BUY YOUR ART
& ANTIQUES
FROM THE
REAL EXPERTS

LOOK FOR THIS SIGN

MEMBERS OF THE BRITISH
ANTIQUE DEALERS' ASSOCIATION

For a full list of members ring 020-7589 4128
or write to 20 Rutland Gate, London SW7 1BD
www.bada.org or enquiry@bada.demon.co.uk

4

The Daily Telegraph

GUIDE TO THE ANTIQUE SHOPS OF BRITAIN

2001/2002

compiled by

Carol Adams

British Library CIP Data Guide to the Antique Shops of Britain. - 2002 (June 2001- May 2002)
1. Great Britain. Antiques trades: Directories - Serials I. Antique Collectors' Club 380. 1' 457451'02541

FRONT COVER: A picture of one of our twelve showrooms . The Portuguese centre table in chestnut in the foreground displays a Scottish rams horn inkwell. The walls are covered in Persian rugs.

Printed in England by The Antique Collectors' Club Ltd., Woodbridge, Suffolk IP12 1DS
Telephone: (01394) 385501   Fax: (01394) 384434
Email: sales@antique-acc.com   Website: www.antique-acc.com
U.S. OFFICE
Market Street Industrial Park, Wappingers' Falls, NY 12590, USA
Telephone: (845) 297 0003   Fax: (845) 297 0068 ORDERS: (800) 252 5231
Email: info@antiquecc.com   Website: http://www.antiquecc.com

**The Tetbury Antique Dealers Association
aims to promote and encourage trade
in the Tetbury area and to assist all visiting
antique dealers and collectors.**

Over twenty shops with over fifty dealers

COTSWOLD ANTIQUE DEALERS' ASSOCIATION

A wealth of Antiques and Fine Art in the heart of England

from a Brass in Northleach Church

Please write to the Secretary
for a free brochure.

FOR ASSISTANCE WITH BUYING, SHIPPING, ACCOMMODATION DURING YOUR VISIT, WRITE TO:

Secretary, CADA, Broadwell House, Sheep Street,
Stow-on-the-Wold, Gloucestershire GL54 1JS
Tel: 01451 830053 Fax: 01451 870028
www.cotswolds-antiques-art.com

ESSENTIAL ANTIQUES

ANTIQUARIUS
Antique Centre
131-141 King's Road,
London SW3

Antiquarius is the most popular and famous antiques centre in London. Newly refurbished and air-conditioned this centre continues to inspire with over 120 dealers offering specialised and general antiques from all periods.

Open Monday to Saturday 10am to 6pm

BOND STREET
Antique Centre
124 New Bond Street,
London W1

London's finest selection of antique jewellery and silver, this elegant centre is situated in the heart of the exclusive Bond Street area.

Open Monday to Saturday 10am to 5.30pm

THE MALL
Antiques Arcade
Camden Passage,
London N1

The Mall is "a focal point of the Camden Passage antiques market area, popular with collectors and interior designers alike".

Open Tuesday, Thursday and Friday 10am to 5pm
Wednesday 7.30am to 5pm & Saturday 9am to 6pm

UNIT ENQUIRIES - EMAIL: ANTIQUE@DIAL.PIPEX.COM
TELEPHONE: 020 7351 5353

L O N D O N - N E W Y O R K - P A R I S

United Kingdom
Gander & White Shipping Ltd.
21 Lillie Road, London SW6 1UE
Tel: 00 44 20 7381 0571
Fax: 00 44 20 7381 5428

Newpound, Wisborough Green, Billingshurst,
West Sussex RH14 0AY
Tel: 00 44 1403 70 00 44
Fax: 00 44 1403 70 08 14

France
Gander & White Shipping Ltd.
8, rue de Duras, 75008 Paris
Tél: 01 43 12 31 32
Fax: 01 43 12 31 33

USA
Gander & White Shipping Inc.
21-44, 44th Road, Long Island City
New York 11101
Tel: 00 1 718 784 8444
Fax: 00 1 718 784 9337

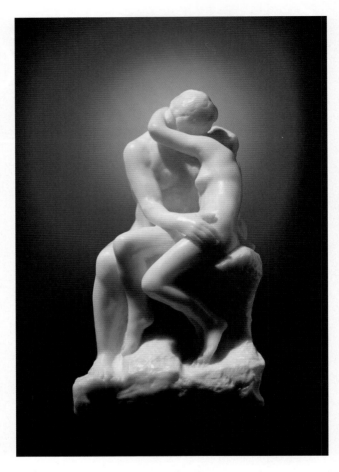
14

KUWAHARA Ltd
Fine art packers & International shippers

No Matter How Large or Small...

- From America to Japan, world-wide door-to-door destination service available.
- Competitive groupage & full-load rates.
- '3 day or less' swift collection policy from any London pick-up point.
- Fine art packing & casing.
- 24 hour security-bonded warehouse.
- Specialists for Far-East markets.
- Insurance cover tailored to your requirements.
- Clients assured of a personalised & professional service.

KUWAHARA Ltd
5 McNICOL DRIVE
LONDON NW10 7AW
Telephone: +44 (0)20 8963 1100
Facsimile: +44 (0)20 8963 0100
Email: kuwahara@uk2.so-net.com

A company who really cares

LAPADA
MEMBER

DragonStone™

ORNAMENTAL STONEWARE

17

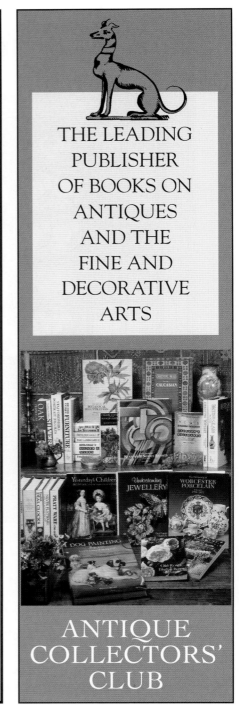

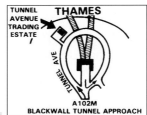

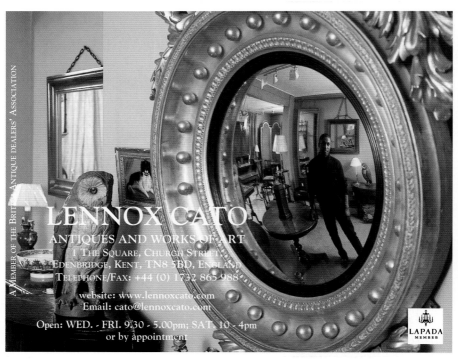

23

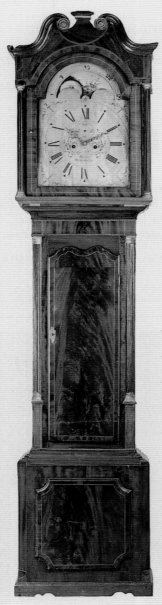

CONTENTS

INTRODUCTION

This is the 30th edition of the **Guide to the Antique Shops of Britain** which is now universally accepted as *the* guide for anybody who wishes to buy antiques in Britain. We are delighted that this year *The Daily Telegraph* has given recognition to the Guide's important and established position in the market place, by having its name associated with us.

Nearly 6,000 establishments are listed in this latest edition and, as usual, every one has been confirmed before reprinting. We appreciate, however, that quantity without quality is meaningless and therefore the range of information we provide is more detailed and up-to-date than in any other publication. We state the obvious facts - name of proprietor, address, telephone number, opening hours and stock and also size of showroom and price range (where supplied). Additional information gives details of major trade association members, the date the business was established, the location and also the parking situation. Whilst none of these points are decisive in themselves, we feel they build up to a useful picture of the sort of establishment likely to be found and may well influence a prospective buyer's decision whether or not to visit a particular shop.

We start preparing the next edition in early 2002. Please let us know of any changes in your area - openings and closures. We do not print information about other dealers without first contacting them, but obviously the more shops in a particular town or village, the more attractive it is to prospective buyers on trips around the country. We would also be grateful for your comments on the Guide and, if you find any information given in the Guide to be incorrect, please let us know. We have occasionally had prospective customers telephoning to say that the stock listed is not what they found when visiting a particular establishment but then refuse to tell us the name of the shop - which means we can do nothing about the complaint. Constructive criticism is welcomed and we look forward to your comments.

ACKNOWLEDGEMENTS

Our main sources of information are still the trade magazines but we would like to thank those dealers who provide information about new shops and closures in their area. Without their assistance our job would be far more difficult.

We would also like to thank those dealers who supported us with advertising - without this revenue each copy would cost £30, instead of £14.95. Each year we include a form at the end of the Guide which dealers can use to up-date details about their own business. In anticipation of next year's Guide, we are grateful to those dealers who make use of this form.

Finally, thanks must go to the editorial team who carry out the mammoth task of up-dating, compiling and indexing the entries each year.

Editor **Carol Adams**
Advertising Sales **Jean Johnson**
Editorial Team **Judith Neal, Diana Dutson**

HOW TO USE THIS GUIDE

The Guide is set out under six main headings; London, Counties, Channel Islands, Northern Ireland, Scotland and Wales. Counties are listed alphabetically, within counties the towns are listed alphabetically and within towns the shops are listed, again alphabetically. London is divided into postal districts.

To make route planning easier there is a map at the beginning of each county, and a list showing the number of shops in any one town or village. The roads indicated on the map are only a broad intimation of the routes available and it is advisable to use an up-to-date map showing the latest improvements in the road system.

Apart from the six main headings above, there are further helpful lists - an alphabetical list of towns, showing the counties in which they will be found for those not familiar with the location of towns within counties, e.g. Woodbridge is shown in the county of Suffolk. One therefore turns to the Suffolk section to look up Woodbridge. This listing is a valuable aid to the overseas visitor. The second is particularly important to British dealers and collectors - giving an alphabetical list of the name of every shop, proprietor and company director known to be connected with a shop or gallery. Thus, if A. Bloggs and B. Brown own an antique shop called Castle Antiques, there will be entries under Bloggs, A., Brown, B., and Castle Antiques. Listings of specialist dealers, auctioneers, shippers and packers, services, and fairs organisers are also included.

We strongly suggest making prior telephone call to confirm opening hours before setting off on a long journey. In the main, dealers are factual and accurate in describing their stock to us but there are probably a few who list what they would like to stock rather than as it is! We would appreciate you letting us know of any such anomalies. Please telephone (01394) 385501 or drop us a postcard and help us to ensure that the Guide remains Britain's premier listing of antique shops and galleries

ABBREVIATIONS IN ENTRIES

BADA:	British Antique Dealers Association.
LAPADA:	London & Provincial Antique Dealers Association
BABAADA:	Bath and Bradford on Avon Antique Dealers Association.
EADA:	Essex Antique Dealers Association.
HADA:	Highlands Antique Dealers Association.
TADA:	Tetbury Antique Dealers Association.
TVADA:	Thames Valley Antique Dealers Association.
CADA:	Cotswold Antique Dealers Association.
CL:	When the business is normally closed in addition to Sunday.
SIZE:	Showroom size. Small - under 60 sq. metres; medium - between 60 and 150 sq. metres; large over150 sq.metres.
LOC:	Location of shop.
SER:	Additional services which the dealer offers.

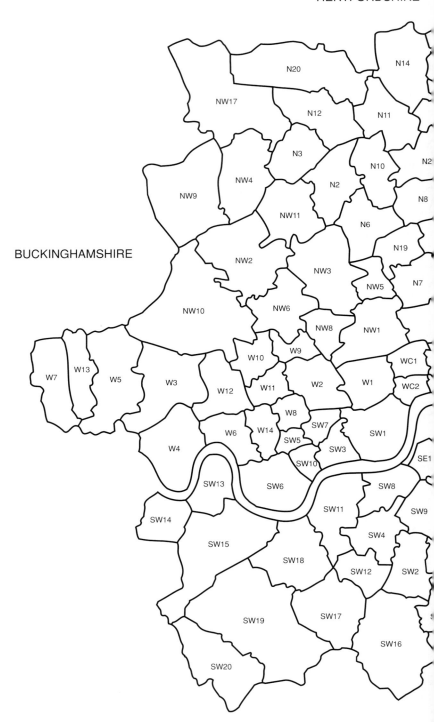

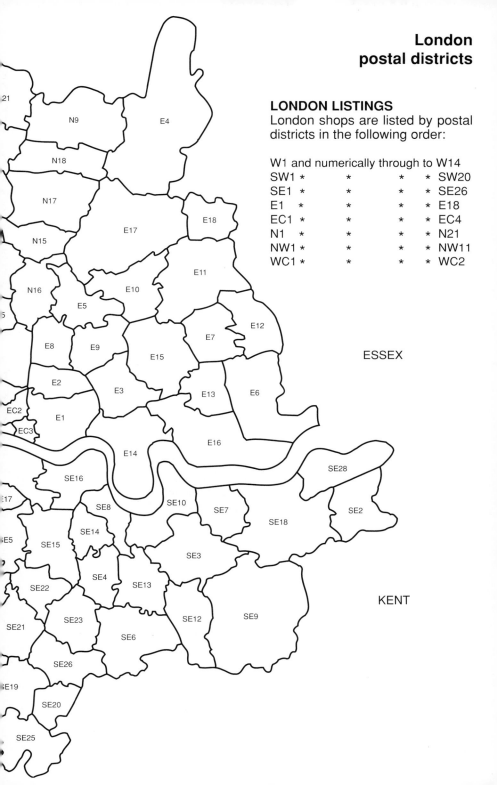

London
postal districts

LONDON LISTINGS
London shops are listed by postal
districts in the following order:

W1 and numerically through to W14
SW1 * * * * SW20
SE1 * * * * SE26
E1 * * * * E18
EC1 * * * * EC4
N1 * * * * N21
NW1 * * * * NW11
WC1 * * * * WC2

David Aaron Ancient Arts & Rare Carpets

22 Berkeley Sq., Mayfair. W1X 7DD. Est. 1910. Open 9.30-6, Sat. by appointment. SIZE: Large. *STOCK: Islamic and ancient art; antique carpets.* PARK: Easy. TEL: 020 7491 9588; fax - 020 7491 9522. SER: Valuations; restorations (trade); buys at auction (as stock). VAT: Stan/Spec.

Aaron Gallery

125 Mount St. W1K 3NS. Open 10-6, Sat. by appointment. *STOCK: Ancient art; Greek, Roman, Egyptian, Near Eastern and Islamic antiquities.* TEL: 020 7499 9434; fax - 020 7499 0072; website - www.aarongallery.com; e-mail - simon@aarongallery.com

Agnew's   BADA

43 Old Bond St. and 3 Albemarle St. W1X 4BA. SLAD. Est. 1817. Open 9.30-5.30, Thurs. 9.30-6.30. CL: Sat. SIZE: Large. *STOCK: Paintings, drawings, watercolours, engravings and sculptures of all schools.* TEL: 020 7629 6176; fax - 020 7629 4359. VAT: Spec.

Adrian Alan Ltd   BADA

66/67 South Audley St. W1K 2QX. LAPADA. Est. 1963. Open 10-6. CL: Sat. SIZE: Large. *STOCK: English and Continental furniture,* *especially fine 19th C; sculpture and works of art.* **TEL: 020 7495 2324; fax - 020 7495 0204; e-mail - enquiries@adrianalan.com; website - www.adrianalan.com. VAT: Stan/Spec.**

Altea Maps & Books

Third Floor, 91 Regent St. W1R 7TB. (Massimo De Martini). PBFA, ABA, ILAB, IMCOS. Est. 1993. Open by appointment. SIZE: Small. *STOCK: Antiquarian maps, 15th-19th C, £50-£5,000; travel books, atlases, 16th-19th C, £200-£20,000; globes, 17th-20th C, £200-£20,000.* LOC: 150 yards from Piccadilly Circus. PARK: NCP nearby. TEL: 020 7494 9060; fax -020 7287 7938. SER: Valuations; restorations (paper, cleaning, colouring and book binding); buys at auction (maps, books and globes). FAIRS: PBFA (June); IMCOS (June); ABA, Chelsea (Nov). VAT: Stan.

Argyll Etkin Gallery

Ramillies Buildings, 1-9 Hills Place, Oxford Circus. W1R 1AG. (Argyll Etkin Ltd). Est. 1954. Open 9-5.30. CL: Sat. SIZE: Medium. *STOCK: Classic postage stamps, postal history and covers, Royal autographs, signed photographs, historical documents and antique letters, 1400-1950, £50-£25,000; stamp boxes and associated writing equipment, 1700-1930, £50-£500.* TEL: 020 7437 7800 (6 lines); fax - 020 7434 1060. SER: Valuations; collections purchased. FAIRS: Major stamp exhibitions worldwide. VAT: Stan.

To fetch a five-figure sum, delft doesn't even need to be perfect. This rare Queen Anne charger realised £10,120 in spite of serious breaks that had been beautifully restored.

From an article entitled 'Not so Potty After All – Early English Pottery' by John Sandon which appeared in the July/August 2000 issue of **Antique Collecting** magazine. For more details and to subscribe see page 147.

BOND STREET
ANTIQUES CENTRE
124 New Bond Street, London W1

"The most prestigious antiques centre
in London"
Antique Monthly

Enquiries: Mike Spooner
Tel: 020-7969 1500 Fax: 020-7969 1639

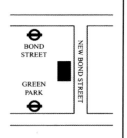

Armour-Winston Ltd
43 Burlington Arcade. W1J 0QQ. Est. 1952.
Open 9-5. Sat. 9.30-2. SIZE: Small. *STOCK:
Jewellery, especially Victorian; gentlemen's
cufflinks, classic watches.* LOC: Off Piccadilly.
Between Green Park and Piccadilly tube stations.
PARK: Savile Row. TEL: 020 7493 8937;
website - www.armourwinston.co.uk. SER:
Valuations; restorations. VAT: Stan/Spec.

Victor Arwas Gallery - Editions Graphiques Gallery Ltd
3 Clifford St. W1. (V. Arwas). Est. 1966. Open
10-6, Sat. 10-2. SIZE: Large. *STOCK: Art
Nouveau and Art Deco, glass, ceramics, bronzes,
sculpture, furniture, jewellery, silver, pewter,
books and posters 1880-1940, £25-£50,000;
paintings, watercolours and drawings, 1880 to
date, £100-£20,000; original graphics, lithographs, etchings, woodcuts, 1890 to date, £5-
£10,000.* LOC: Between New Bond St and Savile
Row. PARK: 50yds. TEL: 020 7734 3944; fax -
020 7437 1859. SER: Valuations; buys at auction.
VAT: Stan/Spec.

Asprey & Garrard Ltd   BADA
**167 New Bond St. W1Y 0AR. Est. 1781. Open
10-6, Sat. 10-5. SIZE: Large. *STOCK:
Furniture, works of art, clocks, silver, jewellery,
glass.* PARK: Albemarle St., entrance No.22.
TEL: 020 7493 6767; fax - 020 7491 0384.
SER: Valuations; restorations (furniture,
jewellery, clocks, silver). VAT: Stan/Spec.**

J & A Beare Ltd   BADA
**7 Broadwick St. W1F 0DA. (J. and A. Beare
Ltd). Est. 1892. Open 9-12.15 and 1.30-5. CL:
Sat. *STOCK: Violins, violas, cellos and bows.*
TEL: 020 7437 1449. SER: Valuations. VAT:
Stan/Spec.**

Paul Bennett
48A George St. W1H 5RF. (M.J. Dubiner). Open
9.30-6. CL: Sat. SIZE: Large. *STOCK: Silver,
1740-1963, £10-£10,000; Sheffield plate.* PARK:

Meters. TEL: 020 7935 1555/7486 8836. VAT:
Stan/Spec.

Bentley & Skinner Ltd
8 New Bond St. W1Y 0SL. LAPADA. Open 10-
5.30. *STOCK: Jewellery, Fabergé, objets d'art.*
PARK: Meters. TEL: 020 7629 0651. SER:
Valuations; repairs. VAT: Stan/Spec.

Peter Biddulph
34 St George St., Hanover Sq. W1R 0ND. Open
10-6. CL: Sat. *STOCK: Violins, violas, cellos and
bows.* TEL: 020 7491 8621; fax - 020 7495 1428.

H. Blairman and Sons Ltd   BADA
**119 Mount St. W1K 3NL. (M.P., P.A. and
W.Y. Levy and L.G. Hannen). Est. 1884. Open
daily. CL: Sat. SIZE: Medium. *STOCK:
English and French antiques, mid-18th to early
19th C; works of art, mounted porcelain,
architect designed furniture, 19th C.* TEL: 020
7493 0444; fax - 020 7495 0766. FAIRS:
Grosvenor House; Fine Art & Antique
Dealers, New York. VAT: Spec.**

Blunderbuss Antiques
29 Thayer St. W1U 2QW. (T. Greenaway). Open
9.30-4.30. *STOCK: Arms and armour, militaria.*
TEL: 020 7486 2444.

Bond Street Antiques Centre
124 New Bond St. W1. (Atlantic Antique Centres
Ltd). Est. 1970. Open 10-5.30, Sat. 11-5.30.
SIZE: Large - 27 dealers. *STOCK: Wide range of
general antiques especially jewellery.* LOC: Bond
St., Oxford St. or Green Park tube stations. TEL:
Enquiries - 020 7969 1500; fax - 020 7969 1639;
e-mail - antique@dial.pipex.com. Below are
listed some of the dealers at this market.

Emmy Abe
Stand 33. *Jewellery and silver.* TEL: 020 7629 1826.

Accurate Trading Co
Stand 1D. (E. Fahimian). *Jewellery.* TEL: 020 7629
0277.

31

N. Bloom & Son (1912) Ltd
Stand 7-9 & 19-20. (Ian Harris). CINOA. LAPADA. *Jewellery, mainly 1860-1960; small silver items, objets d'art and vertu, paintings.* TEL: 020 7629 5060; fax - 020 7493 2528; mobile - 07973 149363; e-mail - nbloom@nbloom.co.uk; internet - http://www.nbloom.co.uk. SER: Valuations; restorations; repairs; buys at auction. VAT: Stan/Spec.

Mr. Cyrlin
Stand 32. *Watches.* TEL: 020 7629 0133.

Adele de Havilland
Stand 18. *Oriental porcelain, netsuke, jade.* TEL: 020 7499 7127.

David Duggan
Stands 1A, 1B. LAPADA. *Vintage watches.* TEL: 020 7491 1362; fax - 020 7408 1727.

Elisabeth's Antiques
Stands 42-44. (Mrs E. Hage). LAPADA. *Jewellery.* TEL: 020 7491 1723; mobile - 07860 550300.

Matthew Foster
Stand 4. *Jewellery.* TEL: 020 7629 4977.

Anthony Green Antiques
Stand 39. *Watches and objects.* TEL: 020 7409 2854; fax - 020 7408 0010.

Massada Antiques
Stand 2. (C.B. and C. Yacobi). LAPADA. Est. 1970. Open Mon.-Fri. 10-5.30. *Jewellery and silver.* TEL: 020 7493 4792/7629 3402.

Nonesuch Antiques
Stand 3. (Mrs E. Michelson). LAPADA. *Jewellery and objects.* TEL: 020 7629 6783.

Resner's   BADA
Stands 5/6. (S. and G.R. Resner, M.P. Daniels) LAPADA. Est. 1918. *Jewellery, £250-£10,000; objets d'art, £200-£1,000; silver, £100-£2,500; all 18th-19th C.* TEL: 020 7629 1413; fax - same; mobile - 07860 704251. SER: Valuations; restorations (jewellery). VAT: Stan/Spec.

Geoff Rowlandson (Jewellery Designer of the Year 1998)
Stand 24. *Jewellery.* TEL: 020 7629 5353.

Sadi & Sahar
Stand 29/30 & 37/37. (Mrs S. Noorani). *Jewellery, glass and porcelain.* TEL: 020 7491 2081.

Nino Santi
Stand 38. *Jewellery and watches.* TEL: 020 7629 3008.

Sergio Tencati
Stand 16. *Jewellery and silver.*

Trianon Antiques and Michael Longmore
Stand 1C. LAPADA. *Jewellery.* TEL: 020 7629 6678.

Matsuko Yamamoto
Stand 14. *Jewellery and porcelain.* TEL: 020 7491 0983.

Bond Street Silver Galleries
111-112 New Bond St. W1Y 0BQ. Open 9-5.30. CL: Sat. PARK: Meters. TEL: 020 7493 6180; fax - 020 7495 3493. Below are listed the dealers at these galleries.

Barnes Jewellers
Fine jewellery. TEL: 020 7495 7554; fax - 020 7495 7556.

Brian Beet
Silver and works of art. TEL: 020 7437 4975; fax - 020 7495 8635.

A. and B. Bloomstein Ltd   BADA
LAPADA. *Silver, Sheffield plate.* **TEL: 020 7493 6180; fax - 020 7495 3493. SER: Valuations; restorations.**

Bruford and Heming
NAG. LAPADA. *Domestic silver especially flatware, jewellery.* TEL: 020 7499 7644/629 4289; fax - 020 7493 5879. SER: Valuations; restorations. VAT: Stan/Spec.

R. Close Jewellery Restoration
TEL: 020 7495 0287.

Adrian Ewart (Gavina Ewart Antiques)   BADA
Silver, porcelain, bronze and ormulu. TEL: 020 7491 7266; 01242 526994.

O. Frydman
Silver, Sheffield and Victorian plate. TEL: 020 7493 4895. VAT: Stan/Spec.

Michael Gardner Antiques
Jewellery and object d'arts. TEL: 020 7495 7592; mobile - 07831 863852.

Graus Antiques
Objets d'art, jewellery and silver. TEL: 020 7629 6680/6651; fax - 020 7629 3361.

M & L Silver Partnership
Silver, old Sheffield and silver plate. TEL: 020 7499 5170; fax - same.

A. Pash & Son
Silver and old Sheffield plate. TEL: 020 7493 5176; fax - 020 7355 3676.

Rare Jewellery Collections Limited
(Elizabeth Powell). *Fine antique and collectable jewellery.* TEL: 020 7499 5414; fax - 020 7499 6906; mobile - 07771 788189; e-mail - info@ rarejewelcollections.com.

Damian Scott
Fine jewellery. TEL: 020 7495 4975; fax - same.

M. Sedler
Silver and plate. TEL: 020 7839 3131.

Guy Steel
Fine jewels. TEL: 020 7495 7554/7594; fax - 020 7495 7556.

D. P. Stern Jewellery and Silver Restoration
TEL: 020 7629 6292; fax - 020 7355 1427.

E. Swonnell (Silverware) Ltd
Silver, Sheffield plate. TEL: 020 7629 9649; fax - same. VAT: Stan/Spec.

David Webb
Old silver, plated ware, decorative objects. TEL: 020 7493 1849; fax - 020 7491 7211.

Zebrak - London
Fine jewels. TEL: 020 7495 7554/7594; fax - 020 7495 7556.

Brandt Oriental Art   BADA
First Floor, 29 New Bond St. W1Y 9HD. (R. Brandt). Est. 1981. Open by appointment. *STOCK: Oriental works of art, £500-£10,000.* TEL: 020 7499 8835; mobile - 07774 989661. VAT: Spec.

Browse and Darby Ltd
19 Cork St. W1X 2LP. SLAD. Est. 1977. *STOCK: French and British paintings, drawings and sculpture, 19th-20th C.* TEL: 020 7734 7984. VAT: Spec.

John Bull (Antiques) Ltd JB Silverware
139A New Bond St. W1S 2TN. LAPADA. Open 9-5. CL: Sat. *STOCK: Antique silver and reproduction giftware, photo frames, cutlery.* TEL: 020 7629 1251; fax - 020 7495 3001; websites - www.jbsilverware.co.uk; www.sales @jbsilverware.co.uk and www.antique-silver. co.uk. VAT: Global/Margin.

Burlington Paintings Ltd   BADA
10 and 12 Burlington Gardens. W1S 3EY. (A. Lloyd, M. Day, J. Lloyd and A. Hardy). Est. 1981. Open 9.30-5.30, Sat. 10-5. SIZE: Small. *STOCK: British and European oil paintings, 19th-20th C, from £1,000.* LOC: Between Old Bond St. and Regent St., facing Savile Row. PARK: APCOA, Old Burlington St. TEL: 020 7734 9984; fax - 020 7494 3770; website - www.burlington.co.uk; e-mail - pictures@ burlington.co.uk. SER: Valuations; restorations (lining, cleaning, reframing oils and watercolours); buys at auction (pictures). VAT: Stan/Spec.

C. & L. Burman   BADA
5 Vigo St. W1X 1AH. (Charles Truman and Lucy Burniston). Open by appointment. *STOCK: 18th-19th works of art including silver,*

glass, furniture, ceramics and sculpture. TEL: 020 7439 6604; fax - 020 7439 6605. SER: Valuations; restorations (silver and metalwork); buys at auction (silver). FAIRS: BADA (March); Grosvenor House (June); Olympia (Nov.). VAT: Spec.

The Button Queen
19 Marylebone Lane. W1U 2NF. (I. and M. Frith). Est. 1953. Open 10-5, Thurs. and Fri. 10-6, Sat. 10-4. SIZE: Large. *STOCK: Antique, old and modern buttons.* LOC: Off Wigmore St. TEL: 020 7935 1505. VAT: Stan.

Carrington and Co. Ltd
170 Regent St. W1R 6BQ. Open 10-6. *STOCK: Regimental jewellery and silver, trophies, watches, clocks.* TEL: 020 7734 3727.

Lumley Cazalet Ltd
33 Davies St. W1K 4LR. SLAD. Est. 1967. Open 10-6. CL: Sat. *STOCK: Late 19th and 20th C original prints including Braque, Chagall, Miro, Matisse, Picasso; drawings by Matisse; drawings and sculpture by Elisabeth Frink.* TEL: 020 7491 4767; fax - 020 7493 8644.

Paul Champkins   BADA
41 Dover St. W1X 3RB. Est. 1995. Open by appointment. SIZE: Small. *STOCK: Chinese, Korean and Japanese art, £1,000-£100,000.* LOC: Off Piccadilly. PARK: Easy. TEL: 020 7495 4600; fax - 01235 751658. SER: Valuations; restorations. FAIRS: Grosvenor House. VAT: Spec.

Antoine Cheneviere Fine Arts   BADA
27 Bruton St. W1. Open 9.30-6. CL: Sat. *STOCK: 18th-19th C furniture and paintings, objets d'art from Russia, Italy, Austria, Sweden and Germany.* TEL: 020 7491 1007.

Andrew Clayton-Payne Ltd
2nd Floor, 14 Old Bond St. W1S 4PP. Open by appointment. SIZE: Small. *STOCK: British paintings and watercolours, 1700-1850, £2,000-£500,000.* PARK: Easy. TEL: 020 7493 6980; fax - 020 7629 9151. SER: Valuations; buys at auction (pictures). VAT: Spec.

Sibyl Colefax & John Fowler
39 Brook St. W1K 4JE. Est. 1933. Open 9.30-5.30. CL: Sat. SIZE: Large. *STOCK: Decorative furniture, pictures, lamps and carpets, 18th-19th C.* PARK: Meters. TEL: 020 7493 2231. VAT: Stan/Spec.

P. and D. Colnaghi & Co Ltd   BADA
15 Old Bond St. W1X 4JL. SLAD. Est. 1760. Open 9.30-6. SIZE: Large. *STOCK: Master*

paintings and drawings, 14th-19th C; English paintings. TEL: 020 7491 7408. SER: Experts and appraisers. VAT: Spec.

Connaught Brown plc
2 Albemarle St. W1X 3HF. (A. Brown). SLAD. Est. 1980. Open 10-6, Sat. 10-12.30. SIZE: Medium. *STOCK: Post Impressionist, Scandinavian and modern works, from £5,000+; contemporary, from £500+.* LOC: Off Piccadilly and parallel to Bond St. PARK: Berkeley Sq. TEL: 020 7408 0362. SER: Valuations; restorations (paintings, drawings, watercolours and sculpture). FAIRS: Olympia. VAT: Stan/Spec.

Sandra Cronan Ltd   BADA
18 Burlington Arcade. W1J 0PN. LAPADA. Est. 1975. Open 10-5. *STOCK: Fine and unusual jewels, 18th to early 20th C, £500-£50,000.* LOC: Off Bond St. TEL: 020 7491 4851; fax - 020 7493 2758. SER: Valuations; design commissions. FAIRS: Fine Art & Antiques; BADA (March): 20th Century, New York (Nov): Grosvenor House (June). VAT: Stan/Spec.

Barry Davies Oriental Art   BADA
1 Davies St. W1K 3DB. Open 10-6. CL: Sat. *STOCK: Japanese works of art, netsuke, lacquer and bronzes.* TEL: 020 7408 0207.

A. B. Davis Ltd
18 Brook St., (Corner of New Bond St). W1Y 1AA. Est. 1920. Open 10-5. CL: Sat. *STOCK: Antique and secondhand jewellery, small silver items and objets d'art.* TEL: 020 7629 1053; 020 7242 7357 (ansaphone).; fax and ansaphone - 020 7499 6454. SER: Valuations; repairs (jewellery and silver). VAT: Stan/Spec.

Richard Day Ltd
173 New Bond St. W1Y 9PB. Open 10-5. CL: Sat. *STOCK: Old Master drawings.* TEL: 020 7629 2991; fax - 020 7493 7569. VAT: Stan.

Demas
31 Burlington Arcade. W1V 9AD. Est. 1953. Open 10-5. CL: Sat. pm. *STOCK: Georgian, Victorian and Art Deco jewellery.* TEL: 020 7493 9496. VAT: Stan.

Dover Street Gallery
13 Dover St. W1S 4LN. (Edmondodi Robilant, Richard Nagy and Charles Beddington). SLAD. Est. 1978. Open Mon.-Fri. 10-6 by appointment. SIZE: Large. *STOCK: Austrian and German Expressionists, including Gustav Klimt, Egon Schiele, 1910-30, from £20,000; Italian and French Old Master paintings, 15th-19th C.* LOC:

Parallel to Albemarle St., opposite The Ritz. TEL: 020 7409 1540; fax - 020 7409 1565; e-mail - info@doverstreetgallery.com; website - www.artnet.com/dover.html. SER: Valuations; buys at auction. FAIRS: New York Fine Art; Tefaf, Maastricht. VAT: Spec.

Charles Ede Ltd
20 Brook St. W1K 5DE. Est. 1970. Open 12.30-4.30 or by appointment. CL: Mon and Sat. *STOCK: Greek, Roman and Egyptian antiquities, £50-£50,000.* PARK: Meters. TEL: 020 7493 4944; fax - 020 7491 2548; e-mail - charlesede@attglobal.net; website - www. charlesede.com. SER: Valuations; buys at auction. VAT: Spec.

Andrew Edmunds
44 Lexington St. W1R 3LH. Open 10-6. CL: Sat. *STOCK: 18th to early 19th C caricature and decorative prints and drawings.* TEL: 020 7437 8594; fax - 020 7439 2551. VAT: Stan/Spec.

Elwes and Hanham Ltd
14 Old Bond St. W1X 3DB. (Ben Elwes and William Hanham). Est. 1993. SIZE: Medium. *STOCK: Old Master and British paintings, 1500-1830.* LOC: 150 yards from Piccadilly. TEL: 020 7491 4966; fax - 020 7491 4976. SER: Valuations. FAIRS: Olympia. VAT: Stan/Spec.

Emanouel Corporation (UK) Ltd
64 & 64a South Audley St. W1K 2QT. (E. Naghi). LAPADA. Est. 1974. Open 10-6, Sat. by appointment only. *STOCK: Important antiques and fine works of art, 18th-19th C; Islamic works of art.* TEL: 020 7493 4350; fax - 020 7629 3125; e-mail - emanouel@emanouel.demon.co.uk VAT: Stan/Spec.

Eskenazi Ltd   BADA
10 Clifford St. W1S 2LJ. (J.E. Eskenazi, P.S. Constantinidi and D.M. Eskenazi). Est. 1960. Open 9.30-6, Sat. by appointment. SIZE: Large. *STOCK: Early Chinese ceramics; bronzes, sculpture, works of art; Japanese porcelain and screens.* TEL: 020 7493 5464; fax - 020 7499 3136. VAT: Spec.

John Eskenazi Ltd   BADA
15 Old Bond St. W1S 4AX. Open 9-6, Sat. by appointment. SIZE: Medium. *STOCK: Oriental art, rugs and textiles; Indian, Himalayan and South East Asian art.* PARK: Meters. TEL: 020 7409 3001; fax - 020 7629 2146; e-mail - john.eskenazi@john-eskenazi.com. SER: Rug conservation. FAIRS: International Asian Art, New York (March); Asian Art, London (Nov.). VAT: Spec.

Essie Carpets
62 Piccadilly. W1V 9HL. (E. Sakhai). Est. 1766. Open 9.30-6.30, Sun. 10.30-6.30. CL: Sat. SIZE: Large. *STOCK: Persian and Oriental carpets and rugs.* LOC: Opposite St. James St. and Ritz Hotel. PARK: Easy. TEL: 020 7493 7766; home - 020 7586 3388. SER: Valuations; restorations; commissions undertaken. VAT: Stan/Spec.

The Fine Art Society plc
148 New Bond St. W1S 2JT. SLAD. Est. 1876. Open 9.30-5.30, Sat. 10-1. SIZE: Large. *STOCK: British fine and decorative arts, 19th-20th C.* PARK: 300yds. TEL: 020 7629 5116. SER: Buys at auction. VAT: Stan/Spec.

Sam Fogg
15d Clifford St. W1S 4JZ. Est. 1971. Open by appointment. *STOCK: Manuscripts, all periods.* TEL: 020 7534 2100; fax - 020 7534 2122. SER: Valuations; buys at auction.

Fortnum and Mason plc
Piccadilly. W1A 1ER. Open 10-6.30. SIZE: Medium. *STOCK: English furniture, 18th-19th C; objects of art, porcelain and decorative paste jewellery.* PARK: Meters. TEL: 020 7734 8040.

H. Fritz-Denneville Fine Arts Ltd
31 New Bond St. W1Y 9HD. SLAD. *STOCK: Paintings, drawings and prints, especially German Romantics, Nazarenes and Expressionists.* TEL: 020 7629 2466; fax - 020 7408 0604. SER: Valuations; restorations; buys at auction.

Deborah Gage (Works of Art) Ltd
38 Old Bond St. W1S 4QW. Est. 1982. Open 9.30-5.30. CL: Sat. *STOCK: European decorative arts and paintings, 17th-18th C; French and British pictures, late 19th to early 20th C, from £5,000.* TEL: 020 7493 3249; fax - 020 7495 1352. SER: Valuations; cataloguing; buys at auction. VAT: Stan/Spec.

Thomas Goode and Co (London) Ltd
19 South Audley St. W1. Est. 1827. Open 10-6. SIZE: Large. *STOCK: China, glass, silver, tableware, ornamental, lamps, mirrors and furniture.* TEL: 020 7499 2823; fax - 020 7629 4230. SER: Restorations. VAT: Spec.

The Graham Gallery
60 South Audley St., Mayfair. W1K 2QW. LAPADA. Est. 1973. Open 10.30-6. SIZE: Large. *STOCK: Library furniture, works of art, oil and sculptures.* PARK: Easy. TEL: 020 7495 3151. VAT: Stan.

Grays Antique Market
South Molton Lane. W1Y 2LP. Open 10-6. CL: Sat. TEL: 020 7629 7034; fax - 020 7493 9344. Below are listed the dealers at this market.

21st Century Keepsakes
Stand VU14. *Collectables*. TEL: 020 7629 7034.

Maria Alcazar
Stands 323. *Jewellery and watches*.

Alexanders Cafe
Stand 117. (Elizabeth Anastos). TEL: 020 7629 3223.

Anthea Antiques
Stand 154/5. (Anthea Geshua) LAPADA. *Jewellery*. TEL: 020 7493 7564.

Antikon Ltd
Stand M13. *Deco and tribal*.

Antique Collectables Ltd
Stand VU7. *Collectables*. TEL: 020 7629 7034.

Arca
Stand 351-3. (R & E Innocentini). *Objets d'art, fans and boxes, Oriental*. TEL: 020 7629 2729.

The Asian Gallery Ltd
Stand 107. *Oriental*. TEL: 020 7629 2935.

Elias Assad
Stand J28-31. *Middle Eastern art*. TEL: 020 7499 4778.

Osman Aytac
Stand 331/2. *Clocks*. TEL: 020 7629 7380.

Colin Baddiel
Stand B25. *Toys*. TEL: 020 7629 1352,

David Baker
Stand M10/11. *Oriental*.

C. Barnes
Stand V5. *Collectables*. TEL: 020 7629 7034.

Don Bayney
Stand C22/3. *Oriental arms and armour*. TEL: 020 7491 7200

Linda Bee
Stand L18-21. *20th C female accessories*. TEL: 020 7629 5921.

Bennett & Thorogood
Stand 109. *Engraving*. TEL: 020 7408 1880.

Barbara Berg
Stand 333. *Jewellery*. TEL: 020 7499 0560.

Beverley R
Stand 343/4. *Jewellery*. TEL: 020 7408 1129.

Biblion
Books. TEL: 020 7629 1374. Stand 356-7. *Lalique and watches*.

Paul Bishop
Stand MB24. *20th C glass*. TEL: 020 7629 7034.

Boris Boskovic
Stand 171. *Jewellery and watches*. TEL: 020 7493 0224.

Britannia
Stand 101-2 &159-60. *Majolica*. TEL: 020 7629 6772.

Nosheen Brohi
Stand 365. *Jewellery*.

S. Brown
Stand M12. *Jewellery*. TEL: 020 7491 4287.

Paul Carney
Stand V8. *Art Deco*. TEL: 020 7629 7034.

P.B. Carpenter
Stand 127. *Paintings, prints and religious art*. TEL: 020 7491 7623.

Christopher Cavey
Stand 178. *Gems and minerals*. TEL: 020 7495 1743.

Cekay
Stand 172. *Walking sticks and curios*.

Continium
Stand 124. (F. and E. Joy). *Oriental*. TEL: 020 7493 4909.

Cyjer Jewellery Ltd
Stand 143/4. *Jewellery*. TEL: 020 7629 3206.

A Hakim Dadajan
Stand A28/29. *Islamic*.

Daisycrest Ltd
Stand 385. *Jewellery*. TEL: 020 7493 6044.

Sharon Dale
Stand VB14. *Jewellery*. TEL: 020 7629 7034.

Alan Darer
Stand A22. *General antiques*. TEL: 020 7629 3644.

Susan Deacon Antiques
Stand L17. *Silver*. TEL: 020 7499 0911.

J. Elton
Stand 175. *Jewellery*. TEL: 020 7629 7469.

Rosemary Erbrich
Stand C26. *General antiques*. TEL: 020 7629 2526.

Fellner and Sellers
Stand A25/B14. *Dolls*. TEL: 020 7629 7034.

Finishing Touch
Stand 176. *Jewellery*. TEL: 020 7495 0592.

Jack First
Stand 310/1. *Silver*. TEL: 020 7409 2722.

Roderick Fiske
Stand FS10. *20th C glass*. TEL: 020 7629 7034.

Forever Young
Stand 371. *Jewellery*.

Peter Gaunt
Stand 120. *Silver.* TEL: 020 7629 1072.

M. Gentry
Stand B16. *Cornish ware.* TEL: 020 7629 7034.

The Gilded Lily
Stand 133-4/145-6. (Korin Harvey). LAPADA. *Jewellery.* TEL: 020 7499 6260.

Jasper Glen Antiques Ltd
Stand 141-2. *Jewellery.* TEL: 020 7629 5511.

Golfania
Stand MG42-3. (Sarah Fabian Baddiel). *Golfiana.* TEL: 020 7629 7034.

Charles Goodall
Stand 131. *Jewellery.*

Gordons Medals Ltd
Stand G14-15. *Coins and medals.* TEL: 020 7495 0900.

R.G. Grahame
Stand 129-30. *Prints.*

Sarah Groombridge
Stand 335-7. LAPADA. *Jewellery.* TEL: 020 7629 0225.

Guest & Gray
Stand H25-28/J10,11,13. *Oriental.* TEL: 020 7408 1252.

Alice Guillesarian
Stand K33/N20. *General antiques.*

Abdul Hadi
Stand A30. *Islamic and antiquities.*

Halstead Hall Antiques
Stand 327. *Jewellery.*

Diane Harby
Stand 148. *Linen and lace.* TEL: 020 7629 5130.

Satoe Hatrell
Stand 156/166. *Jewellery and jet.* TEL: 020 7629 4296.

Lynn and Brian Holmes
Stand 304-6. LAPADA. *Jewellery.* TEL: 020 7629 7327.

Elaine Hopkins
Stand MB27. *Teddies and toys.* TEL: 020 7629 7034.

Peter Hubble
Stand VU6. *Collectables.* TEL: 020 7629 7034.

Mark Hudgell
Stand MB22. *Character mugs.* TEL: 020 7620 7034.

J.L.A.
Stand 123. (Alan Jacobs and Stephen Lack). LAPADA. *Jewellery.* TEL: 020 7499 1681.

Lynda Jackson Antiques
Stand V3. *General antiques.* TEL: 020 7629 7034.

Jacobs Gallery
Stand E18-20. *Islamic.*

Baba Jethwa
Stand 136. *Watches.* TEL: 020 7495 7327.

JUS Watches
Stand 108. *Watches.* TEL: 020 7495 7404.

K & M Antiques
Stand 369-370. (Martin Harris). *Ceramics.* TEL: 020 7491 4310.

K. & Y. Oriental Art
Stand K24-25. *Oriental.* TEL: 020 7491 0264.

Stand G22/3. LAPADA. *Jewellery and diamonds.* TEL: 020 7629 1200.

Kikuchi Trading Co Ltd
Stand 357-8/368. LAPADA. *Jewellery and watches.* TEL: 020 7629 6808.

Barbara Lankester
Stand 339/350. *Jewellery.* TEL: 020 7493 0123.

Lazarell
Stand 325-6. *Silver and objets d'art.* TEL: 020 7408 0154.

Patricia Lennard
Stand 149. *Glass.* TEL: 020 7629 5130.

Lennox Gallery
Stand K10-12. *Numismatics.* TEL: 020 7409 1109.

Paul Lesbirel
Stand 313-5. *Jewellery.* TEL: 020 7629 9681.

Licht & Morrison
Stand 158. *Jewellery.* TEL: 020 7493 7497.

Gary Lloyd
Stand V1. *Silver.* TEL: 020 7629 7034.

Monty Lo
Stand 369-370. *Glass.* TEL: 020 7493 7457.

Michael Longmore
Stand 378-9. LAPADA. *Jewellery.* TEL: 020 7491 2764.

Valerie Lowe
Stand VB6. *Jewellery.* TEL: 020 7629 7034.

Maureen Lusted
Stand B15. *Dolls.* TEL: 020 7629 7034.

M. Marks
Stand 324. *Jewellery.* TEL: 020 7491 0332.

Alison Massey
MG33. *Victorian jet.* TEL: 020 7629 7034.

Mayfair Antiques International Ltd
Stand B22/C15. *Glass.* TEL: 020 7499 9490.

Pete McAskie
Stand A12-13. *Toys.* TEL: 020 7629 2813.

Merchant House Antiques
Stand VU16. *Drink related objects*. TEL: 020 7629 7034.

Ella Misell
Stand 376. *Jewellery*. TEL: 020 7329 3516.

Clive Morley
Stand 121. *Harps*.

Mousa Antiques
Stand A26-7 & B12-3. *Bohemian glass*. TEL: 020 7499 8273.

I. Muskowska
Stand 301. *Silver*. TEL: 020 7491 0143.

Marsha Myers
Stand 386/251. *Silver*. TEL: 020 7493 0768.

Stephen Naegel
Stand B23/C14. *Toys and lead figures*. TEL: 020 7491 3066.

Namdar Antiques
Stand B18/C19. *Glass and ceramics*. TEL: 020 7629 1183.

Howard Neville
Stand 126. *Prints, paintings and religious artefacts*. TEL: 020 7491 7621. Stand G10-1. TEL: 020 7409 0458. SER. Jewellery restoration.

Noritake Collectors Club
Stand FS8. *Japanese porcelain*. TEL: 020 7629 7034.

Glenda O'Connor
Stand A24. *Dolls*. TEL: 020 7629 7034.

Alex Ore
Stand 103. *Diamonds and precious stones*. TEL: 020 7491 3795.

Nabi Ozbek
Stand C20. *Oriental*. TEL: 020 7629 1353.

Mark Paros
Stand MG40. *General*. TEL: 020 7629 7034.

The Pearl Gallery
Stand 328. (B. Clark). *Pearls*. TEL: 020 7409 2743.

Pieces of Time   BADA
Stand M17-9. (Johnny Wachsman). LAPADA. *Pocket watches*. TEL: 020 7629 3272.

Jack Podlewski
Stand 320. *Silver*. TEL: 020 7409 1468.

B. Pragnell
Stand V9. *Dolls and collectables*. TEL: 020 7629 7034.

Ghulam Rasoul
Stand K34-5. *Islamic*. TEL: 020 7495 7422.

RBR Grp
Stand 175. (Olivia Gerrish). *Jewellery*. TEL: 020 7629 4769.

Regal Watches
Stand 128/140. *Watches*. TEL: 020 7491 7722.

A. Rezai
Stand M20-1. *Coins*.

Sabor Safi
Stand C27. *Beads*.

Samiramis
Stand M14-16. (Hamid Ismail). LAPADA. *Islamic*. TEL: 020 7629 1161.

Charlotte Sayers
Stand 360-1. *Jewellery*. TEL: 020 7499 5478.

Second Time Around Ltd/Jadefare
Stand 316-318. *Watches*. TEL: 020 7499 7442.

Chris Seidler
Stand G12-13. *Arms and armour*. TEL: 020 7629 2851.

Shadad Antiques
Stand A16/7. (Farah Hakemi). *Islamic*. TEL: 020 7499 0572.

Shapiro & Co
Stand 380. LAPADA. *Objets d'art and jewellery*. TEL: 020 7491 2710.

Shiraz Antiques
Stand H10-1. (R.P. Kiadah). *Antiquities*. TEL: 020 7495 0635.

Shockett, Byron and Orford
Stand 329-30. *Jewellery*. TEL: 020 7493 2654. Stand E12-13/MB28-9. *African art*. TEL: 020 7408 1043.

Margaret Soane-Sands
Stand 322. *Objets d'art*. TEL: 020 7491 1718.

Solamani
Stand A20/1.(Helen Zokee). *Islamic*. TEL: 020 7491 2562.

Solveig & Anita
Stand 307-9. LAPADA. *Oriental*. TEL: 020 7408 1638.

Boris Sosna
Stand 374-5. *Jewellery*. TEL: 020 7629 2371.

Spectrum
Stand 372-3. (Sylvia Bedwell). *Jewellery*. TEL: 020 7629 3501.

Star Signings Ltd
Stand E16-7. *Football memorabilia*. TEL: 020 7491 1010.

Michael Start
Stand FS4. *Automata*. TEL: 020 7629 7034. Stand 319. *Miniatures*. TEL: 020 7629 6411.

Jane Stewart
Stand L25/27. *Pewter, early 17th C-19th C, £50-£1,000; oak, £500-£1,000; writing slopes, 19th C, £80-£150*. TEL: 020 7355 3333. SER: Valuations; restorations (pewter, oak). VAT: Spec.

Sultani Antiques
Stand K28-31. *Islamic and antiquities*. TEL: 020 7491 3847.

HALCYON DAYS

18th-century English enamels, fans, objects of vertu, tortoiseshell, papier mâché and treen

14 Brook Street, London W1S 1BD
4 Royal Exchange, London EC3V 3LL

Tel: 020 7629 8811
Fax: 020 7409 0280
http://www.halcyondays.co.uk

Tagore Ltd
Stand 302-3. (Ronald Falloon). *Gentlemen's gifts, drinking and smoking paraphernalia.* TEL: 020 7499 0158.

Templar Antiques
Stand A23/B17. *Glass.* TEL: 020 7629 7034.

A. Tendler
Stand 104/170. TEL: 020 7499 1087. SER Jewellery repairs.

Timespec
Stand 366. *Watches.*

Trio
Stand L24. (Teresa Clayton). *Perfume bottles.* TEL: 020 7493 2736.

Michael Ventura-Pauly
Stand 354-5. *Jewellery.* TEL: 020 7495 6868.

Mary Akin Wellard
Stand 165. *General.*

Westleigh Antiques
Stand 339/350. (Pat Sneath). *Jewellery.* TEL: 020 7493 0123.

Westminster Group
Stand 138/150. (Paulette Bates and Richard Harrison). LAPADA. *Jewellery.* TEL: 020 7493 8672.

David Wheatley
Stand 106. LAPADA. *Oriental and fans.* TEL: 020 7629 1352.

Wheels of Steel
Stand B10. (Jeff Williams). *Model toy trains.* TEL: 020 7629 2813.

Wimpole Antiques
Stand 338, 348-9. LAPADA. *Jewellery.* TEL: 020 7499 2889.

R. Yazdani
Stand F14-5. *Islamic.*

ZMS Antiques
Stand 125. *Silver.* TEL: 020 7491 1144.

Richard Green   BADA
147 New Bond St., 33 New Bond St. and39 Dover St. W1S 2TS. SLAD. Open 9.30-6, Sat. 10-12.30. *STOCK: Paintings - Old Master and British; French impressionist and modern British; Victorian sporting and British marine.* **PARK: Meters. TEL: 020 7493 3939; fax - 020 7629 2609; e-mail - paintings@richard-green.com; website - www.richard-green.com.** VAT: Stan/Spec.

Simon Griffin Antiques Ltd
3 Royal Arcade, 28 Old Bond St. W1. (S.J. Griffin). Est. 1979. Open 10-5, Sat. 10-5.30. *STOCK: Silver, old Sheffield plate.* TEL: 020 7491 7367; fax - same. VAT: Stan/Spec.

Hadji Baba Ancient Art
34a Davies St. W1Y 1LG. (Hadji Soleimani). Est. 1939. Open 9.30-6, Sat. and Sun. by appointment. SIZE: Medium. *STOCK: Antiquities and Islamic art.* LOC: Next to Claridges Hotel. PARK: Meters. TEL: 020 7499 9363/9384; fax - 020 7493 5504. SER: Valuations.

Hahn and Son Fine Art Dealers
47 Albemarle St. W1. (P. Hahn). Est. 1870. Open 9.45-5.30. CL: Sat. *STOCK: English oil paintings, 18th-19th C.* TEL: 020 7493 9196. VAT: Stan.

Halcyon Days   BADA
14 Brook St. W1S 1BD. (S. Benjamin). Est. 1950. Open 9.30-6. *STOCK: 18th to early 19th C enamels, treen, papier mâché, tôle, objects of vertu, Georgian and Victorian scent bottles.* **LOC: Hanover Sq. end of Brook St. PARK: Meters and in Hanover Sq. TEL: 020 7629 8811; fax - 020 7409 0280; e-mail - info@halcyondays.co.uk; website - www.halcyondays.co.uk. FAIRS:** Grosvenor House. VAT: Stan/Spec.

Robert Hall   BADA
15c Clifford St. W1X 1RF. Est. 1976. *STOCK: Chinese snuff bottles, Ching dynasty; Oriental*

works of art, 17th-19th C; all £300-£20,000. TEL: 020 7734 4008; fax - 020 7734 4408. SER: Buys at auction. VAT: Stan/Spec.

Hancocks and Co   BADA
52 & 53 Burlington Arcade. W1J 0HH. Est. 1849. Open 9.30-5.30, Sat. 10.30-3.30. SIZE: Medium. *STOCK: Fine estate jewellery and silver.* TEL: 020 7493 8904; fax - 020 7493 8905. VAT: Stan/Spec.

Harcourt Antiques
5 Harcourt St. W1 1DS. (J. Christophe). Est. 1961. Open by appointment only. *STOCK: English, Continental and Oriental porcelain, pre-1830.* PARK: Easy. TEL: 020 7727 6936. VAT: Stan. *Trade Only.*

Brian Haughton Antiques
3B Burlington Gardens, Old Bond St. W1S 3EP. Est. 1965. Open 10-5.30. SIZE: Large. *STOCK: British and European ceramics, porcelain and pottery, 18th-19th C, £100-£50,000.* PARK: Nearby, Savile Row N.C.P. TEL: 020 7734 5491; fax - 020 7494 4604; e-mail - info@haughton. com; website - www.haughton.com. SER: Buys at auction (porcelain and pottery). FAIRS: Organiser - International Ceramics Fair & Seminar, Park Lane Hotel; International Fine Art & Antique Dealers Show, International Fine Art and International Asian Art, New York. VAT: Spec.

Gerard Hawthorn Ltd   BADA
104 Mount St., Mayfair. W1Y 5HE. Open 10-6, Sat. by appointment. *STOCK: Oriental art - Chinese ceramics, porcelain and pottery; cloisonné and painted enamels, jade, hardstones, lacquer, bronzes, metalwork, paintings, textiles, ivory, works of art including Korean, Tibetan and Japanese, 2000BC to 1960.* LOC: Opposite Connaught Hotel. PARK: Easy. TEL: 020 7409 2888; fax - 020 7409 2777. SER: Valuations; restoration; buys at auction; exhibition yearly. FAIRS: New York.

Hennell of Bond Street Ltd.
Founded 1736 (incorporating Frazer and Haws (1868) and E. Lloyd Lawrence (1830))
12 New Bond St. W1Y 0HE. Open 9-5.30, Sat. 10-4. SIZE: Medium. *STOCK: Fine jewellery, silver and watches.* PARK: Meters. TEL: 020 7629 6888. SER: Valuations; restorations (silver, jewellery). VAT: Stan/Spec.

G. Heywood Hill Ltd
10 Curzon St. W1Y 7FJ. (J. Saumarez Smith). Open 9-5.30, Sat. 9-12.30. *STOCK: Books, new* and old, architecture, literature, children's, natural history and illustrated. TEL: 020 7629 0647; fax - 020 7408 0286.

Holland & Holland
31-33 Bruton St. W1X 8JS. Est. 1835. Open 9.30-5.30, Sat. 10-4. SIZE: Medium. *STOCK: Modern and antique guns, rifles, associated items; sporting prints, pictures and antiquarian books; antique sporting objects.* PARK: Meters in Bruton St. TEL: 020 7499 4411; fax - 020 7499 4544.

Holmes Ltd   BADA
24 Burlington Arcade. W1V 9AD. (A.N., B.J. and I.J. Neale). Open 9.30-5. *STOCK: Jewels and silver.* TEL: 020 7629 8380. SER: Valuations; restorations. VAT: Stan.

Howard Antiques
8 Davies St., Berkeley Sq. W1Y 1LJ. Est. 1955. Open 10-6, Sat. by appointment. SIZE: Medium. *STOCK: English and Continental furniture, objects.* PARK: NCP nearby. TEL: 020 7629 2628. SER: Valuations; advice; commissions.

Patrick Jefferson Ltd
94 Mount St., Mayfair. W1Y 5HG. Est. 1978. Open 9.30-5, Sat. 10-5. SIZE: Large. *STOCK: Unusual furniture, works of art, sculpture and paintings, 1700-1930.* LOC: Between Berkeley Square and Park Lane, opposite Scotts. PARK: Easy. TEL: 020 7491 4931; fax - 020 7491 4932. SER: Buys at auction.

C. John (Rare Rugs) Ltd   BADA
70 South Audley St., Mayfair. W1Y 5FE. Est. 1947. Open 9-5. CL: Sat. *STOCK: Textiles, pre-1800, carpets, tapestries, embroideries.* TEL: 020 7493 5288; fax - 020 7409 7030. VAT: Stan/Spec.

Johnson Walker & Tolhurst Ltd BADA
64 Burlington Arcade. W1V 9AF. Est. 1849. Open 9.30-5.30. *STOCK: Antique and secondhand jewellery, objets d'art, silver.* TEL: 020 7629 2615. SER: Restorations (jewellery, pearl-stringing). VAT: Stan/Spec.

Roger Keverne   BADA
2nd Floor, 16 Clifford St. W1S 3RG. Est. 1996. Open Mon.-Fri. 9.30-5.30. SIZE: Large. *STOCK: Oriental art - Chinese jade, lacquer, pottery and porcelain, bronzes, ivories and enamels; all Chinese art from 2500 BC to 1916.* PARK: Meters. TEL: 020 7434 9100; fax - 020 7434 9101. SER: Valuations; restorations; buys at auction. FAIRS: New York (Winter and March Oriental). VAT: Stan/Spec.

D.S. Lavender (Antiques) Ltd BADA
26 Conduit St. W1R 9TA. Est. 1945. Open
9.30-5. CL: Sat. *STOCK: Jewels, miniatures,
works of art.* PARK: Meters. TEL: 020 7629
1782; fax - 020 7629 3106. SER: Valuations.
VAT: Stan/Spec.

The Lefevre Gallery
30 Bruton St. W1X 8JD. (Alex Reid and Lefevre
Ltd). SLAD. Est. 1871. Open 10-5. CL: Sat.
SIZE: Medium. *STOCK: Impressionist,
Contemporary and Modern British paintings.*
LOC: Between Berkeley Sq. and Bond St.
PARK: Meters, Berkeley Sq. TEL: 020 7493
2107; fax - 020 7499 9088. SER: Valuations.
VAT: Spec.

Leuchars and Jefferson
94 Mount St., Mayfair. W1Y 5HG. (Patrick
Jefferson and Hugh Leuchars). Est. 1978. Open
9.30-6, Sat. 10-5. SIZE: Large. *STOCK: English
18th C furniture and works of art.* LOC: Between
Berkeley Square and Park Lane, opposite Scotts.
PARK: Easy. TEL: 020 7491 4931; fax - 020
7491 4932. VAT: Spec.

Liberty
Regent St. W1R 6AH. Est. 1875. Open 10-6.30,
Thurs. 10-8, Fri. and Sat. 10-7. SIZE: Large.
*STOCK: British furniture, ceramics, glass and
metalware, 1860-1930, Gothic Revival, Aesthetic
Movement and Arts & Crafts.* LOC: Regent St.
joins Piccadilly and Oxford Circus. PARK:
Meters and underground in Cavendish Sq. TEL:
020 7734 1234. VAT: Stan.

Maas Gallery
15a Clifford St. W1S 4JZ. (R.N. Maas). SLAD.
Est. 1960. Open Mon.-Fri. 10-5.30. SIZE:
Medium. *STOCK: Victorian and Pre-Raphaelite
paintings, drawings, watercolours and
illustrations.* LOC: Between New Bond St. and
Cork St. PARK: Easy. TEL: 020 7734 2302; fax -
020 7287 4836. SER: Valuations; buys at auction.
VAT: Spec.

Maggs Bros Ltd BADA
50 Berkeley Sq. W1J 5BA. (J.F., B.D. and E.F.
Maggs, P. Harcourt, R. Harding and H. Bett
and J. Collins). ABA. Est. 1853. Open 9.30-5.
CL: Sat. SIZE: Large. *STOCK: Rare books,
manuscripts, autograph letters and medieval
miniatures.* PARK: Meters. TEL: 020 7493
7160 (6 lines); fax - 020 7499 2007; e-mail -
ed@maggs.com; website - www.maggs.com.
VAT: Stan/Spec.

Mahboubian Gallery
65 Grosvenor St. W1X 9DB. (H. Mahboubian).
Open 10-6. CL: Sat. TEL: 020 7493 9112.

Mallett and Son (Antiques) Ltd BADA
141 New Bond St. W1S 2BS. Est. 1865. Open
9.15-6, Sat. 10-4. SIZE: Large. *STOCK:
English furniture, 1690-1835; clocks, 17th-18th
C; china, needlework, paintings and watercolours, objects and glass.* PARK: Meters in
Berkeley Sq. TEL: 020 7499 7411; fax - 020
7495 3179; e-mail - antiques@mallett.co.uk.

Mallett at Bourdon House Ltd
2 Davies St., Berkeley Sq. W1Y 1LJ. Open 9.15-
5.30. SIZE: Large. *STOCK: Continental
furniture, clocks, objets d'art; garden statuary
and ornaments.* PARK: Meters, Berkeley Sq.
TEL: 020 7629 2444; fax - 020 7499 2670. VAT:
Stan/Spec.

Mallett Gallery BADA
141 New Bond St. W1Y 0BS. SLAD. Open
9.30-6, Sat. 11-4. *STOCK: 18th to early 20th C
paintings, watercolours and drawings.* TEL:
020 7499 7411; fax - 020 7495 3179. VAT:
Spec.

Mansour Gallery
46-48 Davies St. W1K 5JB. (M. Mokhtarzadeh).
Open 9.30-5.30, Sat. by appointment. *STOCK:
Islamic works of art, miniatures; ancient glass
and glazed wares; Greek, Roman and Egyptian
antiquities.* TEL: 020 7491 7444/7499 0510.
VAT: Stan.

Map World
25 Burlington Arcade, Piccadilly. W1J 0PT. (J. T.
Sharpe). LAPADA, IMCOS. Est. 1980. Open 10-
5.30. SIZE: Small. *STOCK: Maps, worldwide,
1500-1850, £50-£15,000.* TEL: 020 7495 5377;
fax - same; e-mail - info@map-world.com;
website - www.map-world.com. SER: Valuations; buys at auction.

Marks Antiques BADA
49 Curzon St. W1. (Anthony Marks).
LAPADA. Est. 1945. Open 9.30-6 including
bank holidays. SIZE: Large. *STOCK: Silver,
Sheffield plate.* LOC: Green Park tube,
opposite Washington Hotel. PARK: Meters.
TEL: 020 7499 1788; fax - 020 7409 3183.
SER: Valuations; buys at auction. VAT:
Stan/Spec.

Marlborough Fine Art (London) Ltd
6 Albemarle St. W1. SLAD. Est. 1946. Open 10-
5.30, Sat. 10-12.30. *STOCK: 20th C Masters,
contemporary artists.* PARK: Meters or near
Cork St. TEL: 020 7629 5161.

Marlborough Rare Books Ltd
144-146 New Bond St. W1S 2TR. Est. 1946.
Open 9.30-5.30. CL: Sat. SIZE: Medium.

LONDON W1

Mayfair Carpet Gallery Ltd
3 Old Bond St. W1X 3TD. *STOCK: Persian, Oriental rugs and carpets.* TEL: 020 7493 0126.

Mayfair Gallery
39 South Audley St. W1Y 5DH. (M. Sinai). Open 9.30-6, Sat. by appointment. *STOCK: 19th C antiques and decorative Continental furniture, clocks, chandeliers, Meissen, ivories and objets d'art.* TEL: 020 7491 3435/6; fax - 020 7491 3437; e-mail - mayfair.gallery@dial.pipex.com; website - www.artnet.com/mayfairgallery.htm.

Melton's
27 Bruton Place. W1J 6NQ. (C. Neal). Open 9.30-5.30. CL: Sat. *STOCK: Small antiques and decorative accessories: lamps, prints, porcelain, textiles, English and Continental.* TEL: 020 7409 2938/7629 3612.

Messums (Contemporary)   BADA
8 Cork St. W1X 1PB. LAPADA, SLAD. Open 10-6, Sat. 10-4, other times by appointment. *STOCK: British Impressionist and contemporary paintings and sculpture.* TEL: 020 7437 5545; fax - 020 7734 7018. SER: Valuations; restorations; framing. VAT: Stan/Spec.

Typical incised Della Robbia Pottery marks, including artist's monogram for Cassandia Annie Walker, pattern number and shape numbers with 'Irish Clay' on the edge.

From an article entitled 'The Della Robbia Pottery' by Robert Prescott-Walker which appeared in the February 2001 issue of **Antique Collecting** magazine. For more details and to subscribe see page 147.

Arthur Millner
180 New Bond St. W1S 4RL. Est. 1996. Open by appointment. SIZE: Small. *STOCK: Indian objects, 16th-19th C, £800-£1,200; Indian paintings, 18th-19th C, £200-£400; Islamic art, 16th-18th C, £500-£800.* LOC: Piccadilly end of New Bond St., above David Morris Jewellers. PARK: Old Burlington St. TEL: 020 7499 4484; fax - same; e-mail - info@arthurmillner.com; website - www.arthurmillner.com. SER: Valuations; buys at auction (Indian and Islamic art). FAIRS: Olympia; Arts of Pacific Asia, New York. VAT: Spec.

John Mitchell and Son   BADA
1st Floor, 160 New Bond St. W1S 2UE. SLAD. Est. 1931. Open 9.30-5, Sat. by appointment. SIZE: Small. *STOCK: Old Master paintings, drawings and watercolours, especially flower paintings, 17th C Dutch, 18th C English and 19th C French.* LOC: Nearest tube Green Park. PARK: Meters. TEL: 020 7493 7567. SER: Valuations; restorations (pictures); buys at auction.

Paul Mitchell Ltd   BADA
99 New Bond St. W1Y 9LF. Open 9.30-5.30. CL: Sat. SIZE: Large. *STOCK: Picture frames.* PARK: Meters. TEL: 020 7493 8732/0860. VAT: Stan.

Bashir Mohamed Ltd
8 Broadbent St. W1X 9HH. Open 10-5 by appointment only. CL: Sat. *STOCK: Islamic art, Moghul and south east Asian manuscripts and objects.* TEL: 020 7723 1844. VAT: Spec.

Moira
11 New Bond St. W1. Open 9-6. *STOCK: Fine antique and Art Deco jewellery.* TEL: 020 7629 0160. SER: Valuations; repairs.

Sydney L. Moss Ltd   BADA
51 Brook St. W1Y 1AU. (P.G. Moss). Est. 1910. Open Mon.-Fri. 10-6. SIZE: Large. *STOCK: Chinese and Japanese paintings and works of art; Japanese netsuke and lacquer, 17th-20th C; reference books (as stock).* LOC: From Grosvenor Sq., up Brook St. to Claridges. PARK: Meters. TEL: 020 7629 4670/7493 7374; fax - 020 7491 9278. SER: Valuations and advice; buys at auction. FAIRS: Asian Art, New York (March). VAT: Spec.

The O'Shea Gallery   BADA
120a Mount St., Mayfair. W1K 3NN. ABA. Open 9.30-6, Sat. by appointment only. *STOCK: Maps, topographical, decorative,*

natural history, sporting and marine prints; rare atlases, illustrated books, 15th-19th C, £5-£25,000. LOC: Near Berkeley Sq. TEL: 020 7629 1122; fax - 020 7629 1116; e-mail - osheagallery@paston.co.uk. SER: Decorative framing; restorations. VAT: Stan/Spec.

Richard Ogden Ltd BADA
28 and 29 Burlington Arcade, Piccadilly. W1J 0NX. Est. 1948. Open 9.30-5.15, Sat. 9.30-5. SIZE: Medium. *STOCK: Antique jewellery, rings.* LOC: Near Piccadilly Circus. PARK: Meters and NCP. TEL: 020 7493 9136/7. SER: Valuations; repairs. VAT: Spec.

Omell Galleries
8 Sackville St., Piccadilly. W1X 1DD. Est. 1947. Open 9.30-5; Sat. and Sun. by appointment. SIZE: Medium. *STOCK: Contemporary oils, £400-£6,000.* LOC: Off Piccadilly, near Royal Academy. PARK: Meters. TEL: 020 7734 7477; fax - 020 7734 2112; home - 01344 625958; e-mail - aomell@aol.com. SER: Valuations; restorations (cleaning, repair - oils, watercolours and frames). VAT: Spec.

Paralos Ltd
4th Floor, 23/24 Margaret St. W1W 8RU. (Panagiotis Chantziaras, Louise Bryan and Tim Bryars). Open by appointment. SIZE: Large. *STOCK: Antiquarian books, prints (including decorative and natural history), maps and atlases, printed before 1800; early printing, classics, plate books, voyages and travels, £10-£20,000.* LOC: From Oxford Circus, north up Regent St., second road on right. PARK: Cavendish Sq. TEL: 020 7637 0796; fax - 020 7637 0819; e-mail - paralos@paralos.co.uk; website - www.paralos. co.uk. FAIRS: Map & Print (2nd Mon. monthly), Bonnington Hotel. VAT: Stan. *Trade Only.*

Partridge Fine Arts plc
144-146 New Bond St. W1S 2PF. SLAD. Est. 1911. Open 9-5.30. CL: Sat. SIZE: Large. *STOCK: English and French furniture, objets d'art and silver, 18th-19th C; English, French and Italian paintings, 18th C.* LOC: North of Bruton St., opposite Sotheby's. PARK: Meters. TEL: 020 7629 0834; fax - 020 7495 6266; e-mail - enquiries@partridgeplc.com; website - www.partridgeplc.com. SER: Buys at auction. VAT: Spec.

W.H. Patterson Fine Arts Ltd BADA
19 Albemarle St. W1X 3LA. (W.H. and Mrs. P.M. Patterson and J. Kayll). SLAD. Open 9.30-6. SIZE: Large. *STOCK: 19th C and regular exhibitions for contemporary artists, the*

New English Art Club, Paul Brown, Andrew Coates, Willem Dolphyn and Peter Kuhfeld. LOC: Near Green Park tube station. PARK: Meters. TEL: 020 7629 4119; fax - 020 7499 0119. SER: Valuations; restorations. VAT: Spec.

Pelham Galleries Ltd BADA
24/25 Mount St., Mayfair. W1Y 5RB. (A. and L.J. Rubin). Est. 1928. *STOCK: Furniture, English and Continental; tapestries, decorative works of art and musical instruments.* TEL: 020 7629 0905; fax - 020 7495 4511. VAT: Spec.

Pendulum of Mayfair Ltd
King House, 51 Maddox St. W1. (K. R. Clements and Dr H. Specht). Open 10-6. *STOCK: Clocks, mainly longcase, also bracket, mantel and wall; Georgian mahogany furniture.* TEL: 020 7629 6606; fax - 020 7629 6616. SER: Valuations. FAIRS: Buxton. VAT: Spec.

Ronald Phillips Ltd BADA
26 Bruton St. W1J 6LQ. Est. 1952. *STOCK: English furniture, objets d'art, glass, clocks and barometers.* TEL: 020 7493 2341; fax - 020 7495 0843. VAT: Mainly Spec.

S.J. Phillips Ltd — BADA
139 New Bond St. W1A 3DL. (M.S., N.E.L., J.P. and F.E. Norton). Est. 1869. Open 10-5. CL: Sat. SIZE: Large. *STOCK: Silver, jewellery, gold boxes, miniatures.* LOC: Near Bond St. tube station. PARK: Meters. TEL: 020 7629 6261; fax - 020 7495 6180; website - www.sjphillips.com. SER: Restorations; buys at auction. FAIRS: Grosvenor House; Maastricht. VAT: Stan/Spec.

Piccadilly Gallery
43 Dover St. W1S 4NU. SLAD. Est. 1953. Open 10-5.30, Sat. by appointment. *STOCK: Symbolist and Art Nouveau works, 20th C; drawings and watercolours.* PARK: Meters. TEL: 020 7629 2875; fax - 020 7499 0431. VAT: Spec.

Pickering and Chatto
1st Floor, 36 St George St. W1R 9FA. Est. 1820. Open Mon.-Fri. 9.30-5.30, or by appointment. SIZE: Medium. *STOCK: Literature, economics, politics, philosophy, science, medicine, general antiquarian.* PARK: Meters. TEL: 020 7491 2656; fax - 020 7491 9161; e-mail - rarebooks @pickering-chatto.com.

Nicholas S. Pitcher Oriental Art
1st Floor, 29 New Bond St. W1Y 9HD. Open 10.30-5 by appointment. CL: Sat. except by appointment. SIZE: Small. *STOCK: Chinese and Japanese ceramics and works of art, early pottery, to 18th C, £200-£5,000.* LOC: Four doors from Sotheby's, above Gordon Scott shoe shop. PARK: Nearby. TEL: 020 7499 6621; home - 020 7731 5672. SER: Valuations; buys at auction. VAT: Spec.

Newton Smith Limbird Fielding, A child with a tabby cat, signed l.r. 'Newton Fielding/1851', watercolour over traces of pencil with scratching out, 4¼in. x 7in. (Sotheby's)

From an article entitled 'The Fielding Family' by Charles Hind which appeared in the May 2000 issue of **Antique Collecting** magazine. For more details and to subscribe see page 147.

Portal Gallery
43 Dover St. W1X 3RE. (Lionel Levy and Jess Wilder). Est. 1959. Open 10-5.30, Sat. 10-4. SIZE: Medium. *STOCK: Curios, bygones, artefacts, country pieces and objects of virtue, 19th C, £50-£500; contemporary British idiosyncratic paintings, including Beryl Cook.* TEL: 020 7493 0706; fax - 020 7629 3506.

Jonathan Potter Ltd — BADA
125 New Bond St. W1S 1DY. LAPADA, ABA. Est. 1975. Open 10-6, Sat. by appointment. *STOCK: British and World maps, atlases and travel books, 16th-19th C, £50-£10,000.* PARK: Meters nearby. TEL: 020 7491 3520; fax - 020 7491 9754; e-mail - jpmaps@attglobal.net; website - www.jpmaps.co.uk. SER: Valuations; restorations; colouring; framing; buys at auction (maps and prints); catalogue available. VAT: Stan.

Pyms Gallery — BADA
9 Mount St., Mayfair. W1Y 5AD. (A. and M. Hobart). SLAD. Est. 1975. Open 9.30-6. CL: Sat. *STOCK: British, Irish and French paintings, 18th-20th C.* TEL: 020 7629 2020; fax - 020 7629 2060. SER: Valuations; restorations; buys at auction. VAT: Spec.

Bernard Quaritch Ltd (Booksellers) — BADA
5-8 Lower John St., Golden Sq. W1F 9AU. Est. 1847. Open 9.30-5.30. CL: Sat. SIZE: Large. *STOCK: Rare books and manuscripts.* PARK: Meters, 50yds. TEL: 020 7734 2983; fax - 020 7437 0967; e-mail - rarebooks@quaritch.com; website - www.quaritch.com. SER: Buys at auction. VAT: Stan.

Rabi Gallery Ltd
82P Portland Place. W1N 3DH. (R. Soleymani). Est. 1878. Open 10-6. CL: Sat. *STOCK: Ancient art, antique carpets and works of art.* TEL: 020 7580 9064; fax - 020 7436 0772.

David Richards and Sons
10 New Cavendish St. W1G 8UL. (M. and E. Richards). LAPADA. Open 9.30-5.30. CL: Sat. SIZE: Large. *STOCK: Silver and plate.* LOC: Off Harley St., at corner of Marylebone High St. PARK: Easy. TEL: 020 7935 3206/0322; fax - 020 7224 4423. SER: Valuations; restorations. VAT: Stan/Spec.

Michael Rose - Source of the Unusual
3, 15, 44 Burlington Arcade, Piccadilly and 10 New Bond St. W1J 0QY. *STOCK: Victorian, antique and period diamonds, jewellery and watches.* TEL: 020 7493 0714; 020 7493 0590; website - www.rosejewels.co.uk.

The Royal Arcade Watch Shop
4 Royal Arcade - at 28 Old Bond St. W1S 4SD. Open 10-5.30. SIZE: Small. *STOCK: Modern and vintage Rolex, Cartier, Patek Phillipe.* PARK: Easy. TEL: 020 7495 4882.

Royal Exchange Art Gallery at Cork St.
24 Cork St. W1S 3NJ. Est. 1974. Open 10-6, Sat. 10-1. *STOCK: Fine marine oils, watercolours and etchings.* TEL: 020 7439 6655; fax - 020 7439 6622.

Frank T. Sabin Ltd   BADA
46 Albemarle St. W1X 3FE. (John Sabin). Open 9.30-5.30, Sat. by appointment only. *STOCK: English sporting and decorative prints; English 18th-19th C paintings.* TEL: 020 7493 3288; fax - 020 7499 3593.

Alistair Sampson Antiques Ltd   BADA
120 Mount St., Mayfair. (Formerly of 156 Brompton Rd). W1K 3NN. Open 9.30-5.30. SIZE: Large. *STOCK: English pottery, oak and country furniture, metalwork, needlework, primitive pictures, decorative and interesting items, 17th-18th C.* PARK: Meters. TEL: 020 7409 1799; fax - 020 7409 7717; e-mail - info@alistairsampson.com; website - www.alistairsampson.com. VAT: Spec.

Robert G. Sawers
PO Box 4QA. W1A 4QA. Open by appointment. *STOCK: Books on the Orient, Japanese prints, screens, paintings.* TEL: 020 7794 9618; fax - 020 7794 9571.

Scarisbrick and Bate Ltd
111 Mount St. W1Y 5HE. (A.C. Bate). Est. 1958. Open 9.30-5.30. CL: Sat. SIZE: Medium. *STOCK: Furniture, decorative items, mid-18th C to early 19th C.* Not Stocked: Glass and china. LOC: By Connaught Hotel (off Park Lane). PARK: Meters. TEL: 020 7499 2043/4/5; fax - 020 7499 2897. SER: Restorations (furniture); buys at auction. VAT: Stan.

Seaby Antiquities
14 Old Bond St. W1S 4PP. Est. 1926. Open 10-5. CL: Sat. SIZE: Medium. *STOCK: Antiquities.* LOC: Just off Piccadilly, nearest tube Green Park. TEL: 020 7495 2590; fax - 020 7491 1595.

Bernard J. Shapero Rare Books
32 St George St. W1R 0EA. Est. 1979. Open 9.30-6.30, Sat. 11-5. SIZE: Large. *STOCK: Antiquarian books - travel, natural history and literature (old and modern); antiquarian prints and engravings.* LOC: Near Hanover Sq. and Bond St. TEL: 020 7493 0876. SER: Valuations;

restorations (antiquarian books); buys at auction. FAIRS: Book - London, Paris, New York, San Francisco.

W. Sitch and Co. Ltd.
48 Berwick St. W1F 8JD. (R. Sitch). Est. 1776. Open 8-5. SIZE: Large. *STOCK: Edwardian and Victorian lighting fixtures and floor standards.* LOC: Off Oxford St. TEL: 020 7437 3776; fax - 020 7437 5707. SER: Valuations; restorations; repairs. VAT: Stan.

The Sladmore Gallery of Sculpture
BADA
32 Bruton Place, Berkeley Sq. W1J 6NW. (E.F. Horswell). SLAD. Open 10-6. CL: Sat. SIZE: Large. *STOCK: Bronze sculptures, 19th C - Mene, Barye, Fremiet, Bonheur; Impressionist, Bugatti, Troubetzkoy, Pompon; contemporary, Geoffrey Dashwood birds, Mark Coreth African wildlife, Nic Fiddian-Green horse heads; sporting, polo.* TEL: 020 7499 0365; fax - 020 7409 1381; e-mail - sculpture@sladmore.com; website - www.sladmore.com. SER: Valuations; restorations. VAT: Stan/Spec.

Stephen Somerville (W.A.) Ltd
14 Old Bond St. W1S 4PP. SLAD. Est. 1987. By appointment only. SIZE: Small. *STOCK: Old Master prints and drawings; English paintings, watercolours, prints and drawings, 17th-20th C, £50-£50,000.* LOC: Piccadilly end of Old Bond St. TEL: 020 7493 8363. SER: Buys at auction (as stock). VAT: Spec.

Henry Sotheran Ltd
2/5 Sackville St., Piccadilly. W1X 2DP. Est. 1761. Open 9.30-6, Sat. 10-4. *STOCK: Antiquarian books and prints.* TEL: 020 7439 6151; fax - 020 7434 2019; e-mail - sotherans@sotherans.co.uk; website - www.sotherans.co.uk. SER: Restorations and binding (books, prints); buys at auction. VAT: Stan.

A & J Speelman Ltd   BADA
129 Mount St. W1K 3NX. Est. 1931. Open 9-5.30. SIZE: Large. *STOCK: Chinese and Japanese works of art, Shang era to 19th C.* TEL: 020 7499 5126. SER: Valuations; buys at auction. VAT: Spec.

Spink Leger Pictures   BADA
13 Old Bond St. W1X 4HU. (L.J.Libson). SLAD. Est. 1892. Open Mon.-Fri. 9-5.30. SIZE: Large. *STOCK: British paintings, drawings and watercolours, 17th-20th C and Old Master drawings.* PARK: Meters. TEL: 020 7629 3538; fax - 020 7493 8681. SER: Valuations; restorations.

Stair and Company Ltd BADA
14 Mount St. W1K 2RF. CINOA. Est. 1911.
Open 9.30-5.30, Sat. by appointment. SIZE:
Large. *STOCK: 18th C English furniture, works
of art, mirrors, chandeliers, barometers,
needlework, lamps, clocks, prints.* LOC: Past
Connaught Hotel, towards South Audley St.
PARK: Meters and Adam's Row. TEL: 020
7499 1784; fax - 020 7629 1050; e-mail - stair-
andcompany@talk21.com. SER: Restorations;
decorations. VAT: Spec.

Jacob Stodel BADA
Flat 53 Macready House, 75 Crawford St. W1H
5LP. Est. 1949. *STOCK: Continental furniture,
objets d'art, ceramics, English furniture.* TEL:
020 7723 3732; fax - 020 7723 9813; e-mail -
jacobstodel@aol.com. VAT: Spec.

Stoppenbach & Delestre Ltd
25 Cork St. W1S 3NB. SLAD. Open 10-5.30,
Sat. 10-1. *STOCK: French paintings, drawings
and sculpture, 19th-20th C.* TEL: 020 7734 3534.

Tessiers Ltd BADA
26 New Bond St. W1S 2JY. Open 10-5.
STOCK: Jewellery, silver, objets d'art. TEL:
020 7629 0458; fax - 020 7629 1857. SER:
Valuations; restorations. VAT: Spec.

William Thuillier
14 Old Bond St. W1S 4PP. Open by appointment
only. *STOCK: Old Master paintings and
drawings.* TEL: 020 7499 0106; website -
www.thuillart.com; e-mail - thuillart@aol.com.

Toynbee-Clarke Interiors Ltd
95 Mount St. W1Y 5HG. (G. and D. Toynbee-
Clarke). Est. 1953. Open 11-5.30. CL: Sat. SIZE:
Medium. *STOCK: Decorative English and
Continental furniture and objects, 17th-18th C;
Chinese hand painted wallpapers, 18th C;
French scenic wallpapers, early 19th C; Chinese
and Japanese paintings and screens, 17th-19th C.*
LOC: Between north-west corner of Berkeley Sq.
and Park Lane. PARK: Meters. TEL: 020 7499
4472; fax - 020 7495 1204. SER: Buys at auction.
VAT: Stan/Spec.

M. Turpin Ltd
27 Bruton St. W1J 6QN. LAPADA. Open 10-6 or
by appointment. CL: Sat. SIZE: Large. *STOCK:
English and Continental furniture, mirrors,
chandeliers and objets d'art, 18th C.* LOC:
Between Berkeley Sq. and Bond St. PARK:
Limited and meters. TEL: 020 7493 3275; fax -
020 7408 1869; e-mail - mturpin@mturpin.co.uk;
website - www.mturpin.co.uk.

Jan van Beers Oriental Art BADA
34 Davies St. W1Y 1LG. Est. 1978. Open 10-6.
CL: Sat. SIZE: Medium. *STOCK: Chinese and
Japanese ceramics and works of art, 200BC to
1800AD.* LOC: Between Berkeley Sq. and
Oxford St. PARK: Easy. TEL: 020 7408 0434.
SER: Valuations. FAIRS: Cologne. VAT:
Spec.

Vigo Carpet Gallery
6a Vigo St. W1S 3HF. LAPADA. Open 10-6.
*STOCK: Oriental antique carpets and rugs; re-
creations of hand-made carpets and rugs in
vegetable dyes and hand-spun wool.* TEL: 020
7439 6971; fax - 020 7439 2353. SER: Design.

Rupert Wace Ancient Art Ltd
14 Old Bond St. W1S 4PP. Open Mon.-Fri. 10-5
or by appointment. *STOCK: Ancient Egyptian,
Classical, near Eastern and Celtic antiquities.*
TEL: 020 7495 1623.

Walpole Gallery
38 Dover St. W1S 4NL. SLAD. Open 9.30-5.30.
CL: Sat. except when exhibitions held. *STOCK:
Italian Old Master paintings.* TEL: 020 7499
6626.

Wartski Ltd BADA
14 Grafton St. W1S 4DE. Est. 1865. Open
9.30-5. CL: Sat. SIZE: Medium. *STOCK:
Jewellery, 18th C gold boxes, Fabergé, Russian
works of art, silver.* PARK: Meters. TEL: 020
7493 1141. SER: Restorations; buys at auction.
FAIRS: International Fine Art and Antique
Dealers' Show, New York; European Fine Art:
TEFAF; Maastricht; International Art &
Antique, Palm Beach. VAT: Stan/Spec.

Waterhouse and Dodd BADA
1st and 3rd Floors, 110 New Bond St. W1S
1EQ. (R. Waterhouse and J. Dodd). Est. 1987.
Open 9.30-6, Sat. and Sun. by appointment.
SIZE: Medium. *STOCK: British and European
oil paintings, watercolours and drawings, 1850-
1950, £2,000-£50,000.* LOC: Corner of Brook
St. and Bond St. - entrance on Brook St. TEL:
020 7491 9293. SER: Valuations; restorations;
buys at auction (paintings). FAIRS: Antiques
and Fine Art; Olympia. VAT: Spec.

Captain O.M. Watts
7 Dover St., Piccadilly. W1S 4LD. Open 9-6.
SIZE: Small. *STOCK: Nautical antiques and
collectables, £30-£2,000.* LOC: Near Green Park.
PARK: Meters. TEL: 020 7493 4633; fax - 020
7495 0755. SER: Restorations (scientific
instruments); buys at auction (nautical and
scientific instruments); hire. VAT: Stan.

The Weiss Gallery
1B Albemarle St. W1. Open 10-6. CL: Sat.
*STOCK: Elizabethan, Jacobean and early
European portraits.* TEL: 020 7409 0035. SER:
Valuations; restorations.

William Weston Gallery
7 Royal Arcade, Albemarle St. W1X 3HD.
SLAD. Est. 1964. Open 9.30-5.30, some Sats.
10.30-2. SIZE: Small. *STOCK: Etchings,
lithographs, 1800-1970.* LOC: Off Piccadilly.
TEL: 020 7493 0722; fax - 020 7491 9240. VAT:
Spec.

Rollo Whately Ltd
1st Floor, 9 Old Bond St. W1X 3TA. Est. 1995.
Open 9-6. CL: Sat. SIZE: Small. *STOCK: Picture
frames, 16th-19th C, £500-£2,000.* LOC:
Piccadilly end of Old Bond St. TEL: 020 7629
7861. SER: Valuations; restorations (frames);
search; buys at auction. VAT: Stan.

Wilkins and Wilkins
1 Barrett St., St Christophers Pl. W1M 6DN. (M.
Wilkins). Est. 1981. Open 10-5. CL: Sat. SIZE:
Small. *STOCK: English 17th and 18th C portraits
and decorative paintings, £700-£20,000.* LOC:
Near Selfridges. TEL: 020 7935 9613; fax - 020
7935 4696; info@wilkinsandwilkins.com. VAT:
Stan/Spec.

Wilkinson plc
1 Grafton St. W1X 3LB. Est. 1947. Open 9.30-5.
CL: Sat. *STOCK: Glass especially chandeliers,
18th C and reproduction; art metal work.* LOC:
Nearest underground - Green Park. TEL: 020
7495 2477. SER: Restorations and repairs (glass
and metalwork).

Williams and Son
2 Grafton St. W1X 3LB. (J.R. Williams). Est.
1931. Open 9.30-6. CL: Sat. SIZE: Large.
STOCK: British and European paintings, 19th C.
LOC: Between Bond St. and Berkeley Sq. TEL:
020 7493 4985/5751; fax - 020 7409 7363; e-mail
- art@williamsandson.com; website - www.
williamsandson.com. VAT: Stan/Spec.

Thomas Williams (Fine Art) Ltd
22 Old Bond St. W1S 4PY. Open 9-6. CL: Sat.
STOCK: Old Master drawings, £300-£1,000,000.
TEL: 020 7491 1485; fax - 020 7408 0197. SER:
Valuations; buys at auction (paintings and
drawings).

Linda Wrigglesworth Ltd
34 Brook St. W1K 5DN. LAPADA. Est. 1978.
Open 10-6. CL: Sat. *STOCK: Chinese, Korean
and Tibetan costume and textiles, 14th-19 C.*
LOC: Corner of South Molton Lane. PARK:

Grosvenor Square. TEL: 020 7408 0177. SER: Valuations; restorations; mounting, framing; buys on commission (Oriental). FAIRS: Maastricht; Asian Art, London and New York; Arts Pacific Asia, San Francisco.

Zadah Fine Oriental Carpets

35 Bruton Place. W1X 7AB. LAPADA. Est. 1976. Open 9.30-6. *STOCK: Oriental and European carpets, rugs, tapestries and textiles.* TEL: 020 7493 2622/2673.

W2

Sean Arnold Sporting Antiques

21-22 Chepstow Corner, off Westbourne Grove. W2 4XE. Open 10-6. *STOCK: Sporting antiques and decorative items; golf clubs, 1840-1915, £30-£6,000; tennis racquets, £10-£3,000; vintage luggage.* TEL: 020 7221 2267; fax - 020 7221 5464.

Connaught Galleries

44 Connaught St. W2 2AA. (M. Hollamby). Est. 1966. Open 10-6, Sat. 10-1. SIZE: Medium. *STOCK: Antique and reproduction sporting, historical, geographical and decorative prints.* LOC: Near Marble Arch. PARK: Meters. TEL: 020 7723 1660. SER: Picture framing. VAT: Spec.

Craven Gallery

30 Craven Terrace. W2. (A. Quaradeghini). Est. 1974. Open 11-6, Sat. 3-7, other times by appointment. SIZE: Large and warehouse. *STOCK: Silver and plate, 19th-20th C; furniture, china and glass, Victorian.* LOC: Off Bayswater Rd. PARK: Easy. TEL: 020 7402 2802; home - 020 8998 0769. VAT: Stan. *Trade Only.*

Hosains Books and Antiques

25 Connaught St. W2 2AY. Est. 1979. Open by appointment only. *STOCK: Secondhand and antiquarian books on India, Middle East, Central Asia; miniatures; prints of India and Middle East.* TEL: 020 7262 7900; fax - 020 7433 3126.

Manya Igel Fine Arts Ltd

21/22 Peters Court, Porchester Rd. W2 5DR. (M. Igel and B.S. Prydal). LAPADA. Est. 1977. Open 10-5 by appointment only. SIZE: Large. *STOCK: Mainly modern and contemporary British works, £250-£25,000.* LOC: Off Queensway. PARK: Nearby. TEL: 020 7229 1669/8429; fax - 020 7229 6770. VAT: Spec.

Ian Lieber

The Shop, 29 Craven Terrace, Lancaster Gate. W2 3EL. Est. 1965. Open by appointment. SIZE: Medium. *STOCK: Furniture, early 19th C and decorative; porcelain, objets d'art, paintings, costume jewellery.* LOC: Near Bayswater Rd. TEL: 020 7262 5505; fax - 020 7402 4445. SER: Buys at auction. FAIRS: Olympia. VAT: Stan/Spec.

Daniel Mankowitz

16 Pembridge Sq. W2 4EH. Est. 1970. By appointment only. SIZE: Medium. *STOCK: Furniture, English and Continental, 16th-18th C, £100-£10,000; works of art, English and Continental, 15th-19th C, £50-£5,000; tapestries, 16th-18th C, £200-£3,000.* PARK: Easy. TEL: 020 7229 9270; fax - 020 7229 4687. FAIRS: Olympia. VAT: Spec.

The Mark Gallery   BADA

9 Porchester Place, Marble Arch. W2 2BS. (H. Mark). CINOA. Est. 1969. Open 10-1 and 2-6, Sat. 11-1. SIZE: Medium. STOCK: Russian icons, 16th-19th C; modern graphics - French school. LOC: Near Marble Arch. TEL: 020 7262 4906; fax - 020 7224 9416. SER: Valuations; restorations; buys at auction. VAT: Stan/Spec.

M. McAleer

W2 4SN. (M.J. McAleer). Est. 1969. Open by appointment. *STOCK: Scottish provincial, Irish and small collectable silver.* TEL: 020 7727 7979. SER: Buys at auction (silver).

W3

Remember When

310 Uxbridge Rd., Acton. W3 9QP. Est. 1973. Open 9.30-7 including Sun. *STOCK: Pine furniture.* TEL: 020 8896 2357.

W4

The Chiswick Fireplace Co.

68 Southfield Rd., Chiswick. W4 1BD. (Mrs O'Grady). Open 9.30-5. SIZE: Medium. *STOCK: Original cast iron fireplaces, late Victorian to early 1900's, £200-£1,000; marble, wood and limestone surrounds.* LOC: 8 minutes walk from Turnham Green underground. PARK: Easy. TEL: 020 8995 4011. SER: Restorations. VAT: Stan.

David Edmonds

1-4 Prince of Wales Terrace, Chiswick. W4 2EY. Est. 1985. Open 10.30-6, Sun. 12-4. SIZE: Large. *STOCK: Fine antiques from India and sub-continent, £10-£10,000.* LOC: Off Chiswick High St. PARK: Easy.TEL: 020 8742 1920; fax - 020 8742 3030; mobile - 07831 666436. SER: Valuations; restorations; buys at auction (as stock). VAT: Stan.

J. D. Marshall
38 Chiswick Lane, Chiswick. W4 2JQ. Est. 1985. Open 10-6, Sat. 10-5. SIZE: Medium. *STOCK: Decorative and unusual objects, furniture, bronzes and chandeliers, £100-£50,000; garden statuary and furniture, to £30,000.* LOC: Off A4/M4 at the Hogarth roundabout or Chiswick High Rd. PARK: Easy. TEL: 020 8742 8089; fax - same. SER: Valuations; restorations (oil and water gilding; metal patination and non-ferrous casting). VAT: Spec.

The Old Cinema Antique Department Store
160 Chiswick High Rd. W4 1PR. LAPADA. Est. 1977. Open 10-6, Sun. 12-5. SIZE: Large. *STOCK: General antiques including furniture, gardenalia, decorative and architectural items, 1660-1960, £100-£6,000.* PARK: Easy. TEL: 020 8995 4166; fax - 020 8995 4167; e-mail - theoldcinema@antiques-uk.co.uk; website - www.antiques-uk.co.uk. SER: Restorations. VAT: Stan/Spec.

Oriental Furniture and Arts
11a Devonshire Rd., Chiswick. W4 2EU. (Steven Glynn-Williams). Est. 1993. Open 10-5. SIZE: Small. *STOCK: Oriental furniture, 18th-19th C, to £3,500; Oriental decorative objects, 19th C and modern, £40-£350.* LOC: Off Chiswick High Rd. PARK: Easy. TEL: 020 8987 8571; fax - same. SER: Restorations.

Strand Antiques
46 Devonshire Rd., Chiswick. W4 2HD. Est. 1977. Open 10.30-5.30. SIZE: Medium. *STOCK: French Brocante, chandeliers, garden and kitchen items, corkscrews, glass, jewellery, china, silver, fabrics, furniture, books and other collectors' items, £1-£500.* LOC: Off Chiswick High Rd. 5 mins Turnham Green Tube. PARK: Meters. TEL: 020 8994 1912.

W5

Aberdeen House Antiques
75 St. Mary's Rd. W5 5RH. (N. Schwartz). LAPADA, CINOA. Est. 1971. Open 10-5.30. SIZE: Medium. *STOCK: Furniture and pictures, £150-£4,000; decorative items and textiles, £25-£2,000; china, glass and silver, £25-£1,000; all 18th-20th C.* LOC: On B455 1 mile north of A4. PARK: Easy and at rear. TEL: 020 8567 5194/1223. SER: Valuations. FAIRS: Olympia. VAT: Stan.

Ealing Gallery
78 St. Mary's Rd., Ealing. W5 5EX. (Mrs N. Lane). Open 10.30-5.30. CL: Mon. and Wed.

STOCK: Oil paintings, £250-£1,000; watercolours, £100-£5,000; both 18th-20th C; contemporary paintings, £150-£1,000. LOC: Piccadilly Line underground, South Ealing. PARK: Nearby. TEL: 020 8840 7883; fax - same. SER: Valuations; restorations (oils and watercolours); framing. VAT: Spec.

Harold's Place
148 South Ealing Rd. W5 4QJ. (H. Bowman). Est. 1977. Open 10-6. CL: Wed. SIZE: Medium. *STOCK: Wall plates, commemoratives, porcelain, 19th to early 20th C, £5-£100.* LOC: 1/2 mile north of A4/M4 at Ealing. TEL: 020 8579 4825.

Kitchenalia
122 Pitshanger Lane, Ealing. W5 1QP. (Polly Clewer). Est. 1995. Open 10.15-6, Sun. 12-4. SIZE: Small. *STOCK: Small furniture - pot cupboards, bookshelves, small chests of drawers, 1800-1930, £10-£350.* LOC: Parallel to A40. PARK: Nearby. TEL: 020 8991 1786.

Terrace Antiques
10-12 South Ealing Rd. W5 4QA. (N. Schwartz). Est. 1971. Open 10-5.30. SIZE: Medium. *STOCK: Georgian, Victorian and Edwardian furniture, 1780-1920, £50-£1,000; china, glass and pictures, silver and plate, 1850-1950, £10-£600.* LOC: 1 mile north of A4 on B455. PARK: Easy and opposite. TEL: 020 8567 5194/1223. SER: Valuations. FAIRS: Olympia. VAT: Stan.

Gallé may be better known for Art Nouveau, but this fractured ice vase certainly merited inclusion in Christie's Art Deco sale, where it fetched £3,000.

From an Auction Report by Christopher Wight on Classic Art Deco at Christie's South Kensington, 15th February 2001 which appeared in the April 2001 issue of **Antique Collecting** magazine. For more details and to subscribe see page 147.

LONDON W6

Architectural Antiques

324A & 351 King St. W6 9NH. (G.P.A. Duc).
Est. 1985. Open 9-5, Sat. 10-4. SIZE: Medium.
*STOCK: Marble/stone chimney pieces, 18th-19th
C, £500-£8,000; gilt/painted overmantles, 19th C,
£300-£1,500; antique French doors, £200-
£1,000; bathroom fixtures, basins, £200-£800.*
PARK: Easy and Black Lion Lane. TEL: 020
8741 7883; fax - 020 8741 1109. SER: Valuations. VAT: Stan. *Trade Only.*

Paravent

Flat 10, Ranelagh Gardens, Stamford Brook Ave.
W6 0YE. (M.Aldbrook). Open by appointment
only. *STOCK: Screens, 17th-20th C, £500-
£10,000.* TEL: 020 8748 6323; fax - 020 8563
2912. SER: Restorations; finder (screens). VAT:
Stan/Spec.

Zoom

Arch 65 Cambridge Grove, Hammersmith. W6
0LD. Est. 1973. Open 10-8, Sun. telephone call
advisable. *STOCK: 50's, 60's, 70's furniture,
lighting and unusual retro objects.* LOC: Off
King Street. TEL: 07000 9666 2001; fax - same;
mobile - 07958 372975; e-mail - eddiesandham
@hotmail.com; website - www.retrozoom.com.
SER: Rental for photo shoots, TV and film sets,
styling.

AntikWest AB

150-152 Kensington Church St. W8 4BN. (Bjorn
Gremner and Jonathan Robinson). CINOA. Est.
1979. Open 10-6, Sat. 10-4. SIZE: Small. *STOCK:
Chinese pottery and porcelain, Tang to late 19th C,
£200-£35,000; Chinese furniture, £200-£2,000.*
LOC: 100 yards south of Notting Hill Gate. PARK:
Meters. TEL: 020 7229 4115; website - www.
antikwest.com. FAIRS: Olympia (June); Eurantica,
Brussels; Stockholm, Alvsjo; Helsingborg, Sweden;
Hong Kong International. VAT: Spec.

Valerie Arieta

97b Kensington Church St. W8 7LN. Open 10.30-
5 appointment advisable. *STOCK: American
Indian and Eskimo art; English and Continental
antiques.* TEL: 020 7243 1074/7794 7613.

Garry Atkins

107 Kensington Church St. W8 7LN. (Garry and
Julie Atkins). Est. 1986. Open 10-5.30, Sat. am.
by appointment. SIZE: Small. *STOCK: English
and Continental pottery, to 18th C, £100-
£10,000.* LOC: Between Kensington High St. and

Notting Hill Gate. PARK: Meters. TEL: 020
7727 8737; fax - 020 7792 9010. SER: Valuations; buys at auction (English and Continental
pottery); annual exhibition (March), catalogues
available. FAIRS: International Ceramic; New
York Ceramic. VAT: Spec.

Gregg Baker Asian Art   BADA

132 Kensington Church St. W8 4BH.
LAPADA. Est. 1985. Open 10-6, weekends by
appointment. SIZE: Small. *STOCK: Japanese
and Chinese works of art and screens, mainly
18th-19th C, £500-£100,000.* PARK: Meters.
TEL: 020 7221 3533; fax - 020 7221 4410.
SER: Valuations. VAT: Stan/Spec.

Eddy Bardawil   BADA

106 Kensington Church St. W8 4BH. (E.S.
Bardawil). Est. 1979. Open 10-1 and 2-5.30,
Sat. 10-1.30. SIZE: Medium. *STOCK: English
furniture - mahogany, satinwood, walnut;
mirrors, brassware, tea-caddies, all pre-1830,
£500-£50,000; prints, 18th C.* LOC: Corner
premises, Berkeley Gardens/Church St.
PARK: Easy. TEL: 020 7221 3967; fax - 020
7221 5124. SER: Valuations; restorations
(furniture); polishing. VAT: Stan/Spec.

Baumkotter Gallery

63a Kensington Church St. W8 4BA. (Mrs L.
Baumkotter). LAPADA. Est. 1968. Open 10-
5.30, Sat. by appointment. SIZE: Large. *STOCK:
17th-19th C oil paintings.* TEL: 020 7937 5171;
fax - 020 7938 2312. VAT: Spec.

Berwald Oriental Art   BADA

101 Kensington Church St. W8 7LN. (John R.
Berwald). Est. 1986. Open 10-6, Sat. and Sun
and other times by appointment. SIZE:
Medium. *STOCK: Chinese porcelain, 16th to
early 18th C; Chinese pottery, 200BC to 15th C;
Oriental works of art; all £1,000-£100,000.*
PARK: Meters and nearby. TEL: 020 7229
0800; fax - 020 7229 1101; website - www.
berwald-oriental.com; e-mail - berwald@
aapi.co.uk. SER: Valuations; restorations;
buys at auction (Oriental). FAIRS: International Asian Arts, New York; International
Ceramics, London. VAT: Spec.

David Brower Antiques

113 Kensington Church St. W8 7LN. Est. 1970.
Open 10-6. CL: Sat. SIZE: Large. *STOCK:
Specialist in Meissen, KPM, European and
Oriental porcelain, French bronzes and Japanese
works of art.* PARK: Meters nearby. TEL: 020
7221 4155; fax - 020 7221 6211; e-mail -
David@davidbrower-antiques.com; website -
www.davidbrower-antiques.com. SER: Buys at
auction. VAT: Stan/Spec.

The Lucy B. Campbell Gallery BADA
123 Kensington Church St. W8 7LP. Est. 1983. Open 10-6, Sat. 10-4. SIZE: Medium. *STOCK: Fine decorative prints, 17th-19th C; contemporary originals.* Not Stocked: Maps and sporting prints. PARK: Meters. TEL: 020 7727 2205; fax - 020 7229 4252; e-mail - lucy@lucybcampbell.com; website - www.lucybcampbell.com. SER: Framing. VAT: Stan.

Coats Oriental Carpets
4 Kensington Church Walk, (off Holland St). W8 4NB. (A. Coats). Est. 1973. Open 11-5, Sat. 11-3 or by appointment. SIZE: Medium. *STOCK: Oriental carpets and rugs, kelims, £50-£2,000; Oriental textiles and embroideries, £10-£100; all 19th C.* LOC: Small pedestrian alleyway just off Holland St., off south end of Kensington Church St. PARK: Easy. TEL: 020 7937 0983; home - 020 7370 2355. SER: Valuations; restorations (re-weaving); buys at auction. VAT: Stan/Spec.

Cohen & Cohen BADA
101B Kensington Church St. W8 7LN. Open 10-6, Sat. 11-4. *STOCK: Chinese export porcelain and works of art.* TEL: 020 7727 7677; fax - 020 7229 9653. SER: Valuations; buys at auction. VAT: Stan/Spec.

Garrick D. Coleman
5 Kensington Court. W8 5DL. (G.D. and G.E. Coleman). Est. 1944. Open strictly by appointment only. SIZE: Medium. *STOCK: Chess sets, 1750-1880, £100-£4,000; decorative items, £50-£2,000; glass paperweights, £200-£3,000; conjuring and magic items.* PARK: Easy. TEL: 020 7937 5524; fax - 020 7937 5530; e-mail - coleman-antiques-london@compuserve.com; website - www.antiquechess.co.uk/. VAT: Stan/Spec.

Mrs. M.E. Crick Chandeliers
166 Kensington Church St. W8 4BN. Est. 1897. CL: Sat. *STOCK: English and Continental crystal, glass and ormulu chandeliers, 18th-19th C.* PARK: Meters. TEL: 020 7229 1338; fax - 020 7792 1073.

George Dare
9 Launceston Place, Kensington. W8 5RL. Est. 1980. Open anytime by appointment. SIZE: Medium. *STOCK: English watercolours and oil paintings, mainly 18th-19th C, £100-£2,500.* LOC: Turn left off London bound section of Cromwell Rd., opposite the Forum Hotel. PARK: Easy. TEL: 020 7937 7072; home - same. SER: Restorations; framing; buys at auction (as stock). VAT: Stan.

Davies Antiques
40 Kensington Church St. W8 4BX. (H.Q.V. Davies). LAPADA. Est. 1976. Open 10-5.30, Sat. 10-3. *STOCK: Continental porcelain especially Meissen, 1710-1930.* TEL: 020 7937 9216; fax - 020 7938 2032.

Richard Dennis
144 Kensington Church St. W8. Est. 1967. Open 10-5.30, Sat. 10-2. SIZE: Medium. *STOCK: Contemporary British pottery, including Sally Tuffin at Dennis China Works, Highland Stoneware, Laurence McGowan, Poole, Moorland and Lisa Moorcroft.* LOC: Near Notting Hill Gate tube. TEL: 020 7727 2061. VAT: Stan.

Denton Antiques
156 Kensington Church St. W8 4BN. (M.T. and M.E. Denton). Open 9.30-5.30. CL: Sat. *STOCK: Glass, chandeliers, candelabra, 18th-19th C.* TEL: 020 7229 5866; fax - 020 7792 1073.

H. and W. Deutsch Antiques
111 Kensington Church St. W8 7LN. LAPADA. Est. 1897. Open 10-5. CL: Tues., Wed. and Sat. SIZE: Large. *STOCK: 18th-19th C Continental and English porcelain and glassware; silver, plate and enamel ware, miniature portraits; Oriental porcelain, cloisonné, bronzes, £300-£5,000.* TEL: 020 7727 5984. VAT: Stan/Spec.

Peter Farlow BADA
34 Kensington Church St. W8 4HA. LAPADA. Est. 1986. Open 9.30-5, Sat. 11-4. SIZE: Small. *STOCK: Decorative arts, Gothic Revival furniture, Arts and Crafts.* PARK: NCP Kensington High St. TEL: 020 7937 3388; fax - 020 7937 5588. VAT: Stan/Spec.

C. Fredericks and Son BADA
W8 4BN. (R.F. Fredericks). SIZE: Large. *STOCK: Furniture, 18th C, £500-£15,000.* LOC: Near Notting Hill Gate underground station. TEL: 020 7727 2240; fax - same; mobile - 07831 336937. VAT: Stan/Spec.

Michael German Antiques Ltd BADA
38B Kensington Church St. W8 4BX. LAPADA. Est. 1954. Open 10-5, Sat. 10-3. *STOCK: European and Oriental arms and armour; walking stick specialist.* TEL: 020 7937 2771.

Green's Antique Galleries
117 Kensington Church St. W8 7LN. (S. Green). Open 9-5. SIZE: Medium. *STOCK: Jewellery, 18th C to date; pre-1930 clothes and lace; dolls; china, silver, furniture, paintings, masonic, crocodile and leather items.* PARK: Easy. TEL: 020 7229 9618. VAT: Stan/Spec.

Robert Hales Antiques
131 Kensington Church St. W8 7LP. Est. 1967. Open 9.30-5.30. CL: Mon. and Sat. SIZE: Small. *STOCK: Islamic, Oriental and ethnographic arms and armour; oceanic art, 16th-19th C.* PARK: Easy. TEL: 020 7229 3887. SER: Valuations; buys at auction. VAT: Spec.

Adrian Harrington
64A Kensington Church St. W8 4DB. ABA, ILAB, PBFA. Est. 1970. Open 10-6. SIZE: Medium. *STOCK: Antiquarian books, maps and prints, 15th-20th C, especially bound library sets, English literature, plate books, maps and decorative engravings.* LOC: Half-way up Kensington Church St. PARK: Meters. TEL: 020 7937 1465; fax - 020 7368 0912; e-mail - rare@harringtonbooks.co.uk. SER: Valuations; restorations (bookbinding, prints); framing; buys at auction (antiquarian books). FAIRS: Olympia Book (June); Chelsea Book (Nov). VAT: Stan.

Haslam and Whiteway
105 Kensington Church St. W8 7LN. (T.M. Whiteway). Est. 1969. Open 10-6, Sat. 10-2. SIZE: Small. *STOCK: British furniture, £100-£10,000; British decorative arts, £50-£5,000; Continental and American decorative arts, £50-£500; all 1850-1930.* Not Stocked: Pre-Victorian items. LOC: From Notting Hill Gate tube station, down Kensington Church St. Shop is approx. 300yds. down on right. PARK: Meters. TEL: 020 7229 1145. SER: Valuations; buys at auction. VAT: Stan.

Jeanette Hayhurst Fine Glass BADA
32A Kensington Church St. W8. Open 10-5, Sat. 12-5. STOCK: Glass - 18th C English drinking, fine 19th C engraved, table decanters, contemporary art, scent bottles, Roman and Continental. TEL: 020 7938 1539.

D. Holmes
47c Earls Court Rd. (in Abingdon Villas), Kensington. W8 6EE. Est. 1965. Open Fri. 2-7, Sat. 10-2 or by appointment. *STOCK: Decorative items and furniture, 18th-19th C.* TEL: 020 7937 6961 or 01208 880254; mobile - 07790 431895. SER: Restorations (furniture). VAT: Stan/Spec.

Hope and Glory
(Royal Commemorative Specialists) 131a Kensington Church St. W8 7LP. Open 10-5. *STOCK: Commemorative china.* LOC: Entrance in Peel St. TEL: 020 7727 8424.

Jonathan Horne BADA
66b & 66c Kensington Church St. W8 4BY. Est. 1968. Open 9.30-5.30. CL: Sat. and Sun. except by appointment. SIZE: Medium. STOCK: Early English pottery, needlework and *works of art.* **TEL: 020 7221 5658; fax - 020 7792 3090. VAT: Stan/Spec.**

Valerie Howard
4 Campden St., Off Kensington Church St. W8 7EP. LAPADA. Open 10-5.30, Sat. 10-4.30. *STOCK: Mason's and English Ironstone china, 1810-1860, £50-£10,000; French faience especially from Quimper and Rouen regions, 1750-1920, £20-£3,000; mirrors, 19th C, £500-£2,000.* TEL: 020 7792 9702 (ansaphone at night); fax - 020 7221 7008; e-mail - valeriehoward@quimperpottery.com; web-sites - www.masonsironstonechina.com and www. quimperpottery.com. SER: Valuations; buys at auction (as stock). FAIRS: International Ceramics, Park Lane Hotel (June). VAT: Spec.

Iona Antiques BADA
PO Box 285. W8 6HZ. Est. 1974. Open by appointment only. SIZE: Large. STOCK: 19th C animal paintings, £1,000-£30,000. LOC: 3 minutes walk from Odeon Cinema, Kensington High St. PARK: Nearby. TEL: 020 7602 1193; fax - 020 7371 2843. FAIRS: Grosvenor House, Olympia.

J.A.N. Fine Art
134 Kensington Church St. W8. (Mrs F.K. Shimizu). Est. 1976. Open 10-6, Sat. by appointment. SIZE: Medium. *STOCK: Japanese and Chinese porcelain, 1st to 20th C, from £150; Japanese bronzes and works of art, 15th-20th C, from £150; Japanese paintings and screens, 16th-20th C, from £250; Tibetan thankas and ritual objects, 12th-18th C, from £250.* PARK: Meters. TEL: 020 7792 0736; fax - 020 7221 1380. VAT: Spec.

Japanese Gallery
66d Kensington Church St. W8 4BY. (Mr and Mrs C.D. Wertheim). Est. 1977. Open 10-6. *STOCK: Japanese wood-cut prints; books, porcelain, netsuke.* TEL: 020 7229 2934; fax - same. SER: Free authentification; on-the-spot framing for Japanese prints; sales exhibitions.

Roderick Jellicoe
3A Campden St off Kensington Church St. W8 4EP. Est. 1974. Open 10-5.30, Sat. 10-1. SIZE: Medium. *STOCK: English porcelain, 18th-19th C, £10-£20,000.* PARK: Meters. TEL: 020 7624 6471; mobile - 07775 580051. SER: Valuations; buys at auction (18th C English porcelain). FAIRS: International Ceramics. VAT: Spec.

John Jesse
160 Kensington Church St. W8 4BN. Open 10-6, Sat. 11-4. *STOCK: Decorative arts, 1880-1980, especially Art Nouveau and Art Deco silver, glass, bronzes and jewellery.* TEL: 020 7229 0312; fax - 020 7229 4732; e-mail - jj@johnjesse.com; website - www.johnjesse.com.

VALERIE HOWARD
Specialist in Mason's & other Ironstone China
French Faïence, especially of Quimper

LAPADA
MEMBER

**Weekdays
10–5.30**

**Saturday
10–4.30**

**4 Campden Street (off Kensington Church Street) London W8 7EP
Tel: 020 7792 9702 Fax: 020 7221 7008
E-mail: valeriehoward@quimperpottery.com
Websites: www.masonsironstonechina.com & www.quimperpottery.com**

Howard Jones - The Silver Shop
43 Kensington Church St. W8 4BA. (H. Howard-Jones). LAPADA. Est. 1971. Open 9.30-5.30. SIZE: Small. *STOCK: Silver, antique and modern, £10-£3,000.* Not Stocked: Furniture. PARK: Nearby. TEL: 020 7937 4359; fax - same. VAT: Stan.

Peter Kemp
170 Kensington Church St. W8 4BN. Est. 1975. Open 10-5. CL: Sat. SIZE: Medium. *STOCK: Porcelain - 10th-19th C Chinese, 17th-19th C Japanese, 18th C Continental; Oriental works of art and porcelain, 18th-19th C.* LOC: 200yds. from Notting Hill tube station. PARK: Meters nearby. TEL: 020 7229 2988. SER: Valuations; restorations (porcelain). VAT: Spec.

Kensington Church Street Antiques Centre
58-60 Kensington Church St. W8 4DB. Open 10-6. Below are listed some of the dealers at this Centre. TEL: 020 7376 0425; fax - 020 7937 3400.

Abstract
LAPADA. *Cameo glass and decorative items, both 20th C.* TEL: 020 7376 2652.

Nicolaus Boston
Majolica, Dresser and Aesthetic movement porcelain. TEL: 020 7376 0425; fax - 020 7937 3400. VAT: Stan/Spec.

Didier Antiques
Jewellery and silver, objets d'art, 1860-1960. TEL: 020 7938 2537. VAT: Stan/Spec.

F C R Gallery
20th C fine art and design. TEL: 020 7938 5385.

Freeforms
Mid century decorative arts. TEL: 020 7376 0425.

Gallery 8
19th-20th C decorative arts. TEL: 020 7937 8318; fax - same.

Graven Image
Victorian engravings and limited edition prints. TEL: 020 7376 0425.

Jag
20th C decorative arts, Liberty pewter and silver. TEL: 020 7938 4404; fax - same.

Maurizio Lorenzo
Continental ceramics, 1880-1940 including Zsölnay, Amphora; 20th C decorative arts and sculpture. TEL: 020 7937 6935.

Colin Monk
Oriental porcelain. TEL: 020 7229 3727; fax - 020 7376 1501.

Zeitgeist
Continental Art Nouveau and Art Deco metalware, ceramics and glass. TEL: 020 7938 4817; fax - same.

53

LONDON W8

The Lacquer Chest
71 and 75 Kensington Church St. W8 4BG. (G. and V. Andersen). Est. 1959. Open 9.30-5.30, Sat. 10.30-3. SIZE: Large. *STOCK: Furniture - pine, painted, oak, mahogany; blue and white, Staffordshire, lamps, candlesticks, samplers, prints, paintings, brass, mirrors, garden furniture, unusual items.* LOC: Half-way up left-hand side from High St. PARK: Meters. TEL: 020 7937 1306; fax - 020 7376 0223. VAT: Stan/Spec.

Lev (Antiques) Ltd
97A & B Kensington Church St. W8 7LN. (Mrs Lev). Est. 1882. Open 10.30-5.30. SIZE: Medium. *STOCK: Jewellery, silver, plate, curios.* PARK: Meters. TEL: 020 7727 9248; fax - same. SER: Restorations (pictures).

Lewis and Lloyd   BADA
65 Kensington Church St. W8 4BA. Est. 1968. Open 10.15-5.30, Sat. 10-1.30. SIZE: Medium. *STOCK: Furniture and works of art, 18th-19th C, £2,000-£100,000.* PARK: Easy. TEL: 020 7938 3323; fax - 020 7361 0086. VAT: Spec.

Libra Antiques
131d Kensington Church St. W8. *STOCK: Blue and white pottery, lustre ware.* TEL: 020 7727 2990.

London Antique Gallery
66E Kensington Church St. W8 4BY. (Mr and Mrs C.D. Wertheim). Open 10-6. *STOCK: Porcelain including English, Meissen, Dresden and Sèvres; French and German bisque dolls.* TEL: 020 7229 2934; fax - same. SER: Restorations (prints, porcelain and dolls).

Fay Lucas Gallery   BADA
50 Kensington Church St. W8 4DA. LAPADA. Est. 1977. *STOCK: Fine signed silver holloware, 20th C, £200-£50,000; signed furniture, 20th C, £5,000-£50,000; antique military and sporting jewellery, £100-£3,000.* LOC: Off Kensington High St. PARK: Kensington Town Hall. TEL: 020 7938 3763; fax - 020 7376 1005; e-mail - faylucasgallery@btinternet.com. SER: Valuations; restorations; buys at auction. FAIRS: Olympia (Feb., June, Nov.). VAT: Stan/Spec.

C.H. Major (Antiques) Ltd
154 Kensington Church St. W8 4BN. Est. 1905. Open Mon.-Fri. 10-5.30, Sat. 10-2. SIZE: Large. *STOCK: English furniture, from 1760, £200-£25,000.* PARK: Easy. TEL: 020 7229 1162; fax - 020 7221 9676; e-mail - majorantiques@ukonline.co.uk.VAT: Stan/Spec.

E. and H. Manners   BADA
66a Kensington Church St. W8 4BY. Est. 1986. Open Mon.-Fri. 10-5.30 appointment advisable. *STOCK: European ceramics, pre-19th C, £100-£20,000.* TEL: 020 7229 5516; fax - same; home - 020 8741 7084; e-mail - manners@europeanporcelain.com; website - www.europeanporcelain.com. FAIRS: International Ceramic. VAT: Spec.

S. Marchant & Son   BADA
120 Kensington Church St. W8 4BH. (R.P. Marchant). Est. 1925. Open 9.30-5.30. CL: Sat. *STOCK: Chinese and Japanese pottery and porcelain, jades, cloisonné, Chinese furniture and paintings.* PARK: Easy. TEL: 020 7229 5319/3770; fax - 020 7792 8979. SER: Valuations; restorations (porcelain); buys at auction. VAT: Stan/Spec.

Robert McPherson
at Stockspring Antiques, 114 Kensington Church St. W8 4BH. Est. 1985. Open 10-5.30, Sat. 10-1. *STOCK: Chinese ceramics, 2500 BC to 1800, £5-£10,000.* TEL: 020 7727 7995; website - www.orientalceramics.com. FAIRS: Olympia (June). VAT: Spec.

Michael Coins
6 Hillgate St., (off Notting Hill Gate). W8 7SR. (M. Gouby). Est. 1966. Open 10-5. CL: Mon. and Sat. SIZE: Small. *STOCK: Coins, English and foreign, 1066 A.D. to date; stamps, banknotes and collectors' items.* LOC: From Marble Arch to Notting Hill Gate, turn left at corner of Coronet Cinema. PARK: Easy. TEL: 020 7727 1518; fax - 020 7727 1518; website - www.michael-coins.co.uk. SER: Valuations; buys at auction. VAT: Stan/Spec.

New Century
69 Kensington Church St. W8 4BG. (H.S. Lyons). Est. 1988. *STOCK: Arts and Crafts, aesthetic and Art Nouveau furniture, metal and ceramics, 1870-1920, £20-£3,000.* TEL: 020 7937 2410. SER: Valuations; restorations; buys at auction. VAT: Stan/Spec.

Pawsey and Payne   BADA
PO Box 11830 W8. (Hon. N.V.B. and L.N.J. Wallop). Est. 1910. Open by appointment. *STOCK: English oils and watercolours, 18th-19th C.* TEL: 020 7930 4221; fax - 020 7937 3440; e-mail - nicholas@wallop3.freeserve. co.uk. SER: Valuations; restorations. VAT: Stan/Spec.

Pruskin Gallery
73 Kensington Church St. W8 4BG. *STOCK: Fine Art Nouveau and Art Deco glass, bronzes, silver, furniture, ceramics, paintings, posters and prints.* TEL: 020 7937 1994; evenings - 020 7938 2892.

Raffety & Walwyn   BADA

79 Kensington Church St. W8 4BG. LAPADA, CINOA. Open 10.30-5.30, Sat. 11-2.30. *STOCK: Fine English longcase and bracket clocks, 17th-18th C; carriage clocks and barometers; period furniture.* TEL: 020 7938 1100; fax - 020 7938 2519; website - www.raffetyantiqueclocks.com. SER: Valuations; buys at auction. VAT: Stan/Spec.

Paul Reeves

32B Kensington Church St. W8 4HA. Est. 1976. Open 10-6, Sat. 11-4. *STOCK: Architect designed furniture and artifacts, 1860-1960.* TEL: 020 7937 1594.

Reindeer Antiques Ltd   BADA

81 Kensington Church St. W8 4BG. (Adrian Butterworth). LAPADA. Open 9.30-6, Sat. 10.30-5.30. *STOCK: Period English and Continental furniture and works of art.* PARK: Meters. TEL: 020 7937 3754; fax - 020 7937 7199. VAT: Stan/Spec.

Roderick Antique Clocks

23 Vicarage Gate, Kensington. W8 4AA. (R. Mee). LAPADA. Est. 1975. Open 10-5.15, Sat. 10-3. *STOCK: Clocks - French decorative and carriage, 19th C, £250-£3,500; English longcase and bracket, 18th-19th C, £2,000-£12,000.* LOC: At junction of Kensington Church St. PARK: Easy. TEL: 020 7937 8517. SER: Valuations; restorations (English and French movements and cases). VAT: Spec.

Brian Rolleston Antiques Ltd   BADA

104A Kensington Church St. W8 4BU. Est. 1950. Open 10-1 and 2-5.30. SIZE: Large. *STOCK: English furniture, 18th C.* TEL: 020 7229 5892; fax - same.

Russell Rare Books

Flat 6 Evelyn House, 8-10 Horton St. W8 4NW. (C. Russell). Open by appointment. *STOCK: Antiquarian books.* TEL: 020 7938 4070; fax - 020 7937 5860.

Dyala Salam Antiques

174A Kensington Church St. W8 4DP. Est. 1990. Open 11-5.30, Sat. 11.30-3.30. SIZE: Small. *STOCK: Textiles, glass and furniture from the Ottoman Empire, 18th-19th C, from £200.* PARK: Nearby. TEL: 020 7229 4045; fax - 020 7229 2433. VAT: Spec.

Patrick Sandberg Antiques   BADA

150-152 Kensington Church St. W8 4BN. (P.C.F. Sandberg). Est. 1983. Open 10-6, Sat. 10-4. SIZE: Large. *STOCK: 18th to early 19th C English furniture and accessories - candlesticks,* tea caddies, clocks and prints. TEL: 020 7229 0373; fax - 020 7792 3467. FAIRS: Olympia (Feb., June, Nov). VAT: Spec.

Santos   BADA

21 Old Court House. W8 4PD. Open by appointment only. *STOCK: Chinese export porcelain, 17th-18th C.* TEL: 020 7937 6000; fax - 020 7937 3351; website - www.santoslondon.com. VAT: Spec.

Sinai Antiques Ltd

219-221 Kensington Church St. W8 7LX. (E. Sinai and Sons). KCSADA. Est. 1973. Open 10-6, Sat. and Sun. by appointment. *STOCK: Fine 19th C Continental furniture, clocks, porcelain, chandeliers and objet d'art; Oriental and Islamic decorative arts and antiques.* TEL: 020 7229 6190; fax - 020 7221 0543.

Simon Spero

109 Kensington Church St. W8 7LN. Author of 'The Price Guide to 18th C English Porcelain' and three other standard reference books. Est. 1964. Open 10-5, Sat. by appointment. SIZE: Medium. *STOCK: 18th C English ceramics and enamels.* PARK: Meters. TEL: 020 7727 7413; fax - 020 7727 7414. SER: Valuations; buys at auction; lecturer. VAT: Spec.

Stockspring Antiques   BADA

114 Kensington Church St. W8 4BH. (A. Agnew and F. Marno). LAPADA. Open 10-5.30, Sat. 10-1. *STOCK: English, European and Oriental pottery and porcelain.* TEL: 020 7727 7995; fax - same; e-mail - stockspring@antique-porcelain.co.uk. VAT: Spec.

Pamela Teignmouth and Son

108 Kensington Church St. W8 4BH. (Lady Teignmouth and Mr T. Meyer). Est. 1982. Open 10-6, including Sat. in winter only. SIZE: Medium. *STOCK: English and Continental furniture, 18th-19th C, decorative items, £100-£10,000.* TEL: 020 7229 1602; fax - 020 7792 5042. FAIRS: Olympia (June). VAT: Spec.

Through the Looking Glass Ltd

137 Kensington Church St. W8 7LP. (J.J.A. and D.A. Pulton). Est. 1958. Open 10-5.30. SIZE: Large. *STOCK: Mirrors, 19th C, £500-£10,000.* LOC: 200yds. from Notting Hill Gate. PARK: Side roads. TEL: 020 7221 4026. SER: Gilding. VAT: Spec.

Jorge Welsh Oriental Porcelain & Works of Art   BADA

116 Kensington Church St. W8 4BH. Est. 1987. Open 10-5.30; Sat. 10-2. SIZE: Medium. *STOCK: Chinese export porcelain and Oriental works of art.* LOC: Off Kensington High St.

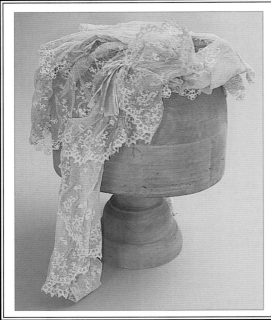

The hat has long been a status-symbol; this theme can make a fascinating collectable category. Married ladies of the Victorian period generally wore a black or white lace cap indoors, of which we have a fine example in our collection. Such caps featured two lengths of lace on either side, known as 'lappets' which were lengthened as the wearer progressed in years.

From an article entitled 'From Royal to Rock 'n' Roll – Hats for the Collector' by Anne Noëlle Tamplin which appeared in the May 2001 issue of **Antique Collecting** magazine. For more details and to subscribe see page 147.

PARK: NCP Bayswater Rd. TEL: 020 7229 2140; fax - 020 7792 3535; website - www.jorgewelsh.com. SER: Valuations; restorations; buys at auction. FAIRS: International Ceramic. VAT: Spec.

Neil Wibrow and Natasha MacIlwaine
77 Kensington Church St. W8 4BG. Open 9-6. *STOCK: 18th C English furniture and works of art.* TEL: 020 7937 2461; fax - 020 7938 3286. VAT: Spec.

Mary Wise & Grosvenor Antiques
BADA
27 Holland St., Kensington. W8 4NA. Est. 1959. STOCK: English porcelain, works of art, bronzes. Not Stocked: English pottery, jewellery. TEL: 020 7937 8649; fax - 020 7937 7179. SER: Buys at auction (Chinese and English porcelain). VAT: Spec.

Yang Guifei
140 Kensington Church St. W8 4JD. (Anne Marie Ellis). KCSADA. Est. 1999. Open 10.30-6, Sat. 10.30-4. CL: Mon. SIZE: Small. *STOCK: Chinese Shanxi lacquer cabinets, 18th-19th C, £2,500-£20,000; Oriental furniture, 18th-19th C, £1,500-£5,000; Han Tang pottery, 206BC to 906AD, £1,500-£15,000.* PARK: Meters. TEL: 020 7792 1637; fax - 020 7792 0529. FAIRS: Asian Art: Daily Telegraph House & Garden. VAT: Margin.

W9

Fluss and Charlesworth Ltd
1 Lauderdale Rd. W9 1LT. (E. Fluss and J. Charlesworth). LAPADA. Est. 1970. Open by appointment. *STOCK: 18th to early 19th C furniture and works of art.* TEL: 020 7286 8339; mobile - 07831 830323. SER: Interior decor. FAIRS: Olympia; LAPADA.

Beryl Kendall, The English Watercolour Gallery
2 Warwick Place, Little Venice. W9 2PX. Est. 1953. Open 2-6, Sat. 11-3.30. CL: Mon. *STOCK: English watercolours, 19th C.* TEL: 020 7286 9902.

Vale Antiques
245 Elgin Ave., Maida Vale. W9 1NJ. (P. Gooley). *STOCK: General antiques.* TEL: 020 7328 4796.

W11

Admiral Vernon Antiques Market
141-149 Portobello Rd. W11. (Angelo Soteriades). Open Sat. 5-5. SIZE: About 200 dealers. *STOCK: Wide range of general antiques and collectables.* TEL: 020 7727 5242; mobile - 07956 277077; e-

mail - info@portobello-antiques.com; website - www.portobello-antiques.co.uk.

Alice's
86 Portobello Rd. W11 2QD. (D. Carter). Est. 1960. Open 9-5. SIZE: Large. *STOCK: General antiques and decorative items.* TEL: 020 7229 8187; fax - 020 7792 2456.

Arbras Gallery
292 Westbourne Grove. W11 2PS. Est. 1972. Open Fri. 10-4, Sat. 7-5. SIZE: 2 floors. *STOCK: General antiques - silver, jewellery, glass, porcelain, clocks, scientific instruments, decorative arts and antiquities.* LOC: 50 yards from Portobello Road. TEL: 020 7229 6772; fax - same. VAT: Stan/Spec.

Axia Art Consultants Ltd
121 Ledbury Rd. W11 2AQ. Est. 1974. *STOCK: Works of art, icons, textiles, metalwork, woodwork and ceramics, Islamic and Byzantine.* TEL: 020 7727 9724.

B. and T. Antiques
79/81 Ledbury Rd. W11 2AG. (Mrs B. Lewis). LAPADA. Open 10-6. *STOCK: Furniture, silver, objets d'art, paintings, 18th C to Art Deco.* TEL: 020 7229 7001; fax - 020 7229 2033; e-mail - bt.antiques@virgin.net.

Sebastiano Barbagallo
15-17 Pembridge Rd., Notting Hill Gate. W11 3HL. Est. 1975. Open 10.30-6 including Sun., Sat. 9-7. SIZE: Medium. *STOCK: Chinese furniture; antiques and handicrafts from India, Tibet, SE Asia and China.* LOC: Just before Portobello Road. TEL: 020 7792 3320; fax - same. VAT: Stan.

P.R. Barham
111 Portobello Rd. W11 2QB. Est. 1951. Open 9-5. SIZE: Large. *STOCK: Victorian, Edwardian, Continental furniture, Oriental porcelain, objets d'art, silver, plate and clocks.* TEL: 020 7727 3397. SER: Valuations; buys at auction.

Barham Antiques
83 Portobello Rd. W11. Est. 1954. Open 9.30-5, Sat. 7-5. SIZE: Large. *STOCK: Victorian and Georgian writing boxes, tea caddies, inkwells and inkstands, glass epergnes, silver plate, clocks, paintings and Victorian furniture.* TEL: 020 7727 3845; fax - same; e-mail - mchlbarham@aol.com. SER: Valuations; buys at auction.

David Black Oriental Carpets
96 Portland Rd., Holland Park. W11 4LN. Est. 1966. Open 11-6. SIZE: Large. *STOCK: Antique and new Oriental room size decorative carpets; tribal rugs, kilims, dhurries, embroideries, £500-£25,000.* LOC: From Notting Hill Gate, second right after Holland Park tube station. PARK: Meters. TEL: 020 7727 2566; fax - 020 7229 4599. SER: Valuations; restorations; cleaning underfelt. VAT: Spec.

Elizabeth Bradwin
Stands 1 & 2, 75 Portobello Rd. W11 2QB. Est. 1989. Open 10.30-4.30, Sat. 7-5. SIZE: Small. *STOCK: Animal subjects, including animalier bronzes, 19th-20th C, £100-£4,000; Vienna bronzes, Staffordshire, carved wood, inkwells, tobacco jars.* PARK: Easy. TEL: 020 7221 1121; home and fax - 020 8947 2629; mobile - 07778 731826; website - www.elizabethbradwin.com. VAT: Spec.

Butchoff Antiques
220 and 229 Westbourne Grove. W11 2SE. LAPADA. Est. 1962. Open 10-6, Sat. 10-3.30. SIZE: Large. *STOCK: Fine 18th-19th C English and Continental furniture, decorative smalls and paintings, £500-£50,000.* TEL: 020 7221 8174; fax - 020 7792 8923.

Caelt Gallery
182 Westbourne Grove. W11 2RH. Est. 1967. Open 9.30-6, Sun. 10.30-6. SIZE: Large. *STOCK: Oil paintings, 17th-20th C, £200-£10,000 but mainly £300-£900.* PARK: Easy. TEL: 020 7229 9309; fax - 020 7727 8746; website - www.caeltgallery.com. VAT: Spec.

Canonbury
174 Westbourne Grove. W11 2RW. (M. Worster). Est. 1965. Open 10-6, Sat. 10-4.30. SIZE: Large. *STOCK: Dutch, English and French furniture; some porcelain.* LOC: Off Portobello Road. PARK: Easy. TEL: 020 7727 4268; fax - 020 7229 5840. SER: Valuations; restorations. VAT: Stan/Spec.

Jack Casimir Ltd   BADA
23 Pembridge Rd. W11 3HG. LAPADA. Est. 1933. Open 10-5.30 and by appointment. SIZE: Large. *STOCK: Brass, copper, pewter, paktong.* Not Stocked: Silver, china, jewellery. LOC: 2 mins. walk from Notting Hill Gate station. PARK: 100yds. TEL: 020 7727 8643. SER: Exports. VAT: Stan/Spec.

Central Gallery (Portobello)
125 Portobello Rd. W11 2DY. Open Sat. 6-3. SIZE: 25+ dealers. *STOCK: 18th C to present day cameos, hardstone, shell, lava, coral, amber, ivory, jet, tortoiseshell, piqué, micro-mosaics, pietra-dura, Art Nouveau, plique é jour, horn pendants, Art Deco, enamels, Austro-Hungarian,*

cut-steel, Berlin iron, Scottish, Victorian silver and gold, Alberts, Albertines, longuards, curbs, gates, fobs, seals, intaglios, pocket watches, vintage wristwatches, cufflinks, fine diamonds, rare gemstones, signed pieces, pearls, from £50-£5,000+. TEL: 020 7243 8027; fax - same. FAIRS: Olympia; Park Lane Hotel (every Sunday); Miami Beach. VAT: Stan/Spec/Global.

The Coach House   BADA

Ledbury Mews North, Notting Hill. W11 2AF. (Jay Arenski and Peter Petrou). LAPADA. Open by appointment only. *STOCK: Fine furniture - Regency, Gothic Revival, Arts & Crafts, Aesthetic, Colonial and Campaign, Islamic and Egyptian Revival; oil paintings including maritime, Old Masters and modern, naïve portraits including animal, watercolours and prints; classical and Vienna bronzes, Grand Tour items, ormolu, metalware and treen; decorative glass, silver and plate, pottery including majolica, equestrian objects and tribal art, £200-£200,000.* Not Stocked: Shipping goods and jewellery. PARK: Easy. TEL: 020 7727 8599/7229 9575; fax - 020 7727 7584; e-mail - arenski@netcomuk.co.uk and peterpetrou@btinternet.com; websites - www.arenski.com and www.peterpetrou.com. SER: Interior decor; shipping arranged. FAIRS: Olympia (June); BADA (May). VAT: Stan/Spec.

Cohen & Cohen (Oriental Porcelain)   BADA

84 Portobello Rd. W11 2QD. (M. and E. Cohen). Est. 1974. Open Fri. 10-4, Sat. 8-4 or by appointment. *STOCK: Chinese porcelain, bronzes, works of art; Japanese prints.* TEL: 020 7229 9458; fax - 020 7229 9653. SER: Valuations; buys at auction. VAT: Spec.

Garrick D. Coleman

75 Portobello Rd. W11. Est. 1944. Open 10.30-4.30, Sat. 8.30-3.30. *STOCK: Chess sets, 1750-1880, £300-£15,000; works of art £50-£3,000; glass paperweights, £200-£3,000; also conjuring and magic items.* TEL: 020 7937 5524; fax - 020 7937 5530; e-mail - coleman-antiques-london@ compuserve.com; website - www. antiquechess. co.uk/. VAT: Stan/Spec.

Sheila Cook

283 Westbourne Grove. W11 2QA. Est. 1970. SIZE: Medium. *STOCK: Textiles, costume and accessories, 1750-1980, £15-£3,000.* PARK: Meters. TEL: 020 7792 8001; fax - 020 7229 3855; e-mail - sheilacook@sheilacook.co.uk; website - www.sheilacook.co.uk. SER: Valuations. VAT: Global/Spec.

The Corner Portobello Antiques Supermarket

282-290 Westbourne Grove. W11. (B. Lipka & Son Ltd). Open Fri. 12-4, Sat. 7-5. SIZE: 150 dealers. *STOCK: General miniature antiques, silver and jewellery.* TEL: 020 7727 2027. SER: Valuations; restorations.

Crawley and Asquith Ltd   BADA

The Studio House, 117 Ladbroke Rd. W11 3PR. Open by appointment. *STOCK: 18th-19th C paintings, watercolours, prints, books.* TEL: 020 7229 0660; fax - 020 7229 2440.

Crown Arcade

119 Portobello Rd. W11. (Angelo Soteriades). Est. 1986. Open Sat. 5.30-5.30. SIZE: Medium. *STOCK: 18th-19th C glass, bronzes, sculpture, silver, jewellery, Arts & Crafts, Art Nouveau, Art Deco.* LOC: Near Westbourne Grove. TEL: 020 7436 9416/7792 3619; mobile - 07956 277077; e-mail - info@portobello-antiques.com; website - www.portobello-collections.co.uk.

Curá Antiques

34 Ledbury Rd. W11 2AB. (G. and M. Antichi). Open 11-6, Sat. 10.30-1. *STOCK: Continental furniture, sculptures, majolica and paintings.* TEL: 020 7229 6880.

Daggett Gallery

1st and 2nd Floors, 153 Portobello Rd. W11 2DY. (Caroline Daggett). LAPADA. Est. 1992. Open 10-5 (prior telephone call advisable) and Sat. 9-3.30. SIZE: Medium. *STOCK: Frames, 18th-20th C, from £1.* LOC: 200 yards from Westbourne Grove towards Elgin Crescent. PARK: Meters. TEL: 020 7229 2248. SER: Restorations (frames); gilding; picture plaques; framing; special paint effects. VAT: Stan/Spec.

Charles Daggett Gallery

1st and 2nd Floors, 153 Portobello Rd. W11 2DY. (Charles and Caroline Daggett). LAPADA. Est. 1977. Open 10-4, prior telephone call advisable, and Sat. 9-3.30. SIZE: Medium. *STOCK: British pictures, 1740-1840.* LOC: 200 yards from Westbourne Grove, towards Elgin Crescent. PARK: Meters. TEL: 020 7229 2248; fax - 020 7229 0193. SER: Restorations (pictures and frames); framing. VAT: Stan/Spec.

John Dale

87 Portobello Rd. W11 2QB. Est. 1950. Open 11-3, Sat. 7-5. SIZE: Medium. *STOCK: General antiques.* TEL: 020 7727 1304. VAT: Stan.

Michael Davidson

54 Ledbury Rd., Westbourne Grove. W11 2AJ. Est. 1961. Open 9.45-12.45 and 1.15-5. CL: Sat. pm. in winter. *STOCK: Regency and period*

furniture, objets d'art. TEL: 020 7229 6088. SER: Valuations. VAT: Stan/Spec.

Delehar
146 Portobello Rd. W11 2DZ. Est. 1919. Open Sat. 9-4. SIZE: Medium. *STOCK: General antiques, works of art.* Not Stocked: Furniture. TEL: 020 7727 9860. VAT: Spec.

Peter Delehar
146 Portobello Rd. W11 2DZ. Est. 1919. Open Sat. 10-4. SIZE: Medium. *STOCK: Unusual scientific and medical instruments.* TEL: 020 7727 9860 (Sat.) or 020 8866 8659; fax - same; internet - www.peterdelehar.co.uk. FAIRS: International Scientific and Medical Instrument (Organiser). VAT: Stan/Spec.

Demetzy Books
113 Portobello Rd. W11. (P. and M. Hutchinson). ABA, PBFA. Est. 1972. Open Sat. 7.30-3.30. SIZE: Medium. *STOCK: Antiquarian leather bound books, 18th-19th C, £5-£1,000; Dickens' first editions and children's and illustrated books, 18th-20th C, £5-£200.* LOC: 20yds. from junction with Westbourne Grove, opposite Earl of Lonsdale public house. PARK: Meters. TEL: 01993 702209. SER: Buys at auction (books). FAIRS: ABA Chelsea; PBFA Russell Hotel, London (monthly); Randolph Hotel, Oxford; ABAA Los Angeles, San Francisco.

Dolphin Arcade
155-157 Portobello Rd. W11. Open Sat. 7-5.30. SIZE: Large - 34 stalls. *STOCK: Jewellery, silver, Oriental porcelain, English pottery, general antiques.* VAT: Stan/Spec.

Gavin Douglas
75 Portobello Rd. W11 2QB. (G.A. and D.J. Douglas). PADA. Est. 1993. Open 10.30-4.30, Sat. 7-5. SIZE: Medium. *STOCK: Neo-classical clocks, 18th -19th C, to £20,000; bronzes, sculpture, porcelain and objects, to £30,000.* PARK: Easy. TEL: 0207 221 1121; 01825 723441; fax - 01825 724418; website - www.antique-clocks.co.uk; e-mail - gavin@antique-clocks.co.uk. SER: Valuations; restorations; buys at auction. VAT: Stan/Spec.

The Facade
196 Westbourne Grove. W11 2RH. Est. 1973. Open Tues.-Sat. 10.30-5. *STOCK: French decorative items and lighting, 1900-1940.* PARK: Easy. TEL: 020 7727 2159. VAT: Stan.

Fairman Carpets Ltd
218 Westbourne Grove. W11 2RH. (D.R.J. and S.J. Page). Open 10-6. *STOCK: Persian and Oriental carpets and rugs.* TEL: 020 7229 2262; fax - 020 7229 2263; e-mail - fairman-carpets@ukonline.co.uk; website - www.fairmancarpets.co.uk. SER: Valuations; repairs; cleaning. VAT: Stan.

Fleur de Lys Gallery
227a Westbourne Grove. W11 2SE. (H.S. Coronel). Est. 1967. Open 10.30-5.30. SIZE: Medium. *STOCK: Oil paintings, 19th C, £2,000-£6,000.* PARK: Easy, but limited. TEL: 020 7727 8595; fax - same; home - 01372 467934; website - www.fleur-de-lys.com; e-mail - henrifdel@panther.netmania.co.uk.

Judy Fox
81 Portobello Rd. and 176 Westbourne Grove. W11. LAPADA. Est. 1970. Open 10-5. SIZE: Large. *STOCK: Furniture and decorative items, 18th-20th C; inlaid furniture, mainly 19th C; pottery and porcelain.* TEL: 020 7229 8130; fax - 020 7229 6998.

J. Freeman
85a Portobello Rd. W11 2QB. LAPADA. Est. 1962. Open 9.30-1 and 2-5, Sat. 9-6. SIZE: Medium. *STOCK: Victorian silver plate, 1830-1870, £10-£150; Sheffield plate, 1790-1830, £20-£100; Victorian and later silver, £5-£200.* LOC: Nearest tube station Notting Hill Gate. PARK: Easy. TEL: 020 7221 5076; fax - 020 7221 5329. VAT: Stan.

Graham and Green
4 Elgin Crescent. W11 2JA. (A. Graham and R. Harrison). Est. 1974. Open 10-6, Sat. 9.30-6, Sun. 11-5. SIZE: Medium. *STOCK: Turkish kelim rugs, European pine and Indian Colonial furniture, re-upholstered Victorian chairs and decorative objects.* LOC: Near Portobello Rd. PARK: Meters nearby. TEL: 020 7727 4594. VAT: Stan.

Gavin Graham Gallery
47 Ledbury Rd. W11 2AA. Est. 1973. *STOCK: Oil paintings.* TEL: 020 7229 4848; fax - 020 7792 9697. VAT: Spec.

Henry Gregory
82 Portobello Rd. W11 2QD. (H. and C. Gregory). Est. 1969. Open 10-4, Sat. 8-5. SIZE: Medium. *STOCK: Victorian decorative objects, silver, plate, jewellery, small furniture and sporting items, £2-£2,000.* LOC: Between Westbourne Grove and Chepstow Villas. PARK: Easy. TEL: 020 7792 9221; fax - same. SER: Export packing and shipping. VAT: Stan/Spec.

Hirst Antiques
59 Pembridge Rd. W11 3HG. Est. 1963. Open 10-6. SIZE: Medium. *STOCK: Four poster and*

half-tester beds; decorative furniture and articles; bronze and marble sculpture. LOC: End of Portobello Rd., near Notting Hill Gate tube station. TEL: 020 7727 9364. SER: Valuations.

J. and B. Antiques

at Geoffrey Van Arcade, 107 Portobello Rd. W11 2QB. (J.E. and C.A. Finch). LAPADA. Est. 1978. Open Sat. 7-4 or by appointment. SIZE: Medium. *STOCK: European works of art, 16th-20th C, £100-£5,000; antiquities, tribal art, £100-£10,000.* TEL: Mobiles - 07768 236921/ 07836 684133. SER: Valuations; buys at auction. VAT: Stan/Spec.

Jones Antique Lighting

194 Westbourne Grove. W11. (Judy Jones). Est. 1978. Open 9.30-6 or by appointment. SIZE: Large. *STOCK: Original decorative lighting, 1860-1960.* Not Stocked: Reproductions. TEL: 020 7229 6866; fax - same. SER: Valuations; repairs; prop hire. VAT: Stan.

Kleanthous Antiques

144 Portobello Rd. W11 2DZ. LAPADA. Open Sat. only 8-4 and by appointment. TEL: 020 7727 3649; fax - 01923 897618; mobile - 07850 375501. Below are listed some of the dealers at this market.

James Forbes Fine Art

Est. 1982. *Works of art, silver and jewellery, from 1700, £50-£5,000.* TEL: 01886 821216.

Kleanthous Antiques Ltd

LAPADA. Est. 1969. Open Sat. 7.30-4 and by appointment. *Specially selected pieces of jewellery - Georgian, Victorian, Art Nouveau, Art Deco, to 1950; vintage pocket and wrist watches by Rolex, Cartier, Patek Phillipe, Vacheron and Constantin, Jaeger le Coultre, Longines, I.W.C., Universal and Omega; English and Continental silver, 18th-20th C; boudoir, desk, carriage and mantel clocks; objects of vertu; furniture. Full guarantee with all purchases.* TEL: 020 7727 3649; fax - 020 7243 2488; mobile - 07850 375501/375502; e-mail - antiques@kleanthous.com. VAT: Stan/Spec.

S. and G. Antiques

(G. Sirett). *Specialist in miniature porcelain cups and saucers, teasets and vases, £25-£500; English and Continental glass, £25-£1,000; Meissen porcelain and objets d'art, £20-£5,000.* TEL: 020 7229 2178 (Sat.); 020 8907 7140; fax - 020 8909 3277; mobile - 07768 366677. VAT: Stan/Spec.

Lacy Gallery

203 Westbourne Grove. W11 2AB. Est. 1960. Open Tues.-Fri.10-5, Sat. 10-4. SIZE: Large. *STOCK: Period frames, 1700-1940; decorative paintings and art.* LOC: Two roads east of

Portobello Rd. PARK: Easy. TEL: 020 7229 6340; fax - 020 7229 9105. VAT: Stan/Spec.

M. and D. Lewis

1 Lonsdale Rd., 172 Westbourne Grove, 83-85 Ledbury Rd. W11. Est. 1960. Open 9.30-5.30, Sat. 9.30-4. *STOCK: Continental and Victorian furniture, porcelain, bronzes.* TEL: 020 7727 3908. VAT: Stan.

M.C.N. Antiques

183 Westbourne Grove. W11 2SB. Open 9.30-6 or by appointment. *STOCK: Japanese porcelain, cloisonné, Satsuma, bronze, lacquer, ivory.* LOC: Near Portobello Rd. market. PARK: Easy. TEL: 020 7727 3796; fax - 020 7229 8839. SER: Buys at auction. VAT: Stan.

Robin Martin Antiques

44 Ledbury Rd. W11 2AB. (Paul Martin). Est. 1972. Open 10-6. SIZE: Medium. *STOCK: English and Continental furniture and works of art, 17th-19th C.* LOC: Westbourne Grove area. TEL: 020 7727 1301; fax - same; mobile - 07831 544055. VAT: Spec.

Mayflower Antiques

117 Portobello Rd. W11. (J.W. Odgers). Est. 1970. Open Sat. 7-5. SIZE: Medium. *STOCK: Clocks, mechanical music, scientific and marine instruments, general antiques.* TEL: Sat. - 020 7727 0381; office - 01255 504079; fax - same; mobile - 07860 843569; e-mail - mayflower@ ukshells.co.uk. VAT: Stan/Spec.

Mercury Antiques   BADA

1 Ladbroke Rd. W11 3PA. (L. Richards). Est. 1963. Open 10-5.30, Sat. 10-1. SIZE: Medium. **STOCK: English porcelain, 1745-1840; English pottery and Delft, 1700-1850; glass, 1780-1850. Not Stocked: Jewellery, silver, plate, Art Nouveau. LOC: Half minute from Notting Hill Gate underground station, turn into Pembridge Rd. and bear left. TEL: 020 7727 5106; fax - 020 7229 3738. VAT: Spec.**

Milne and Moller

W11 2BU. (Mr and Mrs C. Moller). LAPADA. Est. 1976. Open by appointment. SIZE: Small. *STOCK: Watercolours, oils, ceramics and sculpture, 19th C to contemporary.* LOC: Near junction of Westbourne Grove and Ledbury Rd. PARK: Easy. TEL: 020 7727 1679; home - same. SER: Portrait commissioning. FAIRS: Olympia; Chelsea Art. VAT: Spec.

Mimi Fifi

27 Pembridge Rd., Notting Hill Gate. W11 3HG. (Mrs Rita Delaforge). Est. 1990. Open 11-6.30, Sat. 10-7, Sun. 11-4. SIZE: Medium. *STOCK: Vintage and collectable toys and memorabilia,*

20th C, £5-£500; perfume miniatures and related collectables, 19th-20th C, £5-£1,000; advertising and tobacco related collectables, 19th-20th C, £5-£500. LOC: 200 yards from Notting Hill underground. PARK: Nearby. TEL: 020 7243 3154; fax - 020 7938 4222.

Terence Morse and Son Ltd
237 Westbourne Grove. W11 2SE. Est. 1947. Open 10-6, Sat. 11-2. SIZE: Large. *STOCK: Furniture, 18th-19th C, £1,000+.* LOC: 200yds. from Portobello Rd. PARK: Easy. TEL: 020 7229 4059; fax - 020 7792 3284. VAT: Stan/Spec.

Myriad Antiques
131 Portland Rd., Holland Park Ave. W11 4LW. (S. Nickerson). Est. 1970. Open 11-6. SIZE: Medium. *STOCK: Decorative and unusual furniture (including garden) and objects, mainly 19th C, £10-£1,500.* LOC: Between Notting Hill Gate and Shepherds Bush roundabout. TEL: 020 7229 1709. VAT: Stan.

Old Father Time Clock Centre
Portobello Studios, 1st Floor, 101 Portobello Rd. W11 2QB. (John Denvir). Open Fri. 10-1, Sat. 8-2, other times by appointment. *STOCK: Clocks - all types, especially electric (eg. Eureka), mystery, Atmos, novelty, skeleton, carriage, dial and bracket; also spares, books and barometers.* TEL: 020 8546 6299; fax - same; 020 7727 3394; mobile - 07836 712088; website -www. oldfathertime.net; e-mail - clocks@oldfathertime. net.

E.S. Phillips and Sons
99 Portobello Rd. W11 2QB. LAPADA. Est.

1962. Open 10-5. *STOCK: Ecclesiastical antiques and stained glass.* TEL: 020 7229 2113; fax - 020 7229 1963.

Richard Philp   BADA
59 Ledbury Rd. W11 2AA. SLAD. Est. 1961. Open by appointment. *STOCK: Old Master drawings, 16th-17th C English portraiture and Old Master paintings, medieval sculpture, early furniture and 20th C drawings, £50-£40,000.* PARK: Easy. TEL: 020 7727 7915. VAT: Spec.

Piano Nobile Fine Paintings
129 Portland Rd., Holland Park. W11 4LW. (Dr Robert A. Travers). SLAD. Est. 1986. Open Tues.-Sat. 10-5.30. SIZE: Medium. *STOCK: Fine 19th C Impressionist and 20th C Post-Impressionist and Modernist British and Continental oil paintings and sculpture, especially Les Petit Maitres of the Paris Schools, £500-£100,000.* PARK: Easy. TEL: 020 7229 1099; fax - same; e-mail -robert@ pianonobile.fsnet.co.uk; website - www.piano-nobile.com. SER: Valuations; restorations (paintings and sculptures); framing; buys at auction (19th-20th C oil paintings). FAIRS: Grosvenor; 20th C British Art; Olympia: BADA; Art London.

Portobello Antique Co
133 Portobello Rd. W11 2DY. (L. Meltzer and A. Goldsmith). Open Fri. 11-4.30, Sat. 8-4.30, other times by appointment. *STOCK: Porcelain, small furniture, reproduction silver plate and cutlery.* LOC: Off Westbourne Grove. PARK: Easy. TEL: 020 7221 0344; home - 020 8959 8886. VAT: Stan/Spec.

One of four children's pastimes, pub: Valentine (1939). Artist: May Smith (born 1904).

BUMBLEBEE IS BEING SCRUBBED AND SOAPED AND RUBBED AND BLUED AND DRUBBED; WE'LL NEVER MIND IF THEY GET HIM WHITE, HE KNOWS SOME MUD THAT'LL PUT THAT RIGHT.

From an article entitled 'Little Treasures – Collecting Children's Postcards' by Dawn and Peter Cope which appeared in the June 2001 issue of **Antique Collecting** magazine. For more details and to subscribe see page 147.

Justin F. Skrebowski Ground Floor, 177 Portobello Road, London, W11 2DY, UK
Tel/Fax/Answerphone: 020 7792 9742 Mobile: 07774 612474
e-mail: justin@skreb.co.uk website: www.skreb.co.uk

■ Folio Stands/Browsers

■ Display Easels

■ Desk Top Stands

■ Solid Mahogany

■ Beautiful Antique Finish

■ Exported Worldwide

■ Used by Galleries & Museums

■ Ideal for Studies & Homes

Portobello Antique Store

79 Portobello Rd. W11 2QB. (J.F. Ewing). Est. 1971. Open Tues.-Fri. 10-4, Sat. 8-4.30. SIZE: Large. STOCK: Silver and plate, £2-£3,000. LOC: Notting Hill end of Portobello Rd. PARK: Easy weekdays. TEL: 020 7221 1994. SER: Export. VAT: Stan.

Quadrille

146 Portobello Rd. W11 2DZ. (Valerie Jackson-Harris). Open Sat. 9-4. STOCK: Ephemera. TEL: 01923 829079; fax - 01923 825079.

The Red Lion Antiques Arcade

165/169 Portobello Rd. W11. (Angelo Soteriades). Est. 1951. Open Sat. 5.30-5.30. SIZE: 200 dealers. STOCK: General antiques including ethnic antiquities, bronzes, ivory statues, jade, precious metals, dolls, silver and plate, drinking vessels, costumes, Oriental and Western porcelain, furniture, collectables, prints, lace, linen, books, manuscripts, stamps, coins, banknotes, paintings, etchings, sporting memorabilia and curios. TEL: 020 7436 9416; mobile - 07956 277077; e-mail - info@portobello-antiques.com; website - www. portobello-collections.co.uk. SER: Valuations; shipping.

Rezai Persian Carpets

123 Portobello Rd. W11 2DY. Open 9-5. STOCK: Oriental carpets, kilims, tribal rugs and silk embroideries. TEL: 020 7221 5012.

Roger's Antiques Gallery

65 Portobello Rd. W11. (Bath Antiques Market Ltd). Open Sat. 7-4.30. SIZE: 65 dealers. STOCK: Wide range of general antiques and collectables with specialist dealers in most fields, especially jewellery. TEL: Enquiries - 020 7351 5353; fax - 020 7351 5350. SER: Valuations.

Schredds of Portobello

107 Portobello Rd. W11 2QB. (H.J. and G.R. Schrager). LAPADA. Est. 1969. Open Sat. 7.30-3. SIZE: Small. STOCK: Collectors' silver, 17th-19th C, £10-£1,000; Wedgwood, 18th-19th C. TEL: 020 8348 3314; home - same; fax - 020 8341 5971; website - www.schredds.com/. SER: Valuations; buys at auction. FAIRS: Kensington (Jan. and Aug.); Earls Court (Oct.). VAT: Stan/Spec.

The Silver Fox Gallery (Portobello)

121 Portobello Rd. W11 2DY. Open Sat. only 6-3. SIZE: 25+ dealers. STOCK: Jewellery - 18th C to 1960's including Victorian, Art Nouveau, Arts & Crafts, Art Deco, rings (diamond and gemset), earrings, brooches, pendants, gold and silver, Alberts, Albertines, chains longuards, bracelets, curbs, gates, fobs, seals, intaglios, pocket watches, vintage wristwatches, cufflinks, fine diamonds, rare gemstones, cameos, coral, amber, ivory, jet tortoiseshell, piqué, micro-mosaics, pietra-dura, lava, horn pendants, enamels, pearls, Austro-Hungarian cut steel, Berlin iron, Scottish, niello, £50-£5,000+. TEL: 020 7243 8027; fax - same. FAIRS: Olympia; Park Lane Hotel (every Sunday). VAT: Stan/Spec/Global.

Justin F. Skrebowski Prints

Ground Floor, 177 Portobello Rd. W11 2DY. Est. 1985. Open Sat. 9-4, otherwise by appointment. SIZE: Small. STOCK: Prints, engravings and lithographs, 1700-1850, £50-£500; oil paintings, 1700-1900, £200-£1,500; watercolours, drawings including Old Masters, 1600-1900, £50-£1,000; modern mahogany folio stands and easels; frames - gilt, rosewood, maple, carved, 18th-19th C. LOC: Close to Portobello Road. PARK: Meters. TEL: 020 7792 9742; mobile - 07774 612474; e-mail - justin@skreb.co.uk; website - www.skreb. co.uk. SER: Valuations. VAT: Stan/Spec.

Colin Smith and Gerald Robinson Antiques

105 Portobello Rd. W11 2QB. Est. 1979. Open Sat., and Fri. by appointment. SIZE: Large. STOCK: Tortoiseshell, £100-£2,000; silver, ivory and crocodile items. TEL: 020 8994 3783/020 7225 1163. FAIRS: Olympia. VAT: Stan.

Stern Art Dealers

46 Ledbury Rd. W11 2AB. (David Stern).
LAPADA. Est. 1963. Open 10-6. SIZE: Medium.
*STOCK: Oil paintings, 19th-20th C, especially
the Pissarro family, £500-£16,000.* LOC: Off
Westbourne Grove near Portobello. PARK: Easy.
TEL: 020 7229 6187. SER: Valuations;
restorations. VAT: Stan.

Still Too Few

300 Westbourne Grove. W11 2PS. Est. 1995.
Open Sat. 7.30-2. SIZE: Medium. LOC: 50 yards
from Portobello Rd. TEL: 020 7727 7752. Below
are listed the dealers at this address.

David Glick
17th-20th C glass.

Kitchen and Country Antiques
*18th-20th C wood and metalware, pond yachts,
garden tools.*

Frances Wainford
*China and glass, pine furniture, bed and table
linen, 1900-1950's.*

June and Tony Stone Fine Antique Boxes

75 Portobello Rd. W11 2QB. LAPADA. Open
10.30-4.30, Sat. 8-5. *STOCK: Fine boxes
especially tea caddies, 18th-19th C, £200-
£30,000.* TEL: Office - 01273 579333; fax -
01273 588908; Sales - 07092 106600; fax -
07092 106611; e-mail - jts@boxes.co.uk; website
- www.boxes.co.uk. FAIRS: Olympia (June, Nov.
and Feb); LAPADA (Oct.); Claridges (April);
Harrogate (April, Sept.). VAT: Stan/Spec.

Temple Gallery

6 Clarendon Cross. W11 4AP. (R.C.C. Temple).
Est. 1959. Open 10-6, weekends and evenings by
appointment. SIZE: Large. *STOCK: Icons,
Russian and Greek, 12th-16th C, £1,000-£50,000.*
PARK: Easy. TEL: 020 7727 3809; fax - 020
7727 1546; e-mail - templegallery@cs.com;
website - www.temple-russianicons.com. SER:
Valuations; restorations; buys at auction (icons);
illustrated catalogues published. VAT: Spec.

Themes and Variations

231 Westbourne Grove. W11 2SE. (L. Fawcett).
Open 10-1 and 2-6, Sat 10-6. *STOCK: Post war
and contemporary decorative items, furniture,
glass, ceramics, carpets, lamps, jewellery.* TEL:
020 7727 5531; fax - 020 7221 6378.

Tomkinson Stained Glass

87 Portobello Rd. W11 2QB. (S. Tomkinson).
Open 10-5, Sat. 7-5. SIZE: Medium. *STOCK:
Stained glass windows.* LOC: 5 minutes from
Notting Hill Gate underground. PARK: Easy. TEL:

01582 527866; mobile - 07831 861641. SER:
Valuations; restorations (as stock). VAT: Stan.

Christina Truscott

Geoffrey Van Arcade, 105-107 Portobello Rd.
W11 2QB. Est. 1967. Open Sat. 6.45-3.30.
*STOCK: Lacquer, papier-mâché, tortoiseshell,
fans.* TEL: 01403 730554.

Victoriana Dolls

101 Portobello Rd. W11 2BQ. (Mrs H. Bond).
Open Sat. 8-3 or by appointment. *STOCK: Dolls,
toys and accessories.* TEL: Home - 01737
249525.

Virginia

98 Portland Rd., Holland Park. W11 4LQ. (V.
Bates). Est. 1971. Open 11-6. SIZE: Medium.
STOCK: Clothes and lace, 1880-1940, from £100.
LOC: Holland Park Ave. PARK: Easy. TEL: 020
7727 9908; fax - 020 7229 2198. VAT: Stan.

Visto

41 Pembridge Rd., Notting Hill. W11 3HG. (H.
Little and H. Lister). Est. 1997. Open 11-6, Sat.
10-6. SIZE: Small. *STOCK: Ceramics, furniture,
glass and lamps, 1950's-1960's, £5-£600.* LOC:
Between Notting Hill Gate underground and
Portobello Rd. PARK: Nearby. TEL: 020 7243
4392; fax - 020 7243 1374.

Johnny Von Pflugh Antiques

286 Westbourne Grove. W11. Est. 1985. Open
Sat. 8-5 at Portobello Market or by appointment.
SIZE: Small. *STOCK: European works of art,
Italian oil paintings, gouaches, 17th-19th C,
£300-£1,500; fine ironware, 17th-18th C, £300-
£800; medical and scientific instruments, 18th-
19th C, £200-£1,000.* LOC: Off Portobello Rd.
PARK: Easy. TEL: 020 8740 5306. SER:
Valuations; buys at auction (keys, caskets,
medical instruments, Italian oil paintings, and
gouaches). FAIRS: Olympia (June); Little
Chelsea (Scientific and Medical). VAT: Spec.

David Wainwright

63 Portobello Rd. W11 3DB and 251 Portobello
Rd. W11 1LT. Est. 1989. Open 9-6 (No. 63) and
9.30-6.30, Sun. 11-7 (No. 251). SIZE: Large.
*STOCK: Furniture, mainly from the sub-
continent and Far East, 15th-20th C including
18th-19th C cupboards, dining tables and
architectural pieces, £5-£2000; stonework - urns,
mortars, water containers, to 19th C;
contemporary wrought iron.* PARK: Easy. TEL:
020 7727 0707 (No. 63) and 020 7792 1988 (No.
251). FAIRS: Olympia. VAT: Stan.

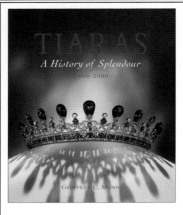

- The majority of photographs and related material are illustrated here for the first time and have been gathered from private collections

- The photographs include those of tiaras from many Royal collections including three designed by Prince Albert for Queen Victoria

- Of great appeal to everyone interested in fashion and style, jewellery, European history and Royalty

- The tiaras are related to a variety of works of art including painting, sculpture and portrait photographs. Whenever possible the original design is shown beside the finished jewel

- Archive photographs from Boucheron and Cartier show jewels of great originality which have now been broken up

Tiaras have always inspired a great fascination and the most beautiful and influential women have been painted, photographed and admired whilst wearing them. Even in the 21st century they are still worn and continue to inspire special poise and elegance. This lavishly illustrated book includes new photographs of a variety of Royal tiaras together with those of French and Russian Imperial provenances. Geoffrey Munn has been granted special access to the photographic archives of many famous jewellers, including Cartier, Boucheron and Fabergé, for his research. Other makers include

Garrards, Castellani, Giuliano, Lalique, Fouquet and Tiffany. Many of these stunning tiaras also have great historical significance and their provenance is explained fully by the author, who is a specialist in jewellery and metalwork. Among the contemporary pieces illustrated are tiaras belonging to Jamie Lee Curtis, Vivienne Westwood, Elton John and Madonna, made by Slim Barratt, Galliano and Versace. This awe-inspiring, sublime text, which incorporates more than 300 majestic colour plates, includes chapters on tiaras as crown jewels, Russian style tiaras, tiaras as a work of art and the relationship between the tiara and the costume ball.

Geoffrey Munn is the Managing Director of Wartski Ltd, a firm of antique dealers in London specialising in European precious metalwork. He is co-author of *Pre-Raphaelite to Arts and Crafts Jewellery* and author of both *Castellani and Giuliano – Revivalist Jewellers of the 19th Century* and *The Triumph of Love – Jewellery 1530-1930*. He is also the jewellery specialist on the BBC's *Antiques Roadshow*.

ISBN 1 85149 375 1
c.400pp., c.350 col., & 100 b.&w. illus.
10¾ x 8⅜in./274 x 235mm. **£45.00/$89.50**

LONDON SW1

Trude Weaver
71 Portobello Rd. W11. LAPADA. Est. 1968.
Open 9-5. CL: Mon. and Tues. SIZE: Medium.
*STOCK: 18th-19th C furniture, selected objects,
textiles.* PARK: Easy. TEL: 020 7229 8738; fax -
same. SER: Valuations.

Wolseley Fine Arts Ltd
12 Needham Rd. W11 2RP. (Rupert Otten and
Hanneke van der Werf). SLAD *STOCK: British
and European 20th C works on paper and
sculpture, works by David Jones, Eric Gill, John
Buckland Wright, Pierre Bonnard, Edouard
Vuillard, Ker Xavier Roussel, Eugeen van
Mieghem, etc.* TEL: 020 7792 2788; fax - 020
7792 2988; e-mail - wolseleyfinearts@ btinternet.
com; website - www.wolseley finearts.com. SER:
Regular catalogues on subscription.

World Famous Portobello Market
177 Portobello Rd. W11. (Angelo Soteriades).
Est. 1951. Open Sat. 5.30-5.30. SIZE: 200
dealers. *STOCK: Stamps, coins, hip flasks, Art
Deco, amber, jewellery, oils, watercolours,
engravings, prints, maps, books, photographs,
objects, teddy bears, toys, dolls, wood, soapstone,
Africana, auction catalogues.* TEL: 020 7436
9416; mobile - 07956 277077; e-mail -
info@portobello-antiques.com; website -
www.portobello-collections.co.uk.

W13

W.13 Antiques
10 The Avenue, Ealing. W13 8PH. Open Tues.,
Thurs. and Sat. 10-5 or by appointment. SIZE:
Medium. *STOCK: Furniture, china and general
antiques, 18th-20th C.* LOC: Off Uxbridge Rd.,
West Ealing. PARK: Easy. TEL: 020 8998 0390;
mobile - 07778 177102. SER: Valuations. VAT:
Stan.

W14

David Alexander Antiques & Kate Thurlow BADA
The Warehouse, 7a North End Rd. W14 8ST.
(Kate Thurlow and Rodney Robertson).
LAPADA, CINOA Est. 1970. Open by
appointment. SIZE: Large. *STOCK: European
furniture, 15th-17th C, £500-£20,000.* LOC: At
junction with Hammersmith Rd., opposite
Olympia Exhibition Hall. PARK: Limited or
meters. TEL: 020 7602 8388; fax - same;
mobile - 07836 588776. SER: Valuations;
restorations (furniture); buys at auction.
FAIRS: Olympia; BADA. VAT: Spec.

Marshall Gallery
67 Masbro Rd. W14 0LS. (D. A. and J.
Marshall). Resident. Est. 1978. Open 10-6, Sat.
10-5. CL: Mon. SIZE: Medium. *STOCK: French
and decorative furniture, £500-£20,000; objects
and lighting, £200-£12,000; pictures, from £100;
all 18th-20th C.* LOC: Just behind Olympia, off
Hammersmith Rd. PARK: Easy. TEL: 020 7602
3317. SER: Restorations (furniture, re-gilding, rewiring). VAT: Spec.

D. Parikian
3 Caithness Rd. W14 0JB. Open by appointment.
*STOCK: Antiquarian books, mythology,
iconography, emblemata, Continental books pre-
1800.* TEL: 020 7603 8375; fax - 020 7602 1178.

J. Roger (Antiques) Ltd BADA
(J. Roger and C. Bayley). Open by appointment only. *STOCK: Late 18th to early 19th C
small elegant pieces furniture, mirrors, prints,
porcelain and boxes.* TEL: 020 7381 2884/7603
7627.

SW1

A.D.C. Heritage Ltd BADA
SW1V 4PB. (F. Raeymaekers and E. Bellord).
Open by appointment only. *STOCK: Silver, old
Sheffield plate.* TEL: 020 7976 5271; fax - 020
7828 7432. SER: Valuations; restorations;
buys at auction.

Didier Aaron (London)Ltd BADA
21 Ryder St., St. James's. SW1Y 6PX. Open 9-
5 by appointment. SIZE: Large. *STOCK:
French furniture, 18th C, £5,000-£500,000; Old
Master and 19th C pictures, £5,000-£500,000;
objets d'art, £1,000-£50,000.* LOC: 20 yds. from
Christie's. TEL: 020 7839 4716; e-mail -
didaaron@aol.com. FAIRS: Paris Biennale.
VAT: Stan/Spec.

Ackermann & Johnson BADA
27 Lowndes St. SW1X 9HY. Est. 1783. Open 9-
5.30, Sat. by appointment. SIZE: Medium.
*STOCK: British paintings and watercolours,
especially sporting, marine and landscapes
including the Norwich School, 18th-20th C.*
PARK: Meters. TEL: 020 7235 6464. SER:
Valuations; restorations. VAT: Spec.

ADEC
227 Ebury St. SW1W 8UT. (A. De Cacqueray).
Open 10-6, Sat. 11-4. *STOCK: French and
Continental furniture, objets d'art.* TEL: 020
7730 5000; fax - 020 7730 0005.

Verner Åmell Ltd
4 Ryder St., St. James's. SW1Y 6QB. SLAD.
Open 10-5.30. CL: Sat. *STOCK: Dutch and
Flemish Old Masters, 16th-17th C; 18th C
French and 19th C Scandinavian paintings.* TEL:
020 7925 2759.

Albert Amor Ltd
37 Bury St., St. James's. SW1Y 6AU. Est. 1903.
Open 9.30-4.30. CL: Sat. SIZE: Small. *STOCK:
18th C English ceramics, especially first period
Worcester and blue and white porcelain.* PARK:
Meters. TEL: 020 7930 2444; fax - 020 7930
9067. SER: Valuations. VAT: Spec.

Anno Domini Antiques   BADA
**66 Pimlico Rd. SW1W 8LS. (F. Bartman). Est.
1960. Open 10-1 and 2.15-6. CL: Sat. pm.
SIZE: Large. STOCK: Furniture, 17th to early
19th C, £500-£20,000; mirrors, 17th-19th C,
£300-£3,000; glass, screens, decorative items
and tapestries, £15-£10,000. Not Stocked:
Silver, jewellery, arms, coins. LOC: From
Sloane Sq. go down Lower Sloane St., turn left
at traffic lights. PARK: Easy. TEL: 020 7730
5496; home - 020 7352 3084. SER: Buys at
auction. VAT: Stan/Spec.**

Antiquus
90-92 Pimlico Rd. SW1W 8PL. (E. Amati). Open
9.30-5.30. SIZE: Large. *STOCK: Classical,
medieval and Renaissance works of art, paintings,
textiles and glass.* LOC: Near Sloane Sq.
underground station. PARK: Meters in Holbein
Place. TEL: 020 7730 8681; fax - 020 7823 6409;
e-mail - enquiries@antiquus-london.co.uk; website
- www.antiquus-london.co.uk.

Appley Hoare Antiques
30 Pimlico Rd. SW1W 8LJ. (Appley & Zoe
Hoare). Est. 1980. Open 10.30-6, Sat. 10.30-4.
SIZE: Medium. *STOCK: French decorative
items, 18th-19th C; painted oak and pine; French
linen.* LOC: Corner Pimlico Green. PARK: Easy.
TEL: 020 7730 7070; fax - 020 7730 8188. VAT:
Spec.

The Armoury of St. James's Military Antiquarians
17 Piccadilly Arcade, Piccadilly. SW1Y 6NH.
Open 9.30-6. SIZE: Small. *STOCK: British and
foreign orders, decorations and medals, 18th C to
date, £50-£50,000; militaria; toy and hand-painted
collectors model soldiers, £4-£4,000.* LOC:
Between Piccadilly and Jermyn St. TEL: 020 7493
5082; e-mail - welcome@armoury. co.uk; website
- www.armoury.co.uk/home. SER: Valuations.
special commissions. VAT: Stan/Spec.

Artemis Fine Arts Limited
15 Duke St., St. James's. SW1Y 6DB. (Timothy
Bathurst, Adrian Eeles and Armin Kunz). SLAD.
Open 9.30-5.30. CL: Sat. *STOCK: Old Master,
19th C and modern paintings, drawings and
prints.* TEL: 020 7930 8733.

Nigel A. Bartlett
25 St Barnabas St. SW1W 8QB. Open 9.30-5.30.
CL: Sat. *STOCK: Marble, pine and stone
chimney pieces.* TEL: 020 7730 3223; fax - 020
7730 2332.

Hilary Batstone Antiques inc. Rosie Uniacke Interiors
8 Holbein Place. SW1W 8NL. LAPADA. Est.
1983. Open 10.30-5.30, Sat. 10.30-3.30. SIZE:
Medium. *STOCK: 19th-20th C decorative
furniture.* TEL: 020 7730 5335. FAIRS:
Decorative Antiques and Textiles, Chelsea. VAT:
Spec.

Chris Beetles Ltd
10 Ryder St., St. James's. SW1Y 6QB. Open 10-
5.30, by appointment at weekends. SIZE: Large.
*STOCK: English watercolours, paintings and
illustrations, 18th-20th C, £500-£50,000.* LOC:
100yds. from Royal Academy. PARK: Meters.
TEL: 020 7839 7551. SER: Valuations; framing.
VAT: Spec.

Belgrave Carpet Gallery Ltd
91 Knightsbridge. SW1. (A.H. Khawaja). Open
9.30-6.30. *STOCK: Hand knotted Oriental
carpets and rugs.* TEL: 020 7235 2541/7245
9749.

Konrad O. Bernheimer Ltd   BADA
**CINOA. Est. 1985. Open by appointment only.
STOCK: Old Master paintings, Chinese
ceramics. TEL: 020 7930 1756; fax - 020 7930
1754.**

Blanchard Ltd
86/88 Pimlico Rd. SW1W 8PL. Est. 1990. Open
10-6, Sat. 10-3. SIZE: Medium. *STOCK: English
and Continental furniture, lighting and objets
d'art.* LOC: Near Sloane Sq. underground station.
TEL: 020 7823 6310; fax - 020 7823 6303. SER:
Valuations; restorations; buys at auction. VAT:
Stan/Spec.

John Bly   BADA
**27 Bury St., St. James's. SW1Y 6AL. (J. and
V. Bly). CINOA Est. 1891. Open 9.30-5.30, Sat.
and Sun. by appointment. STOCK: Fine
English furniture, silver, glass, porcelain and
fine paintings, 18th-19th C. TEL: 020 7930
1292; fax - 020 7839 4775.**

66 Pimlico Road, London S.W.1
020-7730 5496

Fine small Regency rosewood brass inlaid sofa table,
c.1820. 30 in. x 12 in. x 28½in. (high)

J.H. Bourdon-Smith Ltd BADA
24 Mason's Yard, Duke St., St. James's. SW1Y 6BU. Est. 1954. Open 9.30-6. CL: Sat. SIZE: Medium. *STOCK: Silver, 1680-1830, £50-£15,000; Victorian and modern silver, 1830 to date, £25-£10,000.* PARK: Meters. TEL: 020 7839 4714. SER: Valuations; restorations (silver); buys at auction. FAIRS: Olympia (Nov); Harrogate; Grosvenor House; BADA; New York; San Francisco; Hong Kong. VAT: Stan/Spec.

Robert Bowman BADA
8 Duke St., St. James's. SW1Y 6BN. Est. 1992. Open Mon.-Fri. 10-6. SIZE: Medium. *STOCK: Sculpture in bronze, marble and terracotta, early 19th C to early 20th C, £1,000-£200,000.* PARK: Metered bays. TEL: 020 7839 3100; fax - 020 7839 3223. SER: Valuations; restorations (bronze, marble and terracotta). FAIRS: Olympia, Maastricht, Palm Beach, Beverley Hills. VAT: Spec.

Brisigotti Antiques Ltd
44 Duke St., St. James's. SW1Y 6DD. Open 9.30-1 and 2-6. *STOCK: European works of art, Old Master paintings.* TEL: 020 7839 4441; fax - 020 7976 1663.

Camerer Cuss and Co
17 Ryder St., St. James's. SW1Y 6PY. Est. 1788. Open 9.30-5. CL: Sat. SIZE: Medium. *STOCK: Clocks, 1600-1910, £250-£30,000; watches, 1600-1930, £100-£35,000.* TEL: 020 7930 1941. SER: Valuations; restorations (clocks and watches); buys at auction. VAT: Stan/Spec.

John Carlton-Smith BADA
17 Ryder St., St. James's. SW1Y 6PY. Open 9.30-5.30. CL: Sat. *STOCK: Clocks, barometers, chronometers, 17th-19th C.* TEL: 020 7930 6622; fax - same; website - www.fineantique clocks.com. SER: Valuations. VAT: Spec.

Miles Wynn Cato
60 Lower Sloane St. SW1W 8BP. Open Mon.-Fri. 9.30-5.30 and by appointment. *STOCK: English and Welsh pictures and works of art, 1550-1950.* TEL: 020 7259 0306; fax - 020 7259 0305.

Chaucer Fine Arts Ltd
45 Pimlico Rd. SW1W 8NE. Open Mon.-Fri. 10-6 and by appointment. *STOCK: Old Master paintings, sculpture and works of art; 19th C European paintings, 20th C Russian paintings and drawings.* TEL: 020 7730 2972; fax - 020 7730 5861.

Chelsea Antique Mirrors
72 Pimlico Rd. SW1W 2LS. (A. Koll). Est. 1976. Open 10-6, Sat. 10-2. SIZE: Medium. *STOCK: Antique mirrors, £1,000-£25,000.* PARK: Easy. TEL: 020 7824 8024; fax - 020 7824 8233. SER: Valuations; restorations (gilding).

Ciancimino Ltd
99 Pimlico Rd. SW1W 8PH. Open 10-6, Sat. by appointment. *STOCK: Art Deco furniture, Oriental art and ethnography.* TEL: 020 7730 9950/9959; fax - 020 7730 5365.

Classic Bindings
61 Cambridge St. SW1V 4PS. (Sasha Koziell). Est. 1989. Open 9.30-1 and 2-5.30. SIZE: Medium. *STOCK: Bindings, 18th to early 20th C; collectable and decorative antiquarian books.* LOC: Off Warwick Way, Pimlico. PARK: Easy. TEL: 020 7834 5554; fax - 020 7630 6632.

Cobra and Bellamy
149 Sloane St. SW1X 9BZ. (V. Manussis and T. Hunter). Est. 1976. Open 10.30-5.30. SIZE: Medium. *STOCK: Fine art, ceramics and 20th C designer jewellery and furniture, £50-£1,000.* TEL: 020 7730 9993. VAT: Stan.

Cornucopia
12 Upper Tachbrook St. SW1V 1SH. Est. 1967. Open 11-6. SIZE: Large. *STOCK: Jewellery, 20th C clothing and accessories.* PARK: Meters. TEL: 020 7828 5752.

Cox and Company
37 Duke St., St. James's. SW1Y 6DF. (Mr and Mrs R. Cox). Est. 1972. Open 10-5.30, Sat. by appointment. SIZE: Small. *STOCK: European paintings, 19th-20th C, £1,000-£20,000.* LOC: Off Piccadilly. TEL: 020 7930 1987. SER: Valuations; restorations; buys at auction. VAT: Spec.

Crowther of Syon Lodge Ltd
77 Pimlico Rd. SW1W. Open 10-6, Sat. 11-3. *STOCK: Period panelled rooms in pine and oak; chimney-pieces in marble, stone and wood; classical stone and marble statues; wrought iron entrance gates, garden temples, vases, wellheads, lead cisterns, animal figures, seats, fountains and other features.* TEL: 020 7730 8668; website - www.crowthersyonlodge.com. SER: Bespoke summerhouses; quality reproduction ornaments. VAT: Stan/Spec.

Peter Dale Ltd
12 Royal Opera Arcade, Pall Mall. SW1Y 4UY. LAPADA. Est. 1955. Open 9.30-5. CL: Sat. SIZE: Medium. *STOCK: Firearms, 16th-19th C; edged weapons, armour, 14th-19th C; militaria.* LOC: Arcade behind Her Majesty's Theatre and

New Zealand House. PARK: 350yds. Whitcomb St., Public Garage. TEL: 020 7930 3695; fax - 020 7930 2223. SER: Valuations; buys at auction. FAIRS: Arms, spring and autumn. VAT: Spec.

Kenneth Davis (Works of Art) Ltd
15 King St., St. James's. SW1Y 6QU. Open 9-5. CL: Sat. *STOCK: Antique silver and works of art.* TEL: 020 7930 0313; fax - 020 7976 1306.

Shirley Day Ltd
91b Jermyn St. SW1Y 6JB. Est. 1967. *STOCK: Indian, Himalayan and South East Asian sculpture; Japanese screens and paintings.* TEL: 020 7839 2804; fax - 020 7839 3334. VAT: Spec.

Alastair Dickenson Fine Silver Ltd
90 Jermyn St. SW1Y 6JD. Open 9.30-5.30. CL: Sat. SIZE: Small. *STOCK: Fine English, Irish and Scottish silver, 16th to early 19th C; unusual collectable silver - vinaigrettes, wine labels, card cases, caddy spoons, snuff boxes; Arts and Crafts silver including Omar Ramsden.* LOC: Off Duke St. PARK: Meters. TEL: 020 7839 2808; fax - 020 7839 2809; mobile - 07976 283530. SER: Valuations; restorations (repairs, gilding, re-plating), replacement cruet and ink bottles; buys at auction. VAT: Spec.

Simon C. Dickinson Ltd
58 Jermyn St. SW1Y 6LX. (Simon Dickinson, David Ker and James Roundell). SLAD. Open 10-5.30, Fri. 10-4.30. CL: Sat. SIZE: Large. *STOCK: Important Old Master and Modern Master paintings.* LOC: 2 mins. from Piccadilly. TEL: 020 7493 0340; fax - 020 7493 0796. SER: Valuations; restorations; buys at auction. VAT: Spec.

Douwes Fine Art Ltd
38 Duke St., St. James's. SW1Y 6DF. SLAD. Est. 1805. Open 9.30-5.30. CL: Sat. SIZE: Medium. *STOCK: 16th-20th C paintings, drawings and watercolours, Dutch, Flemish, French and Russian schools.* PARK: Meters. TEL: 020 7839 5795. SER: Valuations; restorations. VAT: Spec.

Eaton Gallery
34 Duke St., St. James's and 9 and 12a Princes Arcade, Jermyn St. SW1Y 6DF. (Dr J.D. George). LAPADA. Open 10-5.30. *STOCK: English and European paintings, 19th-20th C and contemporary.* TEL: 020 7930 5950; fax - 020 7839 8076.

N. and I. Franklin   BADA
11 Bury St., St. James's. SW1Y 6AB. Open 9.30-5.30. CL: Sat. *STOCK: Fine silver and works of art.* **TEL: 020 7839 3131; fax - 020 7839 3132.**

Victor Franses Gallery   BADA
57 Jermyn St., St. James's. SW1Y 6LX. Est. 1972. Open 10-5, Sat. by appointment. *STOCK: 19th C animalier bronzes, paintings, watercolours and drawings.* **TEL: 020 7493 6284/7629 1144; fax - 020 7495 3668. SER: Valuations; restorations.**

S. Franses Ltd
Jermyn St. at Duke St., St. James's. SW1Y 6JD. Est. 1909. Open 9-5. CL: Sat. SIZE: Large. *STOCK: Historic and decorative tapestries, carpets, fabrics and textiles.* TEL: 020 7976 1234. SER: Valuations; restorations; cleaning. VAT: Spec.

Charles Frodsham & Co Ltd
32 Bury St., St. James's. SW1Y 6AU. Open Tues.-Fri. 10.30-12.30 and 2-5, other times by appointment. SIZE: Medium. *STOCK: Clocks, watches, marine chronometers and other horological items.* LOC: Between Jermyn St. and St. James's St. PARK: Meters. TEL: 020 7839 1234; fax - 020 7839 2000. VAT: Stan/Spec.

Frost and Reed Ltd (Est. 1808)   BADA
2-4 King St., St James's. SW1Y 6QP. SLAD. Open 9-5.30. CL: Sat. *STOCK: Fine 19th C British and Continental paintings, marine and sporting pictures, Post-Impressionist drawings and watercolours; works by Sir Alfred Munnings, Montague Dawson, Marcel Dyf and Heather St Clair Davis.* **PARK: Meters. TEL: 020 7839 4645; fax - 020 7839 1166. VAT: Spec.**

Gallery '25
26 Pimlico Rd. SW1W 8LJ. (D. Iglesis). Est. 1969. Open 9.30-5.30, Sat. 10-2. SIZE: Medium. *STOCK: Art glass, £100-£5,000; signed furniture, £1,000-£10,000; decorative fine art, £500-£5,000; all 1900-1960's.* TEL: 020 7730 7516; fax - same. SER: Valuations; buys at auction (as stock). FAIRS: Park Lane; Olympia. VAT: Stan/Spec.

General Trading Co Ltd
144 Sloane St. SW1X 9BL. (Julian Geach). LAPADA. Est. 1920. Open 10-6.30. SIZE: Medium. *STOCK: English furniture, £100-£10,000; objects, both 18th-20th C.* PARK: 50yds., underground garage (Cadogan Place). TEL: 020 7730 0411. VAT: Stan/Spec.

Christopher Gibbs Ltd
3 Dove Walk, Pimlico Rd. SW1W 8PH. LAPADA. Est. 1960. Open Mon.-Fri. 9.30-5.30. SIZE: Large. *STOCK: Unusual and decorative paintings, furniture, works of art and sculpture.* TEL: 020 7730 8200; fax - 020 7730 8420. VAT: Spec.

Nicholas Gifford-Mead BADA
68 Pimlico Rd. SW1W 8LS. LAPADA. Est. 1972. Open 9.30-5.30. CL: Sat. SIZE: Medium. *STOCK: Chimney pieces and sculpture, 18th-19th C, from £1,000.* LOC: 3 minutes from Sloane Sq. TEL: 020 7730 6233; fax - 020 7730 6239. SER: Valuations. VAT: Stan/Spec.

Joss Graham
10 Eccleston St. SW1W 9LT. Open 10-6. *STOCK: Textiles including rugs, kelims, embroideries, tribal costume and shawls; jewellery, metalwork, furniture, masks and primitive art - Indian, Middle Eastern, Central Asian and African.* TEL: 020 7730 4370; fax - same; e-mail - joss.graham@btinternet.com.

Martyn Gregory Gallery BADA
34 Bury St., St. James's. SW1Y 6AU. SLAD. Open 10-6. CL: Sat. SIZE: Medium. *STOCK: Early English watercolours, 18th-20th C; British paintings, both £500-£100,000; specialists in pictures relating to China and the Far East.* TEL: 020 7839 3731. SER: Valuations. VAT: Spec.

Ross Hamilton Ltd
95 Pimlico Rd. SW1W 8PH. (Mark Boyce). LAPADA. Est. 1971. Open 9.30-6, Sat. 11-1.30. SIZE: Large. *STOCK: English and Continental furniture, 17th-19th C, £1,000-£100,000; porcelain and objects, 18th-19th C, £1,000-£3,000; paintings, 17th-19th C, £1,000-£10,000+.* LOC: 2 minutes walk from Sloane Square. PARK: Side streets. TEL: 020 7730 3015. VAT: Stan/Spec.

Harris Lindsay BADA
67 Jermyn St. SW1Y 6NY. CINOA. Open 9.30-6. CL: Sat. *STOCK: English, Continental, Oriental furniture; works of art.* TEL: 020 7839 5767; fax - 020 7839 5768. VAT: Spec.

Harrods Ltd
Brompton Rd., Knightsbridge. SW1X 7XL. Open 10-6, Wed., Thurs. and Fri. 10-7. SIZE: Large. *STOCK: Fine Victorian, Edwardian and period furniture; clocks, oil paintings and objets d'art.* PARK: Own. TEL: 020 7730 1234, ext. 5940/2759.

Julian Hartnoll
1st Floor, 14 Mason's Yard, Duke St., St. James's. SW1Y 6BU. Est. 1968. Open by appointment or by chance. *STOCK: 19th-20th C British paintings, drawings and prints especially pre-Raphaelite and works by the kitchen sink artists, including Bratby.* TEL: 020 7839 3842. VAT: Spec.

Harvey and Gore BADA
41 Duke St., St. James's. SW1Y 6DF. (B.E. Norman). Est. 1723. Open 9.30-5. CL: Sat. SIZE: Small. *STOCK: Jewellery, £150-£50,000; silver, £50-£15,000; old Sheffield plate, £125-£15,000; antique paste.* TEL: 020 7839 4033; fax - 020 7839 3313. SER: Valuations; restorations (jewellery and silver); buys at auction. VAT: Stan/Spec.

Hazlitt, Gooden and Fox Ltd
38 Bury St., St. James's. SW1Y 6BB. SLAD. Open 9.30-5.30. CL: Sat. SIZE: Large. *STOCK: Paintings, drawings and sculpture.* PARK: Meters. TEL: 020 7930 6422; fax - 020 7839 5984. SER: Valuations; restorations. VAT: Spec.

Thomas Heneage Art Books
42 Duke St., St. James's. SW1Y 6DJ. LAPADA. Est. 1975. Open 9.30-6 or by appointment. CL: Sat. *STOCK: Art reference books.* TEL: 020 7930 9223; fax - 020 7839 9223; e-mail - artbooks@heneage.com.

Hermitage Antiques plc
97 Pimlico Rd. SW1W 8PH. (B. Vieux-Pernon). Est. 1967. Open 10-6, Sat. 10-5, Sun. by appointment. SIZE: Large. *STOCK: Biedermeier, Empire and Russian furniture; oil paintings; decorative arts; chandeliers; bronzes.* Not Stocked: Silver and jewellery. LOC: Off Sloane Square. PARK: Easy. TEL: 020 7730 1973; fax - 020 7730 6586; e-mail - info@hermitage-antiques.co.uk; website - www.hermitage-antiques.co.uk. VAT: Stan/Spec.

Carlton Hobbs BADA
Est. 1975. Open by appointment only. *STOCK: English and Continental furniture, paintings, chandeliers, works of art, £4,000-£850,000.* TEL: 020 7340 1000; fax - 020 7340 1001; e-mail - chobbs65@aol.com; website - www.interiorinternet.com.

Christopher Hodsoll Ltd inc.
Bennison BADA
89-91 Pimlico Rd. SW1W 8PH. Open 9-6. *STOCK: Furniture, sculpture, pictures and objects.* PARK: Meters. TEL: 020 7730 3370; fax - 020 7730 1516; website - www.hodsoll.com. VAT: Stan/Spec.

Hotspur Ltd BADA
14 Lowndes St. SW1X 9EX. (R.A.B. Kern). Est. 1924. Open 8.30-6, Sat. 9.30-1. SIZE: Large. *STOCK: Fine English furniture, 1680-1800.* LOC: Between Belgrave Sq. and Lowndes Sq. PARK: 2 underground within 100yds. TEL: 020 7235 1918. VAT: Spec.

Christopher Howe

93 Pimlico Rd. SW1W 8PH. and 36 Bourne St. SW1W 8JA. Est. 1982. Open 9-5.30, Sat. 10.30-4.30. SIZE: Large + warehouse nearby. *STOCK: English and European furniture, 16th-20th C, £100-£250,000; decorative objects and lighting.* LOC: Near Sloane Square. PARK: Easy. TEL: 020 7730 7987; fax - 020 7730 0157; e-mail - c.howe@easynet.co.uk. SER: Valuations. VAT: Stan/Spec.

Humphrey-Carrasco

43 Pimlico Rd. SW1W 8NE. (David Humphrey and Marylise Carrasco). Est. 1987. Open 10-6, Sat. 10-5. *STOCK: English furniture and lighting, architectural objects, 18th-19th C.* LOC: 10 minute walk from Sloane Sq. PARK: Easy. TEL: 020 7730 9911; fax - 020 7730 9944. FAIRS: Olympia. VAT: Stan/Spec

Jeremy Ltd   BADA

29 Lowndes St. SW1X 9HX. (M. and J. Hill). Est. 1946. Open 8.30-6, Sat. 9-1. SIZE: Large. *STOCK: English, French and Russian furniture, objets d'art, glass chandeliers, 18th to early 19th C.* PARK: Easy. TEL: 020 7823 2923; fax - 020 7245 6197. FAIRS: Grosvenor House; New York Armory Show. VAT: Spec.

Derek Johns Ltd

12 Duke St., St. James's. SW1Y 6BN. SLAD. Open 9.30-6. *STOCK: Old Master paintings.* TEL: 020 7839 7671; fax - 020 7930 0986.

Keshishian   BADA

73 Pimlico Rd. SW1W 8NE. Est. 1978. Open 9.30-6, Sat. 10-5. SIZE: Large. *STOCK: European and Oriental carpets, to late 19th C; Aubussons, mid 19th C; European tapestries, 16th-18th C; Arts and Crafts and Art Deco carpet specialists.* LOC: Off Lower Sloane St. PARK: Easy. TEL: 020 7730 8810; fax - 020 7730 8803. SER: Valuations; restorations. VAT: Stan/Spec.

John King   BADA

74 Pimlico Rd. SW1W 8LS. Est. 1970. Open 10-6, Sat. by appointment. SIZE: Medium. *STOCK: Fine and unusual antiques, £500-£150,000.* TEL: 020 7730 0427; fax - 020 7730 2515. FAIRS: Olympia (June and Nov). VAT: Spec.

Knightsbridge Coins

43 Duke St., St. James's. SW1. Open 10-6. CL: Sat. *STOCK: Coins - British, American and South African; medals.* TEL: 020 7930 7597/7930 8215.

Kojis Antique Jewellery Ltd

Harrods Fine Jewellery Room, Harrods Ltd., Brompton Rd., Knightsbridge. SW1X 7XL. Open 10-7. *STOCK: Antique and contemporary jewellery and objects; jade.* TEL: 020 7730 1234 ext. 4062/4072.

Bob Lawrence Gallery

93 Lower Sloane St. SW1. Est. 1972. Open 10-6. SIZE: Medium. *STOCK: Decorative arts to Art Deco - furniture, paintings, objects and furnishings, £50-£10,000.* LOC: 2 minutes Sloane Sq., adjacent Pimlico Rd. PARK: Easy. TEL: 020 7730 5900; fax - 020 7730 5902. SER: Valuations; restorations; buys at auction. VAT: Stan/Spec.

Lennox Money (Antiques) Ltd

93 Pimlico Rd. SW1W 8PH. (L.B. Money). Est. 1964. Open 9.45-6. CL: Sat. pm. SIZE: Large. *STOCK: Indian colonial and furniture made of unusual woods; chandeliers and textiles.* LOC: 200yds. south of Sloane Sq. TEL: 020 7730 3070. VAT: Spec.

M. and D. Lewis

84 Pimlico Rd. SW1. Open 9.30-5.30, Sat. 9.30-12, Sun. by appointment. *STOCK: Continental and Victorian furniture, porcelain, bronzes.* TEL: 020 7730 1015; fax - 020 7727 3908 (after 6). VAT: Stan.

Lion, Witch and Lampshade

c/o Muriel Michalos Ltd., 57 Elizabeth St. SW1W 9PP. (Mr and Mrs N. Dixon). Est. 1984. Open by appointment. *STOCK: Unusual decorative objects, 18th to early 20th C, £5-£150; lamps, wall brackets, chandeliers and candlesticks, £50-£1,000; rocking horses.* PARK: Easy. TEL: 020 7730 1774. SER: Restorations (porcelain and glass). VAT: Stan/Spec.

Longmire Ltd (Three Royal Warrants)

12 Bury St., St. James's. SW1Y 6AB. Open 9.30-5.30, Sat. in Nov. and Dec. only. *STOCK: Individual antique jewellery, cufflink and dress sets: antique, signed, platinum, gold, gem set, hardstone, pearl, carved crystal or enamel - four vices, fishing, polo, golfing, shooting, big game, ladybird and pigs.* LOC: Coming from Piccadilly, down Duke St., right into King St. past Christies, first right into Bury St. PARK: Easy. TEL: 020 7930 8720; fax - 020 7930 1898. SER: Custom hand engraving or enamelling in colour - any corporate logo, initials, crest, coats of arms or tartan, any animal (cat, dog etc.), racing silks, sailing burgees, favourite hobbies or own automobiles.

MacConnal-Mason Gallery

14 and 17 Duke St., St. James's. SW1Y 6DB. Est. 1893. Open 9-6. SIZE: Large. *STOCK: Pictures, 19th-20th C.* PARK: Meters. TEL: 020 7839 7693/7409 7323; fax - 020 7839 6797; e-

mail - macconnal-mason@msn.com; website - www.macconnal-mason-gallery.co.uk. SER: Valuations; restorations. VAT: Spec.

The Mall Galleries
The Mall. SW1Y 5BD. Open 10-5 seven days. *STOCK: Paintings.* LOC: Near Trafalgar Sq. TEL: 020 7930 6844; fax - 020 7839 7830; website - www.mallgalleries.org.uk. SER: Contemporary art exhibitions held.

Paul Mason Gallery   BADA
149 Sloane St. SW1X 9BZ. Est. 1969. Open 9-6, Wed. 9-7, Sat. 9-1. *STOCK: Marine, sporting and decorative paintings and prints, 18th-19th*

Fine oak salt box with pierced and carved decoration, West Country, 18th century. (A. & E. Foster)

A whole range of appealing items which appear from time to time in shops and salerooms defy mainstream classification, falling somewhere between 'primitive' bygones, folk-art, 'country smalls', and 'kitchenalia'. Barbara Pearce shows us their charm in an article entitled 'Delightful Oddities!' which appeared in the September 2000 issue of **Antique Collecting** magazine. For more details and to subscribe see page 147.

C; period and old frames, portfolio stands, ship models and nautical items. LOC: Sloane Sq. end of Sloane St. PARK: Easy. TEL: 020 7730 3683; fax - 020 7730 7359. SER: Valuations; restorations (prints, paintings); buys at auction. FAIRS: England and Europe. VAT: Stan/Spec.

Jeremy Mason (Sainsbury & Mason)
145 Ebury St. SW1. Est. 1968. Open 10-1. *STOCK: Period Oriental and European works of art, especially Chinese and Japanese, bronzes, lacquer, porcelain, glass and pictures.* TEL: 020 7730 8331; home - 020 8874 4173; fax - 020 7730 8334. VAT: Spec.

Mathaf Gallery Ltd
24 Motcomb St. SW1X 8JU. LAPADA, SLAD. Est. 1975. Open 9.30-5.30. *STOCK: Paintings, Middle East subjects, 19th C.* TEL: 020 7235 0010. SER: Valuations.

Matthiesen Fine Art Ltd.
7-8 Mason's Yard, Duke St., St. James's. SW1Y 6BU. Est. 1978. Open by appointment only. *STOCK: Fine Italian Old Master paintings, 1300-1800; French and Spanish Old Master paintings.* TEL: 020 7930 2437; fax - 020 7930 1387. SER: Valuations; buys at auction.

McClenaghan
69 Pimlico Rd. SW1W 8NE. Open 10-6: Sat. 10.30-4. *STOCK: English country house furniture, objects and period lighting.* TEL: 020 7730 4187; fax - same; e-mail - mcclenaghan. mcced@virgin.net. VAT: Stan/Spec/Export.

Thomas Mercer (Chronometers) Ltd
32 Bury St., St. James's. SW1Y 6AU. Open Mon.-Fri. 10-5.30, other times by appointment. SIZE: Medium. *STOCK: Marine chronometers.* LOC: Between Jermyn St. and St. James's St. PARK: Meters. TEL: 020 7930 9300; fax - 020 7321 0350. VAT: Stan/Spec.

Messums   BADA
40 Duke St., St James's. SW1Y 6DF. LAPADA. Open Mon.-Fri. 10-6, other times by appointment. SIZE: Medium. *STOCK: Traditional and British Impressionist paintings.* **TEL: 020 7839 5180; fax - same. SER: Valuations; restorations; framing. VAT: Stan/Spec.**

Nigel Milne Ltd
38 Jermyn St. SW1Y 6DN. Est. 1979. Open 9.30-5.30. SIZE: Small. *STOCK: Jewellery, silver frames and objects.* TEL: 020 7434 9343. SER: Valuations. VAT: Stan/Spec.

Mrs Monro Ltd
Jubilee House, 70 Cadogan Place. SW1X 9AH. Est. 1926. Open 9.30-5.30, Fri. 9.30-5. CL: Sat.

SIZE: Medium. *STOCK: Small decorative furniture, £500-£1,000+; china, £50-£500+; rugs; prints; pictures and general decorative items, from £50; all 18th-19th C.* LOC: Between Sloane Sq. and Pont St. PARK: Garage nearby. TEL: 020 7235 0326; fax - 020 7259 6305; e-mail - mrsmonro.co.uk. SER: Restorations (furniture and china). VAT: Stan/Spec.

Moreton Street Gallery
40 Moreton St. SW1V 2PB. (W.M. Pearson - Frasco International Ltd). Est. 1972. Open 9-1 and 2-6. CL: Sat. SIZE: Medium. *STOCK: Contemporary oils, watercolours, limited editions, posters; early engravings - Bunbury, Rowlandson, Hogarth, Gilray and Heath.* LOC: Off Belgrave Rd. PARK: Easy. TEL: 020 7834 7773/5; fax - 020 7834 7834. SER: Valuations; restorations; buys at auction (originals and engravings). VAT: Stan.

Guy Morrison
91a Jermyn St. SW1Y 6JB. SLAD. Open 9.30-5.30. CL: Sat. *STOCK: British paintings from 1900.* TEL: 020 7839 1454.

Peter Nahum at The Leicester Galleries
5 Ryder St. SW1Y 6PY. LAPADA. Open 9.30-5.30. CL: Sat. and Sun. except by appointment. SIZE: Large. *STOCK: British and European paintings, works on paper and bronzes, including the Pre-Raphaelites and Modern British, 19th-20th C, £1,000-£100,000+.* LOC: 100yds. from Royal Academy. PARK: Meters. TEL: 020 7930 6059; fax - 020 7930 4678; e-mail - peternahum@ leicestergalleries.com. SER: Valuations; restorations; framing. VAT: Spec.

Old Maps and Prints
3rd Floor, Harrods, Knightsbridge. SW1X 7XL. Est. 1976. *STOCK: Maps, 16th C to 1890; engravings (all subjects); watercolours.* TEL: 020 7730 1234, ext. 2124.

Ossowski   BADA
83 Pimlico Rd. SW1W 8PH. Est. 1960. Open 10-6. CL: Sat. pm. SIZE: Medium. *STOCK: Carved gilt, 18th C; mirrors, consoles, wood carvings.* TEL: 020 7730 3256. SER: Restorations (gilt furniture). VAT: Stan/Spec.

Anthony Outred   BADA
46 Pimlico Rd. SW1W 8LP. Open 9-6, Sat. 10-5. SIZE: Large. *STOCK: English and Irish furniture especially unusual and amusing, pre 1840, £1,000-£200,000.* LOC: 2 minutes from Sloane Sq. PARK: Meters. TEL: 020 7730 4782; fax - 020 7730 5643; mobile - 07767 848132; e-mail - antiques@outred.co.uk; website - www.outred.co.uk. SER: Finder. FAIRS: Olympia. VAT: Stan/Spec.

Paisnel Gallery
22 Mason's Yard, Duke St., St James's. SW1Y 6BU. (Stephen Paisnel). SLAD. Est. 1977. Open 10-6. CL: Sat. SIZE: Small. *STOCK: Modern British paintings, especially Newlyn and St. Ives Schools, £2,000-£20,000.* LOC: Duke St. runs between Piccadilly and King St. 1 minute from Christies. PARK: St. James Sq. TEL: 020 7930 9293. VAT: Spec.

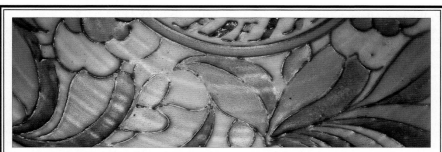

Detail of the Persian Rose pattern designed by Charlotte Rhead for Crown Ducal in the 1930s, showing the tube-lining technique. (Greg Stevenson)

Charlotte Rhead made a significant and influential contribution to the British ceramics industry. She was also one of the first acknowledged female designers of the 20th century. Andrew Casey, whose book on 20th century British ceramic designers is to be published by the Antique Collectors' Club soon, surveys her work. From an article entitled 'Tube-line Variations' by Andrew Casey which appeared in the March 2001 issue of **Antique Collecting** magazine. For more details and to subscribe see page 147.

The Parker Gallery
BADA
28 Pimlico Rd. SW1W 8LJ. (Thomas H. Parker Ltd). SLAD. Est. 1750. Open 9.30-5.30, Sat. by appointment. SIZE: Medium. *STOCK: Historical prints, £45-£1,200; English paintings, £1,000-£30,000; ship models, £95-£30,000.* LOC: 5 minutes from Sloane Sq. TEL: 020 7730 6768; fax - 020 7259 9180. SER: Restorations (as stock); mounting; framing. VAT: Stan/Spec.

Michael Parkin Fine Art Ltd
Studio 4, Sedding St., 1/6 Sloane Sq. SW1W 8EE. SLAD. By appointment only. *STOCK: British paintings, watercolours, drawings and prints, 1860-1960, £50-£10,000.* PARK: Easy. TEL: 020 7730 9784; fax - 020 7730 9718. VAT: Spec.

Trevor Philip and Sons Ltd
BADA
75a Jermyn St., St. James's. SW1Y 6NP. (T. and R. Waterman). Est. 1972. Open 9.30-6, Sat. by appointment only. SIZE: Medium. *STOCK: Early scientific instruments, globes, barometers and ships models; silver and vertu.* PARK: At rear. TEL: 020 7930 2954; fax - 020 7321 0212; e-mail - globe@trevorphilip.com; website - www.trevorphilip.com. SER: Valuations; restorations (clocks and scientific instruments); buys at auction. VAT: Stan/Spec.

Portland Gallery
9 Bury St., St. James's. SW1Y 6AB. SLAD. Est. 1985. Open 10-6. CL: Sat. SIZE: Medium. *STOCK: Scottish pictures, 20th C, £200-£100,000.* TEL: 020 7321 0422. SER: Valuations; buys at auction. VAT: Spec.

Pullman Gallery
14 King St., St. James's. SW1Y 6QU. (Simon Khachadourian). Est. 1980. Open 10-6, Sat. by appointment. SIZE: Medium. *STOCK: Objets de luxe, 19th-20th C, £200-£20,000; automobile art, pre-1950, £1,000-£20,000; collectable cocktail shakers, bar accessories, cigar memorabilia, 1880-1950, £250-£25,000; René Lalique glass, 1900-1940, from £3,000.* LOC: Corner of Bury St., adjacent Christie's. PARK: Easy. TEL: 020 7930 9595; fax - 020 7930 9494; mobile - 07973 141606. VAT: Stan.

Mark Ransom Ltd
62 and 105 Pimlico Rd. SW1W 8LS. Est. 1989. Open 10-6. SIZE: Medium. *STOCK: Furniture - French Empire and Russian, early 19th C; Continental, decorative, from late 18th C, all to £1,000+.* LOC: Close to Sloane Sq. underground - turn left left, 5 minute walk. PARK: Side streets. TEL: 020 7259 0220; fax - 020 7259 0323. VAT: Stan/Spec.

Steven Rich & Michael Rich
39 Duke St., St. James's. SW1Y 6DF. SLAD. Open daily, Sat. by appointment. SIZE: Medium. *STOCK: Master paintings, 16th-19th C; collectors items.* LOC: Just off Piccadilly. PARK: St. James's Sq. TEL: 020 7930 9308; fax - 020 7930 2088. SER: Valuations. VAT: Spec.

Rogier et Rogier
20A Pimlico Rd. SW1W 8LJ. (Miss Lauriance Rogier). Est. 1980. Open 10-6, Sat. 11-4. SIZE: Small. *STOCK: French and Continental painted and country furniture, 18th-19th C, £1,000-£5,000; lamps and wall sconces, 19th C, from £500; decorative antique and reproduction items, from £300.* LOC: 5 minutes walk from Sloane Sq. PARK: Meters. TEL: 020 7823 4780. SER: Restorations (decoration, painted effects, murals, trompe l'oeil). VAT: Spec.

Rossi & Rossi Ltd
91c Jermyn St.,St James's. SW1Y 6JB. (Anna Maria and Fabio Rossi). Est. 1984. Open 10-5, Sat. and Sun. by appointment. SIZE: Medium. *STOCK: Himalayan art, 12th-17th C, to £10,000+; Indian art, 1st-13th C, to £10,000+.* LOC: Off Piccadilly. PARK: Meters. TEL: 020 7321 0208; fax - 020 7321 0546. SER: Valuations; buys at auction. FAIRS: Cultura, Basel. VAT: Spec.

Julian Simon Fine Art Ltd
BADA
70 Pimlico Rd. SW1W 8LS. (M. and J. Brookstone). Open 10-6, Sat. 10-4 or by appointment. *STOCK: Fine English and Continental pictures, 18th-20th C.* TEL: 020 7730 8673; fax - 020 7823 6116; e-mail - juliansimon@compuserve.com; website - www.19thcenturypaintings.com.

Sims, Reed Ltd
43a Duke St., St James's. SW1Y 6DD. Open 10-6, Sat. 10-4. *STOCK: Illustrated rare and in-print books on the fine and applied arts; leather-bound literary sets; contemporary books.* TEL: 020 7493 5660; fax - 020 7493 8468.

Peta Smyth - Antique Textiles
42 Moreton St., Pimlico. SW1V 2PB. LAPADA, GMC. Est. 1977. Open 9.30-5.30. CL: Sat. *STOCK: European textiles and needlework, 17th-19th C, £10-£5,000; tapestries and cushions.* PARK: Easy. TEL: 020 7630 9898; fax - 020 7630 5398. FAIRS: Olympia. VAT: Spec.

Somlo Antiques
BADA
7 Piccadilly Arcade. SW1Y 6NH. Est. 1972. Open 10-5.30, Sat. 10.30-5. SIZE: Medium. *STOCK: Vintage wrist and antique pocket watches, from £1,000.* LOC: Between Piccadilly and Jermyn St. PARK: Meters. TEL: 020 7499 6526. SER: Restorations.

THE PARKER GALLERY
(ESTABLISHED 1750)

28, PIMLICO ROAD, LONDON SW1W 8LJ
TEL: 0207-730 6768   FAX: 0207-259 9180

The Paddle Steamer "Royal Eagle"
Colour print after Jack Spurling, published circa 1933
Size 12 x 17 inches (30.5 x 43 cms)

Guard Mounting, St James's Palace
Coloured line engraving, published circa 1790
Size 10 x 14 inches (25.4 x 35.6 cms)

DEALERS IN PRINTS, PAINTINGS AND WATERCOLOURS OF
THE 18th, 19th & 20th CENTURY, COVERING MARINE,
MILITARY, TOPOGRAPHICAL AND SPORTING SUBJECTS,
MAPS & SHIP MODELS

BADA

Henry Sotheran Ltd
80 Pimlico Rd. SW1W 8PL. Open 10-6, Sat. 10-4. *STOCK: Fine and rare antique prints of architecture, decorative, natural history, travel and topography.* TEL: 020 7730 8756; fax - 020 7823 6090. VAT: Stan.

Robin Symes Ltd
3 Ormond Yard, Duke of York St., St. James's. SW1. Open by appointment only. SIZE: Large. *STOCK: Antiquities, ancient art.* PARK: Meters. TEL: 020 7930 9856/7; 020 7930 5300.

thesilverfund.com
40 Bury St. SW1Y 6AU. (Alastair Crawford and Michael James). Open daily, Sat. and Sun. by appointment. SIZE: Large. *STOCK: Old Georg Jensen silver, £500-£100,000.* LOC: Opposite Christies (King St/Bury St). PARK: NCP Mayfair. TEL: 020 7839 7664; fax - 020 7839 8935; e-mail - dealers@thesilverfund.com. SER: Valuations; restorations. VAT: Stan/Spec.

Bill Thomson - Albany Gallery
1 Bury St., St. James's. SW1Y 6AB. (W.B. Thomson). Open Mon.-Fri. 9-6 by appointment. *STOCK: British drawings, watercolours and paintings, 1700-1850 and some 20th C.* TEL: 020 7839 6119; fax - 020 7839 6614.

Trafalgar Galleries   BADA
35 Bury St., St. James's. SW1Y 6AY. Open 9.30-6. CL: Sat. STOCK: Old Master paintings. LOC: Just south of Piccadilly. TEL: 020 7839 6466.

Tryon Gallery (incorporating Malcolm Innes)
7 Bury St.,St James's. SW1Y 6AL. Open 10-6, Fri.10-5. CL: Sat. *STOCK: Sporting, wildlife and natural history subjects; paintings, bronzes, books, £150-£50,000.* TEL: 020 7839 8083; fax - 020 7839 8085. SER: Valuations; framing; advising; commission buying

Un Francais á Londres
202 Ebury St. SW1W 8UN. Est. 1990. Open 10-6, Sat. 10-4. SIZE: Large. *STOCK: 18th to early 19th C French and Continental furniture.* LOC: Near Pimlico Rd. PARK: Easy. TEL: 020 7730 1771/1881; fax - 020 7730 1661. SER: Valuations; restorations; buys at auction. VAT: Spec

Rafael Valls Ltd   BADA
11 Duke St., St. James's. SW1Y 6BN. SLAD. Est. 1976. Open Mon.-Fri. 9.30-6. STOCK: Fine European paintings. TEL: 020 7930 1144; fax - 020 7976 1596. VAT: Spec.

Rafael Valls Ltd   BADA
6 Ryder St., St. James's. SW1Y 6QB. SLAD. Open Mon.-Fri. 9.30-6. STOCK: Fine European paintings. TEL: 020 7930 0029; fax - 020 7976 1596. VAT: Spec.

Johnny Van Haeften Ltd   BADA
13 Duke St., St. James's. SW1Y 6DB. (J. and S. Van Haeften). SLAD, TEFAF. Est. 1978. Open 10-6, Sat. and Sun. by appointment. SIZE: Medium. STOCK: Dutch and Flemish Old Master paintings, 16th-17th C, £5,000-£5m. LOC: Middle of Duke St. TEL: 020 7930 3062/3; fax - 020 7839 6303. SER: Valuations; restorations (Old Masters); buys at auction (paintings including Old Masters). VAT: Spec.

Waterman Fine Art Ltd
74A Jermyn St., St. James's. SW1Y 6NP. Open 9-6, Sat. 10-4. *STOCK: 20th C paintings and watercolours.* TEL: 020 7839 5203; fax - 020 7321 0212.

Westenholz Antiques Ltd
76-78 Pimlico Rd. SW1W 8LP. Open 10-6, Sat. by appointment. *STOCK: 18th-19th C furniture, pictures, objects, lamps, mirrors.* TEL: 020 7824 8090.

Whitford Fine Art
6 Duke St., St. James's. SW1Y 6BN. (Adrian Mibus). Open 10-6. CL: Sat. *STOCK: Oil paintings and sculpture, late 19th to 20th C; Post War abstract and pop art.* TEL: 020 7930 9332; fax - 020 7930 5577.

Arnold Wiggins and Sons Ltd   BADA
4 Bury St., St. James's. SW1Y 6AB. (M. Gregory). Open Mon.-Fri 9-5.30. STOCK: Picture frames, 16th-19th C. TEL: 020 7925 0195.

Wildenstein and Co Ltd
46 St. James's Place. SW1A 1NS. SLAD. Est. 1934. By appointment only. *STOCK: Impressionist and Old Master paintings and drawings.* TEL: 020 7629 0602; fax - 020 7493 3924.

SW3

Norman Adams Ltd   BADA
8/10 Hans Rd., Knightsbridge. SW3 1RX. Est. 1923. Open 9-5.30, Sat. and Sun. by appointment. SIZE: Large. *STOCK: English furniture, 18th C, £650-£250,000; objets d'art (English and French) £500-£50,000; mirrors, glass pictures, 18th C; clocks and barometers.* LOC: 30yds. off the Brompton Rd., opposite west side entrance to Harrods. TEL: 020 7589 5266;

ANTIQUARIUS

131-141 King's Road, London SW3

"A fine example of what the best antiques centre can offer"

Antique Dealer and Collectors Guide

Enquiries: Mike Spooner

Tel: 020-7969 1500 Fax: 020-7969 1639

fax - 020 7589 1968; e-mail - antiques@norman adams.com; website - www. normanadams.com. **FAIRS: Grosvenor House; BADA. VAT: Spec.**

After Noah
261 King's Rd. Chelsea. SW3 5EL. (M. Crawford and Z. Candlin). *STOCK: Arts and Craft oak and similar furniture, 1880's to 1950's, £1-£1,000; iron, iron and brass beds; decorative items, bric-a-brac including candlesticks, mirrors, lighting, kitchenalia and jewellery.* TEL: 020 7351 2610; fax - same. SER: Restorations. VAT: Stan.

The Andipa Gallery
162 Walton St. SW3 2JL. LAPADA. Est. 1969. Open Tues.-Sat. 11-6. *STOCK: Icons from Byzantium, Greece, Russia, Eastern Europe, Asia Minor and North Africa; Italian Masters and Old Masters, all from 14th-19th C.* TEL: 020 7589 2371. SER: Valuations; restorations; research; collections.

Antiquarius
131/141 King's Rd. SW3. (Atlantic Antiques Centres Ltd). Est. 1970. Open 10-6. LOC: On the corner of King's Rd. and Flood St., next to Chelsea Town Hall. TEL: Enquiries - 020 7969 1500; fax - 020 7969 1639; e-mail - antique@ dial.pipex.com. Below are listed some of the many specialist dealers at this market.

225 Jewellery Exchange
Stand V38. (Mrs Michelle Rowan). LAPADA. *Jewellery and silver.* TEL: 020 7352 8744.

Jaki Abbott
Stand M12. *Jewellery.* TEL: 020 7352 7989; mobile - 07774 864442.

AM-PM
Stands V35. (T.J. Yeganeh) *Vintage watches.* TEL: 020 7351 5654.

Amato Antiques
Stand V9. LAPADA. *Decorative antiques.* TEL: 020 7352 3666.

S. Arena
Stand E5. *General antiques, silver plate, ivory.* TEL: 020 7352 7989.

Arms & Armour Tokugawa
Antique Japanese militaria. TEL: 020 7351 1750.

At the Movies
Stand V3/4. (Liza Tesei). *Vintage and original movie posters.* TEL: 020 7376 7670; mobile - 07770 777411.

Baptista Arts
Stand V10. (John Cox). LAPADA. *Decorative antiques, silver.* TEL: 020 7352 5793.

Beauty & The Beast
Stand Q9-10. (J. Rothman). *Costume jewellery, BP Austrian bronzes, handbags.* TEL: 020 7351 5149.

Alexandra Bolla
Stand J1. *Jewellery.* TEL: 020 7352 7989.

Brown & Kingston
Stand V5/V6. *Staffordshire porcelain, Imari, blue and white.* TEL: 020 7376 8881.

Miss T. Buchinger
Stand Q2. *Jewellery.* TEL: 020 7352 8734.

Mrs V. Carroll
Stand N1. *General antiques.* TEL: 020 7352 8734.

Chelsea Antiques Rug Gallery
Stand V15. (N. Somnez). *Oriental carpets and Persian rugs.* TEL: 020 7351 6611.

Chelsea Clocks
Stand H3-4, R1-2. (P. Dixon). *Clocks and general.* TEL: 020 7352 8646.

Chelsea Military Antiques
Stand N13/14. (Dominic Abbott and Richard Black). *Militaria, swords, revolvers, uniforms, medals (WWII and British Empire).* TEL: 020 7352 0308; mobile - 07889 600844.

Claude & Martine
Stand V16. (C. and M. Latreville) *Fine silver and jewellery.* TEL: 020 7352 5964.

Eli Cohen
Stand Q5. *Jade, netsuke, Oriental art.* TEL: 020 7351 7038.

Glen Dewart
Stand P7/8. *Prints and paintings.* TEL: 0120 7352 4777.

Edge
Stand V17. (D.M. Edge). LAPADA. *Decorative items, furniture, pictures, jewellery.* TEL: 020 7352 2660.

Makiko Featherstone
Stand J9/11. *Silver jewellery, small objets d'art.* TEL: 020 7376 8845.

Ferguson Fine Art
Stands V31/32. (Serena Ferguson). *Fine art and sporting collectables.* TEL: 020 7352 5272.

Flight of Fancy
Stand A9-A11. (Jesse Davis). LAPADA. *Majolica, china, objects, silver.* TEL: 020 7352 4314.

French Glass House
Stand P14/15 N4/5. (M. Aboudara). *Art Deco and Art Nouveau glass.* TEL: 020 7376 5394.

A. Gibson
Stand M10. *Silver and plate, general antiques.* TEL: 020 7352 4690.

Troy Glover
Stand T5/6. *Swedish glass, chandeliers, decorative antiques.*

Brian Gordon
Stand G1. LAPADA. *Silver and plate.* TEL: 020 7352 5808.

Hayman & Hayman
Stands K2/3/4/5. *Photo frames/scent bottles.* TEL: 020 7351 6568.

Mr and Mrs I Howard
Stands T5/6. *Jewellery, silver, watches, porcelain, buttons.* TEL: 020 7351 6140.

Peter & Philip Jeffs - Aesthetics BADA
Stand V2/3. LAPADA. *Silver, ceramics and decorative arts, 1860-1960.* TEL: 020 7352 0395.

D. Kelly
Stand L3, M13. *Books, including reference.* TEL: 020 7352 4690.

The Lace Shop
Stand Q7/8. (Mrs Williamson). *Lace, textiles and decorative antiques.* TEL: Mobile - 07778 659783.

Mrs Larpari
Stand L2. *Jewellery.* TEL: 020 7352 5592.

Le Shop
Stand L9. (A. Kanetti). *Decorative antiques and 1950's glass.* TEL: 020 7352 4690; mobile - 07771 601100.

Mr. E. Lehane
Stand V11. *Tortoiseshell and collectables.* TEL: 020 7349 8638.

Michael Lexton
Stand N8-11. *Silver.* TEL: 020 7351 5980.

Little River
Stand D1/D2. (D. Dykes). *Asian prints, Oriental china, porcelain.* TEL: 020 7376 7348. SER: Restorations (Oriental furniture).

W.D.K. Mandozai
Stand D3. *Oil paintings.* TEL: 020 7352 0518.

Mariad Antiques
(Maria McClean). *Vienna bronzes and vintage jewellery.*

Malcolm Martin
Period mirrors and decorative antiques.

Mrs D. Martin & Miss Jasmin Cameron
Stand M1/14/15/16. *Silver and plate, inkpots and pens, artists materials, glass.* TEL: 020 7351 4154; mobile - 07973 222520.

Mr. Martinez-Negrilo
Stand P1/2/3. *Jewellery, porcelain, glass and paintings de vertus.* TEL: 020 7349 0038; mobile - 07956 406954.

Gerald Mathias
Stand R3-6. *Victorian, Edwardian furniture, clocks, boxes.* TEL: 020 7351 0484.

Mrs Sue Mautner
Stand P13. *40's and 50's costume jewellery.* TEL: 020 7376 4419.

May Avenue
Stand V13. (Zoe Bajcer). *Art Deco ceramics, including Clarice Cliff, Keith Murray.* TEL: 020 7351 5757; mobile - 07710 424033.

Stella McDonald
Stand Q1/Q16. *Furniture.* TEL: 020 7352 8734; 020 8788 4981.

Mrs N. McDonald-Hobley
Stand L7. *Jewellery.* TEL: 020 7351 0154.

William McLeod-Brown
Stand L5-8. *Prints especially botanicals, books.* TEL: 020 7352 4690; workshop - 020 7730 3547.

Mrs Teresa Molloy
Stand E6. *Oil paintings.* TEL: 020 7352 7989.

Mrs. D. Mousavi
Stand D4. *Gold and silver, jade, netsuke.* TEL: 020 7352 8734.

Sue Norman
Stand L4. (Mr and Mrs Alloway). *Blue and white transfer ware.* TEL: 020 7352 7217.

David Odling
Stand G4. *Oil paintings and clocks.* TEL: 020 7352 8734.

Roger Painter
Stand V12. *Antique silver and jewellery.*

Maria Perez
Stand V23/24. *Jewellery.* TEL: 020 7351 1986.

Phillipa & John
Stand J4/5. *Jewellery.* TEL: 020 7352 4690/7351 0294.

A. Poplina
Stand A12. *Oil paintings.* TEL: 020 7352 4733.

Abdul Rabi
Stand P4. *Jewellery and watch repairs.* TEL: 020 7352 8734.

Robert Raymond
Stand V19. LAPADA. *Jewellery.* TEL: 020 7349 0809.

K. Reilly
Stand V4. *Art Nouveau, Art Deco.* TEL: 020 7352 2099.

Alex Ronco
Stand V1. *Bronzes.* TEL: 020 7376 8116.

Simar Antiques
Stand A18-19. (A. Cohen). *Silver.* TEL: 020 7352 7155.

M. Simpson
Stand E1. *Ivory.* TEL: 020 7352 7989.

Mrs Soldati
Stand P9. *Antique jewellery and watches.* TEL: 020 7351 2317.

John Szwarc
Stand G2/3. *Jewellery and cuff-links.* TEL: 020 7352 8201.

G. Tomlinson & Sotiris Papadimitriou
Stand T3-4. LAPADA. *Decorative arts.*

William Wain
Stand J6. *Vintage costume jewellery.* TEL: 020 7351 4905.

Geoffrey Waters
Stand F1-6. LAPADA. *Oriental porcelain and silver.* TEL: 020 7376 5467.

West Country Jewellery
Stand M5/6/7. (David Billing). *Jewellery, objects, silver.* TEL: 020 7376 8252.

XS Baggage
Stand A1,2,3 & 6, B1/4-6, C2. (Mr and Mrs Lehane). *Antique luggage and travel requisites including Louis Vuitton and Asprey; sporting memorabilia.* TEL: 020 7352 7989/7376 8781.

Ziggy
Stand E3/4. (S. Aritake). *General antique watches and lighters.* TEL: 020 7376 5628.

Apter Fredericks Ltd BADA
265-267 Fulham Rd. SW3 6HY. Open 9.30-5.30, Sat. and evenings by appointment. *STOCK: English furniture, 17th to early 19th C.* TEL: 020 7352 2188; fax - 020 7376 5619; e-mail - antiques@apter-fredericks.com. VAT: Stan/Spec.

Joanna Booth BADA
247 King's Rd., Chelsea. SW3 5EL. Est. 1963. Open 10-6. SIZE: Medium. *STOCK: Sculpture, 12th-17th C; tapestries, textiles, 16th-18th C; Old Master drawings, £50-£50,000.* Not Stocked: Silver, glass, pottery, clocks. PARK: Meters. TEL: 020 7352 8998; fax - 020 7376 7350; e-mail - joannabooth@londonweb.net. SER: Buys at auction. VAT: Spec.

Bourbon-Hanby Antiques Centre
151 Sydney St. Chelsea. SW3 6NT. Open 10-6, Sun. 11-5. LOC: Just off Kings Road, opposite town hall. TEL: 020 7352 2106.

Butler and Wilson
189 Fulham Rd. SW3 6JN. *STOCK: Jewellery, Art Deco, vintage bags and clothes, 1950's jewellery, objects and accessories.* TEL: 020 7352 3045.

Campbell's of Walton Street
164 Walton St. SW3 2JL. Open 9.30-5.30. *STOCK: 20th C impressionist and modern British oils and watercolours.* TEL: 020 7584 9268; fax - 020 7581 3499; website - www.campbellsof waltonstreet.co.uk. SER: Master framing, carving, gilding and restorations.

Classic Fabrics with Robin Haydock
Unit 18 Bourbon-Hanby Antiques Centre, 151 Sydney St. SW3 6NT. LAPADA. Open by appointment. *STOCK: Decorative antiques and 18th C textiles.* TEL: 020 7349 9110; fax - same.

Richard Courtney Ltd BADA
112-114 Fulham Rd. SW3 6HU. Est. 1959. Open 9.30-1 and 2-6. CL: Sat. SIZE: Large. *STOCK: English furniture, 18th C, £500-£20,000.* PARK: Easy. TEL: 020 7370 4020. VAT: Spec.

Robert Dickson and Lesley Rendall Antiques BADA
263 Fulham Rd. SW3 6HY. Est. 1969. Open 10-6, Sat. 10-4.30. SIZE: Medium. *STOCK: Late 18th to early 19th C furniture and works of art, £500-£100,000.* PARK: Easy. TEL: 020 7351 0330. VAT: Spec.

Dragons of Walton St. Ltd
23 Walton St. SW3 2HX. (R. Fisher). *STOCK: Mainly painted and decorated furniture; hand*

decorated children's furniture, decorative items.
LOC: Close to Harrods. PARK: Hasker St. or
First St. TEL: 020 7589 3795; fax - 020 7584
4570.

Michael Foster   BADA
**118 Fulham Rd., Chelsea. SW3 6HU. Open
9.30-5.30, Sat. by appointment.** *STOCK: 18th C
English furniture and works of art.* **TEL: 020
7373 3636/3040. SER: Valuations.**

Gallery Lingard
PO Box 33705, Chelsea Manor St. SW3 3FD.
SLAD. Open by appointment only. *STOCK:
Architectural drawings, watercolours, paintings,
prints and books.* TEL: 020 7352 6034; fax -
same.

Gallery Yacou
127 Fulham Rd. SW3 6RT. LAPADA. Open
10.30-6, Sun. 12-5. *STOCK: Decorative and
antique Oriental and European carpets (room-
size and over-size).* LOC: Walking distance from
Bibendum. TEL: 020 7584 2929; fax - 020 7584
3535.

David Gill
60 Fulham Rd. SW3 6HH. LAPADA. Est. 1986.
Open 10-6. SIZE: Medium. *STOCK: Decorative
and fine arts, Picasso, Cocteau ceramics and
drawings, 1900 to present day.* PARK: Onslow
Sq. TEL: 020 7589 5946; fax - 020 7584 9184.
VAT: Stan.

Godson and Coles   BADA
**92 Fulham Rd. SW3 6HR. Est. 1978. Open
9.30-5.30. CL: Sat.** *STOCK: Fine 18th to early
19th C English furniture and works of art.*
TEL: 020 7584 2200; fax - 020 7584 2223.

Green and Stone
259 Kings Rd. SW3 5EL. (R.J.S. Baldwin). Est.
1927. Open 9-5.30, Wed. 9-7, Sat. 9.30-6, Sun.
12-5. *STOCK: 18th-19th C writing and artists'
materials, glass and china.* LOC: At junction
with Old Church St. PARK: Meters. TEL: 020
7352 0837; e-mail - greenandstone@enterprise.
net. SER: Restorations (pictures). VAT: Stan.

James Hardy and Co
235 Brompton Rd. SW3 2EP. Open 10-5.30.
*STOCK: Silver including tableware, and
jewellery.* PARK: Meters. TEL: 020 7589 5050;
fax - 020 7589 9009. SER: Valuations; repairs.

Stephanie Hoppen Ltd
17 Walton St. SW3 2HX. Est. 1962. Open 10-6,
Sat. 12-4. *STOCK: Decorative picture specialist -
watercolours, oils, drawings and prints, antique
and modern.* TEL: 020 7589 3678.

Hungry Ghost
122 Fulham Rd. SW3 6HU. (Virginia Kern).
Open 9.30-5.30. *STOCK: Chinese furniture and
artefacts, 18th-19th C, £50-£8,000.* TEL: 020
7370 6673. VAT: Stan.

Anthony James and Son Ltd   BADA
**88 Fulham Rd. SW3 6HR. Est. 1949. Open
9.30-5.45, Sat. by appointment. SIZE: Large.**
*STOCK: Furniture, 1700-1880, £200-£50,000;
mirrors, bronzes, ormolu and decorative items,
£200-£20,000.* **PARK: Easy. TEL: 020 7584
1120; fax - 020 7823 7618. SER: Valuations;
buys at auction. VAT: Spec.**

Peter Jones at PJ2
1st Floor, Draycott Ave. SW3. Est. 1945. Open
9.30-6, Wed. 10-7. *STOCK: 18th-19th C
furniture.* TEL: 020 7730 3434.

John Keil Ltd   BADA
**1st Floor, 154 Brompton Rd. SW3 1HX. Est.
1959. Open 9.30-5.30. CL: Sat. except by
appointment.** *STOCK: Fine English furniture,
18th to early 19th C.* **LOC: Near Knightsbridge
underground station. PARK: 200 yds. TEL:
020 7589 6454; fax - 020 7823 8235. VAT:
Spec.**

Michael Lipitch Ltd   BADA
98 Fulham Rd. SW3 6HS. *STOCK: 18th to
early 19th C English furniture, decoration and
works of art.* **TEL: 020 7589 7327; fax - 020
7823 9106.**

Peter Lipitch Ltd   BADA
**120/124 Fulham Rd. SW3 6HU. Est. 1954.
Open 9.30-5.30. SIZE: Large.** *STOCK: Fine
English furniture and mirrors.* **TEL: 020 7373
3328; fax - 020 7373 8888. VAT: Spec.**

The Map House   BADA
**54 Beauchamp Place. SW3 1NY. (P. Curtis and
P. Stuchlik). Est. 1907. Open 9.45-5.45, Sat.
10.30-5 or by appointment.** *STOCK: Antique
and rare maps, atlases, engravings and globes.*
**TEL: 020 7589 4325/7584 8559; fax - 020 7589
1041; e-mail - maps@themaphouse.com;
website - www.themaphouse.com. VAT: Stan.**

McKenna and Co
28 Beauchamp Place. SW3 1NJ. (C. and M.
McKenna). LAPADA. Est. 1982. Open 10-6.
SIZE: Medium. *STOCK: Fine jewellery,
Georgian to post war, £250-£25,000; some silver
and objects.* Not Stocked: Pictures and furniture.
LOC: Off Brompton Rd., near Harrods. PARK:
Meters. TEL: 020 7584 1966; fax - 020 7225
2893; e-mail - info@mckennajewels.com;
website - www.mckennajewels.com. SER:
Valuations; restorations. VAT: Stan/Margin.

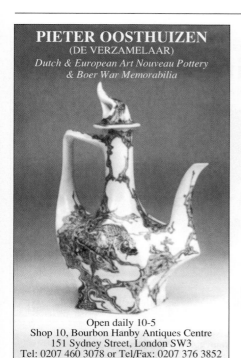

No. 12
12 Cale St., Chelsea Green. SW3 3QU. Open 10-6. *STOCK: French country furniture and accessories.* TEL: 020 7581 5022; fax - 020 7581 3966.

Old Church Galleries
320 King's Rd., Chelsea. SW3 5UH. (Mrs M. Harrington). FATG. Open 10-6. *STOCK: Maps and engravings, from 16th C; sporting and decorative prints.* TEL: 020 7351 4649; fax - 020 7351 4449; e-mail - sales@old-church-galleries.com; website - www.old-church-galleries.com. SER: Framing.

Jacqueline Oosthuizen
23 Cale St., (Off Sydney St.), Chelsea Green. SW3 3QR. LAPADA. Est. 1960. Open 10-5, Sun. by appointment. SIZE: Medium. *STOCK: Staffordshire figures, animals, cottages and toby jugs, 18th-19th C, £80-£8,000; decorative ceramics, 19th-20th C, £60-£6,000.* LOC: Near King's Rd. and Fulham Rd. PARK: Easy. TEL: 020 7352 6071; mobile - 07785 258806. VAT: Stan/Spec.

Jacqueline Oosthuizen
Unit 4 Bourbon-Hanby Antiques Centre, 151 Sydney St. SW3. Open 10-5. *STOCK: Small* selection of Staffordshire figures, animals, cottages and toby jugs. LOC: Just off King's Rd. opposite Town Hall. PARK: Nearby. TEL: 020 7352 6071; mobile - 07785 258806.

Pieter Oosthuizen t/a de Verzamelaar
Shop 10 Bourbon Hanby Antiques Centre, 151 Sydney St. SW3. Est. 1992. Open 10-5. SIZE: Medium. *STOCK: Dutch and European Art Nouveau ceramics, 1880-1930, £30-£8,000; Boer War memorabilia, 1889-1902, £5-£2,000.* LOC: Just off King's Rd. opposite Town Hall. PARK: Nearby. TEL: 020 7460 3078; 020 7376 3852; fax - same. SER: Buys at auction.

Orientalist
152-154 Walton St. SW3 2JJ. (E., H. and M. Sakhai). LAPADA. *STOCK: Oriental, European, antique and reproduction rugs, Aubusson, tapestries, cushions and contemporary rugs.* TEL: 020 7581 2332. SER: Valuations; restorations (cleaning and repairing rugs, carpets and tapestries).

Perez
199 Brompton Rd. SW3 1LA. (Mr Tyran). LAPADA. Est. 1983. Open 10-6. SIZE: Large. *STOCK: Antique carpets, rugs, tapestries and*

Rogers de Rin | **Antiques**

76

Specialists in WEMYSS WARE

76 Royal Hospital Road | London SW3 4HN
Tel: 020 7352 9007 Fax: 020 7351 9407

OPEN 10AM TO 5.30PM, SAT. 10AM TO 1PM. NOW OPEN SUNDAY BY APPOINTMENT.
We would like to buy collections of Wemyss Ware or individual pieces
Website: rogersderin@rogersderine.co.uk

Aubussons. LOC: 50 yards from Harrods. PARK: Easy. TEL: 020 7589 2199 (ansaphone). SER: Valuations; restorations; buys at auction. VAT: Stan/Spec.

Prides of London
15 Paultons House, Paultons Sq. SW3 5DU. Open by appointment only. *STOCK: Fine 18th-19th C English and Continental furniture; objets d'art.* TEL: 020 7586 1227. SER: Interior design.

Rogers de Rin   BADA
76 Royal Hospital Rd., Chelsea. SW3 4HN. (V. de Rin). Est. 1950. Open 10-5.30, Sat. 10-1, Sun. by appointment, SIZE: Small. *STOCK: Wemyss pottery, objets d'art, decorative furnishings (Regency taste), collectors' specialities, 18th-19th C, £50-£10,000.* LOC: Just beyond Royal Hospital, corner of Paradise Walk. PARK: Easy. TEL: 020 7352 9007; fax - 020 7351 9407; e-mail - rogersderin@ rogersderin.co.uk. SER: Buys at auction; free catalogue on request. VAT: Spec.

Charles Saunders Antiques
255 Fulham Rd. SW3 6HY. Open 9.30-5.30, Sat. 10-5. *STOCK: Decorative furniture, objects and lamps, 18th-19th C.* TEL: 020 7351 5242. VAT: Spec.

Christine Schell
15 Cale St. SW3 3QS. LAPADA. Est. 1973. Open 10-5.30. SIZE: Small. *STOCK: Unusual tortoiseshell, silver and enamel objects, late 19th to early 20th C, £150-£2,500.* LOC: North of King's Rd., between Sloane Ave. and Sydney St. PARK: Easy. TEL: 020 7352 5563. SER: Valuations; restorations (tortoiseshell, ivory, shagreen, crocodile, leather, enamels, silver and hairbrush re-bristling). VAT: Stan/Spec.

Robert Stephenson
1 Elystan St., Chelsea Green. SW3 3NT. Open 9.30-5.30, Sat. 10.30-2. *STOCK: Antique and decorative room-sized carpets and kilims; antique Oriental rugs, European tapestries and Aubussons, textiles, needlepoints and cushions; modern Bessarabian kilims, traditional and own contemporary designs.* TEL: 020 7225 2343; fax - same.

Gordon Watson Ltd
50 Fulham Rd. SW3 6HH. LAPADA. Est. 1977. Open 11-6. *STOCK: Art Deco and 1940's glass, jewellery and furniture, £1,000-£50,000; silver by Jensen and Jean E. Puiforcat, 1920's, £500-£30,000.* LOC: At junction with Sydney St. PARK: Sydney St. TEL: 020 7589 3108/7584 6328. VAT: Stan/Spec.

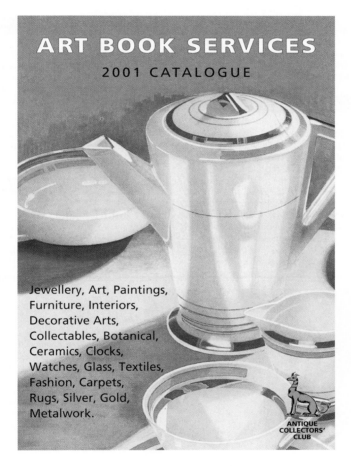

O.F. Wilson Ltd   BADA
Queens Elm Parade, Old Church St. (corner Fulham Rd.), Chelsea. SW3 6EJ. (P. and V.E. Jackson and K.E. Simmonds). LAPADA. Est. 1935. Open 9.30-5.30, Sat. 10.30-1. *STOCK: English and French furniture, mirrors, mantel-pieces, objets d'art.* TEL: 020 7352 9554; fax - 020 7351 0765. SER: Valuations. VAT: Spec.

Clifford Wright Antiques Ltd   BADA
104-106 Fulham Rd. SW3 6HS. Est. 1964. Open Mon.-Fri. 9-5.30, or by appointment. *STOCK: Furniture, period giltwood, looking glasses and consoles, 18th to early 19th C.* TEL: 020 7589 0986; fax - 020 7589 3565. VAT: Spec.

SW4

Antiques and Things
(Mrs V. Crowther). Est. 1986. Open by appointment only. SIZE: Medium. *STOCK: Decorative curtain furniture and fittings; linen, lace, textiles, Victorian to Edwardian, £1-£500; china, glass, kitchenalia, 18th-19th C, £5-£500; English and French furniture, decorative items, 19th C, £20-£2,000.* LOC: Off Lavender Hill, near Clapham junction. TEL: 020 7498 1303; fax - same; mobile - 07767 262096; website - www.antiquesandthings.co.uk.

Places and Spaces
30 Old Town, Clapham. SW4 0LB. (Paul Carroll and Nick Hannam). Est. 1996. Open 10.30-6, Sun. 12-4. CL: Mon. SIZE: Small. *STOCK: Furniture, lighting, art and ceramics, 20th C, £45-£2,000.* LOC: Near Clapham Common underground station. PARK: Meters. TEL: 020 7498 0998; fax - same. SER: Valuations.

SW5

Beaver Coin Room
Beaver Hotel, 57 Philbeach Gdns. SW5 9ED. (J. Lis). Est. 1971. Open by appointment. SIZE: Small. *STOCK: European coins, 10th-18th C; commemorative medals, 15th-20th C; all £5-£5,000.* LOC: 2 mins. walk from Earls Court Rd. PARK: Easy. TEL: 020 7373 4553; fax - 020 7373 4555. SER: Valuations; buys at auction (coins and medals). FAIRS: London Coin and Coinex. VAT: Stan.

SW6

20th Century Gallery
821 Fulham Rd. SW6 5HG. (E. Brandl and H. Chapman). Open 10-6, Sat. 10-1. SIZE: Small. *STOCK: Post impressionist and modern British*

The dial of a mid-18th century astronomical longcase clock by Benson of Whitehaven. In the arch is depicted the rising and setting of the sun, which always occurs at the right time throughout the year because of the raising and lowering of the star-studded blue steel shutters. Also indicated are the sun's declination north or south of the equator, its elevation at midday and position in the zodiac. The aperture in the lower half of the dial shows the state of the tides. Public clocks with astronomical dials were being made some 300 years earlier.

From an article entitled 'Mystery, Novelty and Fantasy Clocks' by Derek Roberts which appeared in the April 2001 issue of **Antique Collecting** magazine. For more details and to subscribe see page 147.

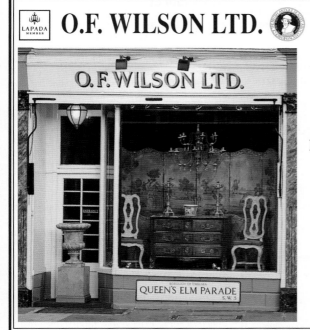

oils and watercolours; original prints. LOC: Near Munster Rd. junction. PARK: Easy. TEL: 020 7731 5888. SER: Restorations (paintings); framing. VAT: Spec.

275 Antiques
275 Lillie Rd., Fulham. SW6 7LL. (David Fisher). Open 10-5.30. SIZE: Medium. *STOCK: English and Continental decorative furniture, £200-£1,200; decorative objects and mirrors, £50-£500; unique American Lucite 1960's table lamps and furniture, £250-£800.* PARK: Easy. TEL: 020 7386 7382.

291 Antiques
291 Lillie Rd., Fulham. SW6 7LL. SIZE: Large. *STOCK: Highly decorative antiques, Gothic style and 18th C splendour; mirrors, garden statuary and textiles.* TEL: 020 7381 5008. SER: Lavish interior design.

This Regency mahogany Pembroke table carries an estimate of £300-£500 at Vost's on 13th September.

From an Action Preview which appeared in the September 2000 issue of **Antique Collecting** magazine. For more details and to subscribe see page 147.

313 Antiques
313 Lillie Rd., Fulham. SW6 7LL. (Marc Costantini Art & Antiques). Open 10.30-5.30. *STOCK: 17th-19th C furniture, £200-£3,000; decorative and interesting objects, £20-£500; pictures especially portrait oils; decorative wood frames, mirrors, carpets.* LOC: From Old Brompton Rd., west for half a mile after crossing Northend Rd. PARK: Easy and nearby. TEL: 020 7610 2380; fax - same;. SER: Shipping arranged.

(55) For Decorative Living
55 New King's Rd., Chelsea. SW6 4SE. (Mrs J. Rhodes). Open 10.30-5.30. *STOCK: Furniture, lighting and decorative items.* TEL: 020 7736 5623. SER: Design.

And So To Bed Limited
638/640 King's Rd. SW6. Est. 1970. Open 10-6. SIZE: Large. *STOCK: Brass, lacquered and wooded beds.* LOC: End of King's Rd., towards Fulham. PARK: Easy. TEL: 020 7731 3593/4/5. SER: Restorations; spares; interior design. VAT: Stan.

The Antique Lamp Shop
at Christopher Wray Lighting, 591-593 King's Rd. SW6 2YW. Est. 1964. Open 10-6. SIZE: Large. *STOCK: Victorian and Edwardian oil lamps, 19th C French and English decorative light fittings, Art Deco wall brackets and pendants, piano candle sconces; also door furniture, old signage and some furniture.* LOC: From Sloane Sq. over Stanley Bridge. TEL: 020 7751 8701; fax - 020 7751 8699. VAT: Stan.

Christopher Bangs   BADA
P O Box 6077. SW6 7XS. LAPADA, CINOA. Est. 1971. Open by appointment only. *STOCK: Domestic metalwork and metalware, works of art, decorative objects.* TEL: 020 7381 3532 (24 hrs); fax - 020 7381 2192 (24 hrs); mobile - 07836 333532; e-mail - cbangs@beeb.net. SER: Research; commission buys at auction; finder. VAT: Stan/Spec.

Sebastiano Barbagallo
661 Fulham Rd. SW6 5PZ. Est. 1975. Open 10.30-6 including Sun., Sat. 9-7. *STOCK: Chinese furnitures; antiques and handicrafts from India, Tibet, SE Asia and China.* TEL: 020 7751 0691.

Barclay Samson Ltd
65 Finlay St. SW6 6HF. Open by appointment only. *STOCK: Pre 1950 original lithographic posters: French, German, Swiss, American, British and Russian Constructivist schools.* TEL: 020 7731 8012; fax - 020 7731 8013; mobile - 07785 306401; e-mail - richard@barclaysamson. com. VAT: Spec.

SALEROOM PRICES

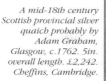

A mid-18th century Scottish provincial silver quaich probably by Adam Graham, Glasgow, c.1762. 5in. overall length. £2,242. Cheffins, Cambridge.

A 19th century Dutch mahogany jardinière with detachable brass liner, 15in. wide. £1,210. Andrew Hartley, Ilkley, West Yorkshire.

A blue-printed footbath, unmarked, c.1820-30, 18¾in. overall length. £2,530. Dreweatt Neate, Newbury, Berkshire.

A George III wax jack, maker Henry Chawner, London 1792, 6¾in. high. £1,100. Wintertons, Lichfield, Staffordshire.

J.R.R. Tolkien, The Hobbit, in dust-wrapper and signed by Tolkien. £3,450. Hamptons, Godalming, Surrey.

An early 20th century Mintons majolica tureen and cover, 11in. diameter. £1,437. Amersham Auction Rooms, Buckinghamshire.

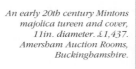

A 5¼in. gauge spirit-fired 4-4-0 locomotive, 34in. long. £770. The Bristol Auction Rooms, Avon.

A creamware coffee pot and cover painted in Pratt enamels, early 19th century, 8¼in. high. £299. Bearne's, Exeter.

From a feature on saleroom prices which appeared in the April 2001 issue of **Antique Collecting** magazine. For more details and to subscribe see page 147.

Robert Barley Antiques

(R.A.Barley). Est. 1965. Open by appointment. SIZE: Medium. *STOCK: Rare and bizarre objects, sculpture and pictures, 2,000BC-2000AD.* TEL: 020 7736 4429; fax - same. VAT: Stan/Spec.

Big Ben Antique Clocks

5 Broxholme House, New King's Rd. SW6 4AA. (R. Lascelles). Est. 1978. *STOCK: Longcase painted dial clocks, from £1,500; also decorative antiques and accessories.* LOC: At junction of Wandsworth Bridge Rd. and New King's Rd. TEL: 020 7736 1770; fax - 020 7384 1957. SER: Buys at auction.

Julia Boston

The Old Stores, The Gasworks, 2 Michael Rd. SW6 2AD. LAPADA, CINOA. Est. 1976. Open 10-6, Sat. 11-5, other times by appointment. SIZE: Large. *STOCK: Tapestry cartoons, 18th-19th C; prints and works of art, 16th-19th C; furniture, 18th-19th C.* LOC: King's Rd. towards Fulham, left Waterford Rd., straight over roundabout, through industrial gates. PARK: Own. TEL: 020 7610 6783; fax - 020 7610 6784; e-mail - julia @juliaboston.com; website -www. juliaboston. com. SER: Restorations (pictures and prints). FAIRS: Decorative (Jan.,April, Sept.). VAT: Spec.

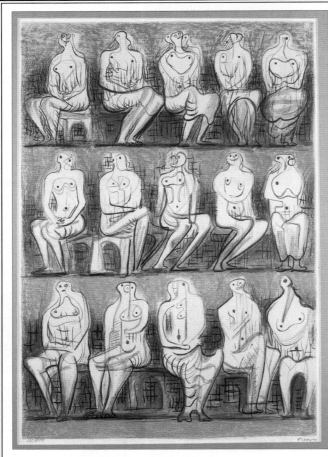

Henry Moore (1898-1986), 'Seated Figures'; bears fake signature and number, lithograph printed in colours, 21in. x 14¼in. Worth about £200? Identical image to the real thing (and then worth £2,500-£3,000) but on the wrong paper.

In his practical approach to spotting fakes and forgeries, Richard Kay identifies seven categories of which the collector should beware. From an article entitled 'Guilty Until Proven Innocent' which appeared in the October 2000 issue of **Antique Collecting** magazine. For more details and to subscribe see page 147.

JULIA BOSTON ANTIQUES

18th & 19th CENTURY ENGLISH & CONTINENTAL FURNITURE
TAPESTRY CARTOONS, ANTIQUE PRINTS & DECORATION

THE OLD STORES, THE GAS WORKS, 2 MICHAEL ROAD, LONDON SW6 2AD
TEL. +44 020 7610 6783   FAX. +44 020 7610 6784

E-mail: julia@juliaboston.com   Website: www.juliaboston.com

89

Caught gazing at her reflection, this sancai courtier represents the Tang pottery at its best. She was given a $170,000-$200,000 estimate at Christie's New York in March this year.

From an article entitled 'Tang Pottery Figures' by Patricia Hunter which appeared in the June 2001 issue of **Antique Collecting** magazine. For more details and to subscribe see page 147.

Alasdair Brown

3/4 The Cranewell, The Gas Works, 2 Michael Rd. SW6 2AD. Est. 1986. Open Wed. and Thurs. 10-6, other days by appointment. SIZE: Medium. *STOCK: Furniture, to £10,000; decorative items, to £5,000; upholstery, lighting and unusual items.* LOC: Behind Christopher Wray (King's Road). PARK: Easy. TEL: 020 7736 6661; fax - 020 7384 3334; e-mail - ab@alasdairbrown. com. SER: Valuations; restorations; finder. FAIRS: Olympia (Feb., June and Nov). VAT: Stan/Spec.

I. and J.L. Brown Ltd

632-636 King's Rd. SW6 2DU. Open 9-5.30. *STOCK: English and French provincial furniture including tables, country chairs, dressers, armoires, side tables and servers; decorative items.* TEL: 020 7736 4141; fax - 020 7736 9164. SER: Restorations; chair re-rushing.

Rupert Cavendish Antiques

610 King's Rd. SW6 2DX. Est. 1980. Open 10-6. SIZE: Large. *STOCK: Louis XVI (Gustavian), Empire, Biedermeier and Art Deco furniture; 20th C oil paintings.* LOC: Just before New King's Rd. PARK: Easy. TEL: 020 7731 7041; fax - 020 7731 8302; e-mail - RCavendish@aol.com; website - www.rupertcavendish.co.uk. SER: Valuations. VAT: Spec.

John Clay

263 New King's Rd., Fulham. SW6 4RB. Est. 1974. Open 10-6. SIZE: Medium. *STOCK: Furniture, £50-£10,000; objets d'art and animal objects, silver and clocks, £10-£5,000; all 18th-19th C.* Not Stocked: Pine. LOC: Close to Parsons Green, A3. PARK: Easy. TEL: 020 7731 5677; e-mail - claycorps@yahoo.com. SER: Restorations (furniture, objets d'art). VAT: Stan/Spec.

Fergus Cochrane and Leigh Warren Antiques

570 King's Rd. SW6 2DY. Est. 1981. Open 10-5. SIZE: Medium. *STOCK: Decorative lighting, furniture and objects, 1700-1930, £100-£3,000.* PARK: Easy. TEL: 020 7736 9166.

Decorative Antiques

284 Lillie Rd., Fulham. SW6 7PX. (Anthony Harley). LAPADA. Est. 1991. Open 10-5.30. SIZE: Medium. *STOCK: French country furniture, 18th C; decorative items.* PARK: Easy. TEL: 020 7610 2694; fax - 020 7386 0103. SER: Valuations; restorations. VAT: Spec.

SALEROOM PRICES

A George III teapot, London 1783, maker's mark 'G.S.', 10½in. wide. £506. Andrew Hartley Fine Arts, Ilkley, West Yorkshire.

19th century gilt metal and shell desk set. £280. The Cotswold Auction Company, Cheltenham.

Ralph Thompson, 'Lion cubs', watercolour, signed lower right, 22½in. x 30¾in, one of a pair. £322. Dreweatt Neate, Newbury, Berkshire.

Graham Greene, The Man Within, 1st edition. £2,475. Hamptons International, Godalming, Surrey.

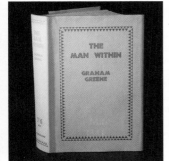

Georgian mahogany bracket clock inscribed 'Tho. Bagley'. £1,800. Hamptons International, Marlborough Saleroom.

A gentleman's steel cased wristwatch by Rolex. £322. Cheffins Grain & Comins, Cambridge.

A Swiss cabinet musical box, c.1880, with 15in. cylinder playing a choice of eight tunes. £2,530. The Bristol Auction Rooms.

From a feature on saleroom prices which appeared in the April 2000 issue of **Antique Collecting** magazine. For more details and to subscribe see page 147.

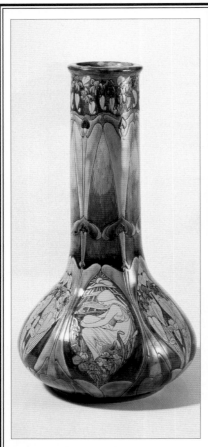

A large Della Robbia Pottery vase, designed by Cassandia Annie Walker, dated 1900, 21in. high.

It can be argued that there were only ever two 'true' Arts and Crafts potteries that adhered to the principles advocated for such by William Morris, says Robert Prescott-Walker. The Medmenham Pottery, near Marlow, Buckinghamshire, was one and the other was the Della Robbia Pottery in Birkenhead, near Liverpool.

From an article entitled 'The Della Robbia Pottery' by Robert Prescott-Walker which appeared in the February 2001 issue of **Antique Collecting** magazine. For more details and to subscribe see page 147.

Charles Edwards   BADA
19A Rumbold Rd. SW6 2HX. Open 9.30-6. *STOCK: Antique and reproduction light fixtures; furniture, 18th-19th C; architectural and decorative items, mirrors, British oil paintings, garden furniture and statuary.* TEL: 020 7736 7172; fax - 020 7731 7388; e-mail - charles@charlesedwards.com

Nicole Fabre
592 King's Rd. SW6 2DX. CINOA Est. 1989. Open 10.30-6, Sat. 11-6, Sun. by appointment only. SIZE: Medium. *STOCK: French furniture, provincial style, French textiles, decorative objects, to 1870.* PARK: Meters. TEL: 020 7384 3112; fax - 020 7610 6410. VAT: Spec.

Fairfax Antiques and Fireplaces
568 King's Rd. SW6 2DY. Open 10-5.30. *STOCK: Cast iron and pine fireplaces, architectural items, balustrades and railings, decorative furniture and collectables.* TEL: 020 7736 5023.

Hector Finch Lighting
88-90 Wandsworth Bridge Rd. SW6 2TF. (Mr and Mrs H. Finch). Est. 1988. Open 10-5.30. SIZE: Medium. *STOCK: Antiques and period lighting, early 20th C contemporary and reproduction.* LOC: Off New King's Rd. PARK: Side streets or Pay and Display. TEL: 020 7731 8886; fax - 020 7731 7408. SER: Restorations (period lighting). VAT: Global.

George Floyd Ltd
592 Fulham Rd. SW6 5UA. Open 8.30-5.30. SIZE: Large. *STOCK: 18th to early 19th C furniture and accessories.* TEL: 020 7736 1649. VAT: Stan/Spec.

Birdie Fortescue Antiques
Studio GJ, Cooper House, 2 Michael Rd. SW6 2AD. LAPADA. Open by appointment only. SIZE: Large. *STOCK: French fruitwood furniture, 18th to early 19th C, £500-£10,000.* LOC: Off King's Rd. TEL: 01206 337567; fax - same; mobile - 07778 263467. FAIRS: Olympia (Feb. and June): Decorative (Jan. and Sept); LAPADA (Oct). VAT: Spec.

Fulham Cross Antiques
318-320 Munster Rd., Fulham. SW6 6BH. SIZE: Large. *STOCK: English, Continental and decorative antique furniture, mirrors and lighting.* TEL: 020 7610 3644.

CHARLES EDWARDS

19A RUMBOLD ROAD, LONDON, SW6 2HX
TEL: +44 (0) 20 7736 7172 FAX: +44 (0) 20 7731 7388
e-mail: charles@charlesedwards.com

Judy Greenwood
657 Fulham Rd. SW6 5PY. Est. 1978. Open 10-5.30. *STOCK: French decorative furniture, lighting, mirrors, beds, quilts.* TEL: 020 7736 6037; fax - 020 7736 1941; e-mail - judyg@dial.pipex.com.

Robin Greer
434 Fulham Palace Rd. SW6 6HX. Est. 1965. Open by appointment. *STOCK: Children's and illustrated books, original illustrations.* TEL: 020 7381 9113; fax - 020 7381 6499. SER: Catalogues issued.

Gregory, Bottley and Lloyd
13 Seagrave Rd. SW6 1RP. Est. 1858. SIZE: Medium. *STOCK: Mineral specimens, £1-£5,000; fossils, £5-£500.* PARK: Easy. TEL: 020 7381 5522; fax - 020 7381 5512. SER: Valuations. VAT: Stan.

Guinevere Antiques
574/580 King's Rd. SW6 2DY. Open 9.30-6, Sat. 10-5.30 (warehouse by appointment only). SIZE: Large + trade warehouse.*STOCK: Period decorative antiques and accessories.* TEL: 020 7736 2917; fax - 020 7736 8267; e-mail - sales@guinevere.co.uk; website- www.guinevere.co.uk.

Gutlin Clocks and Antiques
616 King's Rd. SW6. Est. 1990. Open 9.30-7. SIZE: Medium. *STOCK: Longcase clocks, £2,000-£8,000; mantel clocks, £300-£6,000; furniture and lighting, £500-£3,000; all 18th-19th C.* LOC: 200 yards from beginning of New King's Rd. PARK: Maxwell Rd. TEL: 020 7384 2439; fax - same; home - 020 8740 6830; e-mail - mark@gutlin.com; website - www.gutlin.com. SER: Valuations; restorations (clocks and clock cases); buys at auction (clocks).

Hollingshead and Co
56 Tasso Rd. and 247 Munster Rd., Fulham. SW6. (D. Hollingshead). Est. 1946. Open 8.30-5, Sat. 9-1. SIZE: Medium. *STOCK: Marble and wood mantelpieces, grates, fenders, fire irons, chandeliers, including reproduction, £50-£20,000.* Not Stocked: Furniture. TEL: 020 7385 8519. SER: Valuations; restorations (marblework and wood mantelpieces). VAT: Stan.

House of Mirrors
597 King's Rd. SW6 2EL. (G. Witek). Est. 1960. Open 10-6. *STOCK: Mirrors.* TEL: 020 7736 5885; fax - 020 7610 9188.

HRW Antiques (London) Ltd
26 Sulivan Rd. SW6 3DT. LAPADA. Open 9-5. SIZE: Large. *STOCK: Furniture and objects of art, 18th-19th C.* TEL: 020 7371 7995; fax - 020 7371 9522; e-mail - iain@hrw-antiques.com; website - www.hrw-antiques.com.

P.L. & M. James
590 Fulham Rd. SW6 5NT. Open 8.30-6, Sat. by appointment only. *STOCK: 18th-19th C furniture and objects.* TEL: 020 7736 0183. SER: Restorations (painted and lacquer furniture, gilding, carving). VAT: Stan/Spec.

Christopher Jones Antiques
618-620 King's Rd. SW6 2DU. Open 10-5.30. *STOCK: Continental and British decorative objects and furniture, screens and mirrors, 18th-19th C, £500-£10,000.* TEL: 020 7731 4655; fax - 020 7371 8682VAT: Spec.

Ki Design
594 King's Rd. SW6 2DX. Open Tues.-Sat. 10-6. *STOCK: Japanese furniture.* TEL: 020 7736 5999; fax - 020 7384 3192; e-mail - kidesign@dircon.co.uk.

King's Court Galleries
949/953 Fulham Rd. SW6 5HY. (Mrs J. Joel). Open 10-5.30. *STOCK: Antique maps, engravings, decorative and sporting prints.* TEL: 020 7610 6939; e-mail - sales@kingscourt galleries.co.uk; website - www.kingscourt galleries.co.uk. SER: Framing (on site).

L. and E. Kreckovic
559 King's Rd. SW6. Open 10-6. *STOCK: 18th-19th C furniture.* TEL: 020 7736 0753; fax - 020 7731 5904.

Lewin
638 Fulham Rd. SW6 5RT. (David and Harriett Lewin). Open 10.30-6. SIZE: Medium. *STOCK: Original Dutch colonial furniture and teak and mahogany reproduction colonial-style designs.* TEL: 020 7731 1616. VAT: Stan.

Lunn Antiques Ltd
86 New Kings Rd., Parsons Green. SW6 4LU. Open 10-6. *STOCK: Antique and modern bed linen, nightdresses, christening robes.* TEL: 020 7736 4638; fax - 020 7371 7113. SER: Laundry and restoration (antique linen and lace).

Michael Luther Antiques
590 King's Rd., Chelsea. SW6 2DX. (Michael Luther and Peter Goodwin). Est. 1967. Open 10-6. SIZE: Large. *STOCK: Furniture - 18th-19th C, £500-£10,000; early 20th C, £300-£3,000; lighting, 19th-20th C, £300-£5,000.* LOC: Between Lots Rd. and Wandsworth Bridge Rd. PARK: Nearby. TEL: 020 7371 8492; fax - same. SER: Valuations; buys at auction (furniture). VAT: Spec.

Magpies
152 Wandsworth Bridge Rd., Fulham. SW6 2UH. Open 10-5. SIZE: 4 dealers. *STOCK: China, glass, kitchenalia, collectables, cutlery, door furniture, lighting, silver plate, fireplace accessories and small furniture.* TEL: 020 7736 3738.

Michael Marriott Ltd
588 Fulham Rd. SW6 5NT. Est. 1979. Open 10-5.30. CL: Sat. pm. and Sun. except by appointment. SIZE: Large. *STOCK: English furniture, 1700-1850, £400-£15,000; framed prints, £45-£800.* LOC: Junction of Fulham Rd. and Parsons Green Lane. PARK: Easy. TEL: 020 7736 3110; fax - 020 7736 0568. SER: Valuations; restorations. VAT: Stan/Spec.

David Martin-Taylor Antiques
558 King's Rd. SW6 2DZ. LAPADA. Open 10-6, Sat. 11-5. SIZE: Medium. *STOCK: Classic and decorative furniture and unusual objects, 18th-19th C.* PARK: Easy. TEL: 020 7731 4135; fax - 020 7371 0029; e-mail - dmt@davidmartintaylor.com. SER: Hire. VAT: Stan/Spec.

Megan Mathers Antiques
571 Kings Rd. SW6 2EB. LAPADA. Open 10-6. *STOCK: 18th-19th C English and Continental furniture and decorative objects.* TEL: 020 7371 7837.

Mark Maynard Antiques
651 Fulham Rd. SW6 5PU. Est. 1977. Open 10-5, Sun. by appointment. SIZE: Medium. *STOCK: Decorative items, £25-£300.* LOC: Near Fulham Broadway underground. PARK: Easy. TEL: 020 7731 3533; home - 020 7373 4681. VAT: Stan/Spec.

Mora & Upham Antiques
584 King's Rd. SW6 2DX. (Matthew Upham). Est. 1976. Open 10-6. SIZE: Medium. *STOCK: Furniture, pictures, decorative objects and chandeliers, 18th-19th C.* LOC: Corner premises. PARK: Easy. TEL: 020 7731 4444; fax - 020 7736 0440. SER: Valuations; restorations (pictures, china and furniture). VAT: Spec.

Sylvia Napier Ltd
554 King's Rd. SW6 2DZ. Est. 1972. Open 10-6. SIZE: Large. *STOCK: Furniture - decorative European, 18th-19th C, £100-£15,000; decorative Oriental, 17th-19th C, £200-£7,000; garden, 19th C, £150-£7,000; objets d'art; unusual chandeliers.* LOC: Near junction with Lots Rd. PARK: Easy. TEL: 020 7371 5881. SER: Restorations. VAT: Spec.

Nimmo & Spooner
277 Lillie Rd., Fulham. SW6 7LL. (Catherine Nimmo and Myra Spooner). Est. 1994. Open 10.30-5.30. SIZE: Medium. *STOCK: Furniture including painted dressers and chests of drawers, tables, mirrors, 18th to early 19th C, to £3,500.* LOC: Between Fulham Broadway and Hammersmith. PARK: Nearby. TEL: 020 7385 2724; fax - same. FAIRS: Decorative Antiques & Textiles.

Old World Trading Co
565 King's Rd. SW6. (R.J. Campion). Est. 1970. Open 9.30-6. *STOCK: Fireplaces, chimney pieces and accessories, chandeliers, mirrors, furniture including decorative, works of art.* TEL: 020 7731 4708; fax - 020 7731 1291.

Ossowski
595 King's Rd. SW6 2EL. Est. 1960. Open 9.30-5.30. SIZE: Large. *STOCK: Furniture, 18th C.* TEL: 020 7731 0334. SER: Valuations; restorations. VAT: Stan/Spec.

M. Pauw Antiques
Cooper House, 2 Michael Rd. SW6 2AD. Est. 1985. SIZE: Medium. *STOCK: English and Continental furniture, leather chairs, 18th-19th C; decorative items, lighting fixtures, cast iron, zinc and lead planters.* PARK: Easy. TEL: 020 7731 4022; fax - 020 7731 7356; e-mail - info@mpauw; website - www.mpauw.com. VAT: Stan.

Perez Antique Carpets Gallery
150 Wandsworth Bridge Rd., Fulham. SW6 2UH. (K. Dinari). Est. 1984. Open 10-6.30, Wed. 10-7.30. SIZE: Large. *STOCK: Carpets, 19th C, £400-£40,000; rugs, 18th-20th C, £300-£3,000; textiles, 19th C, £70-£1,500.* PARK: Easy. TEL: 020 7371 9619/9620. SER: Valuations; restorations; buys at auction (Oriental and European carpets, rugs and textiles, tapestries). VAT: Stan/Spec.

The Pine Mine (Crewe-Read Antiques)
100 Wandsworth Bridge Rd., Fulham. SW6 2TF. (D. Crewe-Read). Est. 1971. Open 9.45-5.45, Sat. till 4.30. SIZE: Large. *STOCK: Georgian and Victorian pine, Welsh dressers, farmhouse tables, chests of drawers, boxes and some architectural items.* LOC: From Sloane Sq., down King's Rd., into New King's Rd., left into Wandsworth Bridge Rd. PARK: Outside. TEL: 020 7736 1092. SER: Furniture made from old wood; stripping; export.

Daphne Rankin and Ian Conn
608 King's Rd. SW6 2DX. LAPADA. Est. 1979.
Open 10.30-6. SIZE: Medium. *STOCK: Oriental
porcelain including Chinese, Japanese, Imari,
Cantonese, Satsuma, Nanking, Famille Rose,
£500-£25,000; Dutch Delft; tortoiseshell tea
caddies.* PARK: Maxwell Rd. adjacent to shop.
TEL: 020 7384 1847; fax - same; mobile - 07774
487713; e-mail - daphnerankin@aol.com; website
- www.rankin-conn-chinatrade.com. SER:
Valuations; buys at auction (as stock). FAIRS:
Olympia (June and Nov.). VAT: Stan/Spec.

Redroom
72 Farm Lane, Fulham. SW6 1QA. (Lei Jia). Est.
1997. Open Wed.-Fri. 11-5, Sat. 11-3. SIZE:
Medium. *STOCK: Chinese furniture and works of
art, late 17th-19th C, to £1,500.* LOC: Near
Fulham Broadway. PARK: Easy. TEL: 020 7386
8777; fax - 020 7385 3747; mobile - 07798
801707. FAIRS: Decorative Antiques & Textiles,
Battersea. VAT: Margin.

Reffold
572 King's Rd. SW6 2DY. (K. Jackson). Est.
1968. Open Mon.-Fri. 10-5. SIZE: Medium.
*STOCK: Early furniture, works of art and
paintings.* PARK: Easy. TEL: 020 7736 7145; fax
- 020 7736 0029. VAT: Spec.

Richardson and Kailas Icons   BADA
65 Rivermead Court, Ranelagh Gardens. SW6
3RY. (C. Richardson and M. Kailas).
LAPADA. Open by appointment. *STOCK:
Icons and frescoes.* TEL: 020 7371 0491.

Rogers & Co
604 Fulham Rd. SW6 5RP. (M. and C. Rogers).
LAPADA. Est. 1971. Open 10-6. SIZE: Large.
*STOCK: Furniture, 18th-19th C, £100-£3,000;
upholstery.* LOC: Near Fulham library, Parsons
Green Lane. PARK: Side streets. TEL: 020 7731
8504; fax - 020 7610 6040. SER: Valuations.
VAT: Stan/Spec.

George Sherlock Antiques
588 King's Rd. SW6 2DX. Est. 1968. Open 9.30-
5.30. SIZE: Large. *STOCK: General antiques,
decorative furniture and upholstery, 1650-1900,
£20-£15,000.* PARK: Easy. TEL: 020 7736 3955;
fax - 020 7371 5179. VAT: Stan/Spec.

Simon Horn Furniture Ltd
117-121 Wandsworth Bridge Rd. SW6 2TP.
IDDA. Est. 1981. Open 9.30-5.30, Sun. by
appointment. SIZE: Large. *STOCK: Wooden
classical style bedframes, £500-£5,000; bedside
tables, £150-£650; all 1790-1910 or recent
larger copies.* LOC: South from New King's Rd.,

towards river down Wandsworth Bridge Rd., premises on left at first zebra crossing. PARK: Easy. TEL: 020 7731 1279; fax - 020 7736 3522. SER: Restorations (as stock). FAIRS: House & Garden. VAT: Stan.

Sleeping Beauty Antique Beds
579/581 King's Rd. SW6 2EH. Open 10-5.30. *STOCK: Brass, iron and French wooden beds, 19th C, £500-£15,000.* TEL: 020 7471 4711; e-mail - info@antiquebeds.com; website - www.antiquebeds.com.

Stephen Sprake
283 Lillie Rd., Fulham. SW6 7LL. Open 10.30-5.30. *STOCK: 18th-20th C lighting and furniture.* LOC: 10 mins. from Hammersmith roundabout. PARK: Easy. TEL: 020 7381 3209; fax - 020 7381 9502. VAT: Spec.

Thornhill Galleries Ltd
76 New King's Rd. SW6 4LT. Est. 1880. Open 10-4.30, Sat. 10-1. SIZE: Large. *STOCK: English and French marble, stone and wood chimney-pieces, panelled rooms, architectural features and wood carvings, fire grates and fenders, all 17th-19th C; decorative iron interiors and other fire accessories, 17th-20th C.* LOC: Continuation of King's Rd. Coming from Sloane Sq. shop is on right-hand side. PARK: Easy. TEL: 020 7736 5830. SER: Valuations; restorations (architectural items); buys at auction (architectural items). VAT: Stan/Spec.

Through the Looking Glass Ltd
563 King's Rd. SW6 2EB. (J.J.A. and D.A. Pulton). Est. 1966. Open 10-5.30. SIZE: Large. *STOCK: Mirrors, 18th-19th C.* TEL: 020 7736 7799. SER: Restorations. VAT: Spec.

Ferenc Toth
598A King's Rd. SW6 2DX. (F.I. Toth). Est. 1978. Open 9.30-5.30. SIZE: Medium. *STOCK: Mirrors, furniture and decorative items, 18th-19th C.* LOC: Fulham end of King's Rd., Chelsea. PARK: Easy. TEL: 020 7731 2063; fax - same; home - 020 8932 7954; mobile - 0777 952 4725. SER: Valuations; buys at auction. VAT: Spec.

Trowbridge Gallery
555 King's Rd. SW6 2EB. (M. Trowbridge). LAPADA. Est. 1980. Open 9.30-6, Sat. 10-5.30. SIZE: Large. *STOCK: Decorative prints, 17th-19th C, £35-£3,000.* LOC: Near Christopher Wray Lighting. PARK: Easy. TEL: 020 7371 8733. SER: Valuations; restorations; buys at auction (antiquarian books and prints); hand-made frames; decorative mounting. FAIRS: Decorative Antiques and Textiles, Olympia, LAPADA, City of London. VAT: Stan.

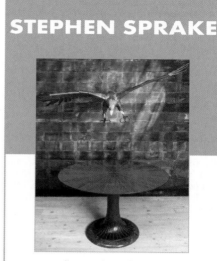
Whiteway and Waldron Ltd
305 Munster Rd., Fulham. SW6 6BJ. (M. Whiteway and G. Kirkland). Est. 1976. Open 10-6, Sat. 11-4. SIZE: Large. *STOCK: Religious antiques including candlesticks, statuary, gothic and carved church woodwork.* LOC: At junction with Lillie Rd. PARK: On forecourt for loading, or Strode Rd. TEL: 020 7381 3195; fax - same; e-mail - sales@whiteway-waldron.co.uk; website-www.whiteway-waldron.co.uk. SER: Buys at auction (religious items). VAT: Stan.

York Gallery Ltd
569 King's Rd. SW6 2EB. (Jane and Gerd Beyer). Est. 1984. Open 10.30-5.30. SIZE: Medium. *STOCK: Antique prints.* TEL: 020 7736 2260; fax - same. SER: Bespoke framing.VAT: Stan.

SW7

Anglo Persian Carpet Co
6 South Kensington Station Arcade. SW7 2NA. Est. 1910. Open 9.30-6. *STOCK: Carpets and rugs.* TEL: 020 7589 5457. SER: Valuations; restorations (carpets and rugs); cleaning.

Atlantic Bay Carpets Gallery   BADA
14 Gloucester Rd. SW7 4RB. (W. Grodzinski).
CINOA. Est. 1945. Open 9-4, Sat. by
appointment. SIZE: Medium. *STOCK: Antique
Oriental and European carpets and textiles;
Islamic and Indian art.* TEL: 020 7689 8489;
fax - 020 7581 8189; e-mail - atlanticbay
gallery@btinternet.com; website - www.
btinternet.com/~atlanticbaygallery/. SER:
Valuations; restorations; buys at auction (as
stock). VAT: Stan/Spec.

Aubrey Brocklehurst   BADA
124 Cromwell Rd. SW7 4ET. Est. 1946. Open
9-1 and 2-5.30 (or later by arrangement), Sat.
10-1. SIZE: Medium. *STOCK: English clocks
and barometers.* TEL: 020 7373 0319; fax - 020
7373 7612. SER: Valuations; restorations;
furniture and clock repairs; buys at auction.
VAT: Spec.

Julie Collino
15 Glendower Place, South Kensington. SW7
3DR. Est. 1971. Open 11-6, Sat. 2-6, Sun. by
appointment. *STOCK: Watercolours, oils,
etchings, £25-£1,000; china, £25-£500; both
19th-20th C; furniture, £50-£2,000.* LOC: Off
Harrington Rd. TEL: 020 7584 4733; home - 020
8568 7440.

The Gloucester Road Bookshop
123 Gloucester Rd., South Kensington. SW7
4TE. (Nicholas Dennys). Est. 1983. Open 8.30-
10.30 pm, Sat. and Sun. 10.30-6.30. SIZE:
Medium. *STOCK: Second-hand hardback and
paperback books, all genres, mainly 19th-20th C,
£1-£50; modern first editions, mainly 20th C, £5-
£500; rare books, 17th-20th C, £70-£1,000.* LOC:
150 yards Gloucester Road underground station.
Come out of station, cross road and turn right.
PARK: Loading; easy weekends. Meters nearby.
TEL: 020 7370 3503; fax - 020 7373 0610. SER:
Valuations; book search.

M.P. Levene Ltd   BADA
5 Thurloe Place. SW7 2RR. Est. 1889. Open
9.30-6. CL: Sat. pm. *STOCK: Silver, old
Sheffield plate, scale silver models, various, all
prices.* LOC: Few minutes past Harrods near
South Kensington station. PARK: Easy. TEL:
020 7589 3755; fax - 020 7589 9908; e-mail -
silver@mplevene.co.uk; website - www.
mplevene.co.uk. SER: Valuations. VAT:
Stan/Spec.

A. & H. Page (Est. 1840)
66 Gloucester Rd. SW7 4QT. Open 9-5.45, Sat.
10-2. *STOCK: Silver, jewellery, watches.* TEL:
020 7584 7349. SER: Valuations; repairs;
silversmith; goldsmith.

The Taylor Gallery Ltd
1 Bolney Gate. SW7 1QW. (J. Taylor). Est. 1986.
Open by appointment only. *STOCK: Irish,
British, China Trade and marine paintings, 19th-
20th C.* TEL: 020 7581 0253.

The Wyllie Gallery
44 Elvaston Place. SW7 5NP. (J.G. Wyllie).
Open by appointment. *STOCK: 19th-20th C
marine paintings and etchings, especially works
by the Wyllie family.* TEL: 020 7584 6024.

SW8

The French House (Antiques) Ltd
125 Queenstown Rd. SW8 3PH. (S.B. and M.J.
Hazell). Est. 1995. Open Thurs., Fri., and Sat.,
other days by appointment. SIZE: Medium.
*STOCK: Wooden beds, 18th-19th, £900-£2,500;
gilt mirrors, 19th C, £300-£2,000; lighting, 19th-
20th C, £200-£1,000; all French.* LOC: Short
drive from Victoria station. PARK: Sidestreets.
TEL: 020 7978 2228; fax - 020 7978 2340;
website - www.thefrenchhouse.co.uk. SER:
Restorations; cabinet making, upholstery, French
polishing and painting. VAT: Stan/Spec.

Heskia   BADA
SW8 5BP. Est. 1877. Open by appointment
only. *STOCK: Oriental carpets, rugs and
tapestries.* TEL: 020 7373 4489. SER: Valuations; cleaning and repairs.

Paul Orssich
2 St. Stephen's Terrace, South Lambeth. SW8
1DH. Open by appointment only. *STOCK: Old,
rare and out of print books on Spain and
Hispanic studies; old maps of all parts of the
world, from £20.* TEL: 020 7787 0030; fax - 020
7735 9612; e-mail - paulo@orssich.com; website
- www.orssich.com.

SW9

Rodney Franklin Antiques
SW9. Est. 1968. Open by appointment only.
*STOCK: French and English mirrors and beds,
furniture, lighting, architectural and garden
items.* TEL: 020 7703 8089. VAT: Stan/Spec.

SW10

Iftikhar Bokhari
57 Uverdale Rd., Chelsea. SW10 0SN. Est. 1963.
Open 10-6. SIZE: Large. *STOCK: Rare
tapestries, carpets, textiles.* TEL: 020 7351

3296/7376 3136; fax - 020 7376 4876; e-mail - ibokhari@freeserve. SER: Valuations; restorations; cleaning; part exchange. VAT: Stan.

Carlton Davidson Antiques
507 King's Rd., Chelsea. SW10 0TX. Est. 1981. Open 10-6. *STOCK: Lamps, chandeliers, mirrors and decorative items, £500-£5,000.* TEL: 020 7795 0905.

Jonathan Clark & Co
18 Park Walk, Chelsea. SW10 0AQ. SLAD. Open 10-6.30, Sat. by appointment. *STOCK: Modern British paintings and sculpture.* TEL: 020 7351 3555; fax - 020 7823 3187.

Collins and Hastie Ltd
5 Park Walk, Chelsea. SW10 0AJ. (Caroline Hastie and Diana Collins). Open 10-6, Sat. by appointment only. SIZE: Large. *STOCK: 20th C contemporary and modern paintings, European and British, £500-£30,000.* LOC: Park Walk runs between King's Rd. and Fulham Rd. PARK: Easy. TEL: 020 7351 4292. SER: Restorations (pictures). VAT: Spec.

The Furniture Cave
533 King's Rd. SW10 0TZ. Est. 1967. Open 10-6, Sun. 11-4. SIZE: Large. LOC: Corner of Lots Rd. PARK: Meters. TEL: 020 7352 4229/5478. SER: Shipping; forwarding. VAT: Stan/Spec. Below are listed the dealers trading from this address.

Paul Andrews Antiques
Basement. *English and Continental decorative furniture; sculpture, Old Master paintings, prints and drawings.* TEL: 020 7352 4584; fax - 020 7351 78165.

Brown's Antique Furniture
First Floor. *Library and dining, and decorative objects, from early 18th C.* TEL: 020 7352 2046; fax - 020 7352 3654.

Stuart Duggan
First Floor. *Georgian and Victorian furniture especially 19th-20th C pianos.* TEL: 020 7352 2046; fax - 020 7352 3654.

Preston Antiques
Ground Floor. *Early 19th C and Regency furniture.* TEL: 020 7352 3775; fax - 020 7352 3759.

Kenneth Harvey
Ground Floor. LAPADA. *Decorative furniture, mirrors, chandeliers, light fittings.* TEL: 020 7352 8645; fax - 020 7376 3225.

Simon Hatchwell Antiques
Ground Floor. Est. 1961. *English and Continental decorative furniture and objets d'art.* TEL: 020 7351 2344; fax - 020 7351 3520.

Lamberty
Unusual English and Continental furniture, chandeliers, works or art, £500-£50,000. TEL: 020 7352 3111; fax - 020 7351 5833; mobile - 07768 736687; e-mail - mail@lamberty.co.uk; website - www.lamberty.co.uk VAT: Spec.

Phoenix Trading Company
Furniture including Indian, porcelain, bronzes. TEL: 020 7351 6543; fax - 020 7352 9803.

Mark Ransom Limited
First Floor. *Continental furniture specialising French Empire; antiquarian books, maps and prints.* TEL: 020 7376 7653; fax - 020 7352 3654.

Anthony Redmile
Basement. *Marble resin neo-classical Grand Tour objects.* TEL: 020 7351 3813; fax - 020 7352 8131.

Steve Thomas
First Floor. *Georgian and Victorian furniture: pedestal desks, writing tables, library, bureaux.* TEL: 020 7352 2046; fax - 020 7352 3654.

York Whiting
Ground Floor. LAPADA. *17th-20th C furniture, English and Continental, paintings, carpets and textiles.* TEL: 020 7376 8530; fax - 020 7352 7994.

Hünersdorff Rare Books
P.O. Box 582. SW10 9RU. ABA. Est. 1969. Open by appointment only. *STOCK: Continental books in rare editions, early printing, science and medicine, illustrated books, Latin America, natural history.* TEL: 020 7373 3899; fax - 020 7370 1244.

Thomas Kerr Antiques Ltd
at L'Encoignure, 517 King's Rd. SW10 0TX. Est. 1977. Open 10-6. SIZE: Large. *STOCK: French country furniture, paintings, mirrors and decorative items.* TEL: 020 7351 6465; fax - 020 7351 4744. VAT: Stan/Spec.

Lane Fine Art Ltd
8 Drayton Gardens. SW10 9SA. (C. Foley). Open by appointment only. *STOCK: Oil paintings, 1500-1850, principally English, major works by the main artists of the period, £10,000-£1million+.* TEL: 020 7373 3130. VAT: Stan/Spec.

Langford's Marine Antiques   BADA
The Plaza, 535 King's Rd. SW10 0SZ. (L.L. Langford). LAPADA. Est. 1941. *STOCK: Ships models, marine instruments, globes, steam engine models.* TEL: 020 7351 4881; fax - 020 7352 0763; e-mail - langford@dircon.co.uk; website - www.langfords.co.uk. SER: Valuations; restorations. VAT: Stan/Spec.

Langton Street Gallery

13 Langton St. SW10 1JR. (P. and C. Kennaugh). Open 10.30-7, Fri. and Sat. 10.30-3. *STOCK: Oils, watercolours, prints, 19th-20th C, £200-£3,000*. TEL: 020 7351 1973.

Stephen Long

348 Fulham Rd. SW10 9UH. Est. 1966. Open 9.30-1 and 2.15-5. CL: Sat. pm. and Sun. except by appointment. SIZE: Small. *STOCK: English pottery, 18th-19th C, to £400; English painted furniture, 18th to early 19th C; toys and games, household and kitchen items, chintz, materials and patchwork, to £1,000*. Not Stocked: Stripped pine, large brown furniture, fashionable antiques. LOC: From South Kensington along road on right between Ifield Rd. and Billing Rd. PARK: Easy. TEL: 020 7352 8226. VAT: Spec.

Mallord Street Antiques

Lower Floor, 498 King's Rd. SW10. (Ginny Mejia). Est. 1987. Open 10-5. SIZE: Small. *STOCK: Decorative furniture and objets d'art, 18th-19th C*. LOC: Near World's End. PARK: Easy. TEL: 020 7351 1442; home/fax - 020 7352 9659. SER: Valuations; buys at auction (furniture). FAIRS: Decorative (Mar. and Sept.). VAT: Stan/Spec.

McVeigh & Charpentier

498 King's Rd. SW10. (Maggie Charpentier). LAPADA. Est. 1979. Open 10.30-5, weekends by appointment only. SIZE: Medium. *STOCK: Continental furniture, mirrors, garden ironwork and stone, 17th-19th C*. LOC: Two blocks down from Earls Court. PARK: In cul de sac adjacent. TEL: 020 7351 1442/7352 6084; home - 020 7937 6459; mobile - 07801 480167. FAIRS: Olympia (June); Harvey (Sept., Jan. and March).

McWhirter

22 Park Walk, Chelsea. SW10 0AQ. (James McWhirter). Open 10-6, Sat. by appointment. SIZE: Medium. *STOCK: Works of art, objects, unusual furniture*. LOC: Near Fulham Road Cinema. PARK: Easy. TEL: 020 7351 5399; fax - 020 7352 9821. VAT: Spec.

Offer Waterman and Co. Fine Art

11 Langton St. SW10 0JL. Est. 1986. Open 9-6.30, Sat. 10-4, Sun. by appointment. SIZE: Small. *STOCK: British paintings, 1900 to date, £500-£5,000*. LOC: Off Kings Rd. PARK: Easy. TEL: 020 7351 0068; fax - 020 7351 2269; e-mail - offerwaterman@msn.com; website - www.waterman.co.uk. SER: Valuations; restorations (as stock); framing; buys at auction (Modern British paintings). FAIRS: Art 2001; 20th C British Art; Olympia. VAT: Stan/Spec.

Orientation

2 Park Walk. SW10 0AD. (Evelyn Soler). Est. 1990. Open 10-6, Sat. by appointment. SIZE: Medium. *STOCK: Continental furniture, 18th-19th C; Chinese porcelain, ceramics, works of art, China trade items, to £20,000*. LOC: Off Fulham Rd. TEL: 020 7351 0234; fax - 020 7351 7535. FAIRS: Olympia. VAT: Spec.

Park Walk Gallery   BADA

20 Park Walk, Chelsea. SW10 0AQ. (J. Cooper). Est. 1988. Open 10-6.30, Sat. 11-4. SIZE: Medium. *STOCK: Paintings, £250-£100,000; watercolours, £250-£20,000; drawings, £200-£15,000; all 19th-20th C English and Continental*. LOC: Off Fulham Rd. PARK: Easy. TEL: 020 7351 0410; fax - same; website - www.jonathancooper.co.uk. SER: Valuations; restorations. FAIRS: Olympia; Watercolours and Drawings, Art London. VAT: Spec.

H.W. Poulter and Son

279 Fulham Rd. SW10 9PZ. Est. 1946. Open 9.30-5. CL: Sat. pm. SIZE: Large. *STOCK: English and French marble chimney pieces, grates, fenders, fire-irons, brass, chandeliers*. PARK: Meters. TEL: 020 7352 7268. SER: Restorations (marble work). VAT: Stan/Spec.

John Thornton

455 Fulham Rd. SW10 9UZ. Open 10-5.30. *STOCK: Antiquarian books especially theology*. TEL: 020 7352 8810.

Vaughan Ltd

G1 Chelsea Harbour Design Centre, Chelsea Harbour. SW10 0XE. Est. 1980. Open 9-5.30. CL: Sat. SIZE: Large. *STOCK: Reproduction 18th-19th C lighting, furniture, decorative objects*. PARK: Easy. TEL: 020 7349 4600. VAT: Stan/Spec.

SW11

Artchaos

176 Northcote Rd., Battersea. SW11 6RE. (John C. Butt). Est. 1991. Open 10-6. CL: Wed. SIZE: Medium. *STOCK: Furniture and lights, £200-£1,000; 1950's and 1960's Italian design, £100-£500; modern paintings,£500-£2,500; all 20th C*. PARK: Nearby. TEL: 020 7924 5856. SER: Valuations; buys at auction.

Braemar Antiques

113 Northcote Rd., Battersea. SW11 6PW. (Maria Elisabeth Ramos-de-Deus and Elizabeth Henderson). Est. 1995. SIZE: Small. *STOCK: Painted furniture including armoires, chests of*

drawers, mirros and lamps; quilts, eiderdowns, china and glass. LOC: Near Clapham junction. PARK: Easy. TEL: 020 7924 5628. FAIRS: Brocante, Kensington.

Eccles Road Antiques
60 Eccles Rd., Battersea. SW11. (H. Rix). Open 10-5. *STOCK: General antiques, pine furniture and smalls.* TEL: 020 7228 1638.

Christopher Edwards
36 Roseneath Rd. SW11 6AH. Est. 1982. Open by appointment. SIZE: Medium. *STOCK: Architecturally inspired furniture, unusual works of art, 19th C, £100-£10,000.* TEL: 020 7223 9962; fax - same; mobile - 07831 707043. SER: Valuations; buys at auction. VAT: Stan/Spec.

Garland Antiques
74 Chatham Rd., Battersea. SW11 6HG. (Garland Beech). Open 10-6, Sun. 12-5. CL: Mon. SIZE: Small. *STOCK: Furniture, 19th C; decorative objects, 18th-19th C.* PARK: Easy. TEL: 020 7924 4284. SER: Restorations (pine stripping, decorative paint finishes, metal polishing).

Gideon Hatch Rugs
1 Port House, Plantation Wharf, Battersea. SW11 3TY. Est. 1985. Open by appointment. SIZE: Small. *STOCK: Oriental and European rugs, 19th to early 20th C, £500-£25,000.* LOC: Off York Rd., behind Homebase. PARK: Easy. TEL: 020 7223 3996; fax - 020 7223 3997. SER: Valuations; restorations; cleaning; buys at auction (rare rugs). FAIRS: Olympia; Battersea. VAT: Stan/Spec.

Northcote Road Antiques Market
155A Northcote Rd., Battersea. SW11 6QB. Open 10-6, Sun. 12-5. SIZE: 30 dealers. *STOCK: Victoriana and Art Deco collectables, silver, glass, furniture, lighting, textiles, jewellery, old advertising.* TEL: 020 7228 6850.

Overmantels
66 Battersea Bridge Rd. SW11 3AG. (Seth Taylor). BCFA. Est. 1980. Open 9.30-5.30. SIZE: Medium. *STOCK: English giltwood mirrors, £400-£3,000; French giltwood mirrors, £700-£3,000; both 18th-19th C. Furniture, 19th C, £200-£2,000.* LOC: 200m south of Battersea Bridge. PARK: Outside shop. TEL: 020 7223 8151; fax - 020 7924 2283. SER: Valuations; restorations (gesso work and gilding). VAT: Stan/Spec.

Pairs Antiques Ltd
Unit 6 Parkfields Industrial Estate, Culvert Rd., Battersea. SW11 5BA. (Iain M. Brunt). Est. 1994. Open by appointment. SIZE: Medium. *STOCK: Pairs only - 18th-19th C furniture, decorative objects and paintings, £500-£20,000.* PARK: Easy. TEL: 020 7622 6446; mobile - 07798 684694; fax -020 7622 3663; e-mail - pairs@aol.com; website - www.antiques. co.uk. SER: Valuations; restorations; buys at auction. VAT: Stan/Spec.

Regent House Gallery
223 St John's Hill. SW11 1TH. (Nick Underwood Thompson). Est. 1988. Open 10-6, Thurs. 10-7.30. CL: Mon. SIZE: Small. *STOCK: Watercolours and paintings, 19th-20th C, £50-£500; prints, drawings, cartoons, 18th-20th C, £10-£200; small antiques, books, 19th to early 20th C, £10-£200.* LOC: Top of St John's Hill, mid-way between Clapham Junction and Wandsworth Town. PARK: Pay and display. TEL: 020 7228 9344; home and fax - 020 7228 9344; e-mail - nick@regent housegallery.com; website - www.regenthouse gallery.com. SER: Framing.

The Woodpigeon
71 Webbs Rd. SW11 6SD. (John Taylor and Barbara Cunnell). Est. 1995. Open Tues.-Sat. 10.30-5.30. SIZE: Small. *STOCK: Country furniture, mainly French - painted armoires and sleigh beds, small decorative items and country antiques, mainly mid to late 19th C, £5-£1,500.* LOC: Parallel with Northcote Rd. PARK: Side roads. TEL: 020 7223 8668; mobile - 07958 787676. SER: Furniture painting and re-upholstery. VAT: Spec.

Robert Young Antiques   BADA
68 Battersea Bridge Rd. SW11 3AG. Est. 1974. Open 10-6, Sat. 10-5. CL: Mon. SIZE: Medium. *STOCK: English oak and country furniture, 17th-18th C, £500-£20,000; English and European treen and objects of folk art, £20-£10,000; English and European provincial pottery and metalwork, £20-£2,500.* LOC: Turn off King's Rd. or Chelsea Embankment into Beaufort St., cross over Battersea Bridge Rd., 9th shop on right. PARK: Opposite in side street. TEL: 020 7228 7847; fax - 020 7585 0489; e-mail - office@robertyoungantiques. com. SER: Valuations; buys at auction (treen and country furniture). FAIRS: Olympia, Chelsea. VAT: Stan/Spec.

SW12

The Kilim Warehouse Ltd
28A Pickets St. SW12 8QB. (J.Luczyc-Wyhowska). Est. 1982. Open 10-5.30, Sat. 10-4. SIZE: Medium. *STOCK: Kilims from Eastern Europe, Asia Minor and beyond, £50-£8,000.* LOC: Near Clapham South tube station and Nightingale Lane. PARK: Easy. TEL: 020 8675

Kate Dyson

THE DINING ROOM SHOP

62-64 White Hart Lane • London SW13 0PZ
Tel: 020-8878 1020   Fax: 020-8876 2367   Email: diningroomshop@cwcom.net

Antique tables and sets of chairs, glass, china, cutlery, prints,
table linen and lace – all for the dining room

3122; fax - 020 8675 8494; website - www.kilim-warehouse.co.uk; e-mail - info@kilim-warehouse.co.uk. SER: Restorations; cleaning. VAT: Stan.

Twentieth Century
(M. Taylor). Est. 1986. By appointment only. *STOCK: Art Deco, Art Nouveau, Arts and Crafts, decorative arts items, £50-£500.* PARK: Easy. TEL: 020 8675 6351; fax - same; e-mail - martin@nbscoms.co.uk. FAIRS: Battersea Art Deco; Loughborough Art Deco; Manchester; Birmingham. VAT: Stan.

SW13

Alton Gallery
2a Suffolk Rd., Barnes. SW13 9PH. Open by appointment only. *STOCK: 19th-20th C British art.* TEL: 020 8748 0606. SER: Framing.

Christine Bridge   BADA
78 Castelnau, Barnes. SW13 9EX. LAPADA, CINOA. Est. 1972. Open anytime by appointment only. SIZE: Medium. *STOCK: Glass - 18th C collectors and 19th C coloured, engraved and decorative, £50-£15,000; small decorative items - papier mâché, bronzes, needlework, ceramics.* LOC: Main road from Hammersmith Bridge. PARK: Easy. TEL: 020 8741 5501; fax - 020 8255 0172; mobile - 07831 126668; e-mail - christine@bridge-antiques.com; website - www.bridge-antiques. com. SER: Valuations; restorations (glass - cutting, polishing, declouding); buys at auction; shipping. FAIRS: Olympia; LAPADA; Chelsea; Brussels; Tokyo; Melbourne; Sydney; Singapore; Santa Monica. VAT: Stan/Spec.

Simon Coleman Antiques
40 White Hart Lane, Barnes. SW13. Est. 1974. SIZE: Large. *STOCK: Country furniture, oak, fruitwood, pine, French and English farm tables, 18th-19th C.* PARK: Easy. TEL: 020 8878 5037. VAT: Stan/Spec.

The Dining Room Shop
62/64 White Hart Lane, Barnes. SW13 0PZ. (K. Dyson). Est. 1985. Open 10-5.30, Sun. by appointment. SIZE: Medium. *STOCK: Formal and country dining room furniture, 18th-19th C; glasses, china, pottery, cutlery, damask and lace table linen, 19th C; associated small and decorative items.* LOC: Near Barnes railway bridge, turning opposite White Hart public house. PARK: Easy. TEL: 020 8878 1020; fax - 020 8876

2367; e-mail - diningroomshop@cwcom.net. SER:
Valuations; restorations; bespoke furniture; finder;
interior decorating. VAT: Stan/Spec.

Joy McDonald Antiques
50 Station Rd., Barnes. SW13 0LP. Resident. Est.
1966. SIZE: Small. *STOCK: 19th-20th C mirrors,
chandeliers and lighting; decorative items and
upholstered chairs.* PARK: Easy. TEL: 020 8876
6184.

New Grafton Gallery
49 Church Rd., Barnes. SW13 9HH. (D. Wolfers).
Est. 1968. Open 10-5.30. CL: Mon. SIZE: Medium.
*STOCK: British paintings and drawings, £150-
£3,000.* LOC: Off Castelnau which runs from
Hammersmith Bridge. PARK: Easy. TEL: 020 8748
8850; home - 020 8876 6294. SER: Valuations;
restorations; buys at auction. VAT: Stan/Spec.

John Spink   BADA
**9 Richard Burbridge Mansions, 1 Brasenose
Dr., Barnes. SW13 8RB. Open by appointment
only.** *STOCK: Fine English watercolours and
selected oils, 1720-1920.* **TEL: 020 8741 6152;**
e-mail - john@johnspink.com

Tobias and The Angel
68 White Hart Lane, Barnes. SW13 0PZ. (A.
Hughes). Est. 1985. Open 10-6. SIZE: Large.
*STOCK: Quilts, textiles, furniture, country and
painted beds, decorative objects, from 1800.*
LOC: Parallel to Barnes High St. PARK: Easy.
TEL: 020 8878 8902; home - 01206 391003.
SER: Interior design. VAT: Stan/Spec.

SW14

The Arts & Crafts Furniture Co Ltd
49 Sheen Lane, East Sheen. SW14 4AB. (Patrick
Rogers). Est. 1985. SIZE: Medium. *STOCK: Arts
and Crafts furniture and effects, Gothic and
Aesthetic movement, 1850-1950, £500-£5,000.*
LOC: Sheen Lane is off Upper Richmond Road
(South Circular A205). PARK: Nearby. TEL: 020
8876 6544; fax - same. SER: Valuations;
restorations including French polishing and
upholstery; buys at auction. VAT: Spec.

Mary Cooke Antiques Ltd   BADA
**12 The Old Power Station, 121 Mortlake High
St. SW14 8SN. LAPADA. Open by appointment.** *STOCK: Silver.* **TEL: 020 8876 5777; fax
- 020 8876 1652.** SER: Valuations; restorations. FAIRS: Chelsea (Autumn); BADA;
LAPADA; Olympia. VAT: Stan/Spec.

Paul Foster's Bookshop
119 Sheen Lane, East Sheen. SW14 8AE. ABA,
PBFA. Est. 1983. Open 10.30-6. SIZE: Medium.

The Clock Clinic
Antique Clocks

Open Tues – Fri 9-6, Sat 9-1, Closed Mondays

85, Lower Richmond Road,
Putney, London, SW15 1EU
Tel: 020-8788 1407 Fax: 020-8780 2838
Website: www.clockclinic.co.uk
Email: clockclinic@btconnect.com

*STOCK: Books - antiquarian, 17th-19th C, £100-
£1,000; out of print, 19th-20th C, £1-£500;
general, 50p-£100.* LOC: 20 yards from South
Circular. PARK: Easy. TEL: 020 8876 7424; fax
- same. FAIRS: Hotel Russell, PBFA monthly.

SW15

R.A. Barnes Antiques
26 Lower Richmond Rd., Putney. SW15.
LAPADA. Open 10-5. CL: Sat. SIZE: Large.
*STOCK: English, Oriental and Continental
porcelain, antiques and collectables; Wedgwood,
ironstone, china, brass, copper, 19th C;
Bohemian and art glass, Regency, Victorian and
some 18th C small furniture, primitive paintings.*
TEL: 020 8789 3371. VAT: Stan/Spec.

The Clock Clinic Ltd
85 Lower Richmond Rd., Putney. SW15 1EU.
(R.S. Pedler). LAPADA, FBHI. Est. 1971. Open
9-6, Sat. 9-1. CL: Mon. *STOCK: Clocks and
barometers.* TEL: 020 8788 1407; fax - 020 8780
2838; e-mail - clockclinic@btconnect.com;
website - www.clockclinic.co.uk. SER: Valuations; restorations (as stock); buys at auction.
VAT: Stan/Spec.

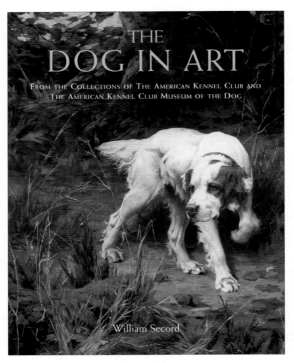

THE
DOG IN ART

William Secord

Chronicled in this monumental volume are the combined encyclopaedic collections of the American Kennel Club and the American Kennel Club Museum of the Dog. Because of the enormity of the two collections, it was impossible to include everything – during the selection process only the very best of the collected works were chosen. The collections are particularly comprehensive, and include not only 19th and 20th century paintings and bronzes, but many watercolours, original prints, silver trophies, porcelains, and antique dog collars, each and every artifact directly related to dogs.

Accompanied by an authoritative text, the exceptional collection of the AKC and the AKC Museum of the Dog, illustrated here in full colour, not only provide a catalogue but also virtually tell the history of the dog in art. It is in this spirit that the book is organised, starting with the Belgian, Dutch and Flemish art in the collections, countries where dog and animal art originated. England – the true home of dog painting – is explored next, then France, and finally America, where animal art was maintained and flourished well into the 20th century. The collections depicted in this volume are a testament to our love for the dog, in all its guises, in conformation dog shows, field and obedience trials, in the sporting field and as a pet. They are also a testament to the many artists, some virtually forgotten until recently, who chose to use their insights and artistic skills to portray the dog on canvas, paper and in porcelain and bronze.

ISBN 1 85149 400 6
360pp., c.390 full colour illus.
£35.00/$80.00

DOG PAINTING
THE EUROPEAN BREEDS

William Secord

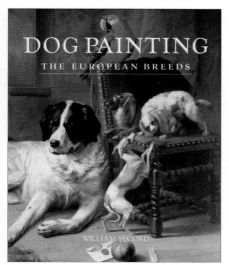

Dog Painting: The European Breeds gives an historical overview of the extraordinary range of dog paintings created in Europe during the nineteenth century. While English artists dominated the field, many prominent European artists produced a wide range of paintings depicting the dog. Over ninety breeds are featured in these paintings, from the lap dogs and hunting dogs of the aristocracy to the common shepherds' dogs who were prized for their keen working abilities.

The book concentrates on the types of dogs and dog paintings which were characteristic to the countries of Europe, and discusses the different national attitudes towards dogs and the organisation of canine societies. It focuses on the many different European breeds, and ninety breeds are discussed in detail under five headings: Working and Herding, Hounds, Toys and Non-Sporting, Terriers, and Sporting Dogs.

Dog Painting: The European Breeds also looks at the art worlds of the different European countries and the numerous artists who portrayed dogs. Just as the breeds developed differently in each of the European countries, so did the various national schools of art, both of which are discussed in detail.

William Secord is President of the William Secord Gallery in New York, specialising in fine nineteenth and twentieth century animal paintings. He is the author of numerous articles on the dog in art as well as the author of the hugely successful *Dog Painting 1840-1940: A Social History of the Dog in Art.* He has recently been appointed to the Board of Directors of the American Society for the Prevention of Cruelty to Animals.

SPECIFICATIONS:
*11 x 9in./280 x 236mm., 400pp., 525 illus., over 450 in colour.***£35.00**

Hanshan Tang Books

Unit 3 Ashburton Centre, 276 Cortis Rd. SW15
3AY. ABA. Open by appointment only. *STOCK:
Second-hand, antiquarian and new books and
periodicals on Chinese, Japanese, Korean and
Central Asian art and culture.* TEL: 020 8788
4464; fax - 020 8780 1565; e-mail - hst@
hanshan.com; website - www.hanshan. com/.

Jorgen Antiques

40 Lower Richmond Rd., Putney. SW15 1JP.
(A.J. Dolleris). Est. 1960. Open 11-5. CL: Mon.
and Sat. SIZE: Large. *STOCK: English and
Continental furniture, 18th to early 19th C, £50-
£5,000.* LOC: Between Putney Bridge and Putney
Common. PARK: Easy. TEL: 020 8789 7329.
VAT: Spec.

Thornhill Galleries Ltd. in association with A. & R. Dockerill Ltd

Rear of 78 Deodar Rd., Putney. SW15 2NJ. Est.
1880. Open 9-5.15, Sat. 10-12. SIZE: Large.
*STOCK: English and French period panelling,
chimneypieces in wood, marble and stone;
architectural items, wood carvings, 17th-19th C
firegrates and fenders, fireplace accessories and
iron interiors.* LOC: Off Putney Bridge Rd.
PARK: Easy. TEL: 020 8874 2101/5669. SER:
Valuations; restorations (architectural items); buys
at auction (architectural items). VAT: Stan/Spec.

SW16

H.C. Baxter and Sons   BADA

**40 Drewstead Rd. SW16 1AB. (T.J., J. and
G.J. Baxter). LAPADA. Est. 1928. Open Wed.
and Thurs. 8.30-5.15, or by appointment.
SIZE: Medium. STOCK: English furniture,
1730-1830, £1,000-£35,000. LOC: Near
Streatham Hill station. PARK: Easy. TEL: 020
8769 5869/5969; fax - 020 8769 0898; e-mail -
partners@hcbaxter.co.uk; website - www.
hcbaxter.co.uk.**

A. and J. Fowle

542 Streatham High Rd. SW16 3QF. Est. 1962.
Open 9.30-7. SIZE: Large. *STOCK: General
antiques, Victorian and Edwardian furniture.*
LOC: From London take A23 towards Brighton.
PARK: Easy. TEL: 020 8764 2896; mobile -
07968 058790.

Rapscallion Antiques Ltd

25 Shrubbery Rd., Streatham. SW16 2AS. (Mrs
P. Barry). Open 10-5. CL: Mon. and Thurs.
STOCK: General antiques and bric-a-brac. TEL:
020 8769 8078.

SW17

Ted Few

97 Drakefield Rd. SW17 8RS. Resident. Est.
1975. Open by appointment. SIZE: Medium.
*STOCK: Paintings and sculpture, 1700-1940,
£500-£5,000.* LOC: 5 mins. walk from Tooting
Bec underground station. TEL: 020 8767 2314.
SER: Valuations; buys at auction. VAT: Spec.

SW18

Earlsfield Bookshop

513 Garratt Lane, Wandsworth. SW18 4SW.
(Charles Dixon). Est. 1985. Open Mon.-Thurs. 4-
6, Fri. 11-6, Sat. 10-5. SIZE: Small. *STOCK:
Books, £1-£50.* LOC: Next to Earlsfield station.
PARK: Limited. TEL: 020 8946 3744.

Just a Second

284 Merton Rd., Wandsworth. SW18 5JN. (James
Ferguson). Est. 1980. Open 9.30-5.30. CL: Mon.
SIZE: Medium. *STOCK: Victorian, Edwardian,
pre-1920's and reproduction furniture and bric-a-
brac.* LOC: 5 minutes from Southfields
underground station. PARK: Easy. TEL: 020 8874
2520. SER: Valuations; restorations.

Mr Wandle's Workshop Ltd

202 Garratt Lane, Wandsworth. SW18 4ED. (S.
Zoil). Open 9-5.30. *STOCK: Victorian and
Edwardian fireplaces and surrounds especially
cast iron.* TEL: 020 8870 5873. SER: Shot-
blasting.

SW19

Adams Room Antiques

20 Ridgway, Wimbledon Village. SW19 4LN.
LAPADA. Est. 1971. Open 10-5. SIZE: Large.
*STOCK: 18th-19th C English and French
furniture especially dining; decorative Regency
chairs, silver.* LOC: 4 miles from King's Rd.,
Chelsea; 1 mile off Kingston by-pass, M3. TEL:
020 8946 7047/8947 4784; fax - 020 8946 7476.
SER: Export orders arranged. VAT: Spec.

Corfield Potashnick

39 Church Rd., Wimbledon Village. SW19 5DQ.
Open Thurs.-Sat. 10.30-5 or by appointment.
STOCK: Fine antique furniture. TEL: 020 8944
9022.

Coromandel

(P. Lang and B. Leigh). Resident. Open at any
time by appointment. SIZE: Small. *STOCK:
Boxes, table cabinets and decorative items,
Anglo-Indian and European Colonial, 17th-19th*

C, *£250-£5,000*. PARK: Easy. TEL: 020 8543 9115; fax - 020 8543 6255; mobile - 07932 102756; e-mail - info@antiqueboxes.com. SER: Restorations (ivory).

The David Curzon Gallery
35 Church Rd., Wimbledon Village. SW19 5DQ. Open 10-6. CL: Mon. SIZE: Medium. *STOCK: Paintings and watercolours, from 1900, £350-£10,000.* LOC: 7 min. walk from Wimbledon Underground/BR. PARK: Reasonable. TEL: 020 8944 6098; fax - same; e-mail - davidcurzon @barclays.net. VAT: Spec.

Shaikh and Son (Oriental Rugs) Ltd
139 Arthur Rd. SW19 8AB. (M. Shaikh). Open 10-6. CL: Sat. pm. *STOCK: Persian carpets, rugs, £100-£10,000.* TEL: 020 8947 9232SER: Repairing and cleaning.

Mark J. West - Cobb Antiques Ltd
BADA
39B High St., Wimbledon Village. SW19 5BY. **Open 10-5.30. SIZE: Large.** *STOCK: Antique glass, £5-£5,000.* **PARK: Easy. TEL: 020 8946 2811. SER: Valuations; buys at auction.** FAIRS: Olympia; Grosvenor House.

SW20

W.G.T.Burne (Antique Glass) Ltd
BADA
PO Box 9465. (Formerly of Chelsea) SW20 9ZD. (Mrs G. and A.T. Burne). Est. 1936. *STOCK: English and Irish glassware, Georgian and Victorian decanters; chandeliers, candelabra and lustres.* **TEL: 020 8543 6319; fax - same; mobile - 07774 725834. SER: Valuations; restorations. VAT: Stan/Spec.**

Chelsea Bric-a-Brac Shop Ltd
12 Lambton Rd. SW20 0LR. (P. and C. Wirth). Est. 1960. Open by appointment only. SIZE: Small. *STOCK: Furniture, 1800-1930, £20-£3,000; reproduction lighting.* LOC: Right from Raynes Park Station, first left, shop 200 yards on right. PARK: Limited. TEL: 020 8946 6894. SER: Restorations (wood). VAT: Stan.

W. F. Turk Antique Clocks
355 Kingston Rd., Wimbledon Chase. SW20 8JX. LAPADA, CINOA. Est. 1970. Open Tues.-Fri. 9-5.30, Sat. 9-4. SIZE: Medium. *STOCK: Clocks, including longcase, 17th-19th C, £4,000-£40,000; bracket, 17th-19th C, £2,000-£40,000; mantel and carriage, 19th C, £450-£5,000.* LOC: Off A3. PARK: Easy. TEL: 020 8543 3231; fax - same. SER: Valuations; restorations. FAIRS: Olympia; LAPADA. VAT: Stan/Spec.

SE1

Antique Trade Warehouse
64 Druid St., Bermondsey. SE1 3LW. (Margaret McCarthy). Est. 1983. Open 9.30-5. SIZE: Warehouse. *STOCK: General antiques and shipping goods.* PARK: Easy. TEL: 020 7394 7856. SER: Valuations.

Bermondsey Antiques Market
Corner of Long Lane and Bermondsey St. SE1. (Bath Antiques Markets Ltd). Est. 1959. Open Fri. 5 am-2 pm. *STOCK: Wide range of general antiques and collectables including specialist dealers in most fields especially jewellery and silver.* LOC: Borough, Tower Hill or London Bridge tube stations. TEL: Enquiries - 020 7969 1500; fax - 020 7969 1639. SER: Valuations; book binding.

Victor Burness Antiques and Scientific Instruments
241 Long Lane, Bermondsey. SE1 4PR. (V.G. Burness). Est. 1975. Open Fri. 6am-1pm or by appointment. SIZE: Small. *STOCK: Scientific instruments, marine items, 19th C, £20-£1,500.* PARK: Easy. TEL: Home - 01732 454591. SER: Valuations. FAIRS: Portman Hotel.

Robert Bush - Antique & Decorative Furniture
169 Bermondsey St. SE1. Open 9.30-5, Fri. 7-5, Sat. by appointment. SIZE: Large. STOCK: Furniture. TEL: 020 7378 1000; e-mail - bush.antiques@virgin.net

The Galleries
157 Tower Bridge Rd., Bermondsey. SE1 3LW. (Alan Bennett). LAPADA. Open 9.30-5.30, Fri. 8-4.30, Sat. and Sun. 12-6. SIZE: Very large. *STOCK: Georgian and Victorian English and Continental furniture, some collectables.* PARK: Easy. TEL: 020 7407 5371; fax - 020 7403 0359. VAT: Stan/Spec.

Penny Farthing Antiques
177 Bermondsey St. SE1. Est. 1976. Open 10-5. CL: Sat. SIZE: Medium. *STOCK: Furniture including shipping, £25-£1,000; longcase clocks, £200-£1,000; general small antiques and shipping items, £5-£200.* LOC: 5 mins. from Tower Bridge. PARK: Usually easy. TEL: 020 7407 5171. VAT: Stan.

Tower Bridge Antiques
159/161 Tower Bridge Rd. SE1 3LW. Open 9-5.30, Sat. 10.30-6, Sun. 11-5. SIZE: Large. *STOCK: Victorian, Georgian and Edwardian furniture, shipping goods.* TEL: 020 7403 3660. VAT: Stan.

LONDON SE1

Giovanni Viventi
173 Bermondsey St. SE1 3UW. Est. 1976. Open 9.30-6.30. CL: Sat. and Sun. except by appointment. SIZE: Large. *STOCK: Furniture and general antiques.* TEL: 020 7407 2566/7403 0022; fax - 020 7403 6808.

Michael Silverman
PO Box 350. SE3 0LZ. *STOCK: Manuscripts, autograph letters, historical documents.* TEL: 020 8319 4452; fax - 020 8856 6006; e-mail - ms@michael-silverman.com; website - www.michael-silverman.com. SER: Catalogue available. *Postal Only.*

Vale Stamps and Antiques
21 Tranquil Vale, Blackheath. SE3 0BU. (H.J. and R.P. Varnham). Est. 1952. Open 10-5.30. CL: Thurs. SIZE: Small. *STOCK: Georgian and Victorian jewellery, £25-£500; ancient and medieval coins, £20-£500.* LOC: Village centre, 100yds. from station. PARK: Nearby. TEL: 020 8852 9817. SER: Valuations. VAT: Stan/Spec.

Wallace Antiques Ltd
56 Tranquil Vale, Blackheath. SE3 0BD. Open 9.30-5.30. *STOCK: Furniture including reproduction.* TEL: 020 8852 2647.

Camberwell Architectural Salvage & Antiques
47 Southampton Way, Camberwell. SE5 7SW. (J. Swan and M. Tree). Est. 1993. Open Tues.-Sat. 10-5. SIZE: Large. *STOCK: Architectural salvage including doors, floorboards, radiators, baths, sinks and taps, 19th-20th C, £15-£600; furniture, 19th-20th C.* LOC: From Camberwell Green towards Peckham - 6th turning on left, just past College of Art. PARK: Easy. TEL: 020 7277 0315.

Robert E. Hirschhorn   BADA
Est. 1979. Open by appointment. *STOCK: Unusual English and Continental country furniture, mainly oak, walnut and fruitwood, and interesting objects, 18th C and earlier.* **TEL: 020 7703 7443; mobile - 07831 405937. FAIRS: BADA (March); Olympia (June and Nov.).**

Wilkinson plc
5 Catford Hill. SE6 4NU. Est. 1947. Open 9-5. CL: Sat. SIZE: Medium. *STOCK: Glass* especially chandeliers, 18th C and reproduction, art metal work. LOC: Opposite Catford Bridge railway station. Entrance through Wickes D.I.Y. car park. PARK: Easy. TEL: 020 8314 1080. SER: Restorations and repairs (glass, metalwork).

Ward Antiques
267 Woolwich Rd., Charlton. SE7. (T. and M. Ward). Est. 1981. Open 9.30-5.30, Sun. 10-2. SIZE: Medium. *STOCK: Victorian fireplaces, Victorian and Edwardian furniture, £50-£1,000.* LOC: From A102 M take Woolwich/Woolwich ferry turn, 100yds. from roundabout, immediately under railway bridge across the road. PARK: Easy. TEL: 020 8305 0963; home - 020 8698 0771.

Antique Warehouse
9-14 Deptford Broadway. SE8 4PA. Est. 1986. Open 10-6, Sun. 11-4. SIZE: Large. *STOCK: Fine furniture, 1750 to 20th C; sofas, chairs, mirrors and oleographs.* TEL: 020 8691 3062. VAT: Stan.

Cobwebs
73 Avery Hill Rd., New Eltham. SE9 2BJ. (Martin Baker). Est. 1991. Open 10-5.30, Sun. 10-2. CL: Mon. am and Thurs. SIZE: Medium - 3 dealers. *STOCK: Furniture, smalls, Oriental items.* LOC: Between A20 and A2 and 5 minutes from New Eltham BR station. PARK: Easy. TEL: 020 8850 5611; website - wwwantique-dealers.eu.com. SER: Valuations.

The Fireplace
257 High St., Eltham. SE9 1TY. (A. Clark). Est. 1978. Open daily. SIZE: Medium. *STOCK: Fireplaces, 19th-20th C, £100-£1,000.* PARK: Adjacent side streets. TEL: 020 8850 4887. SER: Restorations (fireplaces). VAT: Stan.

R.E. Rose FBHI
731 Sidcup Rd., Eltham. SE9 3SA. Est. 1976. Open 9-5. SIZE: Small. *STOCK: Clocks and barometers, 1750-1930, £50-£5,000.* LOC: A20 from London, shop on left just past fiveways traffic lights at Green Lane. PARK: Easy. TEL: 020 8859 4754. SER: Restorations (clocks and barometers); spare parts for antique clocks and barometers. VAT: Stan/Spec.

LAMONT ANTIQUES LTD

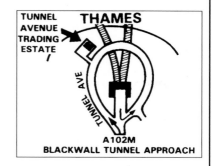

TUNNEL AVENUE TRADING ESTATE

THAMES

TUNNEL AVE

A102M
BLACKWALL TUNNEL APPROACH

ARCHITECTURAL ITEMS
BARS & FITTINGS
STAINED GLASS ETC
PAINTED ITEMS
CONTAINER PACKING

Contact Frank Llewellyn or Neil Lamont

Tunnel Avenue Antique Warehouse
Tunnel Avenue Trading Estate
Greenwich, London SE10 0QH
Telephone: 020-8305-2230
Fax: 020-8305-1805

SE10

Creek Antiques
23 Greenwich South St. SE10 8NW. Est. 1986. Open 11-5, appointment advisable Mon. and Tues. SIZE: Small. *STOCK: Jewellery and silver, from Victorian, £5-£500.* LOC: 200 yards from British Rail station. PARK: Easy. TEL: 020 8293 5721; mobile - 07778 427521; e-mail - creekantiques@ aol.com. SER: Valuations; restorations (jewellery and watch repairs, silversmithing)

Greenwich Antiques Market
Greenwich High Rd. SE10. Est. 1972. Open Sun. 7.30-4.30, and Sat. (June-Sept.). SIZE: 80 stalls. *STOCK: General antiques and bric-a-brac.* LOC: Almost opposite railway station. PARK: Adjacent.

The Greenwich Gallery
9 Nevada St. SE10 9JL. (R.F. Moy). Est. 1965. Open 10-5.30 including Sun. *STOCK: Mainly English oil paintings and watercolours, 18th C to 1950.* TEL: 020 8305 1666. SER: Restorations; framing; exhibitions. VAT: Spec.

The Junk Box
151 Trafalgar Rd., Greenwich. SE10 9TX. (Robert Dodd and Marilyn Allen). Est. 1993. Open 10-5.30 including Sun. SIZE: Small.

STOCK: Furniture, pictures and prints, collectables, 19th-20th C, £5-£1,000. LOC: 1/2 mile east of centre of Greenwich. PARK: Easy. TEL: 020 8293 5715.

The Junk Shop
9 Greenwich South St. SE10 8NW. (T. and R. Moy). Est. 1985. Open 10-5.30 including Sun. SIZE: Large. *STOCK: Larger antique and decorative items, 18th C to 1950s; furniture, architectural antiques, bric-a-brac.* LOC: A202. From London follow A2, then turn left at Deptford - or follow riverside road from Tower Bridge. PARK: Meters. TEL: 020 8305 1666, ext. 25. SER: Restorations (furniture). VAT: Stan/Spec.

Lamont Antiques Ltd
Tunnel Avenue Antique Warehouse, Tunnel Avenue Trading Estate, Greenwich. SE10 0QH. (N. Lamont and F. Llewellyn). LAPADA. Open 9-5.30. CL: Sat. SIZE: Large. *STOCK: Architectural fixtures and fittings, bars, stained glass, pub mirrors and signs, shipping furniture, £5-£25,000.* PARK: Own. TEL: 020 8305 2230; fax - 020 8305 1805. SER: Container packing.

Peter Laurie Antiques
28 Greenwich Church St. SE10 9BQ. Open 10-5 including Sun. CL: Fri. am. *STOCK: Nautical items, navigational instruments, maritime*

curiosities, weapons and photographic items. TEL: 020 8853 5777; fax - same; e-mail - plaurie@maritimeantiques-uk.com; website - www.maritimeantiques-uk.com.

The Warwick Leadlay Gallery
5 Nelson Rd., Greenwich. SE10 9JB. Est. 1974. Open 9.30-5.30, Sun. and Public Holidays 11-5.30. SIZE: Large. STOCK: Antique maps, prints, fine arts, Nelson specialists, 17th-20th C. LOC: Top of Greenwich Market. PARK: Nearby. TEL: 020 8858 0317; fax - 020 8853 1773; e-mail - wlg@easynet.co.uk; website - www.warwick-leadlay.co.uk. SER: Framing; restorations; valuations. VAT: Stan.

Marcet Books
4A Nelson Rd., Greenwich. SE10 9JB. (Martin Kemp). PBFA. Est. 1980. Open 10-5.30 including Sun. SIZE: Small. STOCK: General second-hand and antiquarian books. LOC: In alley off Nelson Rd., leading to Greenwich market. PARK: 200 yards. TEL: 020 8853 5408; fax - same; e-mail - marcet@dircon.co.uk; website - www.marcet.dircon.co.uk SER: Valuations. FAIRS: PBFA 12 monthly at Russell Hotel.

Relcy Antiques
9 Nelson Rd., Greenwich. SE10. (R. Challis). Est. 1958. Open 10-6, including Sun. SIZE: Large. STOCK: English furniture, especially bureaux and bookcases, £50-£15,000; English and Continental pictures, especially marine and sporting, £20-£5,000; instruments and marine items, ships' heads, sextants, telescopes, models, £20-£15,000; all 18th-19th C. Not Stocked: Reproduction. LOC: Central Greenwich - 100 yds. from Dockland Light Railway. TEL: 020 8858 2812. SER: Valuations, restorations (furniture and pictures); buys at auction (Georgian and Victorian furniture, pictures). VAT: Stan/Spec.

Rogers Turner Books
23a Nelson Rd., Greenwich. SE10 9JB. Est. 1975. Open Thurs.-Fri. 10-6 or by appointment. STOCK: Antiquarian books especially on clocks and scientific instruments. TEL: 020 8853 5271; fax - same; Paris - 0033 13912 1191; e-mail - rogersturner@compuserve.com; website - www.rogersturner@abebooks.com. SER: Buys at auction (British and European); catalogues available.

Spread Eagle Antiques
8 Nevada St. SE10 9JL. (R.F. Moy). Est. 1954. Open 10-5.30 including Sun. SIZE: Large. STOCK: Books, period costume, curios, china, bric-a-brac, prints, postcards. Not Stocked: Furniture. LOC: A202. From London follow A2, then turn left at Deptford - or follow riverside road from Tower Bridge. PARK: Easy. TEL: 020 8305 1666. SER: Valuations; restorations (furniture, china, pictures). VAT: Stan/Spec.

Spread Eagle Antiques
1 Stockwell St. SE10 9JL. (R.F. Moy). Est. 1954. Open 10-5.30 including Sun. SIZE: Large. STOCK: Furniture, pictures and decorative items, 18th-19th C. PARK: Easy. TEL: 020 8305 1666; home - 020 8692 1618. SER: Valuations; restorations (pictures, furniture). VAT: Stan/Spec.

The Waterloo Trading Co.
Unit D Tunnel Ave. Trading Estate, Tunnel Ave., Greenwich. SE10 0QH. SIZE: Large. STOCK: Victorian, Edwardian and shipping furniture. TEL: 020 8858 3355; fax - 020 8858 3344; e-mail - boysship@ftech.co.uk. SER: Robert Boys Shipping; packing.

Robert Whitfield Antiques
Tunnel Avenue Antique Warehouse, Tunnel Avenue Trading Estate, Greenwich. SE10 0QH. LAPADA. Open 10-5. CL: Sat. STOCK: Edwardian, Victorian and secondhand furniture, especially bentwood chairs. TEL: 020 8305 2230; fax - 020 8305 1805. SER: Container packing.

SE11

Campbell Wilson
17 West Sq. SE11 4SN. (Neil Wilson). Est. 1996. Open by appointment. SIZE: Large. STOCK: Paintings especially Pre-Raphaelite and Romantic British, 1845-1903; modern British, to 1945. LOC: Directly behind Imperial War Museum. PARK: 1 space available (by arrangement). TEL: 020 7582 2754 fax - same. SER: Buys at auction (Victorian and Modern British paintings). FAIRS: Olympia, Art on Paper, Antiques for Everyone (Glasgow). VAT: Spec.

SE13

Robert Morley and Co Ltd   BADA
34 Engate St. SE13 7HA. Est. 1881. Open 9-5. STOCK: Pianos, harpsichords, clavichords, spinets, virginals. PARK: Own. TEL: 020 8318 5838; fax - 020 8297 0720; website - www.morleypianos.com. SER: Restorations (musical instruments). VAT: Stan.

SE15

Peter Allen Antiques Ltd. World Wide Antique Exporters
17-17a Nunhead Green, Peckham. SE15 3QQ. LAPADA. Est. 1966. Open 8-4. CL: Sat. SIZE: Large. STOCK: Fine Victorian furniture. TEL: 020 7732 1968.

SE20

Bearly Trading of London
202 High St., Penge. SE20 7QB. (Brian Aust). Open 10.30-6.30. *STOCK: Old bears, artist bears, antique furniture including childrens.* LOC: Opposite Kent House Rd., Beckenham, Kent. TEL: 020 8659 0500; fax - 020 8460 3166.

SE21

Acorn Antiques
111 Rosendale Rd., West Dulwich. SE21 8EZ. (Mrs G. Kingham). Open 10-6, Sat. 10-5.30. *STOCK: Furniture, sterling silver, jewellery, ceramics, glassware and fireplace accessories.* TEL: 020 8761 3349.

Francis Jevons
80 Dulwich Village. SE21 7AJ. Est. 1983. Usually open 9.30-1 and 2.30-5.30, Sat. until 5, other times by appointment. CL: Wed. *STOCK: China and small furniture, late 18th to 19th C; interior design, lamps and decorative items.* LOC: Off South Circular leading down from either Gallery or College roads. PARK: Easy. TEL: 020 8693 1991. SER: Valuations; restorations. VAT: Stan/Spec.

SE22

Melbourne Antiques & Interiors
67 and 161 Lordship Lane, East Dulwich. SE22 8EW. (Ian Peters and Ed Jacobs). Est. 1990. Open 10-6 including Sun. SIZE: Large. *STOCK: French beds and armoires, £300-£1,000+; mirrors, £50-£1,000+; commodes, £500-£1,000+; all 19th C; French linen.* LOC: Off South Circular at Dulwich. PARK: Easy. TEL: 020 8299 6565; fax - 020 8299 4257. SER: Restorations (furniture).

SE23

Oddiquities
61 Waldram Park Rd. and 20 Sunderland Rd., Forest Hill. SE23 2PW. (Mrs S.A. Butler). Est. 1966. Open 10-5, Sat. 9.30-1. CL: Thurs. SIZE: Medium. *STOCK: Oil lamps, gas and electric light fitments, 1800-1930; fire furnishings, 1780-1920; all £20-£500; general antiques, 1800-1920, £15-£1,000.* Not Stocked: Coins, stamps, medals, jewellery. LOC: On South Circular Rd., between Catford and Forest Hill. PARK: Opposite. TEL: 020 8699 9574.

SE24

Under Milkwood
379-381 Milkwood Rd., Herne Hill. SE24 0HA.

(Nick and Sue Williams). Est. 1988. Open 9-5.30. SIZE: Medium. *STOCK: Victorian, Edwardian and reproduction mantelpieces, £200-£2,000.* LOC: At rear of Herne Hill station. PARK: Easy. TEL: 020 7733 3921. SER: Valuations; restorations; installations; gas fires; slate hearths.

SE25

Engine 'n' Tender
19 Spring Lane, Woodside Green. SE25 4SP. (Mrs Joyce M. Buttigieg). Est. 1957. Open Thurs. and Fri. 12-5.30, Sat. 10-5.30. SIZE: Small. *STOCK: Model railways, mainly pre 1939; Dinky toys, to 1968; old toys, mainly tinplate.* PARK: Easy. TEL: 020 8654 0386. FAIRS: Local toy.

North London Clock Shop Ltd
Rear of 60 Saxon Rd. SE25 5EH. (D.S. Tomlin). Est. 1960. Open 9-6. CL: Sat. SIZE: Medium. *STOCK: Clocks, longcase, bracket, carriage, skeleton, 18th-19th C.* PARK: Easy. TEL: 020 8664 8089. SER: Restorations (clocks and barometer); wheel cutting, hand engraving, dial painting, clock reconversions. FAIRS: Olympia. VAT: Stan.

SE26

Abbott Antiques and Country Pine
109 Kirkdale, Sydenham. SE26 4QJ. Est. 1972. Open 10-5.30, Sat. 10-5. *STOCK: Victorian and Edwardian pine furniture, general antiques.* LOC: 1/2 mile from South Circular Rd. at Forest Hill. TEL: 020 8699 1363; e-mail - abbottantiques@ btinternet.com.

Behind the Boxes - Art Deco
98 Kirkdale, Sydenham. SE26 4BG. (Ray Owen). Est. 1987. Open 10.30-5, Sun. and Mon. by appointment. SIZE: Large. *STOCK: Furniture, lighting and costume jewellery, 1930's, from £25.* LOC: 1 mile from Crystal Palace. BR station Forest Hill. PARK: Loading, otherwise Fransfield Rd. TEL: 020 8291 6116. SER: Valuations; buys at auction. FAIRS: Decorama and Deco.

T.A. Hillyer
301 Sydenham Rd. SE26 5EW. Est. 1952. Open 9.30-4, Sat. 9.30-2. CL: Mon. and Wed. SIZE: Small. *STOCK: Silver, plate, porcelain, glass, books, bric-a-brac.* PARK: Easy. TEL: 020 8778 6361; home - 020 8777 2506.

Oola Boola Antiques London
139-147 Kirkdale. SE26 4QJ. (R. Scales and S. Bramley). Est. 1968. Open 10-6, Sat.10-5, Sun. 11-5. SIZE: Large. *STOCK: Furniture, £5-£3,000; mahogany, oak, some walnut, Victorian, Arts & Crafts, Art Nouveau, Edwardian, Art Deco and shipping goods.* TEL: 020 8291 9999; fax - 020 8291 5759.

LONDON SE26

Sydenham Antiques Centre
48 Sydenham Rd., Sydenham. SE26 5QF. (Mrs L. Cockton). Est. 1996. Open 10-5. SIZE: Medium. *STOCK: China, glass, silver, collectables, furniture and jewellery, 19th-20th C, £5-£500.* LOC: 2 doors down from Post Office in High St. PARK: Easy and nearby. TEL: 020 8778 1706. SER: Valuations; restorations (china).

Vintage Cameras Ltd
256 Kirkdale, Sydenham. SE26 4NL. (J. Jenkins). Est. 1959. Open 9-5. SIZE: Large. *STOCK: Vintage and classic cameras, £50-£5,000; general photographica, £5-£500; all 1840-2001.* LOC: Near South Circular Rd. PARK: Nearby. TEL: 020 8778 5416; fax - 020 8778 5841; e-mail - i@vintagecameras.co.uk; website - www.vintagecameras.co.uk. SER: Valuations. VAT: Stan.

Yesteryears
99 Kirkdale, Sydenham. SE26 4BG. Open Tues.-Sat. 9.30-5.30. *STOCK: Victoriana, carpets and rugs, 1930's decorative and furniture, lighting and ceramics.* LOC: 1 mile from Crystal Palace. BR station Forest Hill. PARK: Loading, otherwise Fransfield Rd. TEL: 020 8291 6116.

E1

La Maison
107/108 Shoreditch High St. E1 6JN. (Guillaume and Louise Bacou). Open 10-6, Sun. by appointment. SIZE: Large. *STOCK: Beds.* TEL: 020 7729 9646; fax - 020 7729 6399. SER: Restorations. VAT: Margin.

E2

George Rankin Coin Co. Ltd
325 Bethnal Green Rd. E2. Open 10-5. *STOCK: Coins, medals, medallions and jewellery.* TEL: 020 7739 1840/7729 1280; fax - 020 7729 5023.

E4

Record Detector
3 & 4 Station Approach, Station Rd., Chingford. E4 6AL. (N. Salter). Est. 1992. Open 10-6. CL: Thurs. SIZE: Small (2 shops). *STOCK: Secondhand and collectable records, L.P's, E.P's, singles and CD's.* LOC: In forecourt of North Chingford railway station. PARK: Easy. TEL: 020 8529 6361/2938; website - www.salter.co.uk.

Nicholas Salter Antiques
8 Station Approach, Station Rd. E4 6AL. Est. 1971. Open 9.30-5, Fri. and Sat. 9.30-6. CL: Thurs. SIZE: Large. *STOCK: Furniture, 1850-*

1930, £150-£1,500; china and linen, 1870-1950, £30-£150; antiquarian and secondhand books. LOC: Next door to North Chingford station. PARK: Easy. TEL: 020 8529 2938; website - www.Salter.co.uk.

E8

Boxes and Musical Instruments
2 Middleton Rd., Hackney. E8 4BL. (A. and J. O'Kelly). Est. 1974. Open any time by appointment. SIZE: Medium. *STOCK: Boxes - caddies, sewing, writing, snuff, vanity, jewellery and desk, £300-£5,000; musical instruments, plucked string, £1,000-£3,000; all 18th-19th C.* LOC: Off Kingsland Rd., continuation of Bishopsgate. PARK: Easy. TEL: 020 7254 7074; home - same; fax - 0870 125 7669; e-mail - boxes@hygra.com; website - www.hygra.com. SER: Valuations; restorations (exceptional instruments only). Registered with the Conservation Unit of the Museums and Galleries Commission.

E11

Old Cottage Antiques
8 High St., Wanstead. E11 2AJ. (P. Blake and B. Hawkins). Est. 1920. Open Fri. and Sat. 10-5. SIZE: Medium. *STOCK: Furniture, clocks, paintings, 19th-20th C.* LOC: Near Wanstead station and Snaresbrook. TEL: 020 8989 2317/8504 9264; mobile - 07710 031079. SER: Buys at auction. VAT: Stan/Spec.

E17

Collectors Centre - Antique City
98 Wood St. E17. Est. 1978. Open 9.30-5.30. CL: Thurs. SIZE: Large. *STOCK: Antiques, collectables, 40's, 50's, 60's, £1-£500.* PARK: Opposite. TEL: 020 8520 4032. *Trade Only.*

Georgian Village Antiques Market
100 Wood St., Walthamstow. E17 3HX. Est. 1972. Open 10-5. CL: Thurs. SIZE: 10 shops. *STOCK: Clocks, barometers, postcards, collectables, jewellery, brass, copper, stamps, silver, silver plate, crafts.* LOC: 50yds. from Dukes Head. PARK: Adjacent. TEL: 020 8520 6638.

E18

Victoria Antiques
166A George Lane, South Woodford. E18 2HL. (M. A. Holman). Est. 1998. Open 11-5. CL: Tues. SIZE: Small. *STOCK: Clocks and carved chairs, 18th-19th C, £100-£1,000; pictures, 19th C, £50-*

£500. LOC: 2 mins. walk from South Woodford station. PARK: George Lane. TEL: 020 8989 1002. SER: Valuations. VAT: Stan.

EC1

City Clocks
31 Amwell St. EC1R 1UN. (J. Rosson). FBHI. Est. 1960. Open Tues.-Fri. 8.30-5.30, Sat. 9.30-2.30 or by appointment. SIZE: Medium. *STOCK: Clocks, some furniture, 18th-20th C, £100-£12,000.* PARK: Easy. TEL: 020 7278 1154; website - www.cityclocks.co.uk. SER: Valuations; restorations (clocks and watches); buys at auction. VAT: Spec.

Eldridge London
99-101 Farringdon Rd. EC1R 3BT. (B. Eldridge). Est. 1953. Open 12-5, 1st Sat. in month 11-5. CL: Wed. SIZE: Large. *STOCK: Furniture, treen and items of social and historical importance.* PARK: Easy. TEL: 020 7837 0379. VAT: Spec.

Finecraft Workshop Ltd
10 Greville St. EC1N 8SB. (Martyn J. Pummell). NAG. Est. 1955. Open 10.15-5, Sat. 10.15-4.30, Sun. 10.15-2. SIZE: Medium. *STOCK: Jewellery, 19th-20th C, £100-£8,000+.* LOC: Between Farringdon Rd. and Hatton Garden. PARK: Nearby. TEL: 020 7242 3825; fax - 020 7404 0170. SER: Valuations; restorations; re-making and repairing; insurance claims undertaken; buys at auction. FAIRS: Europe and USA. VAT: Stan.

C.R. Frost and Son Ltd
60-62 Clerkenwell Rd. EC1M 5PX. BCWMG; BHI. *STOCK: Quality vintage clocks, watches and barometers.* TEL: 020 7253 0315; fax - 020 7253 7454. SER: Repairs; clock and watch materials; batteries; clock glasses and bevelling to order.

Jonathan Harris (Jewellery) Ltd
63-66 Hatton Garden (office). EC1N 8LE. (E.C., D. I. and J. Harris). Est. 1958. Open 9.30-4.30. CL: Sat. *STOCK: Antique and secondhand rings, brooches, pendants, bracelets and other jewellery, from £100.* PARK: Nearby. TEL: 020 7242 9115/7242 1558; fax - 020 7831 4417. SER: Valuations; export. FAIRS: Basle, Switzerland and Munich, Germany. VAT: Stan/Spec.

Hirsh Ltd
10 Hatton Garden. EC1N 8AH. (A. Hirsh). Open 10-5.30. *STOCK: Fine jewellery, silver and objets d'art.* TEL: 020 7405 6080; fax - 020 7430 0107; e-mail - enquiries@hirsh.co.uk. SER: Valuations; jewellery designed and re-modelled.

R. Holt and Co. Ltd
98 Hatton Garden. EC1N 8NX. Est. 1948. Open 9.30-5.30. CL: Sat. *STOCK: Gemstone* specialists. TEL: 020 7405 5286/0197; fax - 020 7430 1279; e-mail - info@rholt.co.uk. SER: Valuations; restorations (gem stone cutting and testing; bead stringing; inlaid work).

Joseph and Pearce Ltd
63-66 Hatton Garden. EC1. LAPADA. Est. 1896. Open by appointment. *STOCK: Jewellery, 1800-1960, £100-£2,500.* TEL: 020 7405 4604/7; fax - 020 7242 1902. VAT: Stan/Spec. *Trade Only.*

Andrew Lowe
18 Exmouth Market, Clerkenwell. EC1R 4QE. Est. 1998. Open 9.30-6.30, Sat. 10.30-6, Sun. by appointment. SIZE: Large. *STOCK: Period furniture and mirrors, 18th-19th C.* LOC: Off Farringdon Rd., Clerkenwell. PARK: Ping St. TEL: 020 7837 6699. SER: Restorations (mirrors and furniture). VAT: Stan.

A.R. Ullmann Ltd
10 Hatton Garden. EC1N 8AH. (J.S. Ullmann). Est. 1939. Open 9-5, Sat. 9.30-5. SIZE: Small. *STOCK: Jewellery, gold, silver and diamond; silver and objets d'art.* LOC: Very close to Farringdon and Chancery Lane tube stations. PARK: Multi-storey in St. Cross St. TEL: 020 7405 1877; fax - 020 7404 7071; home - 020 8346 2546. SER: Valuations; restorations. VAT: Stan/Spec.

EC2

D. Horton
69 Moorgate. EC2R 6BH. *STOCK: Modern British paintings.* TEL: 020 7588 6004; fax - 020 7588 6005; website - www.hortonlondon.co.uk. SER: Valuations.

LASSCo
St. Michael's, Mark St. (off Paul St.). EC2A 4ER. LAPADA. Est. 1977. Open 10-5. *STOCK: Architectural antiques including panelled rooms, chimney pieces, garden ornaments, lighting, door furniture, stained glass, columns and capitals, stonework, relics and curiosities.* TEL: 020 7749 9944; fax - 020 7749 9941; website - www.lassco.co.uk.

Westland London
St. Michael's Church, Leonard St. EC2A 4ER. Est. 1969. Open 9-6, Sat. 10-5, Sun. by appointment. SIZE: Large. *STOCK: Period and prestigious chimneypieces, architectural elements, panelled rooms, light fittings, statuary, paintings and furniture, £100-£100,000.* LOC: Off Gt. Eastern St. PARK: Easy. TEL: 020 7739 8094; fax - 020 7729 3620; e-mail - westland@westland.co.uk; website - www. westland.co.uk.

EC3

Ash Rare Books
153 Fenchurch St. EC3M 6BB. (L. Worms). Est. 1946. Open 10-5. CL: Sat. SIZE: Small. *STOCK: Books, 1550-1980, £20-£10,000; maps, 1550-1850, £25-£2,000; prints, 1650-1900, £20-£1,000.* LOC: First floor office opposite top of Rood Lane. TEL: 020 7626 2665; fax - 020 7623 9052; e-mail - worms@ashrare.demon.co.uk. SER: Buys at auction (books and maps); picture framing and mount cutting. VAT: Stan.

Halcyon Days
BADA
4 Royal Exchange. EC3V 3LL. (S. Benjamin). Est. 1950. Open 10-5.30. *STOCK: 18th to early 19th C enamels, Georgian and Victorian scent bottles, papier mâché, tôle, objects of vertu, treen, unusual small Georgian furniture.* TEL: 020 7626 1120; fax - 020 7283 1876; e-mail - info@halcyondays.co.uk; website - www.halcyondays.co.uk. FAIRS: Grosvenor House. VAT: Stan/Spec.

Nanwani and Co
2 Shopping Arcade, Bank Station, Cornhill. EC3V 3LA. Est. 1958. CL: Sat. *STOCK: Precious and semi-precious stones, Oriental items, objets d'art.* TEL: 020 7623 8232; fax - 020 7283 2548. VAT: Stan.

Searle and Co Ltd
1 Royal Exchange, Cornhill. EC3V 3LL. Est. 1893. Open 9-5.30. SIZE: Medium. *STOCK: Georgian, Victorian and secondhand silver; Victorian, Edwardian and secondhand jewellery.* LOC: Near Bank Underground - exit 4. PARK: Meters. TEL: 020 7626 2456; fax - 020 7283 6384; e-mail - mail@searleandco.ltd.uk; website - www.searleandco.ltd.uk. SER: Valuations; restorations; repairs; engraving. VAT: Stan/Spec.

N1

After Noah
121 Upper St., Islington. N1 1QP. (M. Crawford and Z. Candlin). Est. 1990. Open 10-6, Sun. 12-5. SIZE: Medium. *STOCK: Arts and Craft oak and similar furniture, 1880's to 1950's, £1-£5,000; iron, iron and brass beds; decorative items, bric-a-brac including candlesticks, mirrors, lighting, kitchenalia and jewellery.* PARK: Side streets. TEL: 020 7359 4281; fax - same. SER: Restorations. VAT: Stan.

Angel Arcade
116-118 Islington High St., Camden Passage. N1

8EG. Open Wed. and Sat. SIZE: Large. *STOCK: Decorative items, some antique.*

Annie's Vintage Costume & Textiles
10 Camden Passage, Islington. N1 8ED. (A. Moss). Open 11-5. CL: Mon. TEL: 020 7359 0796.

The Antique Trader
The Millinery Works, 85/87 Southgate Rd. N1 3JS. (B. Thompson and D. Rothera). Est. 1968. Open Tues.-Sat. 11-6, Sun. 12-5 or by appointment. SIZE: Large. *STOCK: Arts & Crafts and art furniture, £100-£15,000.* LOC: Close to Camden Passage Antiques Centre. PARK: Free. TEL: 020 7359 2019; fax - 020 7359 5792; e-mail - antiquetrader@millinery.demon.co.uk; website - www.milleryworks.co.uk. VAT: Stan/Spec.

R. Arantes - Lalique Glass
Georgian Galleries, Camden Passage, Islington. N1 8DU. Est. 1984. Open Wed. 8-3 and Sat. 10-4. SIZE: Small. *STOCK: René Lalique glass, 1920-30's, £300-£5,000.* LOC: Angel tube station. PARK: Easy and NCP. TEL: Mobile - 07712 189160; fax - 020 7253 5303. SER: Valuations. VAT: Spec.

Art Nouveau Originals c. 1900
5 Pierrepont Row Arcade, Camden Passage, Islington. N1 8EF. (Cathy Turner). Est. 1997. Open Wed. 8-4, Sat. 9-4, other days by appointment. SIZE: Small. *STOCK: Art Nouveau and Arts & Crafts, including small furniture, £50-£1,000+.* TEL: 020 7359 4127; fax - 01733 244717. FAIRS: NEC Antiques for Everyone; LAPADA London and Birmingham; 20th C, Olympia and Earls Court; Penman Chester. VAT: Spec.

Banbury Fayre
6 Pierrepont Row Arcade, Camden Passage, Islington. N1. (N. Steel). Est. 1984. Open Wed., Fri. and Sat. SIZE: Small. *STOCK: Collectables including commemoratives, shipping, Boy Scout movement, Boer War, air line travel.* PARK: 200yds. TEL: Home - 020 8852 5675.

Camden Passage Antiques Market and Pierrepont Arcade Antiques Centre
12 Camden Passage, Islington. N1 8ED. (S. Lemkow). Est. 1960. Open Wed. and Sat. 7.30-3.30. Thurs. - book market. SIZE: Over 400 dealers. *STOCK: Wide range of general antiques and some specialists.* LOC: Behind the Angel, Islington. TEL: 020 7359 0190.

Patric Capon   **BADA**
350 Upper St., Islington. N1 0PD. Est. 1970. Open Wed. and Sat. or by appointment. SIZE:

Medium. *STOCK: Unusual carriage clocks, 19th C, £450-£6,000; 8-day and 2-day marine chronometers, 19th C, £850-£4,500; clocks and barometers, 18th-19th C, £400-£6,500.* LOC: Adjacent Camden Passage. PARK: Easy. TEL: 020 7354 0487; fax - 020 8295 1475; home - 020 8467 5722. SER: Valuations; restorations. FAIRS: Olympia. VAT: Stan/Spec.

Peter Chapman Antiques and Restoration
10 Theberton St., Islington. N1 0QX. (P.J. and Z.A. Chapman). LAPADA, CPTA. Est. 1971. Open 9.30-6. CL: Sun. and public holidays except by appointment. SIZE: Medium. *STOCK: Furniture and decorative objects, 1700-1900; paintings, drawings and prints, 17th to early 20th C; stained glass, hall lanterns; Grand Tour items.* LOC: 5 mins. walk from Camden Passage down Upper St. PARK: Easy. TEL: 020 7226 5565; mobile - 07831 093662; fax - 020 8348 4846; e-mail - pchapmanantiques@easynet.co.uk; website - www.antiques-peterchapman.co.uk. SER: Valuations; restorations (furniture and period objects); buys at auction. VAT: Stan/Spec.

Chapter One
2 Pierrepont Row Arcade, Camden Passage. N1 9EG. (Yvonne Gill). Est. 1993. Open Wed. 9-3, Sat. 9-5 or by appointment. SIZE: Small. *STOCK: Handbags, costume jewellery, vintage accessories, fabrics, bric-a-brac, 1880-1960, £5-£300.* TEL: 020 7359 1185. SER: Jewellery repairs.

Charlton House Antiques
18/20 Camden Passage, Islington. N1 8ED. Open Wed. and Sat. 8-5, Tue. and Fri. 10-4. SIZE: Large. *STOCK: European and Scandinavian furniture, 1840-1930, £100-£5,000; general antiques.* LOC: Near Angel underground station. PARK: Easy. TEL: 020 7226 3141; fax - 020 7226 1123. VAT: Stan/Spec.

Chest of Drawers
281 Upper St., Islington. N1 2TZ. (J. Delf). Open 10-6 including Sun. *STOCK: Pine and oak.* TEL: 020 7359 5909.

Rosemary Conquest
4 Charlton Place, Camden Passage. N1 8AJ. Open 11-5.30, Wed. and Sat. 9-5.30. SIZE: Small. *STOCK: Chandeliers, European decorative items, copper and brass.* PARK: Easy. TEL: 020 7359 0616; home - 020 7254 1208.

Carlton Davidson Antiques
33 Camden Passage, Islington. N1 8EA. Est. 1981. Open Wed.-Sat. 10-4. SIZE: Medium. *STOCK: Lamps, chandeliers, mirrors and*

decorative items, £100-£3,000. LOC: Near Charlton Place. PARK: Meters. TEL: 020 7226 7491. VAT: Stan.

Dean's Antiques
25 Camden Passage, Islington. N1. Open by appointment only. *STOCK: Decorative items.* TEL: 020 7354 9940.

Donay Games & Pastimes
3 Pierrepont Row, Camden Passage, Islington. N1 8EF. (D.C. and C.E. Goddard). Est. 1980. Open Wed. and Sat. 9-4. SIZE: Large. *STOCK: Board and mechanical games - horse racing, cricket, golf and football; treen, paper and metal puzzles including Journet and mechanical Hoffman; chess, backgammon, cribbage, dominoes; card games and scorers; tinplate including Schuco; dice, shakers, mah-jong, marbles, artists' colourboxes; animal bronzes, Punch & Judy, bespoke games tables, 1780-1950, £5-£5,000.* LOC: Near Angel tube station. PARK: Charlton Place. TEL: 020 7359 1880; office - 01444 250230; fax - 01444 250231; e-mail - donay games@aol.com; website - www.donaygames. com.

Eclectica
2 Charlton Place. N1 8AJ. (Liz Wilson). Open 11-6, Wed. and Sat. 9-6. *STOCK: Vintage costume jewellery.* TEL: 020 7226 5625; fax - same.

Feljoy Antiques
Shop 3, Angel Arcade, Camden Passage. N1 8EA. Open Wed. and Sat. 8-4. *STOCK: Chintzware, decorative antiques and textiles.* TEL: 020 7354 5336.

The Fleamarket
7 Pierrepont Row Arcade, Camden Passage, Islington. N1 8EE. Open 9.30-6. CL: Mon. SIZE: Large. 26 stand-holders. *STOCK: Jewellery, furniture, objets d'art, militaria, guns, swords, pistols, porcelain, coins, medals, stamps, 18th-19th C, £1-£500; antiquarian books, prints, fine art, china, silver, glass and general antiques.* PARK: Easy. TEL: 020 7226 8211. SER: Valuations; buys at auction; weapon repairs.

Vincent Freeman
1 Camden Passage, Islington. N1 8EA. Est. 1966. Open 10-5. CL: Mon. and Thurs. SIZE: Large. *STOCK: Music boxes, furniture and decorative items, from £100.* TEL: 020 7226 6178; fax - 020 7226 7231. VAT: Stan/Spec.

Furniture Vault
50 Camden Passage, Islington. N1 8AE. Open Tues.-Sat. 9.30-4.30. *STOCK: Furniture, 18th-20th C; decorative bronzes.* TEL: 020 7354 1047.

Georgian Village
30-31 Islington Green. N1. Open 10-4, Wed. and Sat. 7-5. PARK: Nearby. TEL: 020 7226 1571.

Get Stuffed
105 Essex Rd., Islington. N1 2SL. Est. 1975. Open 1-5, Sat. 1-3. *STOCK: Stuffed birds, fish, animals, trophy heads; rugs; butterflies, insects.* TEL: 020 7226 1364; mobile - 07831 260062; fax - 020 7359 8253; website - www.thegetstuffed. co.uk. SER: Restorations; taxidermy; glass domes and cases supplied.

Gordon Gridley
28 & 41 Camden Passage, Islington. N1 8EA. Est. 1968. CL: Mon. SIZE: Large + warehouse at rear. *STOCK: English and Continental furniture, paintings, decorative objects, metalwork, glass and ceramics, statuary and garden furniture, 17th-19th C, £50-£20,000.* PARK: Business Design Centre or Charlton Place. TEL: 020 7226 0643. SER: Valuations; restorations. VAT: Stan/Spec.

Linda Gumb
9 Camden Passage, Islington. N1. LAPADA. Est. 1981. Open 9.30-4.30, Wed. 7.30-5, Sat. 9-5. SIZE: Medium. *STOCK: Textiles, 18th-19th C; decorative objects, 19th C; all £10-£5,000.* PARK: Easy. TEL: 020 7354 1184; mobile - 07785 248207. SER: Buys at auction. FAIRS: Olympia. VAT: Stan.

Rosemary Hart
8 Angel Arcade, 116 Islington High St. N1 8EG. Est. 1980. Open Wed. and Sat. 9.30-4 , Fri. 10.30-3. SIZE: Small. *STOCK: Silver plated tableware and decorative serving pieces, £5-£500; small silver gifts, from £50.* LOC: Near Angel tube station. TEL: 020 7359 6839; e-mail - rosemaryhart@cwcom.net

House of Steel Antiques
400 Caledonian Rd. N1 1DN. (J. Cole). Est. 1974. Open 11-6, Sat. by appointment. SIZE: Warehouse. *STOCK: Metal items - fireplaces, 18th-19th C, £50-£1,000; spiral staircases, £300-£1,000; balconies, railings, garden furniture, £50-£500; all 19th C.* LOC: Near King's Cross. PARK: Own. TEL: 020 7607 5889. SER: Valuations; restorations (welding, polishing, sandblasting); steel furniture manufactured, items made to order. VAT: Stan.

Diana Huntley
8 Camden Passage, Islington. N1 8ED. LAPADA. Est. 1970. Open Tues. and Fri. 10-4, Wed. 7.30-5, Thurs. by appointment, Sat. 9-5. *STOCK: European porcelain, £50-£10,000; objets d'art; all 19th C.* TEL: 020 7226 4605; fax

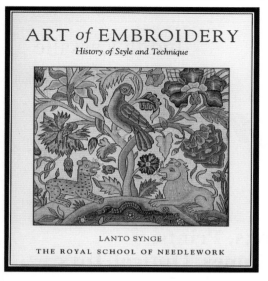

- 020 7359 0240; e-mail - diana@
dianahuntleyantiques.co.uk; website - www.
dianahuntleyantiques.co.uk. SER: Valuations.
VAT: Stan/Spec.

Intercol London
Gallery, 114 Islington High St. (within Camden
Passage). Correspondence - 43 Templars
Crescent, N3 3QR. N1. (Y. Beresiner). Est. 1977.
Open Wed.-Sat. 9-5, other times by appointment.
SIZE: Large. *STOCK: Playing cards, maps and
banknotes and related literature, £5-£1,000+.*
PARK: Easy. TEL: 020 8349 2207; fax - 020
8346 9539; e-mail - yasha@compuserve.com;
website - www.intercol.co.uk. SER: Valuations;
restorations (maps including colouring); buys at
auction (playing cards, maps, banknotes and
books). FAIRS: Major specialist European,
U.S.A. and Far Eastern. VAT: Stan/Spec.

Jonathan James
52/53 Camden Passage, Islington. N1 8EA.
(James and Norman Petre). LAPADA. Est. 1970.
Open 10-4.30, Wed. 9.30-4.30. CL: Mon. SIZE:
Medium. *STOCK: Furniture, 18th-19th C,
£1,000-£20,000.* PARK: 100 yds. TEL: 020 7704
8266; fax - same. SER: Valuations. VAT:
Stan/Spec.

Japanese Gallery
23 Camden Passage, Islington. N1 8EA. Open
9.30-4.30. *STOCK: Japanese woodcut prints;
books, porcelain, screens, kimonos, scrolls,
furniture.* TEL: 020 7226 3347; fax - 020 7229
2934. SER: Framing; free authentification.

Jubilee Photographica
10 Pierrepont Row Arcade, Camden Passage,
Islington. N1 8E. (Beryl Vosburgh). Est. 1966.
Open Wed. and Sat. 10.30-4 or by appointment.
SIZE: Small. *STOCK: Photographica -
apparatus, images, daguerreotypes, ambrotypes,
tintypes, vintage paper prints, stereoscopic cards
and viewers, magic lanterns and slides,
topographical and family-albums, cabinet cards
and cartes de visite, 10p-£1,000.* LOC: From
Piccadilly Circus, take 19 bus to Angel, Islington.
PARK: Meters. TEL: Home - 020 7607 5462; e-
mail - beryl@winks.demon.co.uk. SER: Buys at
auction.

Carol Ketley Antiques
PO Box 16199. N1 7WD. LAPADA. Est. 1979.
Open by appointment. SIZE: Medium. *STOCK:
Mirrors, decanters, drinking glasses, decorative
furniture and objects, 1780-1900, £10-£10,000.*
LOC: Showroom close to Camden Passage.
PARK: Easy. TEL: 020 7359 5529; mobile -

THE MALL
ANTIQUES ARCADE
Camden Passage, London N1

Over 35 Dealers in
Londons premier centre for dealers,
decorators and collectors.

Enquiries: Mike Spooner
Tel: 020-7969 1500 Fax: 020-7969 1639

07831 827284; fax - 020 7226 4589. FAIRS:
Olympia; LAPADA; Decorative Antiques and
Textile. VAT: Global.

Judith Lassalle
7 Pierrepont Row Arcade, Camden Passage,
Islington. N1 8EF. Est. 1765 Cornhill. Open
Wed. 7.30-4, Sat. 9.30-4, other times by
appointment. *STOCK: Books, maps, children's
games, optical toys and rocking horses, 17th C to
1914, £25-£5,000.* PARK: Nearby. TEL: 020
7607 7121; shop - 020 7354 9344. SER:
Valuations; restorations; buys at auction. FAIRS:
Ephemera; PBFA; American Ephemera.

John Laurie (Antiques) Ltd
351/352 Upper St., Islington. N1 0PD. (J.
Gewirtz). LAPADA. Est. 1962. Open 9.30-5.
SIZE: Large. *STOCK: Silver, Sheffield plate.*
TEL: 020 7226 0913/6969; fax - 020 7226 4599.
SER: Restorations; packing; shipping. VAT:
Stan.

Sara Lemkow
12 Camden Passage, Islington. N1 8EA. Open
10-5. *STOCK: Oil lamps, brass, iron, copper,
French enamel, kitchen utensils.* TEL: 020 7359
0190.

Michael Lewis Antiques
6-7 Peabody Yard, Greenman St. N1 8SB.
LAPADA. Est. 1977. Open 9-6, Sun. 12-5. CL:
Mon. SIZE: Small. *STOCK: Pine and country
furniture, British and Irish, 18th-19th C, £100-
£6,500.* LOC: 100yds. north of Camden Passage.
PARK: Easy. TEL: 020 7359 7733. VAT:
Stan/Spec.

London Militaria Market
Angel Arcade, Camden Passage, Islington. N1.
(S. Bosley and M. Warren). Est. 1987. Open Sat.
8-2. SIZE: Large. 35 dealers. *STOCK: Militaria,
1800 to date.* LOC: Near Angel tube station.
PARK: Meters and nearby. TEL: 01628 822503
or 01455 556971.

The Mall Antiques Arcade
359 Upper St., Islington. N1. (Atlantic Antiques
Centres Ltd). Est. 1979. Open 10-5, Wed. 7.30-5,
Sat. 9-6. CL: Mon. LOC: 5 mins. from Angel
tube station. PARK: Meters. TEL: 020 7969
1500; enquiries - 020 7969 1634; e-mail -
antique@dial. pipex.com. Below are listed the
dealers at this Arcade.

Alexandra Alfandary
Stand G9. LAPADA. *Meissen porcelain.* TEL: 020
7354 9762.

Audley Art Ltd
Stand G20. (A. Singer). *Meissen porcelain and oil
paintings.* TEL: 020 7704 9507.

David Bowden
Stand G12. *Oriental and European works of art,
watches.* TEL: 020 7226 3033.

Chancery Antiques Ltd
(R. and D. Rote). *Oriental works of art especially
Japanese Meiji period and Continental porcelain
including Meissen.* TEL: 020 7359 9035; fax - same.

P. Collingridge
Stand G6. *Lighting, brass and furniture.* TEL: 020
7354 9189.

Chris Dunn St. James
Stand G7. *Vintage jewellery.* TEL: 020 7704 0127.

Hallmark Antiques
Stand G15. (Ralph Heller and Raymond
Karpelowsky). *Jewellery and objets de vertu.* TEL:
020 7354 1616; fax - 020 7266 3587.

Heather Antiques
Stand G25. (Mrs. Cohen). *Silver and plate.* TEL:
020 7226 2412.

Patricia Kleinman
Stand G3. LAPADA. *English watercolours, 19th to
early 20th C.* TEL: 020 7704 0798.

Andrew Lineham   BADA
**Stand G19. *Glass and porcelain.* TEL: 020 7704
0195.**

Mario and Sabre Antiques
Stand G23. (M. Barazi and S. Gilmartin). *Porcelain including Meissen, and glass.* TEL: 020 7226 2225.

Military Antiques
(Robert Tredwen). *Military antiques, 1800-1945, £200-£1,000.* TEL: 020 7359 2224; fax - 020 8467 7027. SER:Bu ys at auction. VAT: Spec.

Monika
Stand G16. (M. Jartelius). *Fine period costume jewellery and accessories, 1920's to 1950's.* TEL: 020 7354 3125.

Linda Morgan Antiques
Stand G26. *Jewellery.* TEL: 020 7359 0654.

D. L. Murphy
Stand G4/5. *Silver.* TEL: 020 7345 1204.

Number One The Mall
Stand G1. (Sonia Shea). *Silver, glass and jewellery.* TEL: 020 7354 2839.

Nadine Okker
Stand G8. LAPADA. *Porcelain, glass and bronzes.* TEL: 020 7354 9496.

John Pearman
Stand G24. *Glass and porcelain.* TEL: 020 7359 0591.

Phoenix
Stand B6. (Mr Edwards). LAPADA. *Oriental works of art.* TEL: 020 7226 4474; mobile - 07802 763518.

Mrs Sylvia Powell
Stand G18. LAPADA. *Decorative arts, art pottery, 1870-1894.* TEL: 020 7354 2977.

A bid of £490 secured this late 18th century gilt-metal and agate étui.

From an Auction Report by Tim Ford on the Autumn Fine Art Sale at Bearne's, Exeter on 20th and 21st October, 1998. This feature appeared in the December 1998/January 1999 issue of **Antique Collecting** magazine. For more details and to subscribe see page 147.

Rumours
Stand G4. (J. Donovan). LAPADA. *Art Nouveau and Art Deco china and objets d'art.* TEL: 020 7359 8416.

Gad Sassower
Stand G21. *Bakelite items, gramophones, radios.* TEL: 020 7354 4473; mobile - 07831 326326.

Count Alexander von Beregshasy
Stand G14. *Original vintage French paste and costume jewellery.* TEL: 020 7930 1904.

Michael Young
Stand G22. *Decorative items, model boats.* TEL: 020 7226 2225.

Lower Mall
Eric Edlefsen
Stand B8. *Decorative furniture, Biedermeier.* TEL: 020 7226 1899.

Malcolm D. Stevens
Stand B2/3. LAPADA. *Furniture.* TEL: 020 7359 1020.

Turner Brown Antiques
Stand B9/10. (D. Aron and V. Brown). *Furniture, watches and general antiques.*

Alex Woodage
Stand B7. *Furniture.* TEL: 020 7226 4173.

Laurence Mitchell Antiques Ltd
27 Camden Passage, Islington. N1 8EA. (L.P.J.Mitchell). LAPADA. Est. 1972. Open 10-5, Wed. 8-5, Mon. by appointment. *STOCK: Meissen, European and English porcelain; Oriental works of art, Chinese export and Japanese porcelain.* TEL: 020 7359 7579; fax - 020 7226 1738; e-mail - lawrence.mitchell @ntlworld.com; website - www.121antiques.com. VAT: Stan/Spec.

Michel André Morin
12B Camden Passage and 7 Charlton Place, Islington. N1 8AQ. Open Wed. 8.30-4.30, Sat. 9-4.30, other days by appointment. SIZE: Medium. *STOCK: French decorative furniture, 18th-19th C; French chandeliers.* PARK: Easy. TEL: 020 7226 3803; fax - 020 7704 0708; mobile - 07802 832496. FAIRS: Olympia; Decorative Antique, Battersea.VAT: Spec.

Chris Newland Antiques
Lower Ground Floor, Georgian Village, 30/31 Islington Green. N1. Est. 1964. Open 9-5.30. SIZE: Large. *STOCK: Mahogany furniture, 19th C, £300-£1,000; office furniture, 19th-20th C; shipping furniture, marble, works of art.* PARK: NCP 100 yards. TEL: 020 7359 9805. SER: Valuations; restorations (furniture, French polishing). VAT: Stan/Spec.

RESTALL BROWN & CLENNELL LTD.

Makers of the finest English traditional furniture,
and dealers in antiques, since 1905.

120 QUEENSBRIDGE ROAD, LONDON E2 8PD

TELEPHONE: +44 (0)20 7739 6626

E-MAIL: sales@rbc-furniture.co.uk

Number Nineteen

19 Camden Passage, Islington. N1 8EA. (D. Griffith and J. Wright). Open 10-5. *STOCK: Decorative antiques including military and campaign furniture, leather chairs, pub accessories, club fenders and other fittings from hotels and gentlemen's clubs; quality vintage luggage.* TEL: 020 7226 1126.

Kevin Page Oriental Art

2, 4 and 6 Camden Passage, Islington. N1 8ED. LAPADA. Est. 1968. Open 10-4. CL: Mon. SIZE: Large. *STOCK: Oriental porcelain and furniture, cloisonné, bronzes, ivories.* LOC: 1 min. from Angel tube station. PARK: Easy. TEL: 020 7226 8558. SER: Valuations. VAT: Stan.

Regent Antiques

Barpart House, North London Freight Depot, York Way. N1 0UZ. (T. Quaradeghini). Est. 1983. Open 9-5.30, other times by appointment. SIZE: Large. *STOCK: Furniture, 18th C to Edwardian.* LOC: 1/4 mile from Kings Cross Station. PARK: Own. TEL: 020 7833 5545; fax - 020 7278 2236. SER: Restorations (furniture). VAT: Stan. *Trade Only.*

Relic Antiques at Camden Passage

21 Camden Passage, Islington. N1. (Malcolm Gliksten). Est. 1968. Open Wed. and Sat. 9.30-4.30, other times by appointment. *STOCK: Decorative antiques and painted furniture, childhood memorabilia and paintings, Black Forest carving, fairground art, marine items, period shopfittings, architectural ornaments, trade signs and naive art* PARK: Meters. TEL: 020 7359 2597; fax - 020 7388 2691; mobile - 07831 785059. FAIRS: Chelsea Decorative. VAT: Stan.

Restall Brown and Clennell Ltd

Adelaide Wharf, 120 Queensbridge Rd., E2 8PD. (S. Brown). Open Mon.-Fri. 9-5.30 appointment advisable. *STOCK: English furniture, 17th-19th C.* TEL: 020 7739 6626; fax - 020 7739 6123; e-mail - sales@rbc-furniture.co.uk. VAT: Stan/Spec.

Rookery Farm Antiques

12 Camden Passage, Islington. N1 8ED. *STOCK: Pine and country furniture and bamboo.* TEL: 020 7359 0190.

Marcus Ross Antiques

16 Pierrepont Row Arcade, Camden Passage, Islington. N1 8EF. Est. 1972. Open 10.30-4.30. CL: Mon. *STOCK: Oriental porcelain, general antiques, Victorian walnut furniture.* TEL: 020 7359 8494.

Keith Skeel Antiques

The Merchants Hall, 46 Essex Rd. N1 8LN. LAPADA. SIZE: Very large. *STOCK: Funny, fantastic and fatalistic furniture.* TEL: 020 7359 5633; fax - 020 7226 3780. *Trade Only.*

Staffordshire Pride

4-5 Pierrepont Arcade, Camden Passage, Islington. N1 8EF. (Sharon Racklyeft). Est. 1976. Open Wed. and Sat. 9-3.30. SIZE: Medium. *STOCK: Staffordshire figures, 1800-1870, £50-£300; blue and white china, £10-£50.* PARK: Business Design Centre NCP. TEL: Sat. & Wed. 020 7359 4127; mobile - 07958 453295; home - 020 8341 1943. SER: Valuations. VAT: Stan/Spec.

Style Gallery

1 Ground Floor, Georgian Village, Camden Passage. N1. (M. Webb and P. Coakley-Webb). Open Wed. and Sat. 9.30-4 or by appointment. *STOCK: Art Nouveau, WMF and Liberty pewter, Art Deco bronzes including Preiss and Chiparus, ceramics and glass.* TEL: 020 7359 7867; home - 020 8361 2357; fax - same; mobile - 07831 229640; website - www. styleantiques.co.uk; e-mail - antiqstyle@aol.com.

Sugar Antiques

8-9 Pierrepont Row Arcade, Camden Passage, Islington. N1 8EF. (Elayne and Tony Sugarman). Est. 1990. Open Wed. 6.30-4, Sat. 9-4, other times by appointment. SIZE: Medium. *STOCK: Wrist and pocket watches, 19th-20th C, £25-£2,000; fountain pens and lighters, early 20th C to 1960's, £15-£1,000; costume jewellery and collectables, 19th-20th C, £5-£500.* PARK: Meters. TEL: 020 7354 9896; fax - 020 8931 5642; mobile - 07973 179890; e-mail - tony@sugarantiques.com; website - www.sugarantiques.com. SER: Repairs (as stock); buys at auction (as stock). VAT: Stan.

Swan Fine Art

120 Islington High St., Camden Passage. N1 8EG. (P. Child). Open 10-5, Wed. and Sat. 9-5 or by appointment. SIZE: Medium. *STOCK: Paintings, fine and decorative sporting and animal, portraits, 17th-19th C, £500-£25,000+.* PARK: Easy, except Wed. and Sat. TEL: 020 7226 5335; fax - 020 7359 2225; mobile - 07860 795336. VAT: Spec.

Tadema Gallery   BADA

10 Charlton Place, Camden Passage, Islington. N1. (S. and D. Newell-Smith). LAPADA. Est. 1978. Open Wed. and Sat. 10-5, or by appointment. SIZE: Medium. *STOCK: 20th C abstract art and jewellery, from Art Nouveau to 1960's artist designed pieces.* PARK: Reasonable. TEL: 020 7359 1055; fax - same. SER: Valuations. VAT: Spec.

C. Tapsell

Christopher House, 5 Camden Passage, Islington. N1 8EA. Est. 1970. Open Wed. 9-4.30, Sat. 9-5, other times by appointment. SIZE: Medium. *STOCK: English mahogany and walnut furniture, 18th-19th C, £300-£15,000; Oriental china, 17th-19th C, £20-£5,000; French furniture, 18th-19th C, £500-£5,000.* LOC: Near Angel underground station. PARK: Opposite. TEL: 020 7354 3603. SER: Restorations (furniture); buys at auction (furniture). VAT: Stan/Spec.

The Textile Company

P.O Box 2800, London N1 4DQ. (Judy Wentworth). Est. 1982. Open by appointment only. *STOCK: 18th C silks, British and French printed cottons, patchworks, lace, 1600-1850; Paisley and Kashmir shawls, period costume and accessories.* Not Stocked: Tapestries, upholstery and cushions. TEL: 020 7254 3256. SER: Buys at auction; hire; photographic archive.

Tisdall & Defries Antiques

7 Pierrepont Row Arcade, Camden Passage, Islington. N1 8EE. (M. Tisdall and S. Defries).

Est. 1984. Open Wed. 7-3.30, Sat. 9-3.30, other days by appointment. SIZE: Medium. *STOCK: Sheffield plate, 18th-19th C, £20-£2,000; Victorian plate, 19th to early 20th C, £20-£3,000; silver, 18th-20th C, £50-£5,000.* PARK: NPC nearby. TEL: 020 7226 8211. SER: Valuations; restorations (replating, gilding, repairs); buys at auction (as stock). FAIRS: Newark. VAT: Stan/Spec

Titus Omega

Shop 18, Ground Floor, Georgian Village, Camden Passage. N1. (John Featherstone-Harvey). Est. 1986. Open Wed. 8-3, Sat. 9-4. SIZE: Small. *STOCK: Art Nouveau, 1890-1910, £100-£3,000.* LOC: Islington Green. TEL: 020 7704 8003; home - 020 7688 1295; mobile - 07973 841846. SER: Valuations.

Turn On Lighting

116/118 Islington High St., Camden Passage. N1 8EG. Est. 1976. *STOCK: Lighting, 1840-1940.* TEL: 020 7359 7616; fax - same.

Vane House Antiques

15 Camden Passage, Islington. N1 8EA. (Michael J. Till). Est. 1950. Open 10-5. CL: Mon. and Thurs. *STOCK: 18th to early 19th C furniture.* TEL: 020 7359 1343; fax - same. VAT: Stan/Spec.

Agnes Wilton

3 Camden Passage, Islington. N1 8EA. Open 9.30-3. *STOCK: Furniture, decorative items.* TEL: 020 7226 5679.

Yesterday Child

Angel Arcade, 118 Islington High St. N1. (D. and G. Barrington). LAPADA. Est. 1970. Open Wed. and Sat. 8.30-3. SIZE: Small. *STOCK: Dolls, 1800-1925, £25-£5,000.* PARK: Easy. TEL: 020 7354 1601; home and fax - 01908 583403. SER: Valuations; restorations. VAT: Stan/Spec.

Ying Guoren Ltd

54 Duncan St. N1 8BW. (Rachel Hayward and Damian Hubsch). Open 10.30-6.30, Sun. 11-4. CL: Mon. SIZE: Medium. *STOCK: Chinese country furniture, 19th to mid 20th C, £500-£1,000; Chinese porcelain, 19th C, £50-£150; accessories, late 19th to mid 20th C, £50-£100.* LOC: Off Upper St., Angel end, turn right before Camden Passage. PARK: Easy. TEL: 020 7833 0835; fax - 020 7833 5881. SER: Buys at auction. VAT: Stan.

York Gallery Ltd

51 Camden Passage. N1 8EA. (Jane and Gerd Beyer). Est. 1984. Open Wed. and Sat. 10-5. *STOCK: Antique prints.* TEL: 020 7354 8012. SER: Bespoke framing.

N2

Amazing Grates - Fireplaces Ltd
61-63 High Rd., East Finchley. N2. (T. Tew).
Resident. Est. 1971. Open 10-6. SIZE: Large.
*STOCK: Mantelpieces, grates and fireside items,
£200-£5,000; Victorian tiling, £2-£20; early
ironwork, all 19th C.* LOC: 100yds. north of East
Finchley tube station. PARK: Own. TEL: 020
8883 9590/6017. SER: Valuations; reproduction
mantelpieces in stone and marble; restorations
(ironwork, welding of cast iron and brazing,
polishing); installations. VAT: Stan.

The Antique Shop (Valantique)
9 Fortis Green. N2 9JR. (Mrs V. Steel). Open
Wed., Fri. and Sat. 11-6, Thurs. 11-3, Sun. by
appointment. SIZE: Medium. *STOCK: General
antiques especially original lighting and fenders;
small furniture, pottery, porcelain, glass, oil
paintings, watercolours, prints, mirrors, copper,
brass, unusual items, £5-£500.* LOC: 2 mins. from
East Finchley tube station. PARK: Side street.
TEL: 020 8883 7651. SER: Buys at auction.

Martin Henham (Antiques)
218 High Rd., East Finchley. N2 9AY. Open 10-
6. SIZE: Medium. *STOCK: Furniture and
porcelain, 1710-1920, £5-£3,500; paintings,
1650-1940, £10-£4,000.* PARK: Easy. TEL: 020
8444 5274. SER: Valuations; restorations
(furniture and paintings); buys at auction.

Lauri Stewart - Fine Art
36 Church Lane. N2 8DT. Open 10-5. CL: Mon.
STOCK: Modern British oils and watercolours.
TEL: 020 8883 7719; e-mail - 1ste181072@
aol.com.

N4

Alexander Juran and Co   BADA
at Nathan Azizollahoff, OCC, Top Floor & Lift,
Building A, 105 Eade Rd. N4 1TJ. Est. 1951.
Open 9.15-5.30. CL: Sat. *STOCK: Caucasian
rugs, nomadic and tribal; carpets, rugs,
tapestries.* TEL: 020 7435 0280; fax - same.
SER: Valuations; repairs. VAT: Stan/Spec.

Kennedy Carpets
OCC Building 'G', 105 Eade Rd. N4 1TJ. (M.
Kennedy). LAPADA. Est. 1974. Open 9.30-6.
SIZE: Large. *STOCK: Decorative carpets,
collectable rugs and kelims, mid-19th C to new,
£500-£50,000.* LOC: Off Seven Sisters Road.
TEL: 020 8800 4455; fax - 020 8800 4466. SER:
Valuations; making to order. VAT: Stan.

Joseph Lavian
OCC, Building E, Ground Floor, 105 Eade Rd.
N4 1TJ. LAPADA. Est. 1950. Open 9.30-5.30.
SIZE: Large. *STOCK: Oriental carpets, rugs,
kelims, tapestries and needlework, Aubusson,
Savonnerie and textiles, 17th-19th C.* TEL: 020
8800 0707; fax - 020 8800 0404; mobile - 07767
797707; e-mail - Lavian@Lavian.com; website -
www.Lavian.com. SER: Valuations; restorations.

Teger Trading
318 Green Lanes. N4 1BX. *STOCK: Reproduction bronzes, furniture, marble figures,
paintings, mirrors, porcelain and unusual items.*
TEL: 020 8802 0156; fax - 020 8802 4110. SER:
Restorations; film hire. *Trade Only.*

N5

Nicholas Goodyer
15 Calabria Rd., Highbury Fields. N5 1JB. Est.
1951. Open 9.30-5, but prior telephone call
advisable. CL: Sat. *STOCK: Antiquarian books
especially illustrated.* TEL: 020 7226 5682; fax -
020 7354 4716; e-mail - email@nicholasgoodyer.
com; website - www.nicholasgoodyer.com.

Strike One   BADA
48a Highbury Hill. N5 1AP. (J. Mighell). Est.
1968. Open by appointment. SIZE: Medium.
*STOCK: Clocks, pre-1870, especially early
English wall and Act of Parliament, £2,000-
£25,000; English longcase, 1675-1820, £3,000-
£40,000; English bracket, lantern, skeleton and
French carriage; Vienna regulators;
barometers, music boxes.* PARK: Easy. TEL:
020 7354 2790; fax - same; e-mail -
STRIKEONE@ compuserve.com. SER:
Valuations; restorations (clocks, barometers);
catalogue available. VAT: Stan/Spec.

N6

At the Sign of the Chest of Drawers
164 Archway Rd. N6 5BB. (A. Harms). Open
Tues.-Sat. 10-6. *STOCK: Pine and country
furniture.* TEL: 020 8340 7652

Fisher and Sperr
46 Highgate High St. N6 5JB. (J.R. Sperr). Est.
1945. Open daily 10.30-6. SIZE: Large. *STOCK:
Books, 15th C to date.* LOC: From centre of
Highgate Village, nearest underground stations
Archway (Highgate), Highgate. PARK: Easy.
TEL: 020 8340 7244; fax - 020 8348 4293. SER:
Valuations; restorations (books). VAT: Stan.

Betty Gould and Julian Gonnermann Antiques

408-410 Archway Rd., Highgate. N6 5AT. Est. 1964. Open 10-5.30, Sat. 9.30-5.30. CL: Mon. and Thurs. SIZE: Medium. *STOCK: Furniture, 18th-20th C, £50-£5,000.* LOC: On A1, just below Highgate tube station (corner of Shepherds Hill). TEL: 020 8340 4987. SER: Restorations; French polishing; upholstery.

N7

Dome Antiques (Exports) Ltd

40 Queensland Rd., Islington. N7 7AJ. (Adam and Louise Woolf). LAPADA. Est. 1961. Open Mon.-Fri. and Sat. morning. SIZE: Large. *STOCK: 19th C furniture, £250-£10,000.* LOC: Near junction of Holloway and Hornsey roads. PARK: Easy. TEL: 020 7700 6266; mobile - 07831 805888; fax - 020 7609 1692; e-mail - dome.antiques@dial. pipex.com. SER: Valuations; restorations (furniture). FAIRS: LAPADA (April - NEC: June - Olympia; Oct. - Earls Court). VAT: Stan/Spec.

N8

Centaur Gallery

103 Crouch Hill. N8 9RD. (Dinah Wieliczko). Est. 1960. Open by appointment. *STOCK: Watercolours, prints, sculpture, ethnic and folk art.* TEL: 020 8340 0087.

Katie O'Sullivan, (born London, 7th August 1959), 'The Old Retainer', pencil and watercolour, 17¼in. x 13¾in. Signs work 'Katie O'Sullivan' in script. This charming study is among some 35 works by the artist to be exhibited between 8th-25th November at The Osborne Studio Gallery, 13 Motcomb Street, London SW1X 8LB (tel: 020 7235 9667, www.osg.uk.com). With prices starting from £2,000, the show's theme is drawn from scenes of rural life that are fast disappearing, such as Romany gipsy life and the great horse fair at Chareme in County Cork. The artist can be contacted by writing to The Old Malthouse, Upper Lambourn, Nr Hungerford, Berkshire RG17 8RG. Price guide: drawings, £1,500-£5,000; oil paintings, £6,000-£10,500.

This month Anthony J. Lester features three female artists, all of whom have forthcoming London exhibitions. From an article entitled 'Contemporary British Artists' which appeared in the November 2000 issue of **Antique Collecting** magazine. For more details and to subscribe see page 147.

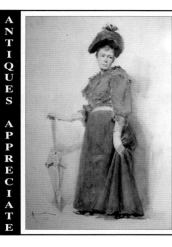

Finchley Fine Art Galleries

983 High Road, North Finchley, London N12 8QR
Telephone: 020-8446-4848 Mobile: 07712 629282
E-mail: finchleyfineart@onetel.net.uk

*200 plus fine 18th-20th Century English watercolours
and paintings in a constantly changing stock. Four
galleries of good quality Georgian, Victorian and
Edwardian furniture, pottery, porcelain, smalls, etc.*

A young lady with a Parasol
by ADOLFO SCARSELLI
born Florence 1866
13½ x 9½ inches
watercolour
signed & dated '93

OPENING TIMES:
MON, TUES, THURS, FRI,
SAT, SUN, 1.00-7.00.
WEDNESDAY
BY APPOINTMENT

(Left margin: ANTIQUES APPRECIATE)
(Right margin: APPRECIATE ANTIQUES)

Sandra Lummis Fine Art
Flat 7, 17 Haslemere Rd. N8 9QP. (Mrs S. Lummis and Dr T. Lummis). Est. 1985. Viewing by appointment. CL: Aug. *STOCK: British art (Modernist school), 20th C from Sickert to contemporary, especially Bloomsbury painters, £500-£50,000.* LOC: From Highgate Hill, along Hornsey Lane, left at 'T' junction, then 1st right. PARK: Easy. TEL: 020 8340 2293; home - same. SER: Commissions; valuations; advice on restoration and framing. VAT: Spec.

Solomon
49 Park Rd., Crouch End. N8 8SY. (Solomon Salim). Est. 1984. Open 9.30-6. SIZE: Medium. *STOCK: Furniture including upholstered and Arts and Crafts, £200-£2,000; decorative items, £100-£500; all 1800-1920.* LOC: 20 minutes off North Circular at Muswell Hill turn-off. PARK: Easy. TEL: 020 8341 1817; e-mail - solomon@solomonantiques.fsnet.co.uk. SER: Valuations; restorations (furniture including upholstery). VAT: Spec.

N10

M.E. Korn
47 Tetherdown, Muswell Hill. N10 1NH. (E. Korn). ABA, PBFA. Est. 1971. Open by appointment. *STOCK: Books - natural history, medical, science, art and literature, 16th-19th C, £10-£1,000.* TEL: 020 8883 5251 (answerphone); fax - same; e-mail - eric@mekornbooks.freeserve.co.uk. SER: Valuations; buys at auction (antiquarian books). FAIRS: PBFA, Russell Hotel monthly; York, Oxford, Cambridge; ABAA in California, Boston, New York and Seattle.

N11

The Collector
4 Queens Parade Close, Friern Barnet. N11 3FY. (Tom Power). Est. 1973. Open 9.30-5.30. SIZE: Large. *STOCK: Decorative ceramics especially Royal Doulton, from 1900, £50-£3,000; Beswick, from 1920, £40-£1,000; Moorcroft, £150-£750.* LOC: Near Arnos Grove. PARK: Easy. TEL: 020 8361 7787; fax - 020 8361 4143. SER: Valuations. FAIRS: Specialist Decorative Art, mainly Royal Doulton. VAT: Stan.

N12

Dean's Antique Emporium
7 Halliwick Court Parade, Woodhouse Rd. N12 0NB. Est. 1976. Open 10-6.30. CL: Wed. SIZE: Small. *STOCK: Victorian, Edwardian, French and Dutch furniture, £500-£1,000.* LOC: Near Muswell Hill. PARK: Nearby. TEL: 020 8368 1858; fax - same; mobile - 07770 445 338. SER: Valuations; restorations.

Finchley Fine Art Galleries
983 High Rd., North Finchley. N12 8QR. (S. Greenman). Est. 1972. Open 1-7, including Sun., Wed. by appointment. SIZE: Large. *STOCK: 18th-20th C watercolours, paintings, etchings, prints, mostly English, £25-£10,000; Georgian, Victorian, Edwardian furniture, to £4,000; china and porcelain - Moorcroft, Doulton, Worcester, Clarice Cliff, £5-£2,000; musical and scientific instruments, bronzes, early photographic apparatus, fire-arms, shotguns.* LOC: Off M25, junction 23, take Barnet road. Gallery on right 3 miles south of Barnet church, opposite Britannia

Road. PARK: Easy. TEL: 020 8446 4848. SER: Valuations; restorations; picture re-lining, cleaning and framing.

N13

Palmers Green Antiques Centre

472 Green Lanes, Palmers Green. N13 5PA. (Michael Webb). Est. 1976. Open 10-5.30, Sun. 11-5. CL: Tues. SIZE: Large. *STOCK: Furniture, general antiques and collectables.* PARK: Nearby. TEL: 020 8350 0878. SER: Valuations. FAIRS: Alexandra Palace; Wembley.

Zeno Booksellers

Est. 1944. *STOCK: Antiquarian books on Greece, Cyprus, Byzantium, Turkey, Middle East and the Balkans.* TEL: 020 8882 1910; fax - same; e-mail - zenobooksellers@ad.com; website - www. thegreekbookshop.com.

N14

C.J. Martin (Coins) Ltd

85 The Vale, Southgate. N14 6AT. LAPADA. Open by appointment. *STOCK: Ancient and medieval coins and ancient artefacts.* TEL: 020 8882 1509/4359.

Southgate Antiques & Collectables

46 Chaseside, Southgate. N14 5PA. Open 10-5. SIZE: Medium - 10 dealers. *STOCK: Gramophones, radios, records, sci-fi, militaria and military medals, blazer badges, general small antique and collector's items including named porcelain and glass, china tableware, silver and gold jewellery, watches, stone necklets; period furniture.* LOC: Near Southgate underground station. TEL: 020 8447 8017. SER: Medals mounted and framed; watch and clock repairs ((John Cant - 07977 202542). VAT: Stan.

N19

Chesney's Antique Fireplace Warehouse

734-736 Holloway Rd. N19 3JF. Est. 1983. Open 9-5.30, Sat. 10-5. SIZE: Large. *STOCK: 18th-19th C marble, stone and timber chimney pieces, £1,000-£150,000; reproduction chimney pieces, £250-£7,500.* LOC: South of Archway roundabout on A1. PARK: Side streets adjacent. TEL: 020 7272 7462; fax - 020 7272 7466. SER: Valuations. VAT: Stan/Spec.

Old School (Gardens & Interiors)

130c Junction Rd., Tufnel Park. N19 5LB. Open 11-7 including Sun. *STOCK: Decorative objects, original pine and reclaimed furniture, period garden furniture and some reproduction, tools and general antiques.* TEL: 020 7272 5603.

N20

Julian Alexander Antiques

40 Station Parade, Totteridge Lane. N20 9QJ. Open 9.30-5. CL: Mon. and Thurs. SIZE: Medium. *STOCK: 18th-20th C furniture, £50-£5,000.* LOC: Close to Totteridge and Whetstone tube station. SER: French polishing; re-upholstery.

The Totteridge Gallery

61 Totteridge Lane. N20 0HD. Est. 1886. Open daily, Sun. by appointment. SIZE: Small. *STOCK: Oil paintings, £1,000-£25,000; watercolours, £300-£10,000; both 18th to early 20th C. Limited edition Russell Flint prints, 20th C, £500-£3,000.* LOC: Opposite Totteridge and Whetstone tube station. PARK: Easy. TEL: 020 8446 7896; website - www.totteridgegallery.com. SER: Valuations; restorations; frame repairs. VAT: Stan/Spec.

N21

Dolly Land

864 Green Lanes, Winchmore Hill. N21 2RS. Est. 1987. Open 9.30-4.30. CL: Mon. and Wed. *STOCK: Dolls, teddies, trains, die-cast limited editions.* PARK: Easy. TEL: 020 8360 1053; fax - 020 8364 1370; website - www.dollyland.com. SER: Restorations; part exchange; dolls' hospital. FAIRS: Doll and Bear.

Winchmore Antiques

14 The Green, Winchmore Hill. N21 1AY. (David Hicks and Stewart Christian). Open 10-6. SIZE: Medium. *STOCK: General antiques, £1-£1,000; architectural brass fittings, fireside accessories, oil lamps and spare parts; all 18th-20th C.* LOC: Junction of 5 roads, at east end of Broad Walk. PARK: Easy. TEL: 020 8882 4800. SER: Valuations; restorations (metal polishing, oil lamps).

NW1

Art Furniture
158 Camden St. NW1 9PA. Open 12-5 including Sun. SIZE: Warehouse. *STOCK: Decorative arts 1851-1951, Arts & Crafts furniture by Heal's, Liberty and others.* LOC: Under railway bridge on Camden St. going south. PARK: Easy. TEL: 020 7267 4324; fax - 020 7267 5199; e-mail - arts-and-crafts@artfurniture.co.uk; website - www.artfurniture.co.uk. SER: Export; hire. VAT: Stan.

Barkes and Barkes
76 Parkway, Camden Town. NW1 7AH. (J .N. and P. R. Barkes). Est. 1976. Open Thurs. 12-7.30, Fri. and Sat. 12-6, and every day during exhibitions. *STOCK: Post-war Russian paintings; British artists - Nick Botting and Mark Pearson.* LOC: Just north of Regents Park. PARK: Next street. TEL: 020 7284 1550; website - www.artrussia.com. VAT: Spec.

Madeline Crispin Antiques
95 Lisson Grove. NW1 6UP. Est. 1971. Open 10-5. *STOCK: General antiques and shipping goods.* TEL: 020 7402 6845. VAT: Stan. *Trade Only.*

Angela Hone Watercolours
LAPADA, CINOA. Open by appointment only. *STOCK: English and French watercolours and pastles, 1850-1930.* TEL: 020 7402 2901.

Laurence Corner
62-64 Hampstead Rd. NW1 2NU. Est. 1955. Open 9.30-6. SIZE: Large. *STOCK: Uniforms, helmets, militaria, theatrical costumes, props, fancy dress, flags.* LOC: From Tottenham Court Rd. - Warren St. end - continue into Hampstead Rd., then Drummond St. is first turning on right by traffic lights. PARK: Easy. TEL: 020 7813 1010; fax - 020 7813 1413. SER: Hire; catalogue on request.

Military History Bookshop
77-81 Bell St. NW1 6TA. (K. W. Barber and M. J. Murphy). Est. 1975. Open 10-5, Sat. 10-2. SIZE: Medium. *STOCK: Military books.* LOC: Off Edgeware Road. PARK: Easy. TEL: 020 7723 2095; fax - 020 7723 4665.

Relic Antiques Trade Warehouse
127 Pancras Rd. NW1 1UN. (Malcolm and Matthew Gliksten). Est. 1968. Open 10-5.30, Sat. and Sun. by appointment. *STOCK: English and French decorative and country; architectural and garden; mirrors and French posters; fairground art, trade signs and marine antiques; shopfittings*

and showcases. PARK: Meters. TEL: 020 7387 6039; fax - 020 7388 2691; mobile - 07831 785059. VAT: Stan.

This and That (Furniture)
50 and 51 Chalk Farm Rd. NW1 8AN. (M.P. Fraser). Est. 1974. Open 10.30-6 including Sun. SIZE: Medium. *STOCK: Country furniture, stripped pine, oak and walnut, 1890-1930.* LOC: Between Roundhouse and Camden Lock. PARK: Easy. TEL: 020 7267 5433. VAT: Stan.

David J. Wilkins
27 Princess Rd., Regents Park. NW1 8JR. Est. 1974. Open by appointment only. SIZE: Large. *STOCK: Oriental rugs.* LOC: Off Regent's Park Rd., near St Mark's church. PARK: Easy. TEL: 020 7722 7608; home - 01799 542246. SER: Valuations; restorations; Oriental rug broker. VAT: Stan.

NW2

G. and F. Gillingham Ltd
62 Menelik Rd. NW2 3RH. Est. 1960. Open by appointment. *STOCK: Furniture, 1750-1950.* TEL: 020 7435 5644; fax - same; mobile - 07958 484140. SER: Valuations; export.

Sabera Trading Co
2 Oxgate Parade, Crest Rd. NW2 7EU. (Sabera Nawrozzadeh). Open 10-6. SIZE: Large. *STOCK: Oriental carpets, 19th-20th C, £100-£12,000; porcelain, early 20th C, £100-£1,000; antiques and fine art, jewellery.* PARK: Easy. TEL: 020 8450 0012; fax - same; home - 020 8450 4058. SER: Valuations.

Soviet Carpet & Art Galleries
303-305 Cricklewood Broadway. NW2 6PG. (R. Rabilizirov). Est. 1983. Open 10.30-5, Sun. 10.30-5.30. CL: Sat. SIZE: Large. *STOCK: Hand-made rugs, £100-£1,500; Russian art, £50-£5,000; all 19th-20th C.* LOC: A5. PARK: Side road. TEL: 020 8452 2445. SER: Valuations; restorations (hand-made rugs). VAT: Stan.

NW3

Patricia Beckman Antiques
(Patricia and Peter Beckman). LAPADA. Est. 1968. Open by appointment. *STOCK: Furniture, 18th-19th C.* TEL: 020 7435 5050/0500. VAT: Spec.

Tony Bingham

11 Pond St. NW3 2PN. LAPADA. Est. 1964. *STOCK: Musical instruments, books, music, oil paintings, engravings of musical interest.* TEL: 020 7794 1596; fax - 020 7433 3662; e-mail - tbingham@easynet.co.uk. VAT: Stan/Spec.

P.G. de Lotz

20 Downside Cres., Hampstead. NW3 2AP. Est. 1967. *STOCK: Antiquarian books on history warfare - naval, military and aviation.* TEL: 020 7794 5709; fax - 020 7284 3058. SER: Catalogue available; search. *Mail Order only.*

Keith Fawkes

1-3 Flask Walk, Hampstead. NW3 1HJ. Est. 1970. Open 10-5.30. *STOCK: Antiquarian and general books.* TEL: 020 7435 0614.

Otto Haas (A. and M. Rosenthal)

49 Belsize Park Gardens. NW3 4JL. Est. 1866. By appointment only. CL: Sat. *STOCK: Manuscripts, printed music, autographs, rare books on music.* TEL: 020 7722 1488; fax - 020 7722 2364.

A collection of three inkwells and three snuff tobacco bottles. (Left to right) (1) America, c.1860, an 'umbrella' ink bottle, 2½in. (2) France, early 19th century, gold ruby red glass, 2¼in. (3) Austria, c.1880, 2¾in. (4) North Germany, c.1820, a snuff preserving bottle, 8¾in. (5) America, c.1840, a snuff preserving bottle, 4in. (6) Scotland (Alloa), c.1820, snuff bottle, 4½in. long.

The text of this article is an extract from Willy Van den Bossche's new book describing the history and evolution of glass bottles from 1500 to 1850. From an article entitled 'Antique Glass Bottles' which appeared in the March 2001 issue of **Antique Collecting** magazine. For more details and to subscribe see page 147.

Hampstead Antique and Craft Market

12 Heath St., Hampstead. NW3 6TE. Est. 1967. Open 10.30-5, Sat. 10-6, Sun. 11.30-5.30. CL: Mon. SIZE: 24 units. *STOCK: General antiques, craft work and gifts.* LOC: 2 mins. walk from Hampstead underground. TEL: 020 7794 3297.

Klaber and Klaber   BADA

PO Box 9445. NW3 1WD. (Mrs B. Klaber and Miss P. Klaber). Est. 1968. Open by appointment. *STOCK: English and Continental porcelain and enamels, 18th-19th C.* TEL: 020 7435 6537; fax - 020 7435 9459; e-mail - info@klaber.com; website - www.klaber.com and e-antiqueporcelain.com. SER: Buys at auction (porcelain, enamels). FAIRS: Grosvenor House. VAT: Spec.

Leask Ward

LAPADA. Open by appointment. *STOCK: Oriental and European antiques and paintings.* TEL: 020 7435 9781; fax - same. SER: Consultancy. VAT: Spec.

Duncan R. Miller Fine Arts   BADA

17 Flask Walk, Hampstead. NW3 1HJ. Open 10-6, Sat. 11-5, Sun. 2-5. SIZE: Small. *STOCK: Modern British and European paintings, drawings and sculpture, especially Scottish Colourist paintings.* LOC: Off Hampstead High St., near underground station. PARK: Nearby. TEL: 020 7435 5462. SER: Valuations; conservation and restoration (oils, works on paper and Oriental rugs); buys at auction. FAIRS: Grosvenor House; BADA. VAT: Spec.

Newhart (Pictures) Ltd

PO Box 1608. NW3 3LB. (Ann and Bernard Hart). Open by appointment only. *STOCK: Oil paintings and watercolours, 1850-1930, from £500.* TEL: 020 7722 2537; fax - 020 7722 4335. SER: Valuations; restorations; framing. VAT: Spec.

Malcolm Rushton - Early Oriental Art

13 Belsize Grove. NW3 4UX. (Dr Malcolm Rushton). Est. 1997. By appointment only, mainly evenings and weekends. SIZE: Small. *STOCK: Fine early Oriental art, neolithic to Tang dynasty, to £15,000.* LOC: Near Belsize Park tube station, off Haverstock Hill. PARK: Easy. TEL: 020 7722 1989. SER: Valuations; restorations (ceramics, sculpture mounting). VAT: Stan.

M. and D. Seligmann   BADA

CINOA Est. 1948. Open by appointment only. *STOCK: Fine vernacular furniture, mainly English, 17th to early 19th C; antiquities and*

objets d'art. TEL: 020 7722 4315; fax - same; mobile - 07946 634429. FAIRS: Olympia (June and Nov.); BADA. VAT: Stan/Spec.

David Wainwright

28 Rosslyn Hill. NW3 1NH. Est. 1989. Open 10-6, Sun. 11-5. SIZE: Large. *STOCK: Furniture from the sub-continent and Far East, 15th-20th C including 18th-19th C cupboards, dining tables and architectural pieces, £5-£2,000; stonework - urns, mortars and water containers, to 19th C; contemporary ironwork.* LOC: Hampstead, on corner of Downshire Hill. PARK: Easy. TEL: 020 7431 5900. FAIRS: Olympia. VAT: Stan.

NW4

Talking Machine

30 Watford Way, Hendon. NW4 3AL. Open 10-5, Sat. 9.30-1.30, prior telephone call advisable. *STOCK: Mechanical music, old gramophones, phonographs, vintage records and 78's, needles and spare parts, early radios and televisions, typewriters, sewing machines, juke boxes, early telephones.* LOC: 1 minute Hendon Central underground station. TEL: 020 8202 3473; fax - same; mobile - 07774 103139; e-mail - talkingmachine@gramophones.ndirect.co.uk; website - www.gramophones.ndirect.co.uk. SER: Buys at auction. VAT: Spec.

NW5

Acquisitions (Fireplaces) Ltd

24-26 Holmes Rd., Kentish Town. NW5. (K. Kennedy). Est. 1970. Open 9-5. SIZE: Large. *STOCK: Fireplaces, Georgian, Victorian, Edwardian reproduction, fire-side accessories, £195-£595.* LOC: 3 mins. walk from Kentish Town tube station. PARK: Easy. TEL: 020 7485 4955. VAT: Stan.

Barrie Marks Ltd

11 Laurier Rd. NW5 1SD. ABA. Open by appointment only. *STOCK: Antiquarian books - illustrated, private press, colourplate, colour printing; modern first editions.* TEL: 020 7482 5684; fax - 020 7284 3149.

Orientalist

74-78 Highgate Rd. NW5 1PB. (E. and H. Sakhai). Est. 1885. SIZE: Large. *STOCK: Rugs, carpets, needlepoints, tapestries and Aubussons, including reproduction.* PARK: Easy and nearby. TEL: 020 7482 0555; fax - 020 7267 9603. SER: Valuations; restorations (cleaning and repairing rugs, carpets and tapestries); buys at auction (Oriental carpets, rugs and textiles). VAT: Stan/Spec.

NW6

H. Baron
76 Fortune Green Rd. NW6 1DS. Open Fri. and Sat. 1-6. *STOCK: Antiquarian music, books on music and iconography, autograph music and letters.* TEL: 020 7794 4041; office and fax - 020 8459 2035.

John Denham Gallery
50 Mill Lane, West Hampstead. NW6 1NJ. Open 10-5. CL: Sat. *STOCK: Paintings, drawings and prints, 17th-20th C, £5-£5,000.* TEL: 020 7794 2635. SER: Restorations; conservation; reframing. VAT: Spec.

Gallery Kaleidoscope
64-66 Willesden Lane. NW6 7SX. (K. Barrie). Est. 1965. Open 10-6. SIZE: Medium. *STOCK: Oils, watercolours, prints, pottery and sculpture, 19th-20th C.* LOC: 10 mins. from Marble Arch. PARK: Easy. TEL: 020 7328 5833; fax - 020 7624 2913. SER: Restorations; framing. VAT: Stan/Spec.

Scope Antiques
64-66 Willesden Lane. NW6 7SX. (K. Barrie). Est. 1966. Open 10-6. SIZE: Large. *STOCK: Furniture, general antiques, decorative items, silver, bric-a-brac.* PARK: Easy. TEL: 020 7328 5833. SER: Restorations (silver). VAT: Stan/Spec.

NW8

Alfies Antique Market
13-25 Church St. NW8. Open Tues.-Sat. 10-6. SIZE: 300 stands with 180+ dealers on 4 floors. TEL: 020 7723 6066; fax - 020 7724 0999; e-mail - post@Alfies.com.

Accurate Trading Co Ltd
Jewellery. TEL: 020 7723 1513.

Beth Adams
Stand G43/44. *Decorative arts, 1860-1950's, £8-£750.* TEL: 020 7723 5613; fax - 020 7262 1576.

Franco Baldini
Decorative antiques. TEL: 020 7723 6105.

David Bennett Antiques
Stand G104/5. *Boxes, scent bottles, small furniture, silver inkwells, fish servers, clocks, brass scales, glasses, decanters, wooden watch stands, 1800-1900, £20-£300.* TEL: 020 7723 0564.

Bibliopola
Stand F17. (Jo Del-Grosso). *Antiquarian illustrated, childrens books; modern first editions, 1600-1940.* TEL: 020 7724 7231.

M. J. Black
Stand F59/61. *Decorative and unusual objects.* TEL: 020 7723 0687.

P. Brooks
Stand G103. *Jewellery, figures, mugs and objets d'art, Georgian to 1960, £25-£1,500.* TEL: 020 7723 0564; mobile - 07785 786395.

Ian Broughton
1950's items. TEL: 020 7723 6105.

Bernie Bruno
Stand G115. *Clocks and watches.* TEL: 020 7723 0564.

Sandra Brunswick
Stand F1-12. *House and garden furnishings, from 18th C.* TEL: 020 7724 9097; fax - 020 8902 5656.

Vincenzo Cafferella
Stand G108/9, G118/9. *Oil paintings.* TEL: 020 7723 0564.

William Campbell
Stand B28-32. *Period picture framer, original frames cut to size, 18th-20th C, £20-£1,000.* TEL: 020 7724 3437.

Wendy Carmichael
Stand S126-129. *Country furniture and decorative antiques, 18th-20th C.*

Castaside
Stand B037-42. (David Smith). *Theatre memorabilia.* TEL: 020 7723 7686.

Linda Chan
Stand G120. *Jewellery.* TEL: 020 7723 0564.

Collectors World
Stand G101, G130/143. (Jo Khan). *Toys including tin plate, Dinky, Meccano, lead soldiers; clocks, watches, cameras, film and TV memorabilia.* TEL: 020 7723 0564; mobile - 07860 791588.

Susie Cooper Ceramics
Stand G70-4, G93-5. (Nick Jones). *Susie Cooper ceramics, from £10.* TEL: 020 7723 0449; fax - 01634 405325.

Cristobal
Stand G125-7. (Steve Miners). *Period costume, jewellery and accessories, 1920's to 1960's, £14-£2,000.* TEL: 020 7724 7789; fax - same; mobile - 07956 388194.

Peran Dachinger
Paintings. TEL: 020 7723 0678.

Gill Danz
Architectural fittings, brass, lighting including chandeliers, decorative items. TEL: 020 7723 0678.

Ann Davey
Textiles. TEL: 020 7706 4123.

Dodo
Stand F73, F83/84. (Liz Farrow). *Posters, tins and advertising signs, 1890-1940.* TEL: 020 7706 1545.

Gerald Dougall
Stand F16. *Decorative antiques, 18th-20th C, £20-£1,000.* TEL: 020 7723 0678.

Antonio Durante
Decorative items. TEL: 020 7723 3439.

East-West Antiques
Stand G113/4, G117. (Colin Thompson). *Books and Oriental objects, from 1800, £5-£500.* TEL: 020 7723 0564.

Eastgates Antiques
Stand 7/9. (Joan Latford) *China teasets, wall plates, cups and saucers; Victorian coloured and Art Deco pressed glass; oil lamps and silver, 19th-20th C, £15-£1,500.* TEL: 020 7258 0312.

Julia Foster
Stand F56. (J. Foster Fogle). *19th C decorative antiques.* TEL: 020 7723 0678; mobile - 07973 146610.

Gardiner and Gardiner
Stand F13/24. (Helen Gardiner). *Ornamental antiques, 18th-19th C.* TEL: 020 7723 5595.

Genie
Stand S57/58. (E. Deimbacher). *Collectables and cutlery, 1900-1970, £2-£100.* TEL: 020 7723 2548.

Brenda Gerwat-Clark
Stand G2/4. *Dolls and teddy bears.* TEL: 020 7724 5650.

Richard Gibbon
Stand G66-68/85/86. *Costume jewellery, 20th C decorative arts, lighting, £10-£2,000.* TEL: 020 7723 0449.

Goldsmith and Perris
Stand G59-62. LAPADA. *Silver and plate.* TEL: 020 7724 7051.

Patricia Gould
Stand F70. *Textiles, 1400-1900, £5-£1,500.* TEL: 020 7723 0429.

Linette Greco
Jewellery. TEL: 020 7262 0766.

Guillou-Emary
Stand G40/1. (Jean Gillou). *General decorative antiques, 18th-20th C, £25-£800.* TEL: 020 7723 5613.

Annie Hartnett and Ann Davey
Stand G35/6. *Textiles, beaded bags, embroidery, period costume, quilts, linen and lace, wedding veils, stoles and collars, 18th C to 1940's, £3-£500.* TEL: 020 7706 4123; fax - 01273 749860.

Henry Hay
Stand S54. *Art Deco, chrome and brass lamps, bakelite telephones, 20th C, £25-£500.* TEL: 020 7723 2548.

George Hepburn
Stand B43/4. *Paintings, 18th-20th C, £50-£2,000.* TEL: 020 7723 3437; mobile - 07721 598487.

Noel Hickey
Stand F54/5. *Decorative antiques.* TEL: 020 7723 0678.

Edward Holden - Old Paintings & Drawings
Stand F122-5, F130. (Holden & Li). *Oils and watercolours, drawings, 17th to early 20th C, £10-£2,000.* TEL: 020 7723 1370; fax - 020 7609 0864.

Frances Houlding
Stand G121-4. *Silver and jewellery.* TEL: 020 7723 1513.

Huxtable's Old Advertising
Stand S3/5. (David Huxtable). *Advertising, collectables, tins, signs, bottles, commemoratives, old packaging, from late Victorian, 50p to £1,000.* TEL: 020 7724 2200; fax - 01727 833445.

Peter Jacques
Stand S59/60. *Brass and architectural fittings.* TEL: 020 7723 6105.

Jay and Gee
Stand B35/6. (Ms and Jacob Fefer). *Bronzes, glass and collectables, Victorian to Art Deco, £10-£2,000.* TEL: 020 7724 3437.

Kitchen Bygones
Stand B51-53. (N. Oakley). *Kitchen antiques - working and decorative, 1800-1940's, £1.50-£500.* TEL: 020 7258 3045; fax - 01923 260453.

Barry Landsman
Stand F103/4. *Watercolours, 18th-19th C, £50-£1,000.* TEL: 020 7723 1370.

Michael Lassere
Stand F40-45. *19th C general antiques, £20-£1,000.* TEL: 020 7723 2688.

Legacy
Stand G50/1. (J. Rosser and W. Garraway). *Postcards, old tins, ephemera, commemoratives, decorative and miniature objects.* TEL: 020 7723 0449.

Sarah Lewis
Stand S40. *Textiles - cushions, curtains, tapestries and embroideries; trims, tassels, prints, linen and lace, silk, shawls and clothes, 19th-20th C, £10-£10,000.* TEL: 020 7723 6105.

Marie-Louise Lowcock
Stand S52. *Millinery, using antique fabrics.* TEL: 020 7723 6105.

Connie Margrie
Stand F50/1. *Soft furnishings and decorative objects, 1830-1930.* TEL: 020 7723 0678.

Marie Antiques
Stand G107, G136/9. (Marie Warner). *Victorian jewellery, Glens silver plate, small furniture, 18th-19th C.* TEL: 020 7723 0564.

Nigel Martin
Stand S44/45. *Textiles.* TEL: 020 7723 1370.

Francesca Martire
Stand F131-7. *Arts and Crafts, 20th C paintings, costume jewellery, decorative arts.* TEL: 020 7723 1370.

Maryam
Stand G25. (R. Fatemi). *Jewellery, 1920- 1960's, £35-1,000.* TEL: 020 7723 1513.

The Maze
Stand G133/4. (S. Thammachote). *Costume jewellery and accessories, 1920's to 1960's, £14-£2,000.* TEL: 020 7724 7789; fax - same; mobile - 07956 388194.

Robert McCoy
Stand F20. *Paintings, 19th-20th C, £50-£500.* TEL: 020 7723 0678.

Nigel McDonald
Stand F23. *Decorative antiques.* TEL: 020 7723 0678.

Margaret Miall
Stand G19. *English and Continental porcelain, glass and furniture, to mid 20th C.*

Modus Vivendi
Stand G79/80. (Helga Wellingham). *Antique and decorative prints.* TEL: 020 7723 0449.

Moji Mohamadi
Jewellery. TEL: 020 7723 0564.

Murray
S48/49. (John Beck). *Pottery - Torquay, North Devon, Honiton and Elton.* TEL: 020 7723 6105.

Bruna Naufal
Stand B1/2. *Modernist furniture, from 1920.* TEL: 020 7724 3437.

Noe & Chiesa
Stand G87-8. *Art Deco and bakelite, 20th C, from £4.* TEL: 020 7723 0449.

Teresa Norton-Gore
Stand S10. *Buttons.* TEL: 020 7723 6105.

K. Norton-Grant
Stand F113/126. *Brass, pewter, pottery and china, 16th-20th C, £1-£250.* TEL: 020 7723 1370.

NS Watches
Stand G1. (M. Heidarieh). *Watches, clocks, prints, pens and silver, from 1850, from £10.* TEL: 020 7724 5650.

Pandora Antiques
Stand G16-18/20/22. *Decorative lamps, ceiling light bowls, furniture, late 18th C.* TEL: 020 7706 3254.

G. Payder
Stand G24. TEL: 020 7723 1513
.

M. Payne
Stand S53. *Jewellery, collectables.* TEL: 020 7723 6105.

Stevie Pearce
Stand G144, T105. *Costume jewellery, fashion accessories, 1900-1970, from £10.* TEL: 020 7723 1513.

Persiflage
(G. Trefor Jones). *Costume.* TEL: 020 7724 7366.

Sam Peters
Stand S14. *Cushion repair/making.* TEL: 020 7723 4990.

Pinnington & Verrinder
Stand G116/129. *Antique luggage, ceramics.* TEL: 020 7723 0564.

Katharine Pole
Stand S105. *Textiles and decorative antiques, 18th-19th C, £5-£500.* TEL: 020 7723 5731.

Angela Regana
Stand S110. TEL: 020 7723 5731. SER: Restorations.

Geoffrey Robinson
Stand G77/78/91/92. *Glass, lighting, chrome, Art Deco, 1925-1960's.* TEL: 020 7723 0449; fax - 020 7 706 3254.

Albert Rockman
Stand G28/9. *China.* TEL: 020 7723 1513.

Rojeh Antiques
Stand B22-27, B33/4. (I. Fayez). *Art Deco furniture, £20-£7,000.* TEL: 020 7724 6960; mobile - 07860 156390; fax - 020 8964 5959.

Anna Sambataro
1950's. TEL: 020 7723 0449.

Hoshang Samii
Stand S102/103. *French decorative antiques, 18th-19th C, £10-£600.* TEL: 020 7723 5731.

Patrick Scola
Stand G63. *Collectables and memorabilia.* TEL: 020 7723 0449

Scott & Lane
Stand G142. *Antiques and collectables.* TEL: 020 7723 0564.

Gloria Sinclair
Stand F118/21. *Porcelain and jewellery, 18th-19th C.* TEL: 020 7724 7118.

Derek Smith
Stand G52/3. *Lamps, china, bakelite and glass, 1920's to 1930's, £60-£350.* TEL: 020 7723 0449.

Kelvin Spooner
Stand S107. *Prints.* TEL: 020 7723 5731.

Elise Taylor
Stand G135. *Jewellery and handbags, 1860-1930.* TEL: 020 7723 0564.

LONDON NW8

Eugene Tiernan
Stand F14. *Decorative antiques, 19th-20th C, £50-£1,500.* TEL: 020 7723 8964; fax - same.

David Tileke - Antique Prints & Engravings
Stand G6-8. *Prints and engravings, 17th-20th C, £5-£500.* TEL: 020 7724 3722.

The Toy Boy
Stand G23. (Paul Mulvey). *TV and film related dolls, toys and autographs, 1960's to 1980's, £1-£2,000.*TEL: 020 7723 1513; mobile - 07973 135906.

Travers Antiques
Stand G33/4. (Paula and S. Kluth). *Furniture and decorative objects, mainly 19th C, £250-£2,000.* TEL: 020 7258 0662.

June Victor
Stand S42-47. *Decorative textiles and antique linen, 17th-20th C, £5-£500.* TEL: 020 7723 6105.

D. F. Wallis
Stand F15. *Medical and scientific items, corkscrews, 19th C, £1-£500.* TEL: 020 7402 1038; fax - same.

Jessica Ward
Stand S100/1. *Decorative antiques, 18th-20th C, £5-£1,000.* TEL: 020 7723 5731.

G. Wetzel
TEL: 020 7723 8731. SER: Restorations.

George Balot Antiques
9 Church St. NW8 8EE. Open Mon.-Fri. 10.30-5.30. SIZE: Large. *STOCK: Furniture, 18th-19th C; opaline glass, mirrors, 19th C; all £500-£4,000.* LOC: Off Lisson Grove, two doors down from Alfies. PARK: Easy. TEL: 020 7258 1803; fax - 020 7258 1809; e-mail - gbalot@dircon.co.uk; website - www.gbalot.dircon.co.uk. VAT: Spec.

Beverley
30 Church St., Marylebone. NW8 8EP. Open 11-7 or by appointment. *STOCK: Art Nouveau, Art Deco, decorative objects.* TEL: 020 7262 1576.

D. and A. Binder
34 Church St. NW8 8EP. Open 10-6. *STOCK: Traditional shop-fittings, counters, cabinets, vitrines and display stands.* LOC: Near Lisson Grove. TEL: 020 7723 0542; fax - 020 7724 0837.

Bizarre
24 Church St., Marylebone. NW8 8EP. (A. Taramasco and V. Conti). Open 10-5. *STOCK: Art Deco and Art Nouveau.* TEL: 020 7724 1305; fax - 020 7724 1316.

Camden Art Gallery
22 Church St. NW8 8EP. (Allen and Anne Silver). Est. 1968. Open 10-5. SIZE: Medium. *STOCK: Oil paintings and furniture, 18th-19th C, £300-£10,000.* LOC: Off Edgware Rd. PARK: Easy. TEL: 020 7262 3613; fax - 020 7723 2333. SER: Valuations; restorations (furniture, picture framing and cleaning). FAIRS: Barbican. VAT: Spec.

Church Street Antiques
8 Church St. NW8 8ED. (Stuart Shuster). Est. 1975. Open 10-5.30. CL: Mon. SIZE: Medium. *STOCK: English brown furniture, 18th to early 20th C, £500-£2,000.* LOC: Between Edgware Rd. and Lisson Grove. PARK: Meters. TEL: 020 7723 7415; fax - 020 7723 7415; home - 020 8952 2249. SER: Valuations; restorations (polishing). FAIRS: NEC. VAT: Stan.

Deuxieme
44 Church St. NW8 8BT. (Victoria Harvey and Jerome Zanotti). *STOCK: Decorative and unusual items, French and English furniture.* TEL: 020 7724 0738; fax - same.

Nicholas Drummond/Wrawby Moor Art Gallery Ltd
6 St. John's Wood Rd. NW8 8RE. (J.N. Drummond). Est. 1972. Open by appointment only. *STOCK: English and European oils, £250-£30,000; works on paper.* LOC: Pass Lords entrance and next lights, house last bow front on left, facing down Hamilton Terrace. TEL: 020 7286 6452; home - same; fax - 020 7266 9070. SER: Valuations; restorations (oils); buys at auction. VAT: Spec.

Robert Franses and Sons
Est. 1969. Open by appointment only. *STOCK: European and Oriental carpets, tapestries, needlework, Turkish village and early Chinese rugs.* TEL: 020 7328 0949. SER: Restorations. VAT: Stan/Spec.

Gallery of Antique Costume and Textiles
2 Church St., Marylebone. NW8 8ED. Open 10-5.30. *STOCK: Curtains, needleworks, paisley shawls, original clothing up to 1940's and English quilts, 19th-20th C; tassles, decorative borders, silk panels, velvets and brocades, £5-£20,000.* LOC: 500yds. from Marylebone tube and 1/2 mile from Marble Arch. PARK: Easy. TEL: 020 7723 9981 (ansaphone); e-mail - info@gact.co.uk; website - www.gact.co.uk.

Patricia Harvey Antiques and Decoration
42 Church St., Marylebone. NW8 8EP. LAPADA. Est. 1961. Open 10-5.30. SIZE: Medium. *STOCK: Decorative furniture, objets,*

PERIOD AND REPRODUCTION OFFICE BOARDROOM AND STUDY FURNITURE

20, Church Street, London, NW8 8EP
Tel 020 7723 7976
Fax 020 7402 6416

Showrooms open Monday-Saturday
Brochure available

accessories and paintings, £100-£20,000. LOC: Between Lisson Grove and Edgware Rd., shop is near Alfies Antique Market. TEL: 020 7262 8989; fax - same; home - 020 7624 1787. SER: Valuations; buys at auction; interior decoration. FAIRS: Decorative Antiques and Textiles. VAT: Stan.

Just Desks

20 Church St. NW8 8EP. (G. Gordon and N. Finch). LAPADA. Est. 1967. Open 9.30-6, Sat. 9.30-5 or by appointment. *STOCK: Victorian, Edwardian and reproduction desks, writing tables, bureaux, chairs, filing cabinets and roll tops.* PARK: Meters/Pay & Display. TEL: 020 7723 7976; fax - 020 7402 6416. VAT: Stan.

Andrew Nebbett Antiques

35-37 Church St., Marylebone. NW8 8ES. 1986. Open 9.30-5.30. CL: Mon. SIZE: Large. *STOCK: Shop fittings, leather chesterfields, decorative, military and ships furniture.* LOC: 50 yards from Alfie's Antique Market. PARK: Easy. TEL: 020 7723 2303; fax - 01404 850221. FAIRS: Decorative Antiques & Textile, Battersea. VAT: Stan/Spec.

No. 28 Antiques

28 Church St. NW8 8EP. (David Tulissio, Dominic de Beaumont and Alan Isenberg). Est. 1998. Open 10-6. SIZE: Medium. *STOCK: Chandeliers, wall lights and lamps, 18th-20th C, £200-£3,000; bronzes and sculpture, 18th-19th C, £200-£4,000; general decorative antiques, 18th-20th C, £100-£5,000; furniture, 19th-20th C, £300-£5,000.* LOC: Opposite Alfie's Antique Market, between Lisson Grove and Edgware Rd. (nearest tube - Edgware Road). TEL: 020 7724 4631; mobiles - 07973 186305/07770 920405/07802 425835. VAT: Stan/Spec.

Silver Belle

48 Church St. NW8 8EP. Est. 1986. Open 9.30-5.30, Sun. and Mon. by appointment. SIZE: Medium. *STOCK: Silver and Sheffield plate, china including tea sets.* PARK: Easy. TEL: 020 7723 2908; fax - same. SER: Valuations; restorations (re-plating).

The Studio

(John Beer). Open by appointment only. *STOCK: British Arts and Crafts, Gothic and Art Deco, especially furniture, 1830-1960's.* TEL: 01242 576080; mobile - 07976 704306. SER: Valuations; buys at auction.

Tara Antiques

6 Church St. NW8 8ED. (G. Robinson). Est. 1971. Open 10-6. CL: Mon. SIZE: Medium. *STOCK: Unusual marble and bronze statuary; Vienna bronzes, silver, furniture, paintings, ivory and tortoiseshell.* PARK: Easy. TEL: 020 7724 2405. SER: Buys at auction. VAT: Stan.

Townsends

81 Abbey Rd., St. John's Wood and 106 Boundary Rd. NW8 0AE. (M.Townsend). Est. 1972. Open 10-6. SIZE: Large + warehouse 96A Clifton Hill. *STOCK: Fireplaces, £250-£6,000; stained glass, £80-£1,000; architectural and garden antiques, £50-£2,000; all mainly 18th-19th C.* LOC: Corner of Abbey Rd. and Boundary Rd. PARK: Easy. TEL: 020 7624 4756; warehouse - 020 7372 4327; fax - 020 7372 3005. SER: Valuations; site surveys; free delivery. VAT: Stan.

Wellington Gallery

1 St John's Wood High St. NW8 7NG. (Mrs K. Barclay). LAPADA. Open 10.30-6. *STOCK: Furniture, 18th-19th C; paintings, Georgian glass, fine porcelain, silver and Sheffield plate, general antiques.* TEL: 020 7586 2620; fax - 020 7483 0716. SER: Valuations; restorations; curtain making, upholstery.

Young & Son

12 Church St. NW8 8EP. (L. and S. Young). Est. 1990. Open 10-6. CL: Mon. SIZE: Medium. *STOCK: Furniture, paintings, £1,000-£5,000; lighting and mirrors, £200-£500; decorative items, £100-£5,000; all 18th-20th C.* LOC: Off Lisson Grove and Edgeware Rd. PARK: Easy. TEL: 020 7723 5910; fax - same; home - 020 8458 3852. SER: Valuations; restorations (gilding, framing, furniture including polishing, paintings relined and restored); buys at auction (fine paintings and furniture). VAT: Stan/Spec.

NW9

B.C. Metalcrafts Ltd
69 Tewkesbury Gardens. NW9 0QU. LAPADA. Est. 1946. Open by appointment only. *STOCK: Lighting, ormolu and marble lamps; Oriental and European vases; clocks, pre-1900, £5-£500.* Not Stocked: Silver. TEL: 020 8204 2446; fax - 020 8206 2871. SER: Restorations and conversions; buys at auction. VAT: Stan/Spec. *Trade Only.*

NW10

David Malik and Son Ltd
5 Metro Centre, Britannia Way, Park Royal. NW10 7PA. Open 9-5. CL: Sat. *STOCK: Chandeliers, wall lights.* PARK: Easy. TEL: 020 8965 4232; fax - 020 8965 2401. VAT: Stan.

NW11

Christopher Eimer
P.O. Box 352. NW11 7RF. *STOCK: Commemorative and historical medals.* TEL: 020 8458 9933; fax - 020 8455 3535.

WC1

Abbott and Holder
30 Museum St. WC1A 1LH. Est. 1936. Open 9.30-6, Thurs. till 7. *STOCK: Pictures, especially watercolours.* TEL: 020 7637 3981. VAT: Spec

Atlantis Bookshop
49a Museum St. WC1A 1LY. Open 11-6. *STOCK: Antiquarian books on the occult and paranormal; occasional related artefacts and paintings.* TEL: 020 7405 2120

Austin/Desmond Fine Art
Pied Bull Yard, 68/69 Great Russell St. WC1B 3BN. (J. Austin). SLAD. Open 10.30-5.30. *STOCK: Modern and contemporary British paintings and prints.* TEL: 020 7242 4443; fax - 020 7404 4480; website - www.austindesmond.com.

Book Art & Architecture & Volume Gallery
12 Woburn Walk, Bloomsbury. WC1. (Prof. Dennis Sharp and Y. Shariff). Est. 1964. Open 11-6. SIZE: Small. *STOCK: Rare, out-of-print and second-hand architectural books and prints, 20th C, £3.50-£350; art, design, planning of*

WELLINGTON GALLERY
No.1, St. John's Wood High Street
London NW8 7NG
Tel: 020 7586 2620
Fax: 020 7483 0716

Antiques, gifts, picture-framing, curtain-making and upholstery

Complete restoration service is available for glass, porcelain, silver, Sheffield plate, oil paintings and furniture.

modern movement; books published by Book Art Ltd. LOC: Pedestrian street off Tavistock Sq. PARK: Nearby. TEL: 020 7387 5006; fax - 020 7787 8286. SER: Valuations; restorations; buys at auction (books and prints). FAIRS: Various book; Historic Buildings Show. VAT: Stan.

Cinema Bookshop
13-14 Great Russell St. WC1B 3NH. (F. Zentner). Est. 1969. Open 10.30-5.30. SIZE: Small. *STOCK: Books, magazines, posters and stills.* LOC: First right off Tottenham Court Rd. PARK: Easy. TEL: 020 7637 0206; fax - 020 7436 9979. SER: Mail order. VAT: Stan.

George and Peter Cohn
Unit 21, 21 Wren St. WC1X 0HF. Est. 1947. Open 9-5, Sat. and Fri. pm. by appointment. *STOCK: Decorative lights.* PARK: Forecourt. TEL: 020 7278 3749. SER: Restorations (chandeliers and wall-lights). *Trade Only.*

Sebastian D'Orsai Ltd
39 Theobalds Rd. WC1X 8NW. (A. Brooks). Open 9-5. CL: Sat. *STOCK: Framed watercolours.* TEL: 020 7405 6663. SER: Restorations (paintings and prints); framing; gilding. VAT: Stan.

135

Fine Books Oriental
38 Museum St. WC1A 1LP. (Jeffrey Somers). PBFA. Est. 1970. Open 9.30-6, Tues. and Thurs. 9.30-5.30. SIZE: Medium. *STOCK: Books.* LOC: Near British Museum. PARK: Meters. TEL: 020 7242 5288; fax - 020 7242 5344.

Michael Finney Antique Prints and Books
31 Museum St. WC1A 1LG. Open 10-6. *STOCK: Prints, 17th-19th C; decorative plate books and watercolours especially David Roberts, Piranesi and Spain.* PARK: Meters. TEL: 020 7631 3533; fax - 020 7637 1813; e-mail - prints@ michaelfinney.co.uk; website - www.michael finney.co.uk.

Robert Frew Ltd
106 Gt. Russell St. WC1B 3NB. ABA, PBFA. Open 10-6, Sat. 10-2. *STOCK: Books, 15th-20th C, £5-£25,000; maps and prints, 15th-19th C, £5-£5,000.* LOC: Turn right off Tottenham Court Rd. to British Museum, shop on left past YMCA. PARK: Easy. TEL: 020 7580 2311. FAIRS: ABA Olympia, Chelsea; PBFA, Hotel Russell; various USA. VAT: Stan.

Jessop Classic Photographica
67 Great Russell St. WC1B 3BN. Open 9-5.30. *STOCK: Classic photographic equipment, cameras and optical toys.* TEL: 020 7831 3640; fax - 020 7831 3956.

Marchmont Bookshop
39 Burton St. WC1H 9AL. (D. Holder). Open 11-6.30. CL: Sat. *STOCK: Literature, including modern first editions.* TEL: 020 7387 7989.

The Museum Bookshop
36 Gt. Russell St. WC1B 3PP. (Ashley Jones). Est. 1982. Open 10-5.30. *STOCK: Books on antiquities - Egyptian, Middle Eastern, classical; glass, ceramics, conservation.* LOC: 3 minutes from Tottenham Court Rd. underground station. PARK: Easy. TEL: 020 7580 4086; fax - 020 7436 4361.

Nortonbury Antiques
BCM Box 5345. WC1N 3XX. LAPADA. Open by appointment. *STOCK: Silver, 17th-19th C.* TEL: 01984 631668; fax - same; mobile - 07774 174092; e-mail - nortonbury.antiques@virgin.net.

Rennies
13 Rugby St. WC1. (Paul and Karen Rennie). Open Tues.-Sat. 12-6.30. *STOCK: Decorative arts, 1880-1960; vintage posters, mainly British.* TEL: 020 7405 0220; e-mail - info@rennart. co.uk; website - www.rennart.co.uk.

Jeremy Seale Antiques/Interiors
44 Bedford Court Mansions, Bedford Ave. WC1B 3AA. Est. 1988. By appointment only. SIZE: Small. *STOCK: Furniture, 18th-19th C, £300-£6,000; decorative items, 19th C; pictures and prints, 18th-19th C; both £50-£500.* TEL: 020 7580 5900; mobile - 07956 457795. SER: Finder; valuations; interior design consultant; homefinder. VAT: Stan/Spec.

Simmons Gallery
53 Lambs Conduit St. WC1N 3NB. (Howard and Frances Simmons). BNTA. Est. 1982. Open Mon.-Fri. 10.30-5.30. SIZE: Small. *STOCK: Coins and medals, from 2000BC to contemporary; scales and weights, ancient to 1900.* LOC: Off Theobalds Rd, Holborn. Close to Gt Ormond St. Hospital. PARK: Meters. TEL: 020 7831 2080; fax - 020 7831 2090. SER: Valuations; buys at auction (coins and medals). FAIRS: London Coin (Feb., June, Sept., Nov); ANA Midsummer Convention (Aug); New York (Dec). VAT: Stan/Spec/Global.

Skoob Books Ltd
11a-15 Sicilian Ave., Southampton Row, Holborn. WC1A 2QH. Est. 1978. Open 10.30-6.30, Sun. 12-5. SIZE: Large. *STOCK: Secondhand books specialising in philosophy, cultural studies, literature, psychology, science. Art house videos.* LOC: In pedestrian arcade, near Holborn Underground. PARK: Easy. TEL: 020 7404 3063; fax - 020 7404 4398; website - www.skoob.com. SER: Publishers of Skoob Seriph, Esoterica and Pacifica series.

Spink and Son Ltd   BADA
69 Southampton Row. WC1B 4ET. Est. 1666. Open 9.30-5.30. CL: Sat. *STOCK: Coins, medals, stamps and bank notes.* TEL: 020 7563 4000. SER: Valuations; buys at auction; commission sales; coin auctions. VAT: Stan/Spec.

WC2

Anchor Antiques Ltd
Suite 31, 26 Charing Cross Rd. WC2H 0DG. (K.B. Embden and H. Samne). Est. 1964. Open by appointment. *STOCK: Continental and Oriental ceramics, European works of art and objets de vertu.* TEL: 020 7836 5686. VAT: Spec. *Trade Only.*

Apple Market Stalls
Covent Garden Market. WC2E 8RF. Open every Monday. SIZE: 48 stalls. *STOCK: General antiques and quality collectables.* TEL: 020 7836 9136.

A.H. Baldwin and Sons Ltd   BADA
11 Adelphi Terrace. WC2N 6BJ. IAPN, BNTA. Est. 1872. Open 9-5. CL: Sat. SIZE: Medium. *STOCK: Coins, 600 BC to present; commemorative medals, 16th C to present, numismatic literature.* LOC: Off Robert St., near Charing Cross. TEL: 020 7930 6879; fax - 020 7930 9450; e-mail - coins@baldwin.sh. SER: Valuations; auctioneers and auction agents for selling and purchasing. VAT: Stan/Spec.

Bell, Book and Radmall
4 Cecil Court. WC2N 4HE. Est. 1974. Open 10-5.30, Sat. 11-4. *STOCK: 20th C first editions English and American literature including detective fiction.* TEL: 020 7240 2161.

Blackwell's
100 Charing Cross Rd. WC2H 0JG. SIZE: Small. *STOCK: Antiquarian and rare modern books.* TEL: 020 7292 5100.

M. Bord (Gold Coin Exchange)
16 Charing Cross Rd. WC2H 0HR. Est. 1969. Open 9.30-6. SIZE: Small. *STOCK: Gold, silver and copper coins, Roman to Elizabeth II, all prices.* LOC: Near Leicester Sq. underground station. TEL: 020 7836 0631/7240 0479. SER: Valuations; buys at auction. FAIRS: All major coin. VAT: Stan/Spec.

Philip Cohen Numismatics
20 Cecil Court. WC2N 4HE. BNTA. Est. 1977. SIZE: Small. *STOCK: English coins, 16th-20th C, £1-£1,000.* LOC: Off Charing Cross Road. TEL: 020 7379 0615; fax - 020 7240 4300. SER: Valuations.

Covent Garden Flea Market
Jubilee Market, Covent Garden. WC2E 8RB. (Sherman and Waterman Associates Ltd). Est. 1975. Open Mon. and Bank Holidays 5-5. SIZE: 200 stalls. *STOCK: General antiques.* LOC: South side of piazza, just off The Strand, via Southampton St. PARK: Easy and N.C.P. Drury Lane. TEL: 020 7836 2139/7240 7405.

David Drummond at Pleasures of Past Times
11 Cecil Court, Charing Cross Rd. WC2N 4EZ. Est. 1962. Open 11-2.30 and 3.30-5.45 and usually 1st Sat. monthly, other times by appointment. SIZE: Medium. *STOCK: Scarce and out-of-print books of the performing arts; early juvenile and illustrated books; vintage postcards, valentines, entertainment ephemera.* Not Stocked: Coins, stamps, medals, jewellery, maps, cigarette cards. LOC: In pedestrian court between Charing Cross Rd. and St. Martin's Lane. TEL: 020 7836 1142; fax - same; e-mail - drummond@poptfsnet.co.uk. VAT: Stan.

W. and G. Foyle Ltd
113-119 Charing Cross Rd. WC2H 0DT. Est. 1904. *STOCK: Antiquarian books.* TEL: 020 7437 5660.

Stanley Gibbons
399 Strand. WC2R 0LX. Est. 1856. Open 8.30-6, Sat. 9.30-5.30. SIZE: Large. *STOCK: Popular and specialised stamps, postal history, catalogues, albums, accessories; autographs and memorabilia.* LOC: Opposite Savoy Hotel. TEL: 020 7836 8444; fax - 020 7836 7342. SER: Valuations. VAT: Stan/Spec.

Gillian Gould at Ocean Leisure
Embankment Place, 11-14 Northumberland Avenue. WC2N 5AQ. Est. 1988. Open 9.30-6, Thurs. 9.30-7, Sat. 9.30-5.30 or by appointment. SIZE: Small. *STOCK: Marine antiques and collectables, scientific instruments, £30-£1,000.* PARK: Meters. TEL: 020 7930 5050; fax - 020 7930 3032; home - 020 7419 0500; fax - 020 7419 0400; mobile - 07831 150060; e-mail - gillgould @dealwith.com. SER: Valuations; restorations; hire; sources gifts for personal and corporate presentation; buys at auction. VAT: Stan.

Grosvenor Prints
28 Shelton St., Covent Garden. WC2H 9JE. Est. 1975. Open 10-6, Sat. 11-4. SIZE: Large. *STOCK: 18th-19th C topographical and decorative prints, specialising in portraits, dogs and British field sports.* LOC: One street north of Covent Garden tube. PARK: Easy. TEL: 020 7836 1979; fax - 020 7379 6695; website - www. grosvenorprints.com; e-mail - grosvenorprints@ btinternet.com. SER: Valuations; restorations; buys at auction. VAT: Stan/Spec.

P. J. Hilton (Books)
12 Cecil Court. WC2N 4HE. (Paul Hilton). Est. 1980. Open 11-6, Sat. 11-5. SIZE: Medium. *STOCK: Antiquarian books, 16th-20th C, £75-£500; secondhand books; leather cloth bindings by the yard.* LOC: Off Charing Cross Rd. TEL: 020 7379 9825. SER: Valuations.

Lee Jackson
2 Southampton St., Covent Garden. WC2E 7HA. PBFA. Est. 1996. Open 10-5.30. SIZE: Large. *STOCK: Maps and views of the world, 16th-19th C, £10-£3,000.* LOC: Off the Strand, opposite the Savoy Hotel. PARK: Meters. TEL: 020 7240 1970; website - www.leejackson.btinternet.co.uk. VAT: Stan.

S. and H. Jewell Ltd
26 Parker St. WC2B 5PH. Est. 1830. Open 9-5.30, Sat. by appointment. SIZE: Large. *STOCK: Furniture*. TEL: 020 7405 8520. SER: Valuations; restorations. VAT: Stan/Spec.

Thomas Kettle Ltd
53a Neal St. WC2H 9PJ. Est. 1974. Open 11-6 and most Sundays 1.30-5. SIZE: Medium. *STOCK: Watches, 1930-1965, £500-£5,000; bespoke and platinum jewellers, £100-£10,000.* LOC: Near Covent Garden tube. PARK: Leicester Sq. TEL: 020 7379 3579. SER: Valuations; restorations (wrist watches). VAT: Stan.

The London Silver Vaults
Chancery House, 53-64 Chancery Lane. WC2A 1QS. Est. 1892. Open 9-5.30, Sat. 9-1. SIZE: 34 shops. *STOCK: Antique and modern silver, plate, jewellery, objets d'art, clocks, watches, collectors' items*. TEL: 020 7242 3844. The following are some of the dealers at these vaults.

A. M. W. Silverware
Vault 52. TEL: 020 7242 3620; fax - 020 7831 3923.

Argenteus Ltd
Vault 2. LAPADA. TEL: 020 7831 3637; fax - 020 7430 0126. VAT: Stan/Spec.

Benjamin Jewellery Ltd
Vault 46. LAPADA. TEL: 020 7831 1380; fax - 020 7831 4629.

Lawrence Block
Vault 28 and 65. Est. 1959. *Silver especially flatware; jewellery*. TEL: 020 7242 0749. SER: Valuations; restorations; buys at auction.

A. Bloom
Vault 27. TEL: 020 7242 6189.

Luigi Brian Antiques
Vault 17. TEL: 020 7405 2484; fax - same.

B.L. Collins
Vault 20. TEL: 020 7404 0628; fax - 020 7404 1451.

P. Daniels
Vault 51. TEL: 020 7430 1327.

B. Douglas
Vault 12/14. LAPADA. TEL: 020 7242 7073.

M.J. Dubiner
Vault 38.

R. Feldman Ltd
Vault 4/6. LAPADA. TEL: 020 7405 6111; fax - 020 7430 0126.

I. Franks
Vault 9/11. LAPADA. Est. 1926. TEL: 020 7242 4035.

Hamilton
Vault 25. TEL: 020 7831 7030; fax - 020 7831 5483.

Gary Hyams
Vault 48. Open 10-5, Sat. 10-1. *Silver and Sheffield Plate*. TEL: 020 7831 4330.

S. Kalms
Vault 31/32. LAPADA. TEL: 020 7430 1254; fax - 020 7405 6206.

B. Lampert
Vault 19. TEL: 020 7242 4121.

Langfords
Vault 8/10. LAPADA. Est. 1940. *Silver and plate especially cutlery*. TEL: 020 7242 5506; fax - 020 7405 0431. SER: Valuations. VAT: Stan/Spec.

Nat Leslie Ltd
Vault 21/22/23. Est. 1940. *Silver and plate, especially cutlery*. TEL: 020 7242 4787; fax - 020 7242 4504. VAT: Stan/Spec.

Linden and Co. (Antiques) Ltd
Vault 7. (H, F, H.M. and S. C. Linden). TEL: 020 7242 4863; fax - 020 7405 9946. VAT: Stan/Spec.

C. and T. Mammon
Vault 31 & 64. TEL: 020 7405 2397.

J. Mammon Antiques
Vault 30. TEL: 020 7242 4704. *Trade Only*.

I. Nagioff (Jewellery)
Vault 63 and 69. (I. and R. Nagioff). Est. 1955. *Jewellery, 18th-20th C, £5-£2,000+; objets d'art, 19th C, to £200*. TEL: 020 7405 3766. SER: Valuations; restorations (jewellery). VAT: Stan.

Percy's
Vault 16. LAPADA. *Candelabra, candlesticks, flatware and collectables*. TEL: 020 7242 3618.

Rare Art
Vault 15. TEL: 020 7405 9968.

Saunders
Vault 60.

David S. Shure and Co
Vault 1. (S. Bulka). Est. 1900. Author. *Silver and plate*. TEL: 020 7405 0011; fax - same. SER: Valuations. VAT: Stan.

Silstar
Vault 29. (B. Stern). Est. 1955. TEL: 020 7242 6740. VAT: Stan/Spec.

B. Silverman   BADA
Vault 26/33. (S. and R. Silverman). Est. 1927. TEL: 020 7242 3269. SER: Valuations; buys at auction. VAT: Stan/Spec.

Jack Simons (Antiques) Ltd
Vault 35 and 37. LAPADA. Est. 1955. TEL: 020 7242 3221. VAT: Stan/Spec.

S. and J. Stodel
Vault 24. TEL: 020 7405 7009; fax - 020 7242 6366.

A. Urbach
Vault 50.

William Walter Antiques Ltd   BADA
Vault 3/5. (R .W. Walter). LAPADA. Est. 1927. TEL: 020 7242 3248; fax - 020 7404 1280. SER: Valuations; restorations (silver, plate).

A. and G. Weiss
Vault 42/44. TEL: 020 7242 8100. VAT: Stan.

Peter K. Weiss
Vault 18. Est. 1955. *Watches, clocks.* TEL: 020 7242 8100; fax - 020 7242 7310. VAT: Stan.

Wolfe (Jewellery)
Vault 41. TEL: 020 7405 2101; fax - same. VAT: Stan/Spec.

Arthur Middleton
12 New Row, Covent Garden. WC2N 4LF. Est. 1968. Open 10-6, Sat. by appointment only. SIZE: Medium. *STOCK: Globes, 1720-1950, from miniatures to large library pairs; scientific instruments - navigation, astronomy, surveying, microscopes, 18th-19th C, £100-£50,000.* LOC: New Row runs between Leicester Sq. and Covent Garden. Shop 300yds. east from Leicester Sq. TEL: 020 7836 7042/7062; fax - 020 7497 2486. SER: Valuations; buys at auction; prop hire. VAT: Stan.

Pearl Cross Ltd
35 St. Martin's Court. WC2N 4AL. Est. 1897. Open 10-5.30. CL: Sat. *STOCK: Jewellery, silver, watches.* PARK: Meters. TEL: 020 7836 2814/7240 0795; fax - 020 7240 2733; e-mail - enquiries@pearlcross.co.uk; website - www.pearlcross.co.uk. SER: Valuations; restorations (jewellery, silver). VAT: Stan/Spec.

Henry Pordes Books Ltd
58-60 Charing Cross Rd. WC2H 0BB. Open 10-7. *STOCK: Secondhand, antiquarian and remainder books on most subjects including antiques.* TEL: 020 7836 9031; fax - 020 7240 4232; e-mail - henrypordes@clara.net; website - www.home. clara.net/henrypordes.

The Rae-Smith Gallery
8 Cecil Court. WC2N 4HE. (John and Felicity Rae-Smith). Est. 1992. Open 11-6, Mon. by appointment. SIZE: Medium. *STOCK: 20th C original cartoon artwork and book illustrations,* £30-£3,000. LOC: Between Charing Cross Road and St. Martin's Lane - Leicester Square underground. PARK: Meters or NCP. TEL: 020 7836 7424; fax - same; e-mail -raesmithg@aol.com. SER: Valuations. FAIRS: Watercolours and drawings. VAT: Margin.

Reg and Philip Remington
18 Cecil Court, Charing Cross Rd. WC2N 4HE. ABA. Est. 1979. Open 10-5, Sat. by appointment. SIZE: Medium. *STOCK: Voyages and travels, 17th-20th C, £5-£1,000.* LOC: Near Trafalgar Sq. TEL: 020 7836 9771. SER: Buys at auction. FAIRS: London Book, Grosvenor House. VAT: Stan.

Bertram Rota Ltd
1st Floor, 31 Long Acre. WC2E 9LT. Est. 1923. Open 9.30-5.30. CL: Sat. *STOCK: Antiquarian and secondhand books, especially first editions, private presses, English literature, and literary autographs.* TEL: 020 7836 0723.

The Silver Mouse Trap
56 Carey St. WC2A 2JB. (A. Woodhouse). Est. 1690. Open 10-5. CL: Sat. SIZE: Medium. *STOCK: Jewellery, silver.* LOC: South of Lincoln's Inn Fields. TEL: 020 7405 2578. SER: Valuations; restorations. VAT: Spec.

Stage Door Prints
9 Cecil Court, Charing Cross Rd. WC2N 4EZ. (A.Reynold). Open 11-6. *STOCK: Prints of performing arts, sports and topographical; signed photographs, maps, Victorian cards, valentines; film shop - posters, stills, books, memorabilia; performing arts book room and bargain basement.* TEL: 020 7240 1683.

Storey's Ltd
3 Cecil Court, Charing Cross Rd. WC2N 4EZ. (T. Kingswood). Est. 1929. Open 10-6. *STOCK: Prints, especially naval and military, topography, antiquarian books.* LOC: Between Charing Cross Rd. and St. Martin's Lane. PARK: Trafalgar Square garage. TEL: 020 7836 3777; fax - 020 7836 3788.

Tomtom
42 New Compton St. WC2H 8DA. (T. S. Roberts). Est. 1990. Open 12-7, Sat. 11-6. CL: Mon. SIZE: Medium. *STOCK: Post war design furniture, art, glass and ceramics, 1940-1980, to £1,000+.* LOC: Adjacent Charing Cross Rd. PARK: Meters. TEL: 020 7240 7909; fax - same; e-mail - sales@tomtomshop.co.uk; website - www.tomtomshop.co.uk. SER: Valuations; buys at auction (designer furniture and post war art). FAIRS: Pier Show, New York. VAT: Spec.

Trafalgar Square Collectors Centre

7 Whitcomb St. WC2H 7HA. (D.C. Pratchett and R.D. Holdich). Est. 1979. Open 10-5. CL: Sat. *STOCK: Coins and military medals, bonds, banknotes, badges and militaria, 18th-20th C, £5-£10,000.* LOC: Next to National Gallery. PARK: NCP. TEL: 020 7930 1979; fax - 020 7930 1152; e-mail - rdhmedals@aol.com. SER: Valuations; buys at auction (coins and military medals). VAT: Stan/Spec.

Travis and Emery

17 Cecil Court, Charing Cross Rd. WC2N 4EZ. ABA. Est. 1960. Open 11-6 including Sun. SIZE: Medium. *STOCK: Musical literature, music and prints.* LOC: Between Charing Cross Rd. and St. Martin's Lane. PARK: Meters. TEL: 020 7240 2129; fax - 020 7497 0790; e-mail - gas@travis-and-emery.com.

Watkins Books Ltd

19 Cecil Court, Charing Cross Rd. WC2N 4EZ. Est. 1880. Open 10-6, Thurs. 10-8, Sat. 10.30-6. *STOCK: Mysticism, occultism, Oriental religions, astrology, psychology, complementary medicine and a wide selection of books in the field of mind, body and spirit - both new and secondhand.* TEL: 020 7836 2182; fax - 020 7836 6700; e-mail - service@watkinsbooks.com; website - www.watkinsbooks.com.

The Witch Ball

2 Cecil Court, Charing Cross Rd. WC2N 4HE. (R. Glassman). Resident. Est. 1969. Open 10.30-6.30. SIZE: Small. *STOCK: Prints relating to the performing arts, from 17th C, 20th C posters.* LOC: 2 mins. from Leicester Sq. tube station. PARK: NCP nearby. TEL: 020 7836 2922; e-mail - thewitchball@btinternet.com; website - www.thewitchball.co.uk.VAT: Stan.

Zwemmer

24 Litchfield St. WC2H 9NJ. Est. 1921. Open 10-6.30, Thurs. 10-8, Sat. 10-6. SIZE: Large. *STOCK: Books on art and fine art; rare and out-of-print catalogue raisonnés.* LOC: Just south of Cambridge Circus, Leicester Sq. underground. TEL: 020 7240 4158.

Two of the earliest Italian maiolica drug jars from the collection of Dr Barney Elliott. (Left) The c.1600 albarello, possibly from Deruta, which brought £1,050; (right) the c.1530-50 albarello, possibly from Naples or Faenza, which sold for £2,600.

From an Auction Report by Christopher Wight on Three Ceramics Collections at Vost's, Newmarket, 28th June 2000 which appeared in the September 2000 issue of **Antique Collecting** magazine. For more details and to subscribe see page 147.

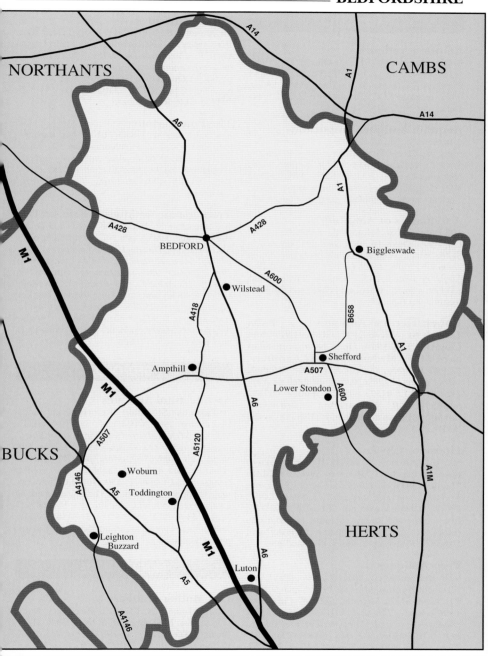

Dealers and Shops in Bedfordshire

				Shefford	1
Ampthill	9	Leighton Buzzard	1	Toddington	1
Bedford	1	Lower Stondon	1	Wilstead	1
Biggleswade	3	Luton	3	Woburn	4

BEDFORDSHIRE

AMPTHILL

Ampthill Antiques
Market Sq. MK45 2EH. (A. Olney). Est. 1980. Open 11-4, Sun. 2-5. SIZE: Large. *STOCK: Furniture, collectables, jewellery, clocks, china, glass, pictures.* LOC: Town centre. PARK: Easy and at rear. TEL: 01525 403344.

Ampthill Antiques Emporium
6 Bedford St. MK45 2NB. Est. 1979. Open 10-5 every day except Tues. SIZE: Large - 40 dealers. *STOCK: Antique furniture.* LOC: 5 mins. from Junction 13, M1. PARK: Easy. TEL: 01525 402131; e-mail - info@ampthillantiques.co.uk; website - www.ampthillantiquesemporium.co.uk.

Antiquarius of Ampthill
107 Dunstable St. MK45 2NG. (Peter Caldwell). Est. 1997. Open 10.30-5, Sun. 1-5. CL: Tues. SIZE: Small. *STOCK: Sitting room and dining room furniture, 1800-1900, to £3,000.* LOC: Town centre. PARK: Nearby. TEL: 01525 841799; e-mail - peter.caldwell@tesco.net SER: Restorations (upholstery).

Robert Harman Antiques   BADA
Church St. MK45 2EH. (Robert Harman Cannell). Est. 1979. Open by appointment only. SIZE: Medium. *STOCK: Furniture, £1,000-£30,000; tea caddies, £200-£10,000; works of art, £200-£20,000, all 18th to early 19th C.* **TEL: 01525 402322; mobile - 07802 535059. SER: Valuations; restorations (furniture); buys at auction. FAIRS: Olympia; BADA. VAT: Spec.**

House of Clocks
102-104 Dunstable St. MK45 2JP. (John Ginty). Resident. Est. 1957. Open 9-5, Sun. 11-5. SIZE: Medium. *STOCK: Clocks including longcase, bracket, carriage and wall, £150-£12,000.* PARK: Behind Market Sq. TEL: 01525 403136; fax - same. SER: Valuations; restorations (clocks). FAIRS: Manchester; Birmingham: Uxbridge: Kettering: Luton. VAT: Stan/Spec.

Paris Antiques
97B Dunstable St. MK45 2NG. (Paul and Elizabeth Northwood). Est. 1985. Open 9.30-5. CL: Mon. SIZE: Medium. *STOCK: Furniture, 18th to early 20th C, £250-£4,000; brass and copper, silver and plate, pictures and smalls.* LOC: Off junction 12, M1. PARK: Opposite. TEL: 01525 840488; home - 01525 861420; mobile - 07802 535059. SER: Valuations; restorations (mainly furniture, some metal); buys at auction.

Pilgrim Antiques
11 Dunstable St. MK45 1BY. (Gary Lester). Est. 1982. Open 10-5.30, including Sun. SIZE: Large. *STOCK: Furniture including dining tables, bookcases, chairs, wardrobes, 18th-20th C, £500-£5,000.* LOC: Town centre. PARK: Rear of premises. TEL: 01525 633023; home - 01525 403266. SER: Restorations.

The Pine Parlour
82a Dunstable St. MK45 2LF. (Lynn Barker). Est. 1989. Open 10-5 including Sun. CL: Mon. SIZE: Small. *STOCK: Pine furniture, 19th C, £200-£800; kitchenalia, £5-£60.* PARK: Easy. TEL: 01525 403030; home - same. SER: Valuations.

Transatlantic Antiques & Fine Art Ltd
101 Dunstable St. MK45 2NG.. (I.J. and D. M. Higgins). Est. 1995. Open 10.30-5 including Sun. SIZE: Large. *STOCK: 19th C furniture, £150-£4,000; glass, ceramics, silver and metalware, 19th C, £5-£3,000; pictures and interesting objects, 18th-19th C, £50-£1,000.* LOC: Main street. PARK: Outside shop and off Market Square. TEL: 01525 403346; fax - same; e-mail - transatlantic@talk21.com; website - www. Antiquesweb.co.uk/transatlantic. SER: Restorations; buys at auction. VAT: Spec.

BEDFORD

Architectural Antiques
70 Pembroke St. MK40 3RQ. (Paul and Linda Hoare). Est. 1989. Open 12-5, Sat. 10-5. SIZE: Medium. *STOCK: Early Georgian to early 20th C fireplaces, £500-£1,000; sanitary ware, from late Victorian, £100-£500; doors, panelling, pews, chimney pots and other architectural items, Georgian and Victorian, £50-£100.* LOC: Follow signs to town centre, turn on The Embankment or Castle Rd., shop is off Castle Rd., near Post Office. PARK: Easy. TEL: 01234 213131/343421. SER: Valuations; restorations; installations, particularly period fireplaces.

BIGGLESWADE

Old Mother Hubbard's
38 Shortmead St. SG18 0AP. (Derry Anne Dynes). Est. 1994. Open 10-5, Sat. 9.30-5. SIZE: Medium. *STOCK: China, 1920's-30's, £15-£100; Victoriana, 19th C, £10-£500; Victorian pine, £100-£1,000.* PARK: Easy. TEL: 01767 600959. FAIRS: Janba; St Ives; Regal Promotions, Dunstable.

Shortmead Antiques
46 Shortmead St. SG18 0AP. (S.E. Sinfield). Open 10.30-4. CL: Mon. and Thurs. SIZE: Small. *STOCK: Furniture, £50-£1,000; boxes, porcelain, silver, bronzes, copper and brass, all pre-1930.* LOC: 1/2 mile from A1. TEL: 01767 601780 (ansaphone).

Simply Oak
Oaktree Farm, Potton Rd. SG18 0EP. (R. Sturman and A. Kilgarriff). Open 10-5, Sun. 11-4. SIZE: Large. *STOCK: Restored oak furniture, late Victorian to 1930's, £100-£2,000.* LOC: Off A1 towards Biggleswade, right turn onto B1040 - 3 miles towards Potton. PARK: Own. TEL: 01767 601559; fax - 01767 312855; e-mail - antiques@ simplyoak.freeserve.co.uk. SER: Valuations; restorations (furniture especially oak).

LEIGHTON BUZZARD

Baroq & David Ball Antiques
59 North St. LU7 7EQ. (Brian Dawson and David Ball). Open 10-5. CL: Thurs. SIZE: Medium. *STOCK: Pottery and porcelain, £10-£500; paintings and watercolours, 18th-20th C, £100-£1,000; furniture, £100-£4,500.* PARK: Easy. TEL: 01525 850900; home - 01908 587766; mobiles - 07767 303501 (B. Dawson) and 07831 11161 (D. Ball).

LOWER STONDON

Memory Lane Antiques
14 Bedford Rd. SG16 6EA. (Elizabeth Henry). Est. 1985. Open 10.30-5, Sun. 11-4. CL: Wed. and Thurs. SIZE: Small. *STOCK: General antiques including 19th oak, silver and plate, glass including coloured.* LOC: On A600 near RAF Henlow. PARK: Easy. TEL: 01462 811029/ 812716; fax - same. SER: Valuations.

LUTON

Bargain Box
4 & 6a Adelaide St. LU1 5BB. Open 9-6, Wed. 9-1. *STOCK: General antiques and collectables.* TEL: 01582 423809.

Bernadette's Antiques & Collectables & Auctioneers
19a Adelaide St. LU1 5BB. Open 9-6, Wed. 9-1. *STOCK: General antiques.* TEL: 01582 423809.

Foye Gallery
15 Stanley St. LU1 5AL. Est. 1960. Open 9.30-5 or by appointment. *STOCK: Engravings, etchings, drawings, watercolours, paintings, maps, books.* TEL: 01582 738487. VAT: Stan.

An estimate of £1,000-£1,500 is placed on this 19th century mahogany longcase clock by Henry Ranorth of Plymouth when it comes under Lawrence's Taunton hammer on 26th September.

From an Auction Preview which appeared in the September 2000 issue of **Antique Collecting** magazine. For more details and to subscribe see page 147.

SHEFFORD

S. and S. Timms Antiques Ltd
2/4 High St. SG17 5DG. LAPADA. Est. 1976.
Open Mon.-Fri. 9.30-5, Sat. and Sun. 11-5 or by
appointment. SIZE: Large. *STOCK: 18th-19th C
Town and Country furniture.* LOC: A507, centre of
village. PARK: Easy. TEL: 01462 851051; mobile
- 07885 458541. FAIRS: LAPADA (London and
NEC); Chelsea; Battersea. VAT: Stan/Spec.

TODDINGTON

Books for Collectors Ltd.
Unit 1, Rear 24/26 High St, LU5 6BY. (Frank
and Shirley Horn). Open 10-4, prior telephone
call advisable. *STOCK: New and secondhand
collectors books.* PARK: Easy. TEL: 01525
875100/01582 738624; fax - 01525 877600.

WILSTEAD (WILSHAMSTEAD)
Nr. Bedford

Manor Antiques
The Manor House, Cottonend Rd. MK45 3BT.
(Mrs S. Bowen). Est. 1976. Open 10-5, Sun. by
appointment. SIZE: Large. *STOCK: Furniture,*

especially dining, 19th C to Edwardian, £100-
£5,000; lighting and oil lamps, Victorian to
1940's; general antiques. LOC: Just off A6, 4
miles south of Bedford. PARK: Own. TEL: 01234
740262; home - same. SER: Restorations
(furniture); buys at auction. FAIRS: London
Decorative. VAT: Stan/Spec.

WOBURN

Christopher Sykes Antiques
The Old Parsonage. MK17 9QL. (C. and M. Sykes).
Est. 1949. Open 9-5. SIZE: Large. *STOCK:
Collectors' items - attractive, early brass, copper
and pewter; scientific and medical instruments;
specialist in rare corkscrews, £10-£800; silver
decanter labels, tastvins and funnels, pottery barrels
and bin labels, glass decanters and tantalus.* LOC: In
main street opposite Post Office on A50. PARK:
Easy. TEL: 01525 290259/290467; fax - 01525
290061; e-mail - sykes.corkscrews@sykes-
corkscrews.co.uk; website - www.sykes-corkscrews.
co.uk. SER: 130 page illustrated mail order catalogue
on corkscrews and wine related antiques available £7
each. VAT: Stan/Spec.

Town Hall Antiques
Market Place. MK17 9PZ. Open Mon.-Sat. 10-5.30,
Sun. 11-5.30. SIZE: Medium. *STOCK: Furniture,*

Woburn Abbey Antiques Centre

WOBURN ABBEY, WOBURN, BEDFORDSHIRE MK17 9WA
Telephone: (01525) 290350 Fax: (01525) 292102

Representing over 60 quality dealers

OPEN EVERY DAY OF THE YEAR
EXCEPT CHRISTMAS

The Centre offers a vast range of quality antiques for the discerning and informed collector or dealer as well as for the casual novice buyer. All items on display are fully described, competitively priced and are vetted for authenticity and accuracy of description. You can buy with confidence at England's most unique and oldest established antiques centre.

£50-£5,000; lighting, clocks, ceramics, glass, silver and plate, £10-£2,000; prints and pictures, £5-£2,000; all 18th to early 20th C; mirrors, domestic metalware; some antiquities; cigarette cards, tools, sporting memorabilia. LOC: Off A5 and off junction 12 or 13, M1. PARK: Easy. TEL: 01525 290950. SER: Valuations; framing.

The Woburn Abbey Antiques Centre

MK17 9WA. Est. 1967. Open every day (including Bank Holidays) 10-5.30. CL: Christmas holidays. SIZE: Over 50 shops and showcases on two floors. STOCK: English and Continental furniture, porcelain, glass, paintings, silver and decorative items. LOC: Exits 12 and 13, M1. On A5 follow signs to Woburn Abbey and after entering grounds, follow signs, The Antiques Centre is in the South Courtyard. PARK: Easy. TEL: 01525 290350; fax - 01525 292102. SER: Carriage for large items; worldwide shipping.

Woburn Fine Arts

12 Market Place. MK17 9PZ. (Z. Bieganski). Est. 1983. Open Tues.-Sun. 2-5. SIZE: Medium. STOCK: Post-impressionist paintings, 1880-1940; European paintings, 17th-18th C; British paintings, 20th C. PARK: Easy. TEL: 01525 290624. SER: Restorations (oils and watercolours); framing.

Silver teaspoon. Rococo decoration to the back of the bowl. Maker's mark (B:C for Benjamin Cartwright II) indicates that this was made between 22 April 1754 and 7 September 1756. (Courtesy Alec Fisher)

From an article by Peter D. Spencer entitled 'Unearthing the Past – Literally!' which appeared in the September 2000 issue of **Antique Collecting** magazine. For more details and to subscribe see page 147.

ANTIQUE COLLECTORS' CLUB

The Antique Collectors' Club was formed in 1966 and quickly grew to a five figure membership spread throughout the world. It publishes the only independently run monthly antiques magazine, *Antique Collecting*, which caters for those collectors who are interested in widening their knowledge of antiques, both by greater awareness of quality and by discussion of the factors which influence the price that is likely to be asked. The Antique Collectors' Club pioneered the provision of information on prices for collectors and the magazine still leads in the provision of detailed articles on a variety of subjects.

It was in response to the enormous demand for information on 'what to pay' that the price guide series was introduced in 1968 with the first edition of *The Price Guide to Antique Furniture* (completely revised 1978 and 1989), a book which broke new ground by illustrating the more common types of antique furniture, the sort that collectors could buy in shops and at auctions rather than the rare museum pieces which had previously been used (and still to a large extent are used) to make up the limited amount of illustrations in books published by commercial publishers. Many other price guides have followed, all copiously illustrated, and greatly appreciated by collectors for the valuable information they contain, quite apart from prices. The Price Guide Series heralded the publication of many standard works of reference on art and antiques. *The Dictionary of British Art* (now in six volumes), *The Pictorial Dictionary of British 19th Century Furniture Design*, *Oak Furniture* and *Early English Clocks* were followed by many deeply researched reference works such as *The Directory of Gold and Silversmiths*, providing new information. Many of these books are now accepted as the standard work of reference on their subject.

The Antique Collectors' Club has widened its list to include books on gardens and architecture. All the Club's publications are available through bookshops world wide and a full catalogue of all these titles is available free of charge from the addresses below.

Club membership, open to all collectors, costs little. Members receive free of charge *Antique Collecting*, the Club's magazine (published ten times a year), which contains well-illustrated articles dealing with the practical aspects of collecting not normally dealt with by magazines. Prices, features of value, investment potential, fakes and forgeries are all given prominence in the magazine.

Among other facilities available to members are private buying and selling facilities and the opportunity to meet other collectors at their local antique collectors' clubs. There are over eighty in Britain and more than a dozen overseas. Members may also buy the Club's publications at special pre-publication prices.

As its motto implies, the Club is an organisation designed to help collectors get the most out of their hobby: it is informal and friendly and gives enormous enjoyment to all concerned.

ANTIQUE COLLECTORS' CLUB
5 Church Street, Woodbridge, Suffolk, IP12 1DS, UK
Tel: (01394) 385501 Fax: (01394) 384434
Email: magazine@antique-acc.com   Website: www.antique-acc.com
——————— *or* ———————
Market Street Industrial Park, Wappingers' Falls, NY 12590, USA
Tel: (845) 297 0003 Fax (845) 297 0068 ORDERS: (800) 252 5231
Email: info@antiquecc.com   Website: www.antiquecc.com

BERKSHIRE

ALDERMASTON, Nr. Reading

Aldermaston Antiques
The Old Dispensary. RG7 4LW. (Vivian and Roger Green). Est. 1994. Open 10-5.30. SIZE: Small + yard. *STOCK: Longcase clocks, furniture, lamps, desks, mainly 19th C; architectural and garden items.* LOC: A340, village centre. PARK: Easy and at rear. TEL: 01189 712370; home -same.

ASCOT

Melnick House of Ascot
16 Brockenhurst Rd. SL5 9DL. (Jackie Collins and Vic Day). Open 10-5. CL: Mon. SIZE: Small. *STOCK: Furniture, 19th-20th C, £200-£2,000; maps and prints, 17th-19th C, £20-£2,000; clocks, 18th-19th C, £600-£1,000.* LOC: South Ascot, short distance from station. PARK: At rear. TEL: 01344 297517; fax - 01344 291800; home - 01344 628383. SER: Restorations (furniture including upholstery, paintings and clocks).

Omell Galleries
The Corner House, Course Rd. SL5 7HL. Est. 1947. Open Tues.-Sat. 9.30-1 and 2-5; Sun. by appointment. SIZE: Medium. *STOCK: Contemporary oils, £400-£6,000.* LOC: Off High St. opposite garage. PARK: Easy. TEL: 01344 873443; fax - 020 7734 2112. SER: Valuations; restorations (cleaning, repair - oils, watercolours and frames). VAT: Spec.

BARKHAM, Nr. Wokingham

Barkham Antique Centre
Barkham St. RG40 4PJ . (Len and Mary Collins). Open 10.30-5 including Sun. SIZE: Large - 50+ dealers. *STOCK: General antiques including furniture, china, kitchenalia, coins, Dinky toys, paintings, glassware, scientific instruments and brass; collectables including Beswick, Moorcroft, Royal Doulton, Wade.* LOC: Off M4, junction 10, A329M to Wokingham, over station crossing to Barkham (B3349), left at Bull public house, centre 300 yds. on left. PARK: Easy. TEL: 0118 976 1355. SER: Valuations; restorations (china, French polishing, upholstery, cabinet making).

BINFIELD

Ulla Stafford Antiques   BADA
Binfield Lodge. RG42 5QB. Open by appointment. *STOCK: Georgian and Continental furniture; European ceramics, 17th-18th C.* TEL: 0118 934 3208; fax - same. VAT: Spec.

BURGHFIELD COMMON, Nr. Reading

Graham Gallery
Highwoods. RG7 3BG. (J. Steeds). Est. 1976. Open by appointment at any time. SIZE: Medium. *STOCK: English watercolours, £50-£1,500; English oil paintings, £200-£8,000; English prints, £25-£200; all 19th to early 20th C.* LOC: 4 miles from Reading on Burghfield road. PARK: Easy. TEL: 0118 9832320; fax - 0118 9831070; website - www.grahamgallery.freeuk.com. SER: Valuations; restorations (cleaning, framing).

CAVERSHAM, Nr. Reading

The Clock Workshop
17 Prospect St. RG4 8JB. (J. M. Yealland FBHI). LAPADA. TVADA. Est. 1980. Open 9.30-5.30, Sat. 10-1. SIZE: Small. *STOCK: Clocks, late 17th to late 19th C, £350-£60,000; barometers, 18th-19th C, £500-£12,000.* LOC: Prospect St. is the beginning of main Reading to Henley road. PARK: North St. TEL: 0118 9470741. SER: Valuations; restorations (clocks, barometers, chronometers, barographs); buys at auction. FAIRS: TVADA; LAPADA; Olympia. VAT: Stan/Spec.

COOKHAM RISE

Cookham Antiques
35 Station Parade. SL6 9BR. (Gary Lloyd Wallis). Est. 1990. Open daily including Sun. SIZE: Large. *STOCK: Furniture including bookcases, desks, chests of drawers, 18th-20th C, £50-£1,000.* PARK: Easy and at rear. TEL: 01628 523224; mobile - 07778 020536. SER: Valuations; restorations.

DATCHET

The Studio Gallery
The Old Bank, The Green, SL3 9JH. (Julian Bettney). Open 11-7, until 6 Sun. CL: Tues. am. and Fri. *STOCK: Fine paintings and prints, 1740-1940; architectural fittings; decorative furniture and fittings, garden items.* LOC: Off junction 5, M4, opposite Manor Hotel. TEL: 01753 544100; fax - same; mobile - 07770 762468; e-mail - Julianbettney@talk21.com. SER: Landscape paintings in oils painted to commission; bespoke framing (hand built, coloured, gilded, marbled, veneered); decorative painting, trompe l'oeil; restorations (oil paintings and frames).

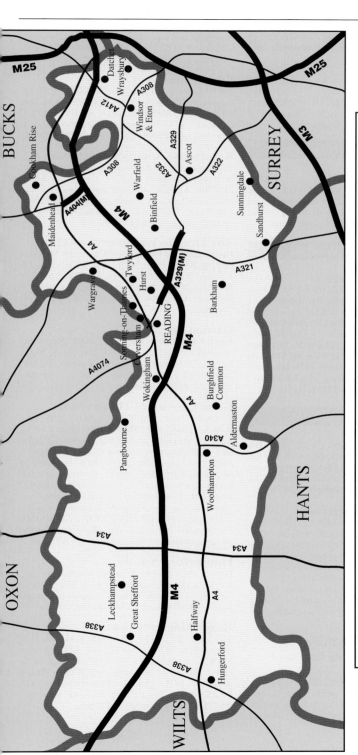

Dealers and Shops in Berkshire

Aldermaston	1	Cookham Rise	1
Ascot	1	Datchet	1
Barkham	1	Great Shefford	1
Binfield	1	Halfway	1
Burghfield Common	1	Horton	1
Caversham	15	Hungerford	1

Hurst	1	Twyford	1
Leckhampstead	1	Warfield	1
Maidenhead	1	Wargrave	1
Pangbourne	1	Windsor and Eton	18
Reading	3	Wokingham	1
Sandhurst	1	Woolhampton	1
Sonning-on-Thames	1	Wraysbury	2
Sunningdale	1		

GREAT SHEFFORD, Nr. Hungerford

Alan Hodgson
No 2 Ivy House, Wantage Rd. RG16 7DA. *STOCK: Boxes, country and general antiques, collectors' items.* LOC: A338, 10 minutes from Hungerford towards Wantage. TEL: 01488 648172. SER: Restorations (furniture).

HALFWAY, Nr. Newbury

Alan Walker   BADA
Halfway Manor. RG20 8NR. TVADA. Open by appointment. *STOCK: Fine barometers and weather instruments.* TEL: 01488 657670; mobile - 07770 728397. SER: Restorations.

HORTON, Nr. Windsor

John A. Pearson Antiques   BADA
Horton Lodge, Horton Rd. SL3 9NU. (Mrs J.C. Sinclair Hill). Est. 1902. By appointment only. SIZE: Large. *STOCK: English and Continental furniture, 1700-1850, £50-£30,000; oil paintings, 17th-19th C, £50-£50,000; decorative objects.* Not Stocked: Items after 19th C. LOC: From London turn off M4, exit 5, past London Airport; from M25 take exit 14. 10 mins from Heathrow. PARK: Easy. TEL: 01753 682136; fax - 01753 687151.

HUNGERFORD

Beedham Antiques Ltd   BADA
Charnham Close. RG17 0EJ. Open 10-5 or by appointment. *STOCK: English oak furniture, 16th-18th C; objects and works of art.* TEL: 01488 684141; fax - 01488 684050. VAT: Spec.

Below Stairs of Hungerford
103 High St. RG17 0NB. (S. Hofgartner). Est. 1974. Open 10-6, including Sun. and Bank Hols. SIZE: Large. *STOCK: Kitchen and decorative garden items, bedroom furniture, lighting, collectables, sporting items and memorabilia, interior fittings and taxidermy, mainly 19th C English, £20-£2,500.* Not Stocked: Reproductions. LOC: Main street. PARK: Easy. TEL: 01488 682317; e-mail - stewart@ belowstairs.co.uk; website - www.belowstairs.co.uk. SER: Valuations. VAT: Stan.

Sir William Bentley Billiards (Antique Billiard Table Specialist Company)
Standen Manor Farm. RG17 0RB. Open by appointment seven days a week. SIZE: Large. *STOCK: Billiard tables, billiard/dining tables; antique and modern accessories including* panelling and brass lights. TEL: 01488 681711; 020 8940 1152; fax - 01488 685197. SER: Restorations; removals and storage.

Bow House
3-4 Faulkner Sq., Charnham St. RG17 0HH. (Jo Preston and Karen Edwards). Open 9.30-5.30, Sun. 10-6. SIZE: Medium. *STOCK: 18th-19th C furniture and decoratives, contemporary accessories and gifts.* PARK: Easy. TEL: 01488 680628.

Bow House Antiques & Interiors
3-4 Faulkner Sq., Charnham St. RG17 0ER. (L.R. Herrington). Open 10.30-4. CL: Mon. SIZE: Medium. *STOCK: Antique furniture, contemporary objets d'art, jewellery and collectables.* LOC: A4. PARK: Easy, own. TEL: 01488 683198; home - 01364 643548.

The Fire Place (Hungerford) Ltd
Hungerford Old Fire Station, Charnham St. RG17 0EP. (E.B. and E.M. Smith). Est. 1976. Open 10-1.30 and 2.15-5. SIZE: Large. *STOCK: Fireplace furnishings and metalware especially fenders; paintings.* LOC: A4. TEL: 01488 683420. VAT: Stan/Spec.

Garden Art
Barrs Yard, 1 Bath Rd. RG17 0HE. (Susan and Arnie Knowles). Open 10-6, Sun. 11-4. SIZE: Large. *STOCK: Period garden items.* PARK: Easy. TEL: 01488 681881; home - 01488 681882. VAT: Stan/Spec.

Great Grooms of Hungerford
Riverside House, Charnham St. RG17 0EP. Open 9.30-5.30, Sun. 10-6. SIZE: Large. *STOCK: Wide variety of specialist dealers in 18th-19th C English and Continental town and country furniture, pottery and porcelain, silver and plate, works of art, metalware, glass, clocks, Oriental, oils and watercolours, prints, clocks and watches.* PARK: Easy. TEL: 01488 682314; fax - 01488 686677; e-mail - antiques@great-grooms.co.uk; website - www.great.grooms.co.uk.SER: Valuations; restorations (furniture including upholstery, pictures, silver, jewellery, ceramics). VAT: Spec.

Hungerford Arcade
High St. RG17 0NF. (Wynsave Investments Ltd). Est. 1972. Open 9.30-5.30, Sun. 11-5. SIZE: Over 80 stallholders. *STOCK: General antiques and period furniture.* PARK: Easy. TEL: 01488 683701.

Roger King Antiques
111 High St. RG17 0NB. (Mr and Mrs R.F. King). Est. 1974. Open 9.30-5. SIZE: Large. *STOCK: Furniture, 1750-1910, £100-£2,000; china, 19th C; oil paintings.* Not Stocked: Silver, jewellery. LOC: Opposite Hungerford Arcade. PARK: Easy. TEL: 01488 682256; website - www.kingantiques.co.uk. VAT: Spec.

The Old Malthouse **BADA**
15 Bridge St. RG17 0EG. (P.F. Hunwick). CINOA. Est. 1963. Open 10-5.30. SIZE: Large. STOCK: 18th to early 19th C walnut and mahogany furniture - dining tables, sets of chairs, mirrors, chests of drawers; clocks, barometers, decorative items and glass. Not Stocked: Orientalia. LOC: A338, left at Bear Hotel, shop is approx. 120 yds. on left, just before bridge. PARK: Front of premises. TEL: 01488 682209; fax - same; e-mail - hunwick@oldmalthouse30.freeserve.co.uk. SER: Valuations. VAT: Spec.

Principia Fine Art
35A High St. RG17 0NF. (M.D.C. Forrer and John Wain). Open 9.30-5.30. STOCK: Collectors items, scientific instruments, maritime, country furniture, treen, pictures, Oriental china, porcelain, books and clocks. TEL: 01488 682873; fax - 01672 511551.

Styles Silver
12 Bridge St. RG17 0EH. (P. and D. Styles). LAPADA. Est. 1974. Open Sat. and any time by appointment. SIZE: Medium. STOCK: Antique, Victorian and secondhand silver including cutlery. PARK: Easy. TEL: 01488 683922; home - same; fax - 01488 683488; mobile - 07778 769559. SER: Repairs; finder.

Turpins Antiques **BADA**
17 Bridge St. RG17 0EG. (Jane Sumner). Open Wed., Fri., and Sat. or by appointment. SIZE: Large. STOCK: 17th-18th C walnut, oak and mahogany furniture and metalware. TEL: 01488 681886; home - 01672 870727. VAT: Spec.

Youll's Antiques
27 and 28 Charnham St. RG17 0EJ. (B. Youll). Open 10.30-5.30 including Sun. STOCK: French and English furniture and decorative items. TEL: 01488 682046; fax - 01488 684335; e-mail - bruce. youll@talk21.com; website - www.youll. com.

HURST, Nr. Reading

Peter Shepherd Antiques
Penfold, Lodge Rd. RG10 0EG. Est. 1962. Open by appointment only. STOCK: Glass, rarities and books. TEL: 0118 934 0755.

LECKHAMPSTEAD, Nr. Newbury

Hill Farm Antiques
Hill Farm, Shop Lane. RG20 8QG. (Mike Beesley). Open 9-5, Sun. by appointment. STOCK: 19th C dining tables, chairs and library furniture. LOC: Off B4494 between Stag public house and church. PARK: Own at rear. TEL: 01488 638541/638361. SER: Restorations; shipping arranged; buys at auction.

MAIDENHEAD

Widmerpool House Antiques
Boulters Lock. SL6. Open by appointment only. *STOCK: English furniture, 18th-19th C; oil paintings, watercolours, prints; porcelain, glass, silver, 19th C.* TEL: 01628 623752.

PANGBOURNE

Rita Butler
4a Station Rd. RG8 7AN. TVADA. Open 10-5. *STOCK: General antiques including brass and bronze, early 19th C to early 20th C especially Art Deco; glass, early 1800's.* TEL: 0118 984 5522; mobile - 07752 936327.

READING

Rupert Landen Antiques
Church Farm, Reading Rd., Woodcote. RG8 0QX. TVADA. Open by appointment only. *STOCK: Late 18th to early 19th C furniture.* TEL: 01491 682396; mobile - 07974 732472.

P.D. Leatherland Antiques
68 London St. RG1 4SQ. Est. 1970. Open 9-5. *STOCK: Furniture, 18th C to 1920's; decorative china, clocks, metalware, mirrors and pictures, £5-£4,000.* PARK: Easy. TEL: 0118 958 1960. VAT: Stan/Spec.

Stables Antique Centre
1a Merchants Place (off Friar St). RG1 1DT. Est. 1972. Open 10-5. SIZE: 2 Floors. *STOCK: General antiques, collectables, Victoriana, advertising items, jewellery and books.* TEL: 0118 959 0290.

SANDHURST

Berkshire Metal Finishers Ltd
3 Factory, Vulcan Close. GU47 9DD. (J.A. and Mrs. J. Sturgeon). Est. 1957. Open 8-1 and 2-6, Sat. 8-1 and 2-4, Sun. 9-1. SIZE: Large. *STOCK: Brass, copper and steel metalware; silver plate.* LOC: Off A30 towards Wokingham on A321, after 1.25 miles turn left into Swan Lane, estate 1st turning right, last factory near car park. PARK: Easy. TEL: 01252 873475; fax - 01252 875434. SER: Restorations (metalware polishing and lacquering).

SONNING-ON-THAMES

Cavendish Fine Arts
The Dower House. RG4 6UL. (Janet Middlemiss and Guy Hazel). LAPADA. TVADA. Open by appointment only. *STOCK: Fine Queen Anne and English Georgian furniture, glass and porcelain.* TEL: 01189 691904; mobile - 07831 295575. VAT: Stan/Spec.

Ash tray. 4¾in. diameter. Engravings on rim in copper and silver framing, inside base has delicately engraved arabesque encrusting. Early 20th century. (£10). (Right) Cigarette dispenser. 3in. high. Calligraphy declares 'You will be saved if you speak the truth'. Note the geometrically bordered interlace decoration on the triangular side. Early 20th century. (£35).

R.S. Morton looks at some good quality work which is available for a modest outlay. From an article entitled 'Damascened Metalwork' which appeared in the September 2000 issue of **Antique Collecting** magazine. For more details and to subscribe see page 147.

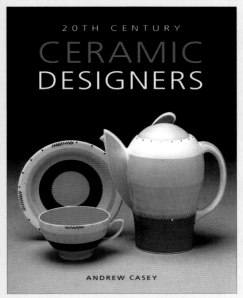

SUNNINGDALE

The Coworth Gallery
9 Coworth Rd. SL5 0NX. (Stephen Paddon). Est. 1985. Open most times, subject to a 'phone call. SIZE: Small. *STOCK: 19th C English and French country furniture, paintings, carpets, decorative items.* LOC: Turn right into Bedford Lane off A30 from London, after I Gladiatori. PARK: Easy. TEL: 01344 626532; mobile - 07831 182076. SER: Restorations.

TWYFORD, Nr. Reading

Bell Antiques
2B High St. RG10 9AE. (Nigel, Chris and Russell Timms). Est. 1980. Open 9.30-5.30, Sun. 10-5.30. SIZE: Small. *STOCK: General antiques including china and glass, silver and plate, small furniture, 18th-20th C, £10-£300.* LOC: Village centre on crossroads. PARK: Nearby. TEL: 0118 934 2501. VAT: Spec.

WARFIELD

Moss End Antique Centre
Moss End Garden Centre. RG12 6EJ. TVADA. Open 10.30-5. CL: Mon. SIZE: Large - 25 dealers. *STOCK: General antiques and collectables.* LOC: A3095. PARK: Own. TEL: 01344 861942.

WARGRAVE

John Connell - Wargrave Antiques
66 High St. RG10 8BY. Open Wed.-Sun. other times by appointment. SIZE: Large - several dealers. *STOCK: Furniture, Georgian-Edwardian; small items, china, glass, metal.* PARK: Nearby. TEL: 01734 402914. SER: Restorations (furniture); silver plating; metal polishing.

Ferry Antiques
70 High St. RG10 8BY. (Kate and Peter Turner). Est. 1982. Open 10-5.30, Sun. 10.30-4.30. CL: Mon. and Tues. SIZE: Medium. *STOCK: Furniture, 18th-19th C, £250-£2,500; glass and porcelain, 18th-19th C, £25-£250; silver and plate, 19th C, £50-£500.* LOC: At crossroads. PARK: 100 yards. TEL: 01189 404415. SER: Valuations; restorations (furniture and clocks). FAIRS: East Berkshire Antiques, Burchetts Green.

WINDSOR AND ETON

The Ancient Art Shop
8 Windsor Royal Station. SL4 1JN. *STOCK: Antiquities.* TEL: 01753 857854.

Art & Antiques and Bridge Miniatures
69 High St., Eton. SL4 6AA. (Vivien and Eddie Rand). Est. 1982. Open 10.30-5.30, Sat. 10.30-6, Sun. 2.30-6. SIZE: Medium. *STOCK: Collectors' items, jewellery, furniture, dolls house miniatures, from Victorian, £1-£600.* LOC: 1st shop over Thames from Windsor at Eton. PARK: Nearby. TEL: 01753 855727; home - 01628 527127. SER: Restorations (furniture, dolls houses, jewellery).

Roger Barnett Antiques
91 High St., Eton. SL4 6AF. Est. 1975. TEL: 01753 867785.

Berkshire Antiques Co Ltd
42 Thames St., Windsor. SL4 1YY. Open 10.30-5.30 including Sun. (Jan.to April - Sun. by appointment). SIZE: Large. *STOCK: Antique and modern designer jewellery; general antiques, china, porcelain and glass, silver and plate, Royal commemoratives, toys and dolls, £10-£25,000.* TEL: 01753 830100; fax - 01753 832278; website - www.users.dircon.co.uk/~jewels; e-mail - jewels@dircon.co.uk. SER: Valuations; repairs.

Dee's Antique Pine
89 Grove Rd. SL4 1HT. (Dee Waghorn). Open 10.30-6, other times by appointment. *STOCK: 19th C pine furniture.* TEL: 01753 865627; fax - 01753 850926; mobile - 07711 902887.

Eton Antique Bookshop
88 High St., Eton. SL4 6AF. TEL: 01753 855534.

Eton Antiques Partnership
80 High St., Eton. SL4 6AF. (Mark Procter). Est. 1967. Open 10-5, Sun. 11-5.30. SIZE: Large. *STOCK: Mahogany and rosewood furniture, 18th-19th C.* LOC: Slough East exit from M4 westbound. PARK: Nearby. TEL: 01753 860752; home - same. SER: Exporting; interior design consultants. VAT: Stan/Spec.

Eton Gallery
(Josephine Smith). LAPADA. TVADA. By appointment only. *STOCK: Fine 18th to early 19th C furniture.* TEL: 01753 860963.

Marcelline Herald Antiques
41 High St., Eton. SL4 6BD. TVADA. Est. 1993. Open Tues.,Thurs., Fri. and Sat. 10-5, other days

by appointment. SIZE: Medium. *STOCK: Furniture including beds, £500-£5,000; mirrors, pelmets and screens, £200-£2,500; ceramics, lamps and prints, £50-£1,000; all 18th to early 19th C.* PARK: Loading only. TEL: 01753 833924; fax - 0118 971 4683; home - same. FAIRS: TVADA; Decorative Antiques and Textiles. VAT: Spec.

J. Manley
27 High St., Eton. SL4 6AX. Est. 1891. Open 10-5. *STOCK: Watercolours, old prints.* TEL: 01753 865647. SER: Restorations; framing, mounting.

Peter J. Martin
40 High St., Eton. SL4 6BD. TVADA. Est. 1963. Open 9-1 and 2-5. CL: Sun. SIZE: Large and warehouse. *STOCK: Period, Victorian and decorative furniture and furnishings, £50-£20,000; metalware, £10-£500, all from 1800.* PARK: 50yds. opposite. TEL: 01753 864901; home - 01753 863987. SER: Restorations; shipping arranged; buys at auction. VAT: Stan/Spec.

Mostly Boxes
93 High St., Eton. SL4 6AF. (G.S. Munday). Est. 1977. Open 10-6.30. *STOCK: Wooden, mother of pearl, and tortoiseshell boxes.* PARK: 100 yds. TEL: 01753 858470. SER: Restorations (boxes). VAT: Spec.

O'Connor Brothers
Trinity Yard, 59 St. Leonards Rd., Windsor. SL4 3BX. *STOCK: Furniture and general antiques.* TEL: 01753 866732. VAT: Stan.

Oriental Rug Gallery Ltd
115-116 High St., Eton. SL4 6AN. (Richard Mathias and Julian Blair). BORDA. Open 10-5. *STOCK: Russian, Afghan, Turkish and Persian carpets, rugs and kelims; Oriental objets d'art.* PARK: Behind showroom. TEL: +44 (0) 1753 623000; fax - same; e-mail - rugs@oriental ruggallery.com; website - www.orientalrug gallery.com.

Rules Antiques
62 St Leonard's Rd. SL4 3BY. (Sue Rule and Kathryn Cale). Open 10.30-6. *STOCK: Fixtures and fittings; brass, metalwork; unusual small furniture; lighting.* TEL: 01753 833210.

Studio 101
101 High St., Eton. SL4 6AF. (Anthony Cove). Est. 1959. SIZE: Medium. *STOCK: Mahogany furniture, some 18th C, mainly 19th C, £50-£1,000; brass, silver plate, 19th C, £10-£200.* LOC: Walk over Windsor Bridge from Windsor and Eton Riverside railway station. PARK: Public, at rear of premises. TEL: 01753 863333.

Times Past Antiques
59 High St., Eton. SL4 6BL. (P. Jackson). MBHI. Est. 1970. Open 10-6, Sun. 12-5. SIZE: Medium.

STOCK: Clocks and music boxes, £100-£3,000; furniture, all 18th-19th C; silver, 19th C, £5-£500. PARK: Reasonable. TEL: 01753 857018; home - same. SER: Valuations; restorations (clocks and watches); buys at auction (clocks). VAT: Stan/Spec.

Turks Head Antiques
98 High St., Eton. SL4 6AF. Open 10-5. CL: Mon. *STOCK: Silver and plate, porcelain, glass and interesting collectables.* TEL: 01753 863939.

The Old Bakery Antiques
Bath Rd. RG7 5RE. (S. Everard). Resident. Est. 1969. *STOCK: Furniture, objets d'art, collectors' items, general antiques.* TEL: 0118 9712116.

Clive Rogers Oriental Rugs
TW19 5PE. TVADA Est. 1974. Open by appointment. SIZE: Medium. *STOCK: Oriental rugs, carpets, textiles; Oriental and Islamic works of art.* LOC: On B376, 10 minutes from Heathrow Airport. PARK: Own. TEL: 01784 481177/481109; fax - 01784 481457; mobile - 07747 114757; e-mail - info@orient-rug.com; website - www.orient-rug.com. SER: Valuations; restorations (as stock); historical analysis commission agents; buys at auction. VAT: Stan/Spec.

Wyrardisbury Antiques
23 High St. TW19 5DA. (C. Tuffs). Est. 1978. Open 10-5. CL: Mon. and Thurs. except by appointment. SIZE: Small. *STOCK: Clocks, £100-£4,000; barometers, small furniture, £100-£1,000.* LOC: A376 from Staines by-pass (A30) or from junction 5 M4/A4 via B470, then B376. PARK: Easy. TEL: 01784 483225. SER: Restorations (clocks).

Wokingham Antiques Centre
152 London Rd. RG40 3HB. (Janice Charlton). Est. 1998. Open 10.30-5.30, 1st Sun. each month 10.30-4.30, other times by appointment. CL: Wed. *STOCK: Furniture, 18th C to 1930's, £50-£2,500; curios, £1-£1,000; porcelain, pottery and silver, to modern collectables, £1-£500.* LOC: Off A329, follow signs for town centre, first shop on right opposite St. Crispin's school. PARK: Easy. TEL: 01189 790202; fax - same. SER: Valuations; restorations (caning, small upholstery, wood); buys at auction.

AMERSHAM

The Cupboard Antiques
80 High St., Old Amersham. HP7 0DS. (N. Lucas). LAPADA. Open 10-5. CL: Fri. SIZE: 4 showrooms. *STOCK: Georgian, Regency and early Victorian furniture and decorative items.* PARK: Easy. TEL: 01494 722882.

Martony Antiques & Collectables
2 Grimsdells Corner, Sycamore Rd. HP6 5EL. (M. P. and A. J. Bainbridge). Est. 1996. Open 10-5. CL: Mon. SIZE: Small. *STOCK: General antiques and collectables, 19th-20th C, £5-£1,000.* LOC: Next door to Red Cross shop. PARK: Easy. TEL: 01494 722666.

Michael and Jackie Quilter
38 High St. HP7 0DJ. Est. 1970. Open 10-5. *STOCK: General antiques, stripped pine, copper, brass, unusual objects.* PARK: Easy. TEL: 01494 433723. VAT: Stan.

Sundial Antiques
19 Whielden St. HP7 0HU. (A. and Mrs M. Macdonald). Est. 1970. Open 9.30-5.30. CL: Thurs. SIZE: Small. *STOCK: English and European brass, copper, metalware, fireplace equipment, 18th-19th C, £5-£500; small period furniture, 1670-1910, £25-£1,500; horse brasses, £10-£300; decorative items, 1750-1910, £5-£500; pottery, porcelain, curios, pre-1914, £10-£750.* Not Stocked: Jewellery, clocks, coins, oil paintings, stamps, books, silver, firegrates. LOC: On A404, in Old Town 200yds. from High St. on right; from High Wycombe, 500yds. from hospital on left. PARK: Easy. TEL: 01494 727955.

BEACONSFIELD

Buck House Antique Centre
47 Wycombe End, Old Town. HP9 1LZ. (C. and B. Whitby). Est. 1979. Open 10-5, Sun. 12-5. CL: Wed. SIZE: Medium - 10 dealers. *STOCK: Wide variety of general antiques including English and Oriental porcelain, clocks, barometers, oak and mahogany furniture, stripped pine, boxes and beds, to 1930's, £5-£5,000.* LOC: A40. TEL: 01494 670714. SER: Valuations.

June Elsworth - Beaconsfield Ltd
Clover House, 16 London End. HP9 2JH. (Mrs J. Elsworth). Est. 1983. CL: Mon. SIZE: Small. *STOCK: Fine English furniture, 18th-19th C; decorative accessories and silver,19th C.* LOC: In old town, on A40. PARK: Easy. TEL: 01494 675611; fax - 01494 671273. VAT: Spec.

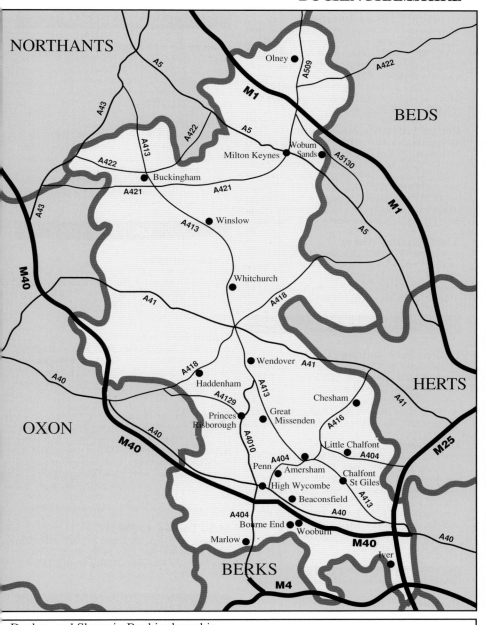

Dealers and Shops in Buckinghamshire

Amersham	4	Haddenham	1	Penn	2
Beaconsfield	5	High Wycombe	2	Princes Risborough	1
Bourne End	2	Iver	1	Wendover	5
Buckingham	1	Little Chalfont	1	Whitchurch	1
Chalfont St. Giles	2	Marlow	4	Winslow	1
Chesham	4	Milton Keynes	1	Wooburn	1
Great Missenden	3	Olney	6		

Grosvenor House Interiors

51 Wycombe End, Beaconsfield Old Town. HP9 1LX. (T.I. Marriott). Est. 1970. Open 10-1 and 2-5. CL: Wed. SIZE: Large. *STOCK: 18th-19th C furniture especially upholstered and mid-19th C walnut; fireplaces and accessories; 19th C watercolours.* PARK: Easy. TEL: 01494 677498. SER: Interior architectural design, fireplace specialists. VAT: Stan/Spec.

Period Furniture Showrooms

49 London End. HP9 2HW. (R.E.W. Hearne and N.J. Hearne). TVADA. Est. 1965. Open Mon.-Sat. 9-5.30. SIZE: Large. *STOCK: Furniture, 1700-1900, £50-£5,000.* LOC: A40 Beaconsfield Old Town. PARK: Own. TEL: 01494 674112; fax - 01494 681046; e-mail - Sales@period-furniture-showrooms.co.uk; website - www.periodfurniture.net. SER: Restorations (furniture). VAT: Stan/Spec.

The Spinning Wheel

86 London End. HP9 2JD. (Mrs M. Royle). Est. 1945. Open 9.30-4.30. CL: Mon. and Wed. *STOCK: English furniture, 18th-19th C, mahogany and oak items, porcelain, glass.* TEL: 01494 673055; home - 01494 873294.

BOURNE END

Bourne End Antiques Centre

67 The Parade. SL8 5SB. (S. Shepheard). Est. 1995. Open 10-5.30, Sun. 1-5.30. SIZE: Large. *STOCK: Furniture - pine, £150-£900, darkwood, £200-£800; both from 19th C; china and glass, £1-£100.* LOC: A4155, 2 miles from Marlow. PARK: Easy. TEL: 01628 533298; home - 01494 525911. VAT: Stan.

La Maison

The Crossings, Cores End Rd. SL8 5AL. (Jeremy D. Pratt). Est. 1995. Open 9.30-5.30, Mon. 1-5, Sat. 10-5.30, Sun. 11-5. SIZE: Medium. *STOCK: French antiques including beds and chandeliers, 19th C, to £1,000.* LOC: Take Marlow by-pass from junction 3, M40. PARK: Easy. TEL: 01628 525858; fax - 01494 670363. SER: Valuations; restorations (re-upholstery). FAIRS: Burchetts Green. VAT: Stan/Spec.

BUCKINGHAM

Buckingham Antiques Centre

5 West St. MK18 1HL. (Peter Walton). Est. 1975. Open 9.15-5.30, Sat. 9-5.30, Wed. and Sun. by appointment. SIZE: Medium. *STOCK: Furniture, 19th C, £50-£1,000; clocks, 18th-20th C, £50-£2,000; general antiques, £2-£500.* LOC: On A422 towards Brackley, near town centre. PARK: Nearby. TEL: 01280 824464; home - same. SER: Valuations; restorations (clocks).

CHALFONT ST. GILES

Gallery 23 Antiques

High St. HP9 4QH. (Mrs A. Vollaro). Est. 1991. Open 10-5. *STOCK: Furniture, clocks, silver, Continental and English porcelain, glass, paintings, prints and watercolours, tapestry cushions.* TEL: 01494 871512.

T. Smith

The Furniture Village, London Rd. HP8 4NN. Est. 1982. Open 10-5 including Sun. SIZE: Medium. *STOCK: Antique pine and architectural items.* LOC: Opposite Pheasant public house. PARK: Easy. TEL: 01494 873031. SER: Valuations; restorations (including upholstery); buys at auction (furniture).

CHESHAM

Chess Antiques

85 Broad St. HP5 3EF. (M.P. Wilder). LAPADA. Est. 1966. Open 9-5, Sat. 10-5. SIZE: Small. *STOCK: Furniture and clocks.* PARK: Easy. TEL: 01494 783043. SER: Valuations; restorations. VAT: Stan/Spec.

Omniphil Prints

Germains Lodge, Fullers Hill. HP5 1LR. (Ross Muddiman). Est. 1953. Open by appointment. SIZE: Warehouse. *STOCK: Rare prints on all subjects and Illustrated London News from 1842.* TEL: 01494 771851.

Queen Anne House

57 Church St. HP5 1HY. (Miss A.E. Jackson). Est. 1918. Open Wed., Fri. and Sat. 9.30-5, other times by appointment. SIZE: Large. *STOCK: Furniture, decorative and furnishing pieces, porcelain figures, other china, glass, silver plate, copper, brass, Victoriana, Persian rugs. Not Stocked: Silver, weapons, jewellery.* PARK: Easy. TEL: 01494 783811. SER: Buys at auction.

M.V. Tooley, CMBHI

at Chess Antiques, 85 Broad St. HP5 3EF. Est. 1960. Open 9-6, Sat. 10-5. SIZE: Small. *STOCK: Clocks and barometers.* TEL: 01494 783043. SER: Valuations; restorations; spare parts.

GREAT MISSENDEN

The Hampden Trading Company

The Old Barn, Solinger Farm, Little Hampden. HP16 9PT. (Callie Hope-Morley). Open by appointment only. *STOCK: 18th-19th C country and painted furniture, textiles, pictures and decorative items.* TEL: 01494 488538; fax - 01494 488818.

The Pine Merchants
52 High St. HP16 0AU. (Mrs J. Peters). Open 10-5.
CL: Mon. SIZE: Medium. *STOCK: Stripped pine
and Victorian bedsteads.* TEL: 01494 862002.

Peter Wright Antiques
(Incorporating Missenden Restorations and
Abbey Clocks & Repairs), 32b High St. HP16
0AU. Est. 1992. Open by appointment only.
SIZE: Small. *STOCK: Clocks, curios and
furniture.* LOC: A413. TEL: 01494 891330. SER:
Restorations; clock repairs.

HADDENHAM

H.S. Wellby Ltd
The Malt House, Church End. HP17 8AH. (C.S.
Wellby). Est. 1820. Open by appointment 9-6.
STOCK: 18th-19th C paintings. TEL: 01844
290036. SER: Restorations. VAT: Spec.

HIGH WYCOMBE

Browns' of West Wycombe
Church Lane, West Wycombe. HP14 3AH. Est. Pre
1900. Open 8-5.30. CL: Sat. *STOCK: Furniture.*
LOC: On A40 approximately 3 miles west of High
Wycombe on Oxford Rd. PARK: Easy. TEL:
01494 524537; fax - 01494 439548. SER:
Restorations and hand-made copies of period chairs.

Windmill Fine Art
2 Windmill Drive, Widmer End. HP15 6BD.
(Ray White). Open by appointment only.
*STOCK: Fine Victorian and early 20th C
watercolours.* TEL: 01494 713757; fax - same;
mobile - 07885 370408. SER: Valuations;
commission search. FAIRS: Most major.

IVER

"Yester-year"
12 High St. SL0 9NG. (P.J. Frost). Resident. Est.
1969. Open 10.30-6. SIZE: Small. *STOCK:
Furniture, porcelain, pottery, glass, metalwork,
18th to early 20th C.* PARK: Easy. TEL: 01753
652072. SER: Valuations; restorations (furniture,
pictures); framing; buys at auction.

LITTLE CHALFONT

Nightingale Antiques
17 Nightingale's Corner. HP7 9PZ. (Lee Andreou).
Est. 1995. Open Tues.-Sat. 10-5.30, Sun. 10-4.
SIZE: Medium. *STOCK: Silver, 18th-19th C, £25-
£1,500; ceramics, 19th-20th C, £25-£1,500;*

furniture, 18th-19th C, £50-£5,000. PARK: Easy.
TEL: 01494 762163. SER: Valuations; restorations
(silver plating, furniture and ceramics).

MARLOW

Glade Antiques   BADA
**(Sonia Garry). LAPADA. CINOA. Open by
appointment only. *STOCK: Fine Oriental
ceramics, bronzes and jades: Chinese items
from Han, Tang, Song, Ming and Quing
periods; Japanese items - mainly Kakiemon,
Nabeshima, Kutani, Satsuma and Imari; also
Korean Koryo, Yi and Choson periods.* TEL:
01628 487255; fax - 01628 487255; mobile -
07771 552328.**

Jack Harness Antiques
Westfield Farm, Henley Rd., Medmenham. SL7.
Est. 1981. Open 9-5 or by appointment. SIZE:
Large warehouse. *STOCK: Pine and country
furniture, especially period pine and original
painted French provincial furniture.* PARK: Easy.
TEL: 01491 410691; fax - same; mobile - 07768
666833; home - 01628 471775. SER: Restorations;
courier. VAT: Stan/Spec. *Mainly Trade.*

Jackdaw Antiques Centre
25 West St. SL7 2LS. (Mr and Mrs Mayle). Est.
1998. Open 10-5.30, Sun. 12-5. SIZE: Large.
*STOCK: Furniture, from Regency, £100-£2,500;
china, from Victorian, £2-£200; limited edition
books, £2-£50; silver, from Victorian, £15-£500.*
LOC: Opposite Waitrose. PARK: Easy. TEL:
01628 898285; home - 01491 680954. SER:
Restorations (furniture, china and glass).

Marlow Antique Centre
35 Station Rd. SL7 1NW. TVADA. SIZE: 30+
dealers. *STOCK: 18th-20th C furniture, collectors'
china from Worcester to Clarice Cliff, Staffordshire
figures and dogs, chandeliers, silver, decorative
glass, writing slopes, tea caddies, postcards, pens,
cuff-links, equestrian items, cameras, jewellery.*
TEL: 01628 473223; fax - 01628 478989.

MILTON KEYNES

Temple Lighting (Jeanne Temple Antiques)
Stockwell House, Wavendon. MK17 8LS. Est.
1968. SIZE: Medium. *STOCK: Victorian,
Edwardian and 1930's light fittings; 19th C
furniture; decorative items.* LOC: Just off A5130
Woburn Sands to Newport Pagnell road. TEL:
01908 583597; fax - 01908 281149.

ANTIQUES AT...WENDOVER
Datelined Antiques Centre
Established 1987
30 dealers offering quality town and country antiques in a period building.
Car park
Monday – Saturday 10-5.30 Sundays & B. Hols 11-5.00
The Old Post Office, 25 High Street, Wendover, Bucks HP22 6DU
Tel: 01296 625335   Website: antiquesatwendover.co.uk

OLNEY

Archer's Antique and Country Furniture
19 High St. MK46 4EB. (Catherine Haslam). Est. 1982. Open 10-5, Sun. 2-5. CL: Wed. SIZE: Medium. *STOCK: 19th C English and Continental pine, mahogany, French and upholstered furniture, to £2,000.* LOC: Past market square on A509. PARK: Easy. TEL: 01234 713050; fax - same. SER: Restorations. VAT: Stan/Spec.

Courtyard Antiques
4 Rose Court. MK46 4BY. (Trisha Sharp). Est. 1993. Open 10-4.30, Sat. 10-5, Sun. 2-5. CL: Wed. SIZE: Medium. *STOCK: Furniture, including pine, 18th-20th C, £50-£1,000; silver, porcelain, glass, figures, 18th C to Art Deco, £5-£500; prints, watercolours, frames, cigarette cards, 18th-20th C, £10-£500; brass and copper.* LOC: Off Market Sq., down alleyway. PARK: Rear access to traders car park. TEL: 01234 712200.

Market Square Antiques
MK46 4BA. (J.D. and H. Vella). Open 10-5, Sun. 12.30-4. *STOCK: Furniture, clocks, china, silver, glass, copper and brass.* TEL: 01234 712172. SER: Restorations.

John Overland Antiques
Rose Court, Market Place. MK46 4BY. Est. 1977. Open 10-4.30. SIZE: Medium. *STOCK: 18th-19th C mahogany and oak furniture, clocks, writing boxes, smalls, brass, copper.* PARK: Market Sq. TEL: 01234 712351. SER: Valuations; restorations (furniture, clocks). VAT: Stan/Spec.

Pine Antiques
10 Market Place. MK46 4EA. (Linda Wilkinson). Open 10-5, Sat. 9.30-5.30, Sun. 12-5. *STOCK: Pine furniture, antique and reclaimed.* TEL: 01234 711065; 01908 510226.

Robin Unsworth Antiques
1 Weston Rd. MK46 5BD. (R. and Z. M. Unsworth). Est. 1971. Open 9-5, Sun. 9-4.30. SIZE: Small. *STOCK: Longcase and wall clocks, £500-£15,000; period and Victorian furniture, £1,000-£10,000; objects of art, £200-£5,000.* LOC: 6 miles from junction 14, M1. PARK: Easy. TEL: 01234 711210; home - 01908 617193.

PENN, Nr. High Wycombe

Country Furniture Shop
3 Hazlemere Rd., Potters Cross. HP10 8AA. (M. and V. Thomas). LAPADA. Est. 1955. Open 9.30-1 and 2-5. SIZE: Large. *STOCK: Furniture, Georgian, £100-£5,000; Victoriana, £5-£2,500; large Victorian dining tables, Victorian dining chairs.* LOC: B474. PARK: Easy. TEL: 01494 812244; home - same. SER: Valuations. VAT: Stan/Spec.

Penn Barn
By the Pond, Elm Rd. HP10 8LB. (P. J. M. Hunnings). Est. 1968. Open Tues.-Sat. 9.30-1 and 2-5. SIZE: Medium. *STOCK: Antiquarian books, maps and prints, 19th C, £5-£500; watercolours and oils, 19th-20th C, £50-£1,500.* LOC: B474. PARK: Easy. TEL: 01494 815691.

PRINCES RISBOROUGH

Well Cottage Antiques Centre
20-22 Bell St. HP27 0AD. Open 9.30-5.30, Sun. and Bank Holidays 1-5. SIZE: Medium. *STOCK: Furniture including pine; silver, jewellery, china, glass, brass, copper, silhouettes, miniatures, treen, pictures and collectables.* LOC: A4010. TEL: 01844 342002.

WENDOVER

Antiques at . . .
Wendover Antiques Centre
The Old Post Office, 25 High St. HP22 6DU. (N. Gregory). Open 10.30-5.30, Sun. and Bank Holidays 11-5. SIZE: Large - 30 dealers + barn housing Aces High Aviation Art Gallery. *STOCK: General antiques dateline 1940/50 - town and country furniture, flatware, kitchenalia, gardenalia, pottery and porcelain, jewellery, Art Deco, Belleek, silver, lamps and lighting, clocks, barometers, telescopes, scientific and medical instruments, beds and bathroom fittings, decorative items, glass, metalware, lace and linen, architectural salvage and antiquities.* PARK: Own. TEL: 01296 625335; evenings - 01296 624633.

Bowood Antiques
Wendover Dean Farm, Bowood Lane. HP22 6PY. (Miss P. Peyton-Jones). LAPADA. Est. 1963. Open 9.30-5, Sat. 10-4.30 - prior telephone call advisable. SIZE: Large. *STOCK: Period furniture, 17th-19th C, £500-£10,000; decorative items, £50-£1,500.* LOC: A413, midway between Amersham and Aylesbury and Gt Missenden and Wendover. PARK: Easy. TEL: 01296 622113; home/fax - 01296 696598. VAT: Spec.

Past Treasures
Downstairs at Antiques At Wendover, The Old Post Office, 25 High St. HP22 6DU. (S. Valledy and M. Ryan). Est. 1996. Open 10.30-5.30, Sun. and Bank Holidays 11-5.30. SIZE: Small. *STOCK: Antiquities including Roman, Egyptian, Chinese and Greek, 2000 BC to 1600 AD, £20-£500; fossils, £5-£150; breweriana, old bottles, pot-lids, enamel advertising signs, £1-£150; collectables, to £50.* PARK: Easy. TEL: Mobile - 07740 203297; home - 01908 227149.

Sally Turner Antiques
Hogarth House, High St. HP22 6DU. LAPADA. Open 10-5. CL: Wed. and Sun. except Dec. SIZE: 7 showrooms + barn. *STOCK: Decorative and period furniture, general antiques and jewellery.* PARK: Rear of shop. TEL: 01296 624402; fax - same; mobile - 07860 201718.

Wendover Antiques
1 South St. HP22 6EF. (R. and D. Davies). LAPADA. Est. 1979. Open mainly Saturdays or by appointment. SIZE: Medium. *STOCK: Furniture, oils, 17th-19th C; decorative prints; 18th C silk embroideries, silhouettes, miniatures, Georgian decanters, silver and Sheffield plate; all £50-£5,000.* LOC: Near village centre on Wendover-Amersham road. PARK: 100yds. TEL: 01296 622078. VAT: Stan/Spec.

WHITCHURCH

Deerstalker Antiques
28 High St. HP22 4JT. (R.J. and L.L. Eichler). Open 10-5.30. CL: Mon. SIZE: Small. *STOCK: General antiques.* TEL: 01296 641505.

WINSLOW

Winslow Antiques Centre
15 Market Sq. MK18 3AB. Est. 1992. Open 10-5, Sun. 1-5. CL: Wed. SIZE: 20 dealers. *STOCK: Furniture, English pottery, silver and jewellery, general antiques.* LOC: A413. TEL: 01296 714540; fax - 01296 714556.

WOOBURN, Nr. High Wycombe

Lafleure Antiques & Decoration
Endsleigh, Town Lane. HP10 0JP. (Peter Lane). TVADA. Open 10-5, Sun. by appointment. CL: Mon. and Wed. *STOCK: Gilded, walnut and marble French furniture, soft furnishings, mirrors and objects, 19th C; paintings and unusual items, curtain accessories, lighting and decorative objects.* LOC: Off M4 on main road between Beaconsfield and Bourne End. TEL: 01628 530461.

Carlo G.V. Manzoni modelling a large clay figure at the Della Robbia Pottery, c.1895. (Private collection)

From an article entitled 'The Della Robbia Pottery' by Robert Prescott-Walker which appeared in the February 2001 issue of **Antique Collecting** magazine. For more details and to subscribe see page 147.

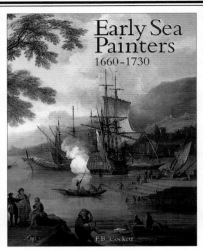

Early Sea Painters
1660–1730

F.B. Cockett

This is an important, newly researched study of the group of early marine painters working in England between 1660 and 1730, about whom little has previously been known or written. Their work was overshadowed by that of the Van de Veldes who dominated the field at the time. However, the many illustrations in this book demonstrate the high quality, broad range and excellent technique to be found in the works of these now much sought after painters.

"This is a delightful work and places on record much interesting material on the less well documented artists working in England from the mid-17th century to the second quarter of the 18th" **Topsail**

ISBN 1 85149 230 5, 160pp., 58 col. 47 b.&w. illus. **£25.00/$49.50**

For a free copy of our catalogue, please contact

ANTIQUE COLLECTORS' CLUB
5 Church Street, Woodbridge
Suffolk, IP12 1DS, UK
Tel: (01394) 385501 Fax: (01394) 384434
Sales Office Direct Fax: (01394) 388994
Email: sales@antique-acc.com
Website: www.antique-acc.com
—— *or* ——
Market Street Industrial Park, Wappingers'
Falls, NY 12590, USA
Tel: (845) 297 0003 Fax: (845) 297 0068
ORDERS: (800) 252 5231
Email: info@antiquecc.com
Website: www.antiquecc.com

BARTON, Nr. Cambridge

Bagatelle Antiques
Burwash Manor Barns, New Rd. CB3 7AY. (A. M. & M. H. Jeffery). Est. 1998. Open 10-5, Sat. 2-5, Sun. by appointment. SIZE: Medium. *STOCK: Furniture, 19th C, £100-£2,000; decorative items, 19th C to 1930's, £10-£250.* LOC: Signed from New Rd. PARK: Easy. TEL: 01223 264400; fax - 01223 264445. SER: Restorations (furniture including re-caning).

BOTTISHAM, Nr. Cambridge

Cambridge Pine
Hall Farm, Lode Rd. CB5 9DN. (Mr and Mrs D. Weir). Est. 1980. Open seven days. SIZE: Large. *STOCK: Pine, 18th-19th C and reproduction, £25-£1,400.* LOC: Midway between Bottisham and Lode, near Anglesey Abbey. PARK: Easy. TEL: 01223 811208; home - same. SER: Copies made in old timber with or without painted finish.

BURWELL

Antiques Emporium
59 High St. CB5 0HD. (S. J. Hunt). Est. 1990. Open 10.30-5, Sun. 11-5, Wed. & Thurs. by appointment. SIZE: Medium. *STOCK: Furniture, 18th-20th C, £100-£1,000; general antiques including china, glass, silver, cameras and radios, £5-£500.* PARK: Easy. TEL: 01638 741155. SER: Valuations; restorations (furniture).

Peter Norman Antiques and Restorations
Sefton House, 55 North St. CB5 0BA. (P. Norman and A. Marpole). Est. 1975. Open 9-12.30 and 2-5.30. SIZE: Medium. *STOCK: Furniture, clocks, arms and Oriental rugs, 17th-19th C, £250-£10,000.* PARK: Easy. TEL: 01638 616914. SER: Valuations; restorations (furniture, oil paintings, clocks, arms). VAT: Stan/Spec.

CAMBRIDGE

20th Century
169 Histon Rd. CB4 3JD. (S. Charles). Open Wed., Thurs. and Fri. 12-5, Sat. 10-5. *STOCK: Decorative arts, 1880-1980.* TEL: 01223 359482.

Jess Applin Antiques   BADA
8 Lensfield Rd. CB2 1EG. Est. 1968. Open 10-5. *STOCK: Furniture, 17th-19th C; works of art.* LOC: At junction with Hills Rd., opposite church. PARK: Pay and display nearby. TEL: 01223 315168. VAT: Spec.

CAMBRIDGESHIRE

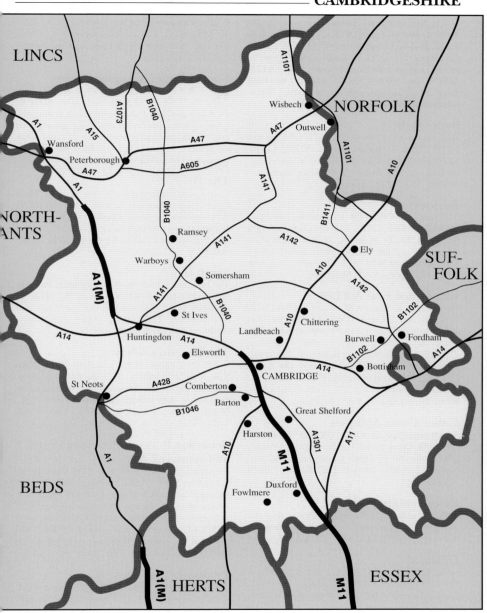

Dealers and Shops in Cambridgeshire

Barton	1	Duxford	1	Harston	1	Somersham	1
Bottisham	1	Elsworth	1	Huntingdon	1	St. Ives	1
Burwell	2	Ely	2	Landbeach	1	St. Neots	1
Cambridge	20	Fordham	1	Outwell	1	Wansford	1
Chittering	1	Fowlmere	1	Peterborough	6	Warboys	1
Comberton	1	Great Shelford	2	Ramsey	2	Wisbech	4

John Beazor and Sons Ltd   BADA

78-80 Regent St. CB2 1DP. Est. 1875. Open 9.15-5, Sat. 10-4 or by appointment. *STOCK: English furniture, late 17th to early 19th C; clocks, barometers and decorative items.* TEL: 01223 355178; fax - 01223 355183; e-mail - martin@johnbeazorantiques.co.uk; website - www.johnbeazorantiques.co.uk. SER: Valuations.

Benet Gallery

26 Long Rd. CB2 2PS. (G.H. and J. Criddle). Est. 1965. Open by appointment. SIZE: Large. *STOCK: Maps and prints of Cambridge, including college views by Ackermann, all periods.* TEL: 01223 248739.

Buckies

31 Trinity St. CB2 1TB. (G. McClure-Buckie). LAPADA. NAG, GMC. Est. 1972. Open 9.45-5. CL: Mon. SIZE: Medium. *STOCK: Jewellery, silver, objets d'art.* PARK: Multi-storey, nearby. TEL: 01223 357910. SER: Valuations; restorations and repairs. VAT: Stan/Spec.

Cambridge Fine Art Ltd

Priesthouse, 33 Church St., Little Shelford. CB2 5HG. (R. and J. Lury). LAPADA. Resident. Est. 1972. Open daily 10-6, Sun. by appointment. SIZE: Large. *STOCK: British and European paintings, 1780-1900; modern British paintings, 1880-1940; British prints by J.M. Kronheim to the Baxter Process.* LOC: Next to church. PARK: Easy. TEL: 01223 842866/843537. SER: Valuations; restorations; buys at auction. VAT: Stan/Spec.

Gabor Cossa Antiques

34 Trumpington St. CB2 1QY. (D. Theobald). Est. 1948. Open 10-6. *STOCK: English ceramics, glass, bijouterie.* LOC: Opposite Fitzwilliam Museum. PARK: 400yds. TEL: 01223 356049. VAT: Global.

Peter Crabbe Antiques

3 Pembroke St. CB2 3QY. Open 10-4.30. *STOCK: Furniture and Oriental porcelain and works of art.* TEL: 01223 357117. VAT: Spec.

G. David

16 St. Edward's Passage. CB2 3PJ. ABA, PBFA. Est. 1896. Open 9-5. *STOCK: Antiquarian books, fine bindings, secondhand and out of print books, selected publishers remainders.* TEL: 01223 354619.

Deighton Bell and Co

20 Trinity St. CB2 1TY. (Heffers Booksellers). Est. 1794. Open 9-5.30. *STOCK: Antiquarian, rare and fine old books, most subjects; illustrated books.* PARK: Multi-storey, 300yds. TEL: 01223 568513. VAT: Stan.

Galloway and Porter Ltd

30 Sidney St. CB2 3HS. ABA. Est. 1900. *STOCK: Antiquarian and secondhand books.* TEL: 01223 367876.

Gwydir Street Antiques Centre

Units 1 & 2 Dales Brewery, Gwydir St. CB1 2LJ. Open 10-5, Sat. 9.30-5.30, Sun. 11-5. *STOCK: Victorian and Edwardian furniture in mahogany, walnut, pine, satinwood and oak; upholstered arm chairs and sofas; lamps, mirrors and other decorative items.* LOC: Off Mill Rd. PARK: Opposite. TEL: 01223 356391.

The Hive

Unit 3, Dales Brewery, Gwydir St. CB1 2LG. Open 10-5, Wed. 10-7, Sun. 11-5. *STOCK: Victorian and Edwardian furniture, antique pine, kitchenalia, period lighting, collectables, pictures and bric-a-brac.* PARK: Opposite. TEL: 01223 300269.

Sarah Key

The Haunted Bookshop, 9 St. Edward's Passage. CB2 3PJ. Est. 1987. Open 10-5. *STOCK: Children's and illustrated books, literature and antiquarian.* TEL: 01223 312913; e-mail - sarahkey@hauntedbooks.demon.co.uk.

The Lawson Gallery

7-8 King's Parade. CB2 1SJ. Est. 1967. Open 9.30-5. SIZE: Medium. *STOCK: Posters, prints, limited editions, specialists in prints of Cambridge both antiquarian and modern.* LOC: Opposite King's College. PARK: Lion Yard. TEL: 01223 313970. VAT: Stan.

Sebastian Pearson Paintings Prints and Works of Art

3 Pembroke St. CB2 3QY. Est. 1989. Open 10.30-5.30. CL: Mon. SIZE: Medium. *STOCK: Oil paintings and watercolours, £300-£3,500; 20th C British prints (etchings and wood engravings), £60-£600.* LOC: City centre. PARK: Nearby. TEL: 01223 323999; home - 01438 871364. SER: Valuations; picture framing; exhibitions of contemporary paintings. VAT: Spec.

Pembroke Antiques

7 Pembroke St. CB2 3QY. (K.N. and R.M. Galey). Open 10-4. CL: Mon. SIZE: Small. *STOCK: Silver, furniture, 18th-19th C; jewellery, 18th-20th C.* LOC: 100 yards off Trumpington St., opposite Pembroke College. PARK: 100 yards. TEL: 01223 363246. VAT: Stan/Spec.

Solopark Plc

Station Rd., Nr. Pampisford. CB2 4HB. (R.J. Bird). Open Mon.-Thurs. 8-5, Fri. and Sat. 8-4, Sun. 9-1. *STOCK: Traditional and new building* materials, timber and period architectural items. TEL: 01223 834663; fax - 01223 834780; e-mail - info@solopark.co.uk; website- www. solopark. co.uk.

Those were the Days
91-93 Mill Rd. CB1 2AW. Est. 1984. Open 9.30-5.30, Sun. 11-5. SIZE: Medium. *STOCK: General antiques including furniture, period lighting and fireplaces, 19th C, £5-£1,500.* LOC: Nearby. TEL: 01223 300440.

Valued History
13 Benet St. CB2 3PT. (Paul Murawski). Est. 1995. Open 10-5. CL: Mon. SIZE: Small. *STOCK: Antiquities, ancient to Tudor, £25-£1,000+; coins and other artifacts, £5-1,000.* LOC: Off King's Parade, near Market Sq. PARK: Multi-storey nearby. TEL: 01223 319319. SER: Valuations. FAIRS: Cumberland Coin. VAT: Spec.

CHITTERING, Nr. Cambridge

Simon and Penny Rumble Antiques
Causeway End Farmhouse. CB5 9PW. Open by appointment. *STOCK: Early oak, country furniture, woodcarving and works of art.* LOC: 6 miles north of Cambridge, off A10. TEL: 01223 861831.

COMBERTON

Comberton Antiques
5a West St. CB3 7DS. (Mrs M. McEvoy). Est. 1980. Open Mon., Fri. and Sat. 10-5, Sun. 2-5. SIZE: Large. *STOCK: Furniture, 1780-1920, £50-£2,000; bric-a-brac, 1830-1920, £5-£100; hand-made Turkish kelims; shipping goods.* LOC: 6 miles west of Cambridge, 2 miles junction 12 M11. PARK: Easy. TEL: 01223 262674; home - 01223 263457.

DUXFORD

Riro D. Mooney
4 Moorfield Rd. CB2 4PS. Est. 1946. Open 9-7. SIZE: Medium. *STOCK: General antiques, 1780-1920, £5-£1,200.* LOC: 1 mile from M11. PARK: Easy. TEL: 01223 832252. VAT: Stan/Spec.

ELSWORTH, Nr. Cambridge

Norman Blackburn
PO Box 971. CB3 8FS. Est. 1974. *STOCK: Prints - decorative, stipple and mezzotints, botanical,* sporting, marine, portraits and views, pre-1860. TEL: 01954 267103; fax - same; mobile - 07714 721846; e-mail - oldprints@normanblackburn. com.

ELY

Mrs Mills Antiques
1a St. Mary's St. CB7 4ER. Open 10-5. CL: Tues. *STOCK: China, jewellery, silver.* Not Stocked: Furniture. TEL: 01353 664268.

Waterside Antiques Centre
The Wharf. CB7 4AU. Est. 1986. Open 9.30-5.30 including Bank Holidays, Sun. 11.30-5.30. SIZE: Large. *STOCK: General antiques.* LOC: Waterside area. PARK: Easy. TEL: 01353 667066.

FORDHAM, Nr. Bly

Phoenix Antiques
1 Carter St. CB7 5NG. Est. 1966. Open by appointment only. SIZE: Medium. *STOCK: Early European furniture, domestic metalwork, pottery and delft, carpets, scientific instruments, treen and bygones.* LOC: Centre of village. PARK: Own. TEL: 01638 720363.

FOWLMERE, Nr. Royston

Mere Antiques
High St. SG8 7SU. (R.W. Smith). Est. 1979. Open 10-1 and 2-6, including Sun. SIZE: Medium. *STOCK: Furniture, porcelain and clocks, 18th-19th C, to £5,000.* PARK: Easy. TEL: 01763 208477; home - 01763 208495. SER: Valuations. VAT: Spec.

GREAT SHELFORD, Nr. Cambridge

The Store Antiques
134 Cambridge Rd. CB2 5JU. (Mick Lambourn-Brown and Warren Dosanjh). Est. 1980. Open 10-4, Sun. 11-4. CL: Mon. SIZE: Medium. *STOCK: Furniture, collectables, architectural and decorative items, bygones, 18th C to Victorian, £5-£1,000.* LOC: Adjacent to Scotsdale's Garden Centre, main road into village. PARK: Easy. TEL: 01223 841070; fax - 01223 839102; home - 01223 276243. SER: Valuations; restorations; buys at auction. FAIRS: Newark.

Storm Fine Arts Ltd
Church Street Barns. CB2 5EL. (Bill & Sue Mason). Resident. Est. 1998. Open by appoint-

MY GOODNESS!
MY GUINNESS!

Dick Henrywood

As we all know, these days there are collectors for just about anything, and the range of so-called collectors' items is vast. Advertising wares have been collectable for many years, with specialist fairs and auctions and plenty of eager buyers for anything rare or unusual. One recent such example was an American 1895 Heinz catalogue of Picklers and Preservers, containing 46 attractive chromolithographed plates, which was sold by Dreweatt Neate of Newbury in June last year for a hefty £1,173. Notable prices like this can, of course, be quoted in any field, but it is the more readily available items which give a clearer guide to the state of any market.

Of all advertising names one of the most recognisable must be Guinness. With well-known slogans such as 'Guinness is Good for You' and 'Guinness for Strength', the company has made particularly effective use of its advertising budgets. Its near obsession with advertising and promotion dates back to the 1920s, but most readers will be familiar with the recent 'Pure Genius', 'Black & White', and similar campaigns.

While much of the company's work has taken the form of traditional posters and printed advertisements, and more recently film and television, Guinness is probably unique in its extensive use of associated promotional wares. They were marketing goods of every description long before the advent of what we now call merchandising. Over the years their output has been vast, but the following list should give a flavour of what can be found.

Alongside the more traditional drinks-related items such as beer mats, ashtrays, mugs, jugs, corkscrews, bottle openers, trays and glasses, we find household wares such as storage jars (figure 2), teapots, mugs, eggcups, cruet sets, plates and teaspoons. There were personal items such as pens, penknives, keyrings, cufflinks, buttons, pendants, clothes brushes, umbrellas (figure 1), and even waistcoats and sun hats alongside the ubiquitous T-shirts. Trinkets such as horse brasses contrast with more expensive items such as watches and clocks (figure 1), cameras and barometers. Stuffed toys vie with mirrors, postcards contrast with a bodhran (an Irish drum) – the lists are virtually endless. It is not surprising that all this proves such a rich vein for collectors.

While all these wares have been collected for some years now, the market received its biggest boost in 1996 when Christie's South Kensington held an auction devoted to Guinness advertising ware and, as with any such specialist sale, prices were generally very strong. Many of the estimates were exceeded by significant margins but despite the special nature of the sale, there were only two hammer prices which reached four figures, and these were both for original artwork by the famous illustrator John Gilroy. Outside the ephemera, the top prices were mostly achieved by lamps (with £690 for a sealion lamp as in figure 3), toucan wall plaques (with £747 for a set of three, again as in figure 3), and the relatively rare toucan jug (£713, similar to the jug in figure 1). This was an exceptional sale and created some exceptional prices, but other salerooms around the country are close to achieving similarly high figures, and some recent reports that the Guinness market has witnessed a downturn could not be further from the truth.

While all Guinness products are sought after, the decorative china wares are particularly popular. These were obtained from various manufacturers, but by far the most prolific supplier was Carltonware. They made household wares such as storage jars (figure 2), cruet sets, mugs and eggcups, alongside more decorative wares such as figures and lampbases. One of the most desirable of the utilitarian items is the toucan jug (figure 1). The single example with a green base at Christie's in 1996 fetched £713 (£620 plus 15% premium), while a slight variant with a sand-coloured base sold at Dreweatt Neate in October 1998 for £715 (£650 plus 10% premium).

The figures include a charming small set of the famous zoo keeper and his animals, each inscribed 'My Goodness! My Guinness!' (figures 1 and 2). These sell for around £50 to £150 each, depending on condition, subject and demand on the day. One particularly desirable figure shows a drayman pulling his own cart, with the horse sitting rather smugly in the back! Two of these sold in May this year for £368 and £345.

Several different lamps were

Above. Figure 1. A typical mix of Guinness wares including an umbrella, a rare Toucan jug and a similar lampbase, two small china figures and a plastic waddling penguin, and a promotional wall clock.

Figure 2. A rare Guinness 'Roglow' heat-driven advertising lamp and various Carltonware ceramics including storage jars, a lampbase and four more of the small china figures.

made, the simplest being of bulbous form printed with a band of running toucans (base only in figure 2). The more desirable are in the form of a penguin, a sealion balancing a spherical shade on his nose (figure 3), or a toucan standing beside a pint of Guinness (base only in figure 1). The toucan lamp is decorated with the wonderful verse:

How grand to be a toucan,
Just think what toucan do.
If he can say as you can,
Guinness is good for you!

Various matching shades were produced. These lamps are all popular and range in price up to more than £500, although some of the simpler types might be found for around £50 or so on a very lucky day! The sealion lamp illustrated here sold relatively recently for £633, helped particularly by being in mint condition, complete with its original box and all internal packing.

Rarest of all is the 'Roglow' advertising lamp, again heat driven, with a three-sided shade projecting various Guinness slogans on to a curved reflector (figure 2). This was clearly made with a very short life in mind, its ephemeral construction probably accounting for its rarity. The example shown here was in amazingly good condition, apparently never used, again with its original box and appropriate packing, including Guinness Park Royal Brewery address labels. It sold for £368.

Perhaps the most evocative of all the Carltonware products are the flying toucan wall decorations, in

the style of the much-derided 1950s set of three graduated ducks flying up the stairs, but in the form of toucans, each balancing two pints of Guinness on its beak (figure 3). If perfect, the set of three will normally sell for around £250, sometimes more, although the set shown here in the original cardboard packing flew to an impressive £483. There was little doubt about the authenticity of this set, but these flying toucans have been extensively reproduced along with other Carltonware Guinness products, particularly the figures. The reproductions are now *very* commonly found in antiques fairs and markets, so *caveat emptor*, let the buyer beware!

All Guinness products are collectable. With beer mats the

cheapest, and lamps amongst the most expensive, there is plenty to interest all collectors, even the most impecunious. While other brewers have produced similar wares, the Guinness name commands a considerable premium. Their output was vast, imaginative, and perhaps most importantly, fun.

Dick Henrywood is the specialist responsible for collectors' items and blue-printed pottery at the auctioneers Dreweatt Neate of Newbury.

This article appeared in the July/August 2000 issue of **Antique Collecting** magazine. For more details of the Antique Collectors' Club magazine see page 147.

Figure 3. A set of Guinness wall toucans complete with original packing, and a popular sealion lamp with heat-driven rotating shade.

167

ment. SIZE: Medium. *STOCK: Paintings and pictures, 1500 to date, £500-£100,000; porcelain, pottery and glass, 1800-1900, £150-£1,500; decorative arts, 1700 to date, £100-£15,000; textiles, 1700-1900, £1,000-£30,000.* PARK: Easy. TEL: 01223 844786; fax - 01223 847871; website - www.stormfinearts.com SER: Valuations; restorations; buys at auction. VAT: Stan.

HARSTON

Antique Clocks
1 High St. CB2 5PX. (C.J. Stocker). Open every day. LOC: On A10, 5 miles south of Cambridge. PARK: Easy. TEL: 01223 870264.

HUNTINGDON

Adams Furniture Centre
The Old Post Office, George St. PE18 6AW. (Stephen Copsey). Est. 1977. Open 9.30-5.30. CL: Thurs. SIZE: Large. *STOCK: Mainly furniture.* LOC: Off Huntingdon ring road. PARK: Easy. TEL: 01480 435100; fax - 01480 454387. SER: Valuations; buys at auction. VAT: Stan/Spec.

LANDBEACH

J.V. Pianos and Cambridge Pianola Company
The Limes, 85 High St. CB4 8DR. (F.T. Poole). Est. 1972. Open Mon.-Fri., evenings and weekends by appointment. SIZE: Medium. *STOCK: Pianos, pianolas and pianola rolls.* LOC: First building on right in Landbeach from A10. PARK: Easy. TEL: 01223 861348/861507; home - same; fax - 01223 441276; website - www...cambridgepianolacompany.co.uk. SER: Valuations; restorations. VAT: Stan.

OUTWELL, Nr. Wisbech

A.P. and M.A. Haylett
Glen-Royd, 393 Wisbech Rd. PE14 8PG. Open 9-6 including Sun. *STOCK: Country furniture, pottery, treen and metalware, 1750-1900, £5-£500.* Not Stocked: Firearms. LOC: A1101. PARK: Easy. TEL: 01945 772427; home - same. SER: Buys at auction.

PETERBOROUGH

Antiques & Curios
249 Lincoln Rd., Millfield. PE2 5NZ. (M. and Mrs R. Mason). Est. 1990. Open 10-5. SIZE: Medium. *STOCK: Pine furniture, 19th C, £50-£500; mahogany and oak furniture, 19th to early 20th C, £50-£500; fireplaces, 19th C, £50-£1,000; collectables, 19th-20th C, £10-£100.* LOC: North from city centre. PARK: Easy. TEL: 01733 314948; home - same. SER: Valuations; restorations (furniture stripping and polishing, fireplaces). FAIRS: Peterborough Festival of Antiques.

Francis Bowers Chess Suppliers
138 Reeves Way, Eastfield. PE1 5LY. Resident. Est. 1991. Open by appointment only. SIZE: Small. *STOCK: Chess books, boards, sets and timers; clocks.* TEL: 01733 562778.

Fitzwilliam Antiques Centre
Fitzwilliam St. PE1 2RX. Open 10-5. SIZE: 25 dealers. *STOCK: General antiques.* LOC: Near city centre. PARK: Easy. TEL: 01733 565415/566346.

Ivor and Patricia Lewis Antique and Fine Art Dealers
Westfield, 30 Westwood Park Rd. PE3 6JL. LAPADA. Open by appointment. *STOCK: Decorative English and French furniture, 19th to early 20th C.* TEL: 01733 344567.

Old Soke Books
68 Burghley Rd. PE1 2QE. (Peter and Linda Clay). Open Tues.-Sat. 10.30-5.30. *STOCK: Antiquarian and secondhand books, paintings, prints, ephemera and postcards, some furniture and small antiques.* TEL: 01733 564147.

G. Smith and Sons (Peterborough) Ltd
1379 Lincoln Rd., Werrington. PE4 6LT. (Mike Groucott). Est. 1902. Open 9-5. SIZE: Medium. *STOCK: General antiques, furniture and clocks.* LOC: Old Lincoln Road, Werrington village. PARK: Easy. TEL: 01733 571630. SER: Restorations.

RAMSEY, Nr. Huntingdon

Abbey Antiques
63 Great Whyte. PE26 1HL. (R. and J. Smith). Est. 1977. Open 10-5 including Sun. CL: Mon. SIZE: Small. *STOCK: Furniture including pine, 1850-1930, £50-£500; porcelain, Goss and crested china, 1830-1950, £3-£500; Beswick, Wade and Fen pottery, Mabel Lucie Attwell, Disney and small collectables.* PARK: Easy. TEL: 01487 814753. SER: Mabel Lucie Attwell Museum and Collectors' Club: Memories UK (Enesco Memories of Yesterday figurines sold). FAIRS: Alexandra Palace.

Antique Barometers
Wingfield, 26 Biggin Lane. PE26 1NB. (William and Helen Rae). Open by appointment. *STOCK: Fine barometers, 18th-19th C, barographs, £400-£10,000.* PARK: Easy. TEL: 01487 814060; home/fax - same; e-mail - antiquebarometers@ talk21.com. SER: Valuations; restorations.

SOMERSHAM, Nr. Huntingdon

T. W. Pawson - Clocks
31A High St. PE28 3JA. Est. 1981. Open by appointment. SIZE: Small. *STOCK: Antique clocks, £150-£5,000; mercury barometers, to mid-19th C.* LOC: Main road through village. PARK: Easy. TEL: 01487 841537; home - same. SER: Restorations, overhauls, repairs (clocks and barometers).

ST. IVES

B.R. Knight and Sons
Quay Court, Bull Lane, Bridge St. PE17 4AU. (M. Knight). Est. 1972. Open Mon., Wed., Fri. 11-2, Sat. 10.30-4.30 or by appointment. SIZE: Medium. *STOCK: Porcelain, pottery, jewellery, paintings, watercolours, prints, decorative arts.* LOC: Off Bridge St. PARK: Nearby. TEL: 01480 468295/300042; e-mail - michaelknight1@ compuserve.com.

ST. NEOTS

Tavistock Antiques
Cross Hall Manor, Eaton Ford. PE19 4AH. Open by appointment. *STOCK: Period English furniture.* TEL: 01480 472082. *Trade Only.*

WANSFORD, Nr. Peterborough

Starlight
16 London Rd. PE8 6JB. Resident. Open Tues.-Fri. 10-1 and 2-5 and most Sats. 10-1 and 2.30-5. *STOCK: Period and new lighting, candles, oil lamps and parts.* LOC: On A1 near A47 junction. PARK: Easy. TEL: 01780 783999; fax - same; e-mail - starlight@lampsandcandles.freeserve. co.uk; website - www.starlight-rpr.co.uk.

WARBOYS

Warboys Antiques
Old Church School, High St. PE28 2SX. (J. Lambden and E. Godfrey). Est. 1986. Open Tues.- Sat. 11-5. SIZE: Medium. *STOCK: Decorative smalls, 18th-20th C; sports equipment, advertising items, 19th-20th C; all £1-£1,500.* LOC: Off A141. PARK: Easy. TEL: 01487 823686; fax - 01480 496296; e-mail - john.lambden@virgin.net; website - www. sportingantiques.co.uk. SER: Valuations. FAIRS: Alexandra Palace.

WISBECH

Antiques & Curios (Steve Carpenter)
96 Norfolk St. PE13 2LF. Est. 1985. Open 9-5, Sun. by appointment. CL: Wed. SIZE: Small. *STOCK: Georgian and Victorian longcase clocks, £1,000-£3,000; Victorian and Edwardian furniture, 19th C, £100-£2,000; bygones and collectables, 18th-20th C, £5-£300.* LOC: Town centre, just off A47. PARK: Easy. TEL: 01945 588441. SER: Valuations; restorations (structural, veneering and polishing).

Peter A. Crofts BADA
Briar Patch, High Rd., Elm. PE14 0DN. Est. 1949. CL: Sat. *STOCK: General antiques, furniture, porcelain, silver, jewellery.* LOC: A1101. TEL: 01945 584614. VAT: Stan/Spec.

Granny's Cupboard
34 Old Market. PE13 1NF. (R.J. Robbs). Est. 1982. Open Tues. and Thurs. 10.30-4, Sat. 10.30-3. SIZE: Small. *STOCK: China, glass, small furniture, Victorian to 1950's, £5-£500.* PARK: Easy. TEL: 01945 589606; home - 01945 870730. FAIRS: The Maltings, Ely.

R. Wilding
Lanes End, Gadds Lane, Leverington. PE13 5BJ. *STOCK: Bamboo furniture and mirrors; period furniture including walnut chests; gilt/polished mirrors.* TEL: 01945 588204; fax - 01945 475712. SER: Veneering; polishing; compo carving; gilding; conversions; replicas. *Trade Only.*

CHESHIRE

Sara Frances Antiques
32 South St. SK9 7ES. (Mrs. F.S. Waterworth). Est. 1990. Open Tues. 10-1, Thurs., Fri. and Sat. 10-4. SIZE: Small. *STOCK: Furniture, 17th-19th C, £100-£6,000; silver, 19th-20th C, £50-£500; decorative items, 17th-20th C, £100-£2,500.* LOC: Off London Rd. PARK: Easy. TEL: 01625 585549/584516; mobile - 07801 458852. SER: Valuations; restorations (furniture and silver).

D.J. Massey and Son
51a London Rd. SK9 7DY. Est. 1900. Open 9.15-5.15, Wed. 9.15-4.45. SIZE: Large. *STOCK: Victorian jewellery, silverware, gold and diamond jewellery.* LOC: On A34. PARK: Easy. TEL: 01625 583565. VAT: Stan/Spec.

Trash 'n' Treasure
48 Sandbach Rd. South. ST7 2LP. (G. and D. Ogden). Est. 1979. Open Tues., Thurs., Fri. and Sat. 10-4. SIZE: Medium. *STOCK: Late Georgian to 1930's furniture, pictures, ceramics, £5-£10,000.* LOC: 10 minutes junction 16, M6. PARK: Nearby. TEL: 01270 872972/873246. SER: Valuations; lectures.

Bizarre Decorative Arts North West
116 Manchester Rd. WA14 4PY. (Malcolm C. and Rebecca Lamb). Resident. Est. 1986. Open 10-6, Sun. by appointment. SIZE: Large. *STOCK: Furniture and lighting, £100-£15,000; figurines, bronzes, ceramics including Clarice Cliff, and jewellery, £5-£2,000; all Art Nouveau and Art Deco.* LOC: A56. PARK: Own. TEL: 0161 926 8895; home - same; fax - 0161 929 8310. SER: Valuations; restorations (furniture and lighting; silver and chrome plating, pewter polishing). FAIRS: NEC Aug; Loughborough Art Deco; Kensington Decorative Arts. VAT: Stan/Spec.

Church Street Antiques
4/4a Old Market Place. WA14 4NP. (Alex Smalley and Nick Stanley). Open 10-5.30, Sun. 12-4. SIZE: Large. *STOCK: Furniture, 18th-19th C, £100-£10,000; silver and plate, 19th C, £50-£1,000; paintings, 19th C to contemporary, £100-£5,000.* PARK: Easy. TEL: 0161 929 5196; fax - same; mobile - 07768 318661; website - www.churchstreetantiques.com. SER: Valuations; restorations. FAIRS: Tatton; Chester; Lakes; Stafford; Newark; NEC. VAT: Spec.

Robert Redford Antiques & Interiors
48 New St. WA14 2QS. (S. and R. Redford). Open 10-6. CL: Mon. and Wed. *STOCK: General antiques, furniture, small silver, porcelain, glass.* PARK: Easy. TEL: 0161 929 8171; home - 0161 926 8232; fax - 0161 928 4827.

Squires Antiques
25 Regent Rd. WA14 1RX. (V. Phillips). Est. 1977. Open 10-5. CL: Mon. and Wed. SIZE: Medium. *STOCK: Small furniture, 1800-1930, £60-£1,500; small silver, 1850-1970, £20-£400; brass, copper and bric-a-brac, 1850-1940, £10-£400; jewellery, porcelain, fire accessories, light fittings and interior design items.* Not Stocked: Large furniture, coins and badges. LOC: Adjacent hospital, and large car park. PARK: Easy. TEL: 0161 928 0749. SER: Valuations.

Derek and Tina Rayment Antiques
BADA
Orchard House, Barton Rd. SY14 7HT. (D.J. and K.M. Rayment). LAPADA. Est. 1960. Open by appointment every day. *STOCK: Barometers, 18th-20th C, from £100.* LOC: A534. PARK: Easy. TEL: 01829 270429; home - same. SER: Valuations; restorations (barometers only); buys at auction (barometers). FAIRS: Olympia; Chelsea; LAPADA NEC. VAT: Stan/Spec.

House of St Clair
Clarence Mill, Clarence Rd. SK10 5JZ. Est. 1970. Open Thurs., Fri. and Sat. 10-5, Sun. 11-5. SIZE: Small. *STOCK: Jewellery, silver, ceramics and glass, 18th to early 20th C, £2-£500.* LOC: Off Macclesfield Silk Rd., through village, left after traffic lights. PARK: Easy. TEL: 01625 576867; home - 0161 449 9978. SER: Valuations; restorations. FAIRS: Buxton, Deanwater Hotel, Stockport Town Hall.

The Lighthouse
68 Palmerston St. SK10 5PW. (Jane and Philip Gwynne). Est. 1999. Open 11-3.30. CL: Wed. SIZE: Small. *STOCK: General antiques and collectibles.* LOC: 4 miles from Macclesfield, through village, opposite Pool Bank car park. PARK: Opposite. TEL: 01625 576500.

Richmond Antiques
Richmond Rd. WA14 2TT. (Joe Freeman). Est.

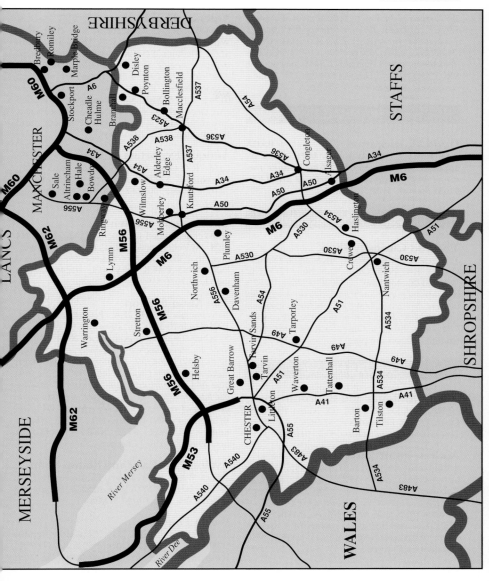

Dealers and Shops in Cheshire

Alderley Edge	2	Congleton	3	Lymm	2
Alsager	1	Crewe	2	Macclesfield	5
Altrincham	4	Davenham	1	Marple Bridge	1
Barton	1	Disley	1	Mobberley	1
Bollington	2	Great Barrow	1	Nantwich	9
Bowdon	1	Hale	1	Northwich	1
Bramhall	1	Haslington	1	Plumley	1
Bredbury	1	Helsby	1	Poynton	2
Cheadle Hulme	2	Knutsford	5	Ringway	1
Chester	26	Littleton	1	Romiley	1
				Sale	1

Stockport	12
Stretton	1
Tarporley	2
Tarvin	1
Tarvin Sands	1
Tattenhall	1
Tilston	1
Warrington	1
Waverton	1
Wilmslow	2

1992. Open 12-6, Sun. by appointment. CL: Mon. *STOCK: Mirrors, 19th C, £300-£2,000; French decorative furniture, 19th C, £150-£500; chandeliers, early 20th C, £200-£700.* LOC: Near Manchester airport, junction 7, M56, junction 19, M6. PARK: Easy. TEL: 01619 281229; home - same. SER: Restorations. VAT: Spec.

BRAMHALL

David H. Dickinson
BADA
P.O. Box 29. SK7 2EJ. Est. 1976. Open by appointment only. STOCK: Fine antique furniture and extraordinary works of art. TEL: 01625 560821. SER: Valuations.

BREDBURY, Nr. Stockport

The Old Curiosity Shop
123 Stockport Rd. West. SK6 2AN. (Sandra Crook). Est. 1984. Open 10-6, Sun. 12-5. CL: Wed. SIZE: Medium. *STOCK: 1920's, 1930's oak furniture, especially barley twist; brass coal buckets, fire tools.* LOC: At junction with Bents Lane. PARK: Forecourt or opposite. TEL: 0161 494 9469; home - same. SER: Restorations (furniture - hand stripping).

CHEADLE HULME

Allan's Antiques and Reproductions
10 Ravenoak Rd. SK8 7DL. (S. Allan). Est. 1979. Open Thurs., Fri. and Sat. *STOCK: Furniture, general antiques, metalware.* TEL: 0161 485 3132.

Andrew Foott Antiques
4 Claremont Rd. SK8 6EG. Est. 1985. Open by appointment only. SIZE: Small. *STOCK: Barometers, 18th-20th C, £200-£2,500; small furniture, 18th-20th C, £500-£3,000.* LOC: 5 minutes from new A34 by-pass. PARK: Easy. TEL: 0161 485 3559; fax - same. SER: Restorations (barometers and furniture). FAIRS: NEC Antiques for Everyone.

CHESTER

Adams Antiques
65 Watergate Row. CH1 2LE. (B. and T. Adams). LAPADA. Est. 1973. Open 10-5. CL: Sun. except by appointment. SIZE: Medium. *STOCK: English and Continental furniture, £200-£4,000; English and French clocks, £150-£4,000; objets d'art, £10-£3,000; all 18th to early 20th C.* PARK: Nearby. TEL: 01244 319421. SER: Valuations; restorations (furniture and clocks). VAT: Stan/Spec.

Aldersey Hall Ltd
Town Hall Sq., 47 Northgate St. CH1 2HQ. (Kim Wilding-Welton). Est. 1990. Open 8.30-5.30. SIZE: Medium. *STOCK: Art Deco and general British ceramics, £5-£500; small furniture, £50-£200; all 1880-1940.* LOC: Between library and Odeon cinema. PARK: Own 100 yards. TEL: 01244 324885. SER: Valuations; buys at auction (Art Deco ceramics). FAIRS: Alexandra Palace, Loughborough, Ardingly, Newark and Birmingham. VAT: Stan/Spec.

Antique Exporters of Chester
CH3 7RZ. Open by appointment only. SIZE: Warehouse. *STOCK: Furniture.* TEL: 01829 741001; home - 01244 570069. SER: Packing. *Export Only.*

The Antique Garden
Grosvenor Garden Centre, Wrexham Rd. CH4 9EB. (Maria Hopwood). Est. 1991. Open Tues.-Sun. 10-4.30. *STOCK: Garden-related bygones.* LOC: A483. PARK: Easy. TEL: 01244 629191; mobile - 07976 539990.

The Antique Shop
40 Watergate St. CH1 2LA. (Peter Thornber). Est. 1985. Open 10-5.30, Sat. 10-6, Sun. (May-Dec.) 1-5, other times by appointment. SIZE: Small. *STOCK: Metalware - brass, pewter, copper, iron, 1700-1900, £35-£350; Doulton - character jugs, figures and series ware, 1890-1960, £35-£350; blue and white transfer printed ware; Prattware pot lids, British Army cap badges; fountain pens; boxes and treen; cranberry glass.* LOC: Off Bridge St. PARK: Nearby. TEL: 01244 316286; home - 0151 327 1725. SER: Restorations (metalwork). FAIRS: Cheshire.

Avalon Post Card and Stamp Shop
1 City Walls, Rufus Court, Northgate St. CH1 2JG. (G.E. Ellis). *STOCK: Postcards, stamps and collectables.* TEL: 01244 318406.

Baron Fine Art
68 Watergate St. CH1 2LA. (S. and R. Baron). LAPADA. Est. 1984. Open 9.30-5.30. *STOCK: Watercolours and oils, some etchings, late 19th to early 20th C, some contemporary, £50-£60,000.* PARK: Easy. TEL: 01244 342520. SER: Restorations; framing. FAIRS: Tatton Park; LAPADA (Jan.); NEC (April, Aug. and Nov). VAT: Stan/Spec.

Boustead-Bland Antiques
59-61 Watergate Row. CH1 2LE. LAPADA. Open 10-5.30. *STOCK: 17th-19th C town and country furniture; portraits, clocks, metalware, pottery, porcelain and lighting.* TEL: 01244 342300/350366.

Cameo Antiques

19 Watergate St. CH1 2LB. Est. 1994. Open 9-5, Sat. 9-5.30. SIZE: Small. *STOCK: Jewellery and English silver, 1800-1990, £20-£2,000; English (including Moorcroft and Sally Tuffin pottery) and Continental porcelain, 1750-1960.* LOC: Off Bridge St. PARK: Easy. TEL: 01244 311467; fax - same. SER: Valuations; restorations. VAT: Stan/Spec.

Deja Vu Antiques

23 Grosvenor St. CH1 2DD. (I. and Mrs A. S. Jones). Open 9.30-5. SIZE: Small. *STOCK: 1920's to 1950's telephones, £50-£500; Victorian pine and walnut furniture, general antiques and reproduction items, £5-£500.* PARK: Nearby. TEL: 01244 315625. SER: Restorations (telephones). FAIRS: Art Deco - Loughborough, Chester, Leeds, Coventry Hilton.

Farmhouse Antiques

21-23 Christleton Rd., Boughton. CH3 5UF. (K. Appleby). Est. 1973. Open 9-5. SIZE: Large. *STOCK: Farmhouse furniture, longcase clocks, Staffordshire pottery, country bygones, mechanical music.* LOC: 1 mile from City centre on A41. PARK: Easy. TEL: 01244 322478; evenings - 01244 318391. SER: Export. VAT: Stan/Spec.

Guildhall Fair - Chester

Watergate St. CH1. Open Thurs. 10-4. SIZE: 40 dealers. *STOCK: General antiques.*

Harris & Holt

Grange Farm, Parkgate Rd., Mollington. CH1 6NP. (Sandra Harris). Est. 1978. Open 10-5, Mon., Tues and Wed. by appointment.SIZE: Medium. *STOCK: English and Continental furniture, £500-£10,000; oil paintings including portraits, £1,000-£10,000; works of art, £100-£5,000; all 17th-19th C.* LOC: A540 Chester to Parkgate road, opposite Banastre Hotel. PARK: Easy. TEL: 01244 851180; fax - 0151 353 8107; mobile - 07860 560875. SER: Valuations; buys at auction. FAIRS: Battersea; Olympia (June). VAT: Spec.

J. Alan Hulme

Antique Maps & Old Prints, 52 Mount Way, Waverton. CH3 7QF. Open Mon.-Sat. by appointment. *STOCK: Maps, 16th-19th C; prints, 18th-19th C.* TEL: 01244 336472.

Jamandic Ltd

22 Bridge St. Row. CH1 1NN. Est. 1975. Open 9.30-5.30, Sat. 9.30-1. SIZE: Medium. *STOCK: Decorative furniture, mirrors, porcelain, pictures and prints.* TEL: 01244 312822. SER: Interior design and decoration; export. VAT: Stan/Spec.

K D Antiques

11 City Walls. CH1 1LD. (Dorothea Gillett). Est. 1990. Open 10-5. SIZE: Small. *STOCK: Stafford-*

HARRIS & HOLT

ANTIQUES, WORKS OF ART & INTERIORS

Opposite the Mollington Banastre Hotel
1 mile out of city centre on A540 - Ample Parking
Opening hours 10-5 p.m. Thurs, Fri, Sat.

Grange Farm, Parkgate Road, Mollington, Chester
Tel/Fax: 01244 851180. Mobile: 07860 560875
www.HarrisAndHolt.com

shire figures, 18th-19th C, £50-£500; wooden boxes, 18th-19th C, £20-£300; collectables, £5-£50. LOC: Town centre, next to Eastgate Clock, wall level. PARK: Nearby. TEL: 01244 314208. FAIRS: Manchester G Mex.

Kayes of Chester

9 St. Michaels Row. CH1 1EF. (A.M. Austin-Kaye and N.J. Kaye). LAPADA. NAG. Est. 1948. Open 9-5.30. SIZE: Medium. *STOCK: Diamond rings and jewellery, 1850-1950, £20-£20,000; silver and plate, 1700-1930, £20-£8,000; small objects and ceramics, 19th to early 20th C, £50-£1,000.* PARK: Nearby. TEL: 01244 327149; fax - 01244 318404; website - www.Kayeschester. com. SER: Valuations; restorations (silver, jewellery and plate); buys at auction. VAT: Stan/Spec.

Lowe and Sons

11 Bridge St. Row. CH1 1PD. Est. 1770. *STOCK: Jewellery and silver, Georgian, Victorian and Edwardian; unusual collectors' items.* TEL: 01244 325850. VAT: Stan/Spec.

Made of Honour

11 City Walls. CH1 1LD. (E. Jones). Open 10-5. *STOCK: Staffordshire figures, British ceramics, boxes, prints and pictures, decorative and collectable items, 18th-19th C.* LOC: Next to Eastgate clock, wall level. TEL: 01244 314208.

Melody's Antique Galleries

30-32 City Rd. CH1 3AE. (M. Melody). LAPADA. Est. 1977. Open 10-5.30 or by appointment. SIZE: Large. *STOCK: 18th-20th C oak, mahogany, walnut and pine furniture; porcelain, silver, plate, lighting, decorative items.* LOC: 400yds. from station. TEL: 01244 328968; fax - 01244 341818. SER: Courier; container packing. VAT: Stan/Spec.

Moor Hall Antiques

27 Watergate Row. CH1 2LE. (John Murphy). Resident. Est. 1992. Open 10-5.30, Mon., Fri. and Sat. 10.30-5.30. SIZE: Large. *STOCK: Furniture, 18th-19th C, £1,000-£2,000; prints, 19th C, £50-£200; modern decorative items, £20-£100.* LOC: City centre. PARK: Easy. TEL: 01244 340095. SER: Restorations (oils, watercolours and furniture). VAT: Stan/Spec.

A 'lace-cut' machine-cut paper with a hand-painted portrait of a young girl at its centre. Similar examples with different painted scenes are known. This one has survived in near mint condition only because it has not been in a watch. Those that have rarely survive intact. c.1830.

Other than the pocket watch itself, there are many related areas worthy of a collector's attention: watch stands, keys, fobs, chains and, perhaps the most humble, the watch-paper. The latter are, however, by no means without interest and importance, as David Penney shows in his article which appeared in the April 2001 issue of **Antique Collecting** magazine. For more details and to subscribe see page 147.

The Old Warehouse Antiques

7 Delamere St. CH1 4DS. (Mr and Mrs M. O'Donnell). Est. 1990. Open 10-5. SIZE: Large. *STOCK: Victorian and Edwardian furniture, £50-£1,000.* LOC: Opposite Delamere bus station. PARK: Nearby. TEL: 01244 383942; mobile - 07790 533850. SER: French polishing. VAT: Spec

Stothert Old Books

4 Nicholas St. CH1 2NX. (Alan and Marjory Checkley). GADAR. Est. 1977. Open 10-5. SIZE: Medium. *STOCK: Books, 17th-20th C, £2-£1,000.* LOC: At junction with Watergate St. TEL: 01244 340756.

Veevers

25 Watergate St. CH1. (Mr and Mrs A. C. Spicer). Est. 1986. Open 9.30-5. SIZE: Medium. *STOCK: Jewellery and silver, 18th-20th C, £5-£5,000; clocks, 19th-20th C, £50-£1,500.* PARK: Limited and nearby. TEL: 01244 400616; e-mail - veevers@fsbdial.co.uk. SER: Valuations; restorations (jewellery and clocks). VAT: Stan/Spec

Watergate Antiques

56 Watergate St. CH1 2LD. (A. Shindler). Est. 1968. Open 9.30-5.30. SIZE: Medium. *STOCK: Porcelain and pottery, jewellery; specialist in silver and silver plate to the Trade.* LOC: From Liverpool first set of traffic lights past Waterfall Roundabout, turn left. PARK: At rear. TEL: 01244 344516; fax - 01244 320350; e-mail - watergate.antiques@the mail.co.uk. VAT: Stan.

Wheatsheaf Antiques

57 Christleton Rd., Boughton. CH3. Est. 1988. Open 11-4, Sun. 12-4. SIZE: Medium. *STOCK: Furniture, 18th C to 1930's, £500-£2,000; vintage clothing, Victorian to 1970's; prints, 18th C to 1930's.* PARK: Adjacent. TEL: 01244 403743; fax - 01244 351713. SER: Restorations. VAT: Spec.

CONGLETON

W. Buckley Antiques Exports

35 Chelford Rd. CW12 4QA. Open 7 days by appointment. *STOCK: Mainly shipping and Victorian furniture.* TEL: 01260 275299. SER: Shipping.

Littles Collectables

8/10 Little St. CW12 1AR. (Mrs J. Storey). Est. 1989. CL: Wed. Open 10-5. SIZE: Medium. *STOCK: Pottery and glass, Doulton, £5-£1,000.* LOC: Town centre. PARK: Nearby. TEL: 01260 299098.

Pine Too and Able to Cane

8/10 Rood Hill. CW12 1LG. (Mrs J.P. Tryon). Open 9.30-5.30. *STOCK: Antique and reproduction furniture; decorative Bèrgere.* LOC: Just

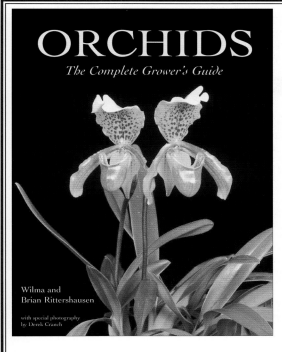

off A34. PARK: Nearby. TEL: 01260 279228; fax - same; mobile - 07808 808980; e-mail - abletocane_uk@yahoo.co.uk. SER: Re-caning.

CREWE

Steven Blackhurst
102 Edleston Rd. CW2 7HD. Est. 1988. Open 9.30-5, Sat. 10-5, Sun. by appointment. CL: Wed. SIZE: Small. *STOCK: Stripped pine, 19th to early 20th C, £25-£600; satinwood furniture, 1900, £100-£500.* LOC: Turn off Nantwich Rd. (A534), shop 250 yards on left. TEL: 01270 258617; home - 01270 665991.

Copnal Books
18 Meredith St. CW1 2PW. (P. Ollerhead). Est. 1980. Open Mon. and Fri. 9.30-4.30, Sat. 9.30-5. SIZE: Small. *STOCK: Books, £1-£50.* LOC: 200 yards north of market. PARK: Easy. TEL: 01270 580470; home - 01270 585622. SER: Valuations; buys at auction.

DAVENHAM, Nr. Northwich

Davenham Antiques Centre
461 London Rd. CW9 8NA. Est. 1985. Open 10-5, Sun. 11-5. CL: Wed. SIZE: 15 dealers. *STOCK: Victorian and Edwardian furniture, china, pictures, silver, clocks, books and collectables.* LOC: Village centre, off A566. TEL: 01606 44350; fax - 01606 782317; e-mail - maxwells@connectfree.co.uk; website - www.antiques-atlas.com/davenham.htm. SER: Shipping.

DISLEY

Mill Farm Antiques
50 Market St. SK12 2DT. (F.E. Berry). Est. 1968. Open every day. SIZE: Medium. *STOCK: Pianos, clocks, mechanical music, shipping goods, general antiques, £50-£10,000.* LOC: A6, 7 miles south of Stockport. PARK: Easy. TEL: 01663 764045; fax - 01663 762690. SER: Valuations; restorations (clocks, watches, barometers, music boxes). VAT: Stan/Spec.

GREAT BARROW, Nr. Chester

Iain Campbell
1 Barrowmore Estate. CH3 7JA. PBFA. Est. 1970. Open by appointment. SIZE: Small. *STOCK: Prints, 18th-19th C, £1-£100; drawings and watercolours, printed ephemera, books, 19th C, £1-£500.* LOC: 1/2 mile from B5132, between A51 and A56. PARK: Easy. TEL: 01829 741499.

FAIRS: Newark DGM; PBFA - London, Oxford, Cambridge, York, Haydock Park, Chester; Ephemera, London (June and Dec.). VAT: Stan.

HALE, Nr. Altrincham

Affordable Antiques
25 Stamford Park Rd. WA15 9EL. (Joel and Kate Freeman). Est. 1996. Open daily, Sun. pm by appointment. SIZE: Medium. *STOCK: Furniture, mid to late Victorian, £100-£600; mirrors, to Victorian, £300-£500.* LOC: From Hale Rd. turn right down Hawthorn Rd., left at bottom, first shop on right. PARK: Easy. TEL: 0161 929 0700; fax - same; home - 01625 525367. SER: Valuations; restorations (French polishing, paint effects); buys at auction.

HASLINGTON, Nr. Crewe

J. Luffman
Bank House, 13 Bradeley Rd. CW1 5PW. Open by appointment. *STOCK: Longcase, bracket and mantel clocks, music boxes, country furniture, paintings and militaria, £5-£20,000.* TEL: 01270 500199; mobile - 07836 592898. SER: Valuations; buys at auction (militaria and paintings).VAT: Spec.

HELSBY

Sweetbriar Gallery
Robin Hood Lane. WA6 9NH. (Mrs A. Metcalfe). Est. 1986. Open 9-5.30 or by appointment to see full stock. *STOCK: Antique and modern paper-weights, £5-£5,000.* LOC: Off M56, junction 14. First left at traffic lights, first right after Elf Garage, past three right turns. Premises on hillside with long, low sandstone wall in front. PARK: Easy. TEL: 01928 723851; home - same; fax - 01928 724153; mobile - 07860 907532; e-mail - sweetbr@globalnet.co.uk; website - www.sweetbriar.co.uk. SER: Valuations; buys at auction (paperweights). FAIRS: Glass (May and Nov.); National Motorcycle Museum (Birmingham); Great Antiques; Shepton Mallet; Newark; Ardingly. VAT: Stan/Spec.

KNUTSFORD

B.R.M. Coins
3 Minshull St. WA16 6HG. (Brian Butterworth). Est. 1968. Open 11-4, Sat. 11-1 or by appointment. SIZE: Small. *STOCK: Coins, medals and bank-*

notes, worldwide, BC to date, from 5p; money boxes, scales and weights. LOC: A50. PARK: Nearby. TEL: 01565 651480; home - 01606 74522. SER: Valuations; buys at auction (as stock).

Cranford Galleries
10 King St. WA16 6DL. (M.R. Bentley). Est. 1964. Open 11-5. CL: Wed. SIZE: Small. *STOCK: Pictures, prints and Victoriana.* Not Stocked: Glass. LOC: Main St. PARK: Easy. TEL: 01565 633646. SER: Framing and mounting. VAT: Stan.

Glynn Interiors
92 King St. WA16 6ED. Est. 1963. Open 10-4. CL: Mon. and Wed. SIZE: Large. *STOCK: Furniture, 1750-1900, £50-£2,000; Victorian chairs, £50-£650.* Not Stocked: Porcelain. LOC: 10 mins. drive after leaving M6 at Exit 19. PARK: Own. TEL: 01565 634418. SER: Restorations (re-upholstery) and cabinet repairs. VAT: Stan/Spec.

Knutsford Antiques Centre
113 King St. WA16 6EH. (David and Patricia McLeod). Est. 1995. Open 10-5, Sun. 12-5. CL: Mon. SIZE: 20+ dealers. *STOCK: Furniture, 18th C, £100-£2,000; pine, £200-£600; ceramics and collectables, £10-£300; British silver, £10-£1,000; books, £1-£50; glass, £10-£100.* LOC: Main street, 5 minutes from junction 19, M6. PARK: Easy. TEL: 01565 654092; website - www.knutsfordantiques.com. SER: Valuations.

Lion Gallery and Bookshop
15a Minshull St. WA16 6HG. (R.P. Hepner). Est. 1964. Open Fri. 10.30-4.30, Sat. 10-4.30. *STOCK: Antiquarian maps, prints and books, watercolours and oils, 16th-20th C; O.S. maps and early directories.* LOC: King St. 3 mins. M6. PARK: Nearby. TEL: 01565 652915; mobile - 07850 270796; fax - 01565 750142. SER: Restorations; binding, cleaning, framing and mounting. VAT: Stan.

LITTLETON, Nr. Chester

John Titchner and Sons
Littleton Old Hall, Little Heath Rd. CH3 7DW. LAPADA. Open 9-5. CL: Sat. *STOCK: Furniture, 18th-19th C.* TEL: 01244 336986.

LYMM

Reflections
11 The Cross. WA13 0HR. (John & Jennie Sprague). Est. 1970. Open 9.30-5, Sun. by appointment. CL: Mon. SIZE: Medium. *STOCK:*

Furniture and smalls, 1850-1950, £5-£1,000. LOC: Village centre, in yard opposite 'Wine Sellers'. TEL: 01925 753555; home - 01925 757331. SER: Valuations; restorations (polishing, repairs; upholstery, modern and traditional).

Willow Pool Garden Centre
Burford Lane. WA13 0SH. (S. Brunsveld). Open 9-6, including Sun. *STOCK: Architectural and general antiques.* TEL: 01925 757827; fax - 01925 758101.

MACCLESFIELD

Gatehouse Antiques
72 Chestergate. SK11 6QQ. (W.H. Livesley). Est. 1973. Open 9-5. CL: Sun. except by appointment and Wed. pm. *STOCK: Small furniture, silver and plate, glass, brass, copper, pewter, jewellery, 1650-1880.* PARK: At rear. TEL: 01625 426476; home - 01625 612841.

Hidden Gem
1,3,5 and 7 Chester Rd. SK10 5SY. (J.C. Tilley). Usually open 11-5 or by appointment. *STOCK: Victorian paintings and general antiques.* TEL: Home - 01625 828348.

Hills Antiques
Indoor Market, Grosvenor Centre. SK11 6SY. (D. Hill). Est. 1968. Open 9.30-5.30. *STOCK: Small furniture, jewellery, collectors' items, stamps, coins, postcards.* LOC: Town Centre. PARK: Easy. TEL: 01625 420777/420467.

D.J. Massey and Son
47 Chestergate. SK11 6DG. Est. 1900. Open 9-5.30. *STOCK: Jewellery, gold and diamonds, all periods.* TEL: 01625 616133.

Mereside Books
75 Chestergate. SK11 6DG. (Miss S. Laithwaite and K. S. Kowalski). Est. 1996. Open 10-5, Mon. and Tues. by appointment. SIZE: Small. *STOCK: Books - secondhand, 20th C, £2-£100; anti-quarian, 19th C, £10-£300; illustrated, 20th C, £10-£1,000.* TEL: 01625 425352; home - 01625 431160. SER: Valuations; restorations (books including re-binding). FAIRS: Buxton Book.

MARPLE BRIDGE, Nr. Stockport

Town House Antiques
21 Town St. SK6 5AA. (Paul and Jeri Buxcey). Open 10-6 most days. *STOCK: Antique pine, French beds and decorative items.* TEL: 0161 427 2228; home - 0161 427 1343.

Coppelia Antiques

Valerie and Roy Clements

Holford Lodge, Plumley Moor Road, Plumley, Nr. Knutsford, Cheshire
WA16 9RS
Telephone: 01565 722197
Fax: 01565 722744
4 miles from J.19, M6

Fine quality mahogany longcase clock, c.1770, London maker, ht. 7ft. 8in. Dial with chapter ring and spandrels with strike-silent in the arch

We currently have one of the finest selections of quality longcase clocks in the U.K. We also stock mantel, bracket, English and Vienna wall clocks. Established 1970, all our clocks are fully restored and guaranteed 1 year. Free delivery U.K. mainland. Why not pay us a visit, you will receive a warm welcome, free coffee and constructive, expert advice.

OPEN 7 DAYS BY APPOINTMENT

MOBBERLEY

David Bedale
WA16 7HR. Est. 1977. By appointment. SIZE: Medium. *STOCK: 18th-19th C furniture, unusual and decorative items.* TEL: 01565 872270. VAT: Stan/Spec.

NANTWICH

Adams Antiques   BADA
Churche's Mansion, Hospital St. CW5 5RY. (Sandy Summers). LAPADA. Resident. Est. 1975. Open by appointment. SIZE: Large. STOCK: Mainly oak and walnut country furniture, dressers, corner cupboards, tables and chairs; longcase clocks, Mason's Ironstone. LOC: A500 to Nantwich to town centre, shop on left. PARK: Own. TEL: 01270 625643; fax - same. SER: Valuations. FAIRS: BADA LAPADA; NEC. VAT: Stan/Spec.

Tim Armitage
99 Welsh Row. CW5 5ET. (T.J. Armitage). Est. 1967. Open by appointment. SIZE: Small. *STOCK: Tin toys, steam models and early advertising.* LOC: Main road into town from

Chester. PARK: Easy. TEL: 01270 626608; home - same. SER: Valuations; buys at auction (toys and models).

Chapel Antiques
47 Hospital St. CW5 5RL. (Miss D.J. Atkin). Est. 1983. Open 9.30-5.30, Wed. 9.30-1 or by appointment. CL: Mon. SIZE: Medium. *STOCK: Oak, mahogany and pine furniture, Georgian and Victorian, £100-£3,000; longcase clocks, pre-1830, £1,000-£3,000; copper, brass, silver, glass, porcelain, pottery and small items, 19th C, £10-£500.* LOC: Enter town via Pillory St., turn right into Hospital St. PARK: Easy. TEL: 01270 629508; home - same. SER: Valuations; restorations (furniture, clocks).

Clock Corner
176 Audlem Rd. CW5 7QJ. (M. J. Green). BHI. Est. 1985. Open by appointment. SIZE: Small. *STOCK: Clocks, 18th-19th C, from £200.* LOC: 1 mile from Nantwich centre on A529 Audlem road. PARK: Easy. TEL: 01270 624481; home - same; e-mail - clock.corner@virgin.net SER: Valuations; restorations (longcase and bracket clocks).

Roderick Gibson
70-72 Hospital St. CW5 5RP. Open 9-5. *STOCK: Furniture and decorative collectors' pieces.* TEL: 01270 625301. VAT: Stan/Global.

Lions and Unicorns
Kiltearn House, 33 Hospital St. CW5 5RL. (J. Pearson). Open by appointment. SIZE: Small. *STOCK: Commemoratives - pottery, porcelain, textiles, glass, tins, metals, books and postcards, £5-£350.* LOC: Town centre, near church. PARK: Easy. TEL: 01270 628892/613830; fax - 01270 626646. SER: Picture framing; rushing and caning; restorations (furniture); buys at auction; catalogue; parcel post worldwide.

Love Lane Antiques
Love Lane. CW5 5BH. (M. Simon). Open 10-5. CL: Wed. SIZE: Small. *STOCK: General antiques, 19th-20th C, £5-£500.* LOC: Two minutes walk from town square. PARK: Nearby. TEL: 01270 626239.

Pillory House
18 Pillory St. CW5 5BD. (D. Roberts). Est. 1968. Open 9-5. CL: Wed. *STOCK: Hand-carved chimney pieces and oak.* TEL: 01270 623524.

Richardson Antiques Ltd
90 Hospital St. CW5 5RP. (Terry Richardson). Est. 1981. Open daily, Sun. by appointment. SIZE: Medium. *STOCK: Furniture, collectables and china.* TEL: 01270 625963; home - 01270 628348. SER: Valuations; restorations (French polishing, upholstery, clocks). VAT: Spec.

NORTHWICH

Northwich Antiques Centre

132 Witton St. (F.J. Cockburn). Est. 1990. Open 10-5 including Sun. CL: Wed. SIZE: Large. *STOCK: Victorian furniture, £50-£1,000+; china, clocks and barometers, Royal Doulton, Beswick.* LOC: Town centre. PARK: Easy. TEL: 01606 47540; fax - 01606 889262. SER: Valuations; restorations; buys at auction.

PLUMLEY

Coppelia Antiques

Holford Lodge, Plumley Moor Rd. WA16 9RS. (V. and R. Clements). Resident. Est. 1970. Open 10-6 every day by appointment. SIZE: Medium. *STOCK: Over 500 clocks (mainly longcase and wall), £1,000-£50,000; tables - Georgian mahogany, wine, oak gateleg and side; bureaux, desks, chests of drawers, lowboys, coffers.* LOC: 4 miles junction 19, M6. PARK: Easy. TEL: 01565 722197; fax - 01565 722744. FAIRS: Buxton (May). VAT: Spec.

POYNTON, Nr. Stockport

Harper Fine Paintings

"Overdale", Woodford Rd. SK12 1ED. (P.R. Harper). Est. 1967. Open by appointment. SIZE: Large. *STOCK: Watercolours, £100-£35,000; oils including European, £250-£60,000.* LOC: From A523 centre of Poynton lights, turn into Chester Rd., over railway. After 1/4 mile turn right, 1st drive on left after railway bridge. PARK: Easy. TEL: 01625 879105; home - same; fax - 01625 850128; e-mail - Peteevette@Aol.com. SER: Valuations; restorations; buys at auction (as stock). VAT: Stan/Spec.

Recollections

69 Park Lane. SK12 1RD. (Angela Smith). Open 10-5. SIZE: Medium. *STOCK: Antique, pre-war and secondhand furniture; costume jewellery and decorative collectables.* PARK: Easy - Civic Centre. TEL: 01625 859373.

RINGWAY, Nr. Altrincham

Cottage Antiques

Hasty Lane. WA15 8UT. (J. and J. M. Gholam). Est. 1967. SIZE: Medium. *STOCK: Furniture, metalware, ceramics, glass, early 18th-mid 19th C.* Not Stocked: Jewellery, jade and ivory. LOC: Off junction 6, M56, off A538, very close to airport. PARK: Easy. TEL: 0161 980 7961. SER: Valuations.

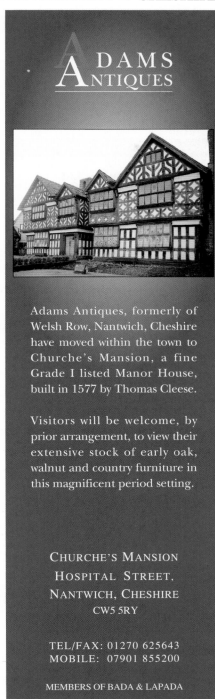

CHESHIRE

Romiley Antiques & Jewellery
42 Stockport Rd. SK6 3ÅA. (P. Green). Est. 1983. Open Thurs., Fri. and Sat. 9-5. SIZE: Medium. *STOCK: Furniture, 18th-19th C, £100-£2,000; ceramics, 18th-19th C, £5-£1,000; jewellery, 19th C, £5-£1,000.* LOC: 5 miles from Stockport. PARK: Nearby. TEL: 0161 494 6920; home - same. SER: Valuations. VAT: Stan/Spec.

Cobwebs of Antiquities Ltd
13 Green Lane. M33 5PN. (Judith Williams). Est. 1996. Open 8.30-5.30. SIZE: Medium. *STOCK: Furniture, 18th-20th C, £50-£4,000; lighting, 20th C, £25-£400; collectables, 18th-20th C, £5-£500.* LOC: M60 towards Altrincham. At Glebelands Road traffic lights, turn right. PARK: Easy. TEL: 0161 905 3554; fax - same; home - 07768 934381. SER: Valuations; restorations (polishing, upholstery and repairs); buys at auction.

Antique Furniture Warehouse
Units 3/4 Royal Oak Buildings, Cooper St. SK1 3QJ. Open 9.30-5. SIZE: Large. *STOCK: English and Continental mahogany, walnut and inlaid furniture, paintings, clocks, shipping goods, pottery, porcelain and curios, decorative items, architectural.* LOC: 2 mins. off M56 towards town centre. PARK: Easy. TEL: 0161 429 8590; fax - 0161 480 5375. VAT: Stan.

Antiques Import Export
20 Buxton Rd., Hevley. SK2 6NU. Open 9.30-5.30. SIZE: Large. *STOCK: American and pre-1930 English furniture, to £5,000.* PARK: Easy. TEL: 0161 476 4013; fax - 0161 477 2684. SER: Valuations; restorations. FAIRS: Newark.

E. R. Antiques Centre
122 Wellington St., off Wellington Rd. South. SK1 1YH. (E. Warburton). Est. 1979. Open 12.30-7.30. SIZE: Medium - 6 dealers. *STOCK: China, pottery, glass, silver, EPNS, costume jewellery, 1820-1960, £5-£200.* LOC: Turn into Edwards St. by the Town Hall, at 'T' junction turn left, shop 500yds. on left at bollards. PARK: Easy. TEL: 0161 429 6646; home - 0161 292 2296.

Flintlock Antiques
28 and 30 Bramhall Lane. SK2 6HR. (F. Tomlinson and Son). Est. 1968. SIZE: Large. *STOCK: Furniture, clocks, pictures, scientific instruments.* TEL: 0161 480 9973. VAT: Stan/Spec.

Halcyon Antiques
435/437 Buxton Rd., Great Moor. SK2 7HE. (Mrs Jill A. Coppock). Est. 1980. Open 10-5. SIZE: Large. *STOCK: Porcelain and glass, £1-£2,000; furniture, £50-£2,000; both 1750-1940: jewellery, silver and plate, linen and lace.* LOC: A6, 2 miles south of town. PARK: Easy. TEL: 0161 483 5038; home - 0161 439 3524.

Highland Antiques
67 Wellington Rd. North. SK4 2LP. (E. Todd). Est. 1970. SIZE: Medium. *STOCK: Silver and plate; Chinese and Japanese pottery, porcelain and furniture, 18th-19th C.* LOC: A6. PARK: Easy. TEL: 0161 476 6660; fax - 0161 476 6669. SER: Valuations; restorations; buys at auction. FAIRS: Manchester. VAT: Stan/Spec.

Imperial Antiques
295 Buxton Rd., Great Moor. SK2 7NR. (A. Todd). LAPADA. Est. 1972. Open 10-5.30, Sun. by appointment. SIZE: Large. *STOCK: Silver and plate, 19th-20th C; porcelain especially Japanese and Chinese, 18th-19th C; both £10-£1,000.* LOC: A6 Buxton Rd., 1.5 miles south of town centre. PARK: Easy. TEL: 0161 483 3322; e-mail - Alfred.todd@imperialantiques.com; website - www.imperialantiques.com. SER: Buys at auction (as stock). VAT: Stan/Spec.

Sue Ledger Antiques
370 Buxton Rd. SK2 7BY. Open 10.30-5. CL: Wed. SIZE: Medium. *STOCK: Pine furniture, decorative items, smalls, £25-£1,000.* LOC: A6. PARK: Easy. TEL: 0161 483 6603.

Limited Editions
35 King St. East. SK1 1XJ. (C.W. Fogg). Est. 1978. Open 9.45-6, Sat. 9.30-5.30. SIZE: Large. *STOCK: Furniture, 19th C, especially dining tables and chairs, £100-£5,000; arm chairs and couches for re-upholstery.* LOC: Off Warren St., next to Sainsbury's. PARK: Own at rear. TEL: 0161 480 1239; e-mail - info@ltd-editions.co.uk; website - www.ltd-editions.co.uk. SER: Valuations; restorations (furniture). VAT: Stan/Spec.

Manchester Antique Company
Mac House, St Thomas's Place. SK1 3TZ. Open 9.30-4.30. SIZE: Large. *STOCK: Antique furniture, English, Continental and shipping goods, mainly walnut and mahogany.* TEL: 0161 355 5566/5577; website - www.manchester-antique.co.uk.

Nostalgia Architectural Antiques
Holland's Mill, Shaw Heath. SK3 8BH. (D. and E. Durrant). Est. 1975. Open Tues.-Fri. 10-6, Sat. 10-5. SIZE: Large. *STOCK: Fireplaces, £200-£50,000; bathroom fittings and architectural items, £50-£2,000; all 18th-19th C.* PARK: At rear. TEL: 0161 477 7706; fax - 0161 477 2267. SER: Valuations. VAT: Stan/Spec.

Page Antiques
424 Buxton Rd., Great Moor. SK2 7JQ. Open Mon.-Sat. SIZE: Large. *STOCK: Georgian to Edwardian furniture, brass, copper, silver, plate, stripped pine especially for Australian and German markets.* LOC: A6. TEL: 0161 483 9202; home - 01663 732358. SER: Courier. VAT: Stan/Spec.

STRETTON, Nr. Warrington

Antiques Etc.
Shepcroft House, London Rd. WA4 5PJ. (M. Clare). Est. 1978. Resident, usually available. SIZE: Medium. *STOCK: Furniture, pine, barometers, clocks, instruments and items of interest, £5-£2,000.* LOC: A49, towards Warrington, through Stretton traffic lights, next turning on left. PARK: Easy. TEL: 01925 730431; mobile - 07836 570663.

TARPORLEY

Marie José Burke
The Pavillion, High St. CW6 0DX. Est. 1959. Open 10-5, appointment advisable. CL: Sat. *STOCK: Period English furniture.* VAT: Spec.

Tarporley Antique Centre
76 High St. CW6 0DP. Open 10-5, Sun. 11-4. SIZE: 9 dealers on two floors. *STOCK: Furniture, ceramics, commemoratives, treen, Studio pottery, glass, oils, watercolours, prints.* LOC: Main road, near Crown public house. PARK: In front of premises and opposite. TEL: 01829 733919. SER: Buys at auction; framing; re-rushing and caning.

TARVIN, Nr. Chester

Antique Fireplaces
The Manor House, Church St. CH3. (Mrs G. O'Toole). Est. 1979. Open Fri., Sat. and Sun. 10-5 or by appointment. SIZE: Medium. *STOCK: Fireplaces and ranges, 18th-19th C, £150-£3,000.* LOC: At junction of A556 and A51. PARK: Easy. TEL: 01829 740936; home - 01606 46717. SER: Valuations; restorations; installations (fireplaces and ranges); new tiles and fenders ordered from suppliers on request. FAIRS: Tatton Park, Knutsford.

TARVIN SANDS, Nr. Chester

Cheshire Brick and Slate Co
Brook House Farm, Salters Bridge. CH3 8HL. (Malcolm Youde). Est. 1978. Open 8-5.30, Sat. 8-4.30, Sun. 10-4. SIZE: Large. *STOCK: Reclaimed conservation building materials, 16th-20th C; architectural antiques - garden statuary, stonework, lamp posts, gates, fireplaces, bathroom suites, chimney pots and ironwork, 18th-20th C, £50-£1,000; furniture, pews, leaded lights, pottery, 18th-20th C, £5-£1,000.* LOC: Directly off A54 just outside Tarvin. PARK: Own. TEL: 01829 740883. SER: Valuations; restorations (fireplaces, timber treatment); building/construction and demolition; renovations. VAT: Stan.

TATTENHALL, Nr. Chester

The Great Northern Architectural Antique Company Ltd
New Russia Hall, Chester Rd. CH3 9AH. Open 9.30-4.30 including Sun. SIZE: Large. *STOCK: Period doors, fire surrounds, stained glass, sanitary ware, garden statuary, furniture and curios.* LOC: Off A41. PARK: Easy. TEL: 01829 770796; fax - 01829 770971. VAT: Stan.

TILSTON, Nr. Malpas

Well House Antiques
The Well House. SY14 7DP. (S. French-Greenslade). Est. 1968. Open by appointment only. SIZE: Small. *STOCK: Collectors' items, china, glass, silver.* LOC: From Whitchurch on A41, take B5395 signposted Malpas. PARK: Easy. TEL: 01829 250332.

WARRINGTON

The Rocking Chair Antiques
Unit 3, St. Peter's Way. WA2 7BL. (M. and N.J. Barratt). Est. 1971. Open 9-5.30. SIZE: Large. *STOCK: Furniture and bric-a-brac.* LOC: Off Orford Lane. PARK: Easy. TEL: 01925 652409; fax - same; mobile - 07774 492891. SER: Valuations; shipping; packing. VAT: Stan.

WAVERTON, Nr. Chester

The White House
Whitchurch Rd. CH3 7PB. (Mrs Elizabeth Rideal). Resident. Est. 1979. Open 10-5. *STOCK: Stripped pine furniture, 19th-20th C, £50-£2,000; Victorian china, 19th C, £5-£100; bric-a-brac.* LOC: A41, 2.5 miles south of Sainsbury's roundabout on Whitchurch Rd. PARK: Easy. TEL: 01244 335063; fax - 01244 335098. VAT: Margin.

WILMSLOW

The Old Sofa Warehouse
Unit 1, 3 Hawthorn Lane. SK9 1AA. (Roger Jackson and Gay Hargreaves-Jones). Est. 1994. Open Thurs. and Fri. 10-5, Sat. 10.30-5, Tues. and Wed. by appointment. SIZE: Large. *STOCK: Victorian and Edwardian sofas, from £200; armchairs, from £95; chaise longue, from £350.* LOC: Town centre. PARK: Nearby. TEL: 01625 536397. SER: Restoration (upholstery); buys at auction.

Wilmslow Antiques
5 Church St. SK9 1AX. (G.M. and S.M. Dale). Est. 1996. Open 10-5. SIZE: Medium - 18 dealers. *STOCK: Wide range of general antiques and fine furniture, 18th-20th C, £5-£1,000+.* LOC: Town centre. PARK: At rear. TEL: 01625 540472; e-mail - pmdale99@aol.com.

CORNWALL

ANGARRACK, Nr. Hayle

Paul Jennings Antiques
Millbrook House. TR27 5HY. Est. 1974. Open by appointment. SIZE: Small. *STOCK: Clocks, furniture, £100-£3,000.* LOC: 1/2 mile from A30. TEL: 01736 754065. VAT: Stan/Spec. *Trade Only.*

BODMIN

Bodmin Antiques Centre
Town End. PL31 1LN. (Ralph and Nola Solomons). Open 10-4. SIZE: Medium - several dealers. *STOCK: Ceramics and glass, £5-£350, small furniture, £10-£350, both 19th-20th C; commemoratives, kitchenalia, toys, brass, 20th C, £5-£75.* LOC: Main road. PARK: Nearby. TEL: 01208 78661; home - 01208 74609; e-mail - bodminantiques@hotmail.com. SER: Valuations.

BOSCASTLE

Newlyfe Antiques
The Old Mill. PL35 0AQ. (Harry Ruddy). Open seven days a week May-Sept. - prior 'phone call advisable at other times. *STOCK: Collectables, small furniture, French beds.* TEL: 01840 250230.

CALLINGTON

Country Living Antiques
Weston House, Haye Rd. PL17 7JJ. (Ian Baxter CBE). Resident. Est. 1990. Open 10-6. SIZE: Large - including barn. *STOCK: 19th C oak and pine country furniture, general antiques, £1-£2,000.* LOC: Town centre. PARK: Own. TEL: 01579 382245; fax - same. SER: Valuations; buys at auction.

CAMBORNE

Victoria Gallery & Bookshop
28 Cross St. TR14 8EX. (B.J. and J.P. Maker). Open Mon.-Fri. 10.30-5.15, other times by appointment. *STOCK: Books, pictures, general antiques, small furniture, silver and jewellery.* TEL: 01209 719268.

CHACEWATER, Nr. Truro

Chacewater Antiques
5 Fore St. TR4 8PS. (Sandra McCall). Est. 1991. Open 10.30-4, Sat. 10-1. CL: Wed. *STOCK: Furniture, 17th-19th C, £100-£1,000; brass and copper, paintings, 19th to early 20th C, £80-£450.* LOC: 5 minutes from Truro. From A30 Chiverton roundabout towards Truro. PARK: Nearby. TEL: 01872 561411; home - 01209 711545.

CREMYLL

Cremyll Antiques
The Cottage, Cremyll Beach, Torpoint. PL10 1HX. *STOCK: Clocks and watches, small items, jewellery.* TEL: 01752 823490. SER: Repairs (barometers, barographs, watches, clocks, jewellery).

DOBWALLS, Nr. Liskeard

Olden Days
Five Lanes. PL14 6JD. (F. J. C. Nancarrow and K. E. C. Trevellian). Est. 1980. Open 9.30-5.30, Sun. 11-5. SIZE: Medium. *STOCK: Furniture, from 19th C, £50-£800; reclaimed and new pine furniture; bric-a-brac and collectables.* LOC: A38 between Liskeard and Bodmin. PARK: Easy and private behind shop. TEL: 01579 321577; home - same; e-mail - dobwallsantiques @talk21. com; website - www.oldendays.org. SER: Buys at auction; furniture made to order. VAT: Stan/Spec.

FALMOUTH

John Maggs
54 Church St. TR11 3DS. (C.C. Nunn). Est. 1900. Open 10-5. SIZE: Medium. *STOCK: Antiquarian prints and maps, exclusive limited editions.* LOC: Main street. PARK: At rear of shop. TEL: 01326 313153; fax - same. SER: Restorations; framing; binding.

Old Town Hall Antiques
3 High St. TR11 2AB. (Mary P. Sheppard and Terence J. Brandreth). Est. 1986. Open 10-5.30, Sun. by appointment. SIZE: Large. *STOCK: Furniture including French armoires, beds and mirrors, 19th C, £100-£2,000; country smalls, some china and collectables, 19th-20th C, £10-£60.* LOC: From edge of Falmouth follow signs towards marina, shop situated on right under road arch (one-way street). PARK: Easy. TEL: 01326 319437; home - 01326 377489. VAT: Global.

Rosina's
4 High St. TR11 2AB. (Mrs R. Gealer). Open 11-4.30. *STOCK: Old dolls, bears, including limited edition, Steiff and artist bears, toys, linen and lace, clothes; modern miniatures. Fairies especially designed for Rosina's.* TEL: 01326 311406; home - 01326 317739. SER: Restorations.

Waterfront Antiques Market
1st Floor, 4 Quay St. TR11 3HH. Open 10-5. SIZE: 20 dealers. *STOCK: Furniture, pottery, porcelain, glass, silver, metalware, kitchenalia, pictures, books, clocks, jewellery, decorative and collectors' items.* TEL: 01326 311491.

GRAMPOUND, Nr. Truro

Pine and Period Furniture
Fore St. TR2 4QT. (S. Payne). Open 10-5. CL:

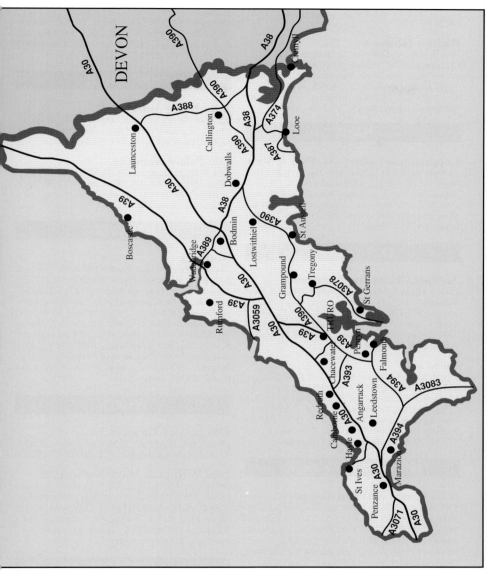

Dealers and Shops in Cornwall

Angarrack	1	Falmouth	4	Penryn	2
Bodmin	1	Grampound	2	Penzance	9
Boscastle	1	Hayle	1	Redruth	1
Callington	1	Launceston	2	Rumford	1
Camborne	1	Leedstown	1	St. Austell	1
Chacewater	1	Looe	2	St. Gerrans	1
Cremyll	1	Lostwithiel	2	St. Ives	3
Dobwalls	1	Marazion	1	Tregony	1
				Truro	6
				Wadebridge	2

Sat. *STOCK: Pine and period furniture.* TEL: 01726 883117.

Radnor House

Fore St. TR2 4QT. (P. and G. Hodgson). Est. 1972. Open 10-5. SIZE: Medium. *STOCK: Furniture and accessories, pre-1900.* Not Stocked: Jewellery, coins and weapons. LOC: A390. PARK: Easy. TEL: 01726 882921; home - same. SER: Valuations; buys at auction. VAT: Stan/Spec.

Copperhouse Gallery - W. Dyer & Sons

14 Fore St. TR27 4DX. (A.P. Dyer). Est. 1900. Open 9-5.30. SIZE: Medium. *STOCK: Watercolours and oils, including Newlyn and St. Ives schools; small antiques, Art Deco pottery.* LOC: Main road. PARK: Easy. TEL: 01736 752787; home - 01736 752960.

Antique Chairs and Museum

Colhay Farm, Polson. PL15 9QS. (Tom and Alice Brown). Est. 1988. Open seven days. SIZE: Large. *STOCK: Chairs, 18th-20th C.* LOC: Signed from A30. PARK: Easy. TEL: 01566 777485; fax - same; home - same. SER: Restorations; buys at auction.

Todd's

2 High St. and 8 Tower St. PL15 8ER. (B. Gallant and T. Mead). Est. 1997. Open 9-5, Sat. 9-4. SIZE: Medium and small. *STOCK: Furniture from 18th C, £100-£2000; ceramics, from 18th C, £10-£400; reproduction period lighting, £40-£500.* PARK: Nearby. TEL: 01566 775007/ 772749; fax - 01566 775007. SER: Restorations. VAT: Stan/Spec.

A.W. Glasby and Son Antiques

The Square. TR27 6DA. (D.E. Glasby). Est. 1936. Open 10.15-12.45 and 2.15-5. CL: Sat. and Mon. SIZE: Large. *STOCK: Furniture, porcelain and clocks, £10-£5,000.* Not Stocked: Coins, medals, scientific instruments. LOC: On main road half-way between Hayle and Helston. PARK: Easy. TEL: 01736 850303.

Dowling and Bray

Fore St., East Looe. PL13 1AE. Est. 1920. *STOCK: General antiques, furniture and brassware.* TEL: 01503 262797.

Tony Martin

Fore St. PL13 1AE. Est. 1965. Open 9.30-1 and 2-5 appointment advisable. CL: Thurs. pm. SIZE: Medium. *STOCK: Porcelain, 18th C; silver, 18th-19th C, both £20-£200; glass, furniture, oils and watercolours.* LOC: Main street. TEL: 01503 262734; home - 01503 262228.

John Bragg Antiques

35 Fore St. PL22 0BN. Open 10-5. *STOCK: Furniture, mainly period mahogany and Victorian.* LOC: 100yds. off A390. TEL: 01208 872827.

Old Palace Antiques

Old Palace, Quay St. PL22 0BS. (D. Bryant). Open 10-1 and 2-5. CL: Wed. pm. *STOCK: Pine, general antiques, books, postcards and collectors' items.* TEL: 01208 872909.

Antiques

The Shambles, Market Place. TR17 0AR. (Andrew S. Wood). Est. 1988. Open Mon.-Fri. 10.15-5.30, also Sats. 1 Nov.-30 April. SIZE: Medium. *STOCK: General antiques and collectors' items including 19th-20th C pottery and porcelain, Victorian to 20th C glass, Art Deco ceramics especially Shelley, Devon and commemorative ware, Goss and crested china, 1950's-60's pottery and glass, bottles.* Not Stocked: Weapons and large furniture. LOC: Main street. PARK: Easy. TEL: 01736 711381; home - same.

Old School Antiques

Church Rd. TR10 8DA. (J.M. Gavin). Open 8.30-6. *STOCK: General antiques.* TEL: 01326 375092.

Neil Willcox & Mark Nightingale

Jobswater, Mabe. TR10 9BT. Open by appointment. *STOCK: Sealed wine and other bottles, British and Continental 1650-1850, and related items.* TEL: 01326 340533; fax - same; e-mail - nightdes@aol.com. SER: Valuations; mail order - catalogue and photos supplied.

Antiques & Fine Art

1 Queens Buildings, The Promenade. TR18 4DL. (Elinor Davies and Geoffrey Mills). Est. 1985. Open 10-4. SIZE: Medium. *STOCK: Furniture, 18th C to Edwardian, to £1,000; brass, copper and ceramics, 18th-19th C, to £250.* LOC: Next to Queen's Hotel. PARK: Nearby. TEL: 01736 350509; home - 01736 350677. SER: Valuations; restorations (furniture); buys at auction (furniture).

James Buchanan Antiques
By appointment only. *STOCK: 17th-20th C furniture, pictures, china, glass, rugs, Newlyn and Hayle copper.* TEL: 01736 762317; mobile - 07967 380168; e-mail - jasperbuchanan@hotmail.com; website - www.newlyncopper.com.

Chapel Street Antiques Arcade
61/62 Chapel St. TR18 4AE. Open 9.30-5. SIZE: 20 dealers. *STOCK: Furniture, pottery, porcelain, glass, silver, metalware, kitchenalia, pictures, books, clocks, jewellery, decorative and collectors' items.* TEL: 01736 363267.

Daphne's Antiques
17 Chapel St. TR18 4AW. Est. 1976. Open 9-5. SIZE: Medium. *STOCK: Early country and 18th-19th C mahogany furniture, Georgian glass, Delft, pottery and decorative objects.* TEL: 01736 361719.

Peter Johnson
62 Chapel St. TR18 4AE. (Peter Chatfield-Johnson). Est. 1961. Open 9.30-5, Mon. by appointment. SIZE: Small. *STOCK: Lighting, 19th-20th C, £25-£500; Oriental ceramics and furniture, 18th-19th C, £25-£2,000; handmade silk lampshades, 20th C, £25-£250.* LOC: Left at top of Market Jew St. PARK: Easy. TEL: 01736 363267; home - 01736 368088. SER: Valuations; restorations (soft furnishings).

Little Jem's
69 Causewayhead. TR18 2SR. (J. Lagden). Open 9.30-5. *STOCK: Antique and modern jewellery (specialising in opal and amber), gem stones, objets d'art, paintings, clocks and watches.* TEL: 01736 351400. SER: Repairs; commissions.

New Street Bookshop
4 New St. TR18 2LZ. (K.E. Hearn). Open 10-5. *STOCK: Books and ephemera.* TEL: 01736 362758.

The Old Custom House
53 Chapel St. TR18 4AF. Open 9-5.30. SIZE: Small. *STOCK: Porcelain and glass, silver plate and small furniture, contemporary paintings.* TEL: 01736 331030.

Tony Sanders Penzance Gallery and Antiques
14 Chapel St. TR18 4AW. Est. 1972. Open 9-5.30. SIZE: Medium. *STOCK: Oils and watercolours, 19th-20th C, £50-£5,000; glass, silver, china and small furniture; specialist in Newlyn and J F Pool of Hayle; copper, contemporary art, paintings and bronzes.* TEL: 01736 366620/368461. VAT: Stan.

The Old Steam Bakery
60A Fore St. TR14 7NU. (Stephen J. Phillips).

Est. 1986. Open 10.30-5. SIZE: Large. *STOCK: Furniture including oak, 19th to early 20th C, £50-£100+; china and glass, early 20th C.* LOC: Next to main Post Office. PARK: Easy. TEL: 01209 315099; home - 01209 710650. SER: Valuations; restorations (furniture). VAT: Stan.

Henley House Antiques
PL27 7SS. (J.L. Neale). *STOCK: Juvenilia, small antiques, bric-a-brac.* TEL: 01841 540322.

Mrs. Margaret Chesterton
33 Pentewan Rd. PL25 5BU. Est. 1965. Open 10-5.30, appointment advisable. CL: Sat. pm. *STOCK: Victoriana, Edwardiana, 1800-1915; some furniture, porcelain, glass, £1-£500; brass, copper, pewter, jewellery, clocks, watercolours.* LOC: Coming from Plymouth, travel direct to St. Austell. Keep on main by-pass until roundabout for Mevagissey and Pentewan Rd. House is 100yds. on left down this road. PARK: Easy. TEL: 01726 72926.

Turnpike Cottage Antiques and Tearooms
The Square. TR2 5EB. (T. and S. Green). Est. 1988. Open 11-1.30 and 3-6, Sun. and wintertime 3-6. CL: Thurs. SIZE: Medium. *STOCK: General antiques, furniture, porcelain, bric-a-brac, £5-£4,000.* LOC: Near church. PARK: Easy, at rear. TEL: 01872 580853; home - same. SER: Valuations; restorations (furniture, watercolours).

Courtyard Collectables
Cyril Noall Sq., Fore St. TR26 1HE. (Janice Mosedale). Est. 1994. Open June to end Sept. 7 days 10-10; Oct., April and May 7 days 10-6; Nov. to March - Tues.-Sat. 10-5. SIZE: Medium. *STOCK: 20th C collectables.* TEL: 01736 798809. SER: Valuations; buys at auction.

Mike Read Antique Sciences
1 Abbey Meadow, Lelant. TR26 3LL. Est. 1974. Open by appointment. SIZE: Small. *STOCK: Scientific instruments - navigational, surveying, mining, barometers, telescopes and microscopes, medical, 18th-19th C, £10-£5,000; maritime works of art and nautical artifacts.* LOC: Turn left on hill in village, heading towards St. Ives. PARK: Easy. TEL: 01736 757237. SER: Valuations; restorations.

Tremayne Applied Arts
Street-an-Pol. TR26 2DS. (Roger and Anne

ALAN BENNETT

18th and 19th century Furniture, Porcelain Silver, Jewellery and Paintings

NEW BRIDGE HOUSE NEW BRIDGE STREET TRURO CORNWALL
Truro 273296

Tonkinson). Est. 1998. Summer - Open 10.30-4.30, Sat. 9.30-1.30. CL: Wed. Winter - appointment advisable. *STOCK: Furniture, china, glass, paintings and prints, late 19th to late 20th C, £50-£1,000.* LOC: Central, close to tourist information office. PARK: Station. TEL: 01736 797779; fax - 01736 793222; home - 01736 753537.

TREGONY, Nr. Truro

Clock Tower Antiques
57 Fore St. TR2 5RW. (The Warne Family). Open 9.30-5, (extended in summer), evenings and Sun. by appointment. SIZE: Medium. *STOCK: Ceramics, including Doulton stoneware, £10-£500; paintings and prints, 19th to early 20th C, £50-£1,000; furniture, 18th to early 20th C, £75-£3,000; brass, copper and treen, £10-£300.* Not Stocked: Silver and jewellery. LOC: Village centre, B3287. PARK: Easy. TEL: 01872 530225; home - same.

TRURO

Alan Bennett
24 New Bridge St. TR1 2AA. Est. 1954. Open 9-5.30. SIZE: Large. *STOCK: Furniture, £50-£5,000; jewellery and porcelain, to 1900, £5-£1,000; paintings and prints, £20-£2,000.* LOC: Eastern side of cathedral. PARK: 100yds. from shop. TEL: 01872 273296. VAT: Stan/Spec.

Blackwater Pine Antiques
Blackwater. TR4 8ET. (J.S. Terrett). Open 9-6. *STOCK: Pine and country furniture.* TEL: 01872 560919. SER: Restorations; stripping; furniture made to order.

Bonython Bookshop
16 Kenwyn St. TR1 3BU. (Rosemary Carpenter). Est. 1996. Open 10.30-4.30. SIZE: Small. *STOCK: Cornish books, £5-£200; topography, £5-£50; art, £5-£100.* PARK: NCP same road. TEL: 01872 262886; e-mail - shop@bonython booksfsnet.co.uk. SER: Valuations; booksearch.

Bric-a-Brac
16A Walsingham Place. TR1 2RP. (Lynne and Richard Bonehill). Est. 1991. SIZE: Small. *STOCK: Militaria, £5-£2,000; small furniture, £20-£1,000; commemorative and crested china, £5-£150; collectors' items and bric-a-brac, 50p-£2,000; all 19th-20th C.* LOC: Town centre, just off Victoria Sq. PARK: Multi-storey nearby. TEL: 01872 225200; e-mail - richard e bonehill3. freeserve.co.uk; website - www. bonehill3. freeserve.co.uk. FAIRS: Lostwithiel.

Collector's Corner
45-46 Pannier Market, Back Quay. TR1 2LL. (Alan McLoughlin and John Lethbridge). Est. 1980. Open 9.30-4.30, Sat. 9-4. SIZE: Small. *STOCK: Stamps, coins, postcards, medals, postal history, militaria, £5-£500.* LOC: City centre. PARK: Nearby. TEL: 01872 272729; home - 01326 573509; mobile - 07811 743404. SER: Valuations.

Pydar Antiques and Pine
Peoples Palace, Pydar St. TR1 2AZ. (D. Severn and J. Poole). Est. 1968. Open 10.30-5 and by appointment. SIZE: Medium. *STOCK: Furniture - English 18th and 19th C, £50-£2,500; Victorian and Edwardian, £50-£2,000; pine, £10-£1,500; silver, plate, porcelain, glass, prints and water-colours, £5-£500.* PARK: Easy. TEL: 01872 223516; home - 01872 510485 or 01637 872034.

WADEBRIDGE

St. Breock Gallery
St. Breock Churchtown. PL27 7JS. (R.G.G. Haslam-Hopwood). Open 10-5. *STOCK: Watercolours, 20th-21st C; furniture, general antiques and objets d'art, £20-£2,000.* LOC: Near Royal Cornwall Showground. PARK: Own. TEL: 01208 812543; fax - 01208 814671; website - www.tomorrows-antiques.com.SER: Restorations; buys at auction.

Victoria Antiques
21 Molesworth St. PL27 7DQ. (M. and S. Daly). Open Mon.-Sat. SIZE: Large. *STOCK: Furniture, 17th-19th C, £25-£10,000.* LOC: On A39 between Bude and Newquay. PARK: Nearby. TEL: 01208 814160. SER: Valuations; restor-ations.. VAT: Stan/Spec.

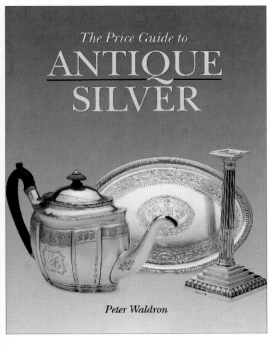

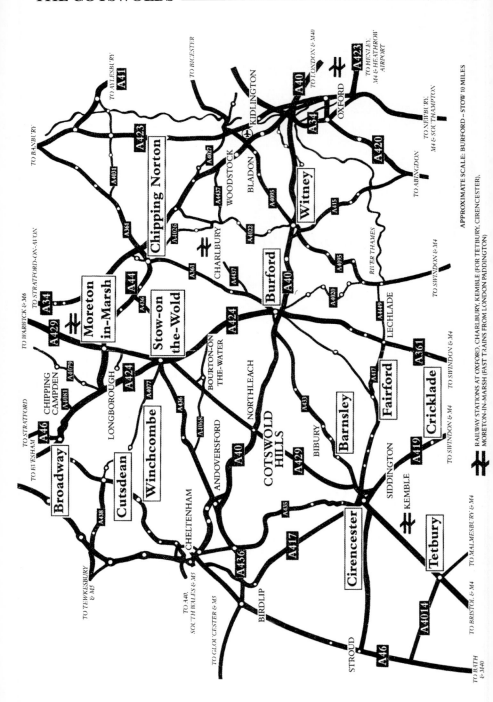

THE COTSWOLD ANTIQUE DEALERS' ASSOCIATION

Buy Fine Antiques and Works of Art at provincial prices in England's lovely and historic countryside

The Cotswolds, one of the finest areas of unspoilt countryside in the land, have been called "the essence and the heart of England." The region has a distinctive  character created by the use of honey-coloured stone in its buildings and dry stone walls. Within the locality the towns and villages are admirably compact and close to each other and the area is well supplied with good hotels and reasonably priced inns. The Cotswolds are within easy reach of London (1½ hour by road or rail) and several major airports.

Cotswold sheep – which inspired the logo for the Cotswold Antique Dealers' Association – a quatrefoil device with a sheep in its centre – have played an important part in the region's history with much of its wealth created by the woollen industry. As for antiques, shops and warehouses of the CADA offer a selection of period furniture, pictures, porcelain, metalwork, and collectables unrivalled outside London.

With the use of the CADA directory on the following pages, which lists the names of its members, their specialities and opening times, visitors from all over the world can plan their buying visit to the Cotswolds. CADA members will assist all visiting collectors and dealers in locating antiques and works of art. They will give you advice on where to stay in the area, assistance with packing, shipping and insurance and the exchange of foreign currencies. They can advise private customers on what can realistically be bought on their available budgets, and if the first dealer does not have the piece which you are selecting he will know of several other members who will. The CADA welcomes home and overseas buyers in the certain knowledge that there are at least fifty dealers with a good and varied stock, a reputation for fair trading and an annual turnover in excess of £15,000,000.

BARNSLEY, Nr. Cirencester

Denzil Verey
Barnsley House. GL7 5EE. CADA. Resident. Est. 1980. Open 9.30-5.30, Sat. 10-5.30, other times by appointment. SIZE: Large. *STOCK: Country furniture, including pine, 18th-19th C; decorative and unusual items, treen, copper, brass, domestic and rural objects, kitchenalia.* LOC: 4 miles from Cirencester on B4425 to Burford, 1st large house in village, set back off road on the right. PARK: Easy. TEL: 01285 740402; fax - 01285 740628. VAT: Stan/Spec.

BROADWAY

Fenwick and Fenwick Antiques
88-90 High St. WR12 7AJ. CADA. Est. 1980. Open 10-6, and by appointment. SIZE: Large. *STOCK: Furniture, oak, mahogany and walnut, 17th to early 19th C; samplers, boxes, treen, Tunbridgeware, Delft, decorative items and corkscrews.* TEL: 01386 853227; after hours - 01386 841724; fax - 01386 858504.

H.W. Keil Ltd   BADA
Tudor House. WR12 7DP. CADA. Est. 1925. Open 9.15-12.45 and 2.15-5.30. SIZE: Large. *STOCK: Walnut, oak, mahogany and rosewood furniture; early pewter, brass and glass, tapestry, glass and works of art, 17th-18th C.* LOC: By village clock. TEL: 01386 852408; fax - 01386 852069. VAT: Spec.

John Noott Galleries   BADA
58 High St., 14 Cotswold Court and at The Lygon Arms, High St. WR12 7AA. LAPADA, CADA. Est. 1972. Open 9.30-1 and 2-5. SIZE: Large. *STOCK: Paintings, watercolours and bronzes, 19th C to Contemporary.* PARK: Easy. TEL: 01386 854868/858969; fax - 01386 854919. SER: Valuations; restorations; framing. VAT: Stan/Spec.

BURFORD

Jonathan Fyson Antiques
50 High St. OX18 4QF. (J.R. Fyson). CADA. Est. 1970. Open 9.30-1 and 2-5.30. SIZE: Medium. *STOCK: English and Continental furniture, decorative brass and steel including lighting and fireplace accessories; club fenders, mirrors, porcelain, glass, jewellery.* LOC: At junction of A40/A361 between Oxford and Cheltenham. PARK: Easy. TEL: 01993 823204; fax - same; home - 01367 860223. SER: Valuations. VAT: Spec.

Gateway Antiques
Cheltenham Rd., Burford Roundabout. OX18 4JA. (M.C. Ford and P. Brown). CADA. Est.

1986. Open 10-5.30 and Sun. pm. SIZE: Large. *STOCK: English and Continental furniture, 18th-early 20th C; decorative accessories.* LOC: On roundabout (A40) Oxford/Cheltenham road. PARK: Easy. TEL: 01993 823678. SER: Valuations. VAT: Stan/Spec.

David Pickup   BADA
115 High St. OX18 4RG. CADA. Est. 1977. Open 9.30-1 and 2-4. Sat. 10-1 and 2-4. SIZE: Medium. *STOCK: Fine furniture, works of art, from £500+; decorative objects, from £100+; all late 17th to mid 20th C, specialising in Arts & Crafts.* PARK: Easy. TEL: 01993 822555. FAIRS: Olympia. VAT: Spec.

Richard Purdon Antique Carpets BADA
158 The Hill. OX18 4QY. CADA. Open 10-6. SIZE: Medium. *STOCK: Antique Eastern and European carpets, village and tribal rugs, needlework, textiles and related items.* TEL: 01993 823777; fax - 01993 823719; e-mail - rp@richardpurdon.demon.co.uk; website - www.purdon.com. SER: Valuations; restorations. VAT: Stan/Spec.

Manfred Schotten Antiques
109 High St. OX18 4RH. CADA. Est. 1974. Open 9.30-5.30 or by appointment. *STOCK: Sporting antiques and library furniture.* TEL: 01993 822302; fax - 01993 822055; website - www.schotten.com. SER: Restorations.

Swan Gallery
High St. OX18 4RE. (D. Pratt). LAPADA. CADA. Est. 1966. Open 10-5.30. SIZE: Large. *STOCK: Country furniture in oak, yew, walnut and fruitwood, 17th-19th C, £300-£12,000; Staffordshire figures and small decorative items, 18th-20th C, £50-£800.* PARK: Easy. TEL: 01993 822244. VAT: Mainly Spec.

CHIPPING CAMPDEN

The Titian Gallery
London House, High St. GL55 6AG. (Ilona Johnson Gibbs). LAPADA, CADA, CINOA. Est. 1976. Open 10-1 and 2-5, Sun. by appointment. SIZE: Medium. *STOCK: Fine 18th-19th C British and European oil paintings and watercolours, to £15,000.* LOC: Near centre of town square. PARK: Easy. TEL: 01386 841789; fax - 01386 849151. SER: Valuations; buys at auction (oils and watercolours). VAT: Spec.

CHIPPING NORTON

Antique English Windsor Chairs - Michael Harding-Hill
at Bugle Antiques 9 Horse Fair. OX7 5AL.

CINOA, CADA. Est. 1971. Open 10-5. *STOCK: 18th and 19th C Windsor chairs, including sets.* TEL: 01608 643322; fax - 01608 644322; e-mail - antique-windsor-chairs@dial.pipex.com; web-site - www.antique-english-windsor-chairs.co.uk. VAT: Stan/Spec.

Key Antiques
11 Horse Fair. OX7 5AL. (J. Riley). LAPADA, CADA. Open 10-5.30 or by appointment. CL: Mon. and Tues. SIZE: Medium. *STOCK: English period oak and country furniture, 17th-19th C; domestic metalware, pottery and associated items.* LOC: On main road. PARK: Easy. TEL: 01608 644992. VAT: Spec.

CIRENCESTER

William H. Stokes   BADA
The Cloisters, 6/8 Dollar St. GL7 2AJ. (W.H.Stokes and P.W.Bontoft). CADA. Est. 1968. Open 9.30-5.30, Sat. 9.30-4.30. *STOCK: Early oak furniture, £1,000-£30,000; brassware, £150-£5,000; all 16th-17th C.* **TEL: 01285 653907; fax - same. VAT: Spec.**

Rankine Taylor Antiques
34 Dollar St. GL7 2AN. LAPADA. CADA. Est. 1969. Open 9-5.30, Sun. by appointment. SIZE: Large. *STOCK: Furniture, 17th to early 19th C, £300-£35,000; glass, 18th-20th C, £8-£350; silver, rare interesting objects and decorative items, 17th-20th C, £20-£4,000.* Not Stocked: Victoriana. LOC: From church, turn right into West Market Place, via Gosditch St. into Dollar St. PARK: Own - private opposite. TEL: 01285 652529. VAT: Spec.

FAIRFORD

Blenheim Antiques
Market Place. GL7 4AB. (N. Hurdle). CADA. Resident. Est. 1972. Open 9.30-6.30. *STOCK: 18th-19th C furniture.* TEL: 01285 712094. VAT: Stan/Spec.

Gloucester House Antiques Ltd
Market Place. GL7 4AB. (Mrs Scilla Chester-Master). CADA. Est. 1972. Open 9-5.30. SIZE: Large. *STOCK: English and French country furniture in oak, elm, fruitwood, pine; pottery, faïence and decorative items.* PARK: Easy. TEL: 01285 712790; home - 01285 653066; fax - 01285 713324. VAT: Spec.

MORETON-IN-MARSH

Astley House - Fine Art
Astley House, High St. GL56 0LL. (David, Nanette & Caradoc Glaisyer). LAPADA. CADA.

Est. 1973. Open 9-5.30 and by appointment. SIZE: Medium. *STOCK: Oil paintings and botanical watercolours, 19th-21st C, £400-£20,000.* LOC: Main street. PARK: Easy. TEL: 01608 650601; fax - 01608 651777; e-mail - astart333@aol.com; website - www.art-uk.com. SER: Restorations (oils and watercolours); framing. VAT: Spec.

Astley House - Fine Art
Astley House, London Rd. GL56 0LE. (David, Nanette & Caradoc Glaisyer). LAPADA. CADA. Est. 1973. Open 10-1 and 2-5 and by appointment. CL: Wed. SIZE: Large. *STOCK: Oil paintings, 19th-21st C; large decorative oils and portraits.* LOC: Town centre. PARK: Easy. TEL: 01608 650608; fax - 01608 651777; e-mail - astart333@aol.com; website - www.art-uk.com. SER: Restorations (oils and watercolours); porcelain framing. VAT: Spec.

Jon Fox Antiques
High St. GL56 0AD. CADA. Est. 1982. Open 9.30-5.30, Sun. 11-4, Tues. by appointment. SIZE: Large. *STOCK: Garden antiques, 19th C, £25-£1,000+; country furniture, bygones and metalware.* PARK: Easy. TEL: 01608 650325. VAT: Spec.

STOW-ON-THE-WOLD

Duncan J. Baggott
Woolcomber House, Sheep St. GL54 1AA. LAPADA. CADA. Est. 1967. Open 9-5.30 or by appointment. SIZE: Large. *STOCK: 17th-20th C English furniture, paintings, domestic metalwork and decorative items; garden statuary and ornaments.* PARK: Sheep St. or Market Sq. TEL: 01451 830662; fax - 01451 832174.

Baggott Church Street Ltd   BADA
Church St. GL54 1BB. (D.J. and C.M. Baggott). CADA. Est. 1978. Open 9.30-5.30 or by appointment. SIZE: Large. *STOCK: English furniture, 17th-19th C; portrait paintings, metalwork, pottery, treen and decorative items.* **LOC: South-west corner of market square. PARK: In market square. TEL: 01451 830370; fax - 01451 832174.**

Christopher Clarke Antiques Ltd
The Fosseway. GL54 1JS. (I.D., D.S. and S.F. Clarke). LAPADA. CADA. Est. 1961. Open 9.30-5.30 or by appointment. SIZE: Large. *STOCK: Furniture, 17th-19th C; works of art, metalware, treen, pictures, decorative items and animal antiques.* LOC: Corner of The Fosseway and Sheep St. PARK: Easy. TEL: 01451 830476; fax - 01451 830300; e-mail - christopherclarke@ barclays.net; website - www.antiques-in-england. com.

Cotswold Galleries

GL54 1AB. (Richard and Cherry Glaisyer). CADA. Est. 1961. Open 9-5.30 or by appointment. SIZE: Large. *STOCK: Oil paintings especially 19th-20th C landscape.* TEL: 01451 870567; fax - 01451 870678. SER: Restorations; framing.

The John Davies Gallery

Church St. GL54 1BB. CADA. Est. 1977. Open 9.30-1.30 and 2.30-5.30. SIZE: Large. *STOCK: Contemporary and late period paintings; limited edition bronzes.* PARK: In square. TEL: 01451 831698; fax - 01451 832477. SER: Restoration and conservation to museum standard.

Fosse Way Antiques

Ross House, The Square. GL54 1AF. (M. Beeston). CADA. Est. 1969. Open 10-5. SIZE: Medium. *STOCK: Mahogany and walnut furniture, oil paintings, £500-£10,000; bronzes, boxes and decorative objects, £150-£2,000, all 18th to early 19th C.* LOC: East side of the Square, behind the Town Hall. PARK: Easy. TEL: 01451 830776. SER: Valuations; buys at auction. VAT: Spec.

Keith Hockin Antiques   BADA

The Square. GL54 1AF. CADA. Est. 1968. Open Thurs., Fri., Sat., 10-5, other times by appointment or ring the bell. SIZE: Medium. STOCK: Oak furniture, 1600-1750; country furniture in oak, fruitwoods, yew, 1700-1850; pewter, copper, brass, ironwork, all periods. Not Stocked: Mahogany. PARK: Easy. TEL: 01451 831058; fax - same. SER: Buys at auction (oak, pewter, metalwork). VAT: Stan/Spec.

Huntington Antiques Ltd

The Old Forge, Church St. GL54 1BE. (M.F. and S.P. Golding). LAPADA. CADA. CINOA. Resident. Est. 1974. Open 9.30-5.30 or by appointment. *STOCK: Early period and fine country furniture, metalware, treen and textiles, tapestries and works of art.* TEL: 01451 830842; fax - 01451 832211; e-mail - info@huntington-antiques.com; website - www.huntington-antiques.com. SER: Valuations; buys at auction. FAIRS: LAPADA; Madrid. VAT: Spec.

Roger Lamb Antiques & Works of Art

The Square. GL54 1AB. LAPADA. CADA. Open 10-5. *STOCK: 18th to early 19th C furniture especially small items, lighting, decorative accessories, oils and watercolours.* TEL: 01451 831371. SER: Search.

Antony Preston Antiques Ltd   BADA

The Square. GL54 1AB. CADA. Est. 1965. Open 9.30-5.30 or by appointment. *STOCK: 18th-19th C English and Continental furniture and objects; barometers and period lighting.* TEL: **01451 831586; fax - 01451 831596. VAT: Stan/Spec.**

Queens Parade Antiques Ltd   BADA

The Square. GL54 1AB. (Antony Preston Antiques Ltd). CADA. Est. 1965. Open 9.30-5.30. SIZE: Large. *STOCK: 18th-19th C furniture, papier mâché, tôle peinte, needlework and period lighting.* LOC: Off Fosse Way. PARK: Easy. TEL: **01451 831586. VAT: Stan/Spec.**

Ruskin Decorative Arts

5 Talbot Court. GL54 1DP. (Anne and William Morris). CADA Est. 1990. Open 9.30-1 and 2-5.30. SIZE: Small. *STOCK: Interesting and unusual decorative objects, Arts & Crafts furniture, Art Nouveau, Art Deco, glass and pottery, 1860-1940.* LOC: Between The Square and Sheep Street. PARK: Nearby. TEL: 01451 832254; fax - 01451 832167; home - 01993 831880. SER: Valuations.

Samarkand Galleries

7 & 8 Brewery Yard, Sheep St. GL54 1AA. (Brian MacDonald). LAPADA. CADA. CINOA. Est. 1979. Open 10-5.30, Sun. by appointment. SIZE: Medium. *STOCK: Tribal and village rugs and artefacts, 19th C, £100-£10,000; fine decorative carpets, 19th-20th C, £1,000-£10,000+; kelims, 19th-20th C, £200-£2,000; also unique contemporary rugs and carpets.* LOC: Street adjacent to Market Sq. PARK: Easy. TEL: 01451 832322; fax - same; e-mail - mac@samarkand.co.uk; website - www. samarkand.co.uk. SER: Exhibitions; valuations; restorations; cleaning. VAT: Stan/Spec.

Stow Antiques

The Square. GL54 1AF. (Mr and Mrs J. Hutton-Clarke). LAPADA. CADA. Resident. Est. 1969. Open Mon.-Sat. 11-1 and 2-5.30 other times by appointment. SIZE: Large. *STOCK: Furniture, mainly Georgian, £500-£30,000; decorative items, gilded mirrors, £50-£10,000.* PARK: Easy. TEL: 01451 830377; fax - 01451 870018. SER: Shipping worldwide.

STRETTON-ON-FOSSE, Nr. Moreton-in-Marsh

Astley House - Fine Art

The Old School. GL56 9SA. (David, Nanette and Caradoc Glaisyer). LAPADA. CADA. Est. 1973. Open by appointment. SIZE: Large. *STOCK: Large decorative oil paintings, 19th-21st C.* LOC: Village centre. PARK: Easy. TEL: 01608 650601; fax - 01608 651777; e-mail - astart333@aol.com; website - www.art-uk.com. SER: Exhibitions; mailing list. VAT: Spec.

TADDINGTON, Nr. Cutsdean

Architectural Heritage
Taddington Manor. GL54 5RY. CADA. Est. 1978. Open 9.30-5.30, Sat. 10.30-4.30. SIZE: Large. *STOCK: Garden ornaments, statues, fountains, temples, seats, urns; chimney pieces in stone; oak and pine panelling.* PARK: Easy. TEL: 01386 584414; fax - 01386 584236; e-mail - puddy@architectural-heritage.co.uk; website - www.architectural-heritage.co.uk. VAT: Stan.

TETBURY

Breakspeare Antiques
36 and 57 Long St. GL8 8AQ. (M. and S. Breakspeare). LAPADA. CADA. Resident. Est. 1962. Open 10-5 or by appointment. CL: Thurs. SIZE: Medium. *STOCK: English period furniture - early walnut, 1690-1740, mahogany, 1750-1835.* PARK: Own. TEL: 01666 503122; fax - same. VAT: Stan/Spec.

Day Antiques   BADA
5 New Church St. GL8 8DS. CADA. TADA. Est. 1975. Open 10-5.30. SIZE: Medium. STOCK: Early oak furniture and related items. TEL: 01666 502413; fax - 01666 505894; e-mail - dayantiques@lineone.net; web-site - www. dayantiques.com VAT: Spec.

Bobbie Middleton
58 Long St. GL8 8AQ. CADA, TADA. Open 10-1 and 2.30-5, Sun. by appointment. *STOCK: Classic country house furniture, mirrors, sconces and upholstered furniture, 18th-19th C.* LOC: Corner New Church St. TEL: 01666 502761; mobile - 07774 192660. VAT: Spec.

WINCHCOMBE

Prichard Antiques
16 High St. GL54 5LJ. (K.H. and D.Y. Prichard). CADA. Est. 1979. Open 9-5.30, Sun. by appointment. SIZE: Large. *STOCK: Period and decorative furniture, £10-£10,000; treen and metalwork, £5-£5,000; interesting and decorative accessories.* LOC: On B4632 Broadway to Cheltenham road. PARK: Easy. TEL: 01242 603566. VAT: Spec.

WITNEY

Colin Greenway Antiques
90 Corn St. OX8 7BU. CADA Resident. Est. 1975. Open 9.30-5, Sat . 10-4, Sun. by appointment. SIZE: Large. *STOCK: Furniture, 17th-20th C; metalware, decorative and unusual items.* LOC:

Witney Antiques
LSA & CJ JARRETT AND RR SCOTT
96-100 CORN STREET, WITNEY,
OXON OX28 6BU, ENGLAND.
TEL: 01993 703902. FAX: 01993 779852.
E-mail: witneyantiques@community.co.uk
Website: www.witneyantiques.com

A rare whitework sampler with bands, including one of two figures based on Sibmacher's Modelbuch published in 1601. English. Circa 1660.

ANTIQUE FURNITURE, CLOCKS & TEXTILES.

Along High St. to town centre, turn right, shop 400yds. on right. PARK: Easy. TEL: 01993 705026; mobile - 07831 585014. VAT: Stan/Spec.

W.R. Harvey & Co (Antiques) Ltd   BADA
86 Corn St. OX8 7BU. CADA. GMC. Open 9.30-5.30, and by appointment. SIZE: Large. STOCK: Fine English furniture, £500-£50,000; clocks, mirrors, objets d'art, £250-£20,000; all 1680-1830. LOC: 300 yds. from Market Place. PARK: Easy. TEL: 01993 706501; fax - 01993 706601; e-mail - antiques@wrharvey.co.uk; website -www.wr harvey.co.uk. SER: Valuations; restorations; consultancy. FAIRS: BADA; Chelsea (March & Sept.); Olympia (June). VAT: Stan/Spec.

Witney Antiques   BADA
96/100 Corn St. OX28 6BU. (L.S.A. and C.J. Jarrett and R.R. Jarrett-Scott). LAPADA, CADA. Est. 1962. Open 10-5. SIZE: Large. STOCK: English furniture, 17th-18th C; bracket and longcase clocks, mahogany, oak and walnut, metalware, needleworks and works of art. LOC: From Oxford on old A40 through Witney via High St., turn right at T-junction, 400yds. on right. PARK: Easy. TEL: 01993 703902/703887; fax - 01993 779852. SER: Restorations. FAIRS: BADA; Grosvenor House. VAT: Spec.

TETBURY ANTIQUE DEALERS' ASSOCIATION

The Antique and Interior Centre
51A Long St. GL8 8AA. TADA. Open 10-5, Sun. 11-5 and most Bank Holidays. SIZE: 8 dealers. *STOCK: Furniture, porcelain, silver and pictures; interior design items.* TEL: 01666 505083.

The Antiques Emporium
The Old Chapel, Long St. GL8 8AA. (D. Sayers). TADA. Est. 1993. Open 10-5, Sun. 1-5. SIZE: Large - 38 dealers. *STOCK: Fruitwood and country furniture, fine oak and mahogany, clocks, china, porcelain, treen, copper and brass, jewellery, silver, kitchenalia, militaria, £1-£15,000.* Not Stocked: Reproductions. PARK: Nearby. TEL: 01666 505281; fax - 01666 505661. SER: Export. VAT: Stan/Spec.

Artique
Talboys House, Church St. GL8 8JG. (George Bristow). TADA. Open 9-5. *STOCK: Interiors, textiles, carpets and kelims and objets d'art from the Orient.* TEL: 01666 503597; fax - same; e-mail - george@artique.demon.co.uk.

Ball and Claw Antiques
45 Long St. GL8 8AA. (Chris Kirkland). TADA. Est. 1994. Open 10-5 and most Sundays 2-5. SIZE: Medium. *STOCK: 17th-19th C furniture, engravings, pictures, linens, textiles, children's decorative toys and general antiques, £5-£5,000.* PARK: Easy. TEL: 01666 502440; mobile - 07957 870423.

Balmuir House Antiques
14 Long St. GL8 8AQ. (P. Whittam). LAPADA. TADA. Open 9.30-5.30, Sun. 2-5.30. SIZE: Large. *STOCK: Furniture, paintings, mirrors, 19th C, £500-£5,000.* LOC: Town centre. PARK: Easy. TEL: 01666 503822; home - same. SER: Restorations (furniture, upholstery, paintings). VAT: Spec.

The Chest of Drawers
24 Long St. GL8 8AQ. (A. and P. Bristow). TADA. Resident. Est. 1969. Open Tues.-Fri. 9.30-6, Mon. by appointment. SIZE: Medium + trade store at The Coach House, 4 The Chipping (open at all times). *STOCK: Late Georgian, Regency and Victorian furniture; country pieces, 17th-18th C; china and brass.* LOC: On A433. PARK: Easy. TEL: 01666 502105; home - same. VAT: Spec.

Day Antiques   BADA
5 New Church St. GL8 8DS. CADA. TADA. Est. 1975. Open 10-5.30. SIZE: Medium.
STOCK: Early oak furniture and related items. TEL: 01666 502413; fax - 01666 505894; e-mail - dayantiques@lineone.net; website - www.dayantiques.com VAT: Spec.

The Decorator Source
39a Long St. GL8 8AA. (Colin Gee). TADA. Open 10-5 or by appointment. SIZE: Large. *STOCK: French provincial furniture - armoires, farm tables, buffets; decorative items and accessories of interest to interior decorators.* PARK: Easy. TEL: 01666 505358. VAT: Stan/Spec.

Anne Fowler
35 Long St. GL8 8AA. TADA. Est. 1995. Open 10-5.30, Sun. by appointment. SIZE: Medium. *STOCK: Mainly French painted and decorative items including garden furniture and accessories, mirrors, faience and pots, wirework, lighting and prints, £20-£2,000.* PARK: Easy. TEL: 01666 504043; home - same; fax - 01666 500256; e-mail - annefowler.fsnet.co.uk. VAT: Stan/Spec.

Gales Antiques
52 Long St. GL8 8AQ. (M.R. Mathews). TADA. Est. 1979. Open 10-5.30. SIZE: Medium. *STOCK: English and French country furniture and decorative items, 17th-19th C, £5-£5,000.* PARK: Easy. TEL: 01666 502686. VAT: Stan/Spec.

Catherine Hunt
No. 13, The Antique & Interior Centre, 51A Long St. GL8 8AA. TADA. *STOCK: Pre-1800 Oriental ceramics, mainly Sung, Yuan, Ming and early Qing including provincial, Asian and European export and palace/imperial ware; Oriental textiles and furniture.* TEL: 01666 505083; 01242 227794; mobile - 07976 319344.

Jester Antiques
10 Church St. GL8 8JG. (Lorna Coles and Peter Bairsto). TADA. Open 10-5.30, including Sun. *STOCK: Longcase and wall clocks, also oil portraits and pictures, Oriental objects, lamps, furniture, decorative items, outside statuary and architectural.* TEL: 01666 505125.

Lyon Oliver Antiques
Laynes House. SN16 9SE. TADA. Prior telephone call advisable. *STOCK: English and Irish country house furniture, large mirrors, upholstery and decorative sculpture.* TEL: 01666 577603; e-mail - lyon@lyon-oliver.demon.co.uk.

The Tetbury Antique Dealers Association aims to promote and encourage trade in the Tetbury area and to assist all visiting antique dealers and collectors.

Over twenty shops with over fifty dealers

For further details contact the secretary:
Colin Gee, 39A Long Street, Tetbury, Glos. GL8 8AA
Telephone (+44) 01666 505358

Bobbie Middleton
58 Long St. GL8 8AQ. CADA, TADA. Open 10-1 and 2.30-5, Sun. by appointment. *STOCK: Classic country house furniture, mirrors, sconces and upholstered furniture, 18th-19th C.* LOC: Corner New Church St. TEL: 01666 502761; mobile - 07774 192660. VAT: Spec.

Peter Norden Antiques
61 Long St. GL8 8AA. TADA. Open 10-5.30, Sun. by appointment. SIZE: Medium. *STOCK: Early oak furniture, 16th-18th C, £250-£10,000; country furniture, 15th-19th C, £75-£10,000; early carvings, metalware, pewter, pottery, treen, 14th-19th C, £10-£20,000.* PARK: Nearby. TEL: 01666 503854; fax - same; home - 01452 770536. SER: Valuations. VAT: Spec.

Porch House Antiques
40/42 Long St. GL8 8AQ. TADA. Open 10-5. *STOCK: 17th-20th C furniture and decorative items.* TEL: 01666 502687.

Sieff
49 Long St. GL8 8AA. LAPADA. TADA. Est. 1994. Open 10-5.30, Sun. by appointment. SIZE: Large. *STOCK: English and French 18th-20th C furniture and objets, £100-£10,000.* PARK: Easy. TEL: 01666 504477; fax - 01666 504478; e-mail

- ssieff@hotmail.com. SER: Valuations; buys at auction. FAIRS: Harvey Decorative Antique & Textile. VAT: Stan/Spec.

Tetbury Gallery
18 Market Place. GL8 8DD. (Jane Maile). FATG. TADA. Open every day. *STOCK: Original and limited edition prints, from Victorian watercolours and oils to contemporary artists including Russell Flint, David Shepherd and Ben Maile.* TEL: 01666 503412.

Tetbury Old Books & Coach House Antiques
4 The Chipping. GL8 8ET. (Tetbury Old Books Ltd and A. & P. Bristow). TADA. Open 10-6, Sun. 11-5. *STOCK: Antiquarian and secondhand books and prints; English antique furniture.* TEL: 01666 504330; fax - 01666 504458; e-mail - oldbooks@tetbury.co.uk.

Westwood House Antiques
29 Long St. GL8 8AA. (Richard Griffiths and Lynne Petersen). TADA. Resident. Open 10-5.30 or by appointment. SIZE: Large. *STOCK: Oak, elm and ash country furniture especially dressers, dresser bases and tables, 17th-19th C; occasional French pieces; decorative pottery, pewter and treen.* TEL: 01666 502328; fax - same; mobile - 07774 952909.

195

CUMBRIA

ALLONBY

Cottage Curios
Main St. CA15 6PX. (B. Pickering). Est. 1965. Open Sat. and Sun. 2-5.

ALSTON

Just Glass
Cross House, Market Place. CA9 3HS. (M.J. Graham). Est. 1987. Open Wed., Thurs., Sat. 11-4, Sun. 12-4. *STOCK: Glass, 1780-1920's, to £800.* LOC: Town centre. PARK: Easy. TEL: Home - 01434 381263; mobile - 07833 994948. FAIRS: Narworth Castle.

BEETHAM, Nr. Milnthorpe

Peter Haworth
Temple Bank. LA7 7AL. Open by appointment. *STOCK: English and Scottish paintings and watercolours, 1850-1950, £100-£25,000.* LOC: 2 miles south of Milnthorpe on A6 to Lancaster. PARK: Easy. TEL: 015395 62352; fax - 015395 63438. SER: Valuations; restorations; commissions.

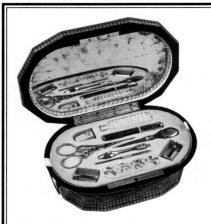

This delightful French amboyna burr fitted necessaire is complete and contains all original fitments and accessories on J. Collins & Son's stand at the BADA Fair. Price £1,450.

From a Fairs Preview which appeared in the March 2000 issue of **Antique Collecting** magazine. For more details and to subscribe see page 147.

BOWNESS ON WINDERMERE

Something Old Something New
(Behind Royal Hotel), St Martin's Parade.. Open 11-5.30 including Sun. SIZE: 3 rooms. *STOCK: Rare vinyl, books, collectables, antiques, bric-a-brac.* TEL: 01524 781718.

J.W. Thornton Antiques Supermarket
North Terrace. LA23 3AU. SIZE: Large. *STOCK: Fine art, general antiques, furniture, shipping and architectural items, pine, bric-a-brac, paintings, decorators items.* TEL: 01229 580284; mobile - 07974 788525. SER: Valuations; buys at auction. VAT: Stan/Spec.

BRAMPTON

The Cumbrian Antiques Centre
St Martin's Hall, Front St. CA8 1NT. (S.T. Summerson-Wright). Est. 1976. Open 10-5, Thurs. 10-6, Sun. 12-6. SIZE: Large. *STOCK: Wide range of general antiques from silver and china to longcase clocks and furniture.* LOC: A69 Carlisle to Newcastle road into village, premises on right as road forks. PARK: Easy. TEL: 016977 42515; fax - same; home - 07889 924843. SER: Valuations; restorations.

Something Old, Something New
46 Main St. CA8 1SB. (Joan Potts). Est. 1980. Open 10-4.30. SIZE: Medium. *STOCK: Victorian stripped pine, £50-£500; oak and mahogany country furniture, smalls.* LOC: A69. PARK: Easy. TEL: 01697 741740; home - 01228 675587. SER: Valuations; buys at auction.

CARLISLE

Carlisle Antiques and Craft Centre
Cecil Hall, Cecil St. CA1 1NT. Open 9-5. SIZE: Large plus trade warehouse (Basement - Fri. and Sat. indoor market - bric-a-brac, collectibles). LOC: Off Warwick Rd. PARK: Easy. TEL: 01228 536910; fax - same. Below are listed the dealers at this centre.

Fine Pine
Stripped pine furniture; mahogany and oak bedroom suites, large furniture, china, quilts.

It's About Time
(B. and W. Mitton). Est. 1985. *Longcase, bracket and carriage clocks, watches; Royal Worcester fine porcelain, jewellery, textiles.* TEL: 01228 36910.

Warwick Antiques
(J. Wardrope). CMBHI. *Period furniture, wall and bracket clocks.* SER: Valuations; restorations (clocks).

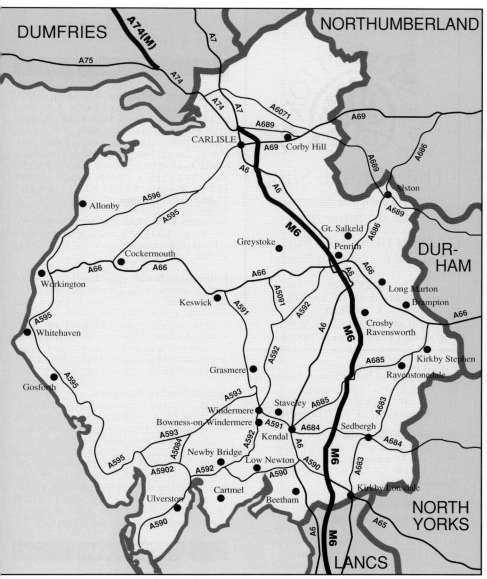

Dealers and Shops in Cumbria

The Antique Shop

English antique furniture,
also decorative items

Open 10.00am – 5.00pm
every day including Sunday

CARTMEL
GRANGE-OVER-SANDS
CUMBRIA
TELEPHONE 015395-36295
MOBILE TELEPHONE 07768 443757

City centre between Fisher St. and Scotch St. PARK: Nearby. TEL: 01228 401281; website - www.cumbriamaps.fsnet.co.uk.

CARTMEL

Anthemion - The Antique Shop BADA LA11 6QD. (J. Wood). LAPADA. Est. 1982. Open 10-5 including Sun. SIZE: Large. *STOCK: English period furniture, 17th to early 19th C, £100-£30,000; decorative items, 17th-19th C, £20-£2, 000.* Not Stocked: Victoriana, bric-a-brac. LOC: Village centre. PARK: Easy. TEL: 01539 536295; mobile - 07768 443757. FAIRS: BADA; NEC; Olympia; Chester. VAT: Stan/Spec.

Norman Kerr - Gatehouse Bookshop
The Square. LA11 6PX. Open by appointment only. *STOCK: Antiquarian books.* TEL: 01539 536247.

Peter Bain Smith (Bookseller)
Bank Court, Market Sq. LA11 6QB. Open 1.30-5 including Sun. From mid Nov. to Easter open Wed.-Sat. 1.30-4.30.*STOCK: Books including antiquarian, especially children's and local topography.* LOC: A590 from Levens Bridge, off roundabout at Lindale by-pass through Grange-over-Sands. PARK: Nearby. TEL: 01539 536369. SER: Valuations.

Simon Starkie Antiques
Gatehouse Cottage, Cavendish St. LA11 6QA. Est. 1980. Open 10.30-4.30, Sun. 11.30-4.30, Mon., Tues. and Thurs. by appointment. SIZE: Small. *STOCK: Oak furniture, 17th-19th C, £100-£8,000; painted country furniture and clocks, 18th-19th C, £50-£2,500; Delftware and pewter, 18th-19th C, £30-£1,000.* LOC: 10 miles from M6, follow signs for Cartmel priory. PARK: Nearby. TEL: 015395 36453; home - 01229 861222. SER: Valuations; buys at auction (furniture and earthenware). VAT: Stan/Spec.

COCKERMOUTH

CG's Curiosity Shop
43 Market Place. CA13 9LT. (Colin Graham and Corinne Ritchie). Est. 1985. Open 10-12.30 and 1.30-5. SIZE: Medium. *STOCK: China, glass, collectables, militaria, from 1800, £5-£1,000+.* LOC: End of main street, over the bridge. PARK: Nearby. TEL: 01900 824418; home - 01697 21108; mobile - 0771 220 6786; e-mail - cgcuriosity@hotmail.com. SER: Valuations; restorations; buys at auction; internet search. FAIRS: Newark.

Clements Antiques
19 Fisher St. CA3 8RF. Est. 1887. Open 9.30-5. CL: Thurs. *STOCK: Silver, jewellery, porcelain and glass.* TEL: 01228 525565; website - www. clements-antiques.co.uk. VAT: Global/ margin.

Maurice Dodd Books
44 Cecil St. CA1 1NT. (R.J. McRoberts). Est. 1945. Open by appointment. *STOCK: Antiquarian books.* TEL: 01228 710456; fax - same; e-mail - doddbook@globalnet.co.uk.

Saint Nicholas Galleries Ltd. (Antiques and Jewellery)
39 Bank St. CA3 8HJ. (C.J. Carruthers). Open 10-5. CL: Mon. SIZE: Medium. *STOCK: Jewellery, silver, plate, Rolex and pocket watches, clocks; collectables; Royal Doulton; Dux, Oriental vases; pottery, porcelain; watercolours, oil paintings; brass and copper.* LOC: City centre. PARK: Nearby. TEL: 01228 544459.

Souvenir Antiques
Treasury Court, Fisher St. CA3 8RF. (J. Higham). Open 10-5. SIZE: Small. *STOCK: Porcelain and pottery, Victorian to Art Deco, £5-£500; coronation ware, crested china, local prints, maps, postcards, Roman and medieval coins, antiquities, costume jewellery.* Not Stocked: Textiles. LOC:

Cockermouth Antiques
5 Station St. CA13 9QW. (E. Bell and G. Davies). Est. 1983. Open 10-5. SIZE: Large. *STOCK: General antiques especially jewellery, silver, ceramics, furniture, pictures, glass, books, metalware, quilts.* LOC: Just off A66, in town centre. PARK: Easy. TEL: 01900 826746; e-mail - elainebell54@aol.com.

Cockermouth Antiques Market
Courthouse, Main St. CA13 9LU. Est. 1979. Open 10-5. SIZE: Large - 4 stallholders. *STOCK: Victorian, Edwardian and Art Deco items, furniture, printed collectables, postcards, books, linen, china, glass, textiles, jewellery and pictures.* LOC: Town centre, just off A66. PARK: 50 yds. TEL: 01900 824346. SER: Restorations (furniture); stripping (pine). VAT: Stan/Spec.

CORBY HILL, Nr. Carlisle

Acanthus Antiques/Country Seat Antiques
The Forge. CA4 8PL. Open 10-4.30. CL: Thurs. SIZE: Medium. *STOCK: 18th-20th C antique furniture and decorative items, paintings and drawings.* LOC: 5 miles from Carlisle on A69 Hexham/Newcastle road. PARK: Easy. TEL: Mobiles - 07760 120431/07710 277490. SER: Upholstery.

CROSBY RAVENSWORTH, Nr. Penrith

Jennywell Hall Antiques
CA10 3JP. (Mrs M. Macadie). Resident. Est. 1975. Open weekends 10-6, also most weekdays but phone call advisable. SIZE: Medium. *STOCK: Oak and mahogany furniture, paintings, interesting objects.* LOC: 5 miles from junction 39, M6. PARK: Easy. TEL: 01931 715288; home - same.

GOSFORTH

Archie Miles Bookshop
Beck Place. CA20 1AT. (Mrs C.M. Linsley). Open 10-5, Sun. 1-5.30, out of season opening times may vary. CL: Mon. *STOCK: Secondhand, antiquarian and out-of-print books, maps and prints.* TEL: 01946 725792.

GRASMERE

Lakes Crafts & Antiques Gallery
3 Oak Bank, Broadgate. LA22 9TA. (Joe and

Sandra Arthy). Est. 1990. Open 15th Mar. - 31st Oct. 9.30-6 including Sun., other times 10-4.30. CL: 5th Jan. - 1st Feb. SIZE: Medium. *STOCK: Books, 18th-20th C, £1-500; collectables and postcards, £1-£100; general antiques, 17th-20th C, £5-£250.* LOC: North side of village, off A591 on Ambleside to Keswick road. PARK: Easy. TEL: 01539 435037; fax - 01539 444271; home - 01539 444234. VAT: Stan.

The Stables
College St. LA22 9SW. (J.A. and K.M. Saalmans). Est. 1971. Open daily 10-6 Easter-November, other times telephone call advisable. SIZE: Small. *STOCK: Brass and copper items, oil lamps, domestic bygones; pottery, silver, prints, books.* Not Stocked: Weapons, furniture. LOC: By the side of Moss Grove Hotel. PARK: Easy. TEL: 01539 435453; home - same.

GREAT SALKELD, Nr. Penrith

G.K. Hadfield
Beck Bank. CA11 9LN. (G.K. and J.V. Hadfield (Hon. FBHI), D.W. and N.R. Hadfield-Tilly). Est. 1972. Open 9-5. *STOCK: Clocks - longcase, dial, Act of Parliament, skeleton, Black Forest, American and carriage; unrestored antique clocks; secondhand, new and out of print horological books; secondhand workshop tools and materials.* LOC: From M6, junction 40 take A686 towards Alston for 3 miles, left on B6412 signed Great Salkeld, about 1.5 miles, turn left at sign for Salkeld Dykes, 1st house on right. TEL: 01768 870111; fax - same; e-mail - gkhadfield@dial.pipex.com. SER: Restoration materials (antique clocks); valuations (clocks and horological books). VAT: Stan/Spec.

GREYSTOKE, Nr. Penrith

Roadside Antiques
Watsons Farm, Greystoke Gill. CA11 0UQ. (K. and R. Sealby). Resident. Est. 1988. Open 10-6 including Sun. SIZE: Medium. *STOCK: Ceramics, longcase clocks, glass, Staffordshire figures, pot-lids, pens, furniture, small collectables, jewellery, mainly 19th C, £5-£2,000.* LOC: B5288 Penrith/Keswick road to Greystoke, through village, first left then left again, premises second on right. PARK: Easy. TEL: 01768 483279.

KENDAL

Below Stairs
125 Stricklandgate. LA9 4RF. (S. and T. Ritchie). Open 10-4. *STOCK: China, brass, copper,*

coloured glass, silver and collectables. LOC: Main street on road towards Windermere. TEL: 01539 741278.

Dower House Antiques

40 Kirkland. LA9 5AD. (Brian Blakemore). Open 9.15-6, Thurs. 9.15-1. *STOCK: Pottery, porcelain, paintings, furniture.* TEL: 01539 722778.

Granary Collectables

29 All Hallows Lane. LA9 4JH. (B. J. Cross). Est. 1998. Open 10-4.30. CL: Mon. SIZE: Small. *STOCK: Small collectables, pictures, kitchenalia, pottery, advertising and unusual items, £5-£100.* LOC: 100 yards from town centre, off main road. PARK: Easy. TEL: 01539 740770. SER: Valuations.

Kendal Studios Antiques

2/3 Wildman St. LA9 6EN. (R. Aindow). Est. 1950. Open 10.30-4, prior telephone call advisable. SIZE: Medium. *STOCK: Ceramics, maps and prints, paintings, oak furniture, art pottery.* LOC: Leave M6 at junction 37, follow one-way system, shop on left. PARK: Nearby. TEL: 01539 723291 (24 hrs. answering service). SER: Finder; shipping. VAT: Stan/Spec.

The Silver Thimble

39 All Hallows Lane. LA9. (V. Ritchie). Est. 1980. Open 10-4. SIZE: Large. *STOCK: Jewellery, silver, glass, linen and lace, porcelain, copper and brass.* LOC: Turn left at second set of traffic lights on main road into Kendal from south, shop 200yds. on right. PARK: Easy. TEL: 01539 731456.

KESWICK

Cat in the Window

29 Station St., (Beneath Ravensworth Hotel). CA12 5HH. (E. Fell). Est. 1980. Open 10.30-4.30. CL: Mon. SIZE: Small. *STOCK: Porcelain and pottery, copper, brass and pewter, small furniture.* LOC: Near Fitz Park. PARK: Easy and nearby. TEL: Mobile - 07989 717088. SER: Valuations; buys at auction. FAIRS: Colin Caygill in Cumbria.

The Country Bedroom

Lake Rd. CA12 5BZ. (W.I. Raw). Est. 1981. Open 9.30-5. *STOCK: Brass beds, iron and brass beds, mattress and base sets for antique beds, mirrors, linen, quilts, £150-£2,000.* LOC: Top of Main St. TEL: 017687 74881; fax - 017687 71424. VAT: Stan.

'Lvivlae' and 'Sambuci' – two English delft syrup jars, c.1680, which sold for respective prices of £2,100 and £2,300.

From an Auction Report by Christopher Wight on Three Ceramics Collections at Vost's, Newmarket, 28th June 2000 which featured in our September 2000 issue of **Antique Collecting** magazine. For more details and to subscribe see page 147.

Haughey Antiques

17th, 18th and 19th century oak, walnut & mahogany furniture

28-30 Market Street, Kirkby Stephen,
Cumbria CA17 4QW

Telephone 017683 71302
Facsimile: 017683 72423
email: haugheyantiques@aol.com

Open Monday - Saturday
10am - 5pm
otherwise by appointment

Rare early 18th century oak joined canopy dresser, Llanrwst, N. Wales.

LAPADA MEMBER

Keswick Bookshop
4 Station St. CA12 5HT. (Jane and John Kinnaird). PBFA. Est. 1994. Open April to end Oct. 10.30-5, prior telephone call essential in winter months. SIZE: Medium. *STOCK: Books, 18th-20th C; prints and maps, 18th-20th C.* LOC: Town centre. PARK: Nearby. TEL: 01768 775535; fax - 01228 528567; home - same. VAT: Stan/Spec.

John Young and Son (Antiques)
12-14 Main St. CA12 5JD. LAPADA. Est. 1890. Open 9-5. SIZE: Large. *STOCK: 17th-20th C. furniture, clocks and decorative items for the home and garden.* LOC: Town centre. PARK: At rear. TEL: 017687 73434; fax - 017687 73306. VAT: Stan/Spec.

KIRKBY LONSDALE

Architus Antiques
14 Main St. (J. Pearson and B. Rigby). Est. 1990. Open 10-4.30, Sat. 10-5.30. SIZE: Medium. *STOCK: Victorian oil lamps, £100-£250; china and glass, jewellery and silver, Victorian to early 20th C.* LOC: First antique shop on left in village from A65 towards Kendal. TEL: 015242 72409; home - 015242 71517. SER: Valuations.

KIRKBY STEPHEN

Haughey Antiques
28/30 Market St. CA17 4QW. (D.M. Haughey). LAPADA. Est. 1969. Open 10-5 or by appointment. SIZE: Large. *STOCK: Furniture, 17th-19th C; garden furniture and statuary.* PARK: Own. TEL: 017683 71302; fax - 017683 72423; e-mail - haugheyantiques@aol.com. SER: Valuations. FAIRS: Olympia; LAPADA, NEC. VAT: Stan/Spec.

David Hill
36 Market Sq. CA17 4QT. Est. 1965. Open Thurs., Fri. and Sat. 9.30-4. SIZE: Medium. *STOCK: Country clocks and furniture, £10-£1,000; both 18th-19th C; glassware, £5-£75; curios, £5-£50; shipping goods, kitchenalia, iron and brassware.* LOC: On A685; M6 junction 38. PARK: Easy. TEL: 0176 83 71598.

LONG MARTON, Nr. Appleby

Ben Eggleston Antiques
The Dovecote, CA16 6BJ. (Ben and Kay Eggleston). Est. 1976. Open strictly by appointment. SIZE: Large. *STOCK: Pine furniture, unstripped and unrestored for the trade, £5-*

£2,500. LOC: 2 miles east of A66 between Appleby and Penrith. PARK: Easy. TEL: 017683 61849; home and fax - same. VAT: Stan/Spec. *Strictly Trade Only.*

LOW NEWTON, Nr. Grange-over-Sands

Utopia Antiques Ltd

Yew Tree Barn. LA11 6JP. (P.J. and Mrs J.Wilkinson). Open 10-5 including Sun. *STOCK: Pine and country furniture, Indian furniture, handicrafts and fabrics.* PARK: Easy. TEL: 015395 30065. VAT: Stan.

W.R.S. Architectural Antiques

Yew Tree Barn. LA11 6JP. (Clive Wilson). Open 10-5, Sun. 12-6 (winter 11-5). *STOCK: General architectural antiques including fireplaces; period furniture.* TEL: 01539 531498.

NEWBY BRIDGE

Townhead Antiques

LA12 8NP. (E.M. and C.P. Townley). LAPADA. Est. 1960. Open 10-5. SIZE: Large. *STOCK: 18th-19th C furniture, silver, porcelain, glass, decorative pieces; clocks, pictures.* LOC: A592. 1 mile from Newby Bridge on the Windermere road. PARK: Easy. TEL: 01539 531321; fax - 01539 530019; e-mail - Townhead@aol.com; website - www.Townhead-Antiques.co.uk. SER: Valuations. VAT: Stan/Spec.

PENRITH

Antiques of Penrith

4 Corney Sq. CA11 7PX. (L. Mildwurf and Partners). Est. 1964. Open 10-12 and 1.30-5, Sat. 10-12.30. CL: Wed. SIZE: Large. *STOCK: Early oak and mahogany furniture, clocks, brass, copper, glass, china, silver plate, metal, Staffordshire figures, curios and paintings.* Not Stocked: Jewellery, books, rugs. LOC: Near Town Hall. PARK: Easy. TEL: 01768 862801. VAT: Stan/Spec/Global.

Brunswick Antiques

8 Brunswick Rd. CA11 7LU. (M. and L. Hodgson). Est. 1985. Open 10-5. SIZE: Small. *STOCK: Furniture, clocks, pottery, glass, metalware, 19th-20th C.* PARK: Easy. TEL: 01768 899338; home - 01768 867164. VAT: Spec.

The Gallery

54 Castlegate. CA11 7HY. (K.G. Plant). Est. 1969. Open by appointment only. SIZE: Small. *STOCK: Paintings and watercolours, 17th-20th*

C, £500-£50,000. LOC: From town centre towards the railway station. TEL: 01768 865538; home - same. SER: Valuations. VAT: Stan/Spec.

Hearth & Home

6 Brunswick Rd. CA11 7LU. Open 9-5. *STOCK: Reproduction furniture and decorative accessories, fireplaces, multi-fuel and gas stoves.* TEL: 01768 867200.

Joseph James Antiques

Corney Sq. CA11 7PX. (G.R. Walker). Est. 1970. Open 9-5. CL: Wed. SIZE: Medium. *STOCK: Furniture and upholstery, 18th C and Victorian, £10-£3,000; porcelain and pottery, £5-£1,000; silver and plate, pictures, £2-£800; all 18th-19th C.* LOC: On the one-way system in the town, 100yds. from the main shopping area (Middlegate), 50yds. from the town hall. PARK: Easy and 100yds. TEL: 01768 862065. SER: Re-upholstery; soft furnishings. VAT: Stan.

Penrith Coin and Stamp Centre

37 King St. CA11 7AY. (Mr and Mrs A. Gray). Resident. Est. 1974. Open 9-5.30. CL: Wed. Sept.-May. SIZE: Medium. *STOCK: Coins, B.C. to date, 1p-£500; jewellery, secondhand, £5-£500; Great Britain and Commonwealth stamps.* LOC: Just off town centre. PARK: Behind shop. TEL: 01768 864185; fax - same. SER: Valuations; jewellery repairs. FAIRS: Many coin. VAT: Stan.

Jane Pollock Antiques

LAPADA. Open by appointment only. *STOCK: Georgian, Victorian and 20th C silver flatware and collectables.* TEL: 01768 88250. FAIRS: Olympia; Chester; Harrogate; Edinburgh. VAT: Global/Margin.

Sandgate Antiques

21 Sandgate. CA11 7TJ. (Steve Bates). Est. 1983. Open Mon., Tues., Fri. and Sat. 10-5 or by appointment. SIZE: Medium. *STOCK: Oak and country furniture, 17th to early 19th C; longcase clocks, Delft, decorative items.* LOC: Near town centre, past bus station up hill on right. PARK: Easy. TEL: 01768 899599; fax - same. VAT: Stan/Spec.

RAVENSTONEDALE, Nr. Kirkby Stephen

The Book House

Grey Garth. CA17 4NQ. (C. and M. Irwin). PBFA. Est. 1963. Open 9-5. CL: Tues. *STOCK: Books, mainly 19th-20th C, £1-£1,000; some postcards, 20th C, 25p-£10.* LOC: Off A685. Square house across road triangle from village school. PARK: Easy. TEL: 015396 23634; home

- same; fax - 015396 23434; e-mail - enquiries@ thebookhouse.co.uk. SER: Valuations. FAIRS: Northern PBFA. VAT: Stan.

Winton Hall Antiques
Rowfoot Farm. CA17 4NN. (S. Baldwick). Resident. Est. 1975. Open 9-5 including Sun. SIZE: Large. *STOCK: Oak and country furniture, 1600-1800, £100-£7,000; mahogany, 1750-1830, £100-£4,000.* LOC: Midway between village and The Fat Lamb Inn, 1.5 miles from A685. PARK: Easy. TEL: 015396 23669. SER: Valuations; buys at auction. VAT: Stan/Spec. *Trade Only.*

SEDBERGH

R. F. G. Hollett and Son
6 Finkle St. LA10 5BZ. (R. F. G. and C. G. Hollett). Est. 1951. Open Wed.-Sat. 10-5. SIZE: Large. *STOCK: Antiquarian books, 15th-20th C, £20-£20,000+; maps, prints and paintings, 17th-19th C, £10-£5,000.* LOC: Town centre. PARK: Free nearby. TEL: 015396 20298; fax - 015396 21396; e-mail - hollett@sedbergh.demon.co.uk; website - www.holletts-rarebooks.co.uk. SER: Valuations. VAT: Stan.

Stable Antiques
Wheelwright Cottage, 15-16 Back Lane. LA10 5AQ. Est. 1970. Open 10-6 or by appointment. *STOCK: Small furniture, brass, copper, silver, china, prints, small collectors' items, treen.* LOC: 5 miles from exit 37, M6. TEL: 015396 20251.

STAVELEY

Staveley Antiques
27/29 Main St. LA8 9LU. (P. John Corry). Est. 1991. Open 10-5, Sun. by appointment. SIZE: Large. *STOCK: Brass and iron bedsteads, 1830-1930, £200-£1,200, French walnut bedsteads, from 1880, £500-£2,000; lighting, 1880-1935, from £50; fire-irons, kerbs and metalware, from 1850, from £50.* LOC: Between Kendal and Windermere on A591 (now bypassed). PARK: Easy. TEL: 01539 821393; home - 01539 821123. SER: Valuations; restorations (brass and iron bedsteads, metalware)

ULVERSTON

A1A Antiques
59B Market St. (J.W. Thornton). Est. 1960. Open by appointment. SIZE: Large. *STOCK: Bric-a-brac, clocks, furniture, shipping items, pictures, decorators items.* PARK: Easy. TEL: 01229

580284. SER: Valuations; restorations; buys at auction. VAT: Stan/Spec.

Elizabeth and Son
Market Hall. (J.R. Bevins). Est. 1960. Open 9-5. CL: Wed. SIZE: Medium. *STOCK: Victorian and Edwardian glass, silver, brass and copper, gold and silver jewellery, books.* LOC: Town centre. PARK: Easy. TEL: 01229 582763.

WHITEHAVEN

Michael Moon - Antiquarian Booksellers
19 Lowther St. CA28 7AL. (M. and S. Moon). SBA, PBFA. Open 9.30-5. SIZE: Large. *STOCK: Antiquarian books including Cumbrian topography.* PARK: Nearby. TEL: 01946 599010. FAIRS: PBFA Northern. VAT: Stan.

WINDERMERE

The Birdcage Antiques
College Rd. LA23 1BX. (Mrs T.A. Griffiths). Est. 1983. Open Wed., Fri. and Sat. 10-5 or by appointment. SIZE: Small. *STOCK: General antiques, glass, brass, copper, pre-1920's lighting, country bygones, Staffordshire, 18th C to 1920; 19th C pottery, small country furniture, 16th -19th C.* LOC: From A591 through village, past end of one-way system, turn right after 50yds. PARK: Alongside shop. TEL: 015394 45063; home - 015394 43041/43310. VAT: Global/Stan.

Joseph Thornton Antiques
4 Victoria St. LA23 1AB. (J.W. Thornton). Est. 1971. Open Tues.-Sat. 10-4.30 or by appointment. SIZE: Large. *STOCK: General antiques, art, architectural and decorators' items, clocks, bric-a-brac.* LOC: 50yds. from railway station. PARK: Easy. TEL: 01229 580284. SER: Valuations; buys at auction. VAT: Stan/Spec.

WORKINGTON

Castle Antiques Bookstore
18 Pow St. CA14 3AG. SIZE: Medium. *STOCK: Books and related ephemera, vintage posters, cigarette cards, postcards, sporting programmes, comics, pictures and prints.* LOC: Just off A66 coming into town. PARK: Opposite. TEL: 01900 607499/601387. SER: Publishers of local histories.

DERBYSHIRE

Alfreton Antiques Centre
11 King St. DE55 7AF. (Helen Dixon). Open 10-4.30, Sun. 11-4.30. SIZE: Large - 40 dealers. *STOCK: Wide range of furniture, ceramics, books, postcards, lighting, metalware, glass, collectables, Deco, costume jewellery, pictures, Langley Artware pottery.* LOC: Off junction 28, M1, A38 to Alfreton, King St. is main street up to traffic lights, shop on right before the lights. PARK: Easy. TEL: 01773 520781; home - 01773 852695; mobile - 07970 786968; e-mail - alfretonantiques@supanet.com; website - www.alfretonantiques.supanet.com. SER: Valuations; Denby replacement service.

Early World Antiques
28 Nottingham Rd. DE55 7HL. (Mark Goddard). Est. 1998. Open 10.30-4.30. CL: Wed. SIZE: Medium. *STOCK: Victorian pine, architectural items, clocks, all 19th C.* LOC: 1.2 mile from A38. PARK: Easy. TEL: 01773 834980; mobile - 07971 544804. SER: Restorations (pine stripping, waxing and polishing); buys at auction (Victorian pine and clocks). FAIRS: Swinderby and Newark.

The South Street Trading Co Ltd
31-32 South St., Riddings. DE55 4EJ. (Richard Evison). Est. 1990. Open 9-5, Sat. by appointment. SIZE: Small. *STOCK: Steam models and advertising figures, 20th C.* LOC: A610 from junction 26, M1 to Codnor. Right at traffic lights, right again to Riddings. PARK: Easy. TEL: 01773 541527; fax - 01773 541527. SER: Valuations; restorations (steam models); buys at auction (steam models). VAT: Stan.

Protective hats can make up another interesting group for collectors. A late 18th century 'bergère' circular sunhat not only provided ladies with shade and glamour; its pastoral simplicity was politically correct in post-revolutionary Europe.

From an article entitled 'From Royal to Rock 'n' Roll – Hats for the Collector' by Anne-Noëlle Tamplin which appeared in the May 2001 issue of **Antique Collecting** magazine. For more details and to subscribe see page 147.

Ashbourne Antiques Ltd
Warehouse, Blake House, Shirley. DE6 3AS. (Robert Allsebrook). Est. 1977. Open by appointment. SIZE: Small. *STOCK: English furniture, 17th-20th C, and hand-made copies.* LOC: A52 Ashbourne/Derby. PARK: Easy. TEL: 01335 361236; mobile - 07970 094883. SER: Restorations; cabinet makers; removals, packing and shipping. VAT: Stan.

Pamela Elsom - Antiques
5 Church St. DE6 1AE. Est. 1963. Open Thurs., Fri. and Sat. 10-5, other days and times by appointment. SIZE: Medium. *STOCK: Furniture, £20-£5,000, metalware, both 17th-19th C; period smalls, general antiques, treen, pottery, glass, secondhand books.* Not Stocked: Coins, militaria. LOC: On A52. PARK: Easy. TEL: 01335 343468/344311. SER: Valuations. VAT: Spec.

J H S Antiques
45 Church St. (Julian H. Snodin). LAPADA. CINOA. Est. 1972. Open 10-5. CL: Mon. and Wed. SIZE: Medium. *STOCK: 17th C oak, £1,000-£7,000; metalware, 17th to early 19th C, £50-£400; carvings, 17th to early 18th C, £300-£1,000.* LOC: A52 from junction 25, M1. PARK: Easy. TEL: 01335 347733. VAT: Spec.

Manion Antiques
23 Church St. DE6 1AE. (Mrs V.J. Manion). Est. 1984. Open Thurs., Fri. and Sat. 10-5, other times by appointment. SIZE: Small. *STOCK: Porcelain, paintings, silver, jewellery, small furniture, £50-£100+.* PARK: Easy. TEL: 01335 343207; home - same; mobile - 07968 067316. SER: Valuations.

Pine and Decorative Items
38 Church St. DE6 1AJ. (M. and G. Bassett). Est. 1980. Open 10-5, Wed. and Sun. by appointment only. SIZE: Small + warehouse. *STOCK: English and French pine and country furniture; garden furniture, ironwork, kitchenalia, 18th C to 1950's, from £10.* TEL: 01335 300061; fax - same; e-mail - mgbassett@aol.com; website - www.antiques-atlas.com. VAT: Stan.

Rose Antiques
37 Church St. DE6 1AJ. Est. 1982. Open 10-5. SIZE: Medium. *STOCK: Furniture, silver, porcelain, jewellery, copper, brass and pine.* LOC: A52. PARK: Easy. TEL: 01335 343822; home - 01283 575301.

Spurrier-Smith Antiques
28, 30 and 39 Church St. DE6 1AJ. (I. Spurrier-Smith). LAPADA. Est. 1973. Open 10-5, Wed.

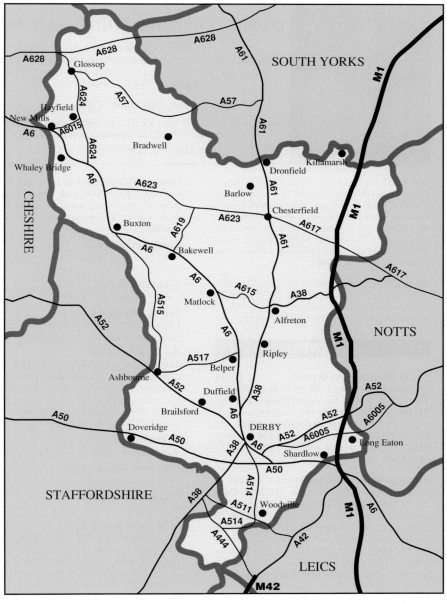

Dealers and Shops in Derbyshire

Alfreton	3	Chesterfield	5	Long Eaton	2
Ashbourne	8	Derby	6	Matlock	1
Bakewell	6	Doveridge	1	Newmills	1
Barlow	2	Dronfield	1	Ripley	2
Belper	2	Duffield	1	Shardlow	1
Bradwell	1	Glossop	1	Whaley Bridge	2
Brailsford	1	Hayfield	2	Woodville	1
Buxton	5	Killamarsh	1		

and Sun. by appointment. SIZE: Large (8 show-rooms) + warehouse. *STOCK: Furniture, oils, watercolours, porcelain, pottery, metalware, instruments, Oriental bronzes, collectables, pine, decorative items. Warehouse - pine and American export goods.* TEL: 01335 343669/342198; home - 01629 822502. SER: Valuations; restorations (furniture). VAT: Stan/Spec.

Kenneth Upchurch

30B Church St. DE6 1AE. Est. 1972. *STOCK: Oil paintings and watercolours, mainly 19th C; pottery and porcelain.* TEL: 01332 754499.

BAKEWELL

Peter Bunting Antiques   BADA

Harthill Hall, Alport. DE45 1LH. LAPADA. Est. 1980. Open by appointment. SIZE: Medium. STOCK: Early oak, country furniture, portraits and period decoration. LOC: On B5056. PARK: Own. TEL: 01629 636203; fax - 01629 636190; mobile - 07860 540870. VAT: Stan/Spec.

Chappells & The Antiques Centre

King St. DE45 1DZ. LAPADA. Est. 1992. Open 10-5, Sun. 11-5. *STOCK: Period furniture, decorative and collectors' items, 17th-20th C.* LOC: King St is signposted B5055, Monyash. PARK: Agricultural Centre (entrance off A6) and Smith's Island (off Baslow Rd.) 5 mins walk from Centre. TEL: 01629 812496; fax - 01629 814531; website - www.chappellsantiquescentre.com. Below are listed the dealers at this market.

Allens

20th C ceramics and secondhand books.

Barbara Austin

Linen, lace and small textile items.

Rex Boyer Antiques

LAPADA 18th-19th C furniture and decorative objects.

Chappell's Antiques & Fine Art   BADA

LAPADA. Est. 1940. 17th-19th C English furniture, oil paintings, porcelain, pottery, metalwork, clocks and decorative items. VAT: Stan/Spec.

Clocks in the Peak

Longcase clocks, specialising in Derbyshire makers.

Compton House

LAPADA. Fine 19th C furniture.

Cottage Antiques

LAPADA. 18th-19th C furniture, glass, treen, textiles, furnishing and decorative items.

De Vine Antiques

(Mr. and Mrs. P.A. Vine). *LAPADA. Est. 1994. British pottery and porcelain including Moorcroft, Worcester, Wedgwood fairyland lustre, Doulton, late 19th to early 20th C, £100-£4,000.* TEL: Mobile - 07885 212684; fax - 01733 390451; home - 01733 223119. VAT: Stan/Spec.

J. Dickinson

Maps, prints and books.

Elizabeth Ann Antiques

Furniture and decorative items.

Elizabeth Antiques

General antiques and collectables.

G.W. Ford & Son Ltd

(I.G.F. Thomson). *LAPADA. Est. 1890. Mahogany and country furniture, 18th-19th C, £50-£5,000; sculpture, 19th to early 20th C, £50-£3,000; various collectable and decorative items, 18th-19th C, £10-£1,200.* TEL: Fax - 01246 410512; home - 01246 410512. SER: Valuations; restorations (furniture, silver and EP). VAT: Stan/Spec.

P.M. & J.J. Furness

Sporting prints.

Ganymede Antiques

18th-19th C clocks, furniture, silver and plate, pewter, brass, pharmaceutical and scientific instruments.

J.H.S. Antiques
LAPADA. *17th to early 19th C country furniture, Staffordshire, treen and metalware.*

Elaine Jackson
Decorative glass 18th C-1930's.

Peter Kelsey Antiques
Furniture and works of art.

Shirley May Antiques & Collectables
Kitchenalia, Cornish, Denby and textiles.

Millennium Antiques
Fine English silver, silver plate, glass and bijouterie.

Walter Moores & Son
18th-19th C furniture and decorative items.

M.F. Morris Antiques
Fine Derby, Royal Crown Derby and Lynton porcelain.

Newton Fine Art
19th-20th C oil paintings and watercolours.

Old Country Antiques
Sporting antiques, luggage, and Beswick animals.

R. Panasiuk
Antique pistols, medals, daggers and war items.

Paraphernalia Lighting
Antique lighting and decorative arts.

Judy Portway
(Benjamin Henry & Co). *Vintage and designer costume jewelley and accessories.*

Renaissance Antiques
Pottery, papier-mâché, metals, glass and objects d'art.

Sandra Wallhead Antiques
19th to early 20th C furniture, Cranberry glass, dolls, jewellery and objects d'art.

N.I. Wilkinson
19th -20th C collectables.

Michael Wisehall Antiques   BADA
Furniture, plate, glass, pictures, metalware and pottery.

Valerie Worden
Small decorative items and jewellery.

Martin and Dorothy Harper Antiques
King St. DE45 1DZ. LAPADA. Est. 1973. Open 10-5, Sun. and other times by appointment. CL: Mon. and Thurs. SIZE: Medium. *STOCK: Furniture, £75-£7,500; metalware, £30-£300; glass, £15-£150; all 17th to late 19th C; needlework, 19th C.* PARK: Easy. TEL: 01629 814757; mobile - 07885 347134. SER: Valuations; restorations; buys at auction. VAT: Stan/Spec.

Lewis Antiques
King St. DE45 1DZ. Est. 1977. Open 10-5, Sun. by appointment. SIZE: Small. *STOCK: Furniture, clocks, barometers, pictures and porcelain, 17th to late 19th C, £50-£5,000.* PARK: Easy. TEL: 01629 813141; e-mail - les@lewisantiques.co.uk; website - www.lewisantiques.co.uk. VAT: Stan/Spec.

Thornbridge Antiques
King St. DE45 1DZ. (Peter Hunt). Open 10-5, Sun. 11-4. CL: Bank Holidays. SIZE: Large. *STOCK: Town and country furniture, 17th-19th C, from £500; clocks, 18th-19th C; objets d'art, porcelain, treen and metalware.* LOC: Near Rutland Hotel. PARK: Easy and nearby. TEL: 01629 814224; fax - same. VAT: Spec.

Water Lane Antiques
Water Lane. DE45 1EU. (M.J. Pembery). Est. 1967. Open 10-5. SIZE: Medium. *STOCK: Furniture, £500-£4,000; metalware, £100-£1,000; objets d'art, £100-£1,500; all 18th-19th C.* LOC: Off Market Sq. PARK: Nearby. TEL: 01629 814161. SER: Valuations; restorations. VAT: Stan/Spec.

BARLOW, Nr. Chesterfield

Byethorpe Furniture
Shippen Rural Business Centre, Church Farm. Est. 1977. Open 9.30-5.30. SIZE: Medium. *STOCK: Oak, mahogany and pine country and classical furniture.* PARK: Easy. TEL: 01142 899111; fax - same; website - www.byethorpe.com. SER: Restorations (furniture); specialist woodwork; upholstery; French polishing; hand-made reproductions. VAT: Stan/Spec.

Hackney House Antiques
Hackney Lane, S18 7TQ. (Mrs J.M. Gorman). Resident. Est. 1984. *STOCK: Furniture, 18th-19th C; prints, clocks, linen, silver.* TEL: 01142 890248.

BELPER

Sweetings (Antiques 'n' Things)
1 & 1a The Butts. DE56 1HX. (K.J. and J.L. Sweeting). Est. 1971. Open daily. SIZE: Large. *STOCK: Pre 1940's furniture including stripped pine, oak, mahogany, satinwood, £20-£1,000.* LOC: Off A6, near Market Place. PARK: Easy. TEL: 01773 825930/822780. SER: Valuations; restorations (pine and satinwood); shipping. VAT: Stan.

DERBYSHIRE

Neil Wayne "The Razor Man"
The Cedars (rear of 55 Field Lane), DE56 1DD. Resident. Est. 1969. Open every day 9.30-6, prior telephone call essential. SIZE: Medium. *STOCK: Razors and shaving items, 18th to early 19th C, £20-£300.* PARK: Easy. TEL: 01773 824157; fax - 01773 825573; e-mail - neil.wayne@derbyshire-holidays.com.

BRADWELL

Bradwell Antiques Centre
Newburgh Hall, Netherside. Est. 1994. Open 10-5, Sun. 11-5. SIZE: 30 dealers. *STOCK: Wide range of general antiques, 18th-20th C, £5-£5,000.* LOC: A625 Hope Valley road, turn opposite Travellers Rest public house on to B6049. PARK: Own. TEL: 01433 621000; fax - same. SER: Restorations (furniture); buys at auction.

BRAILSFORD

Folk & Country Antiques
Derby Rd. DE6 3DA. Variable opening, prior telephone advisable. *STOCK: Painted and country furniture and associated smalls.* TEL: 01335 361217.

BUXTON

The Antiques Warehouse
25 Lightwood Rd. SK17 7BJ. (N.F. Thompson). Est. 1983. Open 10.30-4 or by appointment. SIZE: Large. *STOCK: Furniture, mainly mahogany and walnut, 17th-20th C; paintings, silver, metalware, smalls, clocks including longcase, Victorian brass and iron bedsteads.* LOC: Off A6. PARK: Own. TEL: 01298 72967; home/fax - 01298 22603; mobile - 07808 065745. SER: Valuations; restorations; buys at auction.

Maggie Mays
Unit 10, Cavendish Arcade. SK17. (Mrs. J. Wild). Est. 1993. Open 10.30-5. CL: Mon. *STOCK: Victorian furniture and effects, £35-£800; Art Deco glassware, mirrors, pottery, £20-£500; Edwardian furniture, £100-£800.* LOC: Opposite Turners Memorial on Terrace Road. PARK: Easy. TEL: Mobile - 07831 606003; home - 01663 733935. SER: Valuations; buys at auction.

The Penny Post Antiques
9 Cavendish Circus. SK17 6AT. (D. and R. Hammond). Est. 1978. Open 10-4.30, Sat. 10-5.

SIZE: Small. *STOCK: Pictures, commemoratives, crested china, shaving mugs and other collectables; furniture; general antiques.* LOC: Town centre, opposite Palace Hotel. PARK: Easy. TEL: Home - 01298 25965.

West End Galleries
8 Cavendish Circus. SK17 6AT. (A. and A. Needham). Est. 1955. Open 9-5, Sat. 9-4. SIZE: Medium. *STOCK: French and English furniture; clocks, paintings, works of art, bronzes.* LOC: A6. PARK: Easy. TEL: 01298 24546. VAT: Spec.

What Now Antiques
Cavendish Arcade, The Crescent. SK17 9BQ. (L. Carruthers). Open 10-5, Sun. 2-5. CL: Mon. *STOCK: General antiques and collectables including Art Deco pottery, small silver items, jewellery, textiles, lighting, clocks, Victorian and Edwardian furniture, £1-£1,000.* TEL: 01298 27178; mobile - 07977 369878. SER: Export; valuations; foreign trade.

CHESTERFIELD

Anthony D. Goodlad
26 Fairfield Rd., Brockwell. S40 4TP. Est. 1974. Open by appointment only. *STOCK: General militaria, WWI and WWII.* LOC: Close to town centre. PARK: Easy. TEL: 01246 204004.

N. and C.A. Haslam
414 Chatsworth Rd. S40 3BH. Open Thurs. 1.30-5, Fri. and Sat. 9.30-5. *STOCK: 17th-19th C furniture and decorative items.* TEL: 01246 853672; mobile - 07887 945652. VAT: Stan/Spec.

Alan Hill Books
11 Beetwell St. S40 1SH. Est. 1980. Open 10-5. *STOCK: Antiquarian books, maps and prints.* TEL: 01246 205441; e-mail - alanhillbooks@ supanet.com.

Ian Morris
479 Chatsworth Rd. S40 3AD. Est. 1970. Open 10-4, or by appointment. SIZE: Medium. *STOCK: Furniture, 18th-20th C, £50-£2,000; pictures, small items.* LOC: A619 to Baslow and Chatsworth House. TEL: 01246 235120. VAT: Stan/Spec.

Marlene Rutherford Antiques
401 Sheffield Rd., Whittington Moor. S41 8LS. Est. 1985. Open 10-4, Mon. and Tues. 12-4. CL: Wed. *STOCK: Furniture, pottery, clocks and lamps, £5-£1,000.* PARK: Easy. TEL: 01426 450209; mobile - 07885 665440. SER: Valuations. FAIRS: Bowman, Newark. Pandora.

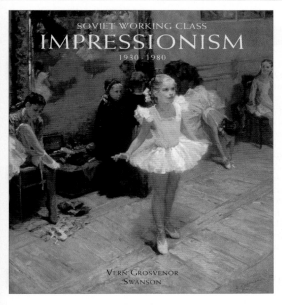

DERBY

Abbey House
115 Woods Lane. DE22 3UE. (Shirley White).
Resident. Est. 1959. Open by appointment.
STOCK: Dolls, teddy bears and all things juvenile.
TEL: 01332 331426; fax - same. SER: Repairs
(dolls and teddies); restorations (furniture).

Derventio Books
43a Sadler St. DE1 1NR. (D. A. Harper). Est.
1996. Open 10.15-5. SIZE: Medium. *STOCK:
Out-of-print, secondhand and antiquarian books
especially modern first editions, Derbyshire,
science fiction, mainly 19th-20th C, 50p to £500;
some antiquarian maps and prints.* LOC: 1st
floor via short passageway off Sadler Gate.
PARK: Opposite. TEL: 01332 343538; website -
www.derventio-books.co.uk SER: Valuations.

Finishing Touches
224 Uttoxeter Old Rd., The Rowditch. DE1 1NF.
(Lynne Robinson). Est. 1994. Open 10-5.30, Sun.
by appointment. CL: Mon. SIZE: Small. *STOCK:
Fire surrounds, £200-£800; pine furniture, £50-
£500; kitchenalia and pottery, £1-£25; all late
19th to early 20th C.* LOC: Off A38 at junction
with A52. PARK: Rear of church. TEL: 01332
721717; website - www.derbyantiques.co.uk.
SER: Restorations.

Friargate Pine Company Ltd
The Pump House, Friargate Goods Wharf,
Stafford St. Entrance. DE1 1JL. (N. J.
Marianski). Open 9-5. *STOCK: Antique and
reproduction pine furniture.* TEL: 01332 341215.

Brian Matsell
1 Friar Gate Court, Friar Gate. DE1 1HE.
LAPADA, CINOA. Resident. Est. 1965. Open by
appointment. SIZE: Large. *STOCK: Georgian
and Regency furniture, decorative antiques,
Oriental porcelain and objects.* LOC: Town
centre. PARK: Easy. TEL: 01332 365211; fax -
01332 367572; mobile - 07747 702741. SER:
Valuations; buys at auction. VAT: Stan/Spec.

Charles H. Ward
12 Friar Gate. DE1 1BU. (M.G. Ward). CL: Wed.
pm. *STOCK: Oil paintings, 19th-20th C; watercolours.* TEL: 01332 342893. SER: Restorations.

DOVERIDGE

Pine Antiques Workshop
Bell Farm, Yelt Lane. DE6 5JU. (M.A. and A.
Groves). Open Tues.-Sat. 9-5.30, other times by
appointment. *STOCK: English and Welsh pine,
pottery, linen and kitchenalia.* TEL: 01889
564898; fax - same.

DRONFIELD

Bardwell Antiques
51 Chesterfield Rd. S18 6XA. (S. Bardwell).
Open Tues., Wed., Thurs. 10-4, Sat. 9-2. *STOCK:
General antiques.* TEL: 01246 412183; fax -
same.

DUFFIELD, Nr. Derby

Wayside Antiques
62 Town St. DE56 4GG. (Mrs J. Harding). Est.
1975. *STOCK: Furniture, 18th-19th C, £50-
£5,000; porcelain, pictures, boxes and silver.*
TEL: 01332 840346. VAT: Stan/Spec.

GLOSSOP

Derbyshire Clocks
104 High St. West. SK13 8BB. (J.A. and T.P.
Lees). Est. 1975. CL: Tues. *STOCK: Clocks.*
TEL: 01457 862677. SER: Restorations (clocks
and barometers).

HAYFIELD, Nr. New Mills

Michael Allcroft Antiques
1 Church St. Open Sat. 2-5, Sun. 1-5, other times
by appointment. *STOCK: Pine furniture and
decorative items.* TEL: 01663 742684; mobile -
07798 781642; fax - 01663 744014.

Paul Pickford Antiques
Top of the Town, Church St. SK22 2JE. Est.
1975. Open Tues., Thurs. and Sat. 11-4, Sun. 1-5,
other times by appointment. SIZE: Medium.
*STOCK: 19th C furniture, stripped pine, lighting
and general antiques, £50-£500.* LOC: Leave the
A6 at Newtown, near Disley, take the A6015.
PARK: Easy. TEL: 01663 747276; home - 01663
743356; e-mail - paul@pickfordantiques.co.uk;
website - www.pickfordantiques.co.uk.

KILLAMARSH

Havenplan's Architectural Emporium
The Old Station, Station Rd. S21 1EN. Est. 1972.
Open Tues.-Sat. 10-3. SIZE: Large. *STOCK:
Architectural fittings and decorative items,
church interiors and furnishings, fireplaces,
doors, decorative cast ironwork, masonry,
bygones, garden ornaments, 18th to early 20th C.*

LOC: M1, exit 30. Take A616 towards Sheffield, turn right on to B6053, turn right on to B6058 towards Killamarsh, turn right between two railway bridges. PARK: Easy. TEL: 01142 489972; fax - same; home - 01246 433315. SER: Hire.

LONG EATON

Goodacre Engraving Ltd
Thrumpton Ave. (off Chatsworth Ave.), Meadow Lane. NG10 2GB. Est. 1948. *STOCK: Longcase and bracket clock movements, parts and castings.* TEL: 01159 734387; fax - 01159 461193. SER: Hand engraving, movement repairs, silvering and dial repainting. VAT: Stan.

Miss Elany
2 Salisbury St. NG10 1BA. (D. and Mrs Mottershead). Est. 1977. Open 9-5. SIZE: Medium. *STOCK: Pianos, 1900 to date, £50-£500; general antiques, Victorian and Edwardian, £25-£200.* PARK: Easy. TEL: 0115 9734835. VAT: Stan.

MATLOCK

Matlock Antiques and Collectables Centre
7 Dale Rd. DE4 3LT. Open 10-4 including Sun., Sat. 10-5. SIZE: Large - 70 dealers. *STOCK: Wide range of general antiques.* LOC: Town centre. PARK: Easy. TEL: 01629 760808.

NEWMILLS, Nr. Stockport

Michael Allcroft Antiques
203 Buxton Rd., Newtown. Open Thurs. and Fri. 11-6.30, Sat. 9.30-1, other times by appointment. SIZE: Large. *STOCK: Edwardian and 1930's furniture.* TEL: Mobile - 07798 781642; fax - 01663 744014.

RIPLEY

Memory Lane Antiques Centre
Nottingham Rd. DE5 3AS. (James Cullen). Est. 1994. Open 10.30-4 including Sun. SIZE: Large. *STOCK: Victoriana and 20th C collectables, pine furniture, specialist in old Denby, Bourne and Langley, lighting.* LOC: 200 yds from town centre - 500 yds from A610 (Sainsburys) roundabout. PARK: Easy. TEL: 01773 570184; mobile - 07703 115626. SER: Valuations; pine stripping; old Denby replacement service.

FAIRS: Derby University; Newark; Abacus; Kedleston Hall; Swinderby.

Taylor Robinson Antiques
6 Market Place. DE5 3FJ. (A. and B. Robinson). Est. 1973. Open 9.30-4.30. SIZE: Medium. *STOCK: Furniture, £100-£1,000; ceramics, copper, £5-£200, all 19th C.* LOC: Opposite Town Hll. PARK: Opposite - Mon.-Thurs. TEL: 01773 743597; home - 01773 603659; mobile - 07885 507420. FAIRS: Newark; Ardingly; Shepton Mallet (DMG); Stafford (Bowmans).

SHARDLOW, Nr. Derby

Shardlow Antiques Warehouse
24 The Wharf. DE7 2GH. Open 10.30-5, Sun. 12-5. CL: Fri. SIZE: Large. *STOCK: Furniture, Georgian to shipping.* LOC: Off M1, junction 24. PARK: Own. TEL: 01332 792899/662899.

WHALEY BRIDGE

Richard Glass
Hockerley Old Hall, Hockerley Lane. Resident. Open by appointment only. SIZE: Small. *STOCK: Oak furniture, 17th-18th C, £1,000-£5,000; paintings, drawings, metal and stoneware, 17th-19th C, £200-£2,000.* LOC: From town centre towards Stockport, turn left at station car park, up hill and 2nd right into Hockerley Lane, up farm track to the end of the lane, house on left. PARK: Easy. TEL: 0161 236 1520; fax - 0161 236 0886. SER: Valuations. VAT: Spec.

Nimbus Antiques
Chapel Rd. (L.M. and H.C. Brobbin). Est. 1978. Open 9-5.30, Sun. 2-5.30. SIZE: Large. *STOCK: Furniture, mainly mahogany, incl. desks, dining tables, clocks, chests, 18th-19th C.* LOC: A6. PARK: Easy. TEL: 01663 734248; home - 01663 733332; website - www.antiques-atlas.com/ nimbus.htm. SER: Valuations; restorations. VAT: Stan/Spec.

WOODVILLE

Wooden Box Antiques
32 High St. DE11 7EH. (Mrs R. Bowler). Est. 1982. Open 10-5 including some Sun. SIZE: Medium. *STOCK: Furniture, Georgian-Edwardian, £75-£400; original cast-iron fireplaces, surrounds, £50-£600; Victorian tiles, country pine furniture, pine doors.* LOC: A511 (was A50), between Ashby-de-la-Zouch and Burton-on-Trent. PARK: Easy. TEL: 01283 212014; home - same.

211

DEVON

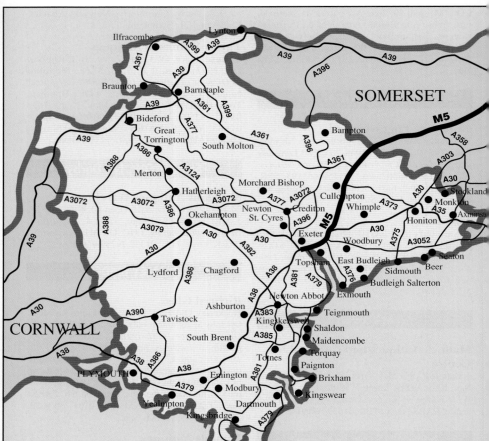

Dealers and Shops in Devon

DEVON

ASHBURTON

Ashburton Marbles
Great Hall, North St. TQ13 7DU. (Adrian Ager). Est. 1976. Open 8-5, Sat. 10-2. SIZE: Warehouse and showroom. *STOCK: Marble and wooden fire-surrounds, decorative cast iron inserts; scuttles, fenders, overmantels, 1790-1910; architectural decorative antiques, garden statuary and related items, chandeliers, soft furnishings and furniture.* PARK: Easy. TEL: 01364 653189; fax - same.

Kessler Ford
9 North St. TQ13 7QJ. (Elisabeth Kessler and Matthew Ford). Est. 1999. Open Tues., Thurs., Fri. 10-5, Sat. 10.30-5. SIZE: Medium. *STOCK: Period oak and Georgian mahogany furniture; pictures, carvings, bronzes.* LOC: Main street. PARK: Easy. TEL: 01364 654310; fax - 01364 652141. SER: Valuations. VAT: Spec.

Moor Antiques
19a North St. TQ13 7QH. (T. and Mrs D. Gatland). Est. 1984. CL: Wed. pm. SIZE: Small. *STOCK: Small furniture, 1780-1900, £250-£2,500; clocks, 1830-1910, £150-£2,000; silver and china, 1800-1900, £25-£500; jewellery, £30-£250.* LOC: A38 town centre, 100 yards past town hall. PARK: Nearby. TEL: 01364 653767. SER: Valuations.

The Shambles
22 North St. TQ13 7QD. Est. 1982. Open 10-5, Sat. 10-4. SIZE: 8 dealers. *STOCK: Country and general antiques and decorative items, £5-£2,000.* LOC: Town centre. PARK: Opposite. TEL: 01364 653848. SER: Valuations. FAIRS: Sandown Park; Westpoint Exeter; Shepton Mallet. VAT: Stan/Spec.

AXMINSTER

W.G. Potter and Son
1 West St. EX13 5HS. Est. 1863. Open 9-5. CL: Sat. pm. SIZE: Medium. *STOCK: Pine, 19th-20th C; some mahogany and oak.* LOC: In main street (A35) opposite church. PARK: Easy. TEL: 01297 32063. SER: Restorations (furniture); buys at auction. VAT: Stan/Spec.

BAMPTON, Nr. Tiverton

Bampton Gallery
2-4 Brook St. EX16 9LY. (Gerald Chidwick). FRICS. Est. 1997. Open 9.30-5.30, Sat. 9.30-1, Sun. and other times by appointment. SIZE:

Medium. *STOCK: Furniture including upholstered, porcelain, pottery and glass, 1750-1900, £10-£10,000; pictures and prints, £10-£1,000.* LOC: Main street. TEL: 01398 331119; fax - same; home - 01398 331354. SER: Restorations (furniture including traditional upholstery and ceramics); buys at auction (porcelain and furniture).

Robert Byles
7 Castle St. EX16 9NS. Est. 1966. Open by chance, knocking or appointment. *STOCK: Early oak, local farmhouse tables and settles, metalwork, pottery, unstripped period pine, architectural items.* TEL: 01398 331515. SER: Restoration materials; replica brass handles for antique furniture. VAT: Stan/Spec.

BARNSTAPLE

Barn Antiques
73 Newport Rd. EX32 9BG. (T. Cusack). Open 9.30-5, Wed. 9.30-1. SIZE: Large. *STOCK: General antiques.* TEL: 01271 323131.

Medina Gallery
80 Boutport St. EX31 1SR. (R. Jennings). Est. 1972. Open 9.30-5. SIZE: Small. *STOCK: Maps, prints, photographs, oils and watercolours, £1-£500.* TEL: 01271 371025. SER: Picture framing, mounting. VAT: Stan.

North Devon Antiques Centre
The Old Church, 18 Cross St. EX31 1BD. (P. Broome and M. Prentice). Est. 1985. Open 10-4.30. SIZE: Large. *STOCK: Furniture, china, clocks, 18th C to 1960's, £5-£2,500; Victorian and Art Deco fireplaces, £100-£900.* LOC: 40 yards off High St. PARK: Nearby. TEL: 01271 375788. SER: Valuations; restorations (woodwork and clocks). FAIRS: Newark, Shepton Mallet, Exeter Westpoint.

Mark Parkhouse Antiques and Jewellery
106 High St. EX31 1HP. Est. 1976. CL: Wed. *STOCK: Jewellery, furniture, silver, paintings, clocks, glass, porcelain, small collectors' items, 18th-19th C, £100-£10,000.* PARK: Nearby. TEL: 01271 374504; fax - 01271 323499. SER: Valuations; buys at auction. VAT: Stan/Spec.

Selected Antiques & Collectables
19 Newport Rd. EX32 9BG. (Helen Chugg). Est. 1994. Open Tues., Thurs., Fri. and Sat. 9.45-4.30. SIZE: Medium. *STOCK: North Devon pottery, 19th C; porcelain and ceramics, glass, collectables, 19th-20th C; linen, books, memorabilia.* PARK: Easy. TEL: 01271 321338 (answerphone). SER: Valuations; restorations (ceramics).

Tudor House
115 Boutport St. EX31 1TD. (C. and D.Pilon). Est. 1980. Open 9.30-3.30,Wed. 9.30-1. SIZE: Large. *STOCK: Furniture and bric-a-brac, late 18th C and reproduction.* LOC: Off M5, Tiverton link road to town centre. PARK: Easy. TEL: 01271 375370; home - 01271 371750. SER: Valuations; restorations (furniture).

BEER

Beer Collectables
Dolphin Courtyard. EX12 3EQ. (L. R. Forkes). Est. 1985. Open 10-5 including Sun. SIZE: Medium. *STOCK: Antique fishing tackle, from £25; jewellery, £50-£2,000; china and smalls, £2-£50.* PARK: Easy. TEL: 01297 24362; home - 01460 65294. SER: Valuations; buys at auction. FAIRS: Taunton, Torquay, Beaminster and some local.

BIDEFORD

J. Collins and Son   BADA
The Studio, 28 High St. EX39 2AN. (J. and P. Biggs). LAPADA, CINOA. Est. 1953. Open by appointment. SIZE: Large. *STOCK: Georgian and Regency furniture; general antiques including framed and restored 19th-20th C oils and watercolours, £100-£100,000.* LOC: From Bideford Old Bridge turn right, then first left into the High St. PARK: Easy. TEL: 01237 473103; fax - 01237 475658; home - 01237 476485; e-mail - biggs@collinsantiques.co.uk; website - www.collinsantiques.co.uk. SER: Valuations; restorations (period furniture, paintings and watercolours); cleaning and framing. FAIRS: BADA (March); Olympia (June, Nov).

Cooper Gallery
Cooper St. EX39 2DA. (Mrs. J. Bruce). Est. 1975. Open 10-4.30, Wed. 10-1.30, Sat. 10-2.30. SIZE: Small. *STOCK: Watercolours, mainly West Country views, late 19th to early 20th C, £200-£2,500.* LOC: Just off the quay, opposite HSBC bank. PARK: Nearby. TEL: 01237 477370; fax - same; home - 01237 423415; e-mail - enq@coopergallery.uk.co. SER: Valuations; restorations (watercolours and oils); buys at auction. VAT: Spec.

The Davies Gallery
74 High St. EX39 2AA. (Jerome and Teresa Davies). Est. 1974. Open 10-5. CL: Wed. SIZE: Medium. *STOCK: Watercolours and oils, including West Country, 19th to early 20th C,* £300-£2,000; Victorian and Edwardian furniture, 1830-1910, £350-£2,000. LOC: Town centre. PARK: Easy. TEL: 01237 422100; fax - same; mobile - 07970 886961; e-mail - jerome.davies@lineone.net. SER: Valuations; restorations (oils and watercolours); framing.

Medina Gallery
20 Mill St. EX39 2JR. (R. Jennings). Est. 1973. Open 9.30-5. SIZE: Medium. *STOCK: Maps and prints, photographs, oils, watercolours, £1-£500.* PARK: Easy. TEL: 01237 476483. SER: Picture framing, mounting. VAT: Stan.

BRAUNTON

Timothy Coward Fine Silver
Marisco, Saunton. EX33 1LG. LAPADA. Open by appointment. *STOCK: Antique and early 20th C silver.* TEL: 01271 890466.

Priced at £650 this Staffordshire pottery figure of a sportsman dating from 1825 can be found on Andrew Dando's stand at The Harrogate Antiques Fair, 29th September-3rd October.

This Fairs Preview appeared in the September 2000 issue of **Antique Collecting** magazine. For more details and to subscribe see page 147.

JOHN PRESITIGE ANTIQUES

Greenswood Court,
Greenswood Road,
Brixham Devon, TQ5 9HN
Tel: 01803 856141
Fax: 01803 851649
E-mail: sales@john-prestige.co.uk

2 WAREHOUSES OF ANTIQUE ENGLISH & CONTINENTAL FURNITURE AND DECORATIVE SMALLS. FULL RESTORATION FACILITIES ON SITE. WE SPECIALISE IN SUPPLING THE AMERICAN AND OVERSEAS TRADE

BRIXHAM

John Prestige Antiques
1 and 2 Greenswood Court. TQ5 9HN. Est. 1971. Open 8.45-6, appointment advisable. CL: Sat. and Sun. except by appointment. SIZE: Large + warehouse. *STOCK: Period and Victorian furniture; shipping goods.* TEL: 01803 856141; home - 01803 853739; fax - 01803 851649; e-mail - sales@john-prestige.co.uk; website - www. john-prestige.co.uk. VAT: Stan/Spec.

Seaward and Around the Clock
Ye Olde Coffin House, King St. TQ5 9TF. (Dr. Paul Strickland). Est. 1996. SIZE: Small. *STOCK: Clocks, 18th-20th C, to £2,500.* PARK: Loading only and nearby. TEL: 01803 856307; home - same. SER: Valuations; restorations; buys at auction (clocks and mechanical items).

BUDLEIGH SALTERTON

Days of Grace
15 Fore St. EX9 6NH. (L. Duriez). *STOCK: Antique lace, vintage textiles and costume, china, jewellery, furniture, interesting decorating items.* TEL: 01395 443730.

Alison Gosling Antiques
46a High St. EX9 6LJ. Est. 1983. Open Mon. and Wed. 11-5, Tues. and Fri. 1.30-5 or by appointment. SIZE: Medium. *STOCK: Furniture, early 18th C to early Victorian, £200-£8,500; porcelain and decorative items, 18th C to 1930's, £20-£1,000.* LOC: Next to Barclay's Bank. PARK: Easy. TEL: 01395 443737; home - 01395 271451. SER: Valuations.

David J. Thorn
2 High St. EX9 6LQ. Est. 1950. Open Tues., Fri. and Sat. 10-1. SIZE: Small. *STOCK: English, Continental and Oriental pottery and porcelain, 1620-1850, £5-£5,000; English furniture, 1680-1870, £20-£5,000; paintings, silver, jewellery, £1-£1,000.* PARK: Easy. TEL: 01395 442448. SER: Valuations. VAT: Stan/Spec.

CHAGFORD

Godolphin Antiques
68 The Square. TQ13 8AE. (S. Freeman). Est. 2000. Open 10-4.30, Wed. 10-1, Sun. 2-5 or by appointment. SIZE: Medium. *STOCK: Watercolours and oils, 18th to early 20th C, £200-£8,000; oak and country furniture, 17th-19th C.* LOC: Off The Square, turn opposite Easton Court Hotel on A382. PARK: Easy. TEL: 01647 433999. SER: Buys at auction (watercolours and oils). FAIRS: Westpoint, Exeter; Shepton Mallet.

Rex Antiques
The Old Cinema. TQ13 8AB. (John Meredith). Est. 1979. Open by appointment. SIZE: Large. *STOCK: Country oak, 16th-19th C, £5-£2,000; Oriental brass and copper, weapons, large unusual items, granite, architectural items, old iron work.* PARK: Easy. TEL: 01647 433405. SER: Buys at auction. VAT: Stan/Spec. *Trade only.*

Whiddons Antiques and Tearooms
6 High St. TQ13 8AJ. (D. Meldrum). Est. 1979. Open 10.30-1 and 2-5.30, Sun. 2-5.30. SIZE: Medium. *STOCK: General and country items - furniture including pine, clocks, prints, paintings, copper, brass, books and collectables.* LOC: Opposite church. PARK: Easy. TEL: 01647 433406; home - 01647 433303.

CREDITON

Musgrave Bickford Antiques
15 East St. EX17 3AT. (Mr and Mrs. D.M. Bickford). Est. 1983. Open by appointment. SIZE: Small. *STOCK: Clocks, barometers, small furniture, mainly 19th C, from £400.* LOC: From Exeter on A377 on right entering one-way system, towards Tiverton. PARK: Easy and at rear by arrangement. TEL: 01363 775042. SER: Restorations (longcase, mantel, wall clock and barometer movements, dials, cases). VAT: Stan/Spec.

CULLOMPTON

Cobweb Antiques
The Old Tannery, Exeter Rd. EX15 1DT. (R. Holmes). Est. 1980. Open 10-5. SIZE: Large. *STOCK: Pine and country furniture, painted, decorative and mahogany items, £5-£2,000.* LOC: Half a mile from junction 28, M5. PARK: Easy. TEL: 01884 855748. SER: Stripping; restorations; packing; courier.

Cullompton Old Tannery Antiques
Exeter Rd. EX15 1DT. (Cullompton Antiques Ltd). Est. 1989. Open 10-5, Sun. by appointment. SIZE: Large. *STOCK: Pine, oak, mahogany and fruitwood country furniture; beds, china, decorative items and mirrors.* LOC: Off M5, junction 28, through town centre, premises on right, approximately 1 mile. PARK: Easy. TEL: 01884 38476; fax - same; e-mail - cullompton-antiques@lineone.net; website - www.cullompton-antiques.ltd.uk.

Miller Antiques
The Old Tannery, Exeter Rd. EX15 1DT. (Nick Miller). Open 10-5.30, Sat. 10-5, Sun. by appointment. SIZE: Large. *STOCK: Furniture, 18th-19th C, £25-£2,000, country, 17th-19th C, £25-£3,000; decorative accessories, £5-£2,000.* LOC: M5 junction 28, bottom of the High St. opposite Somerfield. PARK: Easy. TEL: 01884 38476; fax - same. SER: Valuations; buys at auction.

Mills Antiques
The Old Tannery, Exeter Rd. EX15 1DT. Est. 1979. Open 10-5.30, Sat. 10-5. *STOCK: 17th C to Edwardian furniture; French bedroom suites, country furniture and decorative items.* PARK: Easy. TEL: 01392 860945.

R.C. Associates
The Old Tannery, Exeter Rd. EX15 1DT. Open 10-5.30, Sat. 10-5. *STOCK: French provincial furniture - beds, armoires, tables, buffets.* PARK: Easy.

DARTMOUTH

Chantry Bookshop and Gallery
11 Higher St. TQ6 9RB. (M.P. Merkel). Est. 1969. Open 10.30-5. CL: 15th Jan.-20th Mar. SIZE: Small. *STOCK: Antiquarian books and watercolours; decorative maps, town plans, prints, sea charts and battle plans.* LOC: Next to 'The Cherub' public house. PARK: Nearby. TEL: 01803 832796; home - 01803 834208.

EAST BUDLEIGH

Antiques at Budleigh House
Budleigh House. EX9 7ED. (W. Cook). Est. 1982. Open 10-5, Sat. 10-1. CL: Mon. and Wed. SIZE: Small. *STOCK: 18th-19th C small*

furniture and decorative objects, porcelain, glass, silver and metalware, £5-£1,000. LOC: Opposite Sir Walter Raleigh public house. PARK: Easy. TEL: 01395 445368; home - same. SER: Valuations; buys at auction.

ERMINGTON, Nr. Ivybridge

Mill Gallery
PL21 9NT. (Christopher Trant). Resident. Est. 1984. CL: Sat. SIZE: Small. *STOCK: Oils and watercolours, 18th-20th C, £300-£1,000.* LOC: From A38 take Ivybridge exit, follows signs, 1st premises in village. PARK: Easy. TEL: 01548 830172; website - www.millgallery.com. SER: Valuations; restorations (oils). VAT: Spec.

EXETER

The Antique Centre on the Quay
The Quay. EX2 4AP. Open 10-5 winter, 10-6 summer including Sun. SIZE: 20+ dealers. *STOCK: Antiques - small furniture, collectables, books, pictures, postcards, records, tools and jewellery.* TEL: 01392 493501.

Exeter Rare Books
Guildhall Shopping Centre. EX4 3HG. (R.C. Parry). ABA. PBFA. Est. 1975. Open 10-1 and 2-5. SIZE: Small. *STOCK: Books, antiquarian, secondhand, out-of-print, 17th-20th C; Devon and West Country topography. £5-£500.* LOC: City centre. PARK: Easy. TEL: 01392 436021. SER: Valuations; buys at auction. FAIRS: ABA Chelsea, Bath and Edinburgh.

Fagins Antiques
The Old Whiteways Cider Factory, Hele. EX5 4PW. (C.J. Strong). Open 9.15-5, Sat. 11-5. *STOCK: Furniture, decorative items, architectural and shipping items.* TEL: 01392 882062; fax - 01392 882194; e-mail - cstrong@fagins-antiques.co.uk; website - www.fagins-antiques.co.uk.

Gold and Silver Exchange
Eastgate House, Princesshay. EX4 3JT. *STOCK: Jewellery, watches including Rolex.* TEL: 01392 217478.

Adrian Hornsey Ltd
Langdons, Sidmouth Rd., Clyst St. Mary. EX5 1DR. Open 9-5, other times by appointment. SIZE: Large. *STOCK: Antique and shipping furniture, all periods, and decorative smalls.* TEL: 01392 877395; fax - 01392 877360; e-mail - sales@a-h-antique.com.

The House that Moved
24 West St. EX1 1BA. (L. Duriez). Open 10-5. *STOCK: Lace, shawls, babywear, linen, 1920's costume, Victorian and Edwardian bridal wedding dresses.* TEL: 01392 432643.

McBains Antiques
Exeter Airport Industrial Estate, Westcott Lane. EX5 2BA. LAPADA. Open 9-6, Sat. 10.30-3. SIZE: Large warehouse complex. *STOCK: Georgian, Victorian and Edwardian furniture, arts and crafts, Continental decorative and painted and shipping furniture.* LOC: 3 miles from junction 29,M5. Below are listed the dealers who are trading from this address. TEL: 01392 366261; fax - 01392 365572; e-mail -mcbains@netcomuk.co.uk

Ash Brothers Antiques
Shipping furniture and decorative items. TEL: 01392 364483; fax - same.

McBains Antique Exports
(I.S., G., R. and M. McBain). Est. 1963. *English, French and Belgium furniture suitable for export worldwide.* TEL: 01392 466261; fax - 01392 447304; e-mail - mcbain.exports@zetnet.co.uk SER: Container packing; European courier service.

Miscellany Antiques
Shipping goods. TEL: 01684 566671.

Leon Robertson Antiques
Furniture. TEL: Mobile - 07971 171909.

Tredantiques
Fine quality period furniture and decorative items. TEL: Mobile - 07967 447082; website - www.tredanttiques.com

Mortimers
87 Queen St. EX4 3RP. *STOCK: Jewellery, silver, clocks, watches and objet d'art.* TEL: 01392 279994. VAT: Stan/Spec.

John Nathan Antiques
153/154 Cowick St., St. Thomas. EX4 1AS. (I. Doble). Est. 1950. Open 9-5.30. SIZE: Small. *STOCK: Silver and jewellery, £5-£5,000; clocks, including Georgian and Victorian, £25-£3,000.* LOC: From Exeter inner by-pass over new Exe Bridge, take A30 Okehampton Rd. under railway arch, shop on right. PARK: Easy. TEL: 01392 210864. SER: Valuations; restorations (silver and jewellery); buys at auction. VAT: Stan.

Phantique
47 The Quay. EX2 4AN. Open daily - summer 10.30-5.30, winter 10.30-5. SIZE: Several dealers. *STOCK: Antiques, collectables, prints, books, toys, jewellery.* TEL: 01392 498995.

The Quay Gallery Antiques Emporium
43 The Quay. EX2 4AP. (J. Gould and S. Hornsey). Est. 1984. Open 10-5 including Sun. SIZE: Large - 15 dealers. *STOCK: 18th-20th C oak and mahogany furniture, marine items, porcelain, silver, plate, glass, paintings, prints, antiquities, carpets and decorative items.* LOC: Next to Old Customs House. PARK: Easy. TEL: 01392 213283.

EXMOUTH

Boase Antiques
5 High St. EX8 1NN. Open 10-5. *STOCK: Jewellery, silver, Victorian collectables.* LOC: Town centre. PARK: Easy. TEL: 01395 271528.

Treasures
34 Exeter Rd. EX8 1PS. (L. Treasure). Open 9-5. *STOCK: General antiques.* TEL: 01395 279512.

GREAT TORRINGTON

C Short Antiques
12 Potacre St. EX38 8BH. (C. J. Short). Est. 1985. Open 10-4, Sat. 10-1. SIZE: Small. *STOCK: Victorian pine furniture, £100-£500.* TEL: 01805 624796; home - 01805 624105. SER: Valuations; restorations (pine stripping and polishing). VAT: Stan.

HATHERLEIGH

Hatherleigh Antiques   BADA
15 Bridge St. EX20 3HU. (M. Dann). Open 9-5, prior telephone call advisable. SIZE: Medium. *STOCK: Collectors' furniture and works of art, pre-1700.* PARK: Easy. TEL: 01837 810159/ 810500. VAT: Spec.

HONITON

Jane Barnes Antiques & Interiors
59 High St. EX14 8PW. Open 10-4. CL: Wed. SIZE: Medium. *STOCK: General antiques and country pine, glass, clocks.* LOC: Main St. PARK: Easy. TEL: 01404 41712. SER: Furniture copies made to order.

Roderick Butler   BADA
Marwood House. EX14 1PY. Est. 1948. Open 9.30-5 (during August by appointment only). SIZE: Large. *STOCK: 17th-18th C and Regency furniture, curiosities, unusual items, early metalwork.* LOC: Adjacent to roundabout at eastern end of High St. PARK: In courtyard. TEL: 01404 42169. VAT: Spec.

C & S Antiques
159 High St. EX14 1LJ. (I. Crackston and H. Sledge). Est. 1986. Open 10-5. SIZE: Medium. *STOCK: Oak and period country antiques, copper, brass, ceramics, 17th-19th C.* PARK: Nearby. TEL: 01404 43436.

Fountain Antiques
132 High St. EX14 1JP. (J. Palmer and G. York). Open 9.30-5.30. *STOCK: General antiques including pictures, books and linen.* TEL: 01404 42074.

The Grove Antiques Centre
55 High St. EX14 1PW. (Lesley V. Phillips). Est. 1998. Open 10-5, Sun. 11-4. SIZE: Large. *STOCK: Regency and country furniture, iron and mahogany beds and bedroom suites, Art Deco, glass and porcelain, silver, pictures, tinplate toys and bears, longcase clocks and barometers, carpets.* PARK: Easy. TEL: 01404 43377; fax - 01404 43390.

High Street Books
150 High St. EX14 8JB. (G. Tyson). PBFA. Est. 1978. Open 10-5. CL: Mon. SIZE: Medium. *STOCK: Books, prints and maps, 18th-20th C, £1-£1,000.* LOC: Opposite police station. PARK: Easy. TEL: 01404 45570; fax - same; home - 01404 41771. SER: Valuations; buys at auction (as stock). FAIRS: Major London Book.

Honiton Antique Centre
Abingdon House, 136 High St. EX14 8JP. (N.D.A. and E.K. Thompson). Est. 1985. Open 9.30-5.30. SIZE: Large - 20 dealers. *STOCK: 17th-20th C furniture, metalwork, copper, brass, tools, sporting items, pottery, porcelain, pictures and collectables.* LOC: Exeter end of High St. PARK: Nearby. TEL: 01404 42108.

Honiton Antique Toys
38 High St. EX14 1PJ. (L. and S. Saunders). Est. 1986. Open 10.30-5. CL: Mon. and Thurs. *STOCK: Toys, dolls, teddies and children's books.* PARK: Easy. TEL: 01404 41194; e-mail - honitonantiquetoys38@hotmail.com.

Honiton Clock Clinic
16 New St. EX14 1EY. (David Newton). Est. 1992. Open 10-12.30 and 1.30-4, Sat. 10-1. CL: Thurs. SIZE: Small. *STOCK: Clocks and barometers.* PARK: Nearby. TEL: 01404 47466.

Honiton Fine Art
189 High St. EX14 8LQ. (C.B. and P.R. Greenberg). Est. 1974. Open 11.30-5. SIZE: Medium. *STOCK: English watercolours and oil paintings, 18th-20th C, £300-£5,000; Old Master drawings, Dutch, Italian and French, 16th-18th C, £300-£1,500.* LOC: Town centre. PARK: Easy. TEL: 01404 45942. SER: Valuations; restorations (oil paintings and watercolours).

The Honiton Lace Shop
44 High St. EX14 8PJ. Open 9.30-1 and 2-5. *STOCK: Lace including specialist and collectors; quilts, shawls and other textiles, bobbins and lace making equipment.* TEL: 01404 42416; fax - 01404 47797; e-mail - shop@honitonlace.com; website - www.honitonlace.com.

Honiton Old Bookshop
Felix House, 51 High St. EX14 1PW. (R. Collicott). Est. 1991. Open 10-5.30. *STOCK: Books - travel, childrens' illustrated, topography,*

natural history; plate books and bindings; all £5-£500. LOC: Main street. PARK: Easy. TEL: 01404 47180. SER: Catalogues available (2 per annum). FAIRS: London PBFA; Chelsea ABA. VAT: Stan.

Lombard Antiques
14 High St. EX14 8PU. Est. 1984. Open 10-5.30. SIZE: Small. *STOCK: 18th-19th C English furniture, porcelain and decorative items.* PARK: Easy. TEL: 01404 42140.

Maya Antiques
46 High St. EX14 1PJ. (Antonio Briglia and Pauline Brown). Est. 1996. Open 10-5. SIZE: Medium. *STOCK: Furniture, 18th C, £500-£1,000.* PARK: Easy. TEL: 01404 46009.

Merchant House Antiques
19 High St. EX14 8PR. (C. Giltsoff and R. Kirk). Open 10-5, Sun. by appointment. SIZE: Large. *STOCK: English and French fine and provincial furniture, 17th-19th C; works of art, ironstone and later china, collectables and decorative items, upholstery and furnishings, £10-£20,000+.* PARK: Easy. TEL: 01404 42694; fax - 01404 42471; home - 01884 820944; mobile - 07768 960144.* SER: Valuations. VAT: Stan/Spec.

Otter Antiques
69 High St. EX14 1PW. (Kate Skailes). Open 9.30-5. CL: Thurs. p.m. *STOCK: Fine antique silver and plate including flatware; modern silver.* TEL: 01404 42627; e-mail - otterantiques@ jspencer.co.uk.

Pilgrim Antiques
145 High St. EX14 8LJ. (G. and J.E. Mills). LAPADA. Est. 1970. Open 9-5.30. SIZE: Large - trade warehouse. *STOCK: Period English and Continental furniture.* PARK: Easy. TEL: 01404 41219/45316; fax - 01404 45317. SER: Packing and shipping. VAT: Stan/Spec.

Upstairs, Downstairs
12 High St. EX14 8PU. Open 10-5.30. SIZE: Large. *STOCK: 18th-19th C furniture, porcelain, metalware, pictures and clocks.* PARK: Easy. TEL: 01404 44481/42140.

Wickham Antiques
191 High St. EX14 8LQ. (Edwin Waymouth). Est. 1986. Open 9.30-5. SIZE: Medium. *STOCK: Mahogany and oak period furniture and decorative items.* PARK: Easy. TEL: 01404 44654.

Geoffrey M. Woodhead
53 High St. EX14 8PW. Est. 1950. Open 9.30-5. SIZE: Medium. *STOCK: Secondhand books and magazines.* LOC: A30 opposite largest tree in street. PARK: Limited. TEL: 01404 42969.

ILFRACOMBE

Relics
113 High St. EX34 9ET. (Nicola D. Bradshaw). Resident. Est. 1977. Open 10-5. SIZE: Small. *STOCK: General antiques and small collectables, Victorian and Edwardian.* LOC: Opposite The Bunch of Grapes. PARK: Nearby. TEL: 01271 865486; home - same. SER: Valuations.

KINGSBRIDGE

Avon House Antiques/Hayward's Antiques
13 Church St. TQ7 1BT. (D.H. and M.S. Hayward). Open 10-1 and 2-5. *STOCK: General antiques.* TEL: 01548 853718.

KINGSKERSWELL

Bonstow and Crawshay Antiques
12 Torquay Rd. TQ12 5EZ. (James Bonstow and Simon Crawshay). Est. 1995. Open 10-5, Tues. by appointment. SIZE: Small. *STOCK: English furniture, 18th-19th C, £100-£5,000.* LOC: Torquay to Newton Abbot road. PARK: Easy. TEL: 01803 874291. SER: Valuations; buys at auction (furniture). FAIRS: Devon County, Westpoint. VAT: Spec.

KINGSWEAR, Nr. Dartmouth

David L.H. Southwick Rare Art   BADA
Beacon Lodge, Beacon Lane. TQ6 0BU. Open by appointment. *STOCK: Chinese and Japanese works of art.* TEL: 01803 752533; fax - 01803 752535; e-mail - rareart@ewobell. co.uk.

LYDFORD, Nr. Okehampton

Skeaping Gallery
Townend House. EX20 4AR. Est. 1972. Open by appointment. *STOCK: Oils and watercolours.* TEL: 01822 820383; fax - same. VAT: Spec.

LYNTON

Farthings
Churchill House. EX35 6NF. (Mrs L. R. Farthing and Miss I. J. Farthing). Est. 1996. Open 10-4.30 (4pm in winter) including Sun. SIZE: Small. *STOCK: Pictures, 19th-20th C, £50-£5,000; small furniture, Victorian and Edwardian, £50-£1,000; collectibles, 19th-20th C, £5-£2,000.* LOC: Opposite church. PARK: Easy. TEL: 01598 753744; home - 01598 753465. SER: Valuations; restorations; buys at auction.

Wood's Antiques
29A Lee Rd. EX35 6BS. (Pat and Brian Wood). Est. 1964. Open 9-5.30; in winter Sun. 9.30-2. CL: Thurs. *STOCK: General antiques including small furniture, mainly Victorian, £10-£3,000.* PARK: Easy. TEL: 01598 752722.

MAIDENCOMBE, Nr. Torquay

G.A. Whiteway-Wilkinson
Sunsea, Teignmouth Rd. TQ1 4TP. Est. 1943. Open by appointment only. *STOCK: General antiques, fine art and jewellery.* LOC: Approximately half-way on main Torquay/Teignmouth road. TEL: 01803 329692. VAT: Spec.

MERTON, Nr. Okehampton

Barometer World Ltd
Quicksilver Barn. EX20 3DS. Est. 1979. Open Tues.-Sat. 9-5. SIZE: Medium. *STOCK: Mercurial wheel and stick barometers, 1780-1900, £650-£6,000; aneroid barometers, 1850-1930, £70-£1,200.* LOC: Between Hatherleigh and Torrington on A386. PARK: Easy. TEL: 01805 603443; fax - 01805 603344; website - www.barometerworld.co.uk. SER: Valuations; restorations (barometers). VAT: Stan/Spec.

MODBURY, Nr. Ivybridge

Collectors Choice
27 Church St. PL21 0QR. (Allan Jenkins). Resident. Est. 1994. Open 10-5.30. CL: Some Wed. SIZE: Small. *STOCK: Clocks, £20-£1,000; valve radios, ceramics, fountain pens and small furniture, £5-£500; all 19th-20th C.* LOC: A379 between Plymouth and Kingsbridge. PARK: Easy. TEL: 01548 831111. SER: Valuations; restorations (clocks, fountain pens); clock repairs, cleaning, re-silvering.

Wild Goose Antiques
34 Church St. PL21 0QR. (Mr and Mrs T.C. Freeman). Open 10-5.30. *STOCK: Old pine, country furniture, decorative items.* TEL: 01548 830715. VAT: Stan.

MONKTON, Nr. Honiton

Pugh's Farm Antiques
Pugh's Farm. EX14 9QH. (G. Garner and C. Cherry). Est. 1974. Open 9-5.30. SIZE: Large. *STOCK: General antiques including Victorian and Edwardian furniture and beds; Louis XV and neo-rustique French furniture; copper kitchenalia.* LOC: A30 2 miles from Honiton. PARK: Easy. TEL: 01404 42860; home - same; fax - 01404 47792; website - www.pughs-antiques-export.com; e-mail - sales@pughs-antiques-export.com. SER: Importers and exporters. VAT: Stan.

ANNTERIOR

Since 1987

Our business has been built on quality.....

Hand stripped and finished late
18th to 20th Century pine and antique
furniture complemented by
Designer decorative accessories.

22 Molesworth Road, Millbridge,
Plymouth, Devon
Tel: 01752 558277 Fax: 01752 564471
Email: info@annterior.co.uk

MORCHARD BISHOP, Nr. Crediton

Morchard Bishop Antiques
Meadowbank. EX17 6PD. (J.C. and E.A. Child).
Resident. Open by appointment. *STOCK: Mainly
metalware boxes and pottery.* LOC: 8 miles west
of Crediton, off A377 at Morchard Rd. PARK:
Easy. TEL: 01363 877456.

NEWTON ABBOT

The Attic
9 Union St. TQ12 2JX. (G.W. Gillman). Est.
1976. CL: Mon. and Thurs., prior telephone call
advisable. SIZE: Medium. *STOCK: General
antiques, to £1,000.* LOC: Town centre. PARK:
Easy. TEL: 01626 55124. SER: Valuations.

St Leonards Antiques & Craft Centre
Wolborough St. TQ12 1JQ. (Derick Wilson). Est.
1970. Open 10-4.30 including Sun., Tues. 8-4.30.
SIZE: Large. *STOCK: General antiques, 19th C,
£5-£1,000.* LOC: At start of main road to Totnes.
PARK: Adjacent and opposite. TEL: 01626
335666; fax - same. SER: Valuations; restorations; buys at auction (furniture, decorative
items). FAIRS: All major.

NEWTON ST. CYRES, Nr. Exeter

Gordon Hepworth Fine Art
Hayne Farm, Sand Down Lane. EX5 5DE. (C.G.
and I.M. Hepworth). Est. 1990. Open Wed.-Sat.
during exhibitions or by appointment. SIZE: Large
barn - 2 floors. *STOCK: Modern British paintings,
post-war and contemporary especially West
Country - West Cornwall and St. Ives School,
£300-£5,000.* LOC: A377, 3 miles N.W. of Exeter
turn left by village sign, into Sand Down Lane,
farm entrance on left, after last white house.
PARK: Easy. TEL: 01392 851351; home - same.

OKEHAMPTON

Alan Jones Antiques
Fatherford Farm. EX20 1QQ. Est. 1971. Open
anytime by appointment. SIZE: Large - warehouse
and showroom. *STOCK: Furniture, oak, walnut and
mahogany, some pine; copper, brass, barometers,
clocks.* LOC: On A30, one mile from Okehampton.
PARK: Easy. TEL: 01837 52970; home - 01409
231428. SER: Valuations. VAT: Stan/Spec.

PAIGNTON

Hyde Road Antiques
23 Hyde Rd. TQ4 5BW. (David Pentecost). Est.
1975. Open 10-5, Thurs. 10-12.30 and 1.30-5.
SIZE: Medium. *STOCK: Collectables and
general antiques, 16th-20th C, £1-£5,000.* LOC:
Off Torquay Rd. PARK: Opposite. TEL: 01803
554000. SER: Valuations; restorations (clocks,
furniture, china); buys at auction. FAIRS:
Westpoint and Matford, Exeter.

PLYMOUTH

Annterior Antiques
22 Molesworth Rd., Millbridge. PL1 5LZ. (A.
Tregenza and R. Mascaro). Est. 1987. Open 9.30-
5.30, Sat. 10-5 or by appointment. SIZE: Small.
*STOCK: Stripped pine, 18th-19th C, £50-£3,000;
some painted, mahogany and decorative furniture;
brass and iron beds, 19th C, £250-£1,500;
decorative small items.* LOC: Follow signs to
Torpoint Ferry from North Cross roundabout, turn
left at junction of Wilton St. and Molesworth Rd.
PARK: Easy. TEL: 01752 558277; fax - 01752
564471; e-mail - info@annterior.co.uk. SER:
Buys at auction; finder. VAT: Stan/Spec.

Antique Fireplace Centre
30 Molesworth Rd., Stoke. PL1 5NA. (Brian
Taylor). Est. 1988. Open 10-5 or by appointment.
*STOCK: Fire surrounds - timber, marble, slate,
cast iron, £100-£3,500; Georgian and Victorian*

fire grates, £100-£1,500; original accessories including scuttles, coal boxes, fire irons and overmantels, lamps and lanterns. LOC: 50yds. from Victoria Park, map sent on request. PARK: Easy. TEL: 01752 559441; fax - 01752 605964; website - www.2vu.com/antique.fireplaces. SER: Valuations. VAT: Stan/Spec.

Barbican Antiques Centre
82-84 Vauxhall St., Barbican. PL4 0EX. (T. Cremer-Price). Open 9.30-5 every day. SIZE: 60+ dealers. *STOCK: Silver and plate, art pottery, porcelain, glass, jewellery, furniture, pictures, clocks, collectables.* PARK: Own. TEL: 01752 201752; fax - 020 8546 1618.

New Street Antique Centre
27 New St., The Barbican. PL1 2LS. (Turner Properties). Est. 1980. Open 10-5. SIZE: Medium. *STOCK: Clocks, silver, jewellery, weapons, general antiques.* PARK: Nearby. TEL: 01752 661165. VAT: Stan/Spec.

Parade Antiques Market
17 The Parade, The Barbican. PL1 2JW. (John Cabello). Est. 1982. Open 10-5 including Sun. SIZE: Medium. *STOCK: Collectables, 19th-20th C, £1-£1,000; militaria, 18th-20th C, £1-£7,000.* PARK: Easy. TEL: 01752 221443; fax - 01752 291208.

Michael Wood Fine Art
The Gallery, 1 Southside Ope, The Barbican, PL1 2LL. Est. 1971. Open 9.30-6, other times by appointment. SIZE: Medium. *STOCK: Oils, watercolours, original prints, sculptures, ceramics, art glass and books, contemporary, RA exhibitors, modern British, Newlyn, St Ives and Victorian, £100-£100,000.* TEL: 01752 225533; mobile - 07971 847722. SER: Valuations; conservation/preservation/security advice.

SEATON

Etcetera Etc Antiques
12 Beer Rd. EX12 2PA. (B. Warren and M. Rymer). Est. 1969. Open 10-1 and 2-5. CL: Thurs. SIZE: Medium. *STOCK: General antique furniture, ceramics, glass, brass and decorative items.* PARK: Own. TEL: 01297 21965.

SHALDON

Leigh C. Extence
49 Fore St. TQ14 0EA. Open 9.30-1 and 2.15-5, prior telephone call advisable. CL: Thurs. and Sat. pm. *STOCK: Clocks, 1730-1880.* PARK: Outside shop. TEL: 01626 872636; fax - same; mobile - 07967 802160; e-mail clocks@extence.co.uk; website - www.extence.co.uk. SER: Buys at auction; clock finding service; horological research.

W. J. Woodhams
28 Fore St. TQ14 0DE. Resident. Est. 1970. Open 10-5.30. SIZE: Small. *STOCK: Furniture, £5-£5,000; silver and porcelain, bric-a-brac, £5-£200; all 18th-19th C.* PARK: Easy. TEL: 01626 872630. SER: Valuations; restorations (furniture); buys at auction (furniture). VAT: Stan/Spec.

SIDMOUTH

Gainsborough House Antiques
Libra Court, Fore St. EX10 8AJ. (K.S. Scratchley). Est. 1935. Open 9-5, Sat. 9-12.45. CL: Thurs. pm. except by appointment. SIZE: Small. *STOCK: Small general antiques, 1750-1950, £1-£1,000; medals and militaria, 1700 to date, £1-£1,500.* LOC: Down Fore St., 50 yds from seafront, left down York St., entrance to premises on left. PARK: 100 yds. TEL: 01395 514394; home - 01395 515112. SER: Valuations.

The Lantern Shop Gallery
5 New St. EX10 8AP. (Miss J.M.Creeke). Est. 1974. Open 10-4.45. SIZE: Medium. *STOCK: Lighting including table lamps, 1750-1960, £50-£2,000; shades, £50-£250; English porcelain, 1780-1970, £5-£1,500; watercolours and oils, 1800-1950, £15-£2,000; small furniture, decorative items and collectables, 1750-1970, £5-£1,000; topographical and decorative prints, especially East Devon, 1780-1930, maps, 1620-1880, £10-£700.* LOC: Town centre between Fore St. and Market Place. PARK: Nearby - disabled opposite. TEL: 01395 578462. SER: Silk lampshade-making. VAT: Stan.

The Old Curiosity Shop
Old Fore St. EX10 8LP. (Mr Thomas and Mrs Sally Koch). Open 9-5.30, Sun. 10-5. SIZE: Small. *STOCK: Small items - china and glass, furniture and clocks, Oriental rugs, jewellery and paintings, mainly 18th-19th C.* LOC: Down High St. towards sea, in pedestrianised Old Fore St. PARK: Nearby. TEL: 01395 515299. SER: Valuations; restorations (china); buys at auction (Oriental rugs and works of art). FAIRS: Westpoint, Exeter.

Sidmouth Antiques and Collectors Centre
All Saints Rd. EX10 8ES. Open 10-5 (Easter-end Oct. 10-5.30). SIZE: 10 dealers. *STOCK: Wide range of antiques and collectables, collectors' records, antiquarian and out of print books, postcards, stamps, limited edition plates, pictures and prints, linen, lace and crochet items.* TEL: 01395 512588.

The Vintage Toy and Train Shop
Sidmouth Antiques and Collectors Centre, All

Saints Rd. EX10 8ES. (R.D.N., M.E. and J.W. Salisbury). Open 10-5. *STOCK: Hornby Gauge 0 and Dublo trains, Dinky toys, Meccano and other die-cast and tinplate toys, wooden jig-saw puzzles.* TEL: 01395 512588; home - 01395 513399.

SOUTH BRENT

Philip Andrade   BADA
White Oxen Manor, Rattery. TQ10 9JX. By appointment only. STOCK: English furniture and interesting objects. TEL: 01364 72454; fax - 01364 73061; mobile - 07966 149876. SER: Restorations.

P.M. Pollak
Moorview, Plymouth Rd. TQ10 9HT. (Dr. P.M. Pollak). ABA. Est. 1973. Open by appointment. SIZE: Small. *STOCK: Antiquarian books especially medicine and science; prints, some instruments, £50-£5,000.* LOC: On edge of village, near London Inn. PARK: Own. TEL: 01364 73457; fax - 01364 649126; e-mail - patrick@rarevols.co.uk; website - www.rarevols. co.uk. SER: Valuations; buys at auction; catalogues issued, computer searches.

SOUTH MOLTON

The Antique & Interior Centre
14a Barnstaple St. EX36 3BQ. (S.J. Lock). Open Tues.-Sat.10-5. SIZE: Large. *STOCK: Decorative accessories, fabrics, silks, stained glass, ornamental plasterwork.* LOC: On old A361, 100 yards from town centre. PARK: Nearby. TEL: 01769 573401. SER: Valuations.

The Dragon
80 South St. EX36 3AG. (Mrs J. E. Aker). Est. 1994. Open 9.30-4.30. SIZE: Small. *STOCK: Pine and country furniture, from 19th C; bric-a-brac, books and pictures.* LOC: Near town centre. PARK: Limited or nearby. TEL: 01769 572374; mobile - 07712 079818. SER: Restorations (furniture).

The Dragon and the Phoenix
24 East St. EX36 3DB. Open 10-4. SIZE: Small. *STOCK: Antique Chinese and Tibetan furniture.* PARK: Easy. TEL: 01769 574104; fax - 01769 572580; e-mail - antiques@dragonphoenix.co.uk; website - www.dragonphoenix.co.uk.

Snap Dragon
77 South St. EX36 3AG. (Mrs J. E. Aker). Est. 1994. Open 9.30-4.30. SIZE: Small. *STOCK: Pine and country furniture, kitchenalia and tools, architectural and garden artefacts.* LOC: Near town centre. PARK: Limited and opposite. TEL: 01769 572374; mobile - 07712 079818. SER: Restorations (furniture).

J.R. Tredant
50/50a South St. EX36 4AG. Usually open. *STOCK: General antiques.* TEL: 01769 573006; home - 01769 572416. SER: Valuations.

R M Young Bookseller
17 Broad St. EX36 3AQ. (Mark Young). Est. 1970. Open 10-5, Thurs., Fri. and Sat. 9-5. SIZE: Medium. *STOCK: Books especially Exmoor, the countryside, Henry Williamson, £5-200.* LOC: Main street. PARK: Free nearby. TEL: 01769 573350. SER: Restorations; out-of-print booksearch.

STOCKLAND, Nr. Honiton

Colystock Antiques
Rising Sun Farm. EX14 9NH. (D.C. McCollum). Est. 1975. Open seven days. SIZE: Large. *STOCK: Pine and oak including English, Irish and Continental, 18th-19th C.* TEL: 01404 861271. SER: Container packing and documentation; courier.

TAVISTOCK

King Street Curios
5 King St. PL19 0DS. (T. and P. Bates). Est. 1979. Open 9-4. SIZE: Medium. *STOCK: Pine furniture, postcards, cigarette cards, china, glass, general collectables, jewellery, to £100.* LOC: Town centre.

Tavistock Books
5 Pepper St. PL19 0BD. (D.T. and D.J. Byass). Est. 1993. Open 10-5. CL: Mon. and Wed. SIZE: Small. *STOCK: Antiquarian and secondhand books, £10-£1,000.* LOC: Just off main street, opposite market. PARK: Easy. TEL: 01822 616077. SER: Valuations; buys at auction.

TEIGNMOUTH

Extence Antiques
2 Wellington St. TQ14 8HH. (T.E. and L.E. Extence). Est. 1928. Open 9.30-5. SIZE: Medium. *STOCK: Jewellery, silver, objets d'art.* PARK: Limited. TEL: 01626 773353. VAT: Stan/Spec.

Timepiece
125 Bitton Park Rd. TQ14 9BZ. (Clive and Willow Pople). Est. 1988. Open Tues.-Sat. 9.30-5.30, Sat. 9.30-6. SIZE: Medium. *STOCK: Country furniture (including pine), clocks, 19th C, £25-£2,000; kitchenalia and collectables, 19th-20th C, £1-£100.* LOC: On main Newton Abbot road, next to Bitton Park. TEL: 01626 770275.

TOPSHAM, Nr. Exeter

Mere Antiques
13 Fore St. EX3 0HF. (Marilyn Reed). LAPADA. Resident. Est. 1986. Open 9.30-5.30, Sat. 10-4.30, Sun. by appointment. SIZE: Small. *STOCK: English and Continental porcelain, 19th C, £50-£5,000; Japanese Satsuma - Meiji period, £350-£5,000; furniture, 18th-19th C, £200-£5,000.* PARK: Easy and nearby. TEL: 01392 874224; fax - same. SER: Valuations. FAIRS: NEC; LAPADA. VAT: Spec.

Pennies
40 Fore St. EX3 0HU. (Penelope and Michael Clark). Open 10-5. *STOCK: Antiques and collectables.* TEL: 01392 877020. VAT: Stan/Spec.

TORQUAY

Birbeck Gallery
45 Abbey Rd. TQ2 5NQ. Est. 1952. Open by appointment. SIZE: Medium. *STOCK: Paintings, watercolours and prints, 19th to early 20th C, to £10,000.* LOC: 200yds. up Abbey Rd. from main street roundabout at Torquay GPO. TEL: 01803 291658/297144/324449.

The Schuster Gallery
P O Box 139. TQ1 2XX. ABA. Est. 1973. Open by appointment. *STOCK: Antique prints, maps, medieval manuscripts, fine and rare colour plate books, atlases; children's illustrated books including Beatrix Potter, Kate Greenaway and Alice in Wonderland and related items.* TEL: 01803 211422; fax - 01803 211290; e-mail - tschuster@easynet.co.uk; website - www.acid.co.uk/acid/schus.htm.

Sheraton House Antiques
Sheraton House, 1 Laburnum Row, Torre. TQ2 5QX. (I.S. Hutton). Open 9.45-4.45, Wed. and Sat. 9.45-4. *STOCK: General antiques.* TEL: 01803 293334.

Toby's Architectural Antiques
Torre Station, Newton Rd. TQ2 2DD. (Paul and John Norrish). Est. 1985. Open 10-5, Sun. 10.30-4.30. SIZE: Large. *STOCK: Furniture, 19th C, £25-£1,000; collectables, 19th-20th C, £5-£250.* LOC: Main Newton Abbott road, 1 mile from sea front. PARK: Easy. TEL: 01803 212222; fax - 01803 200523. SER: Valuations; buys at auction. VAT: Spec.

TOTNES

Collards Books
4 Castle St. TQ9 5NU. (B. Collard). Est. 1970.

Open 10-5, restricted opening in winter. *STOCK: Antiquarian and secondhand books.* LOC: Opposite castle. PARK: Nearby. TEL: Home - 01548 550246.

Fine Pine Antiques
Woodland Rd., Harbertonford. TQ9 7SX. Est. 1973. Open 9.30-5, Sun. 11-4. *STOCK: Stripped pine and country furniture.* TEL: 01803 732465; fax - 01803 732771. SER: Restorations; stripping.

Past and Present
94 High St. TQ9 5SN. (James Sturges). CL: Lunch-times. SIZE: Large. *STOCK: Furniture, £100-£2,000; smalls, bygones, £5-£300; all 18th-20th C.* LOC: A38. PARK: 150 yards. TEL: 01803 866086. FAIRS: Sandown Park.

Pedlars Pack Books
4 The Plains. TQ9 5DR. (P. D. and A. Elliott). Est. 1991. Open 9-5. SIZE: Medium. *STOCK: Books, £5-500.* TEL: 01803 866423; home - 01626 364345; e-mail - pedlar@aol.com. SER: Valuations; buys at auction.

Rotherfold Antiques
The Rotherfold. TQ9 5ST. (Mrs S. M. van Heck). Est. 1999. Open 10-1 and 2-5, Thurs. 10-1. *STOCK: Furniture and fine art, 19th C; objets d'art, ceramics, mirrors.* LOC: At the end of The Narrows. PARK: Easy. TEL: 01803 840303.

WHIMPLE, Nr. Exeter

Anthony James Antiques
Brook Cottage, The Square. EX5 2SL. Open by appointment. *STOCK: 17th-19th C furniture and works of art.* LOC: A30 between Exeter and Honiton. PARK: Easy. TEL: 01404 822146. SER: Valuations. VAT: Spec.

WOODBURY, Nr. Exeter

Woodbury Antiques
Church St. EX5 1HN. (H. Ballingull). Est. 1966. Open Mon., Tues., Fri. 10-3, Sat. 10-1, prior 'phone call advisable. SIZE: Large. *STOCK: Victorian and Edwardian furniture and items.* PARK: Easy. TEL: 01395 232727. VAT: Stan/Spec.

YEALMPTON, Nr. Plymouth

Colin Rhodes Antiques
15 Fore St. PL9 2JN. LAPADA. Est. 1969. *STOCK: 17th to early 19th C furniture, paintings and objets d'art.* TEL: 01752 881170/862232. SER: Valuations. VAT: Spec.

DORSET

BEAMINSTER

Cottage Antiques
17 The Square. DT8 3AU. Open 10-5.30 or by
appointment. CL: Wed. *STOCK: Furniture,
paintings, clocks, prints, decorative items.* LOC:
A3066. TEL: 01308 862136.

Good Hope Antiques
2 Hogshill St. DT8 3AE. (D. Beney). Est. 1980.
Open 10-1 and 2-5. CL: Wed. SIZE: Medium.
*STOCK: Clocks especially longcase, bracket and
wall, barometers, £500-£5,000; furniture, £200-
£2,500; all 18th-19th C.* LOC: Town square.
PARK: Easy. TEL: 01308 862119. SER: Valuations; restorations (clocks, including dials;
barometers). VAT: Spec.

BERE REGIS, Nr. Wareham

Dorset Reclamation
Cow Drove. BH20 7JZ. Open 8-5, Sat. 9-4.
*STOCK: Decorative architectural and garden
antiques.* TEL: 01929 472200; fax - 01929 472292.

Legg of Dorchester
The Old Mill, West St. BH20 7HS. (W. and H.
Legg & Sons). Est. 1930. *STOCK: Antique
furniture.* TEL: 01929 472051. VAT: Stan/Spec.

BLANDFORD FORUM

Ancient and Modern Bookshop
(including Garret's Antiques)
84 Salisbury St. DT11 7QE. (Mrs P. Davey). Open
9.30-12.30 and 1.30-4.30. CL: Wed. *STOCK:
Books and small antiques.* TEL: 01258 455276.

Antiques for All
Higher Shaftesbury Rd. DT11 7TA. Est. 1998. Open
9.30-5, Sun. 10.30-5. SIZE: Large. *STOCK:
Furniture, 18th-20th C, £100-£10,000; ceramics and
collectables, 18th-20th C, £5-£1,000; clocks and
barometers, oil lamps, 18th-19th C, £100-£1,000.*
LOC: A354 and A350 roundabout on by-pass; town
exit, 3rd turning on right, 1st left. PARK: Easy. TEL:
01258 458011; fax - 01258 458022. SER: Buys at
auction (furniture, oil lamps and ceramics).

Milton Antiques
Market Place. DT11 7HU. Open 9-5. CL: Wed
pm. SIZE: Medium. *STOCK: Furniture, 18th-
19th C, £50-£2,000; decorative items, 18th-20th
C, £5-£200.* LOC: Opposite parish church,
adjacent to town museum. PARK: Easy. TEL:
01258 450100. SER: Valuations; restorations
including polishing.

BOURNEMOUTH

Allegra's Lighthouse Antiques
85 Poole Rd., Westbourne. BH4 9BB. LAPADA.
Est. 1969. Open 10-5. CL: Wed. *STOCK: Antique
lighting, brass and glass chandeliers, mainly 19th
to early 20th C; period mirrors and 19th C
furniture, £600-£6,000.* TEL: 01202 760003.

Antiques and Furnishings
339 Charminster Rd. BH8 9QR. (P. Neath). Open
10-5.30. *STOCK: Furniture, brass, copper,
china, textiles and decorative objects.* TEL:
01202 527976.

Arcade Antiques
6 Westbourne Arcade, Westbourne. BH4 9AY.
(Richard Samuel). Est. 1984. Open 10-4.30, Wed.
10-1, Fri. and Sat. 9.30-5. SIZE: Medium.
*STOCK: Pottery and porcelain, general antiques,
furniture, collectors' items.* LOC: Just off A35
between Bournemouth and Poole. PARK: Easy.
TEL: 01202 764800; fax - 01202 769537. SER:
Valuations. VAT: Spec.

The Artist Gallery
1086 Christchurch Rd., Boscombe East. BH7
6BQ. Open 9.30-5. CL: Wed. *STOCK: Limited
edition prints and original works of art - David
Shepherd, Sir William Russell Flint, E.R.
Sturgeon, Lowry, Gordon King and others.*
PARK: Forecourt. TEL: 01202 417066.

Boscombe Militaria
86 Palmerston Rd., Boscombe. BH1 4HU. (E.A.
Browne). Est. 1981. Open 10-1 and 2-5. CL:
Wed. *STOCK: German militaria, £10-£500;
British and American militaria, £5-£300, all
1914-1918 and 1939-1945.* LOC: Just off
Christchurch Rd. PARK: Easy. TEL: 01202
304250; fax - 01202 733696. FAIRS: Farnham;
Cheshunt; major South of England Arms.

Boscombe Models and Collectors
Shop
802c Christchurch Rd., Boscombe. BH7 6DD.
(Sylvia Hart). Open Thurs., Fri. and Sat. 10-1 and
2-4.30. *STOCK: Collectors' toys, 19th-20th C,
£1-£1,000.* LOC: On Somerset Rd. TEL: 01202
398884.

Chorley-Burdett Antiques
828-830 Christchurch Rd., Pokesdown. BH7
6DF. (Raymond Burdett). Open 9-5.30. SIZE:
Large. *STOCK: Furniture, pine furniture
including reclaimed late 19th to early 20th C,
£50-£1,000.* LOC: Corner of Warwick Rd.
PARK: Easy. TEL: 01202 423363; fax - same.
VAT: Stan/Spec.

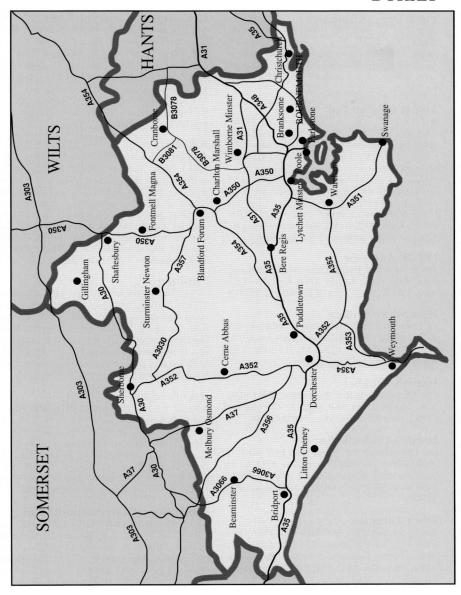

<u>Dealers and Shops in Dorset</u>

				Parkstone	3
				Poole	2
Beaminster	2	Christchurch	4	Puddletown	1
Bere Regis	2	Cranborne	1	Shaftesbury	2
Blandford Forum	3	Dorchester	6	Sherborne	17
Bournemouth	25	Fontmell Magna	1	Sturminster Newton	1
Branksome	3	Gillingham	1	Swanage	2
Bridport	4	Litton Cheney	1	Wareham	1
Cerne Abbas	1	Lytchett Minster	1	Weymouth	6
Charlton Marshall	1	Melbury Osmond	1	Wimborne Minster	3

Peter Denver Antiques
36 Calvin Rd., Winton. BH9 1LN. (P. Denver-White). Est. 1961. Open 11-4. CL: Mon. SIZE: Small. *STOCK: Furniture, porcelain, pictures, glass, Georgian-Edwardian, £5-£800.* LOC: Off main Wimborne Rd. PARK: Easy. TEL: 01202 532536; home - 01202 513911.

Lionel Geneen Ltd
811 Christchurch Rd., Boscombe. BH7 6AP. LAPADA. Est. 1902. Open 9-5, Sat. 9-12, other times by appointment. CL: Lunchtimes. SIZE: Large. *STOCK: English, Continental and Oriental furniture, china and works of art including some bronzes, enamels, ivories, jades, all mainly 19th C, Art Nouveau and Art Deco; specialising in tea, dinner and dessert services.* LOC: Main road through Boscombe. PARK: Easy. TEL: 01202 422961; home - 01202 520417. SER: Valuations. VAT: Stan/Spec.

H.L.B. Antiques
139 Barrack Rd. BH23 2AW. (H.L. Blechman). Est. 1969. SIZE: Large. *STOCK: Collectable items.* PARK: Easy. TEL: 01202 429252/482388.

Hampshire Gallery
18 Lansdowne Rd. BH1 1SD. LAPADA. Est. 1971. *STOCK: Paintings and watercolours, 17th to early 20th C.* TEL: 01202 551211. SER: Valuations; restorations. VAT: Spec.

Hardy's Clobber
874 Christchurch Rd., Boscombe. BH7 6DQ. (J.W. Hardy). Open 10-5. *STOCK: Clothing and fabrics, from Victorian.* TEL: 01202 429794.

Hardy's Collectables
862 Christchurch Rd., Boscombe. BH7 6DQ. (J. Hardy). Open 10-5. SIZE: 20 dealers. *STOCK: Art Deco and Art Nouveau glass and 50's collectables especially Poole pottery.* TEL: 01202 422407/ 303030.

Libra Antiques
916 Christchurch Rd. BH7 6DL. Est. 1967. Open 10-4.30. SIZE: Medium. *STOCK: Silver and plate, objects, furniture, jewellery, metalware.* PARK: Opposite. TEL: 01202 427615; mobile - 07836 680928. VAT: Stan.

G.B. Mussenden and Son Antiques, Jewellery and Silver
24 Seamoor Rd., Westbourne. BH4 9AR. Est. 1948. Open 9-5. CL: Wed. SIZE: Medium. *STOCK: Antiques, jewellery, silver.* LOC: Central Westbourne, corner of R.L. Stevenson Ave. PARK: Easy. TEL: 01202 764462. SER: Valuations. VAT: Stan/Global/Spec.

Geo. A. Payne and Son Ltd
742 Christchurch Rd., Boscombe. BH7 6BZ. (H.G. and N.G. Payne). FGA. Est. 1946. Open 9-5.30. SIZE: Small. *STOCK: Jewellery, 19th-20th C, £10-£3,000; silver, 18th-20th C, £30-£1,000; plate, £10-£200.* LOC: Opposite Browning Ave. and Chessel Ave. PARK: Browning Ave. TEL: 01202 394954. SER: Valuations; gemstone testing; restorations (silver, jewellery, clocks, watches). VAT: Stan/Spec.

R.E. Porter
2-6 Post Office Rd. BH1 1BA. Est. 1934. Open 9.30-5. SIZE: Medium. *STOCK: Silver including early antique spoons, Georgian, £20-£5,000; jewellery, pot lids, Baxter and Le Blond prints, clocks including second-hand.* Not Stocked: Furniture, arms, armour, carpets. LOC: Walking from the Square, take the Old Christchurch Rd., then the first turning on the left. PARK: 300yds. at top of Richmond Hill. TEL: 01202 554289. SER: Valuations. VAT: Stan/Spec.

Portique
15/16/17 Criterion Arcade. BH1 1BU. Est. 1968. *STOCK: Silver, jewellery, Derby china, glass paperweights, cloisonné, clocks.* LOC: Coming from the square take the Old Christchurch Rd. from roundabout, arcade entrance is between first and second turnings on left. TEL: 01202 552979. SER: Repairs and restorations (silver, jewellery). VAT: Stan/Spec.

Recollections
5 Royal Arcade, Boscombe. BH1 4BT. (David and Brenda Francis). Est. 1994. Open 9.30-4.30. CL: Tues. and Wed. SIZE: Medium. *STOCK: Mainly collectables, 1920's to modern, including Poole, royal commemoratives, crested china, Art Deco, Beatrix Potter, Doulton, to £1,000.* LOC: Off pedestrian precinct, opposite Lloyds Bank. PARK: Sovereign centre. TEL: 01202 304441.

Sainsburys of Bournemouth Ltd
23-25 Abbott Rd. BH9 1EU. LAPADA. Est. 1918. Open 8-1 and 2-6, appointment advisable. CL: Sat. *STOCK: Furniture especially bookcases and dining tables, 18th C, to £15,000.* PARK: Own. TEL: 01202 529271; home - 01202 763616; fax - 01202 510028; sales@sainsburys-antiques.com. SER: Custom-made furniture from re-cycled Georgian wood including exceptionally large pieces. VAT: Stan/Spec.

Sandy's Antiques
790-792 Christchurch Rd., Boscombe. BH7 6DD. BDADA. SIZE: 2 large shops + warehouse. *STOCK: Victorian, Edwardian and shipping goods.* TEL: 01202 301190; evenings - 01202 304955. VAT: Stan/Spec.

Sterling Coins and Medals

2 Somerset Rd., Boscombe. BH7 6JH. (W.V. Henstridge). Est. 1969. Open 9.30-4. CL: Wed. pm. SIZE: Small. *STOCK: Coins, medals, militaria, World War II German items.* LOC: Next to 806 Christchurch Rd. TEL: 01202 423881. SER: Valuations. VAT: Stan.

M.C. Taylor

995 Christchurch Rd., Boscombe East. BH7 6BB. (Mark Taylor). MAPH, CMBHI. Est. 1982. SIZE: Small. *STOCK: Clocks, barometers, music boxes and turret clocks, £500-£20,000.* LOC: Opposite St. James' School and Kings Park entrance. PARK: Easy. TEL: 01202 429718. SER: Valuations; restorations. VAT: Stan/Spec.

Victorian Chairman

883 Christchurch Rd., Boscombe. BH7 6AU. (M. Leo). Open 9.30-5. *STOCK: Furniture especially chairs, sofas and tables.* TEL: 01202 420996. SER: Upholstery restoration.

Yesterday Tackle and Books

42 Clingan Rd., Boscombe East. BH6 5PZ. (David and Alba Dobbyn). Open by appointment. *STOCK: Fishing tackle and associated items including taxidermy; books.* TEL: 01202 476586. SER: Catalogues issued.

BRANKSOME

Allen's (Branksome) Ltd

447/449 Poole Rd. BH12 1DH. (D.L and P.J. D'Ardenne). Est. 1948. Open 9-5.30. SIZE: Large. *STOCK: Furniture.* TEL: 01202 763724; fax - 01202 763724. VAT: Stan/Spec.

Branksome Antiques

370 Poole Rd. BH12 1AW. (B.A. Neal). Est. 1973. Open 10-5. CL: Wed. and Sat. SIZE: Medium. *STOCK: Scientific and marine items, furniture and general small items.* PARK: Easy. TEL: 01202 763324; home - 01202 679932. SER: Buys at auction (as stock). VAT: Stan/Spec.

David Mack Antiques

434-436 Poole Rd. and 21 Crommer Rd. BH12 1DF. Est. 1963. Open 9-5.30, Sun. 11-4. SIZE: Large. *STOCK: 18th-19th C tables, chairs, display cabinets, desks, bureaux, bookcases; later furniture.* LOC: 2 doors from Branksome rail station. PARK: Own. TEL: 01202 760005; fax - 01202 765100; website - www.davidmack antiques.co.uk. SER: Restorations. VAT: Stan/Spec.

BRIDPORT

Batten's Jewellers

26 South St. DT6 3NQ. (R. Batten). Open 9.30-5. *STOCK: Jewellery and silver.* TEL: 01308 456910. SER: Valuations; repairs.

Benchmark Antiques

West Allington. DT6 5BJ. (Megan Standage). BAFRA. Est. 1992. Open by appointment. SIZE: Small. *STOCK: English furniture and related items, 1700-1880, £100-£15,000.* LOC: B3167 (West Street) 450yds from town centre. PARK: Easy. TEL: 01308 420941; home - same. SER: Valuations; restorations; buys at auction. FAIRS: NEC; Olympia.

Bridport Antiques Centre

5 West Allington. DT6 5BJ. Open 9-5. SIZE: 10 dealers. *STOCK: Pine and country furniture, lace, linen, porcelain, glass, books, prints, watercolours, oils, postcards, jewellery, classical garden ornaments, taxidermy.* TEL: 01308 425885.

Bridport Old Books

11 South St. DT6 3NR. Open 10-5. *STOCK: Antiquarian and secondhand books and prints.* TEL: 01308 425689.

CERNE ABBAS

Cerne Antiques

DT2 7LA. (I. Pulliblank). Est. 1972. Open 10-1 and 2-5, Sun. 2-5. CL: Mon. and Fri. SIZE: Medium. *STOCK: Silver, porcelain, furniture including unusual items, mainly 19th C, £1-£400.* LOC: A352. PARK: Easy. TEL: 01300 341490; home - same.

CHARLTON MARSHALL, Nr. Blandford Forum

Zona Dawson Antiques

The Old Clubhouse. DT11 9PA. Est. 1958. Open 10-6. CL: Mon. *STOCK: Mainly furniture, clocks, 18th-19th C.* TEL: 01258 453146.

CHRISTCHURCH

J.L. Arditti

20 Twynham Ave. BH23 1QU. Est. 1964. Open by appointment only. SIZE: Medium. *STOCK: Oriental carpets and rugs, 18th to early 20th C, £500-£8,000.* LOC: From town centre take road towards Hurn airport, left turn. PARK: Twynham Avenue. TEL: 01202 485414. SER: Valuations; restorations; cleaning (Persian rugs). VAT: Stan/Spec.

Christchurch Carpets
55/57 Bargates. BH23 1QE. (J. Sheppard). Est. 1963. Open 9-5.30. SIZE: Large. *STOCK: Persian carpets and rugs, 19th-20th C, £100-£1,000.* LOC: Main road. PARK: Adjacent. TEL: 01202 482712. SER: Valuations. VAT: Stan/Spec.

Hamptons
12 Purewell. BH23 1EP. (G. Hampton). Open 10-6. CL: Sat. am. SIZE: Large. *STOCK: Furniture, 18th-19th C; general antiques, clocks, china, instruments, metalware, oil paintings, Chinese and Persian carpets and rugs.* PARK: Easy. TEL: 01202 484000.

Tudor House Antiques
420 Lymington Rd., Highcliffe, BH23 5HE. (P. Knight and D. Burton). LAPADA. Est. 1940. Open 10-5. CL: Mon. and Wed. SIZE: Medium. *STOCK: General antiques.* LOC: Main road, A337. PARK: Easy. TEL: 01425 280440. VAT: Stan/Spec.

CRANBORNE, Nr. Wimborne Minster

Tower Antiques
The Square. BH21 5PR. (P.W. Kear and P. White). Est. 1975. Open 8.30-5.30. CL: Sat. *STOCK: Georgian and Victorian furniture.* TEL: 01725 517552.

DORCHESTER

Box of Porcelain
51d Icen Way. DT1 1EW. (R.J. and Mrs. S.Y. Lunn). Est. 1984. Open 10-5. *STOCK: Porcelain including Worcester, Doulton, Belleek.* LOC: Close town centre, near Dinosaur Museum. TEL: 01305 250856; fax - 01305 265517; e-mail - rlunn@btconnect.com; website -www.boxof porcelain.com. SER: Valuations; Beswick/ Doulton collectors' finder service.

Colliton Antique Centre
Colliton St. DT1 1XH. Open daily, Sun. by appointment. SIZE: 14 dealers. *STOCK: 18th-20th C furniture, £25-£5,000; brass, bric-a-brac, pictures, china, pine, clocks, jewellery and silver, toys.* LOC: By town clock. PARK: Easy. TEL: 01305 269398/260115. SER: Restorations (cabinet work and metalware). VAT: Stan/Spec.

Michael Legg Antiques
8 Church St. DT1 1JN. (E.M.J. Legg). Open 9-5.30 or any time by appointment. SIZE: Medium. *STOCK: 17th-19th C furniture, clocks, porcelain, pictures, silver, glass.* TEL: 01305 264596. SER: Lectures on the Arts. VAT: Stan/Spec.

Legg of Dorchester
Regency House, 51 High East St. DT1 1HU. (W. and H. Legg). Est. 1930. *STOCK: General antiques, Regency and decorative furniture, stripped pine.* TEL: 01305 264964. VAT: Stan/Spec.

John Walker Antiques
52 High West St. DT1 1UT. Open 9.30-5 or by appointment. SIZE: Small. *STOCK: Early furniture, textiles, metalwork, ceramics, wood carvings, 16th-18th C; British folk art, 16th-19th C.* LOC: Main street. PARK: Easy. TEL: 01305 260324. SER: Valuations; buys at auction. VAT: Spec.

Words Etcetera
2 Cornhill. DT1 1BA. (Julian Nangle). PBFA, ABA. Est. 1970. Open 9.30-5.30. SIZE: Medium. *STOCK: Antiquarian and quality second-hand books and prints; remainders on all subjects.* LOC: Close to museum. TEL: 01305 251919; fax - 01305 266898; home - 01258 820415. SER: Buys at auction (books). FAIRS: ABA London (June).

FONTMELL MAGNA

Quarterjack Antiques
The Old Coach House, Lurmer St. SP7 0PA. (Jon Neilson). Est. 1969. SIZE: Small. *STOCK: 18th-19th C glassware, furniture, pictures, corkscrews, walking sticks and horse brasses.* TEL: 01747 812222; website - www.quarterjack.com.

GILLINGHAM

Talisman
The Old Brewery, Wyke. SP8 4NW. LAPADA. Open 9-5, Sat. 10-4. SIZE: Large. *STOCK: Unusual and decorative items, garden furniture, architectural fittings, 18th-19th C; English and Continental furniture.* TEL: 01747 824423/ 824222; fax - 01747 823544. VAT: Stan/Spec.

LITTON CHENEY, Nr. Dorchester

F. Whillock
Court Farm. DT2 9AU. Open by appointment. *STOCK: Maps and prints.* TEL: 01308 482457. SER: Framing.

LYTCHETT MINSTER

Old Button Shop Antiques
BH16 6JF. (T. Johns). Est. 1970. Open Tues.-Fri.

2-5, Sat 11-1. *STOCK: Small antiques, brass, copper, curios, unusual items, and antique Dorset buttons.* TEL: 01202 622169.

Open 9-5. *STOCK: Antiquarian and secondhand books, maps, prints and engravings.* TEL: 01305 848633; fax - 01305 848992. SER: Postal.

MELBURY OSMOND, Nr. Dorchester

Hardy Country
Meadow View. DT2 0NA. Est. 1980. SIZE: Large. *STOCK: Edwardian and Victorian old pine country furniture and antiques, £40-£800.* LOC: Off A37. PARK: Easy. TEL: 01935 83440; website - www.hardycountry.com.

PARKSTONE, Nr. Poole

Derek J. Burgess - Horologist
470 Ashley Rd. BH14 0AD. Open Tues.-Fri. 9-1.30. *STOCK: Clocks, watches.* TEL: 01202 730542. SER: Restorations (clocks and watches of all periods); parts made.

Dorset Coin Company
193 Ashley Rd. BH14 9DL. (E.J. and C.P. Parsons). BNTA, IBNS. Est. 1977. Open 9.30-4, Sat. 9.30-1. *STOCK: Coins, 19th-20th C, £1-£50; banknotes, 20th C, £3-£50.* LOC: Main road through Upper Parkstone. PARK: Easy. TEL: 01202 739606; fax - 01202 739230. SER: Valuations. FAIRS: BNTA Harrogate & London. VAT: Stan/Global/Exempt

Christopher Williams Antiquarian Bookseller
19 Morrison Ave. BH12 4AD. *STOCK: Books especially antiques, art, needlework, lacemaking and leatherbound volumes and sets.* TEL: 01202 743157; fax - same; e-mail - cw4finebooks@lineone.net. FAIRS: Various. *Postal only.*

POOLE

G.D. and S.T. Antiques
(G.D. and S.T.Brown). Open by appointment. *STOCK: General antiques.* TEL: 01202 676340.

Laburnum Antiques
Lonbourne House, 250 Bournemouth Rd. BH14 9HZ. (Doreen Mills). Est. 1998. Open Tues.-Sat. 10-5.30. *STOCK: Fine Georgian and Victorian furniture, smalls, decorative items.* PARK: Forecourt. TEL: 01202 746222; fax - same.

PUDDLETOWN, Nr. Dorchester

Antique Map and Bookshop
32 High St. DT2 8RU. (C.D. and H.M. Proctor).

SHAFTESBURY

Mr. Punch's Antique Market
33 Bell St. SP7 8AE. Open 10-6. SIZE: Large. *STOCK: Wide variety of general antiques, fine art and collectables. Also Punch and Judy collection.* LOC: On corner with Muston's Lane. PARK: Easy 100 yards. TEL: 01747 855775; fax - same. SER: Valuations; restorations; deliveries.

Shaston Antiques
16A Bell St. SP7 8AE. (J. D. Hine). Resident. Est. 1996. Open 9.30-1 and 2-5, Wed. 9.30-1. SIZE: Medium. *STOCK: Furniture, 18th-19th C, £300-£5,000.* LOC: From town centre, turn right opposite Grosvenor Hotel into Bell St. TEL: 01747 850405; home - same. SER: Restorations (furniture).

SHERBORNE

Abbas Antiques
at Sherborne World of Antiques, Long St. DT9 3BS. Open 9.30-5. *STOCK: Small collectables and furniture.* TEL: 01935 816451.

Antiques of Sherborne
1 The Green. DT9 3HZ. (C. and L. Greenslade). Open 10-5. *STOCK: 18th-19th C furniture, sofas and armchairs, chess sets.* TEL: 01935 816549; mobile - 07971 019173; e-mail - clive@antiquesofsherborne.fsnet.co.uk.

Chapter House Books
Trendle St. DT9 3NT. (Carol and Robert Hutchison). PBFA. Est. 1988. Open 10-5. SIZE: Large. *STOCK: Out-of-print, secondhand and antiquarian books, to £400.* LOC: Next to almshouse and abbey. TEL: 01935 816262. SER: Valuations; restorations (bookbinding and repair); book search.

Dodge and Son
28-33 Cheap St. DT9 3PU. (S. Dodge). LAPADA. Open 9-5.30. SIZE: Large. *STOCK: Furniture, all periods, mainly Georgian.* PARK: At rear. TEL: 01935 815151. VAT: Stan/Spec.

Geometrica
3 Westbury. DT9 4RX. Est. 1998. Open Fri. and Sat. 10-4, Mon., Tues. and Thurs. by appointment. SIZE: Small. *STOCK: Ceramics including studio pottery, early and contemporary, glass, 20th C, £25-£50; furniture, 19th-20th C, £50-*

£100; pictures, 20th C, £10-£30. LOC: Opposite abbey entrance off Half Moon St. PARK: Easy. TEL: 01935 814392; home - 01963 220662. SER: Valuations; restorations (ceramics, furniture). FAIRS: Deco.

Greystoke Antiques

Swan Yard, Off Cheap St. DT9 3AX. (F.L. and N.E. Butcher). Est. 1970. Open 10-4.30. *STOCK: Silver, Georgian, Victorian and later; early 19th C English blue transfer printed pottery.* LOC: Off main street. PARK: Adjacent to Swan Yard or outside shop. TEL: 01935 812833. VAT: Stan/Margin/Global.

Heygate Browne Antiques

South St. DT9 3NG. (M. and W. Heygate Browne). Open 10-5. SIZE: Large. *STOCK: 18th-19th C furniture, pottery and porcelain.* LOC: Off Cheap St. towards station. PARK: Easy. TEL: 01935 815487. SER: Valuations; restorations. VAT: Stan/Spec.

Keeble Antiques

2 Tilton Court, Digby Rd. DT9 3NL. (C.P. Keeble). Est. 1965. Open 9-6, Sat. 8.30-6, Sun. 9.30-5.30. SIZE: Medium. *STOCK: Clocks, 19th C, £250-£850; Venetian mirrors, 19th C, £500-£900; books, 16th-20th C, £1-£800; maps, 17th-19th C, £100-£750.* LOC: Adjacent tourist information centre, near abbey. PARK: Easy. TEL: 01935 816199; fax - same; e-mail - info@keebleantiques.co.uk; website - www.keebleantiques.co.uk. SER: Valuations (books and maps).

The Nook

South St. DT9 3LX. (J. Morley). *STOCK: General antiques - furniture, china, glass, brass and copper.* TEL: 01935 813987.

Phoenix Antiques

21 Cheap St. DT9 3PU. (Sally and Neil Brent Jones). Est. 1998. Open 9.30-5.30. SIZE: Medium. *STOCK: Furniture, 17th-20th; lighting, mirrors and furnishings.* LOC: Town centre. PARK: Easy. TEL: 01935 812788. SER: Valuations; restorations. VAT: Spec.

Piers Pisani Antiques

The Music House, The Green. DT9 3HX. Open 10-5. SIZE: Medium. *STOCK: 17th-19th C furniture and furnishings.* TEL: 01935 815209; fax - same. SER: Restorations; upholstery; chairs copied; cabinet-making. VAT: Spec.

Georgina Ryder

The Music House, The Green. DT9 3HX. LAPADA. Est. 1977. Open 10-5. SIZE: Medium. *STOCK: 18th-19th C French furniture and decorative objects.* PARK: Easy. TEL: 01935 815209. SER: Valuations; restorations (upholstery). FAIRS: Olympia; LAPADA; Decorative & Textile, Battersea. VAT: Spec.

Sherborne World of Antiques

Long St. DT9 3BS. Open 9.30-5. SIZE: 40+ dealers. *STOCK: Fine arts, painting, furniture, rugs, objets d'art, jewellery.* LOC: From A30 via Greenhill. PARK: Easy. TEL: 01935 816451.

The Swan Gallery

51 Cheap St. DT9 3AX. (S. and Mrs K. Lamb). Est. 1977. Open 9.30-5, Wed. 9.30-1. SIZE: Large. *STOCK: Watercolours, 18th to early 20th C; oil paintings, antiquarian maps and prints.* PARK: Easy, at rear. TEL: 01935 814465; fax - 01308 868195. SER: Valuations; restorations (paintings, watercolours and prints); framing. VAT: Stan/Spec.

Timecraft Clocks

Unit 2, 24 Cheap St. DT9 3PX. (Gordon M. Smith). Grad. BHI. Est. 1993. Open 10-5.30. SIZE: Small. *STOCK: Clocks, 18th-20th C, £200-£4,000; barometers, 18th-20th C, £80-£1,200; telephones, 20th C, £80-£250.* PARK: Easy. TEL: 01935 817771. SER: Restorations (clock and barometer movements, cases and dials).

John Walker Antiques   BADA

6a Cheap St. Open 10-5 or by appointment. CL: Mon. *STOCK: Early furniture, textiles, metalwork, ceramics, wood carvings, 16th-18th C; British folk art, 16th-19th C.* LOC: Main street. TEL: 01935 812261. VAT: Spec.

Henry Willis (Antique Silver)

38 Cheap St. DT9 3PX. Est. 1973. Open 10-5. SIZE: Small. *STOCK: Silver, 17th-19th C, £15-£1,500.* LOC: Town centre, just off A30. PARK: Nearby. TEL: 01935 816828. SER: Valuations; restorations (silver); buys at auction (silver). FAIRS: Olympia (June). VAT: Stan/Spec.

STURMINSTER NEWTON

Tom Tribe and Son

Bridge St. DT10 1BZ. CMBHI. Resident. Open 9-5, Sat. 9-1 and by appointment. *STOCK: Long-case and mantel clocks, barometers.* PARK: At side of shop. TEL: 01258 472311. VAT: Stan/Spec.

SWANAGE

Georgian Gems Antique Jewellers

28 High St. BH19 2NU. (Brian Barker). NAG.

Est. 1971. Open 9.30-1 and 2.30-5 or by appointment. SIZE: Small. *STOCK: Jewellery, £5-£2,000; silver, £5-£500; both from 1700.* LOC: Town centre. PARK: Nearby. TEL: 01929 424697; freephone - 0800 471 0242. SER: Valuations; repairs; gem testing; special search.

Reference Works

at The Last Resort, 9 Commercial Rd. BH19 1DF. (B. Lamb). Open 10-4, Sat. 10-1. *STOCK: Reference books and catalogues on ceramics, all subjects, new and out-of-print; small range of ceramics, 18th-20th C.* TEL: 01929 424423; fax - 01929 422597; e-mail - RWrefworks@aol.com. SER: Mail order, catalogue available; six newsletters each year; ceramic research and consultancy.

WAREHAM

Heirlooms Antique Jewellers and Silversmiths

21 South St. BH20 4LR. (M. and Mrs G. Young). FGA, DGA, RJDip. Est. 1986. Open 9.15-5. CL: Wed. SIZE: Medium. *STOCK: Jewellery, £30-£1,000; silver, £20-£500; both Georgian to Edwardian.* LOC: On main thoroughfare. PARK: At rear. TEL: 01929 554207. SER: Valuations; restorations; repairs; gem testing.

WEYMOUTH

Books Afloat

66 Park St. DT4 7DE. (J. Ritchie). Open 9.30-5.30. *STOCK: Rare and secondhand books especially nautical; maritime ephemera, liner memorabilia, ship models, paintings, prints.* LOC: Near railway station. PARK: Limited.. TEL: 01305 779774.

Books & Bygones

Great George St. DT4 7AR. (Mrs Denise Nash). Est. 1981. Open 11-5.30, Sun. 12-5. SIZE: Medium. *STOCK: Books including antiquarian, 50p to £1,000; antiques and collectables, from 18th C, £1-£750; ephemera, from 50p.* LOC: Near King's statue, on esplanade. PARK: Easy. TEL: 01305 777231; home - 01305 771529. SER: Valuations; buys at auction.

The Crows Nest

3 Hope Sq. DT4 8TR. (Julia Marko). Open 10-5 including Sun. SIZE: Medium. *STOCK: Collectables including china, glass and nautical items.* LOC: Follow signs for Brewers Quay, shop opposite. PARK: Brewers Quay. TEL: 01305 786930. FAIRS: Shepton Mallet.

Finesse Fine Art

9 Coniston Crescent. DT3 5HA. (Tony Wraight). Open by appointment only. *STOCK: Pre-war motoring accessories - metal mascots and Lalique glassware, including mascots, fine bronzes, automobilia, picnic hampers, £500-£50,000.* TEL: 01305 854286; fax - 01305 852888; mobile - 07973 886937.

Nautical Antique Centre

3a Cove Passage. DT4 8TR. (D.C. Warwick). Est. 1989. Open 10-1 and 2-5 - prior 'phone call advisable, Sat., Sun. and Mon. by appointment. SIZE: Medium. *STOCK: Exclusively nautical, including sextants, logs, clocks, flags, blocks, old sails, rope, bells, ship models, telescopes, ship badges, portholes and memorabilia, also restaurant/pub decorative items, 19th-20th C, £5-£2,000.* LOC: Near Hope Square opposite Brewers Quay, adjacent harbour. PARK: Nearby. TEL: 01305 777838; home - 01305 783180; e-mail - nauticalantiques@tinyworld.co.uk; website - www.nauticalantiquesweymouth.co.uk. SER: Buys at auction (nautical items).

The Treasure Chest

29 East St. DT4 8BN. (P. Barrett). Open 10-1 and 2.30-5. CL: Wed. pm. *STOCK: Maps, prints, coins, medals; army, RN and RAF badges.* PARK: Next door. TEL: 01305 772757. SER: Lost medals replaced; medal mounting - full size or miniature, brooches and new ribbons.

WIMBORNE MINSTER

Four Seasons Gallery

24 West Borough. BH21 1NF. (Nigel Cox). Est. 1996. Open Mon.- Sat. 10-5.30. SIZE: Small. *STOCK: Small 18th-19th furniture, paintings, collectables; contemporary art gallery with regular exhibitions.* LOC: Near minster. PARK: Easy and nearby. TEL: 01202 882204; website - www.fourseasonsgallery.co.uk.

J.B. Antiques

10A West Row. BH21 1LA. (J. Beckett). Est. 1978. Open 10-4, Fri. and Sat. 9.30-4. CL: Wed. SIZE: Small. *STOCK: Copper, £5-£360; brass, £1-£350; furniture, £30-£1,200; all 18th-20th C.* LOC: 2 mins. from Sq. PARK: Nearby. TEL: Home - 01202 882522. SER: Valuations; restorations (metalware); buys at auction (copper).

Minster Books

12 Corn Market. BH21 1HW. (John and Angela Child). Est. 1970. Open 10-5. SIZE: Medium. *STOCK: Books, £5-£100.* LOC: In road at side of minster. PARK: King St. TEL: 01202 883355. SER: Valuations; restorations (book binding).

Edward Barrington-Doulby

23 The Bank. (M. A. Venus). Est. 1990. Open Wed.-Sat. 11-5, Sun. 1-5 in summer. SIZE: Warehouse + shop. *STOCK: 18th-20th C unusual tools, implements, kitchenalia, eccentricities, cast-iron, pottery, pictures, £1-£1,000; 17th-20th C pine, oak, mahogany, rustic and provincial furniture.* PARK: Easy. TEL: 01833 630500; home - 01325 264339.

The Collector

Douglas House, The Bank. DL12 8PH. (Robert A. Jordan). Est. 1970. Open Sat. 10-5 or by appointment. SIZE: Medium. *STOCK: Early furniture and complementary objects, decorative interior fittings and Eastern rugs.* TEL: 01833 637783; fax - same; e-mail - JordanThe Collector@ btinternet.com. SER: Restorations (especially metal work, early furniture and interiors).

Grant's Antiques

26 Newgate. DL12 8NG. (Carl Grant). Resident. Est. 1976. Open Wed., Fri. and Sat. 10.30-5. SIZE: Small. *STOCK: Oak and mahogany furniture, £100-£4,000; pottery, £15-£500; rugs, £50-£500; all 17th-19th C.* TEL: 01833 695700.

Joan and David White Antiques

Neville House, 10 The Bank. DL12 8PQ. Est. 1975. Open Thurs.-Sat. 11-5. *STOCK: Georgian, Victorian and export furniture and decorative items.* LOC: 100yds. from Market Cross. TEL: 01833 638329; home - 01325 374303. VAT: Stan/Spec.

Margaret Bedi Antiques & Fine Art

5 Station Rd. TS23 1AG. LAPADA. Est. 1976. Open by appointment. *STOCK: Mainly English period furniture, 1720-1920; oils and watercolours, 19th-20th C.* LOC: 300yds. off A19, by

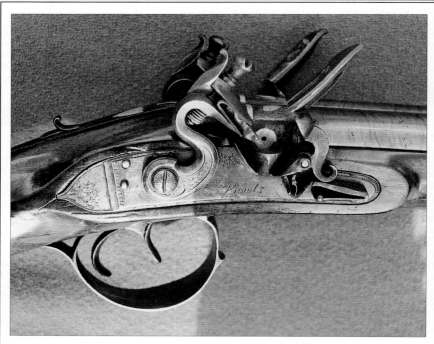

Detail of double-barrel flintlock shot-gun, c.1810 – a gunsmith's perfection. Safety catch, figured walnut stock, gold touch-holes, Damascus barrels. £2,000-£3,000.

From an article entitled 'Antique Guns' by Vivian Crellin which appeared in the September 2000 issue of **Antique Collecting** magazine. For more details and to subscribe see page 147.

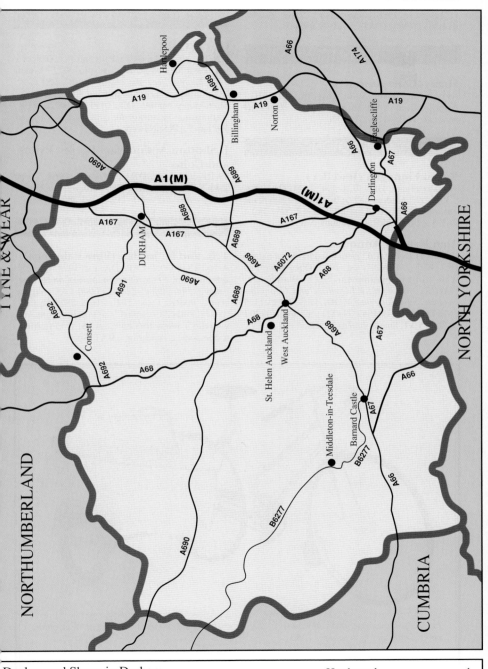

Dealers and Shops in Durham

			Hartlepool	1
			Middleton-in-Teesdale	1
Barnard Castle	4	Darlington	2	Norton	1
Billingham	1	Durham	2	St. Helen Auckland	1
Consett	1	Eaglescliffe	1	West Auckland	1

village green. PARK: Easy. TEL: 01642 782346; mobile - 07860 577637. VAT: Stan/Spec.

CONSETT

Harry Raine Antiques
Kelvinside House, Villa Real Rd. DH8 6BL. Appointment advisable. *STOCK: General antiques.* TEL: 01207 503935.

DARLINGTON

Robin Finnegan (Jeweller)
83 Skinnergate. DL3 7LX. Est. 1974. Open 10-5.30. SIZE: Medium. *STOCK: Jewellery, general antiques, coins and medals, £1-£2,000.* TEL: 01325 489820. SER: Valuations. VAT: Stan.

Alan Ramsey Antiques
Unit 10-11 Dudley Rd, Yarm Road Industrial Estate. DL1 4GG. LAPADA. Est. 1973. Open Mon.-Fri. 9.30-4 or by appointment. SIZE: Warehouse. *STOCK: Victorian, Edwardian and Georgian furniture; interesting pine.* PARK: Easy. TEL: 01325 361679; home - 01642 711311; mobile - 07702 523246. VAT: Stan/Spec. *Trade Only.*

DURHAM

Old & Gold
88 Claypath. DH1 1RG. (Pam and Paul Tracey). Est. 1980. CL: Wed. and Sat. pm. SIZE: Small. *STOCK: Jewellery and china, 19th C, £50-£100.* LOC: 200 yards from Market Place. PARK: Multi-storey nearby. TEL: 0191 386 0728. SER: Valuations; restorations (jewellery); buys at auction. FAIRS: Newark.

J. Shotton Antiquarian Books, Prints and Coins
89 Elvet Bridge. DH1 3AG. Est. 1967. Open 9.30-5. CL: Mon. *STOCK: Antiquarian books, prints, maps and coins.* TEL: 0191 386 4597.

EAGLESCLIFFE, Nr. Stockton-on-Tees

T.B. and R. Jordan (Fine Paintings)
Aslak. TS16 0QN. LAPADA. Est. 1974. Open by appointment. *STOCK: Oil paintings and water-colours, 19th-20th C, £200-£15,000.* LOC: Village centre. PARK: Easy. TEL: 01642 782599; fax - 01642 780473; e-mail - aslak@cwcom.net; website - www.tbrj.cwc.net. SER: Framing; restorations; commissions. VAT: Spec.

Perfect for single mothers nowadays – the circa 1948 Parkes ladies tourer with Watsonian child's sidecar which sold for £350.

From an Auction Report by Christopher Wight on Cycles and Cycling Memorabilia at Phillips, Bayswater, London, 19th August 2000 which featured in our October issue of **Antique Collecting** magazine. For more details and to subscribe see page 147.

(Left to right) A North Country ash and elm armchair, early 19th century, £660. A yew and elm Windsor chair, 19th century, £220. An ash and elm high back Windsor chair, 19th century, £504. A beech and ash comb back Windsor chair, early 19th century, possibly earlier, traces of original paint, £154. A yew and elm Windsor chair, 19th century, £1,155. (Front) A three-legged sycamore milking stool, 19th century, unsold (estimate £100-£150). Andrew Hartley, Ilkley, West Yorkshire.

From a feature on Saleroom Prices which appeared in the December 2000/January 2001 issue of **Antique Collecting** magazine. For more details and to subscribe see page 147.

HARTLEPOOL

Antique Fireplace Centre
134 Lyne St. South, TS24 7LX. (D.J. Crowther). Est. 1983. Open 9-5. SIZE: Large. *STOCK: Victorian and Edwardian fireplaces, Victorian 4-panel pine doors, architectural antiques.* TEL: 01429 279007/222433; mobile - 07774 639754.

MIDDLETON-IN-TEESDALE
Nr. Barnard Castle

Brown's Antiques & Collectables
13 Chapel Row. DL12 0SN. (John and Val Brown). Resident. Est. 1990. Open 10-5, Sun. by appointment. SIZE: Medium. *STOCK: Furniture, metalware and collectables, 18th-20th, £20-£2,000.* LOC: North of A66. PARK: Easy. TEL: 01833 640276; website - www.browns-antiques.co.uk. SER: Buys at auction.

NORTON, Nr. Stockton-on-Tees

Paraphernalia
12 Harland Place, High St. TS20 1AA. (Rena Thomas). Est. 1982. Open 9.30-5. SIZE: Large.

STOCK: Mainly 19th C mahogany furniture, to £1,000. LOC: Next to Red Lion public house. PARK: Easy. TEL: 01642 535940. SER: Restorations (furniture and French polishing). VAT: Stan/Spec.

ST HELEN AUCKLAND

Something Different
34a Maude Terrace. DL14 9BD. Est. 1968. Open 9.30-5.30, Sun. 10-4.30. SIZE: Large. *STOCK: Furniture, clocks, decorative items, 19th-20th C.* TEL: 01388 664366.

WEST AUCKLAND

Eden House Antiques
10 Staindrop Rd. DL14 9JX. (C.W. and M. Metcalfe). Est. 1978. Open daily including Sun. SIZE: Small. *STOCK: Clocks, furniture, 18th-20th C; collectables, bric-a-brac, oak and mahogany reproductions, Continental furniture.* LOC: A68, approx. 7 miles west of A1M. PARK: Easy. TEL: 01388 833013; e-mail - chrismetcalfe01@genie.co.uk; websites - www.edenantiques.co.uk and www.antiques-e.co.uk. SER: Valuations; restorations.

ABRIDGE

Revival
Coach House, Market Place. RM4 1UA. (R. Y. Jefferson). Est. 1988. Open 11-5.30. CL: Fri. SIZE: Large. *STOCK: Furniture, Georgian to Deco, £20-£3,000; china and glass, silver, 1800-1960, £5-£500.* LOC: From London - off M11, junction 5, turn right then left on to A113. From M25, junction 26 follow A121, then B172. PARK: Opposite. TEL: 01992 814000; fax - 01992 814300. SER: Valuations; restorations (ceramics); watch and clock repairs.

BATTLESBRIDGE

Battlesbridge Antique Centre
SS11 7RF. SIZE: Over 80 units within adjacent premises (see below). *STOCK: Wide range from large furniture to jewellery, all periods with specialist dealers for most items.* LOC: A130, midway between Chelmsford and Southend. Junction 29, M25, east on A127 to A130, then north for 3 miles. By rail: Liverpool St.-Southend-on-Sea, change at Wickford for Battlesbridge. PARK: Own. SER: Restorations (furniture); container facilities; nationwide and overseas delivery service.

Cromwell House Antique Centre
TEL: Management : Jim Gallie - 01268 575000; ground floor dealers - 01268 762612; first floor dealers - 01268 734030.

Haybarn and Bridgebarn Antique Centres
(J. P. Pettitt). TEL: 01268 763500/735884.

Muggeridge Farm Buildings
(Jim Gallie). TEL: 01268 575000.

The Old Granary Antique and Craft Centre
(Jim Gallie). TEL: Office - 01268 575000; showrooms - 01268 764197.

BAYTHORNE END

Swan Antiques
The Swan. CO9 4AF. (Mr and Mrs K. Mercado). Est. 1983. Open 9.30-6 including Sun. SIZE: Medium. *STOCK: Furniture, 18th-19th C and some Edwardian, £50-£2,000; porcelain, 19th C, £5-£1,000; small silver and collectables, 19th-20th C, £5-£500.* LOC: A1017 (formerly A604) junction with A1092 to Clare and Long Melford. PARK: Easy. TEL: 01440 785306; home - same. SER: Valuations. FAIRS: Newark.

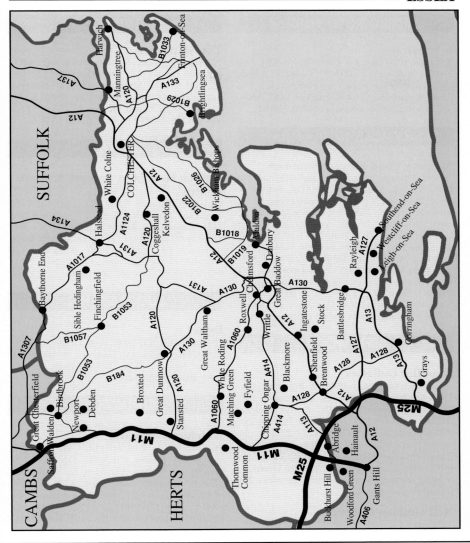

Dealers and Shops in Essex

		Great Waltham	1	Saffron Walden	7
Abridge	1	Colchester	10	Hainault	1	Shenfield	1
Battlesbridge	1	Corringham	1	Halstead	2	Sible Hedingham	4
Baythorne End	1	Danbury	1	Harwich	2	Southend-on-Sea	1
Birdbrook	1	Debden	1	Ingatestone	1	Stansted	3
Blackmore	1	Finchingfield	1	Kelvedon	3	Stock	1
Brentwood	3	Frinton-on-Sea	3	Leigh-on-Sea	8	Thornwood Common	2
Brightlingsea	1	Fyfield	1	Maldon	3	Westcliff-on-Sea	2
Broxted	1	Gants Hill	1	Manningtree	2	White Colne	1
Buckhurst Hill	1	Grays	1	Matching Green	1	White Roding	1
Chelmsford	1	Great Baddow	1	Newport	2	Wickham Bishops	1
Chipping Ongar	1	Great Chesterford	1	Rayleigh	1	Woodford Green	1
Coggeshall	4	Great Dunmow	3	Roxwell	1	Writtle	1

BIRDBROOK, Nr. Halstead

I. Westrope
The Elms. CO9 4AB. Est. 1958. Open 9-5, Sat. 10-1 or by appointment. *STOCK: Furniture, china, dolls house furniture, garden ornaments including birdbaths, fountains, statues, animals.* LOC: A604. TEL: 01440 785795; evenings - 01440 730594.

BLACKMORE, Nr. Ingatestone

Megarry's and Forever Summer
Jericho Cottage, The Duckpond Green. CM4 0RR. (Peter and Judi Wood). EADA. Est. 1986. Open Wed.-Sun. 11-5 or by appointment. SIZE: Medium. *STOCK: Furniture, mainly 18th-19th C, some 20th C, £60-£3,500; ceramics, glass, treen and metalware, 19th-20th C, £5-£200; small silver and plate, jewellery and collectables, 19th-20th C, £5-£100; pine, 19th to early 20th C, £75-£1,000.* LOC: From A12, in Blackmore turn left at war memorial, premises behind Bull garden. PARK: Own. TEL: 01277 821031. SER: Valuations; restorations (furniture including French polishing, clocks and jewellery).

BRENTWOOD

Brandler Galleries
1 Coptfold Rd. CM14 4BM. (J. Brandler). Est. 1973. Open 10-5.30, Sun. by appointment. CL: Mon. SIZE: Medium. *STOCK: British pictures, 20th C, £100-£30,000.* LOC: Near Post Office. PARK: Own at rear. TEL: 01277 222269 (24 hrs); e-mail - art.british@dial-pipex.com; website - www-brandler-galleries.com. SER: Valuations (photographs); restorations (picture cleaning, relining, framing); buys at auction (pictures); 2-3 free catalogues annually.

Neil Graham Gallery
11 Ingrave Rd. CM15 8AP. EADA. FATG. Est. 1977. CL: Mon. SIZE: Large. *STOCK: 19th to early 20th C watercolours, oils and prints, £50-£1,000; Victorian and Edwardian occasional furniture, £100-£1,500; silver, pottery and porcelain, 19th-20th C, £25-£500.* LOC: Near junction of Wilson's Corner, town centre. PARK: Easy and High St. TEL: 01277 215383; fax - same. SER: Valuations; restorations (paintings); buys at auction. VAT: Stan/Spec.

Simpsons - Mirrors & Carvings
449 Ongar Rd. CM15 9JG. (S. Yardy). Open by appointment. *STOCK: Mirrors - antique including pine and new hand-carved; decorative pieces.* TEL: 01277 374541.

BRIGHTLINGSEA

The Shipwreck
22e Marshes Yard, Victoria Place. CO7 0BX. (Michael Kettle). Est. 1994. Open 10.15-5, Sun. 11.15-5. SIZE: Medium. *STOCK: General antiques and collectables, £1-£100.* LOC: Between High St. and Promenade. PARK: Easy. TEL: 01206 307307; mobile - 07980 357456.

BROXTED

Church Hall Farm Antique & Craft Centre
Church Hall Farm. CM6 2BZ. (Jan and Tony Wildman). Est. 1996. Open 10-5 including Sun. SIZE: Large - 60+ dealers. *STOCK: Wide range of general antiques, from smalls to large furniture, £1-£1,500+.* LOC: B1051 next to Whitehall conference centre. PARK: Easy. TEL: 01279 850858; home and fax - same.

BUCKHURST HILL

Depôt
75 Queens Rd. IG9 5BW. (Gail Dean). Open 10-5. *STOCK: Continental furniture, Art Deco and general antiques.* TEL: 020 8504 9945; website - www.depôt-antiques.com.

CHELMSFORD

Hutchison Antiques
163 Main Rd., Broomfield. CM1 7DJ. (G. Hutchison). EADA. Est. 1980. Open 11-5.30, Sun. by appointment. CL: Mon. SIZE: Medium. *STOCK: Furniture, 18th-19th C, £300-£1,000+; china, mainly 19th C, from £50; paintings, from 19th C, from £100.* LOC: On main road, near Broomfield hospital. PARK: Easy. TEL: 01245 441184. SER: Valuations; restorations (as stock).

CHIPPING ONGAR

Future Antiques
204 High St. CM15 9JJ. (S.A., D.A. and G.F. Beecham). EADA. Est. 1970. Open 9.30-5.30, Sun am. by appointment. CL: Mon. and Tues. SIZE: Medium. *STOCK: General antiques, 1760-1930, £50-£3,000.* PARK: Nearby. TEL: 01277 363334; fax - 01277 363506; mobile - 07973 728717; website - www.beechamsfurniture.co.uk. SER: Valuations; specialist chair makers and restorers.

ESSEX

COGGESHALL

Argentum Antiques
1 Church St. CO6 1TU. (Mrs. Dianne M. Carr).
Open 10-5. CL: Wed. SIZE: Medium. *STOCK:
Silver and Old Sheffield plate, 19th-20th C, £100-
£1,000; furniture, mainly oak, 17th-19th C, £200-
£2,000; decorative items, object d'art, garden
ornaments, 19th C.* LOC: Between A120 and
A12, village centre. PARK: Nearby. TEL: 01376
561365. VAT: Spec.

English Rose Antiques
7 Church St. CO6 1TU. (Mark and Iryna Barrett).
Est. 1983. Open 10-5.30, Sun. 10.30-5.30.
*STOCK: English and Continental pine including
dressers, chests, tables and wardrobes, 18th-19th
C, £50-£2,000; fruitwood, ash and elm country
furniture and kitchenalia.* LOC: Town centre.
PARK: Loading or 50 yds. TEL: 01376 562683;
home - same; fax - 01376 563450; mobile -
07770 880790. SER: Valuations; restorations
(stripping, repairing and finishing).

Mark Marchant (Antiques)
3 Market Sq. CO6 1TS. Resident. Est. 1960.
Open 11-5, Sun. 2.30-5.30. SIZE: Small. *STOCK:
Clocks, barometers and music boxes only.* LOC:
A120. PARK: Easy. TEL: 01376 561188. SER:
Valuations; restorations; buys at auction.

Partners in Pine
63/65 West St. CO6 1NS. (W.T. Newton).
Resident. Open 7 days 10-6. *STOCK: Victorian
stripped pine.* TEL: 01376 561972.

COLCHESTER

Barntiques
Lampitts Farm, Turkeycock Lane, Stanway. CO3
5ND. (A. Jones and S. Doubleday). Resident. Est.
1978. Open weekends. SIZE: Medium. *STOCK:
General antiques and pine.* LOC: Turn left at
Eight Ash Green from A604. PARK: Easy. TEL:
01206 210486; home - 01206 212421.

S. Bond and Son
Olivers Orchard, Olivers Lane. CO2 0HH. (R.
Bond). Open by appointment. SIZE: Large.
STOCK: Furniture and pictures. TEL: 01206
331175; mobile - 07710 823800. SER: Restor-
ations; valuations. VAT: Stan/Spec. *Trade only.*

Elizabeth Cannon Antiques
85 Crouch St. CO3 3EZ. Open 10-5. *STOCK:
General antiques including jewellery, silver,
glass, porcelain and furniture.* PARK: Easy.
TEL: 01206 575817.

Castle Bookshop
40 Osborne St. CO2 7DB. (R.J. Green). PBFA
*STOCK: Antiquarian and secondhand books,
maps & prints.* TEL: 01206 577520; fax - same.

Dean Antiques
Mill Farm, Harwich Rd., Gt. Bromley. CO7 7JQ.
Est. 1947. Open 9-5, including Sun. SIZE:
Medium. *STOCK: Country and pine furniture,
18th-19th C.* Not Stocked: Reproductions. LOC:
6 miles from Colchester. 1 1/2 miles off A120
Harwich road, follow signs for Mill Farm
camping. PARK: Own. TEL: 01206 250485;
home - same; fax - 01206 252040. SER:
Valuations.

Grahams of Colchester
19 Short Wyre St. CO1 1LN. Open 9-5.30.
STOCK: Jewellery and silver. TEL: 01206
576808. SER: Valuations; restorations.

Richard Iles Gallery
10a, 10 and 12 Northgate St. CO1 1HA. (R. and
C. Iles). Est. 1970. Open 9.30-4.30. SIZE: Small.
*STOCK: Watercolours, 19th to early 20th C, £75-
£700.* LOC: Off North Hill. PARK: NCP nearby.
TEL: 01206 577877.

E J Markham & Son Ltd
122/3 Priory St. CO1 2PX. (Mrs S. Campbell).
NGA, NPA. Open 8.30-5.30. SIZE: Medium.
*STOCK: Jewellery, 19th-20th C, £25-£8,000;
porcelain, 18th-20th C, £25-£2,000; furniture,
19th-20th C, £100-£1,500.* LOC: Opposite St
Botolph's priory ruins. PARK: NCP Priory St.
TEL: 01206 572646. SER: Valuations;
restorations (porcelain). VAT: Stan.

Revival
23b Drury Rd. CO2 7UY. (Mrs Barbara
Addison). Est. 1999. Open 10.30-4. CL: Mon.
SIZE: Medium. *STOCK: Pine furniture, 19th-
20th C, to £300; sofas and chairs, 19th-20th C, to
£400; bric-a-brac and smalls, old mirrors and
prints, £5-£100.* LOC: From town centre Maldon
Rd. roundabout, follow Maldon Rd., take 6th left
St Helena Rd. Shop at junction with Drury Rd.
PARK: Behind shop. TEL: 01206 506162; home
- 01206 506163. SER: Restorations (wood).

Trinity Antiques Centre
7 Trinity St. CO1 1JN. Est. 1976. Open 9.30-5.
SIZE: 7 dealers + cabinets. *STOCK: General
antiques - small furniture, copper, clocks, brass,
porcelain, silver, jewellery, collectors' items,
Victoriana, maps and prints, linen, pine furniture.*
TEL: 01206 577775.

CORRINGHAM, Nr. Stanford-le-Hope

Bush House
Church Rd. SS17 9AP. (F. Stephens). Est. 1976. Open by appointment. *STOCK: Staffordshire animals, portrait figures, 1770-1901, £50-£5,000.* LOC: Opposite the church. PARK: Own. TEL: 01375 673463; home - same; fax - same; e-mail - francis_j_stephens@hotmail.com. FAIRS: NEC, Birmingham; Earls Court.

DANBURY

Danbury Antiques
Eves Corner (by the Village Green). CM3 4QF. (Mrs Pam Southgate). EADA. Est. 1983. Open 10-5, Wed. 10-1, Sun. 10.30-1. CL: Mon. SIZE: Medium. *STOCK: Jewellery and silver, ceramics, metalware, furniture, 18th to early 20th C, £5-£1,800.* LOC: Off M25, take A12, then A414. PARK: Easy. TEL: 01245 223035. SER: Valuations; restorations (jewellery, upholstery, furniture). FAIRS: Furzehill, Margaretting. VAT: Stan/Spec.

DEBDEN, Nr. Saffron Walden

Debden Antiques
Elder St. CB11 3JY. (Robert Tetlow and Edward Norman). EADA. Est. 1995. Open 10-5.30, Sun. and Bank Holidays 11-4. SIZE: Large. *STOCK: Furniture, 17th-19th C, £100-£10,000; pictures, £50-£5,000, jewellery, silver, glass, porcelain, £5-£500, garden furniture, architectural, £50-£1,000; all 19th C.* LOC: Follow signs to Carver Barracks. PARK: Own. TEL: 01799 543007; fax - 01799 542482. SER: Valuations; restorations. VAT: Stan/Spec.

FINCHINGFIELD

Finchingfield Antiques Centre
The Green. CM7 4JX. (Peter Curry). Est. 1992. Open 10-5.30 including Sun. SIZE: Large - 40 dealers. *STOCK: Wide range of general antiques and collectables.* LOC: From M11, A120 to Gt. Dunmow, then B1057. PARK: Easy. TEL: 01371 810258; fax - same.

FRINTON-ON-SEA

Dickens Curios
151 Connaught Ave. CO13 9AH. (Miss M. Wilsher). Est. 1970. Open 9.45-1 and 2-5.30, Sat. 9.45-1 and 2-5. CL: Wed. pm. SIZE: Small. *STOCK: Postcards and ephemera, Victorian and later items, £5-£200.* Not Stocked: Firearms, watches and clocks. LOC: From Frinton Station quarter of mile down Connaught Ave. PARK: Easy. TEL: 01255 674134.

Frinton Antiques
CO13 9BT. (Mrs. G.M. Pethick). Est. 1952. Open by appointment. *STOCK: Small decorative furniture; fine porcelain, silver, glass and pottery.* TEL: 01255 671894. VAT: Stan/Spec.

Phoenix Trading
130 Connaught Ave. CO13 9AD. (Tom Sheldon). Est. 1996. Open 10-4, Mon. by appointment. SIZE: Large. *STOCK: Pine and painted furniture, 19th C, £500-£1,000.* LOC: Main shopping street. PARK: Easy. TEL: 01255 851094; fax - same. SER: Restorations. FAIRS: Ardingly; Kempton. VAT: Stan/Spec.

FYFIELD

Hay Green Antiques
Herons, Herons Lane. CM5 0RQ. (T. Harding). Open by appointment. *STOCK: Pine, some mahogany and Victorian furniture.* TEL: 01277 899205.

GANTS HILL

Antique Clock Repair Shoppe
26 Woodford Ave. IG2 6XG. (K. Ashton). Est. 1971. Open 10-5. *STOCK: Clocks, pictures, bric-a-brac.* TEL: 020 8550 9540.

GRAYS

Atticus Books
8 London Rd. RM17 5XY. Open Thurs.-Sat. 9-4. *STOCK: Books.* LOC: Town centre, 5 mins from station, 10 mins from M25. TEL: 01375 371200.

GREAT BADDOW

Baddow Antique Centre
The Bringey, Church St. CM2 7JW. Est. 1969. Open 10-5, Sun. 11-5. SIZE: 22 dealers. *STOCK: 18th-20th C furniture, porcelain, silver, paintings, Victorian brass bedsteads, shipping goods.* PARK: Easy. TEL: 01245 476159. SER: Restorations; upholstery.

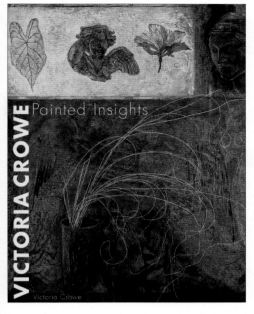

"These are beautiful thoughtful paintings by an artist at the height of her powers. They generate respect for the alternating contradictions of the world, the joy and sadness, the light and the dark"

Derek Hyatt

Victoria Crowe is considered to be among the most critical and original figurative painters currently working in Scotland. Over the last 30 years she has established herself as a painter of work that is instantly recognisable. This complete monograph is the first to focus on this highly acclaimed artist, presenting approximately 120 lavish colour plates. The works featured come from National Collections in both the UK and overseas.

The mysterious, ornate and enigmatic images presented here compliment a personal journey, told from the artist's own perspective. Crowe's highly individual words are punctuated by the voices of critics and art historians, which help to place her work in context. The full range of her exceptional work is covered, including interiors, portraits, self-portraits, still-lifes and landscapes, and work that refuses to be defined by such precise categorisation.

"These paintings emit a rare beauty, an inner glow redolent of life's wonder vitality and abundance yet shot through with a poignant undertow."

Clare Henry

Victoria Crowe studied at the Royal College of Art, London before being invited to teach at Edinburgh College of Art in 1968. An established artist living and working in the Scottish Borders, she has had successful solo exhibitions throughout Britain and worked and exhibited overseas. She has undertaken many prestigious commissions and her work is held in important public and private collections including National Galleries.

"Some indication of the high status in which her formidable artistic proficiency is held can be gleaned from the private and public collections in which she is represented. (H M the Queen and HRH the Duke of Edinburgh, Duke of Devonshire, St John's College, Oxford, National Portrait Galleries of Scotland, England, Denmark, The National Trust for Scotland, etc)"

Anthony Lester

ISBN 1 85149 395 6, 144pp., 120col., 4 b.&w. 11 x 9in./280 x 226mm. **£25.00/$45.00**

GREAT CHESTERFORD, Nr. Saffron Walden

C. and J. Mortimer and Son
School St. CB10 1NN. Est. 1962. Open Thurs.
and Sat. 2.30-5 or by appointment. SIZE:
Medium. *STOCK: Oak furniture, 16th-18th C,
from £500.* LOC: From London on B1383.
PARK: Easy. TEL: 01799 530261.

GREAT DUNMOW

Julia Bennet (Antiques)
Flemings Hill Farm, Gt. Easton. CM6 2ER.
LAPADA. Open by appointment. *STOCK: 18th
C mahogany, 17th-19th C oak and country
furniture, decorative and garden pieces.* TEL:
01279 850279.

Simon Hilton
Flemings Hill Farm, Gt. Easton. CM6 2ER.
Resident. Est. 1937. Open by appointment.
*STOCK: Oil paintings, watercolours and
drawings, £100-£10,000; fine prints and
sculpture, £50-£5,000; all 17th-20th C.* TEL:
01279 850107/850279. SER: Valuations;
restorations (oil paintings, watercolours and
drawings); buys at auction. VAT: Spec.

Memories
Starr Corner, 11A Market Place. CM6 1AX.
(Peter and Denise Berriman). EADA. Est. 2000.
Open 9.30-5. CL: Wed. SIZE: Small. *STOCK:
Furniture especially upholstered, Victorian and
Edwardian, £500-£1,000; clocks especially
longcase, Georgian and Victorian, £2,000-
£4,000; books, 19th-20th C, £5-£25.* LOC: Town
centre. PARK: Free nearby. TEL: 01371 872331;
home - 01279 850915. SER: Buys at auction.

GREAT WALTHAM, Nr. Chelmsford

The Stores
CM3 1DE. (E. Saunders). Est. 1974. Open Wed.-
Sat. 10-5, Sun. 11-4. SIZE: Large. *STOCK:
Period pine and country furniture.* LOC: Village
centre. PARK: At rear. TEL: 01245 360277;
home - 01245 360260.

HAINAULT, Nr. Ilford

Gallerie Antiques
62-70 Fowler Rd. IG6 3XE. (G. Levy, N. Garner
and M. Johnson). EADA. Est. 1998. Open 10-
5.30, Sun. 10-4. SIZE: 80 dealers. *STOCK: Wide
range of general antiques including 18th-20th C
furniture, £500-£1,000; china, porcelain, glass,
linen and lace, books, collectables.* LOC: A1112

Eastern Ave. At Moby Dick public house, turn
towards Hainault Forest Country Park. PARK:
Easy. TEL: 020 8501 2229; fax - 020 8501 2209.
SER: Valuations; restorations (furniture,
paintings, ceramics, clocks, re-caning); buys at
auction. VAT: Stan/Spec.

HALSTEAD

Antique Bed Shop
Napier House, Head St. CO9 2BT. (Veronica
McGregor). Est. 1977. Open Thurs.-Sat., other
times by appointment. SIZE: Large. *STOCK:
Antique wooden bedsteads - 19th C mahogany,
rosewood, chestnut, oak, bergere and painted,
£1,295-£3,500.* Not Stocked: Brass, iron or pine
beds. LOC: On A131 to Sudbury. PARK: Own.
TEL: 01787 477346; fax - 01787 478757.

Townsford Mill Antiques Centre
The Causeway. CO9 1ET. (M.T. Stuckey). Open
10-5, Sun. and Bank Holidays 11-5. SIZE: 70
dealers. *STOCK: General antiques and
collectables.* LOC: On A131 Braintree/Sudbury
road. TEL: 01787 474451.

HARWICH

Harwich Antiques Centre
19 Kings Quay St. CO12 3ER. (David Edwards
and John Tanner). Open 10-5, Sun. 1-5. CL:
Mon. SIZE: Medium. *STOCK: Furniture,
porcelain, china, glass, silverware, jewellery,
19th C, £10-£2,000; collectables, 19th-20th C.*
PARK: Nearby. TEL: 01255 554719. VAT: Stan.

Mayflower Antiques
105 High St., Dovercourt. CO12 3AP. (J.W.
Odgers). Est. 1970. Open by appointment. SIZE:
Medium. *STOCK: Clocks, mechanical music,
scientific and marine instruments, collectors'
items.* LOC: Main road. PARK: Easy. TEL:
01255 504079; mobile - 07860 843569; e-mails -
mayflower@anglianet.co.uk and mayflower@
ukshells.co.uk. VAT: Stan/Spec.

INGATESTONE

Kendons
122a High St. CM4 0BA. Open 9.30-5. CL: Wed.
*STOCK: Jewellery, silver, china, small furniture,
clocks.* TEL: 01277 353625.

KELVEDON, Nr. Colchester

Colton Antiques
Station Rd. CO5 9NP. (Gary Colton). Est. 1993.
Open 8-5, Sun. by appointment. SIZE: Medium.

STOCK: Furniture, 17th to early 20th C, £300-£15,000; decorative items. PARK: Own. TEL: 01376 571504; mobile - 07973 797098. SER: Restorations (furniture). VAT: Stan/Spec.

Kelvedon Antiques
2 High St. CO5 9AG. (Sarah Mabey). Open 10-5. SIZE: Medium. STOCK: Furniture, paintings and decorative items, 18th-19th C. PARK: Easy - own. TEL: 01376 573065; home - same.

G.T. Ratcliff Ltd
Brick House Farm, Braxted Rd. C05 9BS. (F.D. Campbell). Est. 1935. Open by appointment. SIZE: Medium. STOCK: Furniture, mainly 18th-19th C. LOC: A12. PARK: Easy. TEL: 01376 570234; fax - 01376 571764. VAT: Stan. Trade Only, mainly export.

LEIGH-ON-SEA

K.S. Buchan
135 The Broadway. SS9 1PJ. Open 10-5. STOCK: Furniture and general antiques. TEL: 01702 479440.

Collectors' Paradise
993 London Rd. SS9 3LB. (H.W. and P.E. Smith). Est. 1967. Open 10-5.30. CL: Fri. SIZE: Small. STOCK: Clocks, 1830-1930, from £85; bric-a-brac; postcards, 1900-1930s; cigarette cards, 1889-1939. LOC: On A13. PARK: Easy. TEL: 01702 473077.

Deja Vu Antiques
876 London Rd. SS9 3NQ. (Stuart D. Lewis). Est. 1990. Open 9.30-5.30, Sun. 10-2. SIZE: Medium. STOCK: French and English furniture, late 18th to 19th C; antique bedsteads. PARK: Easy. TEL: 01702 470829; e-mail - info@deja-vu-antiques.co.uk; website - www.deja-vu-antiques. co.uk. SER: Valuations; restorations. FAIRS: Newark and Ardingly.

Folly Lane Antiques and Collectables
Clements Arcade, The Broadway. SS9 1PG. (Maurice and Anita James). Est. 1994. Open 9-2.30, Sat. 9-5.30. SIZE: Small. STOCK: Smalls and small furniture, 19th-20th C, £25-1,500; limited edition Teddy bears. LOC: Opposite St. Clements church. TEL: Mobile - 07947 714532.

Pall Mall Antiques
104c/d Elm Rd. SS9 1SQ. (R. and J. Webb). EADA. Open 10-5. CL: Wed. SIZE: Large. STOCK: Porcelain, glass, metalware and collectables. PARK: Own. TEL: 01702 477235; website - www.pallmallantiques.co.uk.

John Stacey and Sons
86-90 Pall Mall. SS9 1RG. Est. 1946. Open 9-5.30. CL: Sat. pm. STOCK: General antiques. TEL: 01702 477051. SER: Valuations; exporters; auctioneers. VAT: Stan.

J. Streamer Antiques
86 Broadway and 212 Leigh Rd. SS9 1AE. Est. 1965. Open 9.30-5.30. CL: Wed. STOCK: Jewellery, silver, bric-a-brac, small furniture. TEL: 01702 472895.

Tilly's Antiques
1801 London Rd. SS9 2ST. (S.T. and R.J. Austen). Est. 1972. Open 10-5. CL: Wed. SIZE: Medium. STOCK: Furniture, 19th C, £100-£500+; Victorian and Edwardian dolls, £100-£500; general antiques, 19th-20th C, £5-£200. LOC: A13. PARK: Easy. TEL: 01702 557170. SER: Valuations; restorations (furniture and dolls).

MALDON

The Antique Rooms
63D High St. CM9 7EB. (Mrs E. Hedley). Est. 1966. Open 10-4. CL: Wed. SIZE: Medium. STOCK: Furniture, pottery, porcelain, glass and silver, costume, linen and lace, jewellery, lace-making equipment, collectors' items. LOC: Just off High St. PARK: Nearby. TEL: 01621 856985.

Clive Beardall Antiques
104B High St. CM9 5ET. BAFRA, EADA. Est. 1982. Open 8-5.30, Sat 8-4. SIZE: Medium. STOCK: Furniture, 18th-19th C, £100-£5,000. LOC: Off High St. up alleyway between Just Fabrics and Peter Foulkes. PARK: Easy. TEL: 01621 857890. SER: Restorations (furniture). VAT: Stan/Spec.

Maldon Antiques and Collectors Market
All Saints Church Hall, London Rd. CM9. Est. 1975. Open first Sat. every month 9-4. LOC: Top of High St., opposite Police Station. PARK: Own. TEL: 01702 230746.

MANNINGTREE

Forty Nine
High St. CO11 1AH. (A. Patterson). Open 10-1 and 2-5. STOCK: General and country antiques. PARK: Easy. TEL: 01206 396170.

F. Freestone
Kiln Tops, 29 Colchester Rd. CO11. Open 9-6, appointment advisable. STOCK: General antiques, furniture, clocks. TEL: 01206 392998.

WEST ESSEX ANTIQUES
Stonehall

Dealer in English and Continental Furniture 18ᵗʰ – 20ᵗʰ C.

e-mail: chris@essexantiques.co.uk   www.essexantiques.co.uk

Tel/Fax: 01279 730609   **Mobile: 07702 492111**

Down Hall Road   15 mins. from M11

Nr. Hatfield Heath   15 mins. Stansted Airport

HERTS. CM17 0RA   45 mins. London

MATCHING GREEN, Nr. Harlow

West Essex Antiques (Stone Hall)
Downhall Rd. CM17 0RA. Est. 1982. Open 9-5, Sat and Sun. by appointment. SIZE: Warehouse. *STOCK: English and Continental furniture, 18th-20th C, £100-£3,000.* LOC: Turning off A1060 at Hatfield Heath. PARK: Own. TEL: 01279 730609; e-mail - chris@essexantiques.co.uk; website - www.essexantiques.co.uk. VAT: Stan.

NEWPORT, Nr. Saffron Walden

Newport Gallery
High St. CB11 3QZ. (W. Kemp and E.C. Hitchcock). Open 9.30-5. CL: Mon. *STOCK: Watercolours, prints and oils.* LOC: On B1383, two miles from Saffron Walden. PARK: At rear. TEL: 01799 540623.

Omega
High St. CB11 3PF. (Tony Phillips and Sybil Hooper). Est. 1982. Open 10-6, Sat. 10-5.30. CL: Thurs. SIZE: Small. *STOCK: Furniture and lighting, 1880-1960, £20-£1,000; jewellery, objects, 1900-1960, £20-£300.* LOC: B1383. PARK: Easy. TEL: 01799 540720; home - same. SER: Valuations; restorations (furniture including French polishing, repairs and re-veneering). FAIRS: Art Deco - Battersea, Brighton, Tunbridge Wells.

RAYLEIGH

F.G. Bruschweiler (Antiques) Ltd
41-67 Lower Lambricks. SS6 8DA. LAPADA. Est. 1963. Open 9-5, Sat. by appointment. SIZE: Warehouses. *STOCK: Furniture, 18th-19th C.* LOC: A127 to Weir roundabout through Rayleigh High St. and Hockley Rd., first left past cemetery, then second left, warehouse round corner on left. PARK: Easy. TEL: 01268 773761/773932; home - 0162 182 8152; fax - 01268 773318; e-mail - fred@fgbruschweiler.demon.co.uk; website - www.fgbruschweilerantiques.co.uk. VAT: Stan.

ROXWELL, Nr. Chelmsford

Freemans Antiques
CM1 4NJ. By appointment only. *STOCK: 17th-18th C oak especially coffers.* TEL: 01245 231286.

SAFFRON WALDEN

Bush Antiques
26-28 Church St. CB10 1JQ. (Mrs J.M. Hosford). EADA. Est. 1962. Open 10.30-4.30. CL: Thurs. SIZE: Medium. *STOCK: English ceramics including blue and white transfer printed pottery, copper lustre and pink lustre, £25-£250; mahogany and country furnitutre, to £1,000; copper and brass, to £250; all 1800-1860.* LOC: 300 yards north of Market Sq., on crossroads with Museum St. PARK: Nearby. TEL: 01799 523277. FAIRS: Bury St. Edmunds (Spring and Autumn).

Ickleton Antiques
4A Gold St. CB10 1EJ. (B. Arbery). Est. 1983. Open 10-4, Mon. 10-3, Sat. 10-5. SIZE: Small. *STOCK: Militaria including badges, medals and weapons; advertising and packaging, postcards.* LOC: Just off centre of town. PARK: Nearby. TEL: 01799 513114; home - 01799 527474. SER: Valuations.

The Interior Design Shop
4 & 5 Rose & Crown Walk. CB10 1JH. (Peter Mileham). Est. 1981. Open 9-5. *STOCK: Victorian mahogany, £200-£3,000; upholstered items, Georgian to 1930's, £300-£2,000; oak and early mahogany, 1790-1900, £300-£2,000.* TEL: 01799 516456; fax - 01799 516699. SER: Valuations; restorations; interior design. VAT: Stan/Spec.

Lankester Antiques and Books
Old Sun Inn, Church St., and Market Hill. CB10 1JW. (P. Lankester). Est. 1965. Open 9.30-5.30. SIZE: Large. *STOCK: Furniture, porcelain, pottery, metalwork, general antiques, books, prints and maps.* TEL: 01799 522685. VAT: Stan

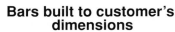

LITTLEBURY ANTIQUES — LITTLEBURY RESTORATIONS
58/60 FAIRYCROFT ROAD SAFFRON WALDEN ESSEX CB10 1LZ
TELEPHONE & FAX: SAFFRON WALDEN (01799) 527961
Evenings and Weekends: (01279) 771530

Barometers, marine antiques, fine ship models, walking sticks, chess sets and other high quality interesting pieces

Expert restoration by craftsmen; barometers, clocks, all forms of furniture repair, replacement of marquetry, all inlay work carefully matched

Business hours 9am-5pm Monday to Friday, Weekend by appointment only
Railway station: Audley End (1½ miles away) London to Cambridge line

Littlebury Antiques - Littlebury Restorations Ltd
58/60 Fairycroft Rd. CB10 1LZ. (N.H. D'Oyly). Est. 1962. Open 9-5. CL: Sat. and Sun. except by appointment. SIZE: Medium. *STOCK: Barometers, marine antiques, chess sets, walking sticks and curios.* PARK: Easy. TEL: 01799 527961; fax - same; home - 01279 771530. SER: Valuations; restorations; buys at auction. VAT: Stan/Spec.

Maureen Morris   BADA
CB11 4TA. LAPADA. Open by appointment. *STOCK: Samplers, needleworks, textiles.* TEL: 01799 521338; fax - 01799 522802; e-mail - mm@antiquesamplers.uk.com.

Saffron Walden Antiques Centre
1 Market Row. CB10 1HA. Est. 1996. Open 10-5.30, Sat. 9-5.30, Sun. 11-5. SIZE: Large - 50+ dealers. *STOCK: Wide range of general antiques.* LOC: Town centre. PARK: Easy. TEL: 01799 524534; fax - 01799 524703.

SHENFIELD

The Chart House
33 Spurgate, Hutton Mount. CM13 2JS. (C.C. Crouchman). Est. 1974. Open by appointment only. SIZE: Small. *STOCK: Nautical items.* PARK: Easy. TEL: 01277 225012; home - same. SER: Hire of nautical items and equipment; buys at auction.

SIBLE HEDINGHAM, Nr. Halstead

Churchgate Antiques
Prayors Farm, Prayors Hill. CO9 3LE. (B. Wilkinson). Est. 1979. Open 10-5, Sun. by appointment. CL: Mon. SIZE: Large. *STOCK: English and Irish period pine, £75-£1,800; architectural antiques - fireplaces, doors, baths, sinks, tiles, garden statuary.* PARK: Easy. TEL: 01787 462269; home - 01787 461311. SER: Valuations. VAT: Stan.

Hedingham Antiques & Interiors
100 Swan St. CO9 3HP. (P. Patterson). EADA. Open 10-12.30 and 1.30-5 or by appointment. SIZE: Small. *STOCK: Silver, plate, china and glass, Victorian to Art Deco; furniture, 1790 to mid 20th C; bric-a-brac and giftwares.* LOC: On A1017, village centre. PARK: Forecourt. TEL: 01787 460360; home - same. SER: Restorations (furniture); silver repairs and re-plating; kitchen studio.

Lennard Antiques
c/o W.A. Pinn & Sons, 124 Swan St. CO9 3HP. LAPADA. Est. 1978. *STOCK: Oak and country furniture, 17th to early 19th C; English Delftware.* LOC: On A1017 opposite Shell garage in middle of village. TEL: 01787 461127. FAIRS: Chelsea; West London; Olympia (June); Harrogate; Chester.

W.A. Pinn and Sons   BADA
124 Swan St. CO9 3HP. (K.H. and W.J. Pinn). LAPADA. Est. 1943. CL: Sun. except by appointment. SIZE: Medium. *STOCK: Furniture, 17th to early 19th C, £100-£5,000; Chinese export porcelain, £25-£1,000; interesting items, prior to 1830, £10-£1,500.* LOC: On A1017 opposite Shell Garage. PARK: On premises. TEL: 01787 461127. FAIRS: Chelsea (Spring and Autumn); Olympia (June); Harrogate. VAT: Stan/Spec.

SOUTHEND-ON-SEA

Lonsdale Antiques
86 Lonsdale Rd, Southchurch. SS2 4LR. (H.M. Clark). Open 9-5.30. CL: Wed. *STOCK: Jewellery, pictures, porcelain, general small antiques.* TEL: 01702 462643.

STANSTED

Harris Antiques (Stansted)
40 Lower St. CM24 8LR. (F.A.D. and B.D.A. Harris BAFRA, and E.V. Bradshaw). Resident. EADA. Est. 1956. Open 9-5, Sun. by appointment only. SIZE: Medium. *STOCK: Quality*

period furniture, ceramics and clocks, 16th-19th C, £200-£20,000+. LOC: Near M11 and Stansted Airport. PARK: Easy. TEL: 01279 812233; home - same. SER: Valuations; restorations (furniture and ceramics). VAT: Spec.

Linden House Antiques
3 Silver St. CM24 8HA. (A.W. and K.M. Sargeant). Est. 1961. Open 9-5.30. CL: Sun. except by appointment. SIZE: Large. STOCK: English furniture, 18th-19th C, £100-£10,000; small decorative items, including library and dining room furniture. LOC: A11. TEL: 01279 812372. VAT: Spec.

Valmar Antiques
Croft House Cottage, High Lane. CM24 8LQ. (John and Marina Orpin). LAPADA. Resident. Est. 1960. Open by appointment. SIZE: Large. STOCK: Furniture and decorative items, £50-£10,000. TEL: 01279 813201; fax - 01279 816962; mobile - 07831 093701; e-mail - valmar-antiques@cwcom.net. FAIRS: Major British.

Sabine Antiques
38 High St. CM4 9BW. (C.E. Sabine). EADA. Est. 1974. Open 10-5 or by appointment. CL: Mon. STOCK: Furniture, from £50; china and glass, from £5. LOC: Village centre on B1007. PARK: Easy. TEL: 01277 840553. SER: Valuations; restorations (furniture); silver plating; framing.

Old Barn Antiques
Hayleys Manor, Uplands Rd. CM16 6PQ. Est. 1971. Open 9-5.30, Sat. and Sun. by appointment. STOCK: French, English and Continental furniture and smalls, 17th-19th C, £20-£5,000. TEL: 01992 579007. VAT: Stan.

Simpsons Antiques & Fine Interiors
Unit 1 Esgors Farm. CM16 6LY. (E. Simpson). Est. 1988. Open 8-1 and 1.30-6.30, Fri. 8-1 and 1.30-3.30, Sat. 9-5.30, Sun. 11-5. SIZE: Large. STOCK: Furniture, 19th C, £20-£4,600. LOC: 1 mile junction 7, M11. PARK: Easy. TEL: 01992 577111; fax - 01992 577112. SER: Valuations; restorations; buys at auction; export.

It's About Time
863 London Rd. SS0 9SZ. (R. and V. Alps and P. Williams). EADA. Est. 1980. Open 9-5.30. SIZE: Large. STOCK: Clocks, 18th-19th C, £200-£5,000; barometers, Victorian and Edwardian

furniture. LOC: A13. PARK: Easy. TEL: 01702 472574; fax - same; home - 01702 205204; website - www.clocking-in.demon.co.uk.

Ridgeway Antiques
66 The Ridgeway. SS0 8NU. (Trevor Cornforth and Charles Jackson). EADA. Est. 1987. Open 10.30-5. SIZE: Small. STOCK: General antiques, £5-£1,000. LOC: A13 London road, right at Chalkwell Ave., right to The Ridgway. PARK: Easy. TEL: 01702 710383. SER: Valuations. FAIRS: Ridgeway and Hallmark.

Fox and Pheasant Antique Pine
CO6 2PS. (J. and J. Kearin). Est. 1978. Open 8-6. SIZE: Small. STOCK: Stripped pine. LOC: A604. PARK: Easy. TEL: 01787 223297. SER: Pine stripping; restorations; kitchens; joinery.

White Roding Antiques
'Ivydene', Chelmsford Rd. CM6 1RG. (F. and J. Neill). Est. 1971. Open by appointment. SIZE: Medium. STOCK: Furniture and shipping goods, 18th-19th C, £10-£1,500. LOC: A1060 between Bishops Stortford and Chelmsford. PARK: Easy. TEL: 01279 876376; home - same. VAT: Stan/Spec.

Barling Fine Porcelain Ltd
(S. Parish). Open by appointment only. STOCK: English porcelain including Royal Worcester, £100-£4,000; watercolours, £300-£2,500. TEL: 01621 890058; e-mail - stuart@barling.uk.com; website - www.barling.uk.com. FAIRS: Wakefield Ceramic; NEC.

Galerie Lev
1 The Broadway. IG8 0HL. Open 10-5. STOCK: Oils, watercolours, collectors' items, silver plate, porcelain. LOC: Near Woodford underground station. TEL: 020 8505 2226. SER: Framing (Trade only).

Whichcraft Jewellery
54-56 The Green. CM1 3DU. (A. Turner). EADA. Est. 1978. Open 9.30-5.30. CL: Mon. SIZE: Small. STOCK: Jewellery, silver and watches, 19th C, £30-£5,000. PARK: Easy. TEL: 01245 420183. SER: Valuations; restorations (jewellery). VAT: Stan/Spec.

Denzil Verey Antiques

Barnsley House,
Barnsley, near Cirencester,
Gloucestershire. GL7 5EE
Tel: 01285 740402

*18th and 19th century country furniture, pine,
treen, and unusual items*

ANDOVERSFORD, Nr. Cheltenham

Julian Tatham-Losh
Brereton House, Stow Rd. GL54 4JN. (Julian and
Patience Tatham-Losh). Resident. Est. 1980. Open
Mon.-Fri. 8-6, at any other time by appointment.
SIZE: Large. *STOCK: 19th C decorative smalls,
bamboo and interesting furniture, majolica, flow
blue, Staffordshire figures and animals, boxes and
caddies, candlesticks, decorative glass, primitive
and folk art items, kitchenalia, mirrors, desk-
related items, brass and copper, luggage, £2-
£10,000.* Not Stocked: Reproductions and
jewellery. LOC: From A40 Oxford to Cheltenham
road take A436 to Stow-on-the-Wold, premises
first house on left. PARK: Own large. TEL: 01242
820646; fax - 01242 820563; mobile - 07850
574924; e-mail - julian@tatham-losh.freeserve.
co.uk. SER: Antique and decorative items supplied
to order, especially repeat bulk shipping items;
courier (air-conditioned transport); free storage.
FAIRS: NEC; Earls Court; Battersea Decorative.
VAT: Stan/Spec. *Trade & Export Only.*

BARNSLEY, Nr. Cirencester

Denzil Verey
Barnsley House. GL7 5EE. CADA. Resident. Est.
1980. Open 9.30-5.30, Sat. 10-5.30, other times

by appointment. SIZE: Large. *STOCK: Country
furniture, including pine, 18th-19th C; decorative
and unusual items, treen, copper, brass, domestic
and rural objects, kitchenalia.* LOC: 4 miles from
Cirencester on B4425 to Burford, 1st large house
in village, set back off road on the right. PARK:
Easy. TEL: 01285 740402; fax - 01285 740628.
VAT: Stan/Spec.

BERKELEY

Berkeley Antiques Market
GL13 9BP. Open 9.30-1 and 2-5. CL: Mon.
SIZE: Large - 10 dealers. *STOCK: General
antiques, oak, mahogany, pine, linen and smalls,
£1-£1,000.* LOC: Village centre, 1 mile from
A38. PARK: Easy. TEL: 01453 511032.

Peter and Penny Proudfoot
16-18 High St. GL13 9BJ. FATG. Est. 1956.
Open 9-6, Sun. by appointment. SIZE: Small.
*STOCK: Furniture, 1600-1900, £100-£3,000;
silver, 1700 to date, £5-£1,000; pictures, 1800 to
date, £20-£3,000.* LOC: Village centre. PARK:
Easy. TEL: 01453 811513; home - same; fax -
01453 511616; e-mail - BerkPix@aol.com. SER:
Valuations; restorations (furniture and oil
paintings). VAT: Stan/Spec.

BIBURY, Nr. Cirencester

Mill Antiques of Bibury
Arlington Mill. GL7 5NL. Open 7 days from 9
am. *STOCK: Antiques, collectables, oils and
prints.* PARK: Easy. TEL: 01285 740199; mobile
- 07788 681998; website - www.bibury.uk.com.

BISHOPS CLEEVE, Nr. Cheltenham

Cleeve Picture Framing
Church Rd. GL52 8RL. (J. Gardner). Open 9-1
and 2-5.30, Sat. 9-1. *STOCK: Prints and pictures.*
TEL: 01242 672785. SER: Framing, cleaning,
restoring (oils, watercolours and prints).

The Priory Gallery
The Priory, Station Rd. GL52 4HH. (R.M. and E.
James). Est. 1977. SIZE: Large. *STOCK: British
and European watercolours and oils, late 19th-
20th C, £500-£50,000.* LOC: A435. PARK: Easy.
TEL: 01242 673226. SER: Buys at auction (as
stock). VAT: Stan/Spec.

BLAKENEY

Lion, Witch and Lampshade
Birmingham House, High St. GL15 4EB. (Mr.
and Mrs. N. Dixon). Open by appointment.

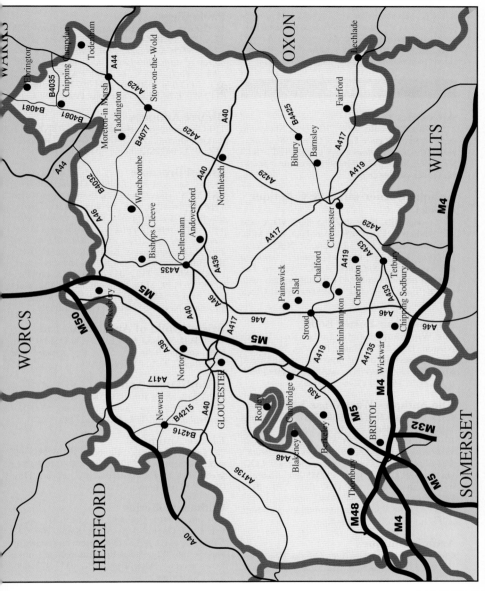

Dealers and Shops in Gloucestershire

Andoversford	1	Chalford	1	Gloucester	4	Stow-on-the-Wold	39
Barnsley	1	Cheltenham	27	Lechlade	5	Stroud	1
Berkeley	2	Cherington	1	Minchinhampton	1	Taddington	1
Bibury	1	Chipping Campden	9	Moreton-in-Marsh	16	Tetbury	25
Bishops Cleeve	2	Chipping Sodbury	1	Newent	1	Tewkesbury	4
Blakeney	1	Cirencester	12	Northleach	3	Thornbury	1
Bristol	28	Ebrington	1	Norton	1	Todenham	1
Cambridge	1	Fairford	4	Painswick	2	Wickwar	1
				Rodley	1	Winchcombe	6
				Slad	1		

STOCK: Unusual decorative objects, 18th to early 20th C, £5-£150; lamps, wall brackets, chandeliers and candlesticks, £50-£1,000; rocking horses. TEL: 01594 516422; fax - same. SER: Restorations (porcelain and glass); lamp rewiring.

BRISTOL

Alexander Gallery
122 Whiteladies Rd. BS8 2RP. (P.J. Slade and H.S. Evans). Open 9-5.30. *STOCK: 19th-20th C paintings, watercolours and prints.* TEL: 0117 9734692; fax - 0117 9466991; website - www.alexander-gallery.co.uk.

Antique Corner with A & C Antique Clocks
86 Bryants Hill, Hanham. BS5 8QT. (D.A. and J.P. Andrews). Est. 1985. Open 10-5. CL: Mon. and Wed. SIZE: Large - 2 floors. *STOCK: Clocks including longcase, wall and mantel; furniture and ceramics, £5-£5,000.* LOC: Next to The Trooper public house, A431 Bristol to Bath road. PARK: Easy. TEL: 0117 9476141. SER: Clock and watch repairs.

Antique Four-Poster Beds
The Workshop, Kennel Lodge Rd., Bower Ashton. BS3 2JT. (Simon Poyntz). Est. 1973. Open Mon.-Fri., out of hours by appointment. *STOCK: Four-poster beds and bedposts and half-tester beds.* TEL: 0117 9632563; fax - same.

The Antiques Warehouse Ltd
430 Gloucester Rd., Horfield. BS7 8TX. (Chris Winsor). Resident. Est. 1994. Open 10-6, Sun. 12-4. SIZE: Large. *STOCK: Furniture, 18th to early 20th C, £200-£2,500; mirrors, from 19th C, £60-£1,000; rugs, from 19th C, £150-£600.* LOC: On the A38 4 miles from M4/M5 interchange, 2 miles from city centre. PARK: Easy. TEL: 0117 942 4500; fax - 0117 942 4140; mobile - 07785 532173. SER: Valuations; restorations (furniture and upholstery). VAT: Stan/Spec.

Arcadia Antiques
Clifton Arcade, Boyces Ave., Clifton. BS8 4AA. Est. 1993. Open 10-5.30. CL: Mon. SIZE: Small. *STOCK: General antiques including sofas and chairs, paintings, jewellery and smalls, £5-£2,500.* LOC: Near The Mall. TEL: 01179 144479.

Aristocratz
115 Coldharbour Rd., Redland. BS6 7SD. (Z. Bouyamourn). Open 9.30-5.30. *STOCK: General antiques, French, Islamic and decorative items.* TEL: 0117 904 0091; mobile - 07770 393020; e-mail - aristocratz@yahoo.com.

Paula Biggs
12 Clifton Arcade, Boyces Ave., Clifton. BS8 4AA. Est. 1978. Open 10-5.30. CL: Mon. SIZE: Small. *STOCK: Silver, 17th-19th C, to £1,000; objects of vertu, 18th-19th C, to £400; collectables, 19th to early 20th C, to £500.* PARK: Limited. TEL: 0117 974 3630; fax - 0117 973 1436; home - 0117 973 9528. SER: Valuations. FAIRS: NEC.

Bizarre Antiques
210 Gloucester Rd., Bishopston. BS7 8NZ. (E.J. Parkin). Open 8.15-5. *STOCK: General antiques.* TEL: 0117 9427888; home - 0117 9503498.

Bristol Brocante
123 St. Georges Rd., College Green, Hotwells. BS1 5UW. (David and Elizabeth Durant). Est. 1966. Open 12-6, Sun. by appointment. SIZE: Small. *STOCK: 19th-20th C French decorative antiques - small furniture, crystal and brass, hanging and wall lights and unusual items, £20-£500.* LOC: Junction of Anchor Rd. and Hotwells Rd., 3 minutes walk from library and city centre. PARK: Meters. TEL: 0117 909 6688; mobile - 07790 253139. SER: Restorations (small repairs and brass cleaning). FAIRS: Kensington Brocante, Newark, Sandown Park, Ardingly.

Bristol Guild of Applied Art Ltd
68/70 Park St. BS1 5JY. Est. 1908. Open 9-5.30, Mon. and Sat. 9.30-5.30. *STOCK: Furniture, late 19th-20th C.* TEL: 0117 9265548.

Bristol Trade Antiques
192 Cheltenham Rd. BS6 5RB. (L. Dike). Est. 1970. SIZE: Large and warehouse. *STOCK: General antiques.* TEL: 0117 9422790.

Cleeve Antiques
282 Lodge Causeway, Fishponds. BS16 3RD. (T. and S.E. Scull). Est. 1978. Open 9.30-5.30. CL: Wed. *STOCK: Furniture and bric-a-brac.* TEL: 0117 9658366; home - 0117 9567008.

Cotham Galleries
22 Cotham Hill, Cotham. BS6 6LF. (D. Jury). Est. 1960. Open 9-5.30. SIZE: Small. *STOCK: Furniture, glass, metal.* LOC: From city centre up Park St. into Whiteladies Rd. Turn right at Clifton Down station. PARK: Easy. TEL: 0117 9736026. SER: Valuations.

Cotham Hill Bookshop
39A Cotham Hill, Cotham. BS6 6JY. (R. Plant). Open 9.30-5.30. *STOCK: Antiquarian and secondhand books especially fine art; antiquarian prints.* TEL: 0117 9732344.

Dusk 'til Dawn
188 Cheltenham Rd. BS6 5RB. Open Tues.-Sat. 10-5. *STOCK: Antique and traditional bedsteads, iron, brass and wood.* TEL: 0117 944 2388.

Flame and Grate
159 Hotwells Rd., Hotwells. BS8 4RU. Open 9-5. *STOCK: Original cast-iron fireplaces, marble surrounds and fireplace accessories.* PARK: Easy. TEL: 0117 9252560/9292930.

Focus on the Past
25 Waterloo St.,Clifton. BS8 4BT. (K. Walker and A. Roylance). Est. 1976. Open 9.30-5.30, Sat. 9.30-6, Sun. 11-5. SIZE: Large. *STOCK: 19th-20th C furniture including mahogany, country, pine, French, English; ceramics, kitchenalia, glass, silver, plate, jewellery, to £1,000+.* LOC: Off Princess Victoria St. PARK: Nearby. TEL: 0117 973 8080. FAIRS: Shepton Mallet, Newark.

Grey-Harris and Co
12 Princess Victoria St., Clifton. BS8 4BP. Est. 1963. Open 9.30-5.30. *STOCK: Jewellery, Victorian; silver, old Sheffield plate.* TEL: 0117 9737365. SER: Valuations. VAT: Stan/Spec.

Chris Grimes Militaria
13 Lower Park Row. BS1 5BN. Open 11-5.30. *STOCK: Militaria, scientific instruments, nautical items.* TEL: 0117 9298205.

Kemps
9 Carlton Court, Westbury-on-Trym. BS9 3DF. Open 9-5.30. *STOCK: Jewellery.* TEL: 0117 9505090.

Robert Mills Architectural Antiques Ltd
Narroways Rd., Eastville. BS2 9XB. Est. 1969. Open 9.30-5. CL: Sat. SIZE: Large. *STOCK: Architectural items, panelled rooms, shop interiors, Gothic Revival, stained glass, church woodwork, bar and restaurant fittings, 1750-1920, £50-£30,000.* LOC: Half mile from Junction 2, M32. PARK: Easy. TEL: 0117 9556542; fax - 0117 9558146; e-mail - robert.mills.ltd @dial.pipex.com; website - www.rmills.co.uk. VAT: Stan.

Oldwoods
4 Colston Yard. BS1 5BD. (S. Duck). Open 11-5.30, Sat. 11-4. *STOCK: Victorian and Edwardian furniture, pine and other woods.* TEL: 0117 9299023. SER: Restorations.

Pastimes
23 Lower Park Row. BS1 5BN. (A.H. Stevens). Est. 1970. Open 10.30-1.45 and 2.45-5, Sat. 10.30-5. SIZE: Medium. *STOCK: Militaria and military books, £1-£1,000.* LOC: Opposite Christmas Steps, off Colston St. PARK: Meters. TEL: 0117 929 9330.

Period Fireplaces
The Old Station, Station Rd., Montpelier. BS6 5EE. (John Ashton and Martyn Roberts). Est. 1987. Open daily. SIZE: Medium. *STOCK: Fireplaces, original and reproduction, £100-£1,000.* LOC: Just off Gloucester Rd. PARK: Easy. TEL: 0117 9444449; website - www. periodfireplaces.co.uk. SER: Valuations; restorations; fitting. VAT: Stan.

Potter's Antiques and Coins
60 Colston St. BS1 5AZ. (B.C. Potter). Est. 1965. Open 10.30-5.30. SIZE: Small. *STOCK: Antiquities, 500 B.C. to 1600 A.D., £5-£500; commemoratives, 1770-1953, £4-£300; coins, 500 B.C. to 1967, £1-£100; drinking glasses, 1770-1953, £3-£200; small furniture, from 1837, £10-£200.* LOC: Near top of Christmas Steps, close to city centre. PARK: NCP Park Row. TEL: 0117 9262551. SER: Valuations; buys at auction. VAT: Stan/Spec.

Simon Poyntz Antique Beds
18 Clifton Rd., Clifton. BS8 1AQ. (Alicia and Simon Poyntz). Est. 1986. Open Tues.-Sat. 10-5, Sun. and other times by appointment. SIZE: Small. *STOCK: Georgian, Regency and Victorian bedposts - made-up into beds £1,600-£3,600; original beds - four-posters, half-testers, £1,850-£4,000; fabrics, cushions, bedlinens.* PARK: Easy. TEL: 0117 974 4450; fax - same; mobile - 07074 632563. SER: Restorations; drape-making; hand-made mattresses and bed bases. VAT: Stan.

Relics - Pine Furniture
109 St. George's Rd., College Green. BS1 5UW. (R. Seville and S. Basey). Est. 1972. Open 10-5.30. SIZE: Large. *STOCK: Victorian style and reclaimed pine furniture; nauticalia, model yachts and Harmony Kingdom figurines.* LOC: Near cathedral, 1/2 mile from city centre. PARK: Easy. TEL: 0117 9268453; fax - same. VAT: Stan.

St. Nicholas Markets
The Exchange Hall, Corn St. BS1 1JQ. (Steve Morris). Est. 1975. Open 9.30-5. *STOCK: Wide range of general antiques and collectors' items.* TEL: 0117 9224014.

CAMBRIDGE, Nr. Gloucester

Bell House Antiques
Bell House. GL2 7BD. (G. and J. Hawkins). Resident. Open 10-1 and 2-5. SIZE: Medium. *STOCK: Furniture, shipping goods, stripped pine, small items, bygones, £5-£500.* LOC: Near Slimbridge, on main A38. PARK: Easy. TEL: 01453 890463. SER: Valuations.

CHALFORD

J. and R. Bateman Antiques
Green Court, High St. GL6 8DS. LAPADA. Est. 1975. Open 9-6 or by appointment. *STOCK: Furniture, oak and country, 17th-19th C; decorative items.* PARK: Easy. TEL: 01453 883234. SER: Restorations; cabinet making, rushing and caning. VAT: Stan/Spec.

CHELTENHAM

Art and Antiques
16/17 Montpellier Walk. GL50 1SD. (Joy Turner). LAPADA. Est. 1950. Open 9-4. CL: Thurs. *STOCK: General antiques.* TEL: 01242 522939. VAT: Stan/Spec.

Austrian representations at Christie's included this Goldscheider group by Stefan Dakon which rated £4,500.

From an Auction Report by Christopher Wight on Classic Art Deco at Christie's South Kensington, 15th February 2001 which appeared in the April 2001 issue of **Antique Collecting** magazine. For more details and to subscribe see page 147.

David Bannister FRGS
26 Kings Rd. GL52 6BG. PBFA. Est. 1963. Open by appointment only. SIZE: Medium. *STOCK: Early maps and prints, 1480-1850, from £25; decorative and topographical prints; atlases and colour plate books.* TEL: 01242 514287; fax - 01242 513890; e-mail - db@antiquemaps.co.uk. SER: Valuations; restorations; lectures; buys at auction. FAIRS: Organiser - Antique Map and Print (Bonnington Hotel). VAT: Stan.

Edward Bradbury and Son
32 High St. GL50 1DZ. (O. Bradbury). Resident. Est. 1986. Open by appointment. SIZE: Small. *STOCK: Works of art, tribal art, furniture, 18th-19th C; books on art reference, monographs on artists and photographers, manuscripts.* PARK: Nearby. TEL: 01242 254952. SER: Valuations. VAT: Spec.

Charlton Kings Antiques Centre
199 London Rd., Charlton Kings. GL52 6HU. Est. 1984. Open 9.30-5.30. SIZE: Large - 11 dealers. *STOCK: General antiques, pine, painted furniture, china, glass, prints, silver, plate, linen, flatware and collectibles, £5-£1,000.* LOC: On A40. PARK: Easy. TEL: 01242 510672.

Cheltenham Antique Market
54 Suffolk Rd. GL50 2AQ. (K.J. Shave). Est. 1970. Open 9.30-5.30. SIZE: 14 dealers. *STOCK: General antiques.* TEL: 01242 529812.

Cheltenham Antiques Centre
50 Suffolk Rd.GL50 2AQ. (Mrs M. Atkinson). Est. 1998. Open 10-5. SIZE: Medium - 20 dealers. *STOCK: Porcelain, glass and silver, furniture, jewellery, Victoriana and clocks; Art Deco, commemorative postcards and books, memorabilia and collectables.* LOC: Close to town centre, off Bath Rd. PARK: Nearby. TEL: 01242 573556; fax - 01242 224564. SER: Valuations; shipping arranged. VAT: Stan.

Cocoa
9 Clarence Parade. GL50 3NY. (Cara Wagstaff). Est. 1973. Open 10-5. SIZE: Small. *STOCK: Lace, antique wedding dresses and accessories, 19th-20th C, £1-£2,000.* TEL: 01242 233588. SER: Re-creations; restorations (period textiles). VAT: Stan.

Giltwood Gallery
30/31 Suffolk Parade. GL50 2AE.. (Mrs G. Butt). Resident. Est. 1992. Open 9-5.30, Sat. 10-5.30. SIZE: Large. *STOCK: Furniture, £500-£1,000; mirrors, £500, all 18th to early 20th C.* PARK: Easy. TEL: 01242 512482; fax - same. SER: Valuations; restorations (upholstery); buys at auction. VAT: Stan/Spec.

Greens of Cheltenham Ltd
15 Montpellier Walk. GL50 1SD. Est. 1946.
Open 9-5. CL: Wed. SIZE: Large. *STOCK: Jewels, objets, porcelain and silver, some furniture.* LOC: Conjunction of Promenade and main shopping centre. PARK: Easy. TEL: 01242 512088; e-mail -steve@greensofcheltenham. co.uk. SER: Buys at auction. VAT: Stan/Spec.

H.W. Keil (Cheltenham) Ltd   BADA
129-131 Promenade. GL50 1NW. Est. 1953. STOCK: Furniture, paintings, 17th-18th C; metalwork, chandeliers. LOC: Opposite Queens Hotel, at top of Promenade. PARK: Easy. TEL: 01242 522509. SER: Upholstery. VAT: Spec.

Latchford Antiques
215 London Rd., Charlton Kings. GL52 6HY. (K. and R. Latchford). Est. 1985. Open 10-5.30. SIZE: Small. *STOCK: Furniture, china, glass and objets d'art, 18th-19th C, £5-£1,000.* LOC: 2 miles from Cheltenham, on A40 towards London at Sixways Shopping Centre, on right. PARK: Easy. TEL: 01242 226263.

The Loquens Gallery
3 Montpellier Avenue. GL50 1SA. Est. 1992. Open 10.15-5. SIZE: Small. *STOCK: 18th-20th C watercolours and some oils.* LOC: Adjacent to The Queens Hotel. TEL: 01242 254313. SER: Valuations: framing; restorations.

Manor House Antiques
42 Suffolk Rd. GL50 2AQ. (J.G. Benton). LAPADA. Est. 1972. Open 10-5.30, other times by appointment only. SIZE: Large. *STOCK: Paintings, furniture, 18th to early 20th C, £500-£20,000.* Not Stocked: Small items, china and jewellery. LOC: A40. PARK: Nearby. TEL: 01242 232780; mobile - 07885 575139.

Manor House Gallery
16 Royal Parade, Bayshill Rd. GL50 3AY. (Geoff Hassell). Resident. Open anytime by appointment. *STOCK: Oils and watercolours, £200-£2,000; prints, under £100; all 20th C.* LOC: Central. PARK: Easy. TEL: 01242 228330; home - same; fax - 01242 228328; e-mail - geoffatmhg@ cwcom; website - mhg-chelt.mcmail.com. SER: Valuations; restorations (oils). VAT: Stan/spec.

Martin and Co. Ltd
19 The Promenade. GL50 1LP. (I.M. and N.C.S. Dimmer). Est. 1890. *STOCK: Silver, Sheffield plate, jewellery, objets d'art.* TEL: 01242 522821; fax - 01242 570430. VAT: Stan/Spec.

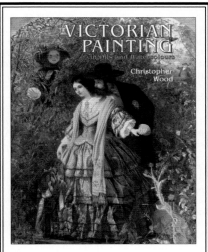

Montpellier Clocks — BADA
13 Rotunda Terrace, Montpellier. GL50 1SW. (B. Bass and T. Birch). Open 9-5.30. *STOCK: Clocks, 17th-19th C; barometers.* LOC: Close to Queens Hotel. PARK: Easy. TEL: 01242 242178; fax - same. SER: Repairs and restorations by West Dean/BADA Dip. conservator.

Patrick Oliver
4 Tivoli St. GL50 2UW. LAPADA. Est. 1896. SIZE: Large. *STOCK: Furniture and shipping goods.* PARK: Easy. TEL: 01242 519538. VAT: Stan/Spec.

Eric Pride Oriental Rugs
44 Suffolk Rd. GL50 2AQ. Est. 1980. Open by appointment only. SIZE: Medium. *STOCK: Rugs and carpets, £100-£4,000; kilims, £300-£2,000; saddle-bags and horse covers, £150-£800; all 19th to early 20th C.* LOC: A40 near Cheltenham College. PARK: Nearby. TEL: 01242 580822 (answerphone); fax - 01242 700549; e-mail - ericpride@hotmail.com; website - www.antique orientalrugs.co.uk. SER: Valuations; restorations (cleaning and repairs).

Q & C Militaria
22 Suffolk Rd. GL50 2AQ. (J.F. and B.M. Wright). OMRS, MCCOFI, BACSEA. Est. 1970. Open 10-5. CL: Mon. SIZE: Medium. *STOCK: Military memorabilia - British orders, decorations and medals; military drums, edged weapons, cap badges.* LOC: A40 ring road. PARK: At rear, off Old Bath Rd. TEL: 01242 519815; fax - same; mobile - 07778 613977; e-mail - john@qc-militaria.freeserve.co.uk; website - www.qcmilitaria.com. SER: Valuations; restorations (drums and military equipment); framing and mounting (medals); buys at auction. FAIRS: OMRS Convention, Aldershot, Yate, Stratford-upon-Avon; Aldershot Collectors (Farnham).

Michael Rayner
11 St. Luke's Rd. GL53 7JQ. Open 10-6, other times by appointment. CL: Mon. and Tues. *STOCK: Books, antiquarian and secondhand.* TEL: 01242 512806.

Scott-Cooper Ltd — BADA
52 The Promenade. GL50 1LY. Est. 1912. *STOCK: Silver, plate, jewellery, clocks, ivory, enamel, objets de vertu.* TEL: 01242 522580. SER: Restorations and repairs (silver and jewellery). VAT: Stan/Spec.

Catherine Shinn Decorative Textiles
7 Suffolk Parade. GL50 2AB. (Catherine and Jenny Shinn). Open 10-5. SIZE: Small. *STOCK: Antique tapestry cushions, hangings, bell pulls; passe menterie and upholstery pieces, old curtains and table covers.* PARK: Suffolk Sq. TEL: 01242 574546; fax - 01242 578495. SER: Valuations; restorations; buys at auction (European textiles). VAT: Stan.

Struwwelpeter Antiques at the Schoolhouse
The Old Schoolhouse, 175 London Rd. GL52 6HN. (Richard Bliss). Est. 1983. Open 10-5.30 or by appointment. SIZE: 6-10 dealers. *STOCK: Period, Victorian and Arts & Crafts furniture; smalls, collectibles, architectural items and pictures.* LOC: A40, 1 mile from town centre, on traffic-light controlled junction adjacent to Holy Apostles church. PARK: Own. TEL: 01242 230088; mobile - 07971 960595. SER: Restorations. VAT: Stan/Spec.

Tapestry
33 Suffolk Parade. GL50 2AE. Open 10-5.30. SIZE: Medium. *STOCK: Antique and decorative furniture and objects, including brass and iron beds, soft furnishings and garden items.* LOC: 10 mins. walk from The Promenade. PARK: Easy. TEL: 01242 512191.

John P. Townsend
Ullenwood Park Farm, Ullenwood. GL53 9QX. Est. 1969. Open 9-5. CL: Sat. SIZE: Medium. *STOCK: Furniture - stripped pine, country and shipping, to 1940's; books.* TEL: 01242 870223.

Triton Gallery
27 Suffolk Parade. GL50 2AE. (L. Bianco). Resident. Open 9-5.30, other times by appointment. *STOCK: Period furniture, 18th C paintings, mirrors and lighting.* TEL: 01242 510477.

Peter Ward Fine Paintings
Nothill Cowley. GL7 7EU.. Open 9-5. *STOCK: 17th-19th C paintings.* TEL: 01285 831327. SER: Valuations; restorations; framing. VAT: Spec.

CHERINGTON, Nr. Tetbury

Paul Nash Antiques
Cherington House. GL8 8SN. LAPADA. Est. 1961. By appointment only. *STOCK: Period furniture and decorative objects.* TEL: 01285 841215; mobile - 07785 570701. VAT: Spec.

CHIPPING CAMPDEN

Antique Heritage
High St. GL55 6AT. (D.B. Smith). Est. 1981. Open 10-5, Sun. 11-4. SIZE: Small. *STOCK: Small items, china, porcelain, tables, boxes, Georgian and Victorian, £15-£400.* LOC: Village centre. PARK: Easy. TEL: 01386 840727.

Cottage Farm Antiques
Cottage Farm, Ashton sub Edge. GL55 6PZ. (A.E. and E.A. Willmore). Est. 1986. Open 8.30-5.30 including Sun. SIZE: Large. *STOCK: Furniture including 19th C wardrobes, 18th-19th C dressers and tables, to £1,500.* LOC: Follow brown tourist signs. PARK: Easy. TEL: 01386 438263; fax and home - same; e-mail - info@ cottagefarm antiques.co.uk; website - www. cottagefarm antiques.co.uk. VAT: Stan/Spec.

The Kettle House
High St. GL55 6HN. (Susie and Charles Holdsworth Hunt). Est. 1988. Open 10-5.30 including Sun. SIZE: Large. *STOCK: 18th-19th C English country furniture, pine, mahogany, oak.* LOC: On village green at Leasebourne end of High St. PARK: Easy. TEL: 01386 840328; e-mail - info@kettlehouse.co.uk; website - www.kettlehouse.co.uk. SER: Valuations.

Pedlars
Lower High St. GL55 6AL. (A. Yates). Open 10-5. *STOCK: General antiques.* TEL: 01386 840680.

Saxton House Gallery
High St. GL55 6HQ. (S.D. and J. Coy). LAPADA. Open 9-5.30. CL: Thurs. SIZE: Medium. *STOCK: Fine English clocks and barometers, unusual carriage clocks, jewellery, Georgian furniture, paintings and watercolours.* LOC: Village centre. PARK: Easy. TEL: 01386 840278. VAT: Stan/Spec.

School House Antiques
School House, High St. GL55 6HB. (G. Hammond). Open 9.30-5 including Sun. (June-Sept.). CL: Thurs. (Oct.-May). *STOCK: Clocks, 18th-19th C; Georgian and Victorian furniture; works of art, oils and watercolours.* TEL: 01386 841474; fax - 01386 841367. SER: Restorations; valuations.

Stuart House Antiques
High St. GL55 6HB. (J. Collett). Est. 1985. Open 10-1 and 2-5.30 including Sun. SIZE: Large. *STOCK: China, 19th C; general antiques, from 18th C; all £1-£1,000.* LOC: Opposite market hall. PARK: Easy. TEL: 01386 840995. SER: Valuations; china search; restorations (ceramics).

Swan Antiques
High St. GL55 6HB. (J. Stocker). Est. 1960. Open 10-1 and 2-4, Thurs. and Sun. by appointment only. SIZE: Medium. *STOCK: Silver, George II to 1920; jewellery including Victorian; porcelain; furniture, 17th C oak to 1860 mahogany; decorative items.* LOC: Village centre. PARK: Easy. TEL: 01386 840759. SER: Gemmologist.

The Titian Gallery
London House, High St. GL55 6AG. (Ilona Johnson Gibbs). LAPADA, CADA, CINOA. Est. 1976. Open 10-1 and 2-5, Sun. by appointment. SIZE: Medium. *STOCK: Fine 18th-19th C British and European oil paintings and watercolours, to £15,000.* LOC: Near centre of town square. PARK: Easy. TEL: 01386 841789; fax - 01386 849151. SER: Valuations; buys at auction (oils and watercolours). VAT: Spec.

CHIPPING SODBURY, Nr. Bristol

Sodbury Antiques
70 Broad St. BS37 6AG. (Millicent Brown). Est. 1986. CL: Wed. SIZE: Small. *STOCK: Porcelain and china, mainly 18th-19th C; antique and secondhand jewellery, £5-£1,000.* PARK: Easy. TEL: 01454 273369.

CIRENCESTER

Walter Bull and Son (Cirencester) Ltd
10 Dyer St. GL7 2PF. Est. 1815. Open 9-5. SIZE: Small. *STOCK: Silver, from 1700, £50-£3,000; objets d'art.* LOC: Lower end of Market Place. PARK: At rear. TEL: 01285 653875; fax - 01285 641751. VAT: Stan/Spec.

Cirencester Arcade
25 Market Place. GL7 2NX. Open Mon.-Sun. SIZE: 70 dealers. *STOCK: General antiques.* TEL: 01285 644214.

Corner Cupboard Curios
2 Church St. GL7 1LE. (P. Larner). *STOCK: General antiques and gramophonalia.* TEL: 01285 655476.

Forum Antiques
Springfield Farm, Perrotts Brook. GL7 7DT. (W. Mitchell). Est. 1986. Open Mon.-Fri. 8.30-5.30 by appointment only. SIZE: Small. *STOCK: Period furniture, pre-1850.* TEL: 01285 831821. SER: Valuations; restorations. VAT: Spec.

Hares
4 Black Jack St. GL7 2AA. Est. 1972. Open 10-5.30, Sun. by appointment. SIZE: Large. *STOCK: Furniture, especially dining tables and long sets of chairs, 18th to early 19th C, £100-£50,000; upholstery and decorative objects.* LOC: Near Market Square. PARK: Own. TEL: 01285 640077; mobile - 07860 350097; e-mail - hares@star.co.uk; website - www.hares-antiques.com. SER: Restorations; traditional upholstery. VAT: Spec.

RANKINE TAYLOR ANTIQUES

Interesting collection of 17th, 18th and 19th century furniture, silver, glass and rare associated objects.

34 DOLLAR STREET, CIRENCESTER, GLOS. GL7 2AN
Telephone: 01285 652529
CUSTOMER CAR PARK OPPOSITE

Thomas and Pamela Hudson
9 Watermoor Rd. GL7 1JW. Resident. Est. 1959. Mail order or by appointment only. *STOCK: Work boxes and needlework tools.* TEL: 01285 652972; website - www.pwhudson.demon.co.uk.

Original Architectural
22 Elliott Rd. GL7 1YS. (Andy Hayward and John Rawlinson). Open 9-5, Sun. 9-4. SIZE: Large. *STOCK: 19th C fireplaces, £160-£550; 17th C oak doors, £350-£750; stone troughs, £500-£1,000, firebacks, £180-£2,000, both 18th C.* LOC: Love Lane Industrial Estate. PARK: Easy. TEL: 01285 653532; fax - 01285 644383; email - john@originaluk.com. SER: Valuations; restorations (doors, fireplaces); buys at auction.

Silver Street Antiques and Things
9 Silver St. GL7 2BJ. (S.A. Tarrant). Resident. Est. 1992. Open 10-5. SIZE: Medium. *STOCK: General antiques including small furniture, £1-£1,500.* LOC: Between Corn Hall and museum. PARK: Nearby. TEL: 01285 641600.

William H. Stokes   BADA
The Cloisters, 6/8 Dollar St. GL7 2AJ. (W.H.Stokes and P.W.Bontoft). CADA. Est. 1968. Open 9.30-5.30, Sat. 9.30-4.30. *STOCK: Early oak furniture, £1,000-£30,000; brassware, £150-£5,000; all 16th-17th C.* TEL: 01285 653907; fax - same. VAT: Spec.

Rankine Taylor Antiques
34 Dollar St. GL7 2AN. LAPADA. CADA. Est. 1969. Open 9-5.30, Sun. by appointment. SIZE: Large. *STOCK: Furniture, 17th to early 19th C, £300-£35,000; glass, 18th-20th C, £8-£350; silver, rare interesting objects and decorative items, 17th-20th C, £20-£4,000.* Not Stocked: Victoriana. LOC: From church, turn right into West Market Place, via Gosditch St. into Dollar St. PARK: Own - private opposite. TEL: 01285 652529. VAT: Spec.

Patrick Waldron Antiques
18 Dollar St. GL7 2AN. Resident. Est. 1965. Open 9.30-1 and 2-6, Sun. by appointment. SIZE: Medium. *STOCK: Furniture, 18th-19th C.* LOC: In street behind church. PARK: Easy and public behind shop. TEL: 01285 652880; home - same; workshop - 01285 643479. SER: Restorations (furniture); buys at auction. VAT: Stan./Spec.

Bernard Weaver Antiques
28 Gloucester St. GL7 2DH. Open by appointment. SIZE: Medium. *STOCK: Furniture, mahogany and oak, 18th-19th C.* LOC: Continuation of Dollar St. PARK: Easy. TEL: 01285 652055. SER: Valuations; restorations.

MARK CARTER

17th-19th century country and mahogany furniture

Open Mon. -Sat. 9.00-5.00 or at other times by appointment

Mobile: 07836-260567

5 Macaroni Wood, Eastleach, Nr. Fairford, Glos. GL7 3NF
Tel: 01367-850483

EBRINGTON, Nr. Chipping Campden

John Burton Natural Craft Taxidermy
21 Main St. GL55 6NL. Est. 1973. Open by appointment. SIZE: Medium. *STOCK: Taxidermy - Victorian and Edwardian cased fish, birds and mammals, from £40-£2,500; glass domes, sporting trophies.* LOC: Village centre. PARK: Easy. TEL: 01386 593231; home - same. SER: Valuations; restorations (taxidermy); buys at auction (taxidermy).

FAIRFORD

Blenheim Antiques
Market Place. GL7 4AB. (N. Hurdle). CADA. Resident. Est. 1972. Open 9.30-6.30. *STOCK: 18th-19th C furniture.* TEL: 01285 712094. VAT: Stan/Spec.

Mark Carter Antiques
5 Macaroni Wood, Eastleach. GL7 3NF. Est. 1979. SIZE: Large - warehouse. *STOCK: English mahogany, oak and fruitwood furniture, 17th-19th C, £500-£10,000.* LOC: Telephone for directions. PARK: Own. TEL: 01367 850587/ 850483; mobile - 07836 260567. SER: Valuations. VAT: Spec.

Blenheim Antiques

AT FAIRFORD

We Sell Town and Country Furniture, Clocks, Pictures and Decorative Objects.

Market Place, Fairford, Glos.
Telephone: 01285 712094
(Easy parking in the Market Place)

GLOUCESTER HOUSE ANTIQUES LTD.

Market Place, Fairford, Glos. GL7 4AB
Tel: 01285 712790 Fax: 01285 713324

We specialise in English and French country furniture, pottery and faïence with a very good selection of armoires and farmhouse tables.

Gloucester House Antiques Ltd
Market Place. GL7 4AB. (Mrs Scilla Chester-Master). CADA. Est. 1972. Open 9-5.30. SIZE: Large. *STOCK: English and French country furniture in oak, elm, fruitwood, pine; pottery, faïence and decorative items.* PARK: Easy. TEL: 01285 712790; home - 01285 653066; fax - 01285 713324. VAT: Spec.

Anthony Hazledine
Antique Oriental Carpets, High St. GL7 4AD. Est. 1976. Mon., Fri. and Sat. 9-5, other days by appointment. SIZE: Small. *STOCK: Oriental carpets and textiles, 18th-19th C, £150-£4,000.* PARK: Easy. TEL: 01285 713400; home and fax - same. SER: Sales; purchases; restoration and cleaning. VAT: Stan/Spec.

GLOUCESTER

Gloucester Antique Centre
1 Severn Rd. GL1 2LE. Est. 1949. Open 10-5, Sun. 1-5. SIZE: 140 dealers. 50p admission charge weekends and Bank Hols. - Trade free. *STOCK: General antiques - furniture, jewellery, silver, clocks, ceramics, collectables.* LOC: Within the Dock area. PARK: Easy. TEL: 01452 529716; fax - 01452 307161.

Arthur S. Lewis
LAPADA. Est. 1969. By appointment. *STOCK: Antique clocks and mechanical music.* TEL: 01452 780258; website - www.arthurlewis antiques.com.

Military Curios, HQ84
(The Curiosity Shop), Southgate. GL1 2DX. (B. Williams). Est. 1964. Open 10-6, including Sun. *STOCK: Medals, badges, (3rd Reich specialities), militaria, blazer badges, Govt. surplus, edged weapons, replicas, air weapons; Jaguar - spares, mascots.* LOC: A38, city centre. PARK: 100 yds (Docks). TEL: 01452 556038; fax - 01452 554056. SER: Valuations; medal find, mounting and framing; costume hire; badge-making; mail order;

A.J. Ponsford Antiques with Decora
Northbrook Rd., off Eastern Avenue, Barnwood. GL4 3DP. (A.J. and R.L. Ponsford). Est. 1962. Open 8-5. CL: Sat. *STOCK: Furniture, 1800-1880, £25-£4,000; furniture, 1650-1800, £200-£15,000.* LOC: 1 mile from junction 11A, M5, to Gloucester over 3 roundabouts, pass walls into Eastern Avenue, pass Royal Mail on right, turn right by McDonalds into Northbrook Road, 150yds on left. PARK: Own. TEL: 01452 307700. SER: Valuations; restorations (furniture); rushing, caning, upholstery, picture framing; manufacturers of period book simulations and decorative accessories. VAT: Stan/Spec.

LECHLADE

Corner House Antiques
High St. GL7 3AE. (John Ffoxe and Audrey Glenn Downes-Hall). Resident. Est. 1997. Open Tues.-Sat. 10-5, Sun. by appointment. SIZE: Small. *STOCK: Silver and small furniture, 17th-19th C; jewellery and porcelain, 18th-19th C.* PARK: Easy. TEL: 01367 252007. SER: Valuations; restorations (wood, silver, glass, porcelain); silver and gold items designed and made.

f@me - Fine Art Multimedia Europe
High St. GL7 3AE. (S. Sheppard). Resident. Open 10-6 including Sun. SIZE: Large - 4 showrooms. *STOCK: Arts & Crafts furniture and 20th C modern art.* PARK: Easy. TEL: 01367 253140; fax - 0137 250252; e-mail - mail@fame limited.com; website - www.famelimited.com.

Jubilee Hall Antiques Centre
Oak St. GL7 3AY. Open 10-5, Sun. 11-5. SIZE: Large. LOC: On left 350 yds from town centre going north towards Burford. PARK: Own. TEL: 01367 253777. SER: Shipping. Listed below are the dealers at this centre.

Mandy Barnes
Georgian and Victorian furniture and decorative objects.

Keith and Lin Bawden
18th-19th C English furniture.

John Calgie
Period furniture, mirrors, copper, brass and interesting objects.

Andrew Crawforth
Antique and Art Nouveau metalwork and interesting objects.

Francoise Daniel
Small silver, ivory, shibayama, toroiseshell, art objects, Tunbridge ware.

Marc Drogin
Antiquities, from 2000 years.

Paul Eisler
18th-19th C ceramics, metalware and treen.

Peter Gibbons
Period pewter, treen, brass, arms and armour, country furniture.

Michael Gray
Period oak and country furniture.

Mark Haillay
Furniture, pottery, glass, small silver and objects of art.

Anita Harris
Porcelain and decorative objects.

Colin and Mary Lee
Glass, porcelain, silver and objects.

Colin Morris
Country furniture, Staffordshire, brass, copper and period objects.

NAAS Antiques
19th C decorative furnishings.

Oak Antiques
(David and Vicky Wilson). *Period country oak furniture and metalware.*

Clive Payne
LAPADA. *Georgian furniture and works of art.*

Mary Pennel
Porcelain, small silver and jewellery.

Judi Pollitt (Times Past)
Antiques ceramics including old blue and white and interesting objects.

Red Lane Antiques
(Terry Sparks). *17th-19th C ironwork, treen, copper and brass.*

Keith Robinson
18th-19th C English furniture, engravings, ceramics, lighting and Japanese and English objects of art.

Fiona Taylor
Sporting antiques including golf, cricket and rowing; antique luggage.

Fred and Margaret Taylor
Small period silver, period glass and porcelain and objects of art.

Jollke van den Berg
Antique metalwork and small arms.

Winson Antiques
Georgian and Victorian furniture and objects.

Lechlade Arcade
5, 6 and 7 High St. GL7 3AD. (J. Dickson). Open 9-5 including Sun. SIZE: 40+ dealers. *STOCK: Bric-a-brac, books, furniture (Mexican pine style), collectables.* TEL: 01367 252832; mobile - 07949 130875.

The Old Ironmongers Antiques Centre
Burford St. GL7. (Mark A. Serle and Geoff Allen). Open 10-5 including Sun. *STOCK: Old ironmongery, £5-£200; furniture including country, £40-£2,000; textiles, £10-£200; Georgian glass, £20-£250; decorative china, £10-£500; treen, £50-£200; militaria including medals, £5-£300; tools and rural implements, £5-£300.* LOC: A361. PARK: Easy. TEL: 01367 252397.

GLOUCESTERSHIRE

MINCHINHAMPTON, Nr. Stroud

Mick and Fanny Wright
The Trumpet. GL6 9JA. Open Wed.-Sat. 10.30-5.30. SIZE: Medium. *STOCK: General antiques - clocks, furniture, china, silver and plate, 50p-£1,000.* LOC: 200 yards west of crossroads at bottom of High St. PARK: Nearby. TEL: 01453 883027; e-mail - thetrumpetantiques@hotmail. com.

MORETON-IN-MARSH

Antique Centre
London House, High St. GL56 0AH. Est. 1979. Open 10-5 including Sun. SIZE: Large. *STOCK: Furniture, paintings, watercolours, prints, pottery, porcelain (including Chinese), domestic artifacts, clocks, silver, jewellery and plate, mainly 17th-19th C, £5-£3,000.* LOC: Centre of High St. (A429). PARK: Easy. TEL: 01608 651084. VAT: Stan/Spec.

Astley House - Fine Art
Astley House, High St. GL56 0LL. (David, Nanette & Caradoc Glaisyer). LAPADA. CADA. Est. 1973. Open 9-5.30 and by appointment. SIZE: Medium. *STOCK: Oil paintings and botanical watercolours, 19th-21st C, £400-£20,000.* LOC: Main street. PARK: Easy. TEL: 01608 650601; fax - 01608 651777; e-mail - astart333@aol.com; website - www.art-uk.com. SER: Restorations (oils and watercolours); framing. VAT: Spec.

Astley House - Fine Art
Astley House, London Rd. GL56 0LE. (David, Nanette & Caradoc Glaisyer). LAPADA. CADA. Est. 1973. Open 10-1 and 2-5 and by appointment. CL: Wed. SIZE: Large. *STOCK: Oil paintings, 19th-21st C; large decorative oils and portraits.* LOC: Town centre. PARK: Easy. TEL: 01608 650608; fax - 01608 651777; e-mail - astart333@ aol.com; website - www.art-uk.com. SER: Restorations (oils and watercolours); porcelain framing. VAT: Spec.

Berry Antiques
3 High St. GL56 0AH. (Chris Berry). LAPADA. Est. 1985. Open 10-5.30, Sun. 11-5.30. CL: Tues. SIZE: Medium. *STOCK: Furniture, late 18th to 19th C, £1,000-£15,000; porcelain, £50-£500; paintings, £200-£10,000; both 19th C.* LOC: Near junction with Broadway road. PARK: Easy. TEL: 01608 652929; home - same. SER: Valuations. FAIRS: NEC, LAPADA (NEC). VAT: Spec.

Simon Brett   BADA
Creswyke House, High St. GL56 0LH. Est. 1972. Open by appointment only. *STOCK: Antique and collectors' fishing tackle and carved wood fish models; portrait miniatures.* TEL: 01608 650751; fax - 01608 651791. VAT: Spec.

An early George III carved mahogany library (drum) table with leathered top, c.1770. 37½in. diameter.

From an article entitled 'The 18th Century British Interior Part II' by Christopher Claxton Stevens which appeared in the October 2000 issue of **Antique Collecting** magazine. For more details and to subscribe see page 147.

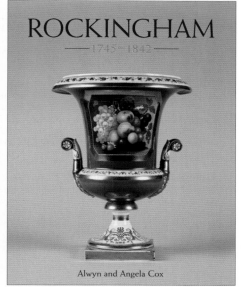

GARY WRIGHT ANTIQUES LTD

Warehouse of over 700 pieces of good quality C18th-C19th furniture at trade prices.

Moreton in Marsh
Gloucestershire
GL56 9NQ

Tel/Fax:
01608 652007
Mobile:
07831653843

Chandlers Antiques

High St. GL56 0AD. (I. Kellam). Prior telephone call advisable. *STOCK: Pottery, porcelain, glass, silver, jewellery, small furniture and general antiques.* TEL: 01608 651347.

Cox's Architectural Reclamation Yard

Unit 10, Fosseway Industrial Estate. GL56 9NQ. (P. Watson). Est. 1991. Open 8.30-6, Sat. 9.30-5, Sun. by appointment. SIZE: Large. *STOCK: Architectural antiques, fire surrounds and places, £250-£500; doors, £50-£100, all 19th C.* LOC: Just off Fosseway, northern end of Moreton-in-Marsh. PARK: Easy. TEL: 01608 652505; fax - 01608 652881; e-mail - coxs@fsbdial.co.uk. SER: Valuations. VAT: Stan.

Dale House Antiques

High St. GL56 0AD. Open 10-5.30, Sun. 11-5. SIZE: Large. *STOCK: 17th-19th C town and country furniture, clocks, barometers, pictures, porcelain and pottery, silver, metalwork, objets.* LOC: Main street. PARK: Easy. TEL: 01608 652950; fax - 01608 652424. VAT: Spec.

Jeffrey Formby Antiques   BADA

Orchard Cottage, East St. GL56 0LQ. LAPADA. Resident. Est. 1994. Open by appointment. SIZE: Small. *STOCK: Fine English clocks, pre 1850, £2,000-£15,000;* *horological books, old and new, £5-£500.* LOC: 100 yards from High St. PARK: Easy. TEL: 01608 650558; website - www.formby-clocks. co.uk. FAIRS: BADA; Olympia; LAPADA (NEC); Guildford. VAT: Spec.

Jon Fox Antiques

High St. GL56 0AD. CADA. Est. 1982. Open 9.30-5.30, Sun. 11-4, Tues. by appointment. SIZE: Large. *STOCK: Garden antiques, 19th C, £25-£1,000+: country furniture, bygones and metalware.* PARK: Easy. TEL: 01608 650325. VAT: Spec.

Grimes House Antiques & Fine Art

High St. GL56 0AT. (S. and V. Farnsworth). Est. 1978. Open 9.30-1 and 2-5, other times by appointment. *STOCK: Old cranberry and antique coloured glass, fine paintings.* TEL: 01608 651029; fax - same; e-mail - grimes_house@ cix.co.uk; websites - www.grimeshouse.co.uk and www.cranberryglass. co.uk.

Lemington House Antiques

Oxford St. GL56 0LA. (K.W. and Y. Heath). LAPADA. Open 10.30-5.30. *STOCK: Early walnut, satinwood, mahogany and oak furniture, 17th-19th C.* LOC: Close to junction with High St. PARK: Own. TEL: 01608 651443.

Seaford House Antiques

Seaford House, High St. GL56 0AD. (Derek and Kathy Young). LAPADA. CINOA. Est. 1988. Open 10-5.30, Tues. by appointment. SIZE: Medium. *STOCK: Furniture, 18th C to Edwardian, £500-£5,000; English and Continental porcelain, mirrors and paintings, 19th C, £100-£3,000.* PARK: Easy. TEL: 01608 652423; fax - same. VAT: Spec.

Simply Antiques

at Windsor House Antiques Centre, High St. GL56 0AD. (G. Ellis). Open 10-5, Tues. and Sun. 12-5. *STOCK: Visiting card cases and small period furniture, mainly 18th to early 19th C.* LOC: In large 17th C premises, adjacent town hall. TEL: 01608 650993; e-mail - info@simplyantiques. org.uk; website - www.simplyantiques.org.uk SER: Finder.

Windsor House Antiques Centre

High St. GL56 0AD. Open 10-5, Tues. and Sun. 12-5. SIZE: 48 dealers. *STOCK: Comprehensive selection of mid-range furniture, from 1650-1914; silver, portrait miniatures, ivory, visiting card cases, French decorative items, English and European porcelain, pottery and glass, objets de vertu, caddies and boxes, brass, copper and pewter.* LOC: Large 17th C premises, adjacent town hall. PARK: Ample. TEL: 01608 650993; fax - 01858 565438; e-mail - windsorhouse@ btinternet.com; website - www.windsorhouse. co.uk

Gary Wright Antiques

Unit 5, Fosseway Business Park, Stratford Rd. GL56 9NQ. Est. 1983. Open 9.30-5.30, Sun. by appointment. SIZE: Large. *STOCK: English and Continental furniture, 18th-19th C, £500-£30,000; unusual and decorative objects, 17th-20th C, £200-£4,000.* LOC: Entrance adjacent to railway bridge on north side of Moreton, on Fosseway (A429). PARK: Easy, TEL: 01608 652007; fax - same; mobile - 07831 653843; e-mail - garywright antiques@FSBDial.co.uk. SER: Valuations; restorations; buys at auction (furniture). VAT: Stan/Spec.

NEWENT

Jillings Antiques - Distinctive Antique Clocks

Croft House, 17 Church St. GL18 1PU. (Doro and John Jillings). LAPADA. Est. 1986. Open by appointment. *STOCK: 18th-19th C English and Continental clocks.* TEL: 01531 822100; fax - 01531 822666; mobile - 07973 830110; e-mail - clocks@jillings.com. SER: Valuations; restorations and repairs; shipping worldwide; free delivery and set up in UK.

NORTHLEACH, Nr. Cheltenham

The Doll's House

Market Place. GL54 3EJ. (Miss Michal Morse). Est. 1971. Open Thurs. Fri. and Sat. 10-5, other times prior telephone call advisable. SIZE: Small. *STOCK: Handmade doll's houses and miniature furniture in one twelfth scale.* LOC: A40. PARK: Easy. TEL: 01451 860431; home and fax - same. SER: Replica houses and special designs to order.

Keith Harding's World of Mechanical Music

The Oak House, High St. GL54 3ET. (K. Harding FBHI and C.A. Burnett CMBHI). Est. 1961. Articles on clocks, musical boxes. Open 10-6 including Sun. *STOCK: Clocks, musical boxes and automata.* TEL: 01451 860181; fax - 01451 861133; website - www.mechanicalmusic.co.uk. SER: Guided tours and demonstrations; valuations; restorations (musical boxes, clocks); buys at auction. VAT: Stan/Spec.

Robson Antiques

New Barn Farm, London Rd. GL54 3LX. Est. 1982. Open daily till late. *STOCK: Furniture, from 18th C, £50-£5,000; garden artefacts.* PARK: Easy. TEL: 01451 861071/861006.

NORTON, Nr. Gloucester

Ronson's Architectural Effects

Norton Barn, Wainlodes Lane. GL2 9LN. (A.P. Jones). Est. 1988. Open 8-5, Sat. 8-1. SIZE: Large. *STOCK: Architectural items including garden ornaments and architectural effects, £25-£1,000; antique pine, £50-£1,000.* LOC: A38 between Gloucester and Tewkesbury. PARK: Easy. TEL: 01452 731236. SER: Buys at auction (garden ornaments and statues). FAIRS: Restorex Period Living, Olympia. VAT: Stan.

PAINSWICK

Craig Carrington Antiques

Pincot House, Pincot Lane. GL6 7QP. Est. 1970. Open by appointment. *STOCK: English and Continental furniture and works of art.* TEL: 01452 813248. SER: Buys at auction. VAT: Spec.

Nina Zborowska   BADA

Damsels Mill, Paradise. GL6 6UD. Est. 1980. By appointment, except during exhibitions (May-June and Oct.-Nov) 11-5 including Sun. SIZE: Medium. *STOCK: Modern British paintings and drawings, St Ives, Newlyn, NEAC and Bloomsbury schools, 1900-1970, £500-£20,000.* LOC: From Cheltenham towards Stroud on A46, take first turning on left to Sheepscombe. PARK: Easy. TEL: 01452 812460; fax - 01452 812912; website - www.ninazborowska.com. SER: Valuations; restorations. FAIRS: Art on Paper; 20th C British Art.

RODLEY, Nr. Westbury on Severn

Kelly Antiques

Landeck, Upper Rodley Rd. GL14 1QZ. (G. Kelly). Resident. Always open. *STOCK: Antique pine.* TEL: 01452 760315.

SLAD, Nr. Stroud

Ian Hodgkins and Co. Ltd

Upper Vatch Mill, The Vatch. GL6 7JY. Open by appointment only. *STOCK: Antiquarian books including pre-Raphaelites and associates, the Brontës, Jane Austen; 19th C illustrated, children's art and literature books.* TEL: 01453 764270; fax - 01453 755233; e-mail - i.hodgkins @dial.pipex.com.

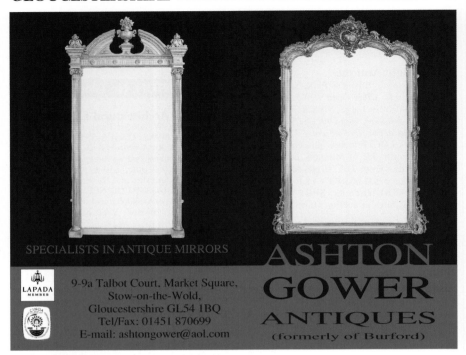

SPECIALISTS IN ANTIQUE MIRRORS

LAPADA
MEMBER

CINOA

9-9a Talbot Court, Market Square,
Stow-on-the-Wold,
Gloucestershire GL54 1BQ
Tel/Fax: 01451 870699
E-mail: ashtongower@aol.com

ASHTON GOWER ANTIQUES
(formerly of Burford)

STOW-ON-THE-WOLD

Ashton Gower Antiques
9/9A Talbot Court, Market Square. GL54 1BQ.
(C. Gower and B. Ashton). LAPADA. Est. 1987.
Open 10-5.30. *STOCK: English and Continental
furniture, mirrors and decorative accessories,
18th-20th C, £25-£5,000.* LOC: Between the
Square and Sheep Street. PARK: Nearby. TEL:
01451 870699; fax - same. SER: Valuations;
restorations; buys at auction. VAT: Stan/Spec.

Duncan J. Baggott
Woolcomber House, Sheep St. GL54 1AA.
LAPADA. CADA. Est. 1967. Open 9-5.30 or by
appointment. SIZE: Large. *STOCK: 17th-20th C
English furniture, paintings, domestic metalwork
and decorative items; garden statuary and
ornaments.* PARK: Sheep St. or Market Sq. TEL:
01451 830662; fax - 01451 832174.

Baggott Church Street Ltd   BADA
**Church St. GL54 1BB. (D.J. and C.M.
Baggott). CADA. Est. 1978. Open 9.30-5.30 or
by appointment. SIZE: Large.** *STOCK:
English furniture, 17th-19th C; portrait
paintings, metalwork, pottery, treen and
decorative items.* **LOC: South-west corner of
market square. PARK: In market square.
TEL: 01451 830370; fax - 01451 832174.**

Oonagh Black
Lower Farm House, Coln Rogers. GL54 3LA.
LAPADA. Est. 1978. Open by appointment.
*STOCK: Country and French provincial furniture,
textiles and related items.* LOC: Just off A429
Fosseway between Cirencester and Stow-on-the-
Wold. PARK: Easy. TEL: 01285 720717/720920;
fax - 01285 720910; home - 01285 720717; mobile
- 07768 568966. FAIRS: Olympia; Harvey
Decorative; Penman. VAT: Spec.

Colin Brand Antiques
Tudor House, Sheep St. GL54 1AA. Est. 1985.
Open 10-1 and 2-5, Sun. by appointment. CL:
Wed. SIZE: Medium. *STOCK: Clocks, small
furniture, £200-£8,000; porcelain, £30-£3,000,
all pre-1900; militaria.* LOC: Opposite Post
Office. PARK: Opposite or main square - private
parking available if notified. TEL: 01451 831760;
fax and home - same. VAT: Spec.

Bryden House Clocks & Antiques
Sheep St. GL54 1JS. (J. and D. Hance). Est. 1990.
Open 10-5.30, Thurs. and Sun. by appointment only.
SIZE: Small. *STOCK: Clocks, furniture, barometers,
18th-19th C, £250-£10,000.* LOC: Opposite Unicorn
Hotel, junction of Fosseway and Sheep Street.
PARK: Opposite. TEL: 01451 832516; home - same.
SER: Restorations (clocks and barometers). FAIRS:
NEC Antiques for Everyone. VAT: Spec.

Durham House Antiques Centre

Sheep Street, Stow-on-the-Wold
Gloucestershire GL54 1AA
Telephone and 24 Hour Fax
Cotswold (01451) 870404
EMail: DurhamHouse@Compuserve.com
Open 7 Days A Week Over 2,000 sq. ft.
30+ Dealers

J. and J. Caspall Antiques
Sheep St. GL54 1AA. Author of "Fire and Light in the Home pre-1820". Est. 1971. Open 10-5.30 or by appointment. *STOCK: Period oak, 16th C to 1760; early metalwork, especially lighting and hearth, early woodcarvings, period domestic and decorative items.* PARK: Nearby. TEL: 01451 831160. VAT: Spec.

Church Street Antiques Centre
3/4 Church St. GL54 1BB. (Mrs G E Niner). Est. 1970. Open 9.45-5. SIZE: Medium - 18 dealers. *STOCK: Furniture, 1680-1930, £50-£4,000; pottery especially Staffordshire, porcelain especially 18th C Worcester, silver, metalwork, jewellery, vintage leather, glass, children's furniture and toys.* PARK: Nearby. TEL: 01451 870186. FAIRS: NEC.

Annarella Clark Antiques
11 Park St. GL54 1AQ. Est. 1968. Open 10-5 or by appointment. SIZE: Medium. *STOCK: Wicker and garden, English and French country and painted furniture, needlework, pottery, quilts and decorative objects.* LOC: Park St. leads from Sheep St., 1st right at lights leading into town. PARK: Easy. TEL: 01451 830535; home - same.

Christopher Clarke Antiques Ltd
The Fosseway. GL54 1JS. (I.D., D.S. and S.F. Clarke). LAPADA. CADA. Est. 1961. Open 9.30-5.30 or by appointment. SIZE: Large. *STOCK: Furniture, 17th-19th C; works of art, metalware, treen, pictures, decorative items and animal antiques.* LOC: Corner of The Fosseway and Sheep St. PARK: Easy. TEL: 01451 830476; fax - 01451 830300; e-mail - christopherclarke@ barclays.net; website - www.antiques-in-england. com.

Cotswold Galleries
GL54 1AB. (Richard and Cherry Glaisyer). CADA. Est. 1961. Open 9-5.30 or by appointment. SIZE: Large. *STOCK: Oil paintings especially 19th-20th C landscape.* TEL: 01451 870567; fax - 01451 870678. SER: Restorations; framing.

Country Life Antiques
Grey House, The Square. GL54 1AF. Open 10-5. *STOCK: Scientific instruments, decorative accessories, pewter, brass, copper, furniture.* PARK: Easy. TEL: 01451 831564; fax - same.

The John Davies Gallery
Church St. GL54 1BB. CADA. Est. 1977. Open 9.30-1.30 and 2.30-5.30. SIZE: Large. *STOCK: Contemporary and late period paintings; limited edition bronzes.* PARK: In square. TEL: 01451 831698; fax - 01451 832477. SER: Restoration and conservation to museum standard.

Durham House Antiques Centre
Sheep St. GL54 1AA. Open 10-5, Sun. 11-5. SIZE: 30+ dealers. PARK: Easy. TEL: 01451 870404; fax - same; e-mail - durhamhouse@ compuserve.com. SER: Buys at auction. FAIRS: NEC (Aug); Newark; Ardingly. Below are listed the dealers at this centre.

Acorn Antiques
(Derek Howe and Stanley Taylor). Est. 1987. *19th C Staffordshire figures and animals.*

Ancient and Oriental Ltd
Ancient art and archaeological items, many periods, lands and cultures.

Aston Antiques
Arts and Crafts and Art Deco lighting, decanters, drinking glasses and ceramics, metalwork and furniture.

Avoncroft Antiques
Oak and mahogany furniture; mantel, wall and carriage clocks; ceramics.

Judi Bland Antiques
Toby jugs, Staffordshire, oak furniture, metalware.

Bread and Roses
19th-20th C kitchen, dairy, laundry and garden collectibles.

Castle Antiques
Pictures, prints, metalware and leather items, ceramics and furniture.

Brian Collyer
English pottery and Staffordshire figures; corkscrews, prints and pictures, small furniture.

Crockwell Antiques
(Philip Dawes). *Longcase clocks, silver, brass and copper, Ironstone china, 18th-19th C furniture.*

Lee Elliott
19th-20th C prints and pictures, specialising in country pastimes.

Jane Fairfield
Elegant silver and plate, Continental porcelain and objet d'art.

Tony and Jane Finnegan
Traditional English and French furniture and mirrors, lighting, decorative accessories including papier mâché and tole.

Anita Harris
French and English decorative furniture and accessories, prints and pictures.

Beryl and Brian Harrison
Linen and lace, tableware and bedclothes.

Erna Hiscock and John Shepherd
Samplers and needlework, early ceramics and blue and white, carvings, country furniture and decorative items.

Harry Horner
Silver and silver plate cutlery; 19th C glassware.

Dorothy Hyatt
Early English porcelain and pottery (Worcester, creamware and blue and white); 18th-19th C drinking glasses.

Ian Kellam
English and Continental porcelain, silver and jewellery, religious objects and objets d'art.

Lineage Antiques
Portrait miniatures, silver and jewellery, tartan and Mauchlineware and objets du vertu.

Little Nells
(Helen Middleton). *Coronation commemoratives, automobilia, Staffordshire and majolica, collectibles and small interesting items.*

Audrey McConnell
Silver and jewellery, picture frames, ceramics, ivory and micromosaics.

Colin Morris
Early carvings, pewter, copper and brass, ceramics, early oak furniture.

Peggy Nichols
Silver and plate, jewellery and glass.

Outram Antiques
(Philip and Dorothy Lipman). *18th-19th C oak and pine country furniture, Ironstone china, prints and decorative items.*

Paper Moon Books
19th-20th C bindings including poetry, prose and history; prayer books and bibles.

Pauline Parkes
19th-20th C Mauchlineware, treen and metal sewing ephemera.

Edith and Brian Prosser Antiques
18th-20th C decorative furniture, mirros, prints, lighting, glass and ceramics.

Quartz and Clay
Arts and Crafts, Art Deco glass and ceramics - Whitefriars, Clarice Cliff and Denby.

Lindsey Richardson Antiques
19th C ceramics including Staffordshire; glass and small decorative items.

Betty Thornley Antiques
Prints and 19th C porcelain, candlesticks and metalware.

Times Past
(Judi Pollitt). *Needlework tools, chatelaines, small silver and objets de vertu*

Wellington Antiques
(Martin Woodford and John Partner). *Quality 19th C mahogany furniture - tables, chairs, chests of drawers, desks and whatnots.*

Paul Wright Antiques
Mahogany furniture, clocks, tea caddies, work boxes and writing slopes; jewellery and silver. SER: Restorations (jewellery); stones supplied and matched.

Yorca Antiques
(Paul and Philippa Hughes). *English porcelain including Derby and Worcester.*

The Fosse Gallery
The Square. GL54 1AF. Est. 1979. Open 10-5.30. SIZE: Large. *STOCK: English and Scottish painters, many RA, RSA and Royal Glasgow Institute members, including Gore, Howard, Ward, Dunstan, Spear, Weight, Morrocco, Donaldson, McClure, Haig, Devlin and Michael Scott.* LOC: Off Fosseway, A429. PARK: Easy. TEL: 01451 831319; fax - 01451 870309. SER: Valuations.

Fosse Way Antiques
Ross House, The Square. GL54 1AF. (M. Beeston). CADA. Est. 1969. Open 10-5. SIZE: Medium. *STOCK: Mahogany and walnut furniture, oil paintings, £500-£10,000; bronzes, boxes and decorative objects, £150-£2,000, all 18th to early 19th C.* LOC: East side of the Square, behind the Town Hall. PARK: Easy. TEL: 01451 830776. SER: Valuations; buys at auction. VAT: Spec.

Fox Cottage Antiques
Digbeth St. GL54 1BN. (Sue London). Est. 1995. Open 10-5. SIZE: 9 dealers. *STOCK: Wide variety of general antiques including pottery and porcelain, silver and plate, metalware, prints, small furniture, country and decorative items, mainly pre 1900, £5-£500.* LOC: Left hand side at bottom of narrow street, running down from The Square. PARK: Nearby. TEL: 01451 870307.

La Chaise Antique

Beauport, Sheep Street, Stow-on-the-Wold, Glos GL54 1AA
Tel: (01451) 830582 Mobile: (07831) 205002

Specialists in leather chairs, upholstery and suppliers of loose leather desk tops. Always available from our new Showroom at Stow-on-the-Wold after 30 years at Faringdon.

Typical example of our leather fully re-upholstered Victorian Chesterfields.

Keith Hockin Antiques BADA
The Square. GL54 1AF. CADA. Est. 1968. Open Thurs., Fri., Sat., 10-5, other times by appointment or ring the bell. SIZE: Medium. *STOCK: Oak furniture, 1600-1750; country furniture in oak, fruitwoods, yew, 1700-1850; pewter, copper, brass, ironwork, all periods.* Not Stocked: Mahogany. PARK: Easy. TEL: 01451 831058; fax - same. SER: Buys at auction (oak, pewter, metalwork). VAT: Stan/Spec.

Hungry Ghost
1 Brewery Yard, Sheep St. GL54 1AA. (Virginia Kern). Est. 1998. Open 9.30-5.30, Sun. 10-4.30. SIZE: Medium. *STOCK: Chinese furniture and artefacts, 18th-19th C, £50-£8,000.* PARK: Nearby. TEL: 01451 870101. VAT: Stan.

Huntington Antiques Ltd
The Old Forge, Church St. GL54 1BE. (M.F. and S.P. Golding). LAPADA. CADA. CINOA. Resident. Est. 1974. Open 9.30-5.30 or by appointment. *STOCK: Early period and fine country furniture, metalware, treen and textiles, tapestries and works of art.* TEL: 01451 830842; fax - 01451 832211; e-mail - info@huntington-antiques.com; website - www.huntington-antiques.com. SER: Valuations; buys at auction. FAIRS: LAPADA; Madrid. VAT: Spec.

Kenulf Fine Arts
Digbeth St. GL54 1BN. (E. and J. Ford). LAPADA. Est. 1978. Open 10-5, Sun. 12-5. *STOCK: 19th to early 20th C oils, watercolours and prints; decorative items, fine period walnut and mahogany furniture.* TEL: 01451 870878; mobile - 07774 107269. SER: Valuations; restorations (oils and watercolours, period framing).

T.M. King-Smith & Simon W. Nutter
Wraggs Row, Fosseway. GL54 1JT. Est. 1975. Open 9.30-5.30. *STOCK: 18th-19th C mahogany and oak furniture, £500-£10,000; silver, porcelain, brass and copper.* LOC: Near traffic lights oppos1te the Unicorn Hotel. TEL: 01451 830658. SER: Buys at auction. VAT: Spec.

La Chaise Antique
Beauport, Sheep St. GL54 1AA. (Roger Clark). LAPADA. Est. 1968. Open 9.30-5.30. CL: Sun. except by appointment. SIZE: Large. *STOCK: Chairs, pre-1860; furniture, 18th-19th C; general antiques, decorators' items.* Not Stocked: Silver, porcelain and glass. PARK: Ample. TEL: 01451 830582; mobile - 07831 205002. SER: Valuations; restorations; upholstery (leather and fabrics); table top liners. FAIRS: NEC (April, Aug., Dec.); LAPADA NEC (Jan.); GAF, Earls Court (Sept./Oct.). VAT: Spec.

Roger Lamb Antiques & Works of Art
The Square. GL54 1AB. LAPADA. CADA.
Open 10-5. *STOCK: 18th to early 19th C
furniture especially small items, lighting,
decorative accessories, oils and watercolours.*
TEL: 01451 831371. SER: Search.

Oriental Gallery
GL56 0QW. (Patricia Cater). Open by
appointment only. *STOCK: Oriental ceramics and
works of art.* TEL: 01451 830944; fax - 01451
870126; e-mail - patriciacaterorg@aol.com;
website - www.patriciacater-orientalart.com

Park House Antiques
Park St. GL54 1AQ. (G. and B. Sutton). Est.
1986. Open 10-5, winter - 11-4.30. CL: Tues. and
all of May. SIZE: Large. *STOCK: Early dolls,
teddy bears, toys, Victorian linen and lace,
porcelain, collectables, small furniture and
pictures.* PARK: Easy. TEL: 01451 830159;
home - same; website - www.TheToymuseum.
co.uk. SER: Museum of dolls, teddies, toys,
textiles and collectables; teddy bears repaired;
antique dolls dressed. VAT: Stan/Spec.

Antony Preston Antiques Ltd   BADA
**The Square. GL54 1AB. CADA. Est. 1965.
Open 9.30-5.30 or by appointment. *STOCK:
18th-19th C English and Continental furniture
and objects; barometers and period lighting.*
TEL: 01451 831586; fax - 01451 831596. VAT:
Stan/Spec.**

Priests Antiques
The Malt House, Digbeth St. GL54 1BN. (A.C.
Priest). Est. 1986. Open 10-5. SIZE: Large.
*STOCK: English furniture, oak, walnut,
fruitwood and mahogany, 17th-19th C.* PARK:
Easy. TEL: 01451 830592; fax - 01451 830592.
SER: Valuations. VAT: Spec.

Queens Parade Antiques Ltd   BADA
**The Square. GL54 1AB. (Antony Preston
Antiques Ltd). CADA. Est. 1965. Open 9.30-
5.30. SIZE: Large. *STOCK: 18th-19th C
furniture, papier mâché, tôle peinte, needlework
and period lighting.* LOC: Off Fosse Way.
PARK: Easy. TEL: 01451 831586. VAT:
Stan/Spec.**

Michael Rowland Antiques
Little Elms, The Square. GL54 1AF. Open 11-
4.30. SIZE: Medium. *STOCK: Furniture,
including Welsh dressers, farmhouse tables, gate
legs, side tables and bureaux, 17th-18th C, £500-
£8,000.* PARK: Easy. TEL: 01451 870089; home
- same. VAT: Spec.

Ruskin Decorative Arts
5 Talbot Court. GL54 1DP. (Anne and William
Morris). CADA Est. 1990. Open 9.30-1 and 2-

5.30. SIZE: Small. *STOCK: Interesting and
unusual decorative objects, Arts & Crafts
furniture, Art Nouveau, Art Deco, glass and
pottery, 1860-1940.* LOC: Between The Square
and Sheep Street. PARK: Nearby. TEL: 01451
832254; fax - 01451 832167; home - 01993
831880. SER: Valuations.

Samarkand Galleries
7 & 8 Brewery Yard, Sheep St. GL54 1AA.
(Brian MacDonald). LAPADA. CADA. CINOA.
Est. 1979. Open 10-5.30, Sun. by appointment.
SIZE: Medium. *STOCK: Tribal and village rugs
and artefacts, 19th C, £100-£10,000; fine
decorative carpets, 19th-20th C, £1,000-
£10,000+; kelims, 19th-20th C, £200-£2,000;
also unique contemporary rugs and carpets.*
LOC: Street adjacent to Market Sq. PARK: Easy.
TEL: 01451 832322; fax - same; e-mail - mac@
samarkand.co.uk; website - www. samarkand.
co.uk. SER: Exhibitions; valuations; restorations;
cleaning. VAT: Stan/Spec.

Arthur Seager Antiques
50 Sheep St. GL54 1AA. Open by appointment.
*STOCK: Period oak, carvings and sculpture,
£500-£20,000.* TEL: 01451 831605.

Stow Antiques
The Square. GL54 1AF. (Mr and Mrs J. Hutton-
Clarke). LAPADA. CADA. Resident. Est. 1969.
Open Mon.-Sat. 11-1 and 2-5.30 other times by
appointment. SIZE: Large. *STOCK: Furniture,
mainly Georgian, £500-£30,000; decorative
items, gilded mirrors, £50-£10,000.* PARK: Easy.
TEL: 01451 830377; fax - 01451 870018. SER:
Shipping worldwide.

Styles of Stow
The Little House, Sheep St. GL54 1JS. (Mr and Mrs
W.J. Styles). Est. 1981. Open 10-5.30. SIZE:
Medium. *STOCK: Longcase (100+) and bracket
clocks, barometers, 18th-19th C, £400-£30,000; fine
furniture, 18th-19th C, £250-£15,000; oils and
watercolours, 19th-20th C, £25-£20,000.* LOC:
Opposite post office. PARK: Easy. TEL: 01451
830455; home and fax - same; e-mail - info@
stylesofstow.co.uk; website - www.styles
ofstow.co.uk. SER: Valuations; restorations; buys at
auction (longcase and bracket clocks). VAT: Margin.

Talbot Court Galleries
Talbot Court. GL54 1BQ. (J.P. Trevers). Est.
1988. Open 9.30-1 and 1.30-5.30. SIZE: Medium.
*STOCK: Prints and maps, 1580-1880, £10-
£5,000.* LOC: Behind Talbot Hotel in precinct
between the Square and Sheep St. PARK:
Nearby. TEL: 01451 832169; fax - 01451
832167. SER: Valuations; restorations (cleaning,
colouring); framing; buys at auction (engravings).
VAT: Stan.

Tudor House Antiques Dealers

Sheep Street, Stow-on-the-Wold, Glos., GL54 1AA
Tel/Fax: 01451 830021

12 dealers trading in furniture, metalware, porcelain, watercolours, sporting goods, lighting, objets-d'art and garden furniture.

Tudor House
Sheep St. (Peter Collingridge and Roy Hooper). Est. 1978. Open 10-5, Sun. by appointment. SIZE: 7 showrooms. *STOCK: Furniture, £500-£10,000; metalware, £50-£2,500; both 1700-1900. Porcelain, 1720-1920, £50-£2,500; watercolours, 1780-1940, £50-£1,000.* LOC: Turn at traffic lights from A429. PARK: At rear. TEL: 01451 830021; fax - same; mobile - 07860 581858. SER: Valuations. VAT: Spec.

Vanbrugh House Antiques
Park St. GL54 1AQ. (J. and M.M. Sands). Resident. Est. 1972. Open 10-6 or by appointment. *STOCK: Furniture and decorative items, 17th to early 19th C; early maps, music boxes, square pianos, clocks and barometers.* LOC: Opposite the Bell Inn. PARK: Easy. TEL: 01451 830797; fax - same. SER: Valuations. VAT: Stan/Spec.

Wyndhams
7a Talbot Court, The Square. GL54 1BQ. (Philip Brown and Kevin Quin). Est. 1988. Open 10-5 or by appointment. SIZE: Medium - 2 showrooms. *STOCK: Fine mid-18th to early 19th C English exotic wood furniture and barometers; fine Art and Crafts and other early 20th C silver; decorative antiques including 19th C Chinese blue and white ceramics, boxes and caddies; brass and ceramic lampbases; late 19th to early 20th C garden watercolours and prints.* LOC: Between The Square and Sheep St. PARK: The Square. TEL: 01451 870067; fax - same; e-mail - antiques@wyndhams.com; website - www.wyndhams.com SER: Valuations. VAT: Spec.

Shabby Tiger Antiques
18 Nelson St. GL5 2HN. (S. Krucker). Est. 1975. Open 11-6. *STOCK: 19th C furniture, pictures, jewellery, silver and plate, china, glass, metalware, decorative items.* LOC: Nelson St. is adjacent to Parliament St. car park. PARK: Opposite. TEL: 01453 759175.

Architectural Heritage
Taddington Manor. GL54 5RY. CADA. Est. 1978. Open 9.30-5.30, Sat. 10.30-4.30. SIZE: Large. *STOCK: Garden ornaments, statues, fountains, temples, seats, urns; chimney pieces in stone; oak and pine panelling.* PARK: Easy. TEL: 01386 584414; fax - 01386 584236; e-mail - puddy@architectural-heritage.co.uk; website - www.architectural-heritage.co.uk. VAT: Stan.

The Antique and Interior Centre
51A Long St. GL8 8AA. TADA. Open 10-5, Sun. 11-5 and most Bank Holidays. SIZE: 8 dealers. *STOCK: Furniture, porcelain, silver and pictures; interior design items.* TEL: 01666 505083.

The Antiques Emporium
The Old Chapel, Long St. GL8 8AA. (D. Sayers). TADA. Est. 1993. Open 10-5, Sun. 1-5. SIZE: Large - 38 dealers. *STOCK: Fruitwood and country furniture, fine oak and mahogany, clocks, china, porcelain, treen, copper and brass, jewellery, silver, kitchenalia, militaria, £1-£15,000.* Not Stocked: Reproductions. PARK: Nearby. TEL: 01666 505281; fax - 01666 505661. SER: Export. VAT: Stan/Spec.

Artique
Talboys House, Church St. GL8 8JG. (George Bristow). TADA. Open 9-5. *STOCK: Interiors, textiles, carpets and kelims and objets d'art from the Orient.* TEL: 01666 503597; fax - same; e-mail - george@artique.demon.co.uk.

Ball and Claw Antiques
45 Long St. GL8 8AA. (Chris Kirkland). TADA. Est. 1994. Open 10-5 and most Sundays 2-5. SIZE: Medium. *STOCK: 17th-19th C furniture, engravings, pictures, linens, textiles, children's*

decorative toys and general antiques, £5-£5,000.
PARK: Easy. TEL: 01666 502440; mobile - 07957 870423.

Balmuir House Antiques
14 Long St. GL8 8AQ. (P. Whittam). LAPADA. TADA. Open 9.30-5.30, Sun. 2-5.30. SIZE: Large. *STOCK: Furniture, paintings, mirrors, 19th C, £500-£5,000.* LOC: Town centre. PARK: Easy. TEL: 01666 503822; home - same. SER: Restorations (furniture, upholstery, paintings). VAT: Spec.

The Black Sheep
51 Long St. GL8 8AA. (Oliver McErlain). Open 10.30-5, Sat. 10-5, Sun. 12-4. SIZE: Small. *STOCK: Traditional English furniture.* PARK: Easy. TEL: 01666 505026.

Breakspeare Antiques
36 and 57 Long St. GL8 8AQ. (M. and S. Breakspeare). LAPADA. CADA. Resident. Est. 1962. Open 10-5 or by appointment. CL: Thurs. SIZE: Medium. *STOCK: English period furniture - early walnut, 1690-1740, mahogany, 1750-1835.* PARK: Own. TEL: 01666 503122; fax - same. VAT: Stan/Spec.

The Chest of Drawers
24 Long St. GL8 8AQ. (A. and P. Bristow). TADA. Resident. Est. 1969. Open Tues.-Fri. 9.30-6, Mon. by appointment. SIZE: Medium + trade store at The Coach House, 4 The Chipping (open at all times). *STOCK: Late Georgian, Regency and Victorian furniture; country pieces, 17th-18th C; china and brass.* LOC: On A433. PARK: Easy. TEL: 01666 502105; home - same. VAT: Spec.

Day Antiques   BADA
5 New Church St. GL8 8DS. CADA. TADA. Est. 1975. Open 10-5.30. SIZE: Medium. *STOCK: Early oak furniture and related items.* **TEL: 01666 502413; fax - 01666 505894; e-mail - dayantiques@lineone.net; website - www.dayantiques.com VAT: Spec.**

The Decorator Source
39a Long St. GL8 8AA. (Colin Gee). TADA. Open 10-5 or by appointment. SIZE: Large. *STOCK: French provincial furniture - armoires, farm tables, buffets; decorative items and accessories of interest to interior decorators.* PARK: Easy. TEL: 01666 505358. VAT: Stan/Spec.

Anne Fowler
35 Long St. GL8 8AA. TADA. Est. 1995. Open 10-5.30, Sun. by appointment. SIZE: Medium. *STOCK: Mainly French painted and decorative items including garden furniture and accessories, mirrors, faience and pots, wirework, lighting and*

prints, £20-£2,000. PARK: Easy. TEL: 01666 504043; home - same; fax - 01666 500256; e-mail - annefowler.fsnet.co.uk. VAT: Stan/Spec.

Gales Antiques
52 Long St. GL8 8AQ. (M.R. Mathews). TADA. Est. 1979. Open 10-5.30. SIZE: Medium. *STOCK: English and French country furniture and decorative items, 17th-19th C, £5-£5,000.* PARK: Easy. TEL: 01666 502686. VAT: Stan/Spec.

Jacqueline Hall Antiques
LAPADA. Est. 1976. Open by appointment. *STOCK: Furniture and mirrors, £500-£4,500; decorative items and objects, 18th-19th C.* TEL: 01666 500247; e-mail - j.hall.antiques@talk21. com. SER: Valuations. FAIRS: BABAADA Decorative, Bath; Decorative Antiques & Textiles, Battersea. VAT: Stan/Spec.

Hampton Gallery
8 Tetbury Upton. GL8 8LP. (P. Downey). Resident. Est. 1969. Open by appointment. SIZE: Large. *STOCK: Weapons, arms and armour, 1700-1880, £100-£25,000.* LOC: Off junction 17, M4. PARK: Easy. TEL: 01666 502971. SER: Valuations; buys at auction (arms). FAIRS: All major. VAT: Spec.

Catherine Hunt
No. 13, The Antique & Interior Centre, 51A Long St. GL8 8AA. TADA. *STOCK: Pre-1800 Oriental ceramics, mainly Sung, Yuan, Ming and early Qing including provincial, Asian and European export and palace/imperial ware; Oriental textiles and furniture.* TEL: 01666 505083; 01242 227794; mobile - 07976 319344.

Jester Antiques
10 Church St. GL8 8JG. (Lorna Coles and Peter Bairsto). TADA. Open 10-5.30, including Sun. *STOCK: Longcase and wall clocks, also oil portraits and pictures, Oriental objects, lamps, furniture, decorative items, outside statuary and architectural.* TEL: 01666 505125.

Merlin Antiques
Shops 4 & 5 Chipping Court Shopping Mall. GL8 8ES. (Miriam and Brian Smith). Est. 1990. Open 9.30-5, Sun. by appointment. SIZE: Medium. *STOCK: Furniture, Georgian to date, £50-£2,000; collectables, glass, pictures, china, jewellery - gold, silver and costume, £2-£500.* PARK: Nearby. TEL: 01666 505008. SER: Valuations; restorations.

Bobbie Middleton
58 Long St. GL8 8AQ. CADA, TADA. Open 10-1 and 2.30-5, Sun. by appointment. *STOCK: Classic country house furniture, mirrors, sconces*

and upholstered furniture, 18th-19th C. LOC: Corner New Church St. TEL: 01666 502761; mobile - 07774 192660. VAT: Spec.

Peter Norden Antiques
61 Long St. GL8 8AA. TADA. Open 10-5.30, Sun. by appointment. SIZE: Medium. *STOCK: Early oak furniture, 16th-18th C, £250-£10,000; country furniture, 15th-19th C, £75-£10,000; early carvings, metalware, pewter, pottery, treen, 14th-19th C, £10-£20,000.* PARK: Nearby. TEL: 01666 503854; fax - same; home - 01452 770536. SER: Valuations. VAT: Spec.

Old Mill Market Shop
12 Church St. GL8 8JG. (Mr and Mrs M. Green). Open 10-5.30, Thurs. 10-1. *STOCK: General antiques, collectables and bric-a-brac.* TEL: 01666 503127.

Porch House Antiques
40/42 Long St. GL8 8AQ. TADA. Open 10-5. *STOCK: 17th-20th C furniture and decorative items.* TEL: 01666 502687.

Sieff
49 Long St. GL8 8AA. LAPADA. TADA. Est. 1994. Open 10-5.30, Sun. by appointment. SIZE: Large. *STOCK: English and French 18th-20th C furniture and objets, £100-£10,000.* PARK: Easy. TEL: 01666 504477; fax - 01666 504478; e-mail - ssieff@hotmail.com. SER: Valuations; buys at auction. FAIRS: Harvey Decorative Antique & Textile. VAT: Stan/Spec.

Tetbury Gallery
18 Market Place. GL8 8DD. (Jane Maile). FATG. TADA. Open every day. *STOCK: Original and limited edition prints, from Victorian water-colours and oils to contemporary artists including Russell Flint, David Shepherd and Ben Maile.* TEL: 01666 503412.

Tetbury Old Books & Coach House Antiques
4 The Chipping. GL8 8ET. (Tetbury Old Books Ltd and A. & P. Bristow). TADA. Open 10-6, Sun. 11-5. *STOCK: Antiquarian and secondhand books and prints; English antique furniture.* TEL: 01666 504330; fax - 01666 504458; e-mail - oldbooks@tetbury.co.uk.

Westwood House Antiques
29 Long St. GL8 8AA. (Richard Griffiths and Lynne Petersen). TADA. Resident. Open 10-5.30 or by appointment. SIZE: Large. *STOCK: Oak, elm and ash country furniture especially dressers, dresser bases and tables, 17th-19th C; occasional French pieces; decorative pottery, pewter and treen.* TEL: 01666 502328; fax - same; mobile - 07774 952909.

GLOUCESTERSHIRE

TEWKESBURY

Berkeley Antiques
132 High St. GL20 5JR. (P. and S. Dennis). Open 9.30-5.30. CL: Thurs. pm. SIZE: Large. *STOCK: Mahogany, oak, walnut and pine, 17th-19th C, £50-£2,000; brass, copper, silver, china and glass.* TEL: 01684 292034. SER: Restorations. VAT: Stan/Spec.

Gainsborough House Antiques
81 Church St. GL20 5RX. (A. and B. Hilson). Open 9.30-5. *STOCK: Furniture, 18th to early 19th C; glass, porcelain.* TEL: 01684 293072. SER: Restorations; conservation.

Tewkesbury Antiques & Collectables Centre
Tolsey Lane (by The Cross). GL20 5AE. Open 9.30-5.30, Sun. 10.30-5.30. SIZE: 10+ units. *STOCK: Furniture, rugs, porcelain, glass, textiles, pictures, kitchenalia.* LOC: Town centre. TEL: 01684 294091.

Whatnots of Tewkesbury
24 St. Mary's Lane. GL20 5SF. (D. Lothian). Est. 1988. Open 11-1 and 1.30-5. SIZE: Small. *STOCK: Small Victorian and Edwardian furniture, £50-£750; pictures and prints, china and pottery, silver, plate and pewter, curios and ethnic items, £10-£500.* LOC: Near river and abbey. PARK: Nearby. TEL: 01684 294154; home - same.

THORNBURY, Nr. Bristol

Thornbury Antiques
3A High St. BS35 2AE. (H. Hill). Est. 1993. Open 10-5. SIZE: Small. *STOCK: Victorian pine furniture, china, glass and jewellery.* PARK: Opposite. TEL: 01454 413722. SER: Valuations. VAT: Spec.

TODENHAM, Nr. Moreton-in-Marsh

Geoffrey Stead
BADA
Wyatts Farm. GL56 9NY. Est. 1963. Open by appointment only. *STOCK: English and Continental furniture, decorative works of art and sculpture.* TEL: 01608 650997; fax - 01608 650597; mobile - 07768 460450; e-mail - geoffreystead@geoffreystead.com.

WICKWAR

Bell Passage Antiques
38 High St. GL12 8NP. (Mrs D.V. Brand). LAPADA. Est. 1966. Open 9-5. CL: Thurs. except by appointment. *STOCK: Furniture, glass, porcelain, some pictures.* LOC: On B4060. PARK: Easy. TEL: 01454 294251; fax - same. SER: Restorations; upholstery; caning.

WINCHCOMBE

Campden Country Pine Antiques
Didbrook Fields Farm, Toddington. GL54 5PE. Open 7 days by appointment. SIZE: Warehouses. *STOCK: Antique pine.* PARK: Easy. TEL: 01242 620950; fax - same. *Trade Only.*

The Clock Shop
11 North St. GL54 5LH. (M. Lovatt). Est. 1994. Open 10-1 and 2-4.30. CL: Mon. SIZE: Small. *STOCK: Antique and period clocks, barometers and gramophones, £100-£3,000.* TEL: 01242 604780; fax - same; website - www.clock-shop-winchcombe.co.uk SER: Valuations; restorations (clocks). VAT: Spec.

Cotswold Antiques. com
Didbrook Fields, Toddington. GL54 5PE. Open 7 days mainly by appointment. SIZE: Large. *STOCK: English and Continental furniture, 17th-19th C.* TEL: 01242 620950; e-mail - Cotsantiks; website - www.Cotswoldantiques.com.

Government House
St Georges House, High St. GL54 5LJ. Open by appointment. *STOCK: Antique and pre-war lighting and accessories.* LOC: Village centre. PARK: Own. TEL: 01242 604562. SER: Spare parts stocked.

In Period
Queen Anne House. GL54 5LJ. (John Edgeler). Resident. Open 9.30-5.30. *STOCK: Furniture, metalwork, glass, ceramics, 1700-1930.* TEL: 01242 602319.

Prichard Antiques
16 High St. GL54 5LJ. (K.H. and D.Y. Prichard). CADA. Est. 1979. Open 9-5.30, Sun. by appointment. SIZE: Large. *STOCK: Period and decorative furniture, £10-£10,000; treen and metalwork, £5-£5,000; interesting and decorative accessories.* LOC: On B4632 Broadway to Cheltenham road. PARK: Easy. TEL: 01242 603566. VAT: Spec.

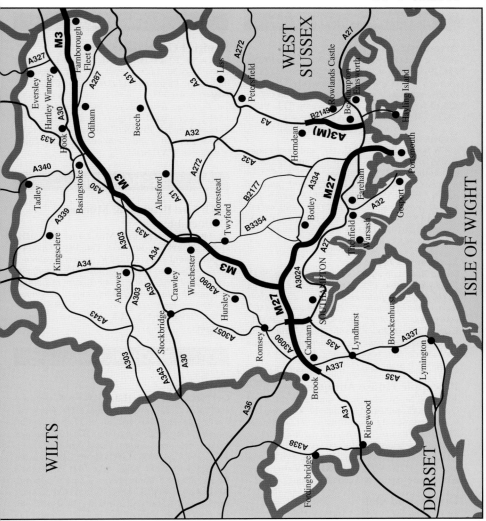

Dealers and Shops in Hampshire

Alresford	5	Farnborough	1	Morestead	1
Andover	1	Fleet	1	Odiham	1
Basingstoke	1	Fordingbridge	2	Petersfield	3
Bedhampton	1	Gosport	2	Portsmouth	5
Beech	1	Hartley Wintney	15	Ringwood	4
Botley	1	Hayling Island	1	Romsey	3
Brockenhurst	2	Hook	1	Rowlands Castle	1
Brook	1	Horndean	1	Southampton	5
Cadnam	1	Hursley	2	Stockbridge	3
Crawley	1	Kingsclere	1	Tadley	1
Emsworth	5	Liss	1	Titchfield	3
Eversley	2	Lymington	7	Twyford	1
Fareham	1	Lyndhurst	2	Warsash	1
				Winchester	12

ALRESFORD, Nr. Winchester

Artemesia
16 West St. SO24 9AT. (D.T.L. Wright). LAPADA. Est. 1972. Open 9.30-5. SIZE: Medium. *STOCK: English and Continental furniture, English, Continental and Oriental porcelain and works of art, £20-£6,000.* LOC: A31. PARK: Nearby. TEL: 01962 732277. SER: Valuations. VAT: Spec.

Evans and Evans
40 West St. SO24 9AU. (D. and N. Evans). LAPADA. Est. 1953. Open Fri. and Sat. or by appointment. SIZE: Medium. *STOCK: Clocks, watches, 1680-1900, £250-£50,000; musical boxes, 19th C, £500-£12,000; Regency and Victorian barometers, £200-£2,000. Stock only as listed.* LOC: A31. Shop on left going east. PARK: Easy. TEL: 01962 732170. SER: Valuations; buys at auction. VAT: Stan/Spec.

Laurence Oxley
Studio Bookshop and Gallery, 17 Broad St. SO24 9AW. ABA. Est. 1951. Open 9-5. SIZE: Large. *STOCK: Antiquarian books, £5-£2,500; topographical prints, £2-£250; maps, £5-£800; watercolours, £100-£10,000.* LOC: B3046. PARK: Easy. TEL: 01962 732188. SER: Valuations; restorations (oil paintings, watercolours, prints, books); framing; book-binding. FAIRS: London ABA. VAT: Stan.

Pineapple House Antiques
49 Broad St. SO24. (Diana Radford). Est. 1969. Open Thurs. and Fri. 11-4, Sat. 10.30-6, Sun. 11-6, other times by appointment. SIZE: Small. *STOCK: Furniture, especially dining tables, chairs, sideboards and dressers, 18th-20th C.* PARK: Easy. TEL: 01962 736575; fax - same; mobile - 07973 254749. SER: Valuations; restorations (repairs and cabinet making).

Underwood Oak
49 West St. SO24 9AB. (Ann and Dale Egerton). Est. 1995. Open 10-5. CL: Wed. SIZE: Small. *STOCK: Oak furniture, 17th-19th C, £200-£10,000.* LOC: Main street. PARK: Easy. TEL: 01962 735677; fax - 01730 267797. SER: Valuations; buys at auction (oak furniture).

ANDOVER

Graylings Antiques
(Nick and Gail Young). Est. 1968. Open by appointment only. *STOCK: Staffordshire portrait figures and animals, 1800-1890, £50-£2,500.* PARK: Easy. TEL: 01264 710077; home - same. SER: Valuations; restorations. FAIRS: NEC; Newark; Shepton Mallett.

BASINGSTOKE

Squirrel Collectors Centre
9 New St. RG21 1DF. (A.H. Stone). Est. 1981. Open 10-5.30. SIZE: Small. *STOCK: Jewellery and silver, Victorian and Edwardian, £5-£4,500; books, postcards, watches, collectors' items, smalls, china, toys and large furniture showroom.* LOC: Near traffic lights at junction with Winchester St. PARK: Nearby. TEL: 01256 464885; e-mail - antiques@onmail.co.uk. SER: Valuations. VAT: Stan.

BEDHAMPTON

J F F Fire Brigade & Military Collectables
Ye Olde Coach House, Mill Lane. PO9 3JH. (Johnny Franklin). Resident. Est. 1982. Open by appointment only. *STOCK: Brass firemen's helmets and fire related memorabilia; military, police and ambulance helmets, cap and collar badges, buttons, uniforms, caps, weapons, equipment, medals and brooches.* PARK: Easy. TEL: 02392 486485. SER: Valuations; buys at auction.

BEECH, Nr. Alton

Jardinique
Old Park Farm, Kings Hill. GU34 4AW. (Edward and Sarah Neish). Resident. Est. 1994. Open 10-5. CL: Sun. and Mon. and Jan. and Feb. except by appointment. SIZE: Very large. *STOCK: Garden ornaments, urns, statuary and furniture, from 17th C, £10-£5,000.* LOC: From Alton on the A339 Basingstoke road, take first left signed Beech, after 1.5 miles premises on left opposite Alton Abbey. PARK: Easy. TEL: 01420 560055; fax - 01420 560050; e-mail - Jardinique@aol.com. SER: Valuations; buys at auction (as stock). VAT: Stan/Spec.

BOTLEY, Nr. Southampton

The Furniture Trading Co
Old Flour Mills. S03 2GB. (L. Davies). Est. 1986. Open 9-5.30, Sun. 12-4. SIZE: Medium. *STOCK: Antique and reproduction furniture, including painted and distressed.* LOC: Off M27, exit 7. PARK: Easy. TEL: 01489 788194; fax - 01489 797337. SER: Valuations; restorations (furniture including upholstery, caning and French polishing); furniture made to order - old and new pine and painted; interior decoration. VAT: Stan.

BROCKENHURST

Antiquiteas

37 Brookley Rd. SO42 7RB. (R. Wolstenholme and S. Hamilton). Resident. Est. 1996. Open 9.30-5, Sun. 10-4. SIZE: Medium. *STOCK: Furniture including pine, £50-£350; china and glass, copper and brass, £10-£100; all 19th-20th C.* LOC: Near watersplash and village post office. PARK: Easy. TEL: 01590 622120. VAT: Stan.

Squirrels

Lyndhurst Rd. SO42 7RL. (Sue Crocket). Est. 1990. Open Wed.-Sun. 10-5, until dusk in winter. *STOCK: Furniture including stripped pine, china especially blue and white, 19th-20th C, to £1,000.* LOC: Take New Forest turn-off from M27. PARK: Easy. TEL: 01590 622433,

BROOK, Nr. Cadnam

F.E.A. Briggs Ltd

Birchenwood Farm. SO43 7JA. Open by appointment. *STOCK: Antique and Victorian furniture.* TEL: 023 8081 2595. SER: Restorations; valuations. VAT: Stan/Spec.

CADNAM

C.W. Buckingham

Twin Firs, Southampton Rd. SO40 2NQ. Resident. Open 9-6 or by appointment. CL: Thurs. *STOCK: Mainly pine, some period and Victorian furniture.* TEL: 023 8081 2122.

CRAWLEY, Nr. Winchester

Folly Farm Antiques

Folly Farm. SO21. (S. Baker). Open 9-5, including Sun. *STOCK: Pine and country furniture.* TEL: 01962 776687.

EMSWORTH

Antique Bed Company

32 North St. PO10 7DG. (Ian and Judi Trewick). Est. 1993. Open 9-5.30, Wed. 9-12.30, Sat. 9-5. SIZE: Small. *STOCK: Iron and brass, brass and wooden beds, 19th C, to £1,000.* LOC: From A259 roundabout in Emsworth, turn towards station. PARK: Nearby. TEL: 01243 376074; fax - same; home - 02392 492772. SER: Restorations (beds).

Clockwise

10 South St. PO10 7EH. (D. Judge). AHS. GMC. Est. 1976. Open daily. SIZE: Small. *STOCK: Longcase, wall, mantel, bracket and carriage clocks, 18th-19th C, £300-£12,000; books and tools.* LOC: A259 off A27, head for harbour. PARK: Easy. TEL: 01243 377558; website - www.clock-wise.co.uk. SER: Valuations; restorations.

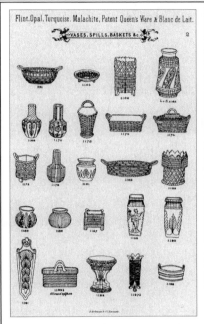

A page from Sowerby's Pattern Book IX, 1882. The text states that the illustrated 'vases, spills, baskets, etc' were available in 'Flint, Opal, Turquoise, Malachite, Patent Queen's Ware & Blanc de Lait'.

The invention of mechanically pressed glass in the late 1820s remains the most revolutionary development in glassmaking since ancient Rome. Rendering obsolete, or automating, production practices that had remained virtually unchanged since time immemorial, pressing enabled the working classes to own glassware for the first time.

From an article entitled '19th Century Pressed Glass' by Andy McConnell which appeared in the November 2000 issue of **Antique Collecting** magazine. For more details and to subscribe see page 147.

Dolphin Quay Antique Centre
Queen St. PO10 7BU. (N. & M. Farmer). Est. 1996. Open 10-5, Sun. and Bank Holidays 10-4. SIZE: Large - 30+ dealers. *STOCK: Fine English, French and country furniture, 18th C to 1939, £50-£5,000; marine antiques; clocks - bracket, mantel, longcase, £100-£5,000; wristwatches, fobs, dress watches, vintage pens, sporting apparel, luggage, conservatory and garden antiques, decorative arts, silver, jewellery, china, paintings, watercolours, prints.* PARK: Own and in square. TEL: 01243 379994; fax - 01243 379251; website - www.dolphin-quay-antiques. co.uk..

Mariners Antiques
Dolphin Quay Antiques Centre, Queen St. PO10 7BU. (Derrick W. Humphrey). Est. 1994. Open 10-5, Sun. 10-4. *STOCK: Nautical antiques, marine paintings and prints, ship models, pond yachts, Royal Navy and shipping line memorabilia, books, 19th to mid 20th C, £5-£3,000.* PARK: Easy. TEL: 01420 476718; fax - same; mobile - 07710 330700; website - www.mariners-antiques.com. SER: Valuations. FAIRS: Ship Show, Westminster, Titanic Society.

Tiffins Antiques
12 Queen St. PO10 7BL. (Phyl Hudson). Est. 1987. Open 10-5. SIZE: Small. *STOCK: General antiques, oil lamps and clocks.* TEL: 01243 372497; home - same.

Eversley Antiques Centre
Church Lane. RG27 0PX. (P. Coombs). Est. 1988. Open 10.30-5.30. CL: Mon. SIZE: Large. *STOCK: Regency, Victorian and Edwardian furniture.* LOC: 1.5 miles from Blackbush airport. PARK: Easy. TEL: 0118 9328518.

Colin Harris Antiques
at Eversley Antiques Centre, Church Lane. RG27 0PX. Est. 1966. Tues.-Sun. 10.30-5.30. *STOCK: General antiques, furniture and decorative items.* LOC: 1.5 miles from Blackbush airport. PARK: Easy. TEL: Home - 0118 973 2580. VAT: Spec.

Elizabethans
58 High St. PO16 7BG. (E.J. Keeble). Est. 1961. Open Mon., Thurs. and Sat. 10-4. *STOCK: Small general antiques including furniture.* TEL: 01329 234964 (answerphone).

Martin and Parke
97 Lynchford Rd. GU14 6ET. (J. Martin and J. Warde). LAPADA. Est. 1971. Open 9-5. SIZE:

Nicholas Abbott

High Street, Hartley Wintney, Hampshire RG27 8NY

*A good selection
of period
furniture
ranging from
1680 to 1830*

Tel/Fax: 01252 842365
e-mail:
nicholasabbott@web-hq.com
website:
www.nicholas-abbott.com

Large. *STOCK: Furniture, shipping goods and books.* TEL: 01252 515311. VAT: Stan.

Bona Arts Decorative Ltd
The Hart Shopping Centre. GU13 8AZ. ADDA. Open 10-5. *STOCK: Clarice Cliff, English pressed glass, 20th C English ceramics.* TEL: 01252 372188; website - www.claricecliff.co.uk. SER: Valuations; restorations (ceramics, bronze, spelter). VAT: Stan.

Mark Collier   **BADA**
24 High St. SP6 1AX. *STOCK: Period and decorative antiques.* **Not Stocked: Coins, medals and stamps. TEL: 01425 652555; fax - 01425 656886.**

Quatrefoil
Burgate. SP6 1LX. (C.D. and Mrs I. Aston). Resident. Est. 1972. Always open. SIZE: Large. *STOCK: Early oak furniture, 16th-18th C, £50-£15,000; carvings and sculpture, 13th-17th C, £20-£20,000; antiquities and coins, £50-£10,000.* LOC: On A338, adjacent Tudor Rose Inn. PARK: Easy. TEL: 01425 653309. VAT: Stan/Spec.

Peter Pan's Bazaar
87 Forton Rd. PO12 4TG. (S.V. Panormo). Est. 1960. CL: Mon., Tues. and Wed. *STOCK: Vintage cameras, early photographica, images, 1850-1950, £5-£1,500.* LOC: Main road into town. PARK: Easy. TEL: 023 9252 4254. FAIRS: Main south of England.

Peter Pan's of Gosport
87 Forton Rd. PO12 4TG. (J. McClaren). Est. 1965. CL: Mon., Tues. and Wed. *STOCK: Jewellery, dolls, toys and miniatures.* LOC: Main road into town. PARK: Easy. TEL: 023 9252 4254. FAIRS: Main south of England.

Nicholas Abbott
High St. RG27 8NY. (C.N. Abbott). LAPADA. Est. 1962. Open 9.30-5.30 or by appointment. *STOCK: English furniture, 18th to early 19th C.* LOC: A30. PARK: Easy. TEL: 01252 842365; fax - same; e-mail - nicholasabbott@web-hq.com; website - www.nicholas-abbott.com

ANDWELLS ANTIQUES LTD

HIGH STREET
HARTLEY WINTNEY
HAMPSHIRE
Tel. (01252) 842305
E-mail: andwellsantiques@btconnect.com
Website: www.andwells-antiques.com

18th and early 19th century furniture

Andwells Antiques Limited
High St. RG27 8NY. LAPADA. Est. 1967. Open 9-5.30, Sat. 9.30-5.30. SIZE: Large. *STOCK: Georgian and Regency furniture, mainly mahogany.* LOC: Main street. PARK: Easy. TEL: 01252 842305; fax - 01252 845149. VAT: Stan/Spec.

Antique House
22 High St. RG27 8NY. (R.M. Campbell and David Campbell). Open 10-5.30, Sun. by appointment. *STOCK: Furniture in walnut, mahogany, rosewood, oak and fruitwoods, 1710-1910; inlaid Edwardian furniture, mirrors, oils, watercolours and prints, £50-£5,000.* PARK: Easy. TEL: 01252 844499; fax/answerphone - 01252 845270. SER: Restorations (furniture and porcelain).

A selection of jasper and jasper dip. (Clockwise from top left) Unmarked blue jasper dip jug and cover sprigged with sylvan scene, £120. Unmarked blue jasper dip jardinière and stand sprigged with fauns and putti, £160. An Adams blue jasper sucrier and cover, £240. A Spode blue jasper dip pot-pourri vase and cover, £160. Unmarked blue jasper coffee cup and saucer, £130.

From an Auction Report by Christopher Wight which appeared in the March 2001 issue of **Antique Collecting** magazine on The Hacking Collection of Davenport, dry-bodied stoneware and other British ceramics held at Phillips Bayswater, 23rd January 2001. For more details and to subscribe see page 147.

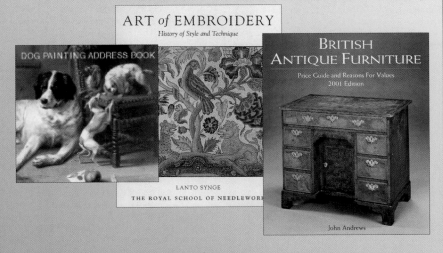

The Antiques Centre

Primrose House, London Rd. RG27 8RJ. (Mrs. Shelagh Lister). Open 10-5, Sun. 12-4. SIZE: Large - 15+ dealers. *STOCK: Fine quality* antique and country furniture, £250-£10,000; clocks, paintings, brass, copper, silver, 18th-20th C; china, including Art Deco, mirrors, decorative antiques for the home and garden, books, £1-£2,000. PARK: Easy. TEL: 01252 843393; mobile - 07836 734838.

Folding flick-comb in a lacquered metal case, British, 1920s-'30s. Case 4in. long. (Private collection)

From an article entitled 'Combs as Love-Tokens' by Jen Cruse and Robert Watts which appeared in the December 2000/January 2001 issue of **Antique Collecting** magazine. For more details and to subscribe see page 147.

Cedar Antiques Centre Ltd

High St. RG27 8NY. (Derek and Sally Green). Open 10-5.30, Sun. 11-5. SIZE: Large - 40+ dealers. *STOCK: Quality furniture, glass, porcelain and pottery, paintings, silver, collectibles from teddy bears to treen.* LOC: A30 village centre. PARK: Opposite. TEL: 01252 843222; fax - 01252 842111; website - www. cedar-antiques-com. VAT: Stan/Spec.

Cedar Antiques Limited

High St. RG27 8NY. (Derek and Sally Green). Est. 1964. Open 9-5.30, Sat. and Sun. 10-4. SIZE: Large. *STOCK: Fine English oak, walnut and country furniture, 17th-18th C, £50-£10,000; French provincial furniture, 1680-1780, £800-£5,000; steel and brasswork, £30-£1,000.* Not Stocked: China, glass, silver. LOC: A30. PARK: Opposite. TEL: 01252 843252; fax - 01252 842111. SER: Valuations; restorations (period furniture); interior design and furnishing. VAT: Stan/Spec.

Cedar Antiques Centre
Hartley Wintney, Hampshire, RG27 8NY

40 Individual Dealers offer a wide variety of good quality antiques and collectables. Charming Courtyard Café serves delicious Lunches, Cream Teas and also houses The T.G. Green Pottery Museum. Space for Dealers with high quality stock sometimes available.

Open: Mon to Sat. 10am to 5.30pm Sunday 11am to 5pm
Tel: 01252 843222 Fax: 01252 842111
www.cedar-antiques.com e-mail: cac@cedar-ltd.demon.co.uk

Cedar Antiques Ltd

Sally & Derek Green specialise in
COUNTRY FURNITURE WITH COLOUR!
Amusing accessories, Pewter, Brass, Textiles & Treen
Tel: 01252 843252 Fax: 01252 842111
www.cedar-antiques.com e-mail: ca@cedar-ltd.demon.co.uk

Bryan Clisby Antique Clocks
at Andwells Antiques, High St. RG27 8NY. Est.
1976. Open 9.30-5.30. SIZE: Large. *STOCK:
Longcase clocks, 1700-1830, £3,000-£20,000;
barometers, 1770-1850, £350-£3,000; bracket,
wall and mantel clocks.* LOC: A30 village centre.
PARK: Easy. TEL: 01252 716436. SER: Valuations; restorations (clocks and barometers).
VAT: Spec.

Deva Antiques
High St. RG27 8NY. (A. Gratwick). Open 9-5.30.
SIZE: Large. *STOCK: 18th-19th C English
mahogany and walnut furniture.* PARK: Easy.
TEL: 01252 843538/843656; fax - 01252 842946.
VAT: Stan/Spec.

Colin Harris Antiques
at Primrose House Antique Centre. RG27 8NY.
Est. 1966. Open 10.30-5.30 including Sun.
*STOCK: General antiques, furniture and
decorative items.* TEL: Home - 0118 973 2580.
VAT: Spec.

David Lazarus Antiques   BADA
**High St. RG27 8NS. Resident. Est. 1973. Open
9.30-5.30; some Sundays, other times by
appointment. SIZE: Medium. *STOCK: 17th to
early 19th C English and Continental furniture;
objets d'art.* LOC: Main street. PARK: Own.
TEL: 01252 842272. VAT: Stan/Spec.**

Old Forge Cottage Antiques
The Green. RG27 8PG. (Sue Carpenter). Open
Tues., Thurs., Fri. and Sat. 10-4, other days by
appointment. SIZE: Medium. *STOCK: Country
and general antiques.* LOC: A30. PARK: Easy.
TEL: 01252 842916.

Phoenix Green Antiques
London Rd. RG27 8RT. (John Biles). Open 9-6,
Sun. 10-5 or by appointment. SIZE: Large.
*STOCK: English and Continental furniture, 17th-
19th C.* TEL: 01252 844430; fax - 01252 849992;
e-mail - JohnBiles@PhoenixGreenAntiques.com;
website- www.PhoenixGreenAntiques.com/
PhoenixGreenDesign.com

A.W. Porter and Son
High St. RG27 8NY. (M.A. Porter). Est. 1844.
Open 9.30-5, Sat. 9.30-4.45. *STOCK: Clocks,
silver, jewellery, glass.* LOC: Opposite Lloyds
Bank. TEL: 01252 842676. SER: Restorations
(clocks). VAT: Stan/Spec.

Sheila Revell Antiques
at Deva, High St. RG27 8NY. Open 9-5.30.
*STOCK: 18th-19th C decorative objects, small
furniture and collectors' items especially tea
caddies and boxes.* TEL: 01252 843538.

Gregory Woodcock

at Phoenix Green Antiques, London Rd. RG27
8RT. Open 9-6, Sun. 10-5 or by appointment.
*STOCK: English and continental furniture and
objets d'art, 17th-20th C.* TEL: 01252 843647;
fax - 01252 849992; e-mail - GregoryWoodcock
@PhoenixGreenAntiques.com; website - www.
PhoenixGreenAntiques.com.

HAYLING ISLAND

J. Morton Lee   BADA

Cedar House, Bacon Lane. PO11 0DN. Est.
1984. Open by appointment. *STOCK: Watercolours, 18th-20th C, £50-£10,000.* **PARK:
Easy. TEL: 023 9246 4444; mobile - 07860
810938. SER: Valuations; buys at auction;
exhibitions in July and Dec. FAIRS: West
London (Jan); Chester (Feb); BADA (March);
Buxton (May); Olympia (Nov); NEC (Aug);
Harrogate (Sept). VAT: Stan/Spec.**

HOOK

Csaky's Antiques

RG27 0AT. Open by appointment only. *STOCK:
Early English and Continental furniture;
carvings, works of art; modern art and sculpture,
specialising in Guy Taplin.* TEL: 01256 880111;
fax - 01256 880601; mobile - 0777 342983; e-
mail - csakyart@btinternet.com.

HORNDEAN

Goss and Crested China Centre and Goss Museum

62 Murray Rd. PO8 9JL. (L.J. Pine). Est. 1968.
SIZE: Medium. *STOCK: Goss, 1860-1930, £2-
£1,000; other heraldic china, Carlton ware,
Charlotte Rhead, Chamelion, 1890-1930, £1-£1,000.* PARK: Easy.
TEL: 023 9259 7440; website - www.gosscrested
china.co.uk. SER: Valuations; collections
purchased. VAT: Stan.

HURSLEY, Nr. Winchester

Hursley Antiques

SO21 2JY. (S. Thorne). Est. 1980. Open 10-6.
STOCK: Pine. LOC: 4 miles from Winchester on
Romsey Rd. PARK: Easy. TEL: 01962 775488.
SER: Coppersmith - restorations and repairs
(metalware).

J. MORTON LEE

FINE WATERCOLOURS

**Cedar House, Bacon Lane,
Hayling Island, Hants. PO11 0DN**

*By appointment (023) 9246 4444
EMail: j.mortonlee@btinternet.com*

*Samuel ATKINS Fl. c.1787-1808
A Frigate at Anchor, smaller Craft nearby
Signed. 11¼" x 15¼" (28.5 x 39.5 cm)*

**ALSO EXHIBITING AT MAJOR
ANTIQUE FAIRS**

The Pine Emporium

The Old Bakery. SO21 2JY. (J. Greatrix). Est.
1993. Open 8.30-6, Sat. 9-5.30, Sun. 11-4. SIZE:
Large. *STOCK: Pine furniture, antique and
reclaimed, from 18th C; oak furniture, from 18th
C.* LOC: 3 miles west of Winchester on A31 to
Romsey. PARK: Easy. TEL: 01962 775449; fax -
01962 775123; website - www.pine-emporium.
com. SER: Valuations; restorations; bespoke
manufacture. VAT: Stan.

KINGSCLERE, Nr. Newbury

Kingsclere Old Bookshop

2A George St. RG20 5NQ. (Dr Tim and Ms R.
Oldham). PBFA. Est. 1978. Open 9-5. SIZE:
Medium. *STOCK: Books and prints, 19th-20th C,
£5-£500.* PARK: Nearby. TEL: 01635 297995;
fax - 01635 297677; e-mail - info@wyseby.co.u;
website - www.wyseby.co.uk. SER: Valuations.
FAIRS: PBFA London. VAT: Stan.

LISS

Plestor Barn Antiques

Farnham Rd. GU33 6JQ. Open 10-5, Sat. 10-2.
SIZE: Large. *STOCK: Furniture, including*

upholstered, Victorian and Edwardian, shipping goods, pine; china and glass, copper and brass. LOC: A325, 2 mins from A3 roundabout, near Spread Eagle public house. TEL: 01730 893922; mobile - 07850 539998.

LYMINGTON

Corfields Ltd
120 High St. SO41 9AQ. Open 9.15-5.30. SIZE: Large. *STOCK: English furniture, porcelain, English School watercolours and oil paintings.* TEL: 01590 673532; fax - 01590 678855. SER: Restorations. VAT: Stan/Spec.

Hughes and Smeeth Ltd
1 Gosport St. SO41 9BG. (P. Hughes and S. Smeeth). ABA. Est. 1976. Open 9.30-5. SIZE: Small. *STOCK: Antiquarian and secondhand books, maps and prints.* LOC: At bottom of High St. PARK: Nearby. TEL: 01590 676324. SER: Valuations; binding; framing. VAT: Stan.

Lymington Antiques Centre
76 High St. SO41 9AL. Open 10-5, Sat. 9-5. SIZE: 30 dealers. *STOCK: General antiques and books.* TEL: 01590 670934.

Barry Papworth
28 St. Thomas St. SO41 9NE. Est. 1960. Open 9-5. SIZE: Small. *STOCK: Diamond jewellery, £50-£4,000; silver, £25-£1,500; both 18th-19th C. Watches, 19th C, £50-£1,000.* LOC: A337 into town, bay window on left. TEL: 01590 676422. SER: Valuations; restorations. VAT: Stan/Spec.

This shipping scene off the French coast by Richard Parkes Bonington can be seen priced at £27,000 on Maurice Deer's stand at the Surrey Antiques Fair, Guildford on 5th-8th October.

From a Fairs Preview which featured in the October 2000 issue of **Antique Collecting** magazine. For more details and to subscribe see page 147.

Robert Perera Fine Art
19 St. Thomas St. SO41 9NB. (R.J.D. Perera). Open 10-1 and 2-5, lunch-times and Sun. by appointment. SIZE: Small. *STOCK: British paintings, 19th-20th C, £100-£5,000; occasional ceramics and sculpture, 19th-20th C, £50-£1,500.* LOC: Top (west) end of main shopping area. PARK: Easy. TEL: 01590 678230; website - www.ART-GALLERY.co.uk.

Platt's of Lymington
15 St Thomas St. SO41 9NB. (Mrs Kay Boyd-Platt). Est. 1997. Open Wed.-Sat. 10-5, other times by appointment. SIZE: Medium. *STOCK: Porcelain including Worcester, Derby, Coalport, Dresden, Sèvres, Volkstedt, Sitzendorf, Wedgwood, Doulton, Minton, George Jones, Samson, 18th-19th C, £10-£1,000; furniture especially small, 18th-19th C, £50-£5,000; artwork and collectables, 18th-20th C, £5-£2,000.* LOC: Next door to King's Arms. PARK: Rear of Waitrose. TEL: 01590 688769; home - same. SER: Valuations. VAT: Stan.

Wick Antiques
Fairlea House, 112 Marsh Lane. SO41 8NE. (Mr and Mrs C. Wallrock). Est. 1985. Open 9-5, Sat. 10-1. SIZE: Medium. *STOCK: French and English furniture, 19th C, £1,000-£15,000; small 19th to early 20th C items, £100-£1,000.* TEL: 01590 677558. SER: Valuations; restorations (furniture polishing, repairs, upholstery and re-gilding); buys at auction. FAIRS: Olympia. VAT: Spec.

LYNDHURST

Lita Kaye of Lyndhurst
13 High St. SO43 7BB. (S. and S. Ferder). Est. 1947. Open 9.30-1 and 2.15-5. SIZE: Large. *STOCK: Furniture, clocks, 1690-1820; decorative porcelain, 19th C.* LOC: A35. PARK: 100yds. in High St. TEL: 023 8028 2337. VAT: Stan/Spec.

Lyndhurst Antiques Centre
19-21 High St. SO43 7BB. (Keith J. Ashley). Est. 1997. Open 10-5. SIZE: Medium. *STOCK: Furniture and clocks, 18th to early 20th C, £50-£5,000; ceramics, 18th to mid 20th C, £5-£1,000; collectables, 20th C, £2-£200.* LOC: Main street by traffic lights. PARK: Loading bay nearby. TEL: 023 8028 4000; fax - 023 8028 2424.

MORESTEAD, Nr. Winchester

Burgess Farm Antiques
SO21 1LZ. (N. Spencer-Brayn). Est. 1970. Open 9-5. SIZE: Large. *STOCK: Furniture, especially*

pine and country, 18th-19th C, £25-£5,000; architectural items - doors, panelling, fire-places. LOC: 2 miles south of Winchester, off Corehampton road at Jackmans Hill corner. PARK: Easy. TEL: 01962 777546. SER: Stripping; export. VAT: Stan/Spec.

ODIHAM

The Odiham Gallery
78 High St. RG25 1HJ. (I. Walker). LAPADA. Open 10-5, Sat. 10-1. *STOCK: Decorative and Oriental rugs and carpets.* TEL: 01256 703415.

PETERSFIELD

The Barn
North Rd. GU31 4AH. (P. Gadsden). Est. 1956. Open 9-5. *STOCK: Victoriana, bric-a-brac; also large store of trade and shipping goods.* TEL: 01730 262958.

The Folly Antiques Centre
Folly Market, College St. GU31 4AD. (Red Goblet Ltd). Est. 1980. Open 9.30-5.30. SIZE: Medium. *STOCK: Furniture, 19th-20th C, £20-£1,000; ceramics and silver, 18th-20th C, £5-£100; jewellery, 19th-20th C; pictures, general antiques.* LOC: Town centre. PARK: Opposite - Festival Hall, Heath Rd. TEL: 01730 266650/ 269888.

The Petersfield Bookshop
16a Chapel St. GU32 3DS. (F. Westwood). ABA. Est. 1918. Open 9-5.30. SIZE: Large. *STOCK: Books, old and modern, £1-£500; maps and prints, 1600-1859, £1-£200; oils and water-colours, 19th C, £20-£1,000.* LOC: Chapel St. runs from the Square to Station Rd. PARK: Opposite. TEL: 01730 263438; e-mail - sales@petersfieldbookshop.com; website - www.petersfieldbookshop.com. SER: Restorations and rebinding of old leather books; picture-framing and mount-cutting. FAIRS: London ABA. VAT: Stan.

A small selection of the thousands of coloured pressed glass vases produced by European glassworks during the inter-war years. The makers of only three can be currently identified: Davidson of Gateshead's purple Cloud vase (fourth from left), the pink bowl at the front, by Val St Lambert, Belgium, and (extreme right) the winged vase by Sowerby. The geometric red vase (centre back) is marked 'TCHECOSLOVAKIE'. £10 to £50 for the most stylish. (Author's collection)

From an article entitled '20th Century Pressed Glass – Part I' by Andy McConnell which appeared in the March 2001 issue of **Antique Collecting** magazine. For more details and to subscribe see page 147.

Academy Books

13 Marmion Rd., Southsea. PO5 2AT. (William Robinson). Open 9-12 and 1-5, Fri. 9-12 and 1-3.30, Sat. 9-5.30. SIZE: Medium. *STOCK: Antiquarian books, 17th C, £5-£500; pictures, prints and postcards, £1-£100; some china, £25-£25.* LOC: Near St. Jude's church. PARK: Opposite. TEL: 023 9281 6632; fax/home - same. SER: Valuations; restorations (books).

A. Fleming (Southsea) Ltd

The Clock Tower, Castle Rd., Southsea. PO5 3DE. Est. 1905. Open 9.30-5.30, Sat. 9.30-1 or by appointment. *STOCK: Furniture, silver and general antiques.* TEL: 023 9282 2934; fax - 023 9229 3501; e-mail - @flemingsantiques. fsnet. co.uk; website - www.flemingsantiques. com. SER: Restorations. VAT: Stan/Spec.

The Gallery

11 and 19 Marmion Rd., Southsea. PO5 2AT. (I. Murphy). Open 10-5. *STOCK: At No.19 - Victorian chairs and chesterfields; at No.11 - furniture, mainly Victorian and Edwardian.* PARK: Nearby. TEL: 023 9282 2016.

Gray's Antique Centre

129-131 Havant Rd., Drayton. PO6 2AA. (Alexandra J. Gray). Est. 1968. Open 10-5, Sun. 12-4. CL: Wed. SIZE: Large - 10 dealers. *STOCK: English and French furniture, 18th-19th C, £200-£5,000; prints and paintings, china, collectables, pine, 18th-20th C, £25-£3,000.* PARK: Easy and side of shop. TEL: 023 9237 6379; mobile - 07811 778601. SER: Restorations (furniture and upholstery).

Oldfield Gallery

76 Elm Grove, Southsea. PO5 1LN. Est. 1970. Open 10-5. CL: Mon. SIZE: Large. *STOCK: Maps and engravings, 16th-19th C, £5-£1,000; decorative prints and some paintings, 19th-20th C, £5-£1,000.* PARK: Nearby. TEL: 023 9283 8042; fax - 023 9283 8042; e-mail - oldfield_maps@compuserve.com; websites - www. antiquemaps.co.uk; www.oldfield-antique maps.co.uk. SER: Valuations; restorations (maps and prints); framing. FAIRS: Bonnington Hotel Map (monthly). VAT: Stan.

Millers of Chelsea Antiques Ltd

Netherbrook House, 86 Christchurch Rd. BH24 1DR. LAPADA. Est. 1897. Open Mon. 9.30-1.30, Tues.-Fri. 9.30-5, Sat. 10-2, other times by appointment. SIZE: Large. *STOCK: Furniture - English and Continental country, mahogany and gilt, military, decorative items, treen, majolica and faïence, 18th-19th C, £25-£5,000.* LOC: On B3347 towards Christchurch. PARK: Own. TEL: 01425 472062; fax - 01425 472727; e-mail - mail@ millers-antiques.co.uk; website - www.millers-antiques.co.uk. FAIRS: Decorative Antiques; Wilton; Great Antiques. VAT: Stan/Spec.

R. Morgan Antiques

90 Christchurch Rd. BH24 1DR. Est. 1984. Open Tues.-Sat. 10-5. SIZE: Small. *STOCK: Militaria and postcards.* LOC: Off A31 into Ringwood, straight over 1st roundabout, left at next roundabout, shop 150yds. on right. PARK: Easy, and at rear. TEL: 01425 479400; fax - same; mobile - 07767 416106. SER: Valuations; restorations. FAIRS: Park Lane; Cumberland Hotel. VAT: Stan/Spec.

Smith & Sons

903 Christchurch Rd. BH7 6AX. (D.R., M. and T. Smith). Est. 1978. Open 9.30-5.30. SIZE: Large. *STOCK: Pine and other woods, 18th-19th C, £30-£1,000.* Not Stocked: Silver, fine china, bric-a-brac. LOC: Almost opposite fire station. PARK: Own. TEL: 01202 429523; home - same; e-mail - enquiries@dsmith&sons.demon.co.uk; website - www.dsmith&sons.demon.co. SER: Makers of cherry and oak replica items; restorations. VAT: Stan.

Lorraine Tarrant Antiques

23 Market Place. BH24 1AN. Est. 1991. Open 10-5. CL: Mon. SIZE: Medium. *STOCK: Victorian furniture, to £1,000; china, glass, collectors items, £5-£100.* LOC: Opposite church. PARK: Easy. TEL: 01425 461123.

Bell Antiques

8 Bell St. SO51 8GA. (M. and B.M. Gay). FGA. Est. 1979. Open 9.30-5.30. CL: Wed. (winter). SIZE: Large. *STOCK: Jewellery and silver, glass, pottery, porcelain, small furniture, prints and maps, mainly 19th-20th C.* LOC: Near market place. PARK: Town centre. TEL: 01794 514719. VAT: Global/Stan/Spec.

Cambridge Antiques

P O Box 169. SO51 6XU. LAPADA. Open by appointment only. SIZE: Large. *STOCK: Furniture, small china, jewellery, paintings.* TEL: 01794 324488; home - 01794 322125. VAT: Stan/Spec.

Romsey Medals
P O Box 169. SO51 6XU. (T. Cambridge, OMRS). Est. 1980. Open by appointment only. *STOCK: Medals, badges, militaria, and commemorative china.* TEL: 01794 324488; home - 01794 322125.

Good Day Antiques and Decor
22 The Green. PO9 6AB. (Gillian Day). Est. 1980. 11-5, Sun. 12-4.30. CL: Tues. and Wed. SIZE: Medium. *STOCK: Furniture, 1812-1940, £100-£1,000; porcelain and pottery, 1800-1950, £25-£500; jewellery and silver, 1840-1970, £25-£1,000; collectables, 19th-20th C, £5-£50.* LOC: Off junction 2, A3(M). PARK: Easy. TEL: 02392 412924; home - 02392 413221. SER: Restorations (silver plating, gilding, engraving and porcelain).

Mr. Alfred's "Old Curiosity Shop" and The Morris and Shirley Galleries
280 Shirley Rd., Shirley. SO15 3HL. Est. 1952. Open 9-6, including Sun. *STOCK: Furniture, 18th-20th C; paintings, porcelain, bronzes, brass, glass, books, silver, jewellery and general antiques.* LOC: On left of main Shirley road, 3/4 mile from Southampton central station. PARK: Own. TEL: 023 8077 4772. SER: Fine art dealer; valuer; auctioneer; curator; restorer; framer.

Amber Antiques
115 Portswood Rd., Portswood. SO17 2FX. (R. Boyle). Est. 1985. Open 10-5, Sat. 9-5, Sun. 11-3. SIZE: Large. *STOCK: Furniture, late Victorian to 1930's, £50-£100.* PARK: Easy. TEL: 02380 583645; fax - same. SER: Restorations (repairs, French polishing). VAT: Stan/Spec.

Meg Campbell
10 Church Lane, Highfield. SO17 1SZ. Est. 1967. Open by appointment only. *STOCK: English, Scottish and Irish silver, collectors' pieces, Old Sheffield plate, portrait miniatures.* TEL: 023 8055 7636. SER: Mail order; catalogues available. VAT: Spec.

Cobwebs
78 Northam Rd. SO14 0PB. (P.R. and J.M. Boyd-Smith). Open 10.30-4. CL: Wed. SIZE: Medium. *STOCK: Ocean liner memorabilia, china, silverplate, ephemera, paintings, furniture, ship fittings, 1840-1990, £5-£5,000.* LOC: Main road into city centre from the east. PARK: 20yds. TEL: 023 8022 7458; fax - same; website - www.cobwebs.uk.com. SER: Valuations. FAIRS: Beaulieu Boat & Auto; Ship Show, Westminster.

H.M. Gilbert and Son
2 1/2 Portland St. SO14 7EB. (R.C. and A.M. Gilbert). ABA. PBFA. Est. 1859. Open 9-5. *STOCK: Antiquarian and secondhand books, £1-£500.* PARK: Easy. TEL: 023 8022 6420; fax - 023 8022 7382. SER: Valuations.

T.R. Baker
at Stockbridge Antique Centre, Old London Rd. SO20 6EJ. Est. 1962. Open 10-5. CL: Wed. SIZE: Large. *STOCK: General antiques, country furniture.* LOC: On White Hart roundabout. TEL: 01264 811008; fax - same. SER: Stripping; restorations; repairs.

Lane Antiques
High St. SO20 6EU. (E.K. Lane). Est. 1981. Open 10-5. CL: Wed. SIZE: Small. *STOCK: English and Continental porcelain, 18th-19th C; silver and plate, decorative items, glass, small furniture.* PARK: Easy. TEL: 01264 810435.

The Wykeham Gallery
High St. SO20 6HE. (Mark Jerram and Gerald Dodson). Est. 1986. Open Tues.-Sat. 10-5. SIZE: Medium. *STOCK: Paintings, sculpture, watercolours, 1890-1940 and contemporary, £150-£15,000.* LOC: Main street. PARK: Easy. TEL: 01264 810364; fax - 01264 810182. SER: Valuations; restorations (paintings and works on paper); buys at auction (19th-20th C pictures). VAT: Spec.

Gasson Antiques and Interiors
P O Box 7225. RG26 5IY. LAPADA. Open by appointment. *STOCK: Georgian, Victorian and Edwardian furniture, clocks, porcelain and decorative items.* TEL: 01189 813636; mobile - 07860 827651.

Alexanders
13 South St. PO14 4DL. Open Thurs.-Sat. 10-5. *STOCK: General antiques including Art Nouveau and Art Deco.* PARK: Easy. TEL: 01329 315962. SER: Restorations (furniture); silver and chrome plating.

HAMPSHIRE

Gaylords
75 West St. PO14 4DG. (I. Hebbard). Est. 1970. Open 9.30-5.30. SIZE: Large. *STOCK: Furniture, from 18th C; clocks, £50-£10,000.* LOC: Off junction 9 M27. PARK: Easy. TEL: 01329 843402; home - 01329 847134. SER: Valuations. VAT: Stan/Spec.

Robin Howard Antiques
6 & 8 South St. PO14 4DJ. Open Tues.-Sat. SIZE: Small. *STOCK: Antique and modern jewellery, silver and plate, boxes and small collectables, £10-£500.* LOC: 1/4 mile from A27. PARK: Easy. TEL: 01329 842794. SER: Valuations.

Twyford Antiques
High St. SO21 1NH. Open 10-5 or by appointment. SIZE: Large. *STOCK: Clocks, furniture.* TEL: 01962 713484. SER: Valuations; restorations (clocks).

Athena Antiques Centre
31 Newtown Rd. SO31 9FY. (Alan and Terri Tonks). Est. 1980. Open 10-1 and 2-5, Mon. 10-

Henry Herbert La Thangue, RA (1859-1929), 'From a Ligurian Spring', oil on canvas, 38in. x 32in., signed, inscribed on a label on the stretcher. Exhibited at the Royal Academy in 1904, this picture turned up at the Torquay auction rooms of Bearne's in 1994, but, carrying an estimate of £60,000-£90,000, failed to sell, although later a private collector purchased the rustic genre composition by private treaty. On 1st March the astute collector sold the painting at Bearne's in Exeter for £330,000. (Bearne's)

From an article entitled 'British Paintings' by Anthony J. Lester which appeared in the July/August 2000 issue of **Antique Collecting** magazine. For more details and to subscribe see page 147.

1. SIZE: Small. *STOCK: Railwayana, 1840 to date, £5-£150; chandeliers, 20th C, £40-£400; china and glass, £5-£300.* LOC: From A27 at Park Gate, down Brook Lane to Warsash and over mini-roundabout. PARK: Easy. TEL: 01489 578093; home - 01489 584633. SER: Valuations; buys at auction. FAIRS: Athena - Wickham, Minstead and Locks Heath. VAT: Stan.

WINCHESTER

Bell Fine Art

67b Parchment St. SO23 8AT. (L.E. Bell). Open 9.30-5.30. *STOCK: Watercolours, oils and prints, 1750-1950, £5-£5,000.* TEL: 01962 860439; fax - same; home - 01962 862947; e-mail - sales@bell-fine-art.demon.co.uk. SER: Valuations; restorations (oils and watercolours); buys at auction. VAT: Spec.

Burns and Graham BADA

27 St. Thomas St. SO23 9HJ. (M. and G. Rollitt). Est. 1971. Open Mon. and Fri. 9.30-5.30, Sat. 9.30-1 or by appointment. *STOCK: English furniture, mirrors, period decorative items, 1680-1840.* LOC: Town centre. PARK: At rear. TEL: 01962 853779; fax - same; mobile - 07771 960393. SER: Valuations. VAT: Stan/Spec.

The Clock Workshop

6a Parchment St. SO23 8AT. (P. Ponsford-Jones). Est. 1997. Open Mon.-Sat. 9-5. SIZE: Medium. *STOCK: Longcase, wall, mantel, bracket and carriage clocks, 18th-19th C, £300-£18,000; barometers, books and tools.* LOC: Central, off main pedestrian precinct, near Smiths. PARK: Easy. TEL: 01962 842331. SER: Valuations; restorations (clocks and barometers).

Peter M. Daly

Rear of Winchester Antiques, 20a Jewry St. SO23 8RZ. PBFA. Open Wed., Fri. and Sat. 10-5. *STOCK: Rare and secondhand books; some pictures and prints, maps.* TEL: Mobile - 07940 335620; home - 01962 867732.

Lacewing Fine Art Gallery

28 St Thomas St. SO23 9HJ. (N. James). Open Tues.-Sat. 10-5. *STOCK: Paintings, watercolours, sculpture, Old Master drawings, 16th-20th C.* TEL: 01962 878700; fax - 01962 870583; e-mail - noeljames@lacewing.co.uk; website - www.lacewing.co.uk.

G.E. Marsh Antique Clocks Ltd BADA

32a The Square. SO23 9EX. Est. 1947. Open 9.30-5, Sat. 9.30-1 and 2-5. *STOCK: English clocks, watches and barometers c1680-1880,*

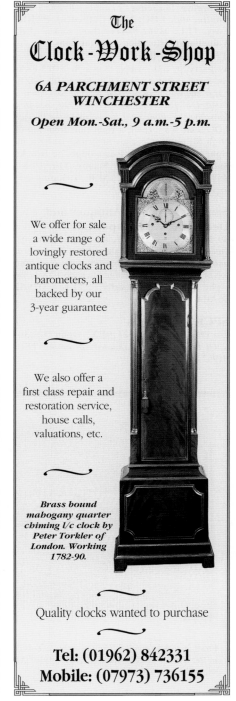

including longcase, bracket, French and Continental. LOC: Near Cathedral. PARK: Easy. TEL: 01962 844443; fax - same. SER: Valuations; restorations; commissions.

The Pine Cellars

39 Jewry St. and 7 Upper Brook St. SO23 8RY. (N. Spencer-Brayn). Est. 1970. Open 10-5. SIZE: Large and warehouses. *STOCK: Pine and country furniture, 18th-19th C, £10-£5,000; painted furniture, architectural items, panelled rooms.* LOC: One way street, a right turn from top of High St. or St. Georges St., shop 100yds. on right. Brook St. premises - opposite Brooks Shopping Centre. PARK: Nearby. TEL: 01962 867014/777546/870102. SER: Stripping and export. VAT: Stan/Spec.

Samuels Spencers Antiques and Decorative Arts Emporium

39 Jewry St. SO23 8RY. (N. Spencer-Brayn). Open 10-5. SIZE: 31 dealers. *STOCK: General antiques.* LOC: One way street, right turn from top of High St. or St. George St., shop 100yds. on right. PARK: Nearby. TEL: 01962 867014/777546.

SPCK Bookshops

24 The Square. SO23 9EX. Open 9-5.30. *STOCK: Secondhand theological books.* TEL: 01962 866617.

Todd and Austin Antiques of Winchester

2 Andover Rd. SO23 7BS. (G. Austin). Est. 1964. Open Tues.-Fri. 9.30-5, Sat. 9.30-12.30. SIZE: Medium. *STOCK: 19th C glass, paperweights, silver tea caddies, boxes, objets d'art and decorative items; late 18th-late 19th C pottery and porcelain, some Oriental porcelain.* LOC: 1 minute from Winchester Station. PARK: Easy. TEL: 01962 869824. SER: Selected range on view at Lainston House Hotel, Sparsholt, Nr Winchester; finder service.

Webb Fine Arts

38 Jewry St. SO23 8RY. (D.H. Webb). Est. 1955. Open 9-5, Sat. 9-1. SIZE: Large - 4 floors. *STOCK: Oil paintings and furniture.* PARK: Own. TEL: 01962 842273. SER: Valuations; restorations (oil paintings); lining and framing; buys at auction (paintings). VAT: Stan/Spec.

Winchester Antiques

20-20A Jewry St. SO23 8RZ. (D. Letts). Est. 1997. Open 10-5. SIZE: Large. *STOCK: Walnut, mahogany and oak furniture, 17th-19th C; collectables, smalls, brass and copper, all £10-£10,000.* LOC: Town centre, 5 minutes from station. PARK: Easy. TEL: 01962 850123; home - 01963 370450. SER: Valuations; restorations (repairs and stripping); buys at auction (furniture).

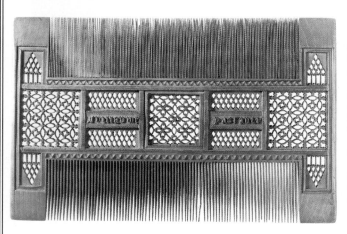

Intricately fretted boxwood comb, French, 15th/ early 16th century. The carved wording indicates a romantic alliance: obverse (shown) 'Guillaume Pascavit', reverse 'Marie Sprat'. 8½in. long, 5¼in. wide. (Ashmolean Museum, Oxford)

From an article entitled 'Combs as Love-Tokens' by Jen Cruse and Robert Watts which appeared in the December 2000/January 2001 issue of **Antique Collecting** magazine. For more details and to subscribe see page 147.

Dear Father Christmas....

We asked six of our regular contributors what would be their ideal Christmas present. Here is John Sandon's reply!

Since joining Phillips in 1975 I have sold around 120,000 lots, ranging from the mundane to the truly wonderful. The problem with my chosen career is that I love porcelain too much. Collecting is genetic and I was born a collector. Customers leave things with me to sell by auction and I want to take them all home. I keep certain pieces in my office for a couple of months researching and cataloguing and they grow on me. I can't bear to part with them and I feel terribly jealous when buyers come and cart them away. Fortunately, most objects I really love I cannot afford, so I control myself and my children don't go without toys and clothes too often!

As a rebellious teenager I was determined to show my father a world of porcelain beyond his beloved Worcester. I decided to collect Caughley, Worcester's deadly rival, which in the 1970s was far more affordable. I scoured Portobello Road every Saturday and in seven years I acquired 150 pieces of Shropshire porcelain. This collecting came to an end through love of a different kind and in 1982 I sold the lot to get married and buy a house. Dad said good riddance, though I was in tears. My Caughley showed me a handsome profit but bricks and mortar just aren't the same. I could never replace the collection and haven't bought a piece of Caughley since.

Twenty years ago a dealer showed me a dish bought cheaply in France and it was love at first sight. It was the Caughley tureen stand illustrated above (main picture) – quite unlike any recorded piece. Very much in French taste with Sèvres-like handles, it has a wonderful *lambrequin* border and extraordinary central painting in bright blue. Caughley were masters of transfer printing but hopeless amateurs when it came to hand painting. Here is crazy chinoiserie where temples from Nankin Willow patterns have been transformed into quaint English farmhouses and a thatched barn. Dotted between are tiny Chinese pavilions completely out of scale. In the story of the Willow Pattern the lovers Koon-se and Chang are transformed into doves and fly away together, an Oriental symbol of their immortal love. Here, though, the Caughley doves are stupidly British, looking as absurd as plaster ducks on a wall.

I wanted this dish so badly and counted all my pennies, but I knew I couldn't afford it. Geoffrey Godden outbid me at the sale and it joined his reference collection in Worthing. Predicting this outcome I had made contingency plans. Before the sale I did the unthinkable and borrowed the dish from Phillips. Back at my flat I secretly made an exact copy (below). Dad provided an unglazed bone china dish from Royal Worcester and I painted it in raw cobalt oxide, copying every scribble and in the process learning a lot about Caughley painting. Back it went to Worcester to be glazed and fired, and although my copy managed to convey the same spirit as the original.

Geoffrey Godden's dish resurfaced at auction a decade later but again I was to be outbid, as I had just moved to a bigger house to make room for my growing family and my porcelain acquisitions were again truncated. The dish sold for under £1,000, a moderate sum for such a rarity but I suppose there are fewer Caughley enthusiasts about now compared to my collecting days. I would love to be given the real dish for Christmas, but at least I have some consolation – a John Sandon fake hanging on my wall is the next best thing!

The above featured in the December 1997/ January 1998 issue of **Antique Collecting** magazine. For more details and to subscribe see page 147.

Bournville Books

95 Whitecross Rd. HR4 0DQ. (Frank Nutt). Est. 1972. Open 9.30-5.30, Sun. by appointment. SIZE: Small. *STOCK: Antiquarian books, £25-£250; leatherbound books for decoration, £4-£12; prints and watercolours, £20-£120; all 19th C*. LOC: 1/2 mile from town centre on Brecon road (A438). PARK: Easy. TEL: 01432 261263; home - same. SER: Valuations. FAIRS: Newark; Bloomsbury Book.

I. and J.L. Brown Ltd

Whitestone Park, Whitestone. HR1 3SE. Open 9-5.30. SIZE: Large. *STOCK: Matched sets of period country chairs, £1,500-£7,500; English country and French provincial furniture, reproduction furniture, decorative items*. LOC: A4103, 4 miles from Hereford towards Worcester. PARK: Easy. TEL: 01432 851991; fax - 01432 851994. SER: Restorations; re-rushing chairs. VAT: Stan/Spec.

Great Brampton House Antiques Ltd

Great Brampton House, Madley. HR2 9NA. (Lady Pidgeon). LAPADA. Est. 1969. Open 9-5, Sat. and Sun. by appointment only. SIZE: Large. *STOCK: English and French furniture and fine art*. TEL: 01981 250244; fax - 01981 251333.

Hereford Antique Centre

128 Widemarsh St. HR4 9HN. (G.P. Smith). Est. 1991. Open 10-5, Sun. 12-5. SIZE: 30 dealers. *STOCK: General antiques and collectables*. PARK: Easy. TEL: 01432 266242. SER: Restorations; shipping.

Warings of Hereford

45-47 St. Owen St. HR1 2JB. Open 9-6 including Sun. *STOCK: Fine 19th C furniture, farmhouse pine; gold and silver*. TEL: 01432 276241.

An impressive Staffordshire figure of Chaucer, c.1820, which fetched £1,150, and a Davenport sauce tureen which rated £580.

From an Auction Report by Christopher Wight which appeared in the March 2001 issue of **Antique Collecting** magazine on The Hacking Collection of Davenport, dry-bodied stoneware and other British ceramics held at Phillips Bayswater, 23rd January 2001. For more details and to subscribe see page 147.

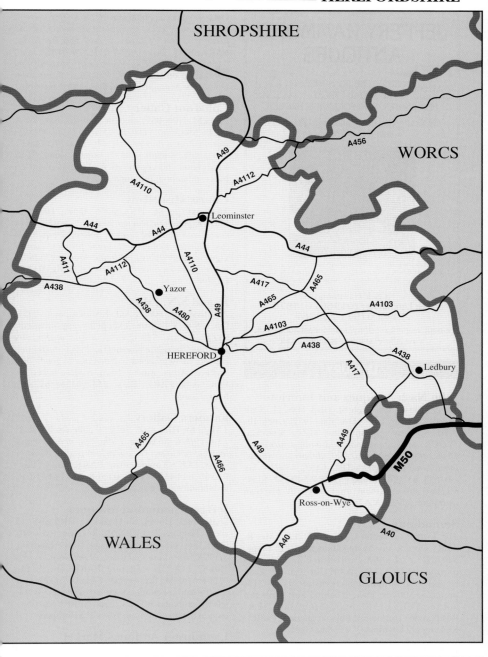

LEDBURY

John Nash Antiques and Interiors
Tudor House, 17c High St. HR8 1DS. (J. Nash and L. Calleja). LAPADA. Est. 1972. Open 10-5.30, Sun. by appointment. SIZE: Medium. *STOCK: Mahogany, oak and walnut furniture, 18th-20th C, £300-£10,000; decorative items, fabrics and wallpapers.* TEL: 01531 635714; fax - 01531 635050; home - 01684 540432. SER: Valuations; restorations; buys at auction (furniture, silver). VAT: Stan/Spec.

Serendipity
The Tythings, Preston Court. HR8 2LL. (Mrs R. Ford). Open 9-5 or by appointment. SIZE: Large. *STOCK: 17th-20th C furniture and general antiques.* LOC: Take A449 for 3 miles from Ledbury, at roundabout turn left on B4215, premises 500yds. on left behind half-timbered house. TEL: 01531 660245/660380. SER: Restorations (furniture); buys at auction. FAIRS: Kensington; Olympia. VAT: Stan/Spec.

LEOMINSTER

Barometer Shop
New St. HR6 8DP. (R. Cookson). Est. 1965.

Open 9-5 or by appointment. *STOCK: Barometers, barographs, clocks, scientific instruments, period furniture.* LOC: Corner of A49 and Broad St. PARK: Easy. TEL: 01568 613652/610200; fax - 01568 610200. SER: Valuations; restorations (workshop on the Register of the Conservation Unit of the Museums and Galleries Commission).

Coltsfoot Gallery
Hatfield. HR6 0SF. (Edwin Collins). Est. 1971. SIZE: Medium. *STOCK: Sporting and wildlife watercolours and prints, £20-£2,000.* PARK: Easy. TEL: 01568 760277; home - same. SER: Restoration and conservation of works of art on paper; mounting; framing.

Courts Miscellany
48A Bridge St. HR6 6DZ. Open 10.30-5. *STOCK: General curios including corkscrews, social and political history, police, fire brigade and sporting items; tools, horse brasses, enamel signs - advertising, military, brewery; studio pottery and commemoratives.* TEL: 01568 612995.

P. and S.N. Eddy
22 Etnam St. HR6 8AQ. Resident. Est. 1951. Open 9-6. CL: Sun. except by appointment. SIZE: Small. *STOCK: Oak and mahogany furniture; saltglaze stoneware, 18th C brass and copper, early metalware, treen and bygones.* Not Stocked: Arms, armour, coins, medals, jewellery. LOC: A44. PARK: Easy. TEL: 01568 612813; home - same.

Farmers Gallery
1 High St. HR6 8LZ. SIZE: 6 galleries. *STOCK: 18th-19th C furniture, paintings, prints, maps, frames, needlework, porcelain and decorative items.* LOC: Town centre. PARK: Easy. TEL: 01568 611413; fax - 01568 611141. SER: Exhibition gallery available.

Jeffery Hammond Antiques
Shaftesbury House, 38 Broad St. HR6 8BS. (J. and E. Hammond). LAPADA. Resident. Est. 1970. Open 9-6, Sun. by appointment. SIZE: Medium. *STOCK: Furniture and works of art, 18th to early 19th C.* LOC: Town centre. PARK: Own. TEL: 01568 614876; fax - same; e-mail - enquiries@ jefferyhammondantiques.co.uk; website - www. jefferyhammondantiques.co.uk. SER: Valuations; buys at auction (furniture). VAT: Stan/Spec.

Leominster Antiques Market
14 Broad St. HR6 8BS. Open 10-5. SIZE: 18 units - 3 floors. *STOCK: Mahogany, oak, pine, kitchenalia, collectables, toys, glass, textiles, silver, postcards, Gaudy Welsh, fine china, pictures, jewellery, tools.* TEL: 01568 612189.

The Old Shoe Box
Church St. HR6. Open 10-5. *STOCK: Furniture, china, prints, watercolours and smalls.* TEL: 01568 611414. SER: Mount cutting; framing.

ROSS-ON-WYE

Baileys Home & Garden
Station Approach. HR9 7BW. (M. and S. Bailey). Est. 1978. Open 9-5. SIZE: Medium. *STOCK: Garden furniture, tools, orchard ladders, junk-style garden painted furniture, kitchenware, quilts, Welsh blankets, French and English lighting, bathrooms (including copper baths, metal washstands), fireplaces, industrial lamps, factory trolleys, machinists' stools, shoe lasts, baskets, bobbins, etc.* LOC: Gloucester side of Ross, just off A40. TEL: 01989 563015; fax - 01989 768172.

Fritz Fryer Antique Lighting
12 Brookend St. HR9 7EG. (F. Fryer and J. Graham). Est. 1981. Open 10-5.30, Sun. by appointment. SIZE: Large. *STOCK: Decorative lighting, original shades, Georgian to Art Deco.* TEL: 01989 567416; fax - 01989 566742. SER: Restorations; lighting scheme design.

Robin Lloyd Antiques
23/24 Brookend St. HR9 7EE. Est. 1970. Open 9.30-5.30. SIZE: Large - 5 showrooms. *STOCK: Country furniture, mainly long tables and early oak, longcase clocks.* LOC: 100yds. downhill from Market Hall. PARK: Nearby. TEL: 01989 562123; fax - same. SER: Export (especially to USA). VAT: Global/Spec.

Merchants House Antiques
36 High St. HR9 5HD. (N. Cockman). Est. 1969. Open 10-5. SIZE: Large. *STOCK: General antiques.* LOC: A40. TEL: 01989 563010. SER: Valuations; restorations; buys at auction. VAT: Spec.

Ross Old Book and Print Shop
51 and 52 High St. HR9 5HH. Open 10-5. CL: Mid-Jan. to mid-Feb. *STOCK: Antiquarian and secondhand books, prints and maps.* TEL: 01989 567458; fax - 01989 567861; e-mail - enquiries @rossoldbooks.wyenet.co.uk; websites - www. antiqueprints.com and www.abebooks.com.

Ross-on-Wye Antiques Centre
Gloucester Rd. HR9 5BU. (Michael Aslanian). Est. 1996. Open 10.30-5, Sun. by appointment. CL: Bank Holidays. SIZE: Large. *STOCK: Wide variety of general antiques and collectables, from BC to 1950's.* LOC: Town centre. TEL: 01989 762290; fax - 01989 762291. SER: Valuations; buys at auction.

Singleton Antiques
29-30 Brookend St. HR9 7EF. (J.W. & A.A. Chapman). Est. 1994. Open 9.30-5.30. SIZE: Medium. *STOCK: Oak, 17th-19th C, £500-£5,000; country furniture, 18th-19th C, £100-£2,000; decorative items and pictures, 19th-20th C, £10-£2,000.* LOC: Main shopping street. PARK: Easy. TEL: 01989 763400; fax - 01989 763200. SER: Valuations. VAT: Stan/Spec.

YAZOR

M. and J. Russell
The Old Vicarage. HR4 7BA. Est. 1969. Usually open Fri. to Mon. and evenings, other times appointment advisable. *STOCK: English period oak and country furniture, some garden antiques.* LOC: 7 miles west of Hereford on A480. TEL: 01981 590674. *Mainly Trade.*

Drawing by L.S. Lowry. £2,179. Biddle & Webb, Birmingham.

From a feature on Saleroom Prices which appeared in the March 2001 issue of **Antique Collecting** magazine. For more details and to subscribe see page 147.

Dobson's Antiques
53 High St. WD5 0AA. Est. 1926. Open 8.30-5.30. CL: Tues. pm. *STOCK: Carved oak, stripped pine, shipping goods, bric-a-brac, £5-£2,000.* LOC: 4 miles north of Watford. TEL: 01923 263186. VAT: Stan/Spec.

BALDOCK

The Attic
20 Whitehorse St. SG7 6QN. (P. Sheppard). Est. 1977. CL: Thurs. SIZE: Small. *STOCK: Small furniture, china, brass and copper, dolls and teddy bears, £5-£100.* LOC: 3 minutes from A1(M). PARK: Easy. TEL: 01462 893880.

Anthony Butt Antiques
7/9 Church St. SG7 5AE. Resident. Usually open. *STOCK: English furniture, 17th-19th C, £500-£5,000; works of art and objects of interest.* Not Stocked: Bric-a-brac, shipping goods. PARK: Easy. TEL: 01462 895272; fax - 01462 894166. SER: Valuations. VAT: Spec.

Howards
33 Whitehorse St. SG7 6QF. (D.N. Howard). Est. 1970. Open 9.30-5.00. CL: Mon. *STOCK: Clocks, 18th-19th C, £200-£5,000.* PARK: Easy. TEL: 01462 892385. SER: Valuations; restorations and repairs (clocks). VAT: Spec.

Ralph and Bruce Moss
26 Whitehorse St. SG7 6QQ. (R.A. and B.A. Moss). Est. 1973. Open 9-6. SIZE: Large. *STOCK: Furniture, £100-£10,000; general antiques, £5-£5,000.* LOC: A505, in town centre. PARK: Own. TEL: 01462 892751; fax - same. VAT: Stan/Spec.

BARNET

C. Bellinger Antiques
91 Wood St. EN5 4BX. Est. 1974. Open Thurs., Fri. and Sat. 10-4 or by appointment. SIZE: Medium. *STOCK: Furniture, silver and plate, smalls.* LOC: Opposite Ravenscroft Park. PARK: Within 100yds. TEL: 020 8449 3467. VAT: Spec.

Scrummager's
188 High St. EN5 5SZ. Est. 1995. Open 10-5, Sat. 10-5.30. SIZE: Medium. *STOCK: Collectibles, £5-£250; pine furniture, £100-£900; jewellery, £10-£250; all 19th-20th C.* PARK: At Hadley Green. TEL: 020 8441 6050.

BERKHAMSTED

Home and Colonial
134 High St. HP4 3AT. (Alison and Graeme Reid-Davies and Liz and Tony Stanton-Kipping). Open 10-5.30, Sun. 11-4.30. CL: Wed. SIZE: Large. *STOCK: Period and country furniture, Arts & Crafts, Art Deco, decorative antiques,*

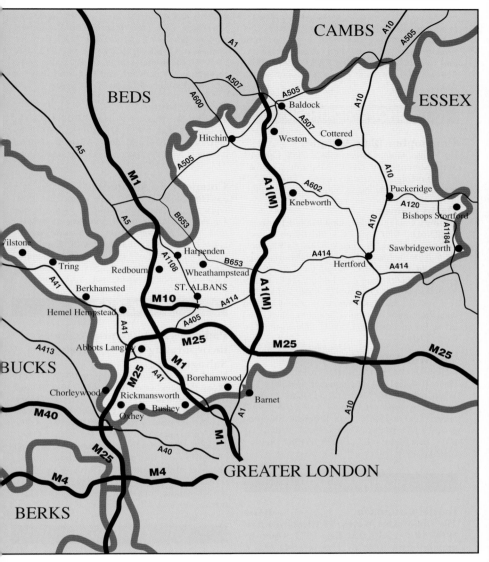

Dealers and Shops in Hertfordshire

Abbots Langley	1	Cottered	1	Redbourn	3
Baldock	4	Harpenden	1	Rickmansworth	2
Barnet	2	Hemel Hempstead	4	Sawbridgeworth	4
Berkhamsted	1	Hertford	5	St. Albans	7
Bishop's Stortford	3	Hitchin	5	Tring	4
Borehamwood	1	Knebworth	1	Weston	1
Bushey	3	Oxhey	1	Wheathampstead	2
Chorleywood	1	Puckeridge	1	Wilstone	1

clocks and barometers, metalware, pictures, porcelain, silver, glass, jewellery, textiles and costume, antiquarian books, radios and gramophones, toys and teddy bears, fireplaces and lighting, £10-£10,000. PARK: Easy. TEL: 01442 877007; website - www.homeandcolonial. co.uk.

BISHOP'S STORTFORD

Christopher Blair Antiques
Ivy House, Gaston Green. CM22 7QS. Open by appointment only. SIZE: Medium. *STOCK: Furniture and decorative items.* TEL: 01279 600566; fax - same.

David Penney
Grooms Cottage, Elsenham Hall, Elsenham. CM22 6DP. BHI. Est. 1973. Strictly no visitors, no stock held on premises. *STOCK: Watches, 18th-19th C, £500-£5,000; watch movements, 18th-19th C, £50-£500; horological books and ephemera, 18th-20th C, £5-£500.* TEL: 01279 814946; fax - 01279 814962. SER: Valuations; restorations; specialist research; postal auction catalogue; buys at auction (watches, clocks and all technical horology). VAT: Stan/Spec. *Mail Order Only.*

The Windhill Antiquary
4 High St. CM23 2LT. (G.R. Crozier). Est. 1951. Open 10-1 and 2-4, appointment advisable. CL: Wed. pm. SIZE: Medium. *STOCK: English furniture, 18th C; carved and gilded wall mirrors, 17th-19th C.* Not Stocked: Shipping goods. LOC: Next to George Hotel. PARK: Up hill - first right. TEL: 01279 651587; home - 01920 821316.

BOREHAMWOOD

Barnet-Cattanach   BADA
The Old Marble Works, 18 Glenhaven Ave. WD6 1BB. LAPADA. Est. 1977. Open by appointment. *STOCK: 18th to early 19th C furniture and accessories.* PARK: Easy. TEL: 020 7727 0460/020 8207 6792; fax - 020 8381 5889. SER: Restorations (furniture). FAIRS: Olympia.

BUSHEY, Nr. Watford

Bushey Antique Centre
39 High St. WD2 1NB. (Graham Lindsay). Est. 1983. Open 9.30-5.30, Sun. 10-4.30. SIZE: 30 dealers. *STOCK: Furniture, 18th-20th C, £50-*

£500; smalls, collectables, clocks, dolls and jewellery, £5-£250; fireplaces and chimney pieces, 18th-19th C, £160-£800. LOC: Between Harrow and Watford. PARK: At rear. TEL: 020 8950 5040; home - same. SER: Valuations; restorations (woodwork and furniture); buys at auction (furniture and fires). VAT: Spec.

Circa Antiques
43 High St., Bushey Village. WD2 1BD. (K. Wildman). Est. 1978. Open 9.30-5.30 or by appointment. SIZE: Medium. *STOCK: General antiques, furniture, porcelain, silver and clocks.* TEL: 020 8950 9233.

Country Life Antiques
33a High St. WD2 1BD. (Peter Myers). Est. 1981. Open 9-5. SIZE: Large. *STOCK: Victorian and Edwardian, European and Scandinavian original pine, French country oak; kitchenalia, water-colours, china and Art Deco.* PARK: Easy. TEL: 020 8950 8575; fax - 020 8950 6982; e-mail - countrylife@busheyherts.freeserve.co.uk; website - www.countrylifeantiques.co.uk. VAT: Stan.

CHORLEYWOOD

Pattison's Architectural Antiques incorporating The Architectural Salvage Store
Unit 6, Darvells Works, Common Rd. WD3 5LP. (Tony Pattison). Open Tues.-Sat. 9.30-5.30, Sun. by appointment. SIZE: Large *STOCK: Doors, glass, 18th C to 1930, £5-£1,000; fireplaces, marble and stone, 18th C to 1920, £500-£3,000; garden ornaments, 19th C to 1950, £1,000-£2,000.* LOC: A404 from junction 18, M25. After .75 mile turn left at lights to town centre, premises 500yds. on right. PARK: Easy. TEL: 01923 284196; fax - 01923 282214; e-mail - tony@ pattant.com. SER: Restorations (glass, marble, stone). VAT: Stan/Spec.

COTTERED

Wareside Antiques
(David Broxup). Est. 1983. Open by appointment only. *STOCK: Furniture, dining tables, sets of chairs.* TEL: 01763 281234.

HARPENDEN

Meg Andrews
Est. 1982. Open by appointment. *STOCK: Worldwide collectable, hangable and wearable antique costume and textiles including Chinese*

embroideries and woven fabrics, robes, shoes, hats, large hangings, Morris and Arts and Crafts embroideries and woven cloths, Paisley shawls, samplers, silkwork pictures; European costumes and textiles. TEL: 01582 460107; home - same; fax - 01582 461112; e-mail - meg.andrews@ cwcom.net. SER: Valuations; advice.

HEMEL HEMPSTEAD

Abbey Antiques - Fine Jewellery & Silver
97 High St., Old Town. HP1 3AH. (L., E., S. and C. Eames). Est. 1962. Open 9.30-5.30. SIZE: Medium. STOCK: Silver, plate, jewellery, £5-£5,000. LOC: M1, junction 8, M25, junction 20, bypass main shopping centre to old town. PARK: Easy. TEL: 01442 264667. SER: Valuations; jewellery design and repair. VAT: Stan/Global.

Cherry Antiques
101-103 High St. HP1 3AH. (A. and R.S. Cullen). Open 9.30-4.30. CL: Wed. pm. SIZE: Medium. STOCK: Victorian, Edwardian, and some period furniture, pine, general antiques, collectors' and decorative items, bric-a-brac, needlework tools, dolls, linens, some silver, plate, jewellery, glass, pottery, porcelain, brass, copper, some shipping items. PARK: Easy. TEL: 01442 264358. VAT: Stan/Spec.

Off the Wall
52 High St.,Old Town. HP1 3AF. (Deborah Tanswell). Est. 1997. Open 10-5.30, Sun. 12-4.30. SIZE: Small. STOCK: Collectables, 1890-1960, £5-£500; porcelain, 1740-1860, £500-£1,000; eccentric European collectables. PARK: Nearby. TEL: 01442 389320. SER: Valuations.

The Pine Emporium
Hilliers Garden Centre, Leighton Buzzard Rd., Piccotts End. (J. Greatrix). Open 9-5.30, Sun. 11-4. STOCK: Pine furniture, antique and reclaimed, from 18th C; oak, from 18th C. TEL: 01442 244644. SER: Restorations; bespoke manufacture.

HERTFORD

Beckwith and Son
St. Nicholas Hall, St. Andrew St. SG14 1HZ. (G.C.M. Gray). Est. 1904. Open 9-1 and 2-5.30. SIZE: Large. STOCK: General antiques, furniture, silver, pottery, porcelain, prints, weapons, clocks, watches, glass. Not Stocked: Fabrics. LOC: A414/B158. PARK: Adjacent. TEL: 01992 582079. SER: Valuations; restorations (fine porcelain, furniture, upholstery, silver, clocks). VAT: Spec.

Gillmark Gallery
25 Parliament Sq. SG14 1EX. (Mark Pretlove and Gill Woodhouse). Est. 1997. CL: Mon. and Wed. pm. SIZE: Medium. STOCK: Maps and prints, 16th-20th C, £10-£5000; secondhand books, 18th-20th C, £1-£5,000. LOC: 15 yards from roundabout at junction of A414 and B158. PARK: Nearby. TEL: 01992 534444; fax - 01992 554734; website - www.gillmark.com. SER: Valuations; restorations (conservation, framing and restoration antique prints and maps). VAT: Stan.

Hertford Antiques
51 St Andrew St. SG14 1HZ. (S.D. Garratt and R.F. Norris). Est. 1994. Open 10-5.30 including Sun. SIZE: Large - 50+ dealers. STOCK: Furniture, jewellery, porcelain, silver, glass, books, £5-£4,000. LOC: Next to St Andrew's Church. PARK: Easy. TEL: 01992 504504.

Robert Horton Antiques
13 Castle St. SG14 1ER. Est. 1972. Open 9-5. STOCK: Clocks, barometers, furniture. TEL: 01992 587546; fax - same. SER: Repairs and restorations (movements, cases, dials). VAT: Stan/Spec.

Tapestry Antiques
27 St. Andrew St. SG14 1HZ. (D.W. and P. Stokes). Est. 1973. Open 10-1 and 2-5, Sat. 10-5.30, Sun. by appointment. CL: Thurs. SIZE: Medium. STOCK: Furniture, 18th-19th C, £100-£1,000; porcelain, 19th to early 20th C, £25-£500; brass and copper, 18th-19th C, £50-£300. LOC: Near railway station. PARK: Easy and behind premises. TEL: 01992 587438. SER: Valuations.

HITCHIN

Michael Gander
10-11 Bridge St. SG5 2DE. Est. 1973. Open Mon. 3-6, Wed., Thurs. and Sat. 9-6, or by appointment. STOCK: Period furniture, metalware, ceramics, glass, pictures. TEL: 01462 432678; mobile - 07885 728976.

Hanbury Antiques
86 Tilehouse St. SG5 2DU. (Mrs M.D. Hanbury). Est. 1988. CL: Wed afternoons. SIZE: Small. STOCK: Period furniture, porcelain, silver, jewellery. LOC: Continuation of Bridge St. PARK: 100 yards. TEL: 01462 420487; home - same. SER: Valuations.

Eric T. Moore
24 Bridge St. SG5 2DF. Open 9.30-5, Sat. 9.30-5.30. STOCK: Secondhand and antiquarian books and maps. TEL: 01462 450497; e-mail - booksales@erictmoore.co.uk; website - www.erictmoore.co.uk. SER: Book binding.

19th & 20th Century
FURNITURE
The Designer-Label Syndrome

John Andrews

Example of typical Victorian Rococo chair. Not designer label. Price going down.

Irwin Stelzer of *The Times* observed recently that data trumps anecdote every time but in the absence of data, anecdote can be indicative. In the ACC we have the data, recorded in the ACC Index with its various sections reported in April, so today, in an attempt to explain the data, maybe it is time for anecdote.

Mothercare has been in trouble with high street sales lately. It appears that buyers of children's clothes are not interested in Mothercare's everyday garments; they want designer-label goods. Marks and Spencer are also in the doldrums. While their troubles are said to relate to a lacklustre style of clothing, they may partly be from the fact that St Michael is not regarded as exactly designer-label either. Much the same is happening to the retailing of antique furniture of the 19th and particularly the 20th century.

The collector of pre-1800 furniture is generally happy with the fact that it is in period, of a style the collector cherishes, and in good condition. That a piece can be attributed to a famous cabinetmaker

or designer is an added bonus which can multiply the price much further, but it is not nearly as important as it is becoming with post-1800 furniture. This is emulating the current retail preoccupation with labels. It is of course true that the 19th and 20th centuries saw a vast expansion in output of furniture as production methods developed more rapid means of replicating functions previously performed by hands trained during laborious apprenticeships. If one is to be selective when collecting from the enormous range of the 19th and 20th century therefore, one argument suggests that the label of a renowned designer or cabinetmaker is the only distinguishing feature which will provide the cachet all keen collectors seek to acquire.

If, starting in the Regency period, one examines this current preoccupation, astonishment at the combined effect of the Gillows and Hackwood Park provenance on a set of chairs and a long table – a 30-seater – comes into perspective. The prices rising from £150,000 which were realised for these pieces still

cause raised eyebrows. Can it be that Gillows, once considered an agreeably competent firm with the good grace to leave very detailed records of their work, thus earning the blessing of all furniture history researchers, are now considered for pre-1830 furniture to have the sort of effect on price which was once reserved for Thomas Hope and George Smith? Gillows date back to the 18th century as suppliers of quality furniture to the gentry but in the second half of the 19th century they too became rather more prolific than the individual cabinetmakers of yore. The Gillows label does not always qualify for automatically celestial pricing but it seems that its early-days importance has grown.

When we come to the Victorian period it is possible that the designer-label syndrome can be having negative, as well as price-

Chair by Alvar Aalto in laminated beech and plywood, 1931-2. Made in Finland. Sold at Christie's South Kensington for £27,600 in March.

Chair by Gerald Summers 1933-4. Made from one sheet of moulded laminated plywood. Sold at Christie's South Kensington for £13,800 in March.

enhancing overtones. The architect-designers of the Victorian period are many and are now well-known. From Pugin to Godwin, Morris to Voysey, the list is well-established and will doubtless, from time to time, be augmented by new discoveries. When the work of these celebrities is put on the market the vendors make sure that the full details are prominently available. Examples this year include a Burges cabinet for £195,000 and a William Watts/Godwin armchair for £21,500 although there have been one or two disappointments on Bevan pieces, the name not being, perhaps, quite high enough in the label pecking order.

Where it is possible that a negative effect is taking place is on the anonymous Rococo furniture that has been the happy mainstay of Victorian furniture collecting. I mentioned in April that the prolixity of reproductions of this style was reducing prices of the real thing. Now it may seem that the figured walnut, scrolled, balloon-backed, cabriole-legged much-produced style is suffering from a decline in fashion plus a lack of designer-label attraction. At Phillips on 18th May there were several disappointments: two sets of six balloon-back chairs failed to sell even at estimates of £200 or so per chair. This may be compared to retail prices of £400 per chair at the height of the Victorian Rococo boom. A loo table of similar style also failed to sell at a modest price. On the other hand, a damaged Gillows burr walnut and marquetry breakfast table of circa 1870 did not find a buyer either, so here the designer label did not compensate for condition – or can it be that the style is now considered passé? It is probably too early to jump to conclusions at a relatively unexciting time for unattributed Victorian furniture, which continues to provide a substantial volume of trade but has none of the excitement currently being generated by the 20th century.

The later Arts and Crafts, Art Nouveau and Art Deco furniture which we have several times dealt with in these pages continues to gain ground. Ambrose Heal is probably one of the best-regarded innovative designers, less quixotic than Liberty's can sometimes be yet not as safely traditional as Gordon Russell and the Cotswolds school. Not that the traditionalists lack followers. How else to account for

Early 20th century kidney-shaped mahogany desk, reproduction Sheraton, made by Wytock and Reid of Edinburgh. Sold for £9,725 at Phillips New Bond Street in May.

the prices recently being paid for Robert 'Mouseman' Thompson of Kilburn, whose designer label – that image of a mouse – provides a sure-fire identification? A sideboard from the 1940s by Thompson recently fetched £6,000 at a provincial auction whereas an unattributed sideboard in that plain oak, panelled, safe, adze-and-iron strapped style much associated with the '30s and '40s would be remarkable to achieve more than a few hundred pounds – surely an example of the designer label's enormous influence.

Another example: at the Phillips 18th May sale a 20th century mahogany kidney-shaped desk – a classic reproduction of a Sheraton original – fetched £9,725. The vendors had done their homework well, pointing out that the makers, Wytock and Reid of Edinburgh, became the most prominent art manufacturers and retailers in that city by the end of the 19th century. Every little label helps.

To this now well-accepted furniture must be added an increasing interest in more Modernist furniture, not just of the famed Continentals but of British designers and craftsmen who serve to provide the labels sought by enthusiastic pursuers of hoped-for 'antiques of the future'. Up to now, tubular furniture has been much to the fore, along with the remarkable designs of Charles Eames, Marcel Breuer, Mies van der Rohe and others, but now the moulded plywood of Alvar Aalto, Jacobsen

and post-1945 designers has started to come into its own. I am grateful to Simon Andrews (no relation) of Christie's South Kensington for drawing attention to the chair here illustrated which is by Gerald Summers and which fetched £13,800 at auction in March, a sale at which an Aalto laminated chair fetched £27,600.

The laminated birch lounge chair designed by Gerald Summers for *Makers of Simple Furniture* in 1933-34 was cut from a single sheet of birch laminate. It was sold for £3-15s-0d to what appears to have been a small elite clientele. Its tremendous advantage was that it was cut and formed into a finished chair without the need for any other materials or bracing and was contoured to fit the human body. Unfortunately for Summers and the manufacturers, the Aalto-designed chairs imported into England by Finmar were cheaper, so only 120 of these chairs were made.

Thinking of what is happening to Victorian Rococo, at £13,800 one might ask how soon before someone starts moulding Summers in plywood again? Ah, comes the answer, for designer-label furniture, provenance will remain just as important as ever. Unlike anonymity?

This article appeared in the July/August 1999 issue of **Antique Collecting** *magazine. For more details and to subscribe see page 147.*

HERTFORDSHIRE

Phillips of Hitchin (Antiques) Ltd
BADA
The Manor House. SG5 1JW. (J. and B. Phillips).
Est. 1884. Open 9-5.30. SIZE: Large. *STOCK:
Furniture, walnut and mahogany, 18th to early
19th C, £500-£20,000.* LOC: In Bancroft, main
street of Hitchin. PARK: Easy. TEL: 01462
432067; fax - 01462 441368. SER: Restorations
(furniture); books on collecting. VAT: Spec.

Tom Salusbury Antiques
7 Nutleigh Grove. SG5 2NH. Est. 1963. Open by
appointment only. SIZE: Small. *STOCK:
Furniture, to 1910, £100-£3,000.* LOC: 3 miles
from A1, junction 8. PARK: Easy. TEL: 01462
441520; fax - same. SER: Valuations; restorations
(especially upholstery). VAT: Stan/Spec.

KNEBWORTH

Hamilton Billiards & Games Co.
Park Lane. SG3 6PJ. (H. Hamilton). Est. 1980.
Open 9-5, weekends and evenings by
appointment. SIZE: Large. *STOCK: Victorian
and Edwardian billiard tables, £3,000-£18,000;
19th C convertible billiard/dining tables and
accessories, £30-£5,000; indoor and outdoor
games.* LOC: Near railway station. PARK: Easy.
TEL: 01438 811995. SER: Valuations;
restorations (billiard tables and furniture); buys at
auction (as stock). VAT: Stan.

OXHEY, Nr. Watford

Thwaites and Co
33 Chalk Hill, WD19 4BL. Est. 1971. Open 9-5,
Sat. 9.30-12.30. *STOCK: Stringed instruments,
from violins to double basses.* TEL: 01923
232412. SER: Restorations.

PUCKERIDGE

St. Ouen Antiques
Vintage Corner, Old Cambridge Rd. SG11 1SA.
(J., J. and S.T. Blake and Mrs P.B. Francis). Est.
1918. Open 10.30-5. SIZE: Large. *STOCK:
English and Continental furniture, decorative
items, silver, porcelain, pottery, glass, clocks,
barometers, paintings.* TEL: 01920 821336. SER:
Valuations; restorations.

REDBOURN, Nr. Hemel Hempstead

Bushwood Antiques
Stags End Equestrian Centre, Gaddesden Lane.

HP2 6HN. LAPADA. Est. 1967. Open 8.30-4,
Sat. 10-4. *STOCK: 18th-19th C furniture,
accessories and objects of art.* LOC: Telephone
for directions. TEL: 01582 794700; fax - 01582
792299; website - www.bushwood.co.uk.

J.N. Antiques
86 High St. AL3 7BD. (M. and J. Brunning). Est.
1975. Open 9-6. SIZE: Medium. *STOCK:
Furniture, 18th-20th C, £5-£3,000; brass and
copper, porcelain, 19th C, £5-£100; pictures,
19th-20th C.* PARK: 50 yds. TEL: 01582 793603.
SER: Valuations. VAT: Spec.

Tim Wharton Antiques
24 High St. AL3 7LL. LAPADA. Est. 1970. Open
10-5.30, Sat. 10-4. CL: Mon. and usually Thurs.
*STOCK: Oak and country furniture, 17th-19th C;
some mahogany, 18th to early 19th C; copper,
brass, ironware and general small antiques.* LOC:
On left entering village from St. Albans on A5183.
PARK: Easy. TEL: 01582 794371; mobile - 07850
622880; e-mail - tim@timwhartonantiques.co.uk;
website - www.timwhartonantiques.co.uk. VAT:
Stan/Spec.

RICKMANSWORTH

Clive A. Burden Ltd
Elmcote House, The Green, Croxley Green. WD3
3HN. Est. 1966. Open by appointment only.
SIZE: Medium. *STOCK: Maps, 1500-1860, £5-
£1,500; natural history, botanical and Vanity
Fair prints, 1720-1870, £1-£1,000; antiquarian
books, pre-1870, £10-£5,000.* TEL: 01923
778097/772387; fax - 01923 896520. SER:
Valuations; buys at auction (as stock). VAT:
Stan.

Galliard Antiques
144 High St. WD3 1AB. (Ellen Harriman). Open
10-6, Fri. 10-7. *STOCK: Clocks, furniture, china,
silver, militaria, pictures, bronzes, coins, Art
Nouveau, Art Deco.* TEL: 01923 778087; fax -
01923 720618.

SAWBRIDGEWORTH

Arcane Antiques Centre
Unit E2 First Floor, The Maltings, Station Rd.
CM21 9JX. (Nicola Smith and Nigel Hoy).
EADA. Est. 1998. Open 10-5, Sat. and Sun. 11-5.
CL: Mon. SIZE: Large. *STOCK: 18th C to
Edwardian furniture, £500-£8,000; English and
French, Chinese and Japanese ceramics, 17th-
20th C, £15-£500; jewellery, from Victorian, £5-
£2,000; glass and silver, tools, 18th-19th C, £5-
£500; Art Deco accessories, £5-£50.* LOC: From

Harlow on A1184, take right at first mini roundabout in Sawbridgeworth into Station Rd., over river bridge and first right into maltings. Shop 100 yards on left. PARK: Easy. TEL: 01279 600562; fax - same. SER: Restorations (jewellery and silver).

Charnwood Antiques
Unit E2 Ground Floor, The Maltings, Station Rd. CM21 9JX. (Nigel Hoy). EADA. Open 10-5, Sat. and Sun. 11-5. CL: Mon. SIZE: Large. *STOCK: Furniture, 18th C to Edwardian, £500-£8,000.* LOC: From Harlow on A1184, turn right at first mini roundabout into Station Rd., over river bridge, first right into maltings. Shop 100 yards on left. PARK: Easy. TEL: 01279 600652; fax - same; mobile- 07957 551899. SER: Restorations (furniture including French polishing and traditional upholstery, desk re-leathering, brass ware supplied and fitted: clock cases and movements); cabinet making, carving and turning.

The Herts and Essex Antiques Centre
The Maltings, Station Rd. CM21 9JX. Est. 1982. Open 10-5, Sat. and Sun. 10.30-5.30. SIZE: Large - over 100 dealers. *STOCK: General antiques and collectables, £1-£2,000.* LOC: Opposite B.R. station. PARK: Easy. TEL: 01279 722044.

Riverside Antiques Ltd
The Maltings, Station Rd. CM21 9JX. (Chris Scott and John Maynard). EADA. Est. 1998. Open 10-5 including Sun. SIZE: Large. *STOCK: General antiques, art and collectables.* PARK: Easy. TEL: 01279 600985; fax - 01279 726398. SER: Valuations; restorations.

ST. ALBANS

By George! Antiques Centre
23 George St. AL3 4ER. Open 10-5, Sun. 1-5. SIZE: 20 dealers. *STOCK: A wide range of general antiques, jewellery and collectables.* LOC: 100yds. from Clock Tower. PARK: Internal courtyard (loading) and Christopher Place (NCP) nearby. TEL: 01727 853032. SER: Restorations.

The Clock Shop - Philip Setterfield of St. Albans
161 Victoria St. AL1 3TA.. Est. 1974. Open 11-4. CL: Thurs. *STOCK: Clocks and watches.* LOC: City station bridge. TEL: 01727 856633; fax - same. SER: Restorations; repairs (clocks, watches, barometers). VAT: Stan/Spec.

Forget-me-Knot Antiques
at Over the Moon, 27 High St. AL3 4EH. (Heather Sharp). Est. 1987. Open 9.30-5.30, Sun. by appointment. *STOCK: Mainly Victorian jewellery and collectables, specializing in silver name brooches.* TEL: 01727 848907. SER: Valuations. VAT: Stan.

James of St Albans
11 George St. AL3 4ER. (S.N. and W. James). Est. 1957. Open 10-5, Thurs. 10-4. *STOCK: Furniture including reproduction; smalls, brass and copper; topographical maps and prints of Hertfordshire.* TEL: 01727 856996. VAT: Stan/Spec.

Magic Lanterns
at By George! Antiques Centre, 23 George St. AL3 4ES. (Josie A. Marsden). Est. 1987. Open 10-5, Thurs. 11-5, Sat. 10-5.30, Sun. 1-5. SIZE: Medium. *STOCK: Lighting - candle, gas and early electric, 1800-1950's, £35-£1,000; small furniture, prints, mirrors, china, metalware, fire accessories, 1850-1950, £25-£500.* LOC: Near the abbey. PARK: Multi-storey nearby. TEL: 01727 853032/865680.

Oriental Rug Gallery Ltd
42 Verulam Rd. AL3 4DQ. (R. Mathias and J. Blair). Open 9-6, Sun. 10.30-4. *STOCK: Russian, Afghan, Turkish and Persian carpets, rugs and kelims; Oriental objets d'art.* TEL: +44 (0) 1727 841046; fax - same; e-mail - rugs@orinetalrug gallery.com; website - www.orientalruggallery. com.

Christopher Wharton Goldsmiths
1 George St. AL3 4ER. FGA DGA. Est. 1967. Open 9-5.30. SIZE: Medium. *STOCK: Silver and plate, 18th-20th C, £20-£2,000; jewellery, mainly*

Queen Mother commemorative plate made by Mary Wondrausch, 12in. diameter, £150.

From the News and Views feature which appeared in the September 2000 issue of **Antique Collecting** magazine. For more details and to subscribe see page 147.

Eighteenth and nineteenth century English furniture

Antiques purchased

Collins Antiques

Wheathampstead

Hertfordshire AL4 8AP England
Telephone: 01582 833111
www.antique-finder.co.uk

Junction 4 on the A1(M) 5 miles

modern, £20-£5,000. LOC: Near clock tower. PARK: Pay and Display at bottom of street or multi-storey, city centre. TEL: 01727 859489; fax - 01727 855474. SER: Registered valuer (jewellery and silver); goldsmithing, gem testing; buys at auction (silver). VAT: Stan.

TRING

John Bly   BADA
The Old Billiards Room, Church Yard. HP23 5AG. Est. 1891. Open Wed.-Sat. 9.30-4.30. SIZE: Large. STOCK: English furniture. TEL: 01442 890802.

Country Clocks
3 Pendley Bridge Cottages, Tring Station. HP23 5QU. (T. Cartmell). Resident. Est. 1976. Open daily, prior 'phone call advisable. SIZE: Small. *STOCK: Clocks, 18th-19th C.* LOC: One mile from A41 in village, cottage nearest canal bridge. PARK: Easy. TEL: 01442 825090. SER: Restorations (clocks).

Farrelly Antiques
The Long Barn, 50 High St. HP23 5AG. (P. Farrelly). Open 9-4. *STOCK: Furniture.* TEL: 01442 891905. SER: Restorations. VAT: Spec.

New England House Antiques
50 High St. HP23 5AG. (Jennifer and Suj Munjee). Est. 1990. Open 10.30-5. CL: Mon. SIZE: Large - 6 showrooms on 3 floors. *STOCK: Fine Georgian and Victorian furniture, £100-£10,000; paintings, glass, silver, decorative furnishings specialising in antique table lights and hand-made shades.* LOC: A41 towards Aylesbury. PARK: Next to shop. TEL: 01442 827262; home - 01462 431914; website - www.newenglandhouseantiques.co.uk. SER: Valuations; restorations (paintings, metalwork and furniture); searches undertaken. VAT: Stan/Spec.

WESTON, Nr. Hitchin

Weston Antiques
Weston Barns, Hitchin Rd. (M.A. Green). Est. 1974. Open Tues.-Sat. 10.30-5.30. SIZE: Small. *STOCK: Period furniture, longcase and mantel clocks, mainly 18th-19th C.* LOC: Off B197, near junction 9 A1(M). PARK: Easy. TEL: 01462 790646; fax - 01462 680304; mobile - 07802 403800; e-mail - greencoantiques@BTinternet.com; website - www.antiques-shop.co.uk. SER: Valuations; restorations (furniture and clocks); buys at auction. VAT: Spec.

WHEATHAMPSTEAD

Collins Antiques (F.G. and C. Collins Ltd.)
Corner House. AL4 8AP. (S.J. and M.C. Collins). Est. 1907. Open 9-1 and 2-5. SIZE: Medium. *STOCK: Furniture, mahogany, 1730-1920, £100-£8,000; oak, 1600-1800, £50-£5,000; walnut, 1700-1740, £75-£3,000.* Not Stocked: Silver. LOC: London, A1(M) junction 4 to B653. PARK: Easy. TEL: 01582 833111. VAT: Stan/Spec.

The Old Bakery Antiques
3 Station Rd. AL4 8BU. (Maurice Shifrin). Open 10-6, Sun. 11-4. CL: Wed. SIZE: Large. *STOCK: 19th C furniture, £500-£1,000.* PARK: Easy, own. TEL: 01582 831999; fax - 01582 831555. VAT: Stan/Spec.

WILSTONE, Nr. Tring

Michael Armson (Antiques) Ltd
The Old Post Office, 34 Tring Rd. HP23 4PB. Open 8-2. SIZE: Large. *STOCK: Furniture, 17th-19th C.* TEL: 01442 890990; fax - 01442 891167; mobile - 07860 910034.

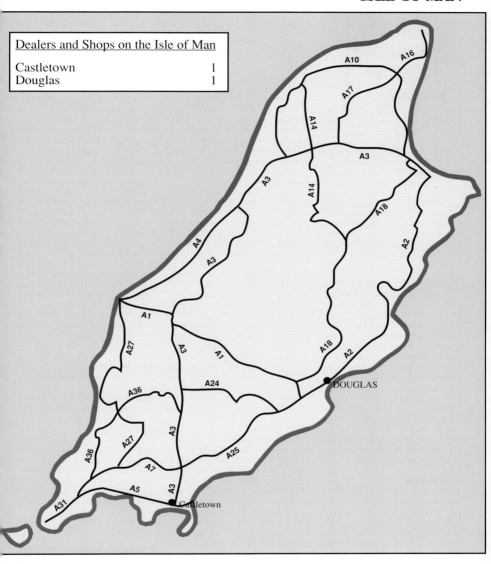

Dealers and Shops on the Isle of Man

Castletown	1
Douglas	1

CASTLETOWN

J. and H. Bell Antiques
22 Arbory St. IM9 1LJ. Est. 1965. Open Wed., Fri. and Sat. 10-5. SIZE: Medium. *STOCK: Jewellery, silver, china, early metalware, furniture, 18th-20th C, £5-£5,000.* TEL: 01624 823132 or 01624 822414. VAT: Stan/Spec.

DOUGLAS

John Corrin Antiques
73 Circular Rd. IM1 1AZ. Est. 1972. Open Sat. 10-4.30 otherwise by appointment. SIZE: Medium. *STOCK: Furniture, 18th-19th C, £100-£6,000; clocks, barometers, 19th C.* LOC: From the promenade, travel up Victoria St., this becomes Prospect Hill and Circular Rd. is on left. PARK: Easy. TEL: 01624 629655; home - 01624 621382.

WINE ANTIQUES
Robin Butler

A mahogany brass-bound wine cooler. The open top models pre-date the lidded variety and are sought because they are dual purpose – they can be used as planters. This example of c.1760 is in particularly good condition and without restoration. At £6,300 it is surprisingly little different in price from what it would have been five years ago. (Robin Butler)

Wine antiques as an area of collecting is less than twenty years old. Its appeal, apart from the fact that many pieces are totally practical today, is that the subject crosses the boundaries of glass, ceramics, silver and furniture as well as adding fresh disciplines such as corkscrews. Price rises have been uneven. Even in the narrow field of wine labels, some categories have moved ahead rapidly in price during the past twelve months, while others have remained almost static. Similar patterns can be observed across the entire discipline and are mainly because of the specific demands of the collecting community.

Wine Bottles
Wine bottles with dated seals are becoming very difficult to find and any 17th or early 18th century examples are commanding well over £1,000, with the finest near to ten times that amount. Unsealed late 18th and early 19th century bottles are plentiful enough and can be bought for less than £100.

Bin Labels
Like many antiques, bin labels are harder to find than they were. Plain white pottery 'coat-hanger' labels with angular or rounded shoulders and marked with names like SHERRY, PORT or MADEIRA, can still be found for about £50-£60 but more interesting names are £100+. Spelling mistakes command a premium, as do any which are out of the ordinary, such as those having lettering other than black. Delftware bin labels with magenta lettering are much sought and can be £500 or more, while blue lettering is dearer again. All these figures are higher than last year, with the best increasing in price more than the ordinary.

Corkscrews
Plain T corkscrews can still be found for less than £30, or considerably less if the worm is damaged. Those with an original brush start from £50 which is little changed from last year. However, the collector market for well-preserved patented corkscrews is rushing ahead. Even Thomason and King's patents, the most frequently encountered of the complex patents, are increasingly hard to find, and command prices 25%+ more than last year, making £400-£800 depending on rarity and condition. Rare patents have increased in price more than all others with fine examples selling for £3,000+. Some of the highest prices for the top collectors' pieces appear to have been concentrated in one auction saleroom.

Wine Tasters
French silver *tastevins* have risen very little in price, if at all, during the past year. Most post-date 1830 and are still to be found for £100-£250. By contrast, pre-Revolution (1789) *tastevins* of any quality and condition are £700-£1,500. English tasters are hard to find and can be many times the above figures. Porcelain tasters have always been of trophy significance to collectors and can now reach £5,000.

Wine Coolers
There are two types of wine cooler, the variety which accommodates a single bottle on the table, and the piece of furniture which will take many. Table wine coolers in silver are among the grandest of antiques and the best examples have followed the trend of all the most sought antiques with prices escalating heavily, in exceptional cases well into six-figure sums. Less grand examples have moved little, except where the cooler has some quirk of design which elevates it above the ordinary. Porcelain wine coolers are sought like all large decorative pieces in that medium, and while Dr Wall period Worcester pairs might make £10,000-£15,000, early 19th century Davenport examples will be about a third of that price, around £3,000-£4,000. Georgian mahogany octagonal brass-bound coolers have changed little if at all in several years and can still be found in the £2,200-£4,500 range depending on colour and condition. However, as soon as some distinctively superior design or top quality example appears on the market, the value can multiply several or many times. Sarcophagus-shaped models have found more favour and moved ahead appreciably. Georgian sideboards with cellaret drawers have risen in price substantially in the past year while their later cousins have risen moderately.

Wine Funnels
Silver wine funnels have surged in price again. Whereas a year ago it was quite possible to find a Georgian example for £500-£600, it is now hard to find one for less than £700, and many are £800-£1,100. There is a shift in popularity from the earlier, 18th century models to the more robust type which appeared from about 1805, and which are generally heavier in gauge. Practicality, condition and quality are the determining factors here.

One of a pair of silver coasters, London 1808, by Rebecca Eames and Edward Barnard. At £1,200, they have hardly changed in price for several years. (Robin Butler)

Decanters

Georgian decanters are becoming harder to find, especially in pairs, and are rising as a result. Singles can be had for £180-£280 with pairs of circa 1810 making three times as much, while 18th century models command a premium of about 25%. This represents about a 15%-20% increase on last year. Specialist decanters with masonic engraving, faux wine labels or Jacobite engraving have risen somewhat more. Decanters from the 1830s and '40s have remained almost static in price and can be bought for well under £100 each, often below £50. Victorian 'shaft and globe' decanters can be found for £30-£100 as singles, and £100-£300 for pairs, which is little different from a year ago.

Claret Jugs

Claret jugs are popular and have risen substantially over the year. Animal models are especially favoured. Ducks and cockatoos with silver mounts can be had for £3,000-£4,000, but rarities like seals and walruses can double or treble that figure. Silver mounted jugs in the Elizabethan manner can be bought for £1,200-£2,400, a little up, but later models have changed little and can still be had for a few hundred pounds. Silver plated models find little favour, and like last year can be, though seldom are, less than £100, while unmounted glass models have moved with the decanter market.

Wine Labels

Ordinary silver wine labels, such as reeded edge rectangular examples, bearing names like 'madeira', 'sherry' or 'hock', are probably cheaper now than they were a year ago. Unmarked (i.e. pre-1790) silver labels can be as little as £40, and marked ones £55-£65. On the other hand, the heavy, early 19th century, cast labels by Edward Farrell or Paul Storr are now four-figure objects and rising quickly. In between, pretty labels and those with unusual names or with spelling mistakes are being avidly sought by collectors, and the price rise during the past year has been about 25% to the £120-£450 level.

Wine Coasters

A few years ago, the sharp rise in the price of papier mâché coasters begot a rash of reproductions and fakes. As a result, the market cooled markedly, but during the past year, the prices of such coasters have

A group of good, but not exceptional, mid-18th century wineglasses. Dating from c.1740-65, they have surged ahead in price as they have become more difficult to locate. Slight damage, however, severely reduces the desirability. (Robin Butler)

begun to harden, and pretty pairs can be seen around the £500 mark. Silver coasters seem less sought than they were and have remained almost static in price during the last twelve months, with ordinary but pleasant examples making £1,200-£2,800 a pair. The only coasters to increase in price have been the important models, such as the Regency silver gilt models by Digby Scott and Benjamin Smith, or Paul Storr.

Drinking Glasses

English drinking glasses have shown marked gains recently. From early balusters to late 18th century facet stems, there have been overall increases with balusters increasing by around 25%, while facet stems by perhaps 15% or so. Ordinary, but perfect, opaque white twists can seldom be seen below £200, but as with all categories, the more rare the glass, the greater the rise in price with colour twists at £1,500-£5,000+ and Beilbys in a similar price bracket.

Space prevents a complete listing of all categories of antique wine paraphernalia. However, it may be gathered from the above that the more desirable collectables have shown a clear move forward, with increments of 20%+ not uncommon. At the same time, many perfectly respectable antique wine artefacts have changed little or not at all over the same period. The inference is that objects with individuality, in fine or better condition, and preferably with a practical use, have fared considerably better than standard pieces, or those for which the vendor should be making some excuse.

Robin Butler is a member of the British Antique Dealers' Association with a shop in Bristol (tel: 0117 973 3017); he specialises in period furniture, silver and wine related items.

This article appeared in the July/August 2000 issue of **Antique Collecting** magazine. For more details and to subscribe see page 147.

A set of four Old Sheffield Plate labels. In silver these would excite little interest and would sell for £400-£500 the set. However, as very early examples of OSP (c.1760), they would be almost double the price. (Robin Butler)

BEMBRIDGE

Windmill Antiques

1 Foreland Rd. PO35 5XN. (E.J. de Kort). LAPADA. Est. 1970. Open Wed.- Sat. 10-1 and 2.15-4. SIZE: Medium. *STOCK: Furniture, silver, porcelain, jewellery.* TEL: 01983 873666. SER: Valuations; buys at auction. VAT: Stan/Spec.

CHALE

Curios of Chale

3 Church Place. PO38 2HA. (Michael Gregory). Est. 1985. Open 12-6 including Sun. SIZE: Large. *STOCK: Architectural items, fireplaces, £50-£500; general antiques, curios and taxidermy, £5-£500; mostly 19th C.* LOC: Off Military Rd., near Black-Gang. PARK: Easy. TEL: 01983 730230; mobile - 07811 835159. SER: Valuations.

COWES

Charles Dickens Bookshop

65 High St. PO31 7RL. *STOCK: Antiquarian and secondhand books, especially 19th-20th C English literature, nautical and children's.* TEL: 01983 280586.

Flagstaff Antiques

Tudor House, Bath Rd. PO31 7RH. (T.A.M. Cockram). Est. 1970. Open from 10 am. CL: Wed. SIZE: Small. *STOCK: Jewellery, 19th-20th C, £50-£2,000; porcelain, 19th C, £25-£1,000; pictures, 19th-20th C, £10-£1,000.* LOC: 100 yards from The Parade. PARK: Easy. TEL: 01983 200138. SER: Valuations; restorations (porcelain and silver).

Galerias Segui

75 High St. PO31 7AJ. Est. 1976. Open 10-5. SIZE: Medium. *STOCK: Pine furniture, £60-£600; prints and watercolours, £15-£200; bric-a-*

Donald Grant, MBE (born 1930), 'Giraffe', oil on canvas, 24in. x 34in., signed. Following a varied career which began in 1946 as an apprentice shipbuilding draughtsman with Swan Hunter, Grant turned to painting and after an exhibition in Birmingham, two London galleries took notice. Soon his wildlife subjects became much sought after but in 1989, following a promotional tour of Canada, he suffered a serious stroke which has curbed his artistic progress. Estimated at £2,000-£3,000, this fine painting sold on 17th May at Christie's South Kensington auction of 'Wildlife Art' for £4,700. (Christie's South Kensington)

From an article entitled 'British Paintings' by Anthony J. Lester which appeared in the July/August 2000 issue of **Antique Collecting** magazine. For more details and to subscribe see page 147.

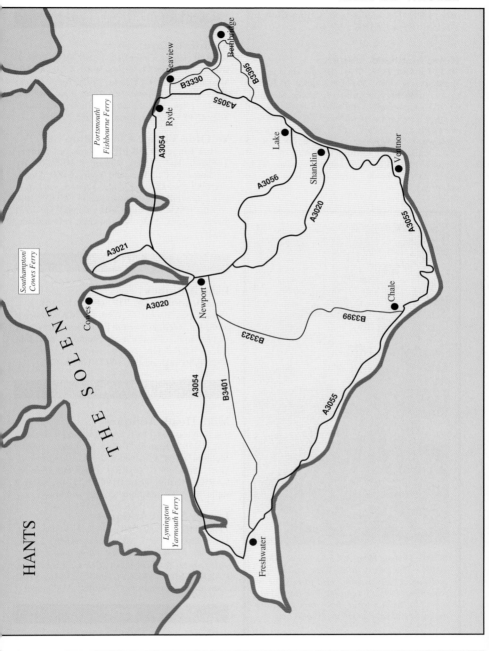

Portsmouth/ Fishbourne Ferry

Southampton/ Cowes Ferry

THE SOLENT

HANTS

Lymington/ Yarmouth Ferry

Bembridge
Seaview
B3330
B3395
A3055
Ryde
A3054
Lake
Ventnor
Shanklin
A3056
A3020
A3055
A3021
Chale
Newport
A3020
Cowes
B3399
B3323
A3054
B3401
A3055
Freshwater

---

brac. LOC: Between Island Sailing Club and Midland Bank. PARK: 200yds. TEL: 01983 292148.

Royal Standard Antiques
70-72 Park Rd. PO31 7LY. (Dennis and Caroline Bradbury). Resident. Est. 1992. Open 10.30-5.30 or any time by appointment. SIZE: Medium. *STOCK: Georgian, Victorian, Edwardian and French provincial furniture, £100-£1,000+; architectural items, £20-£500; pictures, commemoratives, breweriana, £5-£500.* LOC: 5 mins. walk from hydrofoil terminus; corner of Victoria Rd. PARK: Own, behind premises. TEL: 01983 281672; home - same. SER: Restorations; upholstery.

William Holman Hunt, A.R.S.A., R.S.W. (1827-1910), 'The Lost Child'. Watercolour and bodycolour, 5in. x 3¼in. Sold for £8,165 in November 1998. A gem-like Pre-Raphaelite work, a major (but not unreasonably expensive) addition to any good collection.

From an article on watercolours by Richard Kay of Phillips which appeared in the July/August 1999 issue of **Antique Collecting** magazine. For more details and to subscribe see page 147.

Aladdin's Cave
147/149 School Green Rd. PO40 9BB. (Mrs J. Dunn). Est. 1984. Open 9.30-4.30. SIZE: Medium. *STOCK: China, collectors' items, glass, linen, old pine, furniture, memorabilia, books, 19th-20th C, £5-£500.* PARK: Easy. TEL: 01983 752934; home - 01983 753846.

Ye Olde Village Clock Shop
3 Moa Place. PO40 9DS. (Ron and Sandra Tayler). Est. 1970. Open 9.30-1 or by appointment. CL: Tues and Thurs. SIZE: Small. *STOCK: Clocks - longcase, Vienna, carriage, bracket, French and novelty, 17th-19th C, £300-£6,000.* PARK: Easy. TEL: 01983 754193; home - same. SER: Valuations; restorations (clocks).

Lake Antiques
Sandown Rd. PO36 9JP. (P. Burfield). Est. 1982. Open 10-4. CL: Wed. *STOCK: General antiques, Georgian and Victorian furniture, clocks.* LOC: On the main Sandown-Shanklin Rd. PARK: On forecourt. TEL: 01983 406888/865005; mobile - 07710 067678.

Mike Heath Antiques
3-4 Holyrood St. PO30 5AU. (M. and B. Heath). Est. 1979. Open 9.30-5. CL: Thurs. SIZE: Medium. *STOCK: General antiques and bric-a-brac, 19th-20th C, £5-£500.* LOC: Off High St. PARK: Nearby. TEL: 01983 525748; home - same. SER: Restorations (copper and brass).

Lugley Street Antiques
13 Lugley St. PO30 5HD. (D.A. Newman). Est. 1986. Open 9.30-5. CL: Thurs. SIZE: Large. *STOCK: Furniture, clocks, china and collectables, late 18th to early 20th C, £5-£2,500.* PARK: Meters. TEL: 01983 523348. SER: Valuations; restorations (furniture). VAT: Spec.

Hayter's
19-20 Cross St. PO33 2AD. (R.W. and F.L. Hayter). Est. 1956. Open 9-1 and 2-5. CL: Thurs. SIZE: Large. *STOCK: Furniture including*

Victorian. LOC: Through main traffic flow from sea front to town centre. TEL: 01983 563795. VAT: Stan/Spec/Global.

Royal Victoria Arcade
Union St. PO33 2LQ. Open 9-5.30; basement market open Thurs., Fri. and Sat. in summer. TEL: 01983 564661. Below are listed some of the dealers in this Arcade.

Crocus
Collectables, art deco to 1950's.

Echoes
Costume jewellery, militaria and general antiques.

Uriah's Heap
Jewellery, writing equipment, instruments, china, glass and collectables.

Uriah's Heap
9 Royal Victoria Arcade, Union St. PO33 2LQ. (F. Cross). Open Wed., Fri. and Sat. 10-5. *STOCK: Small antiques, china, silver, collectables, linen, lace, fountain pens, jewellery.* TEL: 01983 564661.

SEAVIEW

Rex Gully Antiques
Regent House, High St. PO34 5EX. Est. 1970. Open 10-1, Sat. 10-5, Sun. (summer only) 12-5, other times by appointment. SIZE: Small. *STOCK: Pine, £100-£1,000; pottery, brass and copper, £10-£300; all 19th C.* LOC: From Ryde towards Seaview, follows signs for Seaview Hotel. PARK: Easy. TEL: 01983 613362; fax - same; home - 01983 872725. SER: Valuations; buys at auction (furniture). VAT: Stan/Spec.

SHANKLIN

The Shanklin Gallery
67 Regent St. PO37 7AE. Open 9-5. SIZE: Medium. *STOCK: Oils, watercolours, engravings, prints, maps, 17th-20th C, £10-£2,000.* LOC: Town centre near railway station. PARK: Easy. TEL: 01983 863113. SER: Valuations; restorations (oils, watercolours and prints); framing.

VENTNOR

Peter Goodall
29 Pier St. PO38 1SX. Est. 1965. Open by appointment only. SIZE: Medium. *STOCK: Engravings, etchings, lithographs and aquatints, 17th-20th C, £5-£1,000.* TEL: 01983 856116. SER: Valuations.

Ultramarine
40B High St. PO38 1LG. (Milly Stevens). Open 10-1, Thurs. and Fri. 10-4, Sat. 10-2. CL: Wed. SIZE: Small. *STOCK: 20th C collectables including jewellery, china, studio pottery, textiles and glass, £5-£500.* LOC: Central. PARK: Nearby. TEL: 01983 854062.

Ventnor Rare Books
19 Pier St. PO38 1ST. (N.C.R. and T.A. Traylen). ABA. *STOCK: Antiquarian and secondhand books, prints.* TEL: 01983 853706; fax - 01983 853357.

At Sotheby' South, a set of five oak hall chairs in the George II style will be offered in the International Sale on 24th-27th July. The set is estimated to make £1,200-£1,800.

From an Auction Report which appeared in the July/August 2000 issue of **Antique Collecting** magazine. For more details and to subscribe see page 147.

Roger Kirby Antiques

Caroline Farm, Ridge Row, Acrise Nr. Folkstone, Kent CT18 8JT
Tel: 01303 893230 Fax: 01303 891478

Specialist Dealer & Authority in 16th to late 18th Century English Furniture & Works of Art.
Always a fine selection of furniture in stock waiting for a good home. Valuations & probate
undertaken. We are always pleased to purchase Furniture & Works of Art of the above period.

An extremely rare Northamptonshire Coffer, date 1500 to 1540. Superb colour
and patination and in my opinion a much better example than the one that is
illustrated in Victor Chinnery's book.

ACRISE, Nr. Folkestone

R. Kirby Antiques
Caroline Farm, Ridge Row. CT18 8JT. Open by
appointment 7 days. *STOCK: Early period oak,
16th-18th C, and works of art.* TEL: 01303
893230; e-mail - KIRBYR.@FSBusiness.co.uk.

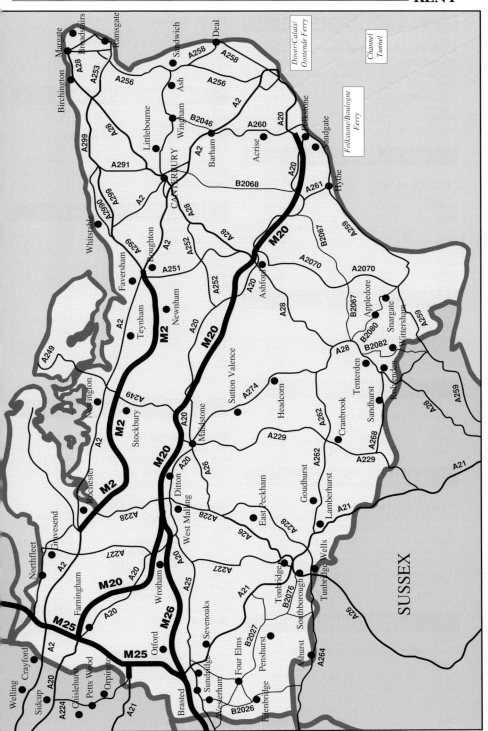

APPLEDORE, Nr. Ashford

Richard Moate Antiques and Back 2 Wood Pine Stripping

The Old Goods Shed, Station Rd. TN26 2DF. Est. 1987. Open 8.30-5, Sat. 9-3. *STOCK: Unstripped and finished pine furniture.* LOC: Adjacent to station. PARK: Easy. TEL: 01233 758109; mobile - 07831 655414; home - 01233 860400. VAT: Stan/Margin.

ASH, Nr. Canterbury

Henry's of Ash

51 The Street. CT3 2EN. (P.H. Robinson). Est. 1988. Open 10-12 and 2-5. CL: Tues. pm and Wed. SIZE: Small. *STOCK: General antiques, linen, Victorian and Art Deco, £5-100; small furniture, £50-£500.* LOC: Main street. PARK: Outside. TEL: 01304 812600. SER: Buys at auction (small items). FAIRS: Copthorne; Ashford; Bromley.

ASHFORD

County Antiques

Old Mill Cottage, Kennett Lane, Stanford North. TN25 6DG. (B. Nilson). Open by appointment. *STOCK: General antiques.* TEL: 01303 813039.

ASHURST

The Baldfaced Stag

(Mike Roberts). *STOCK: Fire surrounds, chimney pieces, garden statuary and sculptures, light fittings.* TEL: 01892 740877.

BARHAM, Nr. Canterbury

Stablegate Antiques

CT4 6QD. (Mr and Mrs M.J. Giuntini). Est. 1989. Open by appointment. SIZE: Large. *STOCK: Georgian and Victorian dining tables, chairs, sideboards, bureaux, davenports, chests of drawers; silver plate, china, clocks, jewellery, glass, objets d'art, collectables, copper, brass, etc.* LOC: Village just off the A2 to Dover. PARK: Easy. TEL: 01227 831639; mobile - 07802 439777.

BECKENHAM

Beckenham Antiques & Collectors' Market

Public Hall, Bromley Rd. BR3. Est. 1979. Open Wed. only 8.30-2. SIZE: 20 stalls. *STOCK: General antiques.* TEL: 020 8660 1369.

Pepys Antiques

9 Kelsey Park Rd. BR3 2LH. (S.P. Elton). Est. 1969. Open 10-2. CL: Wed. *STOCK: Furniture, paintings, clocks, silver, porcelain, copper, brass.* LOC: Central Beckenham. TEL: 020 8650 0994.

BIRCHINGTON, Nr. Margate

John Chawner

36 Station Approach. CT7 9RD. Open 10.30-12.30 and 2-5. CL: Tues. *STOCK: Clocks, barometers, smalls and bureaux.* PARK: Easy. TEL: 01843 843309. SER: Repairs (clocks and barometers).

BOUGHTON, Nr. Faversham

Clockshop

187 The Street. ME13 9BH. (S.G. Fowler). LBHI. Resident. Est. 1968. Open 10-6. SIZE: Small. *STOCK: Clocks.* PARK: Easy. TEL: 01227 751258. SER: Repairs (clocks).

Jean Collyer Antiques

194 The Street. ME13 9AL. (Mrs J.B. Collyer). Est. 1977. Open by appointment only. SIZE: Small. *STOCK: Porcelain, glass, furniture, general antiques, 18th to mid-19th C.* PARK: Easy. TEL: 01227 751454; home - 01227 752831. SER: Valuations. VAT: Stan/Spec.

BRASTED, Nr. Westerham

David Barrington

The Antique Shop. TN16 1JA. Est. 1947. Open 9-6. SIZE: Medium. *STOCK: Furniture, 18th C.* LOC: A25. PARK: Easy. TEL: 01959 562537. VAT: Stan/Spec.

Cooper Fine Arts Ltd

Swan House, High St. TN16 1JJ. (J. Hill-Reid). Est. 1976. Open 10-6. SIZE: Medium. *STOCK: Furniture, sculpture, oils and watercolours, 1750-1950, £100-£10,000.* PARK: Easy. TEL: 01959 565818. VAT: Stan/Spec.

Courtyard Antiques

High St. TN16 1JE. (H. La Trobe). Open 10-5, Sun. and Bank Holidays 12.30-4.30. SIZE: Medium. *STOCK: 19th C furniture (including extending dining tables), silver, jewellery, glass, ceramics, Tunbridge ware, watercolours, prints and objets d'art.* PARK: Easy. TEL: 01959 564483; fax - 01732 454726. SER: Restorations (furniture); French polishing; re-leathering.

Peter Dyke

Kentish House, High St. TN16 1JE. Est. 1977. Open 10-5.30. SIZE: Small. *STOCK: Furniture, 18th-19th C, £500-£10,000; paintings, 19th-20th C, £500-£1,000+; decorative objects, 19th C, £150-£1,000.* LOC: A25. PARK: Easy. TEL: 01959 565020. SER: Valuations; buys at auction. VAT: Spec.

Kashan Carpets Ltd.

High St. TN16 1JA. (J. Caslake). Open 10-6, Sun. by appointment. *STOCK: Oriental carpets and rugs, £250-£10,000; kilim stools, £85-£550; kilim and carpet cushions, £20-£75.* TEL: 01959 565866; fax - same. SER: Valuations; restorations; hand-cleaning; kilim stools and cushions made to order. FAIRS: Olympia (June).

Keymer Son & Co. Ltd

Swaylands Place, The Green. TN16 1JY. Est. 1977. Open 10-1 and 2.30-5. CL: Sat. SIZE: Small. *STOCK: 18th-19th C furniture, £100-£3,000.* LOC: A25. PARK: Easy. TEL: 01959 564203; fax - 01959 561138.

Roy Massingham Antiques

The Coach House. TN16 1JJ. LAPADA. Open by appointment. *STOCK: 18th-19th C furniture, pictures and decorative items.* TEL: 01959 562408; mobile - 07860 326825.

Old Manor House Antiques

The Green. TN16 1JL. Open daily. *STOCK: Clocks, barometers, lighting, copper and brass, mirrors, furniture and general antiques.* TEL: 01959 562536.

Southdown House Antiques

High St. TN16 1JE. Est. 1978. Open 10-5. *STOCK: Furniture, mainly 19th C mahogany and walnut, decorative items, porcelain, glass, metalware, textiles, £50-£4,000.* PARK: Own. TEL: 01959 563522. VAT: Spec.

Graham Stead Antiques

Southdown House, High St. TN16 1JE. Open 10-5. *STOCK: Furniture, mainly 19th C mahogany and walnut, decorative items and porcelain, £50-£3,000.* PARK: Own. TEL: 01959 563522. VAT: Spec.

Dinah Stoodley & Celia Jennings

High St. TN16 1JE. Est. 1965. Open 9.30-5.30. SIZE: Medium. *STOCK: Oak and country furniture, 1600-1800; ceramics, 1600-1880; European woodcarving and sculpture, 1400-1700.* LOC: A25. PARK: Easy. TEL: 01959 563616. VAT: Spec.

Tilings Antiques

High St. TN16 1JA. (Penny Fawcett). Est. 1974. Open 10-5.30 or by appointment. SIZE: Medium. *STOCK: Furniture, decorative items, 18th-19th C, £20-£2,000.* LOC: Village centre on A25. PARK: Easy. TEL: 01959 564735; mobile - 07885 103234. VAT: Stan/Spec.

The Village Antique Centre

4 High St. TN16 1JE. (Ms K. Phillips). Est. 1983. Open 10-5, including Sun. SIZE: Large. *STOCK: Furniture, ceramics, silver, jewellery, glass, decorative and collectable items, 15th-20th C, £5-£10,000.* LOC: A25 between Sevenoaks and Westerham. PARK: Own. TEL: 01959 564545; home - 01293 824173. SER: Valuations; restorations (furniture).

W.W. Warner (Antiques)   BADA

The Green, High St. TN16 1JL. (C.S. Jowitt). Est. 1957. Open 10-5. *STOCK: 18th-19th C English and Continental pottery, porcelain, glass, furniture.* LOC: A25. PARK: Easy. TEL: 01959 563698. SER: Valuations; restorations.

BROADSTAIRS

Broadstairs Antiques and Collectables

49 Belvedere Rd. CT10 1PF. (P. Edwards). Est. 1980. Open winter 10-4.30 (closed Wed), April-end Sept. 10-5, including Wed. *STOCK: General antiques, linen, lace, china and small furniture.* PARK: Easy. TEL: 01843 861965.

CANTERBURY

Antique and Design

The Old Oast, Hollow Lane. CT1 3SA. (Steve Couchman). Est. 1988. Open 9-6, Sun. 10-4. SIZE: Large. *STOCK: Pine furniture, decorative items, 1800-1950, £5-£1,500.* LOC: M2 from London, Canterbury exit, straight at first roundabout, right at second and third roundabouts, left at second pedestrian lights, shop 500 yds. TEL: 01227 762871. SER: Restorations; buys at auction; import and export. VAT: Stan/Spec.

R. J. Baker

16 Palace St. CT1 2DZ. Est. 1979. Open 9.30-5. CL: Mon. SIZE: Small. *STOCK: Silver and jewellery, 18th-19th C, £500-£2,000; handmade modern silverware, modern jewellery.* LOC: 5 minutes from cathedral, opposite The King's School. PARK: Easy. TEL: 01227 463224. SER: Valuations; restorations; gold and silversmiths; manufacturers. VAT: Stan/Spec.

Burgate Antique Centre
10c Burgate. CT1 2HG. (V. Reeves). Est. 1986. Open 10-5. SIZE: 14 dealers. *STOCK: General antiques and collectables.* LOC: City wall overlooking cathedral gardens. TEL: 01227 456500.

The Canterbury Bookshop
23a Palace St. CT1 2DZ. (David Miles). Open 10-5. *STOCK: Antiquarian and secondhand books, children's books, prints.* TEL: 01227 464773; fax - 01227 780073.

William Lionel Wyllie, The Final Port of Call, c.1900, oil on panel, 20in. x 12in. (Private collection)

From an article entitled 'The Great Age of British Marine Art 1815-1900 – Marine Painting Part III' by James Taylor which appeared in the May 2001 issue of **Antique Collecting** magazine. For more details and to subscribe see page 147.

Chaucer Bookshop
6-7 Beer Cart Lane. CT1 2NY. (Sir Robert Sherston-Baker Bt.). ABA, PBFA. Est. 1956. Open 10-5. *STOCK: Books and prints, 18th-20th C, £5-£150; maps, 18th-19th C, £50-£250.* LOC: 5 minutes walk from cathedral, via Mercery Lane and St. Margaret's St. PARK: Castle St. TEL: 01227 453912; fax - 01227 451893; e-mail - chaucerbooks@canterbury.dialnet.com. SER: Valuations; buys at auction (books, maps and prints). VAT: Stan.

Coach House Antiques
2A Duck Lane, St. Radigunds. CT1 2AE. Est. 1975. Open daily. SIZE: Large. *STOCK: General antiques, small furniture, ceramics, glass, linen, books, collectors' items and bygones.* Not Stocked: Jewellery. TEL: 01227 463117.

Conquest House Antiques
17 Palace St. CT1 2DZ. (C.C. Hill and D.A. Magee). Open 9-5. *STOCK: 18th-19th C furniture and decorative items.* TEL: 01227 464587; fax - 01227 451375.

H.S. Greenfield and Son, Gunmakers (Est. 1805)
4/5 Upper Bridge St. CT1 2NB. (T.S. Greenfield). *STOCK: English sporting guns, in pairs and singles; Continental sporting guns, firearms.* TEL: 01227 456959. SER: Valuations; restorations (antique firearms). VAT: Stan.

Nan Leith's Brocanterbury
Errol House, 68 Stour St. CT1 2NZ. Resident. Open Mon., Wed., Fri. and Sat. 1-6 or by appointment. *STOCK: Art Deco, Victoriana, pressed glass, costume jewellery.* LOC: Close to Heritage Museum. TEL: 01227 454519.

Michael Pearson Antiques
Open by appointment only. *STOCK: 17th-18th C furniture including early oak and country; clocks and wood carvings.* TEL: 01227 459939. SER: Valuations; restorations (clocks and furniture).

Rastro Antiques
44a High St. CT1 2SA. (J. Coppage). Est. 1981. Open 10-5. SIZE: 8 dealers. *STOCK: Bric-a-brac, vintage clothing, books, stamps, ephemera.* LOC: Up narrow lane off High St. PARK: Nearby. TEL: 01227 463537.

The Saracen's Lantern
8-9 The Borough. CT1 2DR. (W.J. Christophers). Est. 1970. *STOCK: General antiques, silver, jewellery, clocks, watches, Victorian bottles and pot-lids, Georgian, Victorian and Edwardian furniture.* LOC: Near Cathedral opposite King's School. PARK: At rear, by way of Northgate and St. Radigun's St. TEL: 01227 451968.

DOUGLAS BRYAN **CATHERINE BRYAN**

DOUGLAS BRYAN
Early Oak & Country Furniture
SPECIALISING IN 17TH & 18TH CENTURY OAK FURNITURE
THE OLD BAKERY, ST. DAVID'S BRIDGE, CRANBROOK, KENT TN17 3HN
TEL: 01580 713103 FAX: 01580 712407
Visits By Appointment

LAPADA MEMBER

Town and Country Furniture
141 Wincheap. CT1 3SE. (A. Hollinhurst). Est. 1986. Open 10-5. SIZE: Medium. *STOCK: Furniture, country collectables, 50p-£1,000.* LOC: A28 Wincheap road. PARK: Nearby. TEL: 01227 762340. SER: Paint and metal stripping; restorations (furniture); French polishing; lead light repairs; reclaimed pine furniture made to order.

Victorian Fireplace
Thanet House, 92 Broad St. CT1 2LU. (J.J. Griffith). Est. 1980. Open 10-5.30. CL: Mon. SIZE: Medium. *STOCK: Georgian to Victorian fireplaces.* LOC: Town centre. PARK: Nearby. TEL: 01227 767723. SER: Restorations; fitting. VAT: Stan/Spec.

CRANBROOK

Douglas Bryan   BADA
The Old Bakery, St. David's Bridge. TN17 3HN. (Douglas and Catherine Bryan). LAPADA. Est. 1971. Open by appointment. SIZE: Medium. *STOCK: Mainly English oak and country furniture, 17th-18th C; woodcarvings, some metalware.* LOC: Adjacent Tanyard car park - off road towards Windmill. PARK: Adjacent. TEL: 01580 713103; fax - 01580 712407; mobile - 03747 37303.

Cranbrook Antique Centre
15 High St. TN17. (Mrs S. Bisram). Open 10-5. SIZE: 7 dealers - 2 floors. *STOCK: 19th C furniture, collectables and silver.* TEL: 01580 712173.

CHISLEHURST

Chislehurst Antiques
7 Royal Parade. BR7 6NR. (Mrs M. Crawley). LAPADA. Est. 1976. Open Mon., Fri., Sat., 10-5, Sun. 11-4. SIZE: Large. *STOCK: Furniture, 1760-1910; lighting - oil, gas, electric, 1850-1910; decorative antiques.* LOC: Half mile from A20, 3 miles from M25. PARK: Easy. TEL: 020 8467 1530; mobile - 07773 345266. VAT: Spec.

Michael Sim
1 Royal Parade. BR7 5PG. Open 9-6 including Sun. SIZE: Medium. *STOCK: English furniture, Georgian and Regency, £500-£50,000; clocks, barometers, globes and scientific instruments, £500-£50,000; Oriental works of art, £50-£5,000; portrait miniatures, £300-£5,000; animalier bronzes, £1,000-£10,000.* LOC: 50yds. from War Memorial at junction of Bromley Rd. and Centre Common Rd. PARK: Easy. TEL: 020 8467 7040; home - same; fax - 020 8857 1313. SER: Valuations; restorations; buys at auction. VAT: Spec.

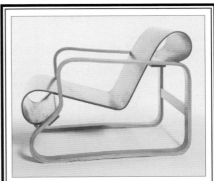

A No.41 Paimio Sanatorium lounge chair by Alvar Aalto for Oy Huonekalu-Rakennustyotehdas, Finland, 1931-1932. Sold for £16,000.

From an article entitled 'Scandinavian Furniture 1930-1975' by Dan Tolson which appeared in the December 2000/January 2001 issue of **Antique Collecting** magazine. For more details and to subscribe see page 147.

LENNOX CATO
ANTIQUES & WORKS OF ART

1 The Square, Church Street,
Edenbridge, Kent TN8 5BD
Tel: 01732 865988 Mobile: 07836 233473

Website: www.lennoxcato.com
Email: cato@lennoxcato.com

Cranbrook Gallery
21B Stone St. TN17 3HF. (P.J. and N.A. Rodgers).
Open Tues.-Sat. 9.30-5. *STOCK: Watercolours,
prints and maps, 18th-19th C*. TEL: 01580
720720; e-mail - cranbrookg@ aol.com.

Swan Antiques
Stone St. TN17 3HF. (R. White). Est. 1982. Open
10-1 and 2-5 and by appointment. CL: Mon. and
Wed. SIZE: Medium. *STOCK: Country furniture,
17th-19th C, from £500+; folk art and nâive
paintings*. LOC: Town centre. PARK: Easy. TEL:
01580 712720; home - 01580 291864. SER:
Valuations; buys at auction. FAIRS: Olympia;
Battersea Decorative and Fine Art. VAT: Spec.

Vestry Antiques
3 Stone St. TN17 3HF. (Mrs Lynn Dawkins). Est.
1992. Open 9.30-5. *STOCK: 18th-19th C oak,
mahogany, pine and decorative items*. LOC: Next to
church. PARK: Nearby (loading and unloading only
outside shop). TEL: 01580 713563. SER: Valuations.

CRAYFORD

Watling Antiques
139 Crayford Rd. DA1 4AS. Open 10-6.30.
STOCK: General antiques and shipping goods.
TEL: 01322 523620.

DEAL

J. Clarke-Hall Ltd
75 Middle St. CT14 6HN. Est. 1934. *STOCK:
English literature especially Samuel Johnson and
the 18th C*. TEL: 01304 375467. *Mail Order
Only*.

Decors II Ltd
67 Beach St. CT14 6HY. (N. Loftus-Potter). Est.
1973. Open 9.30-7 including Sun; in winter Fri.-
Mon. or by appointment. *STOCK: Decorative
items, general antiques and fabrics (including
modern)*. PARK: Easy. TEL: 01304 368030; fax -
same; home - same; e-mail - potter@ decors
antiques.com; website - www. decorsantiques.
com.

Pretty Bizarre
170 High St. CT14 6BQ. (Philip Hartley). Open
Fri. and Sat. 10-4.30 or by appointment. SIZE:
Medium. *STOCK: Art Deco to 1970's ceramics
and collectables*. TEL: Mobile - 07973 794537.

Quill Antiques
12 Alfred Sq. CT14 6LR. (A.J. and A.R. Young).
Open 9-5.30. *STOCK: General antiques,
porcelain, postcards*. TEL: 01304 375958.

Serendipity
125 High St. CT14 6BB. (M. and K. Short). Est.
1976. Open 10-1 and 2-4.30, Sat. 9.30-4.30 or by
appointment. SIZE: Medium. *STOCK: Staffordshire
figures, ceramics, pictures, furniture*. PARK: Easy.
TEL: 01304 369165; home - 01304 366536. SER:
Valuations; restorations (ceramics, oil paintings).

DITTON, Nr. Maidstone

Pinions Collectors Centre
429 London Rd. ME20 6DB. (John Wright). Est.
1999. Open 7 days 10-5. SIZE: Small. *STOCK:
General antiques and collectables, from 18th C,
£5-£500*. LOC: A20, 3 miles west of Maidstone.
PARK: Own. TEL: 01622 790923; home - same.

EAST PECKHAM, Nr. Tonbridge

Desmond and Amanda North
The Orchard, Hale St. TN12 5JB. Est. 1971. Open
daily, appointment advisable. SIZE: Medium.
*STOCK: Oriental rugs, runners, carpets and
cushions, 1800-1939, £60-£3,500*. LOC: On B2015,
400yds south of roundabout at northern end of Hale
Street bypass. PARK: Easy. TEL: 01622 871353;
home - same. SER: Valuations; restorations
(reweaving, re-edging, patching, cleaning).

Chevertons of Edenbridge Ltd
English and Continental Antique Furniture

Taylour House, 67-73 High Street, Edenbridge, Kent, TN8 5AL
Tel: (01732) 863196/863358   Fax: (01732) 864298
e-mail: chevertons@msn.com

Edenbridge is
16 miles from Gatwick Airport,
35 miles from London,
37 miles from Brighton,
68 miles from Dover,
13 miles from Tunbridge Wells,
10 miles from East Grinstead
and 8 miles from Westerham.

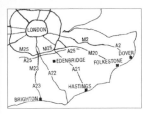

Opening hours

Monday to Saturday,
9am - 5.30pm

Car Park on premises

**TWENTY-FIVE
SHOWROOMS**

One of the largest selections of affordable antiques in the south of England

EDENBRIDGE

Lennox Cato
BADA
1 The Square, Church St. TN8 5BD. (Mr and Mrs Cato). LAPADA. Est. 1975. Open 9.30-5.30, Sat. 10-4. SIZE: Medium. *STOCK: 18th-19th C English and Continental furniture and related items, including mirrors.* **TEL: 01732 865988; mobile - 07836 233473; e-mail - cato@lennoxcato.com; website - www.lennoxcato.com. SER: Valuations; restorations. FAIRS: Olympia (Spring, Summer, Winter); BADA (London and Harrogate). VAT: Stan/Spec.**

Chevertons of Edenbridge Ltd
Taylour House, 67-73 High St. TN8 5AL. (D. and A. Adam). LAPADA. Open 9-5.30. SIZE: 25 showrooms. *STOCK: Furniture and accessories, £250-£25,000.* LOC: From Westerham, on B2026 to Edenbridge. PARK: Own. TEL: 01732 863196/863358; fax - 01732 864298; e-mail - chevertons@msn.com. VAT: Stan/Spec.

FARNINGHAM

Adams Arts & Antiques Ltd
The Old Forge, High St. DA4 0DG. (J. Adams and R. K. Dagger). Open 9.30-5 including Sun.

CL: Wed. pm. SIZE: Medium. *STOCK: Unusual and distinctive garden and interior statuary.* LOC: Close to junction M25/M20. TEL: 01322 866877; fax - same. FAIRS: Hampton Court; Tatton Park. VAT: Stan.

P.T. Beasley
Forge Yard, High St. DA4 0DB. (P.T. and R. Beasley). Est. 1964. CL: Tues. *STOCK: English furniture, some pewter, brass, Delft, woodcarvings.* LOC: Opposite Social Club. TEL: 01322 862453.

Farningham Pine
High St. DA4. (P. and Mrs. T.A. Dzierzek). Est. 1987. Open 10-5. CL: Wed. *STOCK: Pine furniture, from 1830, £25-£5,000.* LOC: 1 mile from M25, junction 3, on A20, first turn off (A225), before Brands Hatch if heading south. PARK: Easy. TEL: 01322 863168/863230; fax - 01322 863168. VAT: Stan/Spec.

FAVERSHAM

Collectors' Corner
East St/Crescent Rd. ME13 8AD. Est. 1952. Open 10-5. CL: Thurs. SIZE: Small. *STOCK: Collectors' items - cigarette and post cards, badges, jewellery, prints, antique and second-hand wood-working and engineering tools.* LOC:

Opposite P.O., at only set of traffic lights. PARK: Easy and at rear by arrangement. TEL: 01795 539721; home - 01795 536642. SER: Valuations.

Squires Antiques (Faversham)
3 Jacob Yard, Preston St. ME13 8NY. (A. Squires). Est. 1985. Open 10-5. CL: Wed. and Thurs. *STOCK: General antiques.* TEL: 01795 531503.

FOLKESTONE

Alan Lord Antiques
71 Tontine St. CT20 1JR. (A.G., J.A. and R.G. Lord). Est. 1956. Open 9-5. CL: Sat. pm. SIZE: Large. *STOCK: Period and Victorian furniture, china, silver. Rear warehouse - trade and shipping goods.* LOC: Road up from harbour. PARK: Easy. TEL: 01303 253674 anytime. VAT: Stan/Spec.

G. and D.I. Marrin and Sons
149 Sandgate Rd. CT20 2DA. ABA. Est. 1949. Open 9.30-1 and 2.30-5.30. CL: Mon. SIZE: Large. *STOCK: Maps, early engravings, topographical and sporting prints, paintings, drawings, books, engravings.* TEL: 01303 253016; fax - 01303 850956; e-mail -marrinbook@clara.co.uk; website - www. marrinbook.clara.net. SER: Restorations; framing. VAT: Stan.

FOUR ELMS, Nr. Edenbridge

Treasures
The Cross Roads. TN8 7NH. (B. Ward-Lee). Open 10-5. *STOCK: Copper, brass, glass, porcelain, silver, jewellery, linen, books, toys, pine, small furniture and collectables.* TEL: 01732 700363.

Yew Tree Antiques
The Cross Roads. TN8 7NH. (G. Nixon). Est. 1984. Open 10-5. SIZE: Medium. *STOCK: Porcelain and copper, 19th-20th C, £5-£500; glass, jewellery, linen, small furniture and collectables.* LOC: Off A25 - B269. PARK: Easy. TEL: 01732 700215.

GOUDHURST

Mill House Antiques
High St. Est. 1968. Open 10-5. CL: Wed pm. SIZE: Medium. *STOCK: Oak, pine country and painted furniture and associated items, 18th C to Victorian, £5-£1,000.* LOC: Off A21 on to A262, village about 3 miles. PARK: Easy. TEL: 01580 212476; home - 01580 211703. SER: Valuations.

GRAVESEND

Alan Wood
Open by appointment. *STOCK: Specialist in Staffordshire portrait figures.* TEL: 01474 533722.

HEADCORN, Nr. Ashford

Penny Lampard
31-33 High St. TN27 9NE. (Mrs P. Lampard). Est. 1981. Open 9.30-5.30. SIZE: Large. *STOCK: Stripped pine and decorative items for interior design.* PARK: Easy. TEL: 01622 890682. FAIRS: Sutton Valence. VAT: Stan.

HYTHE

Malthouse Arcade
High St. CT21 5BW. (Mr and Mrs R.M. Maxtone Graham). Est. 1974. Open Fri., Sat. and Bank Holiday Mon. 9.30-5.30. SIZE: Large - 37 stalls. *STOCK: Furniture, jewellery and collectors' items.* LOC: West end of High St. PARK: 50yds. TEL: 01303 260103; home - 01304 613270.

Owlets
99 High St. CT21 5JH. Open 9-5. *STOCK: Antique and estate jewellery and silver.* TEL: 01303 230333: e-mail - alison@owlets.co.uk; website - www.owlets.co.uk.

Samovar Antiques
158 High St. CT21 5JR. (Mrs F. Rignault). Open 9.30-5, Wed. 9.30-1. *STOCK: 19th C furniture, French provincial furniture, Oriental carpets and rugs and general antiques.* PARK: Own. TEL: 01303 264239.

LAMBERHURST

The China Locker
TN3 8HN. (G. Wilson). Open by appointment only. SIZE: Small. *STOCK: Prints, 18th-19th C, £5-£40.* TEL: 01892 890555. FAIRS: Local.

LITTLEBOURNE, Nr. Canterbury

Jimmy Warren Antiques
Cedar Lodge, 28 The Hill. CT3 1TA. Est. 1969. Open 10-5 including Sun. *STOCK: Decorative antiques and garden ornaments.* LOC: A257. PARK: Own. TEL: 01227 721510; e-mail - enquiries@jimmywarren.co.uk; website - www.jimmywarren.co.uk. SER: Valuations. VAT: Stan/Spec.

MAIDSTONE

Gem Antiques
10 Gabriels Hill. Est. 1969. Open 10-5. SIZE: Small. *STOCK: Clocks and barometers, £200-£10,000; jewellery, £5-£10,000.* TEL: 01622 763344. SER: Valuations; restorations; repairs.

Newnham Court Antiques
Newnham Court Shopping Village, Bearsted Rd. ME14 5LH. (Mr and Mrs Draper). Est. 1991. Open 9-5.45, Sun. 10.30-4.30. SIZE: Medium. *STOCK: Dining furniture including sideboards and cabinets, late Victorian to 1930's, £300-£2,500; collectables, £1-£250.* PARK: Easy. TEL: 01622 631526. VAT: Stan/Spec.

MARGATE

Furniture Mart
Grotto Hill. CT9 2BU. (R.G. Scott). Est. 1971. CL: Wed. SIZE: Large. *STOCK: General antiques £1-£1,500; shipping goods.* LOC: Corner of Bath Place. TEL: 01843 220653. SER: Restorations; restoration materials supplied; container packing. VAT: Global/Stan.

NEWINGTON, Nr. Sittingbourne

Newington Antiques
58-60 High St. (Georgina McKinnon). LAPADA. Est. 1979. Open 10-5, Sun. 10-2 or by appointment. CL: Mon. and Wed. SIZE: Large. *STOCK: Furniture, late 18th to late 19th C, £500-£3,000; pre-1930 smalls, pictures, decorative items, £50-£4,000.* LOC: On the A2 close to A249. PARK: Own. TEL: 01795 844448; fax - 01795 841448; website - www.antiqueskent.co.uk. SER: Valuations; restorations (furniture, china, metal). FAIRS: Battersea Antiques & Textiles; NEC; Earls Court.

NEWNHAM, Nr. Sittingbourne

Periwinkle Press
47 The Street. ME9 0LN. (A.L. and C. Swain). Est. 1967. Open 9-6, Sun. 12-6. *STOCK: Antiquarian books and prints, maps, watercolours.* LOC: Village centre. PARK: Easy. TEL: 01795 890388; e-mail - cswain1805@ aol.com. SER: Restorations (prints and oils); framing.

NORTHFLEET

Northfleet Hill Antiques
36 The Hill. DA11 9EX. (Mrs M. Kilby). Est.

1986. Open Mon., Tues., Fri., some Sats. 10-5 and by appointment. SIZE: Small. *STOCK: Furniture, 19th to early 20th C, £50-£800; bygones and collectables, £1-£100.* LOC: A226 near junction with B261 and B2175. PARK: Easy (behind Ye Olde Coach and Horses Inn). TEL: 01474 321521.

ORPINGTON

Antica of Green Street Green
48 High St., Green Street Green. BR6 6BJ. Open 10-5.30. *STOCK: General antiques.* TEL: 01689 851181.

OTFORD

Ellenor Antiques and Tea Shop
11a High St. TN14. (Ellenor Hospice Care). Open 10-5. SIZE: Medium. *STOCK: Furniture, ceramics, glass, 18th to early 20th C, £5-£1,500.* LOC: Towards Sevenoaks, 3 miles south of junction 4, M25. PARK: Nearby. TEL: 01959 524322. SER: Items sold on donation or commission basis for hospice charity.

Mandarin Gallery - Oriental Art
The Mill Pond, 16 High St. TN14 5PQ. (J. and M.C. Liu). Est. 1984. Open 10-5. CL: Wed. SIZE: Medium. *STOCK: Chinese rosewood and lacquer furniture, 18th-19th C; jade and soap stone, ivory and wood carvings.* Not Stocked: Non-Oriental items. LOC: A225. PARK: Easy. TEL: 01959 522778; home - 01732 457399; fax - same. SER: Restorations (Chinese rosewood furniture).

Otford Antiques & Collectors Centre
26-28 High St. TN15 9DF. (Mr and Mrs David Lowrie). Open 10-5, Sun. 11-4. SIZE: Large. *STOCK: Furniture and collectables, to £800+.* PARK: Easy. TEL: 01959 522025; fax - 01959 525858. SER: Restorations (polishing, caning and upholstery).

PENSHURST, Nr. Tonbridge

Buxton House Stores
TN11 8BT. (Sali Morant and Jonny Farringdon). Est. 1995. Open Thurs., Fri., Sat. 12-5, Sun. 2-5. *STOCK: Furniture, textiles, linens and decorative items, £2-£250.* LOC: Main road. PARK: Easy. TEL: 01892 870220; home - same; website - www.wizzo.demon.co.uk/.

PETTS WOOD

Beehive
22 Station Sq. BR5 1NA. Est. 1994. Open 9.30-5, Sat. 9.30-4.30. SIZE: 50 dealers. *STOCK: Collectables, china, glass, jewellery and furniture, 19th-20th C, £1-£1,000.* PARK: Easy. TEL: 01689 890675.

RAMSGATE

Granny's Attic
2 Addington St. CT11 9JL. (Penelope J.Warn). Est. 1987. Open 10-5. CL: Thurs. pm. SIZE: Medium. *STOCK: Pre-1940's items, £2-£500.* LOC: Left off harbour approach road or right off Westcliffe Rd. PARK: Easy. TEL: 01843 588955; home - 01843 596288.

Thanet Antiques Trading Centre
45 Albert St. CT11 9EX. (Mr and Mrs R. Fomison). Est. 1971. Prior 'phone call advisable. SIZE: Large. *STOCK: Furniture and bric-a-brac, 18th-20th C, £1-£5,000.* LOC: From London Rd. right to seafront. With harbour on right turn first left down Addington St., then last right. PARK: Own. TEL: 01843 597336; home - 01843 597540.

ROCHESTER

Baggins Book Bazaar - The Largest Secondhand Bookshop in England
19 High St. ME1 1PY. Open 10-6 including Sun. *STOCK: Secondhand and antiquarian books.* TEL: 01634 811651; fax - 01634 840591.

Cottage Style Antiques
24 Bill Street Rd. ME2 4RB. (W. Miskimmin). Open 9.30-5.30. *STOCK: General and architectural antiques.* TEL: 01634 717623.

Field Staff & Woods
93 High St. ME1 1LX. (Jim Field, Jane Staff and John Woods). Open 10-5. SIZE: Large - 3 showrooms. *STOCK: General antiques and collectables.* LOC: Centre of High St. TEL: 01634 846144/840108.

Francis Iles
Rutland House, La Providence, High St. ME1 1LX. (The Family Iles). Est. 1960. Open 9.30-5.30. SIZE: Large. *STOCK: Over 700 works, all mediums including sculpture, mainly 20th C, £50-£10,000.* PARK: 40yds. TEL: 01634 843081; fax - 01634 846681. SER: Restorations (cleaning and relining); framing. VAT: Stan/Spec.

Kaizen International Ltd
88 High St. ME1 1JT. (Jason Hunt). Est. 1997. Open 9-5.30, Sun. 12-4. SIZE: Medium. *STOCK: General antiques including antique and secondhand jewellery.* PARK: Nearby. TEL: 01634 814132; website - kaizenInternational. com. SER: Valuations; restorations (jewellery).

Langley Galleries
143 High St. ME1 1EL. (K.J. Cook). Est. 1978. Open 9-5.30. *STOCK: Prints, watercolours, oils, 19th-20th C.* TEL: 01634 811802. SER: Restorations and cleaning (watercolours and oils); framing.

Memories
128 High St. ME1 1JT. (Mrs V.A. Lhermette). Est. 1985. Open 9-5, Sun. 11-5. SIZE: Medium. *STOCK: Small furniture, £50-£500; china, £5-£75; both 1900-1950; pictures, late Victorian to Edwardian, £20-£70; collectables, bric-a-brac, linen and books.* PARK: Opposite. TEL: 01634 811044.

ROLVENDEN, Nr. Cranbrook

Falstaff Antiques
63-67 High St. TN17 4LP. (C.M. Booth). Est. 1964. Open 9-6, Sun. by appointment. SIZE: Medium. *STOCK: English furniture, £5-£700; china, metal, glass, silver, £1-£200.* Not Stocked: Paintings. LOC: On A28, 3 miles from Tenterden, 1st shop on left in village. PARK: Easy. TEL: 01580 241234. SER: Valuations. VAT: Stan/Spec.

Harriet Ann Sleigh Beds
Cherry Garden Farm, Hastings Rd. TN17 4PL. (Mrs R. Churchod). Est. 1987. Open by appointment only. SIZE: Medium. *STOCK: Eastern European*

FREEMAN & LLOYD

A superb small Hepplewhite period mahogany chest of drawers with brushing slide. Original handles. Circa 1780.

Est. 1968

Member of the British Antique Dealers Association Ltd.

The finest selection of 18th and early 19th century furniture and associated items in Kent

44 SANDGATE HIGH STREET
FOLKESTONE, KENT CT20 3AP
TEL: 01303 248986
FAX: 01303 241353

(5 mins. from Channel Tunnel entrance)

---

and Scandinavian sleigh beds; French fruitwood doubles or singles; European pine armoires, chests and cabinets; bedside lights, bedroom decorative accessories especially childrens. PARK: Easy. TEL: 01580 243005. SER: Mattresses available to order; reproduction beds in certain styles.

Kent Cottage
39 High St. TN17 4LP. (Mrs R. Amos). Open by appointment. STOCK: Porcelain - Continental including Meissen, and English; English scent bottles, silver and small furniture. LOC: A28, 3 miles S.E of Tenterden. PARK: Easy. TEL: 01580 241719.

J.D. and R.M. Walters
10 Regent St. TN17 4PE. Est. 1977. Open 8-6, Sat. 11-4.30 or by appointment. SIZE: Small. STOCK: Mahogany furniture, 18th-19th C. LOC: A28 turn left in village centre onto B2086, shop on left. PARK: Easy. TEL: 01580 241563; home - same. SER: Handmade copies of period furniture including chairs; restorations (GMC). VAT: Stan/Spec.

SANDGATE, Nr. Folkestone

Christopher Buck Antiques   BADA
56-60 High St. CT20 3AP. Est. 1983. Open 10-5. CL: Wed. SIZE: Medium. STOCK: English furniture, 18th C, £500-£30,000; decorative items,

18th-19th C, £100-£2,000. LOC: 5 mins. from M20 and Channel Tunnel. PARK: Easy. TEL: 01303 221229. SER: Valuations; restorations (furniture); buys at auction. FAIRS: Olympia (June and Nov); BADA(March). VAT: Stan/Spec.

Finch Antiques
40 High St. CT20 3AP. (Robert and Sylvia Finch). Est. 1978. Open 9.30-6, Sun. 11-5. SIZE: Medium. STOCK: Furniture, 1800-1920, £150-£3,000; silver plate and writing items, £5-£400. PARK: Easy. TEL: 01303 240725. SER: Restorations (furniture, French polishing).

Michael Fitch Antiques
95-99 High St. CT20 3BY. LAPADA. Open 10-5.30, Sun. by appointment. STOCK: Georgian, Victorian and Edwardian furniture and clocks. TEL: 01303 249600; fax - same.

Freeman and Lloyd Antiques   BADA
44 High St. CT20 3AP. (K. Freeman and M.R. Lloyd). LAPADA. Est. 1968. Open 10-5.30, Mon., Wed. and Fri. by appointment only. SIZE: Medium. STOCK: Fine Georgian and Regency English furniture; clocks, paintings and other period items. LOC: On main coast road between Hythe and Folkestone (A259). PARK: Easy. TEL: 01303 248986; fax - 01303 241353; mobile - 07860 100073. SER: Valuations. FAIRS: Olympia (Feb., June, Nov.); BADA (March). VAT: Spec.

David Gilbert Antiques
30 High St. CT20 3AP. Est. 1975. Open 9-5. SIZE: Medium. *STOCK: Furniture, smalls, glass, 1790-1930, £5-£1,000.* LOC: A259. PARK: Easy. TEL: 01303 850491; home - 01304 812237. SER: Valuations.

Jonathan Greenwall Antiques
61-63 High St. CT20 3AH. LAPADA. Est. 1964. Open 9.30-5. SIZE: Large. *STOCK: Furniture, to 19th C; decorative items, jewellery, oils and watercolours, prints and maps, sculpture and bronzes.* LOC: Folkestone-Brighton road. PARK: Easy. TEL: 01303 248987. SER: Valuations.

Old English Oak
102 High St. CT20 3BY. (A. Martin). *STOCK: Oak furniture and interesting items.* TEL: 01303 248560.

Old English Pine
100 High St. CT20 3BY. (A. Martin). Open 10-6. *STOCK: Pine furniture and interesting items.* TEL: 01303 248560.

SANDHURST

Forge Antiques and Restorations
Rye Rd. TN18 5JG. (James Nesfield). Est. 1975. Open 10-1 and 2-5, Sat. 10-5, Sun. and Mon. by appointment. *STOCK: Victorian and Edwardian furniture, £100-£1,200; ceramics, 18th-20th C, £5-£1,000.* LOC: A268. PARK: Own. TEL: 01580 850308; home - 01580 850665. SER: Valuations; restorations (furniture). FAIRS: Penshurst, Ardingly, Maidstone. VAT: Spec.

SANDWICH

All Our Yesterdays & Chris Baker Gramophones
3 Cattle Market. CT13 9AE. (Sandie and Chris Baker). Est. 1994. Open 10.30-2.30, Fri. 10.30-2, Sat. 10.30-3.30, Sun. by appointment. CL: Wed. *STOCK: General antiques, gramophones and associated items, £5-£1,000.* PARK: Behind Guildhall. TEL: 01304 614756; e-mail - chrisbaker@uk.packardbell.org. SER: Repairs (gramophones, phonographs, etc).

Delf Stream Gallery
14 New St. CT13 9AB. (N. Rocke). Est. 1985. Open 10-5. CL: Tues. and Wed. SIZE: Small. *STOCK: European and American art pottery, 19th-20th C, £25-£4,000.* LOC: Main one-way road in town centre, around corner from Guildhall. PARK: Easy. TEL: 01304 617684; home - same; fax - 01304 615479. SER: Valuations; restorations (as stock); buys at auction. FAIRS: NEC.

James Porter Antiques
5 Potter St. CT13 9DR. Est. 1948. Open 9.30-5.30. CL: Wed. *STOCK: Period furniture, brass and copper.* TEL: 01304 612218.

Nancy Wilson
Monken Quay, Strand St. CT13 9HP. Est. 1960. Open 11-5, other times by appointment. SIZE: Large. *STOCK: Period furniture, longcase clocks, £100-£5,000.* LOC: 100yds. from King's Arms public house. PARK: Easy. TEL: 01304 612345; home - same.

SEVENOAKS

The Antiques Centre
120 London Rd., Tubs Hill. TN13 1BA. (Ruth Harrison). Est. 1964. Open 10-1 and 2-4.30, Wed. and Sat. 10-1, other times by appointment. *STOCK: Furniture, 17th-19th C; interesting and decorative items.* LOC: Near station, on left side of hill. PARK: Opposite or in driveway. TEL: 01732 452104. VAT: Stan/Spec.

Neill Robinson Blaxill
21 St. John's Hill. TN13 3NX. FBHI. Open 9-6, appointment preferred. *STOCK: Clocks, barometers, decorative items and furniture, 17th-19th C.* LOC: 1 mile from High St. PARK: Easy. TEL: 01732 454179; website - www.antiques-clocks.co.uk. SER: Valuations; restorations.

Gem Antiques
28 London Rd. TN13 1AP. Est. 1969. Open 10-5. SIZE: Small. *STOCK: Clocks and furniture, 17th-19th C, £500-£10,000; jewellery, 18th-20th C, £10-£10,000.* LOC: Near Post Office. PARK: Nearby. TEL: 01732 743540. SER: Valuations; restorations (as stock). VAT: Spec.

Time to Remember
18 London Rd., Dunton Green. TN13 2UE. (A. Lyons). Est. 1982. Open Mon. and Tues. 10-5, Thurs.-Sat. 10-6. SIZE: Large. *STOCK: Clocks and watches, period furniture, porcelain, glass, toys, bric-a-brac.* LOC: London road into town, opposite Whitmore's Vauxhall showroom. PARK: Easy. TEL: 01732 454549. SER: Valuations; restorations (clocks and watches, furniture).

SIDCUP

Sidcup Antique and Craft Centre
Elm Parade, Main Rd. DA14 6NF. (M.H. and G.M. Tripp). Est. 1993. Open 10-5 including Sun. SIZE: 100+ dealers. *STOCK: Wide range of antiques and craft items.* LOC: M25, junction 3 then A20 to Sidcup (Queen Mary's Hospital). Premises near traffic lights, opposite police station. PARK: Easy. TEL: 020 8300 7387.

Ward Antiques

105 Main Rd. DA14 6ND. (T. and M. Ward). Est. 1981. *STOCK: Victorian fireplaces, Victorian and Edwardian furniture.*

SNARGATE (Romney Marsh)

Judith Peppitt

The Old Rectory. TN29 0EW. Open by appointment. *STOCK: English watercolours, 19th-20th C.* LOC: 1 mile off A2070, adjoining Snargate Church. PARK: Easy. TEL: 01797 344516.

SOUTHBOROUGH, Nr. Tunbridge Wells

Henry Baines

14 Church Rd. TN4 0RX. LAPADA. Est. 1968. Open Tues.-Fri. 10-5, Sat. 10-4.30, prior telephone call advisable. *STOCK: Early oak and country furniture especially tables and sets of chairs; French provincial furniture and decorative items.* PARK: Easy. TEL: 01892 532099. VAT: Stan/Spec.

STOCKBURY

Steppes Hill Farm Antiques   BADA

The Hill Farm, South St. ME9 7RB. (W.F.A. Buck). Est. 1965. Always open, appointment advisable. SIZE: Medium. STOCK: English porcelain, pottery, pot-lids, 18th-20th C, to £30,000; small silver; caddy spoons, wine labels, silver boxes, furniture, 18th-19th C, to £10,000. LOC: 5 mins. from M2 on A249. Enquire in village for Steppes Hill Antiques. PARK: Easy. TEL: 01795 842205. SER: Valuations; buys at auction. FAIRS: BADA; International Ceramics. VAT: Spec.

SUNDRIDGE, Nr. Sevenoaks

Sundridge Gallery

9 Church Rd. TN14 6DT. (T. and M. Tyrer). Open 10-5.30. *STOCK: Watercolours and oils, 19th-20th C; some Oriental rugs.* TEL: 01959 564104.

SUTTON VALENCE, Nr. Maidstone

Sutton Valence Antiques

North St. ME17 3AP. (T. and N. Mullarkey). LAPADA. Est. 1971. Open 9-5, Sun. 10-4 or by appointment. SIZE: Large. *STOCK: Furniture including shipping, porcelain, clocks, silver, metalware, 18th-20th C.* LOC: On A274

Maidstone/Tenterden Rd. PARK: Side of shop. TEL: 01622 843333; fax - 01622 843499; e-mail - svantiques@aol.com; website - www. svantiques. co.uk SER: Valuations; restorations; container packing and shipping; courier; buys at auction.

TENTERDEN

Flower House Antiques

90 High St. TN30 6JB. (Barry Rayner and Quentin Johnson). Open 9.30-5.30, Sun. by appointment. SIZE: Medium. *STOCK: English and Continental furniture, 16th to early 19th C; Oriental works of art, 16th-19th C; pictures, lighting, mirrors, objets d'art.* LOC: A28. PARK: Easy and private. TEL: 01580 763764. SER: Valuations; restorations. VAT: Spec.

Garden House Antiques

116 High St. TN30 6HT. (H. Kirkham). Resident. Always open. *STOCK: Mainly 18th-19th C furniture, paintings and porcelain; old fishing reels and rods.* PARK: Easy. TEL: 01580 763664. SER: Valuations; interior design.

The Lace Basket

at Garden House, 116 High St. TN30 6HD. (C. Walls). Open 10.30-5. *STOCK: Textiles, Victorian linen and lace, samplers and quilts.* PARK: Opposite. TEL: 01580 763664. SER: Valuations.

Tenterden Antiques and Silver Vaults

66 High St. TN30 6AU. (T.J. Smith). Open 10-5 including Sun. *STOCK: Clocks, silver, telephones and general antiques.* TEL: 01580 765885.

TEYNHAM, Nr. Sittingbourne

Jackson-Grant Antiques

The Old Chapel, 133 London Rd. ME9 9QJ. (D.M. Jackson-Grant). Est. 1966. Open 10-5, Sun. 1-5. SIZE: Large. *STOCK: General antiques, French furniture, bookcases and long tables, beds, smalls, 18th C to Art Deco, £5-£500.* LOC: A2 between Faversham and Sittingbourne. PARK: Easy. TEL: 01795 522027; home - same; mobile - 07831 591881; e-mail - david.jackson-grant@talk21.com. VAT: Stan/Spec.

TONBRIDGE

Barden House Antiques

1-3 Priory St. TN9 2AP. (Mrs B.D. Parsons). Open 10-5. SIZE: 5 dealers. *STOCK: General antiques and collectables.* TEL: 01732 350142; evenings - 01732 355718.

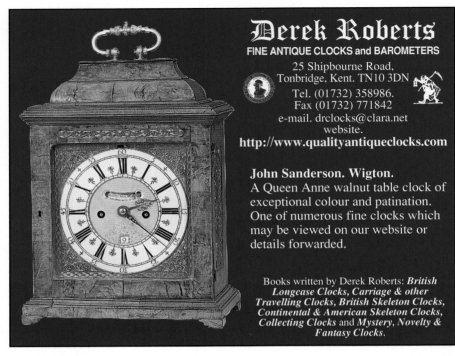

Derek Roberts Fine Antique Clocks
& Barometers **BADA**
25 Shipbourne Rd. TN10 3DN. Author of
several books on clocks. Est. 1968. Open 9.30-
5.30 or by appointment. SIZE: Large. *STOCK:*
Fine restored clocks, mostly £2,000-£100,000.
LOC: A227. From London A21 take B245
Hildenborough to Tonbridge, left 20 yds
before first lights, left again and 50 yds up on
right. PARK: Easy. TEL: 01732 358986; fax -
01732 771842; e-mail - drclocks@clara.net;
website - www.qualityantiqueclocks.com. SER:
Cabinet making. VAT: Spec.

B.V.M. Somerset
Stags Head, 9 Stafford Rd. TN9 1HT. Est. 1948.
Open 11-6.30. *STOCK: Clocks, £500-£5,000.*
LOC: Off High Street beside castle. TEL: 01732
352017. SER: Valuations; restorations (cabinets,
gilt and French polishing); buys at auction
(longcase and bracket clocks). VAT: Stan.

TUNBRIDGE WELLS

Aaron Antiques
77 St. Johns Rd. TN4 9TT. (R.J. Goodman).
Open 9-5. *STOCK: Clocks and pocket watches,*
paintings and prints; period and shipping
furniture; English, Continental and Oriental
porcelain; antiquarian books, postcards, coins
and medals. TEL: 01892 517644. VAT:
Stan/Spec.

Amadeus Antiques
32 Mount Ephraim. TN3. (P.A. Davies). Open
10-5, Sun. by appointment. SIZE: Medium.
STOCK: Unusual furniture, to Art Deco, £50-
£5,000; china and bric-a-brac, £25-£500;
chandeliers, £100-£1,000. LOC: Near hospital.
PARK: Easy. TEL: 01892 544406; 01892
864884. SER: Valuations.

The Architectural Emporium
55 St John's Rd. TN4 9TP. (Mike Roberts). Open
10-5.30. SIZE: Medium. *STOCK: Fireplaces,*
garden statuary, lighting, decorative salvage,
Georgian to Edwardian. LOC: A26 towards
Southborough. PARK: John St. TEL: 01892
540368. VAT: Stan/Spec.

Baskerville Books
13 Nevill St. TN2 5RU. Est. 1982. Open 10-5.
SIZE: Small. *STOCK: Antiquarian and*
secondhand books; small collectible antiques and
occasional period and shipping furniture. LOC:
50 yards from entrance to Pantiles. PARK:
Nearby. TEL: 01892 526776. SER: Valuations.

Nicholas Bowlby

9 Castle St. TN1 1XJ. Est. 1981. Open 10-5.30. CL: Mon. and Wed. SIZE: Large. *STOCK: 19th-20th C watercolours, contemporary paintings and sculpture, £200-£20,000.* LOC: Near The Pantiles. TEL: 01892 540049; e-mail - nicholasbowlby @hotmail.com: website - www.nicholasbowlby. co.uk SER: Valuations; restorations; buys at auction (watercolours and drawings). VAT: Spec.

Calverley Antiques

30 Crescent Rd. TN1 2LZ. (P. A. Nimmo). Est. 1995. Open 10-5.30 including Sun. *STOCK: Furniture including European pine and 1920's oak.* LOC: Near police station and Assembly Hall. PARK: Multi-storey next door. TEL: 01892 538254. SER: Valuations; restorations (furniture). FAIRS: Ardingly.

Chapel Place Antiques

9 Chapel Place. TN1 1YQ. (J. and A. Clare). Open 9-6. *STOCK: Silver photo frames, antique and modern jewellery, old cutlery, porcelain including hand-painted Limoge boxes.* TEL: 01892 546561.

Claremont Antiques

48 St John's Rd. TN4 9NY. (Anthony Broad). Open 10-5.30, other times by appointment. SIZE: Large. *STOCK: Irish, French, Eastern European, pine, hardwood and painted country furniture, 18th-19th C; decorative items, all £10-£5,000.* LOC: On A26 London Road, by St John's church. PARK: Easy. TEL: 01892 511651; fax - 01892 517360; e-mail - ant@claremontantiques.com; website - www.claremontantiques.com. VAT: Stan/Spec.

Corn Exchange Antiques Centre

64 The Pantiles. TN2 5TN. (B. Henderson). Open 10-5. *STOCK: Furniture, silver, mirrors, pictures, ceramics, glass and collectables.* TEL: 01892 539652.

Glassdrumman Antiques

7 Union Square, The Pantiles. TN4 8HE. (Graham and Amanda Dyson Rooke). Open Tues.-Sat. 10-5.30. SIZE: Medium. *STOCK: Silver, jewellery, watches, clocks, furniture, decorative items, 18th-19th C.* PARK: Nearby. TEL: 01892 538615; fax - same.

Hall's Bookshop

20-22 Chapel Place. TN1 1YQ. Est. 1898. Open 9.30-5. *STOCK: Antiquarian and secondhand books.* TEL: 01892 527842.

Kent & Sussex Gold Refiners

7 Vale Rd. (Mr and Mrs A.C. Padley). NAG. Est. 1926. Open 9-5.30. CL: Wed. *STOCK: Antique and modern jewellery, silver and plate, £15-£100,000.* LOC: Around corner from High St. PARK: Nearby. TEL: 01892 526084; fax - 01892 543602. SER: Valuations; restorations (antique silver and jewellery). VAT: Stan/Spec.

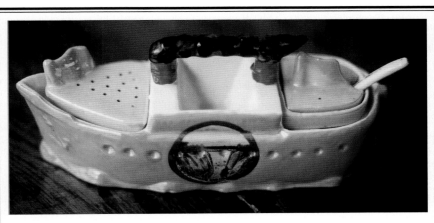

A cruet, modelled as a liner, c.1910, 6in. long, £25.

By the end of the 19th century, a great diversity of cheap seaside souvenirs was available. Christopher Spencer trawls the Falmouth antique shops to find out what is still around today in his article entitled 'Oh, I do like to be beside the Seaside' which appeared in the February 2001 issue of **Antique Collecting** magazine. For more details and to subscribe see page 147.

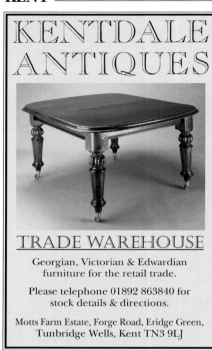

KENTDALE ANTIQUES

TRADE WAREHOUSE

Georgian, Victorian & Edwardian
furniture for the retail trade.

Please telephone 01892 863840 for
stock details & directions.

Motts Farm Estate, Forge Road, Eridge Green,
Tunbridge Wells, Kent TN3 9LJ

Kentdale Antiques
Motts Farm Estate, Forge Rd., Eridge Green. TN3 9LJ. (C. Bigwood and T. Rayfield). Open by appointment. SIZE: Warehouse. *STOCK: Mostly mahogany and walnut furniture.* TEL: 01892 863840; fax - same. VAT: Stan/Spec.*Trade only.*

Howard Neville Antiques
21 The Pantiles. TN4. (H.C.C. Neville). Est. 1967. Open by appointment. SIZE: Medium. *STOCK: General antiques, furniture, sculpture and works of art, 16th-18th C.* PARK: Easy. TEL: 01892 511461; home - 01435 882409. SER: Valuations; restorations. VAT: Spec.

The Pantiles Antiques
31 The Pantiles. TN2 5TD. (Mrs E.M. Blackburn). Est. 1979. Open 10-5. SIZE: Medium. *STOCK: Georgian, Victorian and Edwardian furniture; 19th C porcelain, silver.* PARK: Easy. TEL: 01892 531291.

Pantiles Spa Antiques
4/5/6 Union House, The Pantiles. TN4 8HE. (J.A.Cowpland). Est. 1979. Open 9.30-5, Sat. 9.30-5.30. SIZE: Large. *STOCK: Victorian and Georgian furniture especially dining tables and chairs, £200-£10,000; pictures, £50-£3,000; clocks, £100-£5,000; porcelain, £50-£2,000;* silver, £50-£1,000; all 17th-19th C; dolls, bears and toys. PARK: Nearby. TEL: 01892 541377; fax - 01435 865660; e-mail - psa.wells@ btinternet. com; website - www.antiques-tun-wells-kent. co.uk. SER: Restorations (furniture); 30 mile radius free delivery (large items). VAT: Spec.

Phoenix Antiques
51-53 St. John's Rd. TN4 9TP. Est. 1982. Open 10-5.30 or by appointment. SIZE: Large. *STOCK: 18th-19th C French, English, original painted and country furniture, decorative furnishings, original gilt overmantel mirrors, garden statuary.* LOC: On A26 from A21 into town, by St. John's Church. PARK: Easy. TEL: 01892 549099.

Redleaf Gallery
1 Castle St. TN1 1XJ. (Nick Hills). Open Tues.-Sat. 10.30-5.30. *STOCK: 19th-20th C watercolours and modern British paintings.* LOC: Off High St. PARK: Nearby. TEL: 01892 526695. VAT: Spec.

Ian Relf Antiques
132/134 Camden Rd. TN4. Open 9.30-1.30 and 2.30-5.30. *STOCK: Mainly furniture.* TEL: 01892 538362.

John Thompson
27 The Pantiles. TN2 5TD. Est. 1982. Open 9.30-1 and 2-5. SIZE: Medium. *STOCK: Furniture, late 17th to early 19th C; paintings 17th-20th C; decorative items.* Not Stocked: Jewellery, silver and militaria. PARK: Linden Road or Warwick Park. TEL: 01892 547215. VAT: Spec.

Tunbridge Wells Antiques
12 Union Sq., The Pantiles. TN4 8HE. (N.J. Harding). Est. 1980. Open 9.30-5. SIZE: Large. *STOCK: Antiques and collectables including silver, jewellery, Georgian and Victorian furniture, soft furnishings, Victorian Staffordshire figures, clocks and watches, Tunbridgeware, antique-related reference books.* PARK: Nearby. TEL: 01892 533708; e-mail - twantique@aol. com. SER: Valuations; shipping. VAT: Stan/Spec.

Up Country
The Corn Stores, 68 St. Johns Rd. TN4 9PE. (G.J. Price and C.M. Springett). Est. 1988. Open 9-5.30. SIZE: Large. *STOCK: British and European country furniture, £50-£5,000; associated decorative and interesting items, £5-£500; all 18th-19th C.* LOC: On main London Rd. to Southborough and A21 trunk road which joins M25 and M26 at Sevenoaks intersection. PARK: Own at rear. TEL: 01892 523341. VAT: Stan.

Variety Box
16 Chapel Place. TN1 1YQ. Est. 1955. Open 9.45-5. CL: Wed. SIZE: Small. *STOCK: Tunbridge ware and sewing antiques, 19th C, £5-£150; hatpins, 20th C, £5-£60; small collectables, 18th-20th C, £5-£50.* LOC: 2 minutes from Pantiles towards High St. PARK: Limited. TEL: 01892 531868. FAIRS: Ardingly, Newark, Alexandra Palace.

The Vintage Watch Co.
The Old Pipe House, 74 High St. TN1 1YB. (F. Lawrence). Open Wed.-Sat. 10-5. *STOCK: Pre-1950's fine wrist watches, pocket watches.* SER: Restorations.

WELLING

The Emporium Antiques, Collectibles & Craft Centre
138-140 Upper Wickham Lane. DA16 3DP. Open 10-5. SIZE: Medium. *STOCK: Royal Doulton, Wade, Kevin Francis, Sylvac, Beswick, Winstanley cats, Lladro, Lorna Bailey, Wedgwood, Brian Wood, £10-£300.* LOC: From Bexleyheath, right at Welling corner on High St. into Upper Wickham Lane. TEL: 020 8855 8308; fax - same.

WEST MALLING

The Old Clock Shop
63 High St. ME19 6NA. (S.L. Luck). Est. 1970. Open 9-5. SIZE: Large. *STOCK: Grandfather clocks, 17th-19th C; carriage, bracket and wall clocks.* LOC: Half a mile from M20. PARK: Easy. TEL: 01732 843246; website - www.theold clockshop.co.uk. VAT: Spec.

Rose and Crown Antiques
40 High St.. (Candy and Julian Lovegrove). Est. 1995. Open Tues.-Sat. 9.30-5.30. SIZE: Medium. *STOCK: General antiques including furniture, 18th to early 20th C.* PARK: Free. TEL: 01732 872707; fax - 01732 872810; website - www. antiqueswestmalling.co.uk. SER: Restorations (furniture including French polishing and upholstery)

WESTERHAM

Apollo Antique Galleries
19 -21 Market Sq. TN16 1AN. LAPADA. Open 9.30-5.30. SIZE: Large. *STOCK: Georgian, Victorian and Edwardian furniture; 19th C oils and watercolours; bronze and marble statuary; clocks, silver.* TEL: 01959 562200; fax - 01959 562986. VAT: Stan./Spec.

Castle Antiques Centre
1 London Rd. TN16 1BB. (Stewart Ward Properties). Est. 1986. Open 10-5, Sun. 1-6. SIZE: Small - 8 dealers. *STOCK: General antiques, tools, linen, collectables, retro clothing.* LOC: Just off town centre. PARK: Easy - nearby. TEL: 01959 562492. SER: Valuations; props for stage productions.

London House Antiques
4 Market Sq. TN16 1AW. Est. 1977. Open 10-5, Sun. by appointment only. SIZE: Medium. *STOCK: Furniture, 18th-19th C, £500-£10,000; paintings, prints and engravings, 19th-20th C, £100-£2,000; English and German teddy bears and dolls, 19th-20th C, £100-£3,000; clocks and bronzes, 19th C, £300-£5,000; silver and porcelain, 19th-20th C, £50-£1,500.* LOC: Off M25, junction 6 on A25 to Westerham. PARK: Easy. TEL: 01959 564479.

Marks Antiques
5 The Green. TN16 1AS. (Alan and Michael Marks). Est. 1954. Open 9.30-5. SIZE: Medium. *STOCK: Furniture, £500-£30,000; clocks, barometers, porcelain, bronzes and pictures, £200-£3,000: all 18th-19th C.* LOC: A25. PARK: Easy. TEL: 01959 562017; home - 01268 542621. SER: Valuations; restorations (furniture, including upholstery); buys at auction (furniture). VAT: Stan/Spec.

Regal Antiques
2 Market Sq. TN16 1AW. (T. Lawrence). Open Wed.-Sat. 10-5. *STOCK: Antique jewellery, fine paintings, portrait miniatures, porcelain, vintage watches.* TEL: 01959 561778. SER: Picture restorations.

Denys Sargeant
21 The Green. TN16 1AX. Est. 1949. Open 9.30-5.30. *STOCK: Glass especially chandeliers and candelabras, decanters and lustres.* TEL: 01959 562130. SER: Restoration and cleaning (chandeliers, candelabras, lustres); electrification. VAT: Stan/Spec.

Taylor-Smith Antiques
4 The Grange, High St. TN16 1AH. LAPADA. Open 10-5. CL: Wed. *STOCK: Fine 18th-19th C furniture; paintings, porcelain, glass and decorative items.* TEL: 01959 563100; fax - 01959 561561.

Taylor-Smith Books
2 High St. TN16 1RF. LAPADA. Open by appointment. *STOCK: Books by Sir Winston Churchill and related items.* TEL: 01959 561561; fax - 01959 561561.

Westerham Antiques Warehouse
The Old Sorting Office, Fullers Hill, London Rd. TN16 1AA. (R.W. Barr). Open 10-5.30. *STOCK: 18th-19th C furniture especially dining tables and sets of chairs.* TEL: 01959 561622; fax - 01959 562986.

Westerham House Antiques
The Old Sorting Office, Fullers Hill, London Rd. TN16 1AA. (R.W. Barr). Open 10-5.30. *STOCK: 18th-19th C English furniture, animal and figurative bronzes, oil paintings.* TEL: 01959 561622; mobile - 07885 883441.

WHITSTABLE

Laurens Antiques
2 Harbour St. CT5 1AG. (G. A. Laurens). Est. 1965. Open 9.30-5.30. SIZE: Medium. *STOCK: Furniture, 18th-19th C, £300-£500+.* LOC: Turn off Thanet Way at Whitstable exit, straight down to

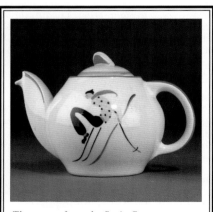

The teapot from the Susie Cooper nursery ware breakfast set, decorated with the extremely rare 'Skier' pattern, which sold for £1,600.

From an Auction Report by Christopher Wight on 20th Century British Decorative Arts at Christie's South Kensington, London, 4th May 2000 which appeared in the July/August issue of **Antique Collecting** magazine. For more details and to subscribe see page 147.

one-way system in High Street. PARK: Easy. TEL: 01227 261940; home - same. SER: Valuations; restorations (cabinet work); buys at auction.

Tankerton Antiques
136 Tankerton Rd. CT5 2AN. (Mrs. F. Holland). Est. 1985. Open 10-5, Tues. 10-4, Wed. 10-1. CL: Mon. SIZE: Medium. *STOCK: Furniture, Regency to 1930's, £50-£1,500; china, from 18th C, to £1,500; glass, Regency to 1930's, to £400; clocks and barometers, from 1800, £30-£2,500; French, English and German costume jewellery, £30-£300.* LOC: From A299 Thanet Way take A290/B2205 turn off to Whitstable. Through town and into Tankerton. Shop on right just past roundabout. TEL: 01227 266490; mobile - 07702 244064. SER: Valuations.

WINGHAM, Nr. Canterbury

Silvesters
33 High St. CT3 1AB. (S.N. Hartley and G.M.A. Wallis). LAPADA. Est. 1953. Open 9.30-5 by appointment. *STOCK: Furniture, Georgian and Victorian; decorative items, silver, porcelain, glass.* LOC: At main junction in town. TEL: 01227 720278 and 01843 841524.

WITTERSHAM

Old Corner House Antiques
6 Poplar Rd. TN30 7PG. (G. and F. Shepherd). Open Wed.-Sat. 10-5 or by appointment. *STOCK: General antiques, country furniture, samplers; 18th-19th C English pottery including blue and white and creamware; watercolours, 19th to early 20th C.* PARK: Easy. TEL: 01797 270236.

WROTHAM

Barnaby's
High St. TN15 7AD. (Cordelia McCartney). Resident. Open 9-5, Wed. 9-1, Sun. by appointment. SIZE: Medium. *STOCK: Smalls, collectables, 1850-to date, £5-£50; furniture, Victorian to date, £50-£1,000; pictures, 20th C, £10-£100.* PARK: Easy. TEL: 01732 886887; fax/home - same; e-mail - cordelia@cordeliamc. free-online.co.uk.

Charles International Antiques
The Poplars, London Rd. TN15 7RR. (Mr and Mrs C. Bremner). LAPADA. Est. 1968. Open 9-4.30. *STOCK: Victorian, Edwardian and shipping goods.* LOC: A20. TEL: 01732 823654; e-mail - c.bremner@antiques2.demon.co.uk; website -www.collect.com/charles. SER: Full container and documentation facilities.

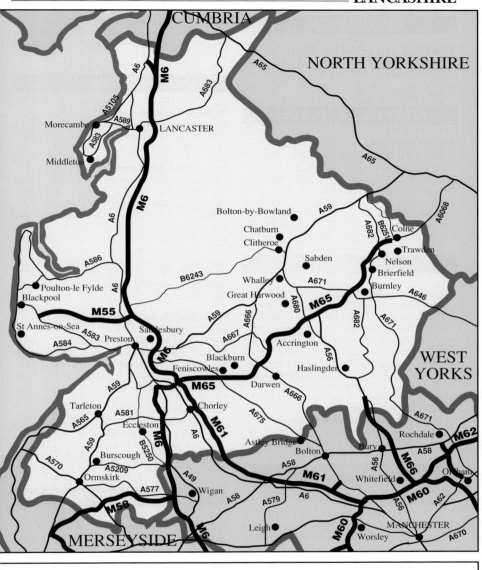

Dealers and Shops in Lancashire

Accrington	1	Bury	1	Lancaster	4	Rochdale	3
Astley Bridge	1	Chatburn	1	Leigh	1	Sabden	2
Blackburn	2	Chorley	1	Manchester	22	Samlesbury	1
Blackpool	3	Clitheroe	2	Middleton Village	1	St. Annes-on-Sea	1
Bolton	4	Colne	2	Morecambe	3	Tarleton	1
Bolton-by-Bowland		Darwen	4	Nelson	3	Trawden	1
	2	Eccleston	2	Oldham	4	Whalley	1
Brierfield	1	Feniscowles	1	Ormskirk	1	Whitefield	1
Burnley	3	Great Harwood	1	Poulton-le-Fylde	1	Wigan	4
Burscough	1	Haslingden	4	Preston	8	Worsley	1

ACCRINGTON

The Coin and Jewellery Shop
129a Blackburn Rd. BB5 0AA. Est. 1977. Open 9.30-5. CL: Wed. *STOCK: Coins, jewellery and small antiques.* TEL: 01254 384757.

ASTLEY BRIDGE, Nr. Bolton

Alpine Antiques
15 Sharples Ave. BL1 7HB. (B. and M. Carney). Est. 1970. Open by appointment. SIZE: Small. *STOCK: Glass, pottery, silver and jewellery, collectables.* LOC: Just off main Blackburn road, turn immediately at Texaco garage. PARK: Own frontage. TEL: 01204 303364; fax - same. SER: Valuations; restorations; buys at auction. FAIRS: Chester monthly; Northgate Arena.

BLACKBURN

Ancient and Modern
17 New Market St. BB1 7DR. Est. 1943. Open 9-5.30. *STOCK: Jewellery, Georgian to date, up to £30,000; clocks, vintage and modern watches including Rolex, Cartier, Patek; militaria and silver; diamond merchants.* LOC: Town centre, opposite side entrance of Marks & Spencer. PARK: Easy. TEL: 01254 677866. SER: Valuations; repairs; restorations.

Mitchell's Antiques
76 Bolton Rd. BB2 3PZ. (S. Mitchell). Open 9-5. *STOCK: General antiques, gold and silver jewellery, wrist watches.* TEL: 01254 664663.

BLACKPOOL

Chard Coins
521 Lytham Rd. FY4 1RJ. Est. 1965. Open 9-5. CL: Sat. SIZE: Large. *STOCK: Paintings and furniture, English and ancient coins, gold bullion coins, jewellery and silver, £50-£20,000+.* LOC: Between Central Promenade south and Blackpool Airport main gates, 1/4 mile from airport. PARK: Easy. TEL: 01253 343081. SER: Valuations. VAT: Stan/Spec.

Ann and Peter Christian
400/402 Waterloo Rd., Marton. FY4 4BL. Open 10-5.30. *STOCK: Decorative arts and pine furniture.* TEL: 01253 763268.

Nostalgia
95 Coronation St. FY1 4QE. (P.Jackson). Est. 1978. Open 10-4, including Sun. in summer.

SIZE: Small. *STOCK: Royal commemoratives, 19th-20th C, £5-£150.* LOC: Town centre, near Winter Gardens. PARK: Easy. TEL: 01253 293251.

BOLTON

Bolton Antique Centre
96 Great Moor St. BL3 6DS. Open 10-4.30. *STOCK: General antiques and collectables.* TEL: 01204 362694.

Drop Dial Antiques
Last Drop Village, Hospital Rd., Bromley Cross. BL7 9PZ. (I.W. and I.E. Roberts). Est. 1975. Open every afternoon except Mon. and Fri. SIZE: Small. *STOCK: Clocks, mainly English and French, 18th-20th C, £100-£4,000; mercury barometers, 19th-20th C, £100-£500; paintings, silver and general antiques, £20-£500.* Not Stocked: Stamps and armour. PARK: Easy. TEL: 01204 307186; home - 01257 480995. SER: Valuations; restorations (clocks and barometers). VAT: Stan/Spec.

Ironchurch Antiques Centre
Blackburn Rd. BL1 8DR. (P.J. Wilkinson). Est. 1975. Open 10-5 including Sun. SIZE: Large. *STOCK: Furniture, china, glass, clocks, books, jewellery, 17th C to date, £1-£10,000.* PARK: Free nearby. TEL: 01204 383616. SER: Valuations; restorations.

G. Oakes and Son
160-162 Blackburn Rd. BL1 8DR. Est. 1958. Open 9-5. *STOCK: Furniture and bric-a-brac.* TEL: 01204 526587; e-mail - ycs12@dial. pipex.com. SER: Shipping and packing; buys at auction. VAT: Stan.

BOLTON-BY-BOWLAND, Nr. Clitheroe

Farmhouse Antiques
23 Main St. BB7 4NY. (M. Howard). Est. 1980. Open Sat., Sun. and Bank Holidays 12-4.30 (Sundays only in winter) or by appointment. SIZE: Small. *STOCK: Textiles, bed and table linen, quilts, christening robes, lace, samplers, embroideries, bags, buttons, trimmings, beads, jewellery, Victoriana.* LOC: Off A59, past Clitheroe, through Sawley to village. PARK: Easy. TEL: 01200 441457/447294.

Harrop Fold Clocks (F. Robinson)
Harrop Fold, Lane Ends. BB7 4PJ. Est. 1974. Open by appointment. SIZE: Medium. *STOCK: British clocks, barometers, 18th-19th C, £1,000-£10,000.* LOC: Through Clitheroe to Chatburn and

Grindleton. Take Slaidburn road, turn left after 3 miles. PARK: Own. TEL: 01200 447665; home - same. SER: Valuations; restorations (clocks).

J.H. Blakey and Sons Ltd (Est. 1905)
Burnley Rd. BB9 5AD. *STOCK: Furniture, brass, copper, pewter, clocks, curios.* TEL: 01282 613593. SER: Restorations. VAT: Stan.

Brun Lea Antiques
3/5 Standish St. BB11 1AP. Open 9.30-5.30. *STOCK: General antiques and shipping goods.* TEL: 01282 413513.

Brun Lea Antiques (J. Waite Ltd)
Unit 1, Rear Elm Street Mill, Travis St. BB10 1DG. Open 8.30-5.30, Fri. and Sat. 9-4, Sun. 12-4. SIZE: Large warehouse. *STOCK: Georgian furniture to 1930's shipping goods.* TEL: 01282 413513; fax - 01282 832769.

King's Mill Antique Centre
Unit 2 King's Mill, Queen St., Harle Syke. (Michael and Linda Heuer). Open 10-5, Thurs. 10-8, Sun. 11-5. SIZE: Large. *STOCK: Furniture and bric-a-brac, Edwardian and Victorian, £5-£1,000.* LOC: From General Hospital, follow brown tourist signs for Queen's Mill. PARK: Easy. TEL: 01282 431953; mobile - 07803 153752. SER: Export.

West Lancs. Antique Exports
Victoria Mill, Victoria St. L40 0SN. (W. and B. Griffiths). LAPADA. Est. 1959. Open 9-5.30, Sat. and Sun. 10-5 . SIZE: Large. *STOCK: Shipping furniture.* TEL: 01704 894634; fax - 01704 894486. SER: Courier; packing and shipping. VAT: Stan.

Newtons
151 The Rock. BL9 0ND. (Newtons of Bury). Est. 1931. Open 9-5. SIZE: Small. *STOCK: General antiques, 18th-19th C, £5-£500.* Not Stocked: Continental furniture. LOC: From Manchester through Bury town centre, shop is on left 200yds. before Fire Station. PARK: 50yds. behind shop. TEL: 0161 764 1863. SER: Valuations; restorations (furniture). VAT: Stan.

T. Brindle Antiques
6 and 8 Sawley Rd. BB7 4AS. LAPADA. Open 9.30-5.00, Sat. and other times by appointment. *STOCK: Antique and decorative items.* TEL: 01200 440025; fax - 01200 440090; e-mail - tbrindle@globalnet.co.uk; website - www.antique web.co.uk/tbrindle/.

Antiques and Crafts Centre
Botany Bay Villages Ltd., Canal Mill, Botany Brow. PR6 9AF. Open daily including Sun. SIZE: Large - 5 floors. *STOCK: Porcelain, china and jewellery; furniture, memorabilia and curios and crafts.* LOC: Opposite junction 8, M61. PARK: Easy. TEL: 01257 261220. VAT: Stan.

Heskin Hall Antiques
Heskin Hall, Wood Lane, Heskin. PR7 5PA. (Harrison Steen Ltd). Est. 1996. Open 10-5.30 seven days. SIZE: Large - 70+ dealers. *STOCK: Wide range of general antiques.* LOC: B5250. PARK: Easy. TEL: 01257 452044; fax - 01257 450690. SER: Valuations; restorations.

CLITHEROE

Folly Antiques
22 Moor Lane. BB7 1BE. (N.P. Medd). Est. 1967. Open 9-6, Wed. and Sun. by appointment. SIZE: Medium. *STOCK: Decorative and upholstered items, furniture, £100-£2,000; pictures, brass and objects, £5-£2,000; all 19th-20th C; garden furniture, small architectural items, 18th-20th C, £20-£2,000.* LOC: 15 miles from junction 31, M6, via A59. PARK: Opposite. TEL: 01200 429461. VAT: Stan/Spec.

Lee's Antiques
59 Whalley Rd. BB7 1EE. (P.A. Lee). *STOCK: General antiques.* TEL: 01200 424921; home - 01200 425441.

COLNE

Enloc Antiques
96 Keighley Rd. BB8 0PH. Est. 1978. Open 9-5, Sun. 12-4. SIZE: Large. *STOCK: Pine - antique, reclaimed timber, reproduction.* TEL: 01282 867101; fax - 01282 867601. SER: Restorations (hot stripping, polishing and joinery). VAT: Stan.

Ingleside Antiques
13 Keighley Rd. BB8 0LP. (J. Fry). Est. 1988. Open 10-5. CL: Tues. and Thurs. SIZE: Medium. *STOCK: General antiques especially longcase, wall and mantel clocks and barometers, 1740-1910, £25-£4,500.* LOC: Just through centre of Colne. PARK: Easy. TEL: 01282 860046; home - same. SER: Valuations; restorations (clocks).

DARWEN

Belgrave Antique Centre
Britannia Mill, 136 Bolton Rd. Est. 1998. Open 9.30-5, Sun. 10-4.30. SIZE: Large - 40 dealers. *STOCK: Porcelain, pottery, glass, furniture, architectural, collectables.* LOC: Opposite India Mill. PARK: At rear. TEL: 01254 777714. SER: Valuations. FAIRS: Newark, Ardingly, Swinderby.

Cottage Antiques
135 Blackburn Rd. BB3. SIZE: Small. *STOCK: Fine porcelain including Crown Derby, Worcester and Doulton, £100-£2,000; 19th C furniture, £100-£5,000.* LOC: A666 towards Blackburn, opposite St Cuthbert's Church. PARK: Opposite. TEL: 01254 775891 or 01254 676840 (24 hour).

Two mechanical clockwork tennis playing figures made by Bing of Nuremburg, Bavaria, c.1910.

From an article entitled 'Lawn Tennis Memorabilia' by Gerald Gurney which appeared in the June 2000 issue of **Antique Collecting** magazine. For more details and to subscribe see page 147.

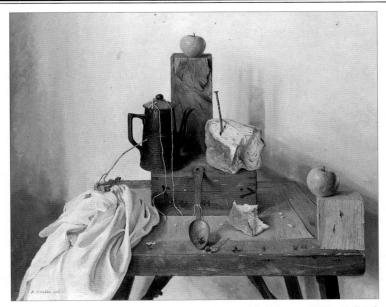

Arthur Frederick Easton, ROI, (born Horley, Surrey, 9th February 1939), 'Still Life with Nail in Bread', oil on board, 36in. x 30in. Signs work 'A Easton'.

From an article entitled 'Contemporary British Artists' by Anthony J. Lester which appeared in the April issue of **Antique Collecting** magazine. For more details and to subscribe see page 147.

Grove Antiques
Hampden Mill, Springdale. (V. Cooney). Open 10-2.30. *STOCK: General antiques.* TEL: 01254 776644. SER: Valuations.

K.C. Antiques
538 Bolton Rd. BB3 2JR. (K. and J. Anderton). Resident. Open 9-6, Sun. 12-5. *STOCK: Georgian, Victorian and Edwardian furniture and decorative items.* LOC: A666. PARK: Easy. TEL: 01254 772252. SER: Buys at auction. VAT: Stan/Spec.

ECCLESTON

Bygone Times International Plc
Grove Mill, The Green. PR7 5PD. (S. Higham). Open 9-5 including Sun. SIZE: 2 warehouses. *STOCK: Architectural antiques and memorabilia.* TEL: 01257 453780; e-mail - enquire@bygonetimes.co.uk.

The Cutlery Ghost
7 The Carrington Centre. PR7 5UP. (R. W.

Metcalf). Open Wed., Thurs. and Sat. SIZE: Small. *STOCK: Silver plated cutlery £50-£100; glass, linen and china, £5-£25; all 1900-1939.* LOC: Village centre - 4 miles from junction 27, M6. PARK: Easy. TEL: 01257 451281. SER: Restorations (silver plate). FAIRS: Newark, Ardingly, Stoneleigh. VAT: Spec.

FENISCOWLES, Nr. Blackburn

Old Smithy
726 Preston Old Rd. BB2 5EP. (R.C. Lynch). Est. 1967. Open 9.30-5. SIZE: Large. *STOCK: Period and Victorian fireplaces, pub and architectural items, violins and musical instruments, pictures and prints, furniture, shipping items, jewellery, brass, copper, Victorian lace and linen.* LOC: Opposite Fieldens Arms. PARK: Own or nearby. TEL: 01254 209943/580874. SER: Valuations; restorations (wooden items); buys at auction. FAIRS: Park Hall, Charnock Richard, Newark, Lincs.

LANCASHIRE

GREAT HARWOOD, Nr. Blackburn

Benny Charlesworth's Snuff Box
51 Blackburn Rd. BB6 7DF. (N. Walsh). Est. 1984. Open 10-5. SIZE: Small. *STOCK: Furniture, china, linen, costume jewellery, teddies.* LOC: 200yds. from town centre, off A680. PARK: Next to shop. TEL: 01254 888550. FAIRS: Local.

HASLINGDEN

P.J. Brown Antiques
8 Church St. BB4 5QU. Open 10-5, Sat. and Sun. by appointment. SIZE: Medium. *STOCK: Georgian, Victorian and Edwardian furniture, shipping goods, old advertising items, bottles and related items.* LOC: Town centre, off Bury Road/Regent St. PARK: Easy. TEL: 01706 224888. VAT: Stan/Spec.

Fieldings Antiques
176, 178 and 180 Blackburn Rd. BB1 2LG. Est. 1956. Open 9-4.30, Fri. 9-4. CL: Thurs. SIZE: Large. *STOCK: Longcase clocks, £30-£2,000; wall clocks, sets of chairs, pine, period oak, French furniture, glass, shipping goods, toys, steam engines, veteran cars, vintage and veteran motor cycles.* PARK: Easy. TEL: 01706 214254; mobile - 07973 698961; home - 01254 263358.

Holden Wood Antiques Centre
St Stephen's Church, Grane Rd. BB4 4AT. (Peter & Mary Crossley and John Ainscough). Est. 1997. Open 10-5.30 including Sun. SIZE: Large. *STOCK: Furniture, 18th-19th C, £200-£600; ceramics including figures, glass, 19th C, £50-£200.* PARK: Own. TEL: 01706 830803. SER: Valuations; restorations.

P.W. Norgrove - Antique Clocks
38 Bury Rd. BB4 5LR. Open by appointment only. *STOCK: Longcase, wall, bracket and mantel clocks.* TEL: 01706 211995; mobile - 07788 164621.

LANCASTER

The Assembly Rooms Market
King St. LA1. Open Tues.-Sat. 10-4.30. SIZE: Several dealers. *STOCK: General antiques, period and costume jewellery, Victorian to '60's costume and retro fashion, books.* TEL: Market Superintendent - 01524 66627.

G.B. Antiques Ltd
Lancaster Leisure Park, Wyresdale Rd. LA1 3LA. (Mrs G. Blackburn). Open 10-5 including Sun. SIZE: Large. 100+ dealers. *STOCK: Porcelain, glass and silver, late 19th to early 20th C; small furniture, Victorian to early 20th C.* LOC: Off M6, junction 33 or 34. PARK: Easy. TEL: 01524 844734; fax - 01524 844735; home - 01772 861593. SER: Valuations; buys at auction. VAT: Stan/Spec.

Lancaster Leisure Park Antiques Centre
Wyresdale Rd. (on site of former Hornsea Pottery Plant). LA1 5LA. Open every day 10-5. SIZE: 140 dealers. *STOCK: Wide range of general antiques.* LOC: Off M6, junction 33. TEL: 01524 844734.

Lancastrian Antiques & Co
70/72 Penny St. LA1 1XN. (S.P. and H.S. Wilkinson). Open 10-4. CL: Wed. *STOCK: Furniture, lighting, paintings, bric-a-brac.* TEL: 01524 847004.

LEIGH

Leigh Jewellery
3 Queens St. (R. Bibby). Open 9.30-5.30, Wed. 9.30-12.30. *STOCK: Jewellery.* TEL: 01942 607947/722509; mobile - 07802 833467.

MANCHESTER

A.S. Antique Galleries
26 Broad St, Salford. M6 5BY. (A. Sternshine). Est. 1975. Open Thurs., Fri. and Sat. 10-5.30 or by appointment. SIZE: Large. *STOCK: Art Nouveau and Art Deco bronzes, bronze and ivory figures, silver, glass, furniture, jewellery, lighting and general antiques.* Not Stocked: Weapons. LOC: On A6, one mile north of Manchester city centre, next to Salford University College. PARK: Easy. TEL: 0161 737 5938; mobile - 07836 368230; fax - 0161 737 6626. SER: Valuations; restorations; commission purchasing.

Antique Fireplace Warehouse
1090 Stockport Rd, Levenshulme. M19 2SU. (D. McMullan & Son). Open 9-6, Sun. 11-5. *STOCK: Fireplaces and architectural items.* TEL: 0161 431 8075.

Antiques Village
The Old Town Hall, 965 Stockport Rd., Levenshulme. M19 3NP. Est. 1978. Open 10-5.30, Sun. 11-4. SIZE: 40+ dealers. *STOCK: Furniture*

and clocks, reproduction pine, fireplaces, collectables. LOC: A6 between Manchester and Stockport. PARK: Own. TEL: 0161 256 4644; fax - same; mobile - 07976 985982. SER: Valuations; restorations; pine stripping; picture framing. FAIRS: Newark.

Bus Stop Curios
1 Beech Rd., Chorlton-cum-Hardy. M21 8BX. (John and Jean Higginbotham). Resident. Est. 1989. Open Thurs. 11-5.30, Fri. 11.15-5.45, Sat. 10.30-4.30. SIZE: Medium. STOCK: Militaria, WW1 & WW2, £1-£100; Victorian and Art Deco pottery and glass and smalls, £1-£100. PARK: Easy. TEL: 0161 860 6232.

Cathedral Jewellers
38 Thomas St. M4 1ER . Open 9.30-5. STOCK: Jewellery. TEL: 0161 832 3042.

Empire Exchange
1 Newton St., Piccadilly. M1 1HW. (David Ireland). Est. 1975. Open every day 9-7.30 except Christmas day. SIZE: Large. STOCK: General small antiques including silver, pottery, clocks and watches, ephemera, autographs, football memorabilia, records, books and comics, 18th-20th C, £5-£10,000. PARK: Easy. TEL: 0161 236 4445; fax - 0161 273 5007; home - 0161 256 1140. SER: Valuations. VAT: Stan/Spec.

Family Antiques
405/407 Bury New Rd., Prestwich. M25. (J. and J. Ditondo). Open daily. STOCK: General antiques. TEL: 0161 798 0036.

Fernlea Antiques
Failsworth Mill, Ashton Rd West, Failsworth. M35 0FD. (A.J. and Mrs B. McLaughlin). Open 10-5. STOCK: General antiques and shipping goods. TEL: 0161 682 0589.

Forest Books of Cheshire
in The Ginnel, 18-22 Lloyd St. M2 5WA. (Mrs E. Mann). Open 9.30-5.30. CL: Bank Holiday weekends and Christmas-New Year. STOCK: Antiquarian, art, collecting, drama and humanities books and prints. TEL: 0161 834 0747; 0161 833 9037 (The Ginnel); e-mail - info@fbooks. co.uk; website - www.fbooks.co.uk.

Fulda Gallery Ltd
19 Vine St., Salford. M7 3PG . (M.J. Fulda). Est. 1969. Open by appointment only. STOCK: Oil paintings, 1500-1950, £500-£30,000; watercolours, 1800-1930, £350-£10,000. LOC: Near Salford Police Station off Bury New Rd. TEL: 0161 792 1962; mobile - 07836 518313. SER: Valuations; restorations; buys at auction.

Gibb's Bookshop Ltd
10 Charlotte St. M1 4FL. Est. 1926. STOCK: Books. TEL: 0161 236 7179.

The Ginnell Gallery Antique Centre
18-22 Lloyd St. M2 5WA. (Mr and Mrs J.K. Mottershead). Est. 1973. Open 9.30-5.30. STOCK: Art Deco and Art Nouveau, 1950's pottery, furniture, glass, antiquarian and other books. LOC: Opposite Town Hall. TEL: 0161 833 9037.

In-Situ Manchester
Talbot Mill, 44 Ellesmere St., Hulme. M15 4JY. (Laurence Green). Est. 1983. Open Tues.-Sat. 10-5.30. SIZE: Large. STOCK: Architectural items including fireplaces, doors, panelling, sanitary ware, radiators, flooring, glass, gardenware, staircasing. TEL: 0161 839 5525; mobile - 07712 435821.

In-Situ Manchester South
Architectural Antiques
149 Barton Rd., Stretford. M32 8DN. (A. Whyman and S. Newsham). Open 9-5.30, Sun. 10-4. STOCK: Architectural antiques, fireplaces, radiators, flooring, stoves, doors, glass, lighting, sanitaryware. TEL: 0161 865 2110; fax - same; e-mail - andrew.whyman@virgin.net.

Irving Antique Toys
c/o Ginnel Gallery, 18-22 Lloyd St. M2 5WA. SIZE: Large. STOCK: Tinplate, trains, Dinkies, teddies and dolls. LOC: Off Albert Square. TEL: 0161 833 9037; home - 0161 740 9601; mobile - 07703 811715.

Eric J. Morten
Warburton St., Didsbury. M20 6WA. Est. 1959. Open 10-6. SIZE: Medium. STOCK: Antiquarian books, 16th-20th C, £5-£5,000. LOC: Off Wilmslow Rd., near traffic lights in Didsbury village. A34. PARK: Easy. TEL: 0161 445 7629 and 01265 277959. SER: Valuations; buys at auction (antiquarian books).

R.J. O'Brien and Son Antiques Ltd
Failsworth Mill, Ashton Rd. West, Failsworth. M35 0FD. Est. 1970. Open 9-5. CL: Sat. SIZE: Very large. *STOCK: Furniture, Victorian, Edwardian and 1930's; shipping goods, general antiques and pianos.* PARK: Own. TEL: 0161 688 4414; mobile - 07850 485201. SER: Container and courier service.

Premiere Antiques
371 Bury New Rd., Prestwich. M25 5AW. (S. Harris). GADAR. *STOCK: Furniture, mainly Victorian and Edwardian inlaid.* TEL: 0161 773 0500; fax - 0161 792 0232. SER: Restorations (furniture).

Prestwich Antiques Ltd
371-373 Bury New Rd., Prestwich. M25. (T. Finn and Y. Gray). Est. 1973. Open 10.30-6, Sun. 11.30-5. SIZE: Large. *STOCK: Victorian four-poster beds and associated furniture.* LOC: Off junction 17, M62. PARK: Own at rear. TEL: 0161 798 0911; home - 01282 618270. SER: Valuations; restorations (upholstery, polishing and repairs). VAT: Stan/Spec.

Secondhand and Rare Books
Corner Church St/High St. M4 1PN. Open 12-4. *STOCK: Books.* TEL: 0161 834 5964 or 01625 861608.

St. James Antiques
STOCK: Jewellery, silver and paintings. TEL: 0161 773 4662; mobile - 07808 521671.

Village Antiques
416 Bury New Rd., Prestwich. M25 1BD. (R. Weidenbaum). Est. 1981. Open 10-5, Wed. 10-1. SIZE: Medium. *STOCK: 19th C pottery and porcelain, £5-£300; 18th C glass; small furniture; Art Deco clocks, figurines and lamps; Art Nouveau figurines.* LOC: Village centre, 2 mins. from M62. PARK: Easy - side and opposite. TEL: 0161 773 3612.

MIDDLETON VILLAGE, Nr. Morecambe

G.G. Exports
Newfield House, Middleton Rd. LA3 3PP. (G. Goulding). Est. 1970. Always available but prior telephone call essential. SIZE: Large. *STOCK: Shipping goods, £30-£5,000, English and European furniture.* LOC: On main road between Morecambe promenade and Middleton village. PARK: Easy. TEL: 01524 850757; fax - 01524 851565. SER: Courier; packing; 40ft containers weekly worldwide. VAT: Stan. *Trade Only.*

MORECAMBE

The Magpies Nest
Unit 1 Plaza Arcade and 48 Pedder St. LA4 5YJ. (B. Byrne). Open 10-5. CL: Wed. *STOCK: Bric-a-brac, cutlery, china, glass, militaria.* TEL: 01524 423328.

Tyson's Antiques
Clark St. LA4 5HT. (George, Andrew and Shirley Tyson). Est. 1952. Open Sat. 8-11.30, other times by appointment. SIZE: Large. *STOCK: Georgian, Victorian and Edwardian furniture.* PARK: Easy. TEL: 01524 416763/425235/420098; mobile - 07971 836892; website - www.tysons-antiques. freeserve.co.uk. VAT: Stan/Spec. *Trade Only.*

Luigino Vescovi
135 Balmoral Rd. LA3 1HJ. Est. 1970. Open by appointment every day. SIZE: Warehouse. *STOCK: Georgian and Victorian furniture, inlaid Edwardian and plated ware, £50-£10,000.* PARK: Easy. TEL: 01524 416732; mobile - 07860 784856. VAT: Stan/Spec/Export

NELSON

Colin Blakey Fireplaces
115 Manchester Rd. BB10 2LS. Est. 1906. Open 9.30-5.30, Sat. 9.30-5, Sun. 12-4. *STOCK: Fireplaces and hearth furniture, paintings and prints.* LOC: Exit 12, M65. PARK: Opposite. TEL: 01282 614941. SER: Manufacturers and suppliers of hand-carved marble fireplaces and hardwood mantels. VAT: Stan.

Brittons - Watches
34 Scotland Rd. BB9 7UU. Est. 1970. CL: Tues. *STOCK: Jewellery and collectors' watches.* PARK: Opposite. TEL: 01282 697659; fax - 01282 618867; website - www.brittons-watches. co.uk.

Brooks Antiques
7 Russell St. BB9 7NL. (D. and S.A. Brooks). Est. 1987. Open 9-5, Sun. and Tues. by appointment. SIZE: Medium. *STOCK: Furniture, £50-£2,000; smalls, £5-£500; both 1750-1930; postcards, ephemera, early 20th C, to £20.* LOC: Town centre, 2 mins. from junction 13, M65. PARK: Easy. TEL: 01282 698148; home - 01282 866234. SER: Valuations.

OLDHAM

Charles Howell Jeweller
2 Lord St. OL1 3EY. (N.G. Howell). NAG. Est. 1870. Open 9.15-5.15. SIZE: Small. *STOCK: Edwardian and Victorian jewellery, £25-£2,000; silver, early to mid 20th C, £40-£1,500; watches, Victorian to mid 20th C, £50-£800.* LOC: Town centre, off High St. PARK: Limited or by arrangement. TEL: 0161 624 1479. SER: Valuations; restorations (jewellery and watches); buys at auction (jewellery and watches). VAT: Stan/Spec.

CONTAINER SERVICE

USA JAPAN EUROPE KOREA AUSTRALIA

30,000 SQ FT WAREHOUSE FULL OF GEORGIAN, VICTORIAN, EDWARDIAN, 1930s SHIPPING FURNITURE, PIANOS CONTINENTAL FURNITURE ALSO STOCKED

20FT FROM £5000
40FT FROM £8000

ALL CONTAINERS BOUGHT FROM US PACKED FREE OF CHARGE

REFERENCES AVAILABLE

FOR MORE INFORMATION CONTACT RONAN O'BRIEN @ R.J. O'BRIEN & SON ANTIQUES LTD MANCHESTER M35 0FD ENGLAND

TEL/FAX 00 44 161 688 4414
EMAIL OBANTIQUES@BTINTERNET.COM EXPORTS@OBALTD.FSNET.CO.UK

WEBSITE

WWW.ANTIQUE-EXPORTS.COM

SHOP WHERE THE ENGLISH TRADE SHOPS

H.C. Simpson and Sons Jewellers (Oldham)Ltd
37 High St. OL3 5AW. Open 9-5.30. *STOCK: Clocks, jewellery, watches.* TEL: 0161 624 7187. SER: Restorations (clocks).

Valley Antiques
Soho St. OL4 2AD. (J. Chadwick). Est. 1973. Open 10-6. SIZE: Warehouse. *STOCK: General antiques including stripped pine, oak furniture, 19th C, £25-£600.* PARK: Easy. TEL: 0161 624 5030. SER: Valuations; restorations (pine stripping, upholstery, clocks).

Waterloo Antiques
16 Waterloo St. OL1 1SQ. (B.J. and S. Marks). Est. 1969. Open 9.30-5. SIZE: Medium. *STOCK: General antiques, furniture, jewellery.* LOC: Town centre. TEL: 0161 624 5975; fax - same; e-mail - bmarks46@hotmail.com. SER: Valuations.

ORMSKIRK

Alan Grice Antiques
106 Aughton St. L39 3BS. Open 10-6. *STOCK: Period furniture.* PARK: Easy. TEL: 01695 572007.

POULTON-LE-FYLDE

Ray Wade Antiques
P O Box 39. FY6 9GA . Est. 1978. Trades at fairs or by appointment. *STOCK: Decorative items, sculpture, European and Oriental works of art, paintings.* TEL: 01253 700715; fax - 01253 702342; mobile - 07836 291336; e-mail - antiques@r-wades.demon.co.uk. SER: Finder; valuations; buys for export. VAT: Stan/Spec.

PRESTON

The Antique Centre
56 Garstang Rd. PR1 1NA. (Paul Allison). Open 9-5.30, Sat. 9.30-5.30, Sun. 10.30-5.30. SIZE: 35 dealers. *STOCK: Furniture, including pine, Georgian, Victorian and Edwardian; porcelain, silver, clocks, bric-a-brac and pictures.* TEL: 01772 882078; fax - 01772 252842. SER: World-wide shipping; containers.

European Fine Arts and Antiques
10 Cannon St. PR1 3NR. (B. Beck). Est. 1970. Open 9.30-5.30. SIZE: Medium. *STOCK: Victorian paintings and furniture, to £2,000.* LOC: Town centre - Fishergate. PARK: Loading only and nearby. TEL: 01772 883886; fax - 01772 823888. SER: Valuations; buys at auction (paintings and furniture). VAT: Stan/Spec.

Hackler's Jewellers
6b Lune St. PR1. (N.E. Oldfield). FBHI. *STOCK: Antique clocks.* TEL: 01772 258465. VAT: Stan.

Halewood and Sons
37 Friargate. PR1 2AT. Est. 1867. CL: Thurs. pm. *STOCK: Antiquarian books and maps.* TEL: 01772 252603.

Nelson's Antiques
113 New Hall Lane. PR1 5PB. (W. and L. Nelson). Open 9.30-5.30 or by appointment. *STOCK: General antiques and collectors' items, dolls.* LOC: Half mile from junction 31, M6. PARK: Easy. TEL: 01772 794896/862066. SER: Valuations.

Preston Antique Centre
The Mill, New Hall Lane. PR1 5UH. Open 8.30-5.30, Sat.10-4, Sun. 10-5. SIZE: Large - 40+ dealers. *STOCK: General antiques, Georgian, Victorian and Edwardian; shipping furniture.* TEL: 01772 794498/654531/651548; fax - 01772 651694; e-mail - prestonantiques@hotmail.com; website - www.antiques-atlas.com/preston.htm.

Preston Book Co
68 Friargate. PR1 2ED. Est. 1950. Open 9.30-5.30. *STOCK: Antiquarian books.* TEL: 01772 252613. SER: Buys at auction.

Priory Collectables
7 Priory Lane, Penwortham. (David Howden). Est. 1988. Open Tues., Thurs., Fri. 1-5, Sat. 10-5, Sun. trade by appointment. SIZE: Small. *STOCK: Cutlery and silver plate, from 1850, £5-£500; collectables including china, glass, clocks, toby jugs, Wade, Sylvac, small furniture.* LOC: Turn right at traffic lights in Penwortham into Priory Lane. PARK: Easy. TEL: 01772 752090.

ROCHDALE

Antiques and Bygones
100 Drake St. OL16 1PQ. (K. and E. Bonn). Est. 1983. Open 10-4, Sat. 10-2. CL: Mon. and Tues. SIZE: Small. *STOCK: Pottery, coins and medals, jewellery, 19th-20th C, £5-£50.* TEL: 01706 648114.

S.C. Falk
LAPADA. Open by appointment only. *STOCK: Fine English period furniture.* TEL: 01706 644946. VAT: Stan/Spec.

Owen Antiques
114 Buersill Avenue. OL16 4TX. (J.G.T. Owen). Est. 1891. Open by appointment. *STOCK: Mainly paintings, clocks, radios; old scarce, rare and unusual books.* TEL: 01706 353270. SER: Valuations; restorations (clocks and furniture).

SABDEN, Nr. Clitheroe

Walter Aspinall Antiques
Pendle Antiques Centre, Union Mill, Watt St. BB7 9ED. Est. 1964. Open 9-5, Sat. and Sun. 11-4 or by appointment. SIZE: Large. *STOCK: Furniture and bric-a-brac.* LOC: On Pendle Hill between Clitheroe and Padiham. TEL: 01282 778642; fax - 01282 778643. SER: Export; packing; courier; containers; wholesale.

Pendle Antiques Centre Ltd
Union Mill, Watt St. BB7 9ED. Est. 1993. Open 10-5, Sun. 11-5 (other times by appointment for Trade). SIZE: 10 dealers. *STOCK: Furniture and bric-a-brac.* LOC: Over Pendle Hill, off the A59 between Clitheroe and Padiham. TEL: 01282 776311; fax - 01282 778643; e-mail - sales@pendleantiquescentre; www - pendle antiquescentre.co.uk.

SAMLESBURY, Nr. Preston

Samlesbury Hall
(Dating from 1325). Preston New Rd. PR5 0UP. (Samlesbury Hall Trust). Est. 1969. Open 11-4.30, but prior telephone call advisable. Admission - adults £2.50, children £1. CL: Mon. SIZE: Large. *STOCK: General collectable antiques.* LOC: Exit 31, M6 on A677 between Preston and Blackburn. PARK: Easy. TEL: 01254 812010/2229.

ST. ANNES-ON-SEA

The Victorian Shop
19 Alexandria Drive. FY8 1JF. (G.O. Freeman). Open 10-5. *STOCK: General antiques.* TEL: 01253 725700.

TARLETON

R.H. Latham Antiques
6 Gorse Lane. PR4 6UJ. Est. 1958. Open by appointment only. SIZE: Medium + warehouse at Old Cornmill Antique Centre, 64 South Road, Bretherton. *STOCK: Antique stripped pine furniture and interesting associated smalls.* TEL: 01772 812900; mobile - 07801 948320. SER: Shipping and courier; pine stripping.

TRAWDEN, Nr. Colne

Jack Moore Antiques and Stained Glass
The Old Rock, Keighley Rd. BB8 8RW. Open Mon.-Fri. 9-5 or by appointment. SIZE: Large. *STOCK: Furniture and stained glass.* PARK: Easy. TEL: 01282 869478; home - same; fax - 01282 865193; mobile - 07802 331594. SER: Restoration and manufacture of stained glass; container packing; courier. VAT: Stan.

WHALLEY, Nr. Blackburn

Edmund Davies & Son Antiques
32 King St. BB7 9SL. (E. and P. Davies). Est. 1960. Open 10-5. SIZE: Medium + trade warehouse. *STOCK: Oak and country furniture, longcase clocks, to £10,000; jewellery, to £500.* Not Stocked: Reproductions. LOC: A59 (11 miles from M6). PARK: Easy. TEL: 01254 823764. VAT: Stan/Spec.

WHITEFIELD, Nr. Manchester

Henry Donn Gallery
138/142 Bury New Rd. M45 6AD. Est. 1954. Open 9.30-5. *STOCK: Paintings, 19th-20th C, £20-£100,000.* LOC: Off M60, junction 17 towards Bury. TEL: 0161 766 8819. SER: Valuations; framing; restorations (pictures). VAT: Stan/Spec.

WIGAN

Corner Cupboard Antiques
49 Preston Rd., Standish. WN6 0JH. (Mrs B. Calderbank). Est. 1980. Open Thurs. and Fri. 10-4. SIZE: Small. *STOCK: Dolls, china and furniture, 20th C, £5-£500.* LOC: A49. PARK: Easy. TEL: 01257 426454. SER: Valuations.

Colin de Rouffignac
57 Wigan Lane. WN1 2LF. Open 10-4.30. CL: Wed. *STOCK: Furniture, jewellery, oils and watercolours.* TEL: 01942 237927.

John Robinson Antiques
172-176 Manchester Rd., Higher Ince. WN2 2EA. Est. 1965. Open any time. SIZE: Large. *STOCK: General antiques.* LOC: A577 near Ince Bar. PARK: Easy. TEL: 01942 247773/241671. SER: Export packing. VAT: Stan. *Export and Trade Only.*

Wiend Books & Collectables
8-12 The Wiend. WN1 1PF. (Paul and Roslyn Morris). Est. 1996. Open 9.30-5. CL: Tues. SIZE: Medium. *STOCK: Books, £5-£80; ephemera, £1-£20; advertising items, Wade, £5-£25; all 19th-20th C.* LOC: Between Market Place and Millgate. PARK: Millgate. TEL: 01942 820500; fax - same. SER: Valuations. FAIRS: Bolton Reebok Stadium; Haigh Hall; Bury Drill Hall.

WORSLEY, Nr. Manchester

Northern Clocks
Boothsbank Farm, Leigh Rd. M28 1LL. (R.M. Love and Miss M.A. Love). Est. 1998. Open by appointment. SIZE: Large. *STOCK: Provincial longcase and bracket clocks, 18th C.* LOC: Off junction 13, M60. PARK: Easy. TEL: 0161 790 8414; home - same; fax - 0161 703 7567. SER: Valuations; restorations. VAT: Stan.

See Rutland county listing for
Empingham, Manton, Oakham,
Uppingham and Wing

BROUGHTON ASTLEY, Nr. Leicester

Old Bakehouse Antiques and Gallery
10 Green Rd. LE9 6RA. (S.R. Needham). Open
Thurs.-Sat. 10-6, Sun. 2-5. *STOCK: Period
furniture.* PARK: Easy. TEL: 01455 282276.

CASTLE DONINGTON

The Book Shop
17 Borough St. DE74 2LP. (Michael and Margaret
Fletcher). Est. 1970. Open 9-5, Sat. 9-12. CL: Wed.
SIZE: Small. *STOCK: Books - aviation history,
military, railway and antiquarian; pictures and
prints, die cast toys.* LOC: Opposite village church.
PARK: Easy. TEL: 01332 814391. SER: Valuations;
restorations (book-binding); framing. FAIRS:
Donington; airshows - Duxford, Waddington,
Cottesmore, Cosford and Woodford, RIAT, IPMS.

COALVILLE

Keystone Antiques
9 Ashby Rd. LE67 3LF. (I. and H. McPherson).
LAPADA. FGA. Est. 1979. Open 10-5, Sat. 10-4.
CL: Wed. SIZE: Medium. *STOCK: Jewellery,
Victorian and Georgian, £25-£1,500; silver,
1700-1920, £20-£500; small collectable items,
18th-19th C, £15-£300; furniture, cranberry,
needlework tools, Victorian and Georgian table
glass.* LOC: A115, town centre. PARK: At rear.
TEL: 01530 835966. SER: NAG registered
valuer; gem testing. VAT: Stan/Spec.

EARL SHILTON

The Glory Hole
69 High St. LE9 7DH. (M. Crowston). Est. 1994.
Open 10-5.30, Sun. 10-2. SIZE: Large. *STOCK:
Victorian and Edwardian furniture, £100-£1,000;
porcelain, 1860-1930's, £5-£50.* PARK: Easy. TEL:
01455 847922; mobile - 07710 101364; website -
www.thegloryhole.co.uk. SER: Valuations;
restorations including door stripping; buys at auction
(furniture). FAIRS: Newark and Ardingly.

GREAT GLEN, Nr. Leicester

Sitting Pretty
45a Main St. LE8 9GH. (Jennifer Jones-
Fenleigh). Est. 1979. Open Thurs., Fri. and Sat.
10-5.30, other days by appointment. *STOCK:
Upholstered furniture, 18th-20th C, £50-£1,000.*

LOC: Off A6. PARK: Easy. TEL: 0116 259
3711; home - same. SER: Valuations; restorations
(re-upholstery, French polishing, caning and
rushing). VAT: Spec.

HINCKLEY

House Things Antiques
Trinity Lane, 44 Mansion St. LE10 0AU. (P.W.
Robertson). Est. 1976. Open 10-6. SIZE: Small.
*STOCK: Stripped pine, satinwood, oak and
walnut, mainly Victorian and Edwardian, £50-
£600; small collectors' items, 1860-1930s, £5-
£100; cast iron fireplaces, brass and iron beds,
1890-1920's, £50-£1,000.* LOC: On inner ring
road 200yds. from Leisure Centre. PARK: Easy.
TEL: 01455 618518; home - 01455 212797.

HOBY, Nr. Melton Mowbray

Withers of Leicester
The Old Rutland, Church Lane. LE14 3DU. (S.
Frings). Est. 1860. Open 9-5.30. CL: Thurs. pm.
and Sat. SIZE: Medium. *STOCK: Furniture,
17th-19th C, £50-£3,000; china, 18th-19th C,
£10-£300; oil paintings, 19th C, £5-£500.* Not
Stocked: Jewellery and coins. PARK: Easy. TEL:
01664 434803. SER: Valuations; restorations
(furniture). VAT: Stan/Spec.

IBSTOCK, Nr. Leicester

Mandrake Stevenson Antiques
101 High St. LE67 6LJ. Est. 1979. Open 10-5,
Sat. 10-1. CL: Wed. SIZE: Small. *STOCK:
Furniture, pre 1930's.* PARK: Easy. TEL: 01530
260898. SER: Valuations; restorations (furniture).

KNIPTON, Nr. Grantham

Anthony W. Laywood
NG32 1RF. Est. 1967. Open by appointment.
SIZE: Medium. *STOCK: Antiquarian books, pre-
1850, £20-£2,000.* LOC: 1.5 miles off the
Grantham-Melton Mowbray road. PARK: Easy.
TEL: 01476 870224; fax - 01476 870198; e-mail
- laywood@globalnet.co.uk. SER: Valuations;
buys at auction.

LEICESTER

Betty's
9 Knighton Fields Rd. West. LE2 6LH. (A. Smith).
Est. 1968. Open 9.30-5. SIZE: Small. *STOCK:
Satinwood and pine items, brass and copper,
pictures.* LOC: Off Saffron Lane. PARK: Easy. TEL:
0116 2839048. SER: Valuations; buys at auction.

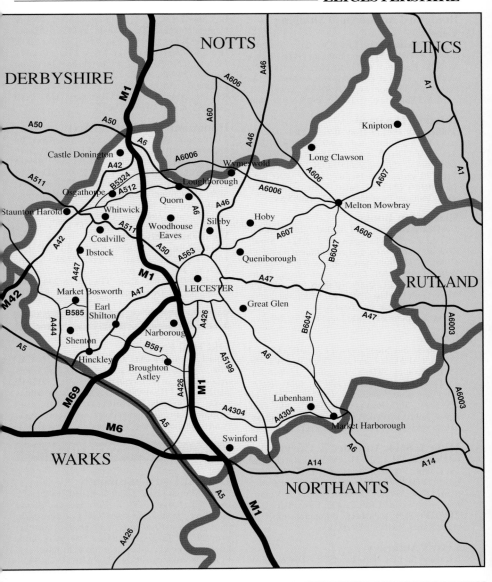

Dealers and Shops in Leicestershire

Boulevard Antique and Shipping Centre

63 King Richard's Rd. LE3 5QG. Open Mon.-Fri. 9-6 or anytime by appointment. SIZE: Large. *STOCK: Furniture including oak, mahogany and shipping; general antiques, some smalls.* LOC: A46 from junction 21, M1. PARK: Own. TEL: 0116 233 8828; fax - 0116 233 8823. VAT: Stan.

Britain's Heritage

Shaftesbury Hall, 3 Holy Bones. LE1 4LJ. (Mr and Mrs J. Dennis). Est. 1980. Open 9.30-5.30, Sat. 9.30-5. SIZE: Large. *STOCK: Fireplaces, 18th-20th C, £100-£25,000.* LOC: Off Vaughan Way, 70 yards from Holiday Inn. PARK: Easy. TEL: 0116 2519592. SER: Valuations; restorations (antique fireplaces). VAT: Stan/Spec.

Clarendon Books

144 Clarendon Park Rd. LE2 3AE. (Julian Smith). PBFA. Est. 1984. Open 10-5. SIZE: Small. *STOCK: Antiquarian and second-hand books, £1-£500.* LOC: Between London Rd. (A6) and Welford Rd. (A50), 2 miles south of city centre. PARK: Easy. TEL: 0116 270 1856; fax - 0116 270 9020; home - 0116 270 1914. SER: Valuations; restorations (repair and binding); buys at auction (books and maps). FAIRS: London H D; PBFA.

Corry's

24 Francis St., Stoneygate. LE2 2BD. (Mrs E.I. Corry). LAPADA. Est. 1962. Open 10-5. CL: Fri. SIZE: Medium. *STOCK: Furniture, 18th-19th C, £500-£10,000; paintings, 19th C, £100-£8,000; silver, porcelain, 18th-20th C, £5-£5,000.* TEL: 0116 270 3794. SER: Restorations. FAIRS: NEC (Jan., April, Aug.); LAPADA London; Robert Baileys'; Dorchester; Claridges; Park Lane. VAT: Spec.

Hide & Seek Antiques & Curios

60A Queens Rd. LE2 1TU. (Michael Haynes). Est. 1981. Open 10.30-6, Sat. 10-6. CL: Thurs. SIZE: Small. *STOCK: Hardwood furniture and interesting items, 18th-20th C, to £800.* LOC: Off Victoria Park, near London Rd. PARK: Easy. TEL: 0116 212 0210. SER: Valuations; restorations especially architectural. FAIRS: Newark.

Letty's Antiques

6 Rutland St. LE1 1RA. Est. 1952. *STOCK: Silver, jewellery, china and brass.* TEL: 0116 2626435.

Oxford Street Antique Centre

16-26 Oxford St. LE1 5XU. Open 10-5.30, Sat. 10-5, Sun. 2-5. SIZE: Large warehouse. *STOCK: Period furniture, shipping goods, pine, bric-a-brac and general antiques, 18th to mid-20th C, 50p-£5,000.* LOC: Main ring road. PARK: Own. TEL: 0116 2553006; fax - 0116 2555863. SER: Container loading facilities. VAT: Stan/Spec.

The Rug Gallery

50 Montague Rd., Clarendon Park. LE2 1TH. (Dr.

Roy Short). Est. 1987. Open Fri. and Sat. 10-4 or by appointment. SIZE: Medium. *STOCK: Oriental rugs and kilims, early 19th to 20th C, £100-£2,000; Swat, Afghan, Indian and Chinese furniture, 18th-19th C, £50-£1,000; tribal embroidery and jewellery, 19th-20th C, £10-£1,000.* LOC: From London Rd. A6, take Victoria Park Rd., to Queen's Rd., then Montague Rd. PARK: Easy. TEL: 0116 2700085; home - 0116 2700113.

Hammond Smith (Fine Art)

431 London Rd. LE2 3JW. Est. 1981. Open by appointment. SIZE: Small. *STOCK: British watercolours, 1750-1950, £300-£10,000; British etchings, 19th-20th C, £100-£500.* TEL: 0116 270 9020; fax - same; mobile - 07973 483231. SER: Valuations; restorations (watercolours and prints cleaned, mounted and framed); buys at auction (watercolours). VAT: Spec.

West End Antiques

1 Lothair Rd., Off Aylestone Rd. LE2 7QE. Est. 1986. Open Tues.-Sat. 10-4.30. SIZE: Small. *STOCK: Furniture, porcelain, silver, 19th C, £25-£1,000.* PARK: Easy. TEL: 0116 244 0086. FAIRS: Castle Donington.

LONG CLAWSON, Nr. Melton Mowbray

Old Hall Farm

Hose Lane. LE14 4NG. Open 8.30-5.30. *STOCK: Pine, French antiques, gas (electric) wall lights and shades, architectural items.* TEL: 01949 860274; fax - 01949 861231. SER: Restorations (oak, mahogany, architectural items, pine stripping); furniture, windows and doors made from reclaimed pine.

LOUGHBOROUGH

Lowe of Loughborough

37-40 Church Gate. LE11 1UE. Est. 1846. CL: Sat. SIZE: Large. *STOCK: Furniture and period upholstery from early oak, 1600 to Edwardian; mahogany, walnut, oak, £20-£8,000; clocks, bracket and longcase, £95-£2,500; porcelain, maps, copper and brass.* Not Stocked: Jewellery. LOC: Opposite parish church. PARK: Own. TEL: 01509 212554/217876. SER: Upholstery; restorations; interior design. VAT: Stan/Spec.

LUBENHAM, Nr. Market Harborough

Leicestershire Sporting Gallery and Brown Jack Bookshop

The Old Granary, 62 Main St. LE16 9DG. (Reg Leete). Est. 1958. Prior 'phone call advisable. SIZE: Large. *STOCK: Oil paintings, prints including Vanity Fair and sporting; engravings, maps,*

OAKTREE ANTIQUES

Fine 17th-19th century town and country furniture,
longcase clocks & works of art

The Drapers House
Main Street
Lubenham
Market Harborough
Leicestershire LE16 9TF

Tel: 01858 410041
Mobile: 07710 205696

Open 10am-6pm
Wed-Sun inclusive

furniture (including mahogany and oak); antiquarian and illustrated books, histories of fox hunts, prints, horse brasses, martingales, swingers - all stock dateline 1960. LOC: Centre of village. PARK: Rear of village green opposite. TEL: 01858 465787.

Oaktree Antiques
The Drapers House, Main St. LE16 9TF. (Gillian Abraham and John Wright). Open Wed.-Sun. 10-6. SIZE: Medium. *STOCK: Town and country furniture, 17th-19th C; longcase clocks, Georgian to early Victorian.* LOC: 1 mile east of Market Harborough, close to A14, M1 and M6. PARK Opposite, on village green. TEL: 01858 410041; mobile - 07710 205696. VAT: Spec.

Stevens and Son
61 Main St. LE16 9TF. (M.J. Stevens). Resident. Est. 1977. Open 10-5. *STOCK: General antiques, mainly furniture.* LOC: A427 via junction 20 M1. TEL: 01858 463521. SER: Restorations (furniture).

MARKET BOSWORTH

Bosworth Antiques
10 Main St. CV13 0JW. (John Thorp). Est. 1986. Open 10-1 and 2-5, Sat. 10-5. CL: Tues. *STOCK: General antiques, 19th-20th C.* PARK: Easy. TEL: 01455 292134. SER: Valuations.

Corner Cottage Antiques
7 Market Place, The Square. CV13 0LF. (J. and B. Roberts). Est. 1969. Open 10-5 or by appointment. *STOCK: 18th-20th C furniture, silver, paintings; clocks, porcelain, glass, brass and copper, general antiques.* PARK: Easy. TEL: 01455 290344; home - 01455 282583. VAT: Global/Stan/Spec.

Country Pine Antiques
4 Main St. CV13 0JW. (M. and A. Boylan). Est. 1980. Open 10-5.30, Thurs. 10-3. CL: Mon. SIZE: Medium. *STOCK: Stripped pine and interesting and unusual decorative items.* LOC: Off A447 in Market Place. PARK: Easy. TEL: 01455 291303.

P. Stanworth (Fine Arts)
The Grange, 2 Barton Rd. CV13 0LQ. (Mr and Mrs G. and Mr James Stanworth). Resident. Est. 1965. Open by appointment. SIZE: Medium. *STOCK: Oil paintings and watercolours, 18th to early 20th C.* LOC: Road just off town square. PARK: Easy. TEL: 01455 291023. VAT: Spec.

MARKET HARBOROUGH

Graftons of Market Harborough
92 St Mary's Rd. LE16 7DX. (F. Ingall). Est. 1967. Open Mon., Tues., Fri. and Sat. 10-5.30, other times by appointment. *STOCK: Oils, watercolours, etchings and engravings, 18th-19th C.* TEL: 01858 433557.

Walter Moores and Son
P O Box 5338. LE16 7WG. (Peter Moores). LAPADA. Est. 1925. Open by appointment only. *STOCK: Georgian furniture; complementary Victorian items.* TEL: 07071 226202; fax - same; mobile - 07710 019045. FAIRS: Most major. VAT: Spec.

J. Stamp and Sons
The Chestnuts, 15 Kettering Rd. LE16 8AN. (M. Stamp). Resident. Est. 1947. Open 8-5.30, Sat. 9-12.30 or by appointment. SIZE: Medium. *STOCK: Mahogany and oak furniture, 18th-19th C, £500-£5,000; Victorian furniture, £250-£2,500; Edwardian furniture, £100-£1,000.* LOC: A6. PARK: Easy. TEL: 01858 462524; fax - 01858 465643. SER: Valuations (furniture); restorations (furniture). VAT: Stan/Spec.

MELTON MOWBRAY

Flagstones Pine & Interiors
24 Burton St. LE13 1AF. (Julie Adcock). Est. 1986. Open 9.30-5.15. SIZE: Medium. *STOCK: English and European pine furniture, 18th-20th C; new and reclaimed wood reproductions, including kitchens.* PARK: Easy. TEL: 01664 566438; website - www.flagstonespine.co.uk. SER: Restorations; stripping; waxing. VAT:Stan.

347

NARBOROUGH

Ken Smith Antiques Ltd
215-217 Leicester Rd. LE9. (K.W. Sansom). LAPADA. Est. 1888. Open 9.30-5, Sun. 11-5. SIZE: Large. *STOCK: Furniture, mainly 1880-1930, £100-£5,000; clocks, smalls and paintings.* TEL: 0116 286 2341; fax - 0116 275 3151. VAT: Stan/Spec.

OSGATHORPE, Nr. Loughborough

David E. Burrows
Manor House Farm. LE12 9SY. LAPADA. Est. 1973. *STOCK: Pine, oak, mahogany and walnut furniture, clocks, £100-£10,000.* LOC: Junction 23, M1, turn right off Ashby road, farm next to church; or A42. TEL: 01530 222218; mobile - 07702 059030; fax - 01530 223139; e-mail - david.burrows2@virgin.net. VAT: Stan/Spec.

QUENIBOROUGH, Nr. Leicester

J. Green and Son
1 Coppice Lane. LE7 3DR. (R. Green). Resident. Est. 1932. Appointment advisable. SIZE: Medium. *STOCK: 18th-19th C English and Continental furniture.* LOC: Off A607 Leicester-Melton Mowbray Rd. PARK: Easy. TEL: 0116 2606682. SER: Valuations; buys at auction. VAT: Stan/Spec.

QUORN

Quorn Pine and Decoratives
The New Mills, Leicester Rd. LE12 8ES. (S. Yates and S. Parker). Open 9-6, Sat. 9.30-5.30. *STOCK: Pine and country furniture.* TEL: 01509 416031. SER: Stripping and restorations (pine). VAT: Stan/Spec.

SHENTON, Nr. Market Bosworth

Whitemoors Antiques and Fine Art
CV13 6BZ. Est. 1987. Open Mon.-Fri. 11-4 (winter) 11-5 (summer), Sat. in June and Bank Holidays 11-5. SIZE: Large - 20+ unitholders. *STOCK: Furniture, £25-£2,000; smalls, £5-£200; prints and pictures, Victorian to early 20th C, £40-£400.* LOC: A5 onto A444 towards Burton-on-Trent, first right then second left. PARK: Easy. TEL: 01455 212250; home - 01455 212981.

SILEBY, Nr. Loughborough

R. A. James Antiques
Ammonite Gallery, 15a High St. LE12 7RX. *STOCK: Mainly stripped pine, general antiques.* TEL: 01509 812169; mobile - 07713 132650.

STAUNTON HAROLD

Ropers Hill Antiques
Ropers Hill Farm. LE65 1SE. (S. and R. Southworth). Est. 1974. Open by appointment. SIZE: Small. *STOCK: General antiques, silver and metalware.* LOC: On old A453. PARK: Easy. TEL: 01530 413919. SER: Valuations.

SWINFORD, Nr. Lutterworth

Old Timers
High St. LE17 6BL. (M. S. Harris). Est. 1994. Open every day except Sun., but appointment preferred. SIZE: Small. *STOCK: Clocks and furniture, some brass and copper.* LOC: Village centre, half a mile from junction 19, M1, M6 and A14. PARK: Own. TEL: 01788 860311; fax - same; e-mail - info@old-timers.co.uk; website - www.old-timers.co.uk. SER: Valuations; restorations.

WHITWICK, Nr. Coalville

Charles Antiques
3 Market Place. LE67 5AE. (Brian Haydon). Est. 1970. Open afternoons, Sat. 10-12 and 2-4, Wed. and Sun. by appointment. CL: Mon. SIZE: Small. *STOCK: Clocks, 18th C, £25-£4,000; furniture, 19th C, £50-£1,000; china.* LOC: A511. PARK: Easy. TEL: 01530 836932; home - same; mobile - 07831 204406. SER: Buys at auction. VAT: Stan/Spec.

WOODHOUSE EAVES, Nr. Leicester

Paddock Antiques
The Old Smithy, Brand Hill. LE12 8SS. (M., C.A. and T.M. Bray). Open Thurs. - Sat. 10-5.30, other times by appointment. *STOCK: Furniture, 1750-1910, to £5,000; porcelain, 1750-1940's, to £3,500; prints and glass.* PARK: Easy.

WYMESWOLD, Nr. Loughborough

N. Bryan-Peach Antiques
28 Far St. LE12 6TZ. Resident. Open 10-6, Sun. by appointment. SIZE: Medium. *STOCK: Clocks, barometers, watches; 18th-19th C furniture, £50-£5,000.* PARK: Easy. TEL: 01509 880425. SER: Valuations; restorations; buys at auction. VAT: Spec.

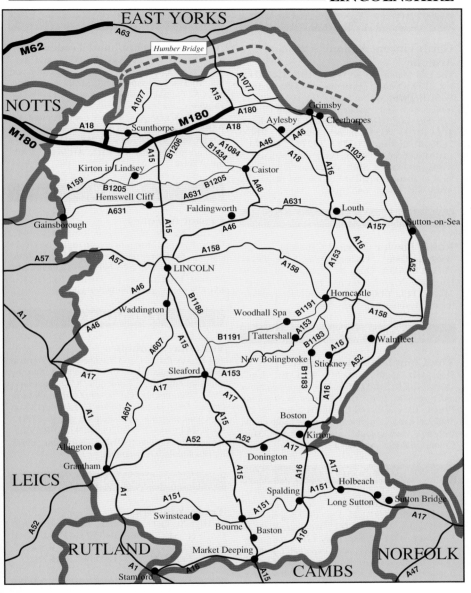

LINCOLNSHIRE

ALLINGTON, Nr. Grantham

Garth Vincent Antique Arms and Armour

The Old Manor House. NG32 2DH. LAPADA. Est. 1979. Open by appointment. SIZE: Medium. *STOCK: Militaria including firearms, swords, rapiers and daggers; armour, 16th-19th C, £50-£15,000.* LOC: Opposite church. PARK: Easy. TEL: 01400 281358; home - same; fax - 01400 282658; mobile - 07785 352151; e-mail - garthvincent@compuserve.com; website - www.guns.uk.com. SER: Valuations; restorations; buys at auction. FAIRS: London and major city Arms; NEC (Aug). VAT: Spec.

AYLESBY, Nr. Grimsby

Robin Fowler (Period Clocks)

Washing Dales, Washing Dales Lane. DN37 7LH. LAPADA. Open by appointment. SIZE: Large. *STOCK: Clocks and barometers, 17th-18th C.* TEL: 01472 751335. SER: Restorations (clocks, barometers).

BASTON, Nr. Peterborough

The Complete Automobilist

Dept. GD, 35 Main St. PE6 9NX. Est. 1967. Open 9-5. CL: Sat. *STOCK: Hard-to-get parts for older vehicles.* LOC: On A15, east of Stamford. PARK: Easy. TEL: 01778 560312; fax - 01778 560738; e-mail - colincrabbe@compauto.co.uk; website - www.completeautomobilist.com. SER: Colour catalogue available £2.

BOSTON

Tony Coda Antiques

121 High St. PE21 8TJ. Est. 1967. Open 9.30-12.30 and 1.30-5.30. SIZE: Medium. *STOCK: Furniture, 17th-19th C, from £100; paintings, 19th C, to £500; china, silver and clocks, to £200.* LOC: From A16 turn right at roundabout into London Rd. and then to High St. PARK: Easy. TEL: 01205 352754; home - 01205 722104. SER: Valuations. FAIRS: International Antique and Collectors.

Portobello Row Antique & Collectors' Centre

93-95 High St. PE21. Open 10-4. SIZE: 9 dealers. *STOCK: Shipping furniture, kitchenalia, blue and white china, 1940's-70's clothing, bric-a-brac.* TEL: 01205 368692.

BOURNE

Antique & Secondhand Traders

The Warehouse, 39 West St. (C.A. and A.L. Thompson). Est. 1962. Open Mon., Tues., Fri. and Sat. 10-5 or by appointment. SIZE: Warehouse. *STOCK: Furniture - antique, Victorian, Edwardian, shipping, oak, reproduction and modern, £50-£5,000.* LOC: On A15, 8 miles from Stamford A1. PARK: Own. TEL: 01778 394700; mobiles - Alan - 07885 694299; Clyde - 07958 941728. SER: Valuations. FAIRS: Newark; Ardingly. VAT: Spec/Global.

CAISTOR

Caistor Antiques

12 High St. LN7 6TX. (Susan Rutter). Est. 1982. Open by appointment day or night. *STOCK: Pottery, furniture, jewellery, dolls, linen, 18th-20th C.* LOC: Off A46 between Grimsby and Market Rasen. PARK: Own. TEL: 01472 851975; home - same. SER: Valuations.

CLEETHORPES

Yesterday's Antiques

86 Grimsby Rd. DN35 7DP. (Jeanette and Norman Bishop). Resident. Est. 1983. Open 9-5, Sun. by appointment. SIZE: Large. *STOCK: Furniture, £50-£2,000; fireplaces, £500-£1,000; French beds, clocks, £300-£1,200; all 19th C.* LOC: A180 on right entering town, opposite Esso garage. PARK: Easy. TEL: 01472 343020/504093. SER: Valuations; restorations (polishing, stripping, clock repairs, fireplace renovation).

DONINGTON, Nr. Spalding

Trade Antiques

47 High St. PE11 4TA. (P.E. Poole). Est. 1961. CL: Sat. SIZE: Medium. *STOCK: General shipping goods, clocks and watches.* LOC: A152. PARK: Easy. TEL: 01775 821491. *Trade Only.*

FALDINGWORTH, Nr. Market Rasen

Brownlow Antiques Centre

Lincoln Rd. LN8 3SF. (Sylvia and Alex Stephens). Est. 1994. Open Tues.-Sat. 10-6 (10-5 Oct.-March), Sun. 12-5. SIZE: Large. *STOCK: Furniture, 18th C to pre-1940, £50-£3,000; bric-a-brac, collectables, from £2.* LOC: A46 towards Grimsby, 10 miles north of Lincoln. PARK: Own. TEL: 01673 885367; home - same. FAIRS: Local.

GAINSBOROUGH

S. Carrick's Antiques and Shipping
130 Trinity St. DN21 5PD. Open 8.30-5. STOCK: General antiques and shipping furniture. TEL: 01427 611393/810409; mobile - 07850 470966.

Stanley Hunt Jewellers
22 Church St. DN21. (S. and R.S. Hunt). Est. 1952. Open 9-5. CL: Wed. SIZE: Medium. STOCK: Antique jewellery. LOC: Main street from Market Place. PARK: Easy. TEL: 01427 613051; home - same. SER: Valuations; restorations (gold, silver, clocks).

Pilgrims Antiques Centre
66 Church St. DN21 2JR. Est. 1986. CL: Mon. and Wed. SIZE: Large. STOCK: Jewellery, miniatures, silver, silhouettes, paintings, textiles, ceramics and books, £5-£1,000; furniture, £50-£1,000. LOC: Near Old Hall. PARK: Easy. TEL: 01427 810897. SER: Valuations. FAIRS: Newark; Birmingham.

GRANTHAM

Grantham Clocks
30 Lodge Way. NG31 8DD. (R. Conder). Resident. Open by appointment. STOCK: Clocks. PARK: Easy. TEL: 01476 561784. SER: Restorations.

Grantham Furniture Emporium
4-6 Wharf Rd. NG31 6BA. (K. and J.E. Hamilton). Est. 1970. Open 10-4, Sun. 11-4. CL: Mon. and Wed. SIZE: Large. STOCK: Victorian, Edwardian and shipping furniture, £5-£3,000. LOC: Town centre, near Post Office. PARK: Own at rear. TEL: 01476 562967.

Harlequin Antiques
46 Swinegate. NG31 6RL. (A.R. and Mrs S.B. Marshall). Est. 1996. Open from 9. SIZE: Medium. STOCK: Furniture and china, 19th C, £50-£500; collectables, 19th-20th C, £50-£100. LOC: 100 yards from High St., opposite Blue Pig public house. PARK: Easy. TEL: 01476 563346. SER: Valuations.

Notions Antiques Centre
2a Market Place. NG31 6LQ. (Mrs S. Checkley). Est. 1984. Open 10-5, Sat. 9.30-5. SIZE: 21+ dealers. STOCK: China, collectables, decorative accessories and furniture, mainly 19th-20th C, £1-£1,000. LOC: Down from Angel and Royal Hotel. PARK: Easy. TEL: 01476 563603. SER: Valuations; repairs. FAIRS: Newark; Ardingly.

Wilkinson's
The Tyme House, 1 Blue Court. NG31 6NJ. (M. and P. Wilkinson). Est. 1935. Open 10-4.30. CL: Wed. SIZE: Small. STOCK: Jewellery, watches and silver, 19th C, £50-£5,000. PARK: Nearby. TEL: 01476 560400 and 01529 413149. SER: Valuations; restorations (including clock and watch movements); buys at auction (rings and watches). VAT: Spec.

GRIMSBY

Abbeygate Gallery & Antiques Centre
14 Abbeygate. DN31 1JY. Open Tues.-Sat. 10-4.30. SIZE: Medium. STOCK: Pottery and glass, militaria, coins and medals, £5-£100; small furniture, £25-£500; all 19th-20th C. TEL: 01472 361129.

Bell Antiques
68 Harold St. DN32 7NQ. (V. Hawkey). Est. 1964. Open by appointment, telephone previous evening. SIZE: Large. STOCK: Antique pine and grandfather clocks. Not Stocked: Reproduction. PARK: Easy. TEL: 01472 695110; home - same.

HEMSWELL CLIFF, Nr. Gainsborough

Astra House Antiques Centre
RAF Hemswell. DN21 5TL. (M. Frith). Open daily including Sun. 10-5. SIZE: 50 dealers. STOCK: Wide variety of general antiques and shipping goods, including Victorian, Edwardian and Continental furniture and smalls. LOC: Near Caenby Corner Roundabout A15/A631. TEL: 01427 668312.

Fairburn Books
Upper Floor, Building 2, Hemswell Antiques Centre, Caenby Corner Estate. DN21 5TJ. (Elaine Lonsdale). PBFA. Est. 1988. Open daily including Sun. SIZE: Small. STOCK: Antiquarian and second-hand books and ephemera. PARK: Easy. TEL: 01977 678193; mobile - 07710 480581. SER: Valuations; book-binding. FAIRS: PBFA.

Hemswell Antiques Centres
Caenby Corner Estate. DN21 5TJ. (Robert Miller). Est. 1986. Open 10-5 including Sun. SIZE: 270+ dealers. STOCK: Period furniture, 17th-19th C; watercolours and oils, 19th C; silver and plate, clocks, porcelain, china, jewellery, dolls, toys, books, prints, clothes. LOC: A15 from Lincoln then A631 towards Gainsborough, 1 mile from roundabout, follow signs. PARK: Easy. TEL: 01427 668389; fax - 01427 668935; e-mail - info@hemswell-antiques.com. SER: Restorations (oak, mahogany and pine; upholstery); delivery.

Kate
Kate House, Caenby Corner Estate. DN21 5TJ. (Mr Shamsa). Open 9-4.30, Sat. 10-1. STOCK: Pine including reproduction. TEL: 01427 668724/668904; fax - 01427 668905.

Adriatic (24,679 tons, White Star) was the ship that Captain Smith (later of Titanic) called unsinkable. He never used the word to describe the Titanic. Artist: Montague B. Black.

From an article entitled 'Ocean Liner Postcards and Marine Art' by Robert Wall which appeared in the February 2001 issue of **Antique Collecting** magazine. For more details and to subscribe see page 147.

Second Time Around
Hemswell Antique Centre, Caenby Corner Estate, Gainsborough. DN21 5TJ. (G.L. Powis). Open 10-5 including Sun. *STOCK: Longcase and bracket clocks, pre 1830, £1,650-£35,000.* LOC: A15 from Lincoln to Caenby Corner roundabout, left towards Gainsborough for 1 mile (A631). PARK: Easy. TEL: 01427 668389; home - 01522 543167; mobile - 07860 679495. SER: Restorations (clocks).

HOLBEACH, Nr. Spalding

P.J. Cassidy (Books)
1 Boston Rd. PE12 7LR. Est. 1974. Open 10-6. SIZE: Medium. *STOCK: Books, 19th-20th C, £2-£300; maps, prints and engravings, 17th-19th C, £10-£500.* LOC: 1/4 mile from A17. PARK: Nearby. TEL: 01406 426322; fax - same; e-mail - bookscass@aol.com. SER: Valuations; framing and mount cutting. VAT: Stan.

HORNCASTLE

G. Baker Antiques
16 South St. LN9 6DX. Est. 1974. Open 9-5, Wed. 9-1, Sun. by appointment. SIZE: Small.
STOCK: Furniture, 18th-20th C, £10-£10,000. LOC: A153. PARK: Easy. TEL: 01507 526553; mobile - 07767 216264. SER: Valuations; restorations (furniture). FAIRS: Swinderby and Newark. VAT: Stan/Spec.

Clare Boam
22-38 North St. LN9 5DX. Est. 1977. Open 9-5, Sun 2-4.30. SIZE: Large. *STOCK: Furniture and bric-a-brac, 19th-20th C, to £1,000.* LOC: Louth/Grimsby road out of town. PARK: Easy. TEL: 01507 522381; home - same. VAT: Global.

Great Expectations
37-43 East St. LN9. (Clare Boam). Est. 1977. Open 9-5, Sun. and Bank Holidays 1-4.30. SIZE: Large. *STOCK: Wide variety of general antiques including pine, oak, mahogany, kitchenalia, luggage, books, china, glass, collectables, 50p to £1,000.* LOC: A158, 100 yards from traffic lights. PARK: At rear or in street opposite. TEL: 01507 524202; home - 01507 522381. SER: Restorations (china, glass and furniture).

Lindsey Court Architectural Antiques
Lindsey Court. LN9 5DH. (Lindsay White). Open 10-4, Sun. by appointment. *STOCK: Architectural antiques, English, French and Spanish reclamations, York stone flagging and garden statuary, £50-£10,000.* LOC: Behind the library. PARK:

Own. TEL: 01507 527794; fax - 01507 526670; mobile - 07768 396117; e-mail - lndsy150@ netscapeonline.co.uk; sales@1starchitectural.co.uk; website - www. 1starchitectural.co.uk. SER: Container and shipping. VAT: Stan/Global.

North Street Antiques & Interiors
48 North St. LN9 5DX. (Mrs Vivien Hallberg). Est. 1985. Open 10-4, Sun. and evenings by appointment. SIZE: Medium. *STOCK: Smalls, pre 1900, £100-£3,000; portrait miniatures, 18th-19th C, £250-£1,000; small furniture, 18th-19th C, £200-£2,000; silver, ceramics, 18th-19th C glass, objets de vertu.* LOC: Left off Lincoln Rd. into town, last shop in right, opposite Jobcentre. PARK: Easy. TEL: 01507 525835; home - 01526 388359. SER: Valuations; buys at auction. FAIRS: Swinderby, Newark, Lincoln, Uppingham, Louth, Barnsdale Country Club.

Alan Read - Period Furniture
60 & 62 West St. LN9 5AD. Open 10-4.30. CL: Mon. and Wed. *STOCK: 17th-19th C furniture, early oak, walnut and decorative items.* TEL: 01507 524324/525548. SER: Bespoke copies; interior design.

Seaview Antiques
Stanhope Rd. LN9 5DG. (M. Chalk and Tracey Collins). Open 9-5. SIZE: Large + warehouse. *STOCK: Victorian, Edwardian and decorative furniture; smalls, brassware, silver and plate, lamps, boxes.* LOC: A158. PARK: Easy. TEL: 01507 524524.

Laurence Shaw Antiques
77 East St. LN9 6AA. Open 8.30-5. SIZE: Medium. *STOCK: Furniture, china, glass, metalware, books, collectables, general antiques, 17th-20th C.* LOC: Opposite Tourist Information Centre. TEL: 01507 527638. SER: Consultant; valuations. VAT: Global/Spec.

Staines Antiques
25 Bridge St. LN9 5HZ. (Mrs M. Staines). Est. 1991. Open 10-5. CL: Mon. SIZE: Medium. *STOCK: Furniture, pictures and clocks, £50-£5,000; ceramics, £20-£500; all 18th-20th C.* LOC: A158 Lincoln to Skegness road, turn off by-pass towards town centre. Shop 200 yards on right, opposite Antiques Centre. PARK: Easy and nearby. TEL: 01507 527976; home - same. SER: Valuations.

KIRTON

Kirton Antiques
3 High St. PE20 1DR. (A.R. Marshall). LAPADA. Est. 1973. Open 8.30-5, Sat. 8.30-12 or by appointment. SIZE: Large - warehouse. *STOCK: Furniture, all periods; painted pine,*

chairs, decorative items, glass, metal, pottery, china, picture frames. TEL: 01205 722595; evenings - 01205 722134; fax - 01205 722895. VAT: Stan.

KIRTON IN LINDSEY

Mr Van Hefflin
12 High St. DN21 4LU. Est. 1820. Open 10-5. *STOCK: Jewellery, curios, silver, paintings.* PARK: Easy. TEL: 01652 648044. SER: Guide.

LINCOLN

Annette Antiques
77 Bailgate. LN1 3AR. (Mrs A. Bhalla). Est. 1972. Open Tues.-Sat. 2-6. SIZE: Small. *STOCK: Porcelain, glass and small silver, 19th-20th C; clocks, silver flatware, watercolours, prints and drawings, 18th-20th C; all £10-£500.* LOC: 2 minutes from castle and cathedral. PARK: Nearby. TEL: 01522 546838; home - 01205 260219. SER: Restorations (furniture). FAIRS: Alexandra Palace.

Michael Brewer
Northgate Lodge, Northgate. LN2 1QS. Est. 1954. Open by appointment. SIZE: Medium. *STOCK: Furniture, oil paintings, silver, porcelain, bronzes, works of art.* Not Stocked: Coins. LOC: Close to Cathedral. PARK: 20yds. TEL: 01522 545854. SER: Valuations; buys at auction. VAT: Stan/Spec. *Trade Only.*

C. and K.E. Dring
111 High St. LN5 7PY. Open 10-5.30. CL: Wed. *STOCK: Victorian and Edwardian inlaid furniture; shipping goods, porcelain, clocks, musical boxes, tin-plated toys, trains and Dinkys.* TEL: 01522 540733/792794.

Golden Goose Books
20 and 21 Steep Hill. LN2 1LT. (R. West-Skinn and Mrs A. Cockram). Est. 1983. Open 10-5.30. CL: Wed. *STOCK: Antiquarian and secondhand books, maps and prints.* TEL: 01522 522589; home - 01673 878622.

David J. Hansord & Son BADA
6 & 7 Castle Hill. LN1 3AA. (David, John and Anne Hansord). Est. 1972. Open 10-1 and 2-5. SIZE: Large. *STOCK: Furniture, clocks, barometers, works of art, 18th C, £50-£25,000.* LOC: In square between cathedral and castle. PARK: Castle Hill. TEL: 01522 530044; fax - same; home - 01522 731088. SER: Valuations; restorations (furniture, barometers and clocks); buys at auction. FAIRS: Olympia (June and Nov). VAT: Spec.

LINCOLNSHIRE

Harlequin Gallery
22 Steep Hill. LN2 1LT. (R. West-Skinn). Est. 1962. Open 10-5.30. *STOCK: Antiquarian and secondhand books, antique maps and prints.* TEL: 01522 522589; home - 01673 858294. SER: Restoration (globes).

Dorrian Lambert Antiques
64 Steep Hill. LN1 1YN. (R. Lambert). Est. 1981. Open 10-5, Wed. and Sun. by appointment. SIZE: Medium. *STOCK: Small furniture, clocks, chairs, pottery, porcelain, jewellery, books, sporting antiques, books and collectables, 18th to early 20th C.* PARK: Loading only or nearby. TEL: 01522 545916; home - 01427 848686. SER: Valuations; restorations (clocks). FAIRS: Newark.

Mansions
5a Eastgate. LN2 1QA. Open 10-5. *STOCK: General antiques, decorative items, period lighting.* TEL: 01522 513631/560271.

Rowletts of Lincoln
338 High St. LN5 7DQ. (A.H. Rowlett). Open 9-5. *STOCK: Antique and secondhand jewellery.* TEL: 01522 524139.

Timepiece Repairs
43 Steep Hill. LN2 1LU. (R. Ellis and D.A. Linton). FBHI. Est. 1978. Open 10-5, Sat. 10-4.30. CL: Mon. and Wed. SIZE: Small. *STOCK: Clocks and watches, 18th-20th C, £10-£8,000; barometers, 19th-20th C, £100-£1,500.* LOC: Near cathedral. PARK: 100 metres. TEL: 01522 525831; home - 01522 881790. SER: Valuations; restorations (movements, dials and cases); buys at auction (horological). VAT: Stan/Spec.

James Usher and Son Ltd
incorporating John Smith & Son, 26 & 27 Guildhall St. LN1 1TR. Open 9-5.30. *STOCK: Silver, jewellery.* TEL: 01522 527547/523120.

The Chapel Emporium Antique Centre
London Rd. PE12. (J.A. Beck and B. Hill). Est. 1984. Open 10-5 including Sun. SIZE: Large. *STOCK: Furniture, 18th-19th C, £100-£2,000; collectables, 19th-20th C, 50p-£300; ephemera, 19th C, 50p-£25.* LOC: Opposite playing fields. PARK: Easy. TEL: 01406 364808.

J.W. Talton
15-19 Market St. PE12 9DD. (J., W. and J.J. Talton). Resident. Est. 1952. Open 9-5, Wed. 9-12. SIZE: Small. *STOCK: General antiques.* LOC: On old A17. PARK: Easy. TEL: 01406 362147; home - same. SER: Restorations (furniture and cabinet making).

A Barn Full of Brass Beds
Abbey House, Eastfield Rd. LN11 7HJ. (J.J. Tebbs). Est. 1985. Open by appointment. SIZE: Large. *STOCK: Brass and iron beds, 1860-1910, £250-£1,000.* LOC: 1/4 mile from Louth on right, off Eastfield Rd. PARK: Easy. TEL: 01507 603173; home - same. SER: Valuations; restorations. VAT: Stan.

Jocelyn Chatterton
82 Westgate. LN11 9YD. Open by appointment (and by appointment in London). SIZE: Small. *STOCK: Formal Chinese court costume, Qing dynasty, £200-£5,000; informal Chinese costume, 19th to early 20th C, £50-£3,000; Chinese dress accessories and embroidery, 19th to early 20th C, £20-£500.* LOC: Adjacent St James' church (large spire) in town centre. PARK: Available by appointment. TEL: 01507 602251; fax - 01507 608239; e-mail - jocelyn@cixi.demon.co.uk; website - www.cixi.demon.co. SER: Buys at auction (Chinese costume). FAIRS: NEC; Hali Oriental Textile; Earls Court; New York.

Old Maltings Antique Centre
38 Aswell St. LN11 9HP. (Norman and Margaret Coffey). Est. 1980. Open 10-4, Wed. and Fri. 10-4.30, Sat. 10-5. SIZE: Large - over 40 cabinets. *STOCK: Furniture including Victorian and Edwardian, collectables, ceramics, glass, jewellery.* LOC: 2 minutes walk from town centre. PARK: Easy. TEL: 01507 600366. SER: Valuations; restorations; pine stripping.

Market Deeping Antiques & Craft Centre
50-56 High St. PE6. (J. Strutt and C. Stubbins). Resident. Est. 1995. SIZE: Large. *STOCK: General antiques, bric-a-brac and craft items.* LOC: A15. PARK: Easy. TEL: 01778 380238.

Portland House Antiques
23 Church St. PE6 8AN. (G.W. Cree and V.E. Bass). Est. 1987. Open Mon.-Sat. or by appointment. SIZE: Medium. *STOCK: Porcelain, glass, furniture, 18th-19th C, £100-£10,000.* PARK: Easy. TEL: 01778 347129; home - same. SER: Buys at auction. VAT: Stan/Spec.

Junktion
The Old Railway Station. (J. Rundle). Est. 1981. Open Wed., Thurs. and Sat. SIZE: Large. *STOCK: Early advertising, decorative and architectural items; toys, automobilia, mechanical antiques and*

GERTRUDE JEKYLL

The Making of a Garden

An Anthology

Compiled by
Cherry Lewis

This anthology encompasses a rich legacy of gardening lore left to us by Gertrude Jekyll, (1843-1932) one of the great gardeners of the century and certainly one of the most influential. Her ten gardening books were published between 1899 and 1937 and it is from these that the excerpts in this anthology have been selected.

Trained at art school, Gertrude Jekyll developed strongly held views on design, form and the use of colour in the garden, and it is these views which are reflected in this selection which takes us through the year, season by season. Her observations will entertain those who delight in reading about the heart and soul of gardening as well as educate those with a more practical bent. Gertrude Jekyll's genius is to enthuse the reader to action by her straightforward, no nonsense approach which keeps her and her readers from becoming a slave to the garden or its plants.

The book is illustrated, not only with Gertrude Jekyll's own black and white photographs and drawings, but also with watercolours and paintings by contemporary artists.

Cherry Lewis's selection was based on the aim of going for 'observations' which would not only entertain those who delight in reading about the heart and soul as well the maintaining of a garden; but also to enthuse those who feel they want but can never quite get down to their gardens. As she points out, it is impossible to read Gertrude Jekyll without feeling spurred on because she never makes a mystery of gardening and her approach is so straightforward, down-to-earth and practical.

Here then is a rich legacy of gardening lore, its delights, disasters, its pleasures and practicalities. Since she wrote, times have changed: many of the plants referred to are no longer commonly seen or available; the classification of plant names is being altered continuously; gardens have shrunk in size and gardening help in quantity. What is remarkable is that so many of Gertrude Jekyll's writings remain relevant today.

Skilful editing has resulted in a truly representative selection which succeeds in conveying 'the lesson I have thoroughly learnt, and wish to pass on to others, is to know the enduring happiness that the love of a garden gives'.

ISBN 1 870673 27 1, 192pp., 151 col., 162 duotone illus., 10 b.&w. illus. **£25.00/$49.50**

bygones; early slot machines, wireless, telephones, bakelite, 20th C collectables. Not Stocked: Porcelain and jewellery. LOC: B1183 Boston to Horncastle. PARK: Easy. TEL: 01205 480087/ 480068.

SCUNTHORPE

Antiques & Collectables & Gun Shop
Rear of 251 Ashby High St. DN16 2SQ. (J.A. Bowden). Open 9-5. *STOCK: Clocks, furniture, arms and collectables.* TEL: 01724 865445/ 720606. SER: Restorations and repairs (clocks and guns).

SLEAFORD

Mill Antiques
19A Northgate. NG34 7BH. (John Noble and A. Crabtree). Est. 1988. Open 9-5. SIZE: Medium. *STOCK: General antiques including furniture, porcelain and pictures, 18th-20th C, £5-£2,500.* LOC: 100 yds. from Market Square. PARK: Loading only. TEL: 01529 413342; home - 01529 415101. SER: Valuations; restorations (furniture and porcelain).

Wilkinson's
The Little Tyme House, 13 Southgate. NG34 7SU. (M. and P. Wilkinson). Est. 1935. Open 10-4.30. CL: Wed. and Thurs. SIZE: Small. *STOCK: Jewellery, watches and silver, £50-£2,000.* PARK: Nearby. TEL: 01529 413149 and 01476 560400. SER: Valuations; restorations (including clock and watch movements); buys at auction (rings and watches). VAT: Stan.

SPALDING

Dean's Antiques
"The Walnuts", Weston St. Mary's. PE12 6JB. (Mrs B. Dean). Est. 1969. Open daily. SIZE: Medium. *STOCK: General antiques, farm and country bygones, £2-£200.* LOC: On Spalding to Holbeach main road A151. PARK: Easy. TEL: 01406 370429.

Penman Clockcare
Unit 5 Pied Calf Yard, Sheepmarket. PE11 1BE. (Michael Strutt). BWCMG. Est. 1998. Open 9-5. *STOCK: Clocks 18th-20th C; watches, 19th-20th C.* LOC: In yard behind Pied Calf public house, opposite PO. PARK: Nearby. TEL: 01755 714900; home - 01755 840955. SER: Valuations; restorations (clocks and watches).

Spalding Antiques
1 Abbey Path, The Crescent. PE11 1AY. (John Mumford). Est. 1980. Open 10-5, Thurs. 10-12 and 1.30-5, Sat. 10-4. SIZE: Medium. *STOCK: Clocks, furniture and smalls, 19th C, £10-£3,000.* LOC: Opposite Sessions House. PARK: Victoria St. TEL: 01775 713185. SER: Valuations.

STAMFORD

Dawson of Stamford Ltd
6 Red Lion Sq. PE9 2AJ. (J. Dawson). Open 9-5.30. *STOCK: Fine antique furniture, jewellery and silver.* LOC: Town centre between St. John's church and All Saint's church. TEL: 01780 754166. VAT: Stan/Spec.

Hunters Antiques & Interior Design
9a St. Mary's Hill. PE9 2DP. Open 9.30-5.30. SIZE: Medium. *STOCK: Period mahogany and country furniture, decorative items.* LOC: Just over town bridge, on the left. PARK: George Hotel. TEL: 01780 757946; fax - same; mobile - 07976 796969. SER: Restorations (furniture, clocks and barometers). VAT: Stan/Spec.

Graham Pickett Antiques
7 High St., St Martins. PE9 2LF. (G.R. Pickett). Est. 1990. Open 10-5.30, Thurs. 10-4. SIZE: Medium. *STOCK: Furniture - country, 1650-1900, French provincial, 1700-1900, both £50-£2,000; French and English beds, 1750-1900, £350-£2,000.* LOC: From A1 north into town, on right by 1st lights opposite George Hotel. PARK: Easy. TEL: 01780 481064; home - 01780 764502; mobile - 07710 936948; e-mail - graham@pickett antiques.demon.co.uk. FAIRS: Newark IACF. VAT: Stan/Spec.

Sinclair's
11/12 St. Mary's St. PE9. (J.S. Sinclair). Est. 1970. Open 9-5.30. SIZE: Large. *STOCK: Oak country furniture, 18th C, £200-£3,000; Victorian mahogany furniture, £100-£1,000; Edwardian furniture.* LOC: Near A1. PARK: George Hotel. TEL: 01780 765421. VAT: Stan/Spec.

St. George's Antiques
1 St. George's Sq. PE9 2BN. (G.H. Burns). Est. 1974. Open 9-1 and 2-4.30. CL: Sat. SIZE: Shop + trade only warehouse. *STOCK: Period and Victorian furniture, some small items.* TEL: 01780 754117; home - 01780 460456. VAT: Stan/Spec.

St. Martins Antiques Centre
23a High St., St. Martin's. PE9 2LF. (P. B. Light). Open every day 10-5. SIZE: 50 dealers. *STOCK: Georgian, Victorian and Edwardian furniture, country pine, Art Deco and Arts &*

Crafts furniture, porcelain, glass, copper, brass, clocks and watches, silver, jewellery, military books, leather and willow, paintings, prints, textiles, fireplaces, surrounds and grates, 20th C lighting and other artefacts, collectables and ephemera. TEL: 01780 481158; fax - same; e-mail - peter@st-martins-antiques.co.uk.

Staniland (Booksellers)
4/5 St. George's St. PE9 2BJ. (V.A. and B.J. Valentine-Ketchum). Est. 1973. Open 10-5. SIZE: Large. *STOCK: Books, mainly 19th-20th C, £1-£2,000.* LOC: High St. PARK: St. Leonard's St. TEL: 01780 755800; e-mail - stanilandbooksellers @btinternet.com.

Andrew Thomas
Old Granary, 10 North St. PE9 2YN. Est. 1970. Open 9-6. SIZE: Large. *STOCK: Pine and country furniture in original paint; ironware.* LOC: From south take old A1 through Stamford. Turn right at second set of traffic lights, warehouse on right. PARK: Opposite. TEL: 01780 762236; home - 01780 410627. VAT: Stan.

Vaughan Antiques
45 Broad St. PE9 1PX. (Barry and Lindy Vaughan). LAPADA. Est. 1993. Open 10-5. SIZE: Large. *STOCK: 18th-19th C furniture and decorative items.* TEL: 01780 765888.

STICKNEY

B and B Antiques
Main Rd. PE22 8AD. (B.J. Whittaker and J. Shooter). Open by appointment. *STOCK: General antiques.* PARK: Easy. TEL: 01205 480204.

SUTTON BRIDGE

The Antique Shop
100 Bridge Rd. PE12 9SA. (R. Gittins). Est. 1973. Open 9-5.30, Sun. 11-5. SIZE: Large - 8 showrooms + trade warehouse. *STOCK: Victorian furniture, glass, china, oil lamps and clocks.* Not Stocked: Pine. LOC: On old A17 opposite church. PARK: Easy. TEL: 01406 350535. VAT: Spec.

Bridge Antiques
30-32 Bridge Rd. PE12 9UA. Open 8-5. CL: Sat. SIZE: Large. *STOCK: Shipping furniture - barleytwist, linenfold, pineapple, Jacobean styles.* LOC: Old A17. PARK: Easy. TEL: 01406 350704/351669.

Old Barn Antiques & Furnishings
48-50 Bridge Rd. PE12 9UA. (S. and Mrs T.J. Jackson). Open 9-5, Sat. 10-5, Sun. 11-4. SIZE: Large + trade warehouse. *STOCK: 19th-20th C furniture - oak, mahogany, walnut, pine and upholstered.* LOC: Village centre, 200 yds from swing-bridge. PARK: Easy. TEL: 01406 359123; fax - 01406 359158; mobile - 07956 677282. VAT: Spec.

Old Barn Antiques Warehouse
220 New Rd. PE12 9QE. (S. and Mrs T. Jackson). Open Mon.-Fri. 9-5.30 or by appointment. SIZE: Large. *STOCK: 19th -20th C furniture - shipping goods, oak - carved, pineapple, Jacobean, distressed, barley twist; mahogany, walnut and pine original, unrestored and reclaimed timber copies.* LOC: 1 mile out of village, turn by Barclays Bank. PARK: Own. TEL: 01406 350435; fax - 01406 359158; mobile - 07956 677228. SER: Storage; container and export facilities. *Trade & Export Only.*

SUTTON-ON-SEA

Knicks Knacks Emporium
41 High St. LN12 2EY. (Mr and Mrs R.A Nicholson). Est. 1983. Open 10.30-1 and 2-5, including Sun. CL: Mon. SIZE: Medium + small warehouse. *STOCK: Victorian gas lights, brass and iron beds, cast-iron fireplaces, bygones, curios, tools, collectables, pottery, porcelain, Art*

LINCOLNSHIRE

Deco, Art Nouveau, advertising items, furniture and shipping goods, £1-£1,000. LOC: A52. PARK: Easy. TEL: 01507 441916; fax - same; home - 01507 441657.

SWINSTEAD

Robin Shield Antiques   BADA
Tyton House, 11 Park Rd. NG33 4PH. LAPADA. Est. 1974. Open by appointment anytime. SIZE: Medium. *STOCK: Furniture and paintings, £200-£20,000; works of art, £100-£5,000; all 17th-19th C.* **PARK: TEL: 01476 550892; mobile - 07860 520391. SER: Valuations; buys at auction. VAT: Stan/Spec.**

TATTERSHALL

Wayside Antiques
Market Place. LN4 4LQ. (G. Ball). Est. 1969. Open anytime by appointment. *STOCK: General antiques.* LOC: A158. PARK: Easy. TEL: 01526 342436.

WADDINGTON, Nr. Lincoln

J. and R. Ratcliffe
The Manor, Manor Lane. LN5 9QD. Est. 1954. Appointment advisable. *STOCK: English and Continental furniture, 1600-1830.* LOC: 4 miles from Lincoln on Grantham road. PARK: Opposite. TEL: 01522 720996.

WAINFLEET, Nr. Skegness

Haven Antiques
Bank House, 36 High St. PE24 4BJ. (Colin and Julie Crowson). Est. 1980. Open daily except Thurs., Sun. by appointment. SIZE: Small. *STOCK: General antiques, jewellery, porcelain and collectibles.* LOC: A52. PARK: Easy and opposite. TEL: 01754 880661; home - same. SER: Valuations.

WOODHALL SPA

Underwoodhall Antiques
The Broadway. LN10 6ST. Open 10-5. CL: Wed. SIZE: Medium. *STOCK: Furniture, £10-£1,000; porcelain and china, £5-£500; general antiques, £1-£500; pictures, £5-£500, all 1750 to date.* LOC: B1191. PARK: Easy. TEL: 01526 353815; e-mail - underwoodhall@supanet.com.

V.O.C. Antiques
27 Witham Rd. LN10 6RW. (D.J. and C.J. Leyland). LAPADA. Resident. Est. 1970. Open 9.30-5.30, Sun. 2-5. SIZE: Medium. *STOCK: 17th-19th C furniture, to £5,000; period brass and copper, pottery, porcelain and pictures.* LOC: B1191. PARK: Easy. TEL: 01526 352753; fax - same; home - same. SER: Valuations.

Winyard and Green
Unit 1 Broadway Centre, The Broadway. LN10 6ST. (Mrs S. Green). Est. 1995. Open 10.30-4.30, Sun. 2-4.30. SIZE: About 30 cabinets. *STOCK: Dolls, oil lamps, £95-£395; porcelain, jewellery, curios.* PARK: Easy. TEL: 01526 354711.

Possibly the most famous handbag in the world is the Hermes Kelly. At Christie's the late 1960s example in light brown baby crocodile skin sold to an enthusiast for £3,200. Another collector paid £1,100 for the 1950s bag of black calf skin.

From an Auction Report by Christopher Wight on Quilts, Costume and Textiles held at Christie's South Kensington on 6th March 2001 which appeared in the May 2001 issue of **Antique Collecting** magazine. For more details and to subscribe see page 147.

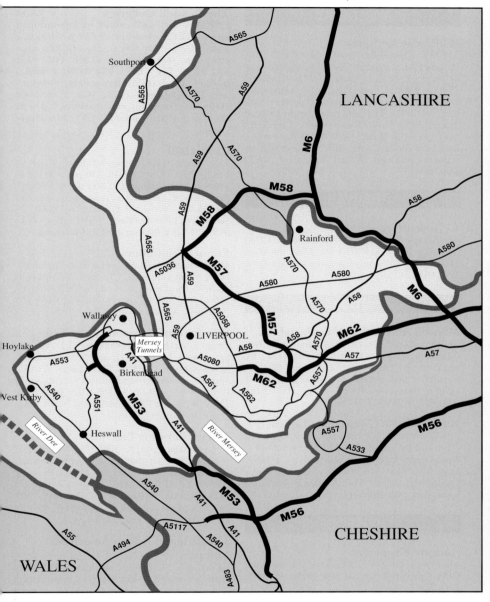

Dealers and Shops on Merseyside

Birkenhead	1	Liverpool	13	Wallasey	3
Heswall	1	Rainford	1	West Kirby	1
Hoylake	2	Southport	11		

BIRKENHEAD

Bodhouse Antiques
379 New Chester Rd., Rock Ferry. CH42 1LB. (G. and F.M. Antonini). Open 9-5, Sat. and Sun. by appointment. SIZE: Large. *STOCK: Furniture, 19th C; ceramics, from 19th C; silver plate, 18th-20th C; all £5-£1,000+; prints and pictures, 19th C, £25-£1,000+.* LOC: 1/2 mile from Birkenhead Tunnel, A41 towards Chester. PARK: Easy. TEL: 0151 644 9494; home - 0151 652 6433; e-mail - francesantonini@ic24.net. SER: Packing; courier; regular containers to Italy and Spain. VAT: Stan/Spec.

HESWALL

C. Rosenberg
The Antique Shop, 120-122 Telegraph Rd. CH60 0AQ. Est. 1960. Open 10-5. CL: Mon. and Wed. *STOCK: Jewellery, silver, porcelain, objets d'art.* TEL: 0151 342 1053.

HOYLAKE

Mansell Antiques and Collectables
Mulberry House, 128-130 Market St. CH47 3BH. (Gary Mansell). Open 9-5.30 and by appointment. CL: Wed. SIZE: Large. *STOCK: Furniture, pine, china, decorative arts.* LOC: A540 in town centre. PARK: At rear. TEL: 0151 632 0892; mobile - 07944 883021.

Kevin Whay's Clocks & Antiques
The Quadrant. CH47 2EE. Est. 1969. Open Fri. 10-4 and by appointment. *STOCK: Clocks, barometers, furniture and jewellery.* PARK: Easy. TEL: 0151 336 3432; fax - same; e-mail - kevin@lots.uk.com. SER: Restorations (clocks, barometers, dials and cases).

LIVERPOOL

Antique Fireplaces
43a Crosby Rd. North, Waterloo. (J.Toole). Est. 1978. Open 10-5, Sat. 10-5.30. SIZE: Medium. *STOCK: Fireplaces, 18th-19th C, £100-£1,000+; doors, 19th C, from £35.* PARK: Easy. TEL: 0151 949 0819. SER: Valuations; restorations. VAT: Stan.

Boodle and Dunthorne Ltd
Boodle House, Lord St. L2 9SQ. Est. 1798. Open 9-5.30. *STOCK: Jewellery and some silver.* TEL: 0151 227 2525. VAT: Stan/Spec.

The Boydell Galleries   BADA
LAPADA. Est. 1851. Open by appointment only. SIZE: Medium. *STOCK: English watercolours, 18th-20th C, £50-£10,000; maps and prints, 16th-19th C, £1-£2,000.* TEL: 0151 932 9220; fax - 0151 924 0199; e-mail - boydellgalleries@btinternet.com; website - www.boydellgalleries.co.uk. SER: Valuations; cleaning; framing; restorations; buys at auction. FAIRS: National. VAT: Stan/Spec/Global.

Circa 1900
11-13 Holts Arcade, India Buildings, Water St. L2 0RR. Est. 1989. Open 10-2.30 and 3.30-6, Sat. and Sun. by appointment. SIZE: Small. *STOCK: Art Nouveau, classic Art Deco, decorative and applied arts, 1860-1940, £10-£1,000+.* LOC: 100 yards from Liver Buildings. PARK: Easy. TEL: 0151 236 1282; fax - same. SER: Valuations.

Edward's Jewellers
45a Whitechapel. (R.A. Lewis). FGA. Est. 1967. Open by appointment. CL: Sat. SIZE: Small. *STOCK: Jewellery, silver and plate, 19th-20th C, £50-£1,000.* LOC: City centre. TEL: 0151 236 2909. SER: Valuations.

Kensington Tower Antiques Ltd
Christ Church, 170 Kensington. L7 2RJ. (R. Swainbank). Est. 1960. Open 9-5, Sat. and Sun. by appointment. CL: Mon. SIZE: Large. *STOCK: Shipping goods, general antiques.* LOC: A57. PARK: Easy. TEL: 0151 260 9466; fax - 0151 260 9130; home - 0151 924 6538. VAT: Stan. *Trade Only.*

Maggs Shipping Ltd
66-68 St Anne Street. L3 3DY. (G. Webster). Est. 1965. Open 9-5, weekends by appointment. *STOCK: General antiques, period and shipping smalls, £1-£1,000.* LOC: In town centre by Central station. PARK: Meters. TEL: 0151 207 2555; evenings - 01928 564958. SER: Restorations; container packing, courier.

The Original British American Antiques
Halsall Hall, 2 Carrmoss Lane, Halsall. L39 8SA. (John Nolan). Est. 1970. Open by appointment including Sun. and evenings. SIZE: Large. *STOCK: Export items, especially for US decorator market.* LOC: On A5147. TEL: 01704 540808; mobile - 07714 322252. SER: Courier; packing and shipping. VAT: Stan/Spec. *Trade Only*

E. Pryor and Son
110 London Rd. L3 5NL. (Mr Wilding). Est. 1876. Open 8-4. CL: Wed. *STOCK: General antiques, jewellery, Georgian and Victorian*

silver, pottery, porcelain, coins and medals, clocks, paintings, ivory and carvings. TEL: 0151 709 1361. VAT: Stan.

Ryan-Wood Antiques
102 Seel St. L1 4BL. Est. 1972. Open 9.30-5. *STOCK: Furniture, paintings, china, silver, curios, bric-a-brac, Victoriana, Edwardiana, Art Deco.* TEL: 0151 709 7776; home/fax - 0151 709 3203; mobile - 07050 094779; e-mail - pdw@ ryan-wood.freeserve.co.uk; website - www.ryan-wood.freeserve.co.uk. SER: Restorations; valuations. VAT: Stan/Spec.

Stefani Antiques
497 Smithdown Rd. L15 5AE. (T. Stefani). Est. 1969. Open 10-5. SIZE: Medium. *STOCK: Furniture, to 1910, £200-£2,000; jewellery, £25-£2,000; pottery, silver, old Sheffield plate, porcelain, bronzes.* LOC: On main road, near Penny Lane. PARK: Easy. TEL: 0151 734 1933; home - 0151 733 4836. SER: Valuations; restorations (furniture including French polishing and upholstery).

Swainbanks Ltd
Christchurch, 170 Kensington. L7 2RJ. Open 9-5 or by appointment. CL: Sat. SIZE: Large. *STOCK: Shipping goods and general antiques.* TEL: 0151 260 9466/924 6538; fax - 0151 260 9130. SER: Containers. VAT: Stan.

Theta Gallery
29-33 Parliament St. (J. Matson). Open by appointment. SIZE: Warehouse. *STOCK: General antiques, especially furniture and clocks.* TEL: 0151 709 1217. *Trade Only.*

RAINFORD, Nr. St. Helens

Colin Stock
BADA
8 Mossborough Rd. WA11 8QN. Est. 1895. Open by appointment. *STOCK: Furniture, 18th-19th C.* TEL: 0174 488 2246.

SOUTHPORT

Birkdale Antiques
119a Upper Aughton Rd., Birkdale. PR8 5EX. (John Napp). Est. 1996. CL: Mon. SIZE: Small. *STOCK: English and Continental furniture, £200-£2,000.* LOC: From Lord St. West into Lulworth Rd., second left into Aughton Rd., over railway crossing into Upper Aughton Rd. PARK: Easy. TEL: 01704 550117; home - 01704 567680. SER: Valuations; restorations (furniture including polishing); buys at auction. FAIRS: Stafford, Newark, Swinderby.

C.K. Broadhurst and Co Ltd
5-7 Market St. PR8 1HD. Est. 1926. Open 9-5.30. *STOCK: Rare books, first editions, art and architecture, collecting.* TEL: 01704 532064/ 534110; fax - 01704 542009.

King Street Antiques
27 King St. PR8 1LH. (John Nolan). Open 10-5. *STOCK: General antiques.* TEL: 01704 540808; mobile - 07714 322252.

Molloy's Furnishers Ltd
6-8 St. James St. PR8 5AE. (P. Molloy). Est. 1955. Open daily. SIZE: Large. *STOCK: Mahogany and oak, shipping and Edwardian furniture.* LOC: Off A570 Scarisbrick New Road. PARK: Easy. TEL: 01704 535204; fax - 01704 548101. VAT: Stan.

John Nolan - King Street Antiques
29 King St. PR8 1LH . Open Mon.-Sat. *STOCK: Furniture and decorative items.* TEL: 01704 540808; mobile - 07714 322252; home - 01704 841065. SER: Courier; packing and shipping.

Osiris Antiques
104 Shakespeare St. PR8. (C. and P. Wood). Est. 1983. Open 10.45-4.45, Sat. 11-5.15, Sun. by appointment. CL: Tues. SIZE: Small. *STOCK: Art Nouveau and Art Deco, £10-£1,000; period clothing and accessories, 1850-1950, £5-£200; jewellery, 1880-1960, to £150.* LOC: Just out of town, off main road leading to motorway. PARK: Easy. TEL: 01704 500991; mobile - 07802 818500; home - 01704 560418. SER: Valuations; buys at auction (Art Nouveau, Art Deco); lectures given on Decorative Arts 1895-1930.

David M. Regan
25 Hoghton St. PR9 0NS. Est. 1983. Open Mon., Wed., Fri. and Sat. 10-5. SIZE: Small. *STOCK: Roman and English coins, £3-£300; post and cigarette cards, small collectables.* TEL: 01704 531266. SER: Valuations.

The Southport Antiques Centre
27/29 King St. PR8 1LH. (J. Nolan). Open 10-5. TEL: 01704 540808; mobile - 07714 322252. Below are listed the dealers at this centre.

British-American Antiques
Shipping goods.

Evergold Ltd
Antique and decorative items. SER: Packing and shipping for USA.

Halsall Hall Antiques
Country furniture.

King St. Antiques
General antiques.

John Nolan
Period furniture.

Pine Country Antiques
Country pine furniture.

S.M. Collectors Items
Smalls.

The Spinning Wheel Antiques
1 Liverpool Rd., Birkdale. PR8 4AR. (Roy and Pat Bell). Est. 1966. Open 10.30-5. CL: Tues. SIZE: Small. *STOCK: Antiques and collectables, old golf items, £5-£5,000+.* TEL: 01704 568245/567613; fax - same; e-mail - roypat@patroy.fsnet.co.uk.

Tony and Anne Sutcliffe Antiques
130 Cemetery Rd. and warehouse - 37A Linaker St. PR8. Est. 1969. Open 8.30-5 including Sun. or by appointment. SIZE: Large. *STOCK: Shipping goods, Victorian and period furniture.* LOC: Town centre. TEL: 01704 537068; home - 01704 533465; mobile - 07860 949816/480376. SER: Containers; courier. VAT: Stan/Spec.

Weldons Jewellery and Antiques
567 Lord St. PR9 0BB. (H.W. and N.C. Weldon). Est. 1914. Open 9.30-5.30. SIZE: Medium. *STOCK: Furniture, clocks, watches, jewellery, silver, coins.* Not Stocked: Militaria. PARK: Easy. TEL: 01704 532191; fax - 01704 500091. SER: Valuations; restorations. VAT: Stan.

Arbiter
10 Atherton St., New Brighton. CH45 2NY. (W.D.L. Scobie and P.D. Ferrett). Resident. Est. 1983. Open Wed.-Sat. 1-5 or by appointment. *STOCK: Decorative arts, 1850-1980; base metal and treen, £20-£2,000; Oriental, ethnographic and antiquities, £40-£1,500; original prints and drawings, £80-£500.* LOC: Opposite New Brighton station. PARK: Easy. TEL: 0151 639 1159. SER: Valuations; buys at auction; consultant.

Decade Antiques & Interiors
62 Grove Rd. CH45 3HW. (A.M. Duffy). Open 10-5. SIZE: Medium. *STOCK: General antiques, textiles, decorative items, Continental furniture.* LOC: From junction 1, M53, take A554 to Wallasey/New Brighton, turn right into Harrison Drive then left into Grove Rd. TEL: 0151 638 0433/639 6905; fax - 0151 638 9995.

Victoria Antiques/City Strippers
155-157 Brighton St. CH44 8DU. (J.M. Colyer). Open 9.30-5.30. *STOCK: Pre-1930 furniture.* TEL: 0151 639 0080.

Helen Horswill Antiques and Decorative Arts
62 Grange Rd. CH48 4EG. Open 10-5 or by appointment. SIZE: Medium. *STOCK: Furniture, 17th-19th C; decorative items.* LOC: A540. PARK: Easy. TEL: 0151 625 2803/8660.

An earthenware beaker decorated with a nursery pattern, 'Who Said Dinner?' Designed by Charlotte Rhead for Crown Ducal, early 1930s.

Charlotte Rhead made a significant and influential contribution to the British ceramics industry. She was also one of the first acknowledged female designers of the 20th century. Andrew Casey, whose book on 20th century British ceramic designers is to be published by the Antique Collectors' Club soon, surveys her work. From an article entitled 'Tube-line Variations' by Andrew Casey which appeared in the March 2001 issue of **Antique Collecting** magazine. For more details and to subscribe see page 147.

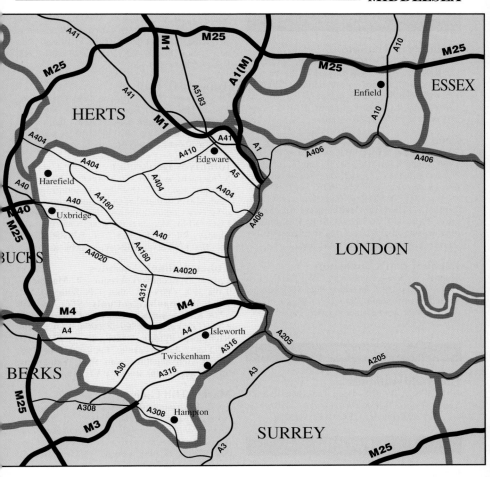

Dealers and Shops in Middlesex

					Isleworth	1
Edgware	1	Hampton	3	Twickenham	9
Enfield	1	Harefield	1	Uxbridge	1

EDGWARE

Edgware Antiques
19 Whitchurch Lane. HA8 7JZ. (E. Schloss). Est. 1972. Open Thurs.- Sat. 10-5 or by appointment. SIZE: Medium. *STOCK: Furniture, pictures, silver and plate, brass and copper, clocks, bric-a-brac, porcelain and shipping goods.* PARK: Easy. TEL: 020 8952 1606; home - 020 8952 5924.

ENFIELD

Gallerie Veronique
66 Chase Side. EN2 6NJ. (Veronica Aslangul). Est. 1993. Open 10-3, Sat. 10-5. CL: Sun (except by appointment) and Wed. SIZE: Medium. *STOCK: Furniture, 1820-1920, £100-£1,000.* LOC: Near junction A10 and M25. PARK: Easy. TEL: 020 8342 1005; fax - 020 8342 1005; mobile - 07770 410041. SER: Restorations (French polishing and upholstery).

Hunter's of Hampton
76 Station Rd. TW12 2AX. (Robin and Julia Hunter). Est. 1990. Open Mon. 10-5.30, Fri. and Sat. 10-6, other times by appointment. *STOCK: Victorian and Edwardian furniture, mirrors, etc, £50-£1,500.* LOC: Off High St. PARK: Easy. TEL: 020 8979 5624; fax - same.

Peco
72 Station Rd. TW12 2BT. (C.D. Taylor). Est. 1969. Open 8.15-5.15. SIZE: Large. *STOCK: Doors, 18th-20th C, £75-£250; fireplaces including French and marble, 18th-19th C, £495-£5,500; stoves.* LOC: 1.5 miles from Hampton Court. Turning off Hampton Court/Sunbury Rd. PARK: Own. TEL: 020 8979 8310. SER: Restorations (marble, stained glass, cast iron fireplaces, doors); stained glass made to order. VAT: Stan.

Ian Sheridan's Bookshop
Thames Villa, 34 Thames St. TW12 2DX. Est. 1960. Open 10.30-5 including Sun. SIZE: Large. *STOCK: Antiquarian and secondhand books.* LOC: 1 mile from Hampton Court Palace. TEL: 020 8979 1704.

Harefield Antiques
42 High St. UB9 6BS. Open Tues.-Sat. 10-5.30, Sun. 11-5. *STOCK: Furniture, militaria, jewellery, collectables.* TEL: 01895 825224.

Crowther of Syon Lodge Ltd
Busch Corner, London Rd. TW7 5BH. Open 9-5, Sat. and Sun. 11-4.30. SIZE: Large. *STOCK: Period panelled rooms in pine and oak; chimneypieces in marble, stone and wood; classical stone and marble statues; wrought iron entrance gates, garden temples, vases, wellheads, lead cisterns, animal figures, seats, fountains and other features.* LOC: Just off the A4, half-way between the West End and London Airport. TEL: 020 8560 7978; website - www.crowthersyonlodge.com. SER: Bespoke summerhouses; quality reproduction ornaments. VAT: Stan/Spec.

Ailsa Gallery
32 Crown Rd. (C.A. Wiltshire). Open Thurs., Fri. and Sat. 10-5, other times by appointment. SIZE: Small. *STOCK: Paintings, 19th-20th C, £200-£3,000; bronze, decorative arts, small furniture, silver and glass.* LOC: Off St. Margarets Rd., near station. PARK: Easy. TEL: 020 8891 2345; home - 020 8892 0188.

Anthony C. Hall
30 Staines Rd. TW2 5AH. Est. 1966. Open Mon., Tues., Thurs. and Fri. 10-5. SIZE: Medium. *STOCK: Antiquarian books.* PARK: Easy. TEL: 020 8898 2638; fax - 020 8893 8855; website - www.hallbooks.co.uk.

John Ives Bookseller
5 Normanhurst Drive, St. Margarets. TW1 1NA. Resident. Est. 1977. Open by appointment at any time. SIZE: Medium. *STOCK: Scarce and out of print books on antiques and collecting, £1-£500.* LOC: Off St. Margarets Rd. near its junction with Chertsey Rd. PARK: Easy. TEL: 020 8892 6265; fax - 020 8744 3944. SER: Valuations (as stock).

Tobias Jellinek Antiques   BADA
Unit 4, 29 Broadway Avenue, St Margarets. TW1 2PX. (Mrs D.L. and T.P. Jellinek). Est. 1963. By appointment only. SIZE: Small. *STOCK: Fine early furniture and objects, 16th-17th C or earlier, £500-£5,000+.* LOC: Near Richmond Bridge. PARK: Easy. TEL: 020 8892 6892; home - same; fax - 020 8744 9298; e-mail - toby@jellinek.com. SER: Valuations; buys at auction (as stock). VAT: Stan/Spec.

Marble Hill Gallery
70/72 Richmond Rd. TW1 3BE. (D. and L. Newson). Est. 1974. Open 10-5.30. *STOCK: English and French marble and natural stone, pine and white Adam-style mantels.* PARK: Easy. TEL: 020 8892 1488; website - www.marblehill.co.uk. VAT: Stan/Spec.

David Morley Antiques
371 Richmond Rd. TW1 2EF. Est. 1968. Open 10-1 and 2-5. CL: Wed. SIZE: Medium. *STOCK: General antiques, collectors' items, old toys.* Not Stocked: Large furniture. LOC: Approx. 200yds. from Richmond Bridge. PARK: In side road (adjacent to shop). TEL: 020 8892 2986.

Phelps Antiques
133-135 St. Margarets Rd. TW1 1RG. (R.C. Phelps). LAPADA. Est. 1870. Open 10-5.30, Sat. 9.30-5.30, Sun. 12-4. SIZE: Large - several dealers. *STOCK: Furniture, 1800-1920's and small collectables.* LOC: Adjacent St. Margaret's station. PARK: Easy, at rear of shop. TEL: 020 8892 1778/7129; fax - 020 8892 3661; website - www.phelps.co.uk; e-mail - antiques@phelps.co.uk. SER: Restorations. VAT: Stan/Spec.

Rita Shenton

142 Percy Rd. TW2 6JG. Est. 1973. Open by appointment only. SIZE: Medium. *STOCK: Clocks, watches, barometers, sundials, scientific instruments, automata and ornamental turning books, £1-£1,000.* LOC: Continuation of Whitton High St. PARK: Easy. TEL: 020 8894 6888; fax - 020 8893 8766; e-mail - rita@shentonbooks. demon.co.uk; website - www.shentonbooks. demon.co.uk. SER: Valuations; buys at auction (horological books); catalogues available. *International postal service.*

Twickenham Antiques Warehouse

80 Colne Rd. TW2 6QE. (A. Clubb and E. Robinson). Est. 1985. Open 9.30-1 and 2-5, Sat. 10-4, Sun. 10-2. SIZE: Medium. *STOCK: European furniture, 1700-1920, £50-£2,000.* LOC: Off London Rd. PARK: Easy. TEL: 020 8894 5555; mobile - 07973 132847. SER: Valuations; restorations (French polishing, cabinet work, carving). VAT: Spec.

UXBRIDGE

Antiques Warehouse (Uxbridge)

34-36 Rockingham Rd. UB8 2TZ. Est. 1966. Open 10-6. SIZE: Large. *STOCK: General antiques, shipping items, £1-£4,000.* PARK: Easy. TEL: 01895 256963/271012. VAT: Stan.

A Worcester finger bowl and stand printed with 'The Siesta' and 'Le Chalet des Palmes'. About 1758-60. Diameter of stand 5⅞in.

From an article entitled '18th Century Overglaze Printed English Porcelain – The Joseph Handley Collection' by Simon Spero which appeared in the October 2000 issue of **Antique Collecting** magazine. For more details and to subscribe see page 147.

ACLE, Nr. Norwich

Ivy House Antiques
Ivy House, The Street. NR13 3BH. (N. Pratt).
Est. 1970. Open 9-5. SIZE: Small. *STOCK:*
Furniture, porcelain, pottery, glass, metalware,
18th-20th C, £25-£2,000; pictures, £50-£500.
LOC: Village centre. PARK: Easy. TEL: 01493
750682; home - same. SER: Valuations. FAIRS:
Norwich. VAT: Stan/Spec.

ATTLEBOROUGH

A.E. Bush and Partners
Vineyards Antiques Gallery, Leys Lane. NR17
1NE. (A.G., M.S. and J.A. Becker). Est. 1940.
Open 9-1 and 2-5.30. SIZE: Large. *STOCK:*
Walnut and mahogany, 18th-19th C. LOC: Town
outskirts. PARK: Easy. TEL: 01953 454239/
452175. SER: Restorations; wholesale antiques and
export; storage; buys at auction. VAT: Stan/Spec.

AYLSHAM

Sheila Hart and John Giles
NR11 7QQ. LAPADA. Open by appointment.
STOCK: Furniture, 18th-19th C, £200-£5,000;
objects, £50-£1,000. PARK: Easy. TEL: 01263
768216; fax - same. *Trade Only.*

Pearse Lukies
The Old Vicarage. NR11. Open preferably by
appointment. *STOCK: Period oak, sculpture,*
objects, 18th C furniture. TEL: 01263 734137.
Trade Only.

BAWDESWELL, Nr. East Dereham

Norfolk Polyphon Centre
Wood Farm. NR20 4RX. (N.B. Vince). Open
weekends, week days preferably by appointment.
STOCK: Mechanical music - polyphons, cylinder
musical boxes, organs, orchestrions, automata.
LOC: On B1145, 1 mile east of Bawdeswell
village and junction with A1067. TEL: 01362
688230. VAT: Stan/Spec.

BRANCASTER STAITHE, Nr. King's Lynn

Staithe Antiques
Coast Rd. PE31 8BJ. (Anne and Tony Webb).
Open Tues.-Sun. *STOCK: 18th-19th C furniture,*
china, glass and pictures. TEL: 01485 210600.
SER: Restorations.

BURNHAM MARKET

The Brazen Head Bookshop & Gallery
Market Place. PE31 8HD. (David S. Kenyon).
Open 9.30-5.30. SIZE: Large. *STOCK: Rare, out-*
of-print and secondhand books. LOC: On green,
opposite PO. PARK: Easy. TEL: 01328 730700;
fax - 01328 730929; e-mail - brazenheadbook
@aol.com. SER: Valuations; framing.

M. and A. Cringle
The Old Black Horse. PE31 8HD. Est. 1965.
Open 10-1 and 2-5. CL: Wed. SIZE: Medium.
STOCK: 18th to early 19th C furniture, £50-
£2,000; china, glass, pottery, prints, maps, £10-
£500; modern china and decorative items. Not
Stocked: Large furniture. LOC: In village centre.
PARK: Easy. TEL: 01328 738456. VAT: Spec.

Anne Hamilton Antiques
North St. PE31 8HG. (A. Hudson). Open 10-1 and
2-5. SIZE: Medium. *STOCK: Georgian furniture;*
porcelain, decorative items. LOC: 20yds. from
village green towards coast. PARK: Easy. TEL:
01328 738187; fax - same. VAT: Stan/Spec.

Market House BADA
PE31 8HF. (D.H. and J. Maufe). Resident. Est.
1978. Open 10-6, but appointment advisable.
SIZE: Medium. **STOCK: English furniture -**
walnut, mahogany, rosewood, late 17th to mid-19th
C; works of art, mirrors, small decorative items. Not
Stocked: Silver, jewellery, clocks, porcelain, or
any reproductions. LOC: B1355, large Queen
Anne house on green in village centre. PARK:
Easy. TEL: 01328 738475; fax - 01328 730750.
SER: Valuations; buys at auction. FAIRS:
Olympia (Nov.); BADA (March). VAT: Spec.

COLTISHALL

Roger Bradbury Antiques
Church St. NR12 7DJ. Est. 1967. Open by
appointment. *STOCK: Cargoes - Tek Sing,*
Nanking, Vung Tao, Diana. PARK: Easy. TEL:
01603 737444. VAT: Stan.

Coltishall Antiques Centre
High St. NR3 7AA. (I. Ford). Est. 1980. Open 10-
4.30. SIZE: Several specialists. *STOCK: A wide*
variety of items including 19th C porcelain and
pottery, silver and silver plate, copper, brass,
lamps, furniture, jewellery, collectors' items,
militaria, glass, bijouterie. LOC: B1150 on corner
of main street. PARK: Easy. TEL: 01603 738306.

Gwendoline Golder
Point House, 5 High St. NR12 7AA. Est. 1974.
Open 11-5. CL: Sun. except by appointment.
STOCK: General antiques and collectors' items.
PARK: Easy. TEL: 01603 738099.

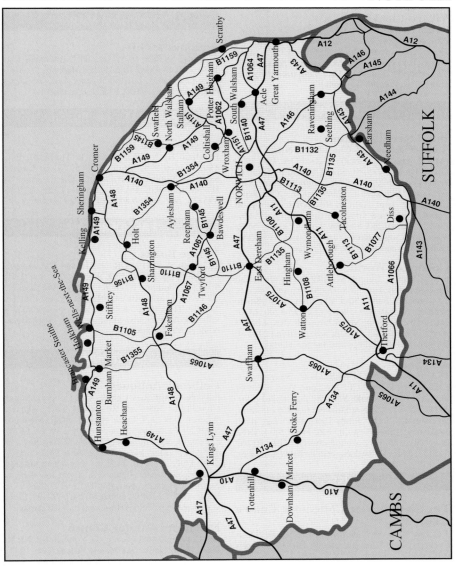

Dealers and Shops in Norfolk

Acle	1	East Dereham	1	North Walsham	2	Stiffkey	2
Attleborough	1	Fakenham	3	Norwich	25	Stoke Ferry	1
Aylsham	2	Great Yarmouth	7	Potter Heigham	1	Swaffham	2
Bawdeswell	1	Heacham	1	Raveningham	1	Swafield	1
Brancaster Staithe	1	Hingham	2	Reepham	1	Tacolneston	1
Burnham Market	4	Holkham	1	Scratby	1	Thetford	1
Coltishall	4	Holt	11	Seething	1	Tottenhill	1
Cromer	3	Hunstanton	3	Sharrington	1	Twyford	1
Diss	2	Kelling	1	Sheringham	4	Watton	1
Downham Market	1	King's Lynn	5	South Walsham	1	Wells-next-the-Sea	2
Earsham	1	Needham	1	Stalham	1	Wroxham	1
						Wymondham	3

Village Clocks
9 High St. NR12 7AA. Open Mon.-Sat. *STOCK: Clocks - 18th-19th C longcase and bracket, regulators, wood and marble.* LOC: Main Norwich to North Walsham road. PARK: Easy. TEL: 01603 736047. SER: Valuations; restorations (cases and movements).

CROMER

Bond Street Antiques
6 Bond St. and 38 Church St. NR27 9DA. (M.R.T. and J.A. Jones). NAG, FGA. Est. 1970 Open 9-1 and 2-5.30. SIZE: Medium. *STOCK: Jewellery, silver, porcelain, china, glass, small furniture, 18th-20th C, £50-£5,000.* LOC: From Church St. bear right to Post Office, shop on opposite side on street further along. PARK: Easy. TEL: 01263 513134; home - same. SER: Valuations; restorations (watches and jewellery); gem testing and analysis. VAT: Stan.

Collectors World
6 New Parade, Church St. NR27 9EP. (John and Irene Nockels). Est. 1988. Open 10-1 and 2-4, Sat. 10-1 and 2-5, Sun. 2.30-5. CL: Mon. SIZE: Small. *STOCK: Collectables, 19th-20th C, £5-£100.* LOC: Near traffic lights on Norwich road. PARK: Limited at rear. TEL: 01263 515330; home - 01263 514174. FAIRS: Norfolk Showground and Swinderby.

A.E. Seago
15 Church St. NR27 9ES. (D.C. Seago). Est. 1937. Open 9.30-4. CL: Sun. and Wed. October to April. SIZE: Small. *STOCK: Furniture, 1790-1910, £25-£2,500.* Not Stocked: Garden furniture, oil paintings. LOC: From Sheringham take main coast road, then New St. into High St. PARK: Easy. 50 yds away around church. TEL: 01263 512733. SER: Valuations; restorations (furniture).

DISS

The Antiques & Collectors Centre (Diss)
3 Cobbs Yard, St Nicholas St. IP22 4LB. (Dean Cockaday and Chris Beecham). Est. 1997. Open 9.30-5. SIZE: Large. *STOCK: Royal commemoratives, 19th-20th C: Victorian to 1930's porcelain, £50-£100; modern collectables, 1930's-70's, £25-£50.* LOC: Next to Diss Ironworks, off St. Nicholas St. PARK: Easy. TEL: 01379 644472. VAT: Spec.

Diss Antiques & Interiors
2 & 3 Market Place. IP22 4JT. LAPADA. Open 9-5. SIZE: Large. *STOCK: Furniture, barometers, clocks, jewellery, porcelain, copper, brass.* PARK: Nearby. TEL: 01379 642213; e-mail - sales@ dissantiques.co.uk. SER: Repairs (as stock). VAT: Stan/Spec.

DOWNHAM MARKET

Antiques & Gifts
47 Bridge St. PE38 9DW. (B. and T. Addrison). Est. 1980. Usually open 10-5. SIZE: Medium. *STOCK: Furniture - pine, oak, mahogany; brass and iron beds, Victorian to 1930.* PARK: Free nearby.

EARSHAM, Nr. Bungay

Earsham Hall Pine
Earsham Hall. NR35 2AN. (R. Derham). Est. 1976. Open 9-5, Sun. 10.30-5. SIZE: Large. *STOCK: Pine furniture.* LOC: On Earsham to Hedenham Rd. PARK: Easy. TEL: 01986 893423; fax - 01986 895656. SER: Containers.

EAST DEREHAM

Village Books
20A High St. NR19 1DR. (J.A.R. and J.W. James). Est. 1996. Open 9.30-4.30, Wed. 9.30-1, Sat. 9.30-5. SIZE: Medium. *STOCK: Books, 19th-20th C, £1-£150.* LOC: Just off Market Place. PARK: Nearby. TEL: 01362 853066; fax - same; e-mail - villagebooksdereham@ukonline.co.uk. SER: Book binding. VAT: Stan.

FAKENHAM

Colbrook Antiques
Fakenham Antiques Centre, Old Congregational Church, 14 Norwich Rd. NR21 8AZ . (Brian Weeks). Est. 1989. Open 10-4.30. SIZE: Medium. *STOCK: Furniture, 18th to early 20th C, £100-£2,000; clocks, 18th-19th C, £150-£2,000; pictures and prints, china, glass, 19th to early 20th C, £50-£500.* LOC: Turn off A148 at roundabout towards town, right at traffic lights, left at next roundabout, centre is 50 yards on right. TEL: 01238 862941; home - 01485 576138; mobile - 07867 797198. SER: Valuations; restorations (furniture); buys at auction.

Fakenham Antique Centre
Old Congregational Church, 14 Norwich Rd. NR21 8AZ. (Julie Hunt and Mandy Allen). Est. 1984. Open 10-4.30, until 5 on Fri.and Sat. Easter-Sept. SIZE: 20 dealers. LOC: Turn off A148 at roundabout to town, at traffic lights turn up Queens Rd., left at second mini-roundabout, centre 50yds. on right opposite Godfrey DIY. PARK: Easy. TEL: 01328 862941; home - 01328 830225. SER: Restorations (furniture); polishing; replacement handles; cane and rush seating repairs.

Sue Rivett Antiques and Bygones
6 Norwich Rd. NR21. (Mrs S. Rivett). Est. 1969. Open 10-1. *STOCK: General antiques and bygones.* LOC: On Norwich Rd. into Fakenham. TEL: 01328 862924; home - 01263 860462.

GT. YARMOUTH

Barry's Antiques
35 King St. NR30 2PN. Open 9.30-5. SIZE: Large. *STOCK: Jewellery, porcelain, clocks, glass, pictures.* LOC: In main shopping street. PARK: Opposite. TEL: 01493 842713. VAT: Stan/Spec.

David Ferrow
77 Howard St. South. NR30 1LN. ABA, PBFA. Est. 1940. Open 10-5. CL: Thurs. SIZE: Large. *STOCK: Books, some antiquarian maps, local prints, manuscripts.* LOC: From London, sign before river bridge to The Docks, keep to nearside, turn left and then right to car park. PARK: Easy. TEL: 01493 843800; home - 01493 662247. SER: Valuations; restorations (books and prints). VAT: Stan.

Folkes Antiques and Jewellers
74 Victoria Arcade. NR30 2NU. (Mrs J. Baldry). Est. 1946. Open 10-4. *STOCK: General antiques especially jewellery and collectables.* LOC: From A47 into town centre, shop on right. PARK: Easy. TEL: 01493 851354. SER: Valuations. FAIRS: Local collectors.

Gold and Silver Exchange
Theatre Plain. NR30 2BE. (C. Birch). Open 9.30-5.15. *STOCK: Coins, medals and secondhand jewellery.* TEL: 01493 859430.

Peter Howkins Antiques
132 King St. NR30 2PQ. Est. 1946. Open 9.30-4. *STOCK: Furniture, silver, pottery, glass, bronzes, Georgian-Edwardian.* LOC: From Norwich through town one-way system to road signposted Lowestoft which intersects King St. PARK: Easy. TEL: 01493 851180. SER: Valuations; restorations.

Peter Howkins Jewellers
135 King St. NR30 2PQ. Open 9-5. *STOCK: Jewellery, silver, crystal, porcelain, pottery, Georgian to present day.* TEL: 01493 844639. SER: Valuations; restorations.

Wheatleys
16 Northgate St., White Horse Plain and Fullers Hill. NR30 1BA. Est. 1971. Open 9.30-5, Thurs. 9.30-1. SIZE: Large. *STOCK: Jewellery and general antiques.* LOC: 2 minutes walk from Market Place. PARK: Easy. TEL: 01493 857219. VAT: Stan.

HEACHAM, Nr. King's Lynn

Peter Robinson
Pear Tree House, 7 Lynn Rd. PE31 7HU. Est. 1880. Open 9-5. Appointment advisable Mon. and Sat. SIZE: Small. *STOCK: Furniture, 1600-1900, £10-£5,000; china, 1750-1900, metalwork, 1700-1870; both £2-£1,000.* LOC: Shop on left on entry to village. PARK: Easy. TEL: 01485 570228. SER: Valuations; buys at auction. VAT: Stan/Spec.

HINGHAM, Nr. Norwich

Mongers
15 Market Place. NR9 4AF. (Sam and Trudie Coster). Est. 1995. Open 9.30-5.30. SIZE: Large. *STOCK: Fireplaces, 1700-1930, £400-£900; sanitaryware, 1870-1950, £250-£1,000; Victorian and Edwardian garden antiques, £50-£500.* LOC: B1108. PARK: Easy. TEL: 01953 851868; fax - 01953 851870. SER: Restorations (pine stripping, bath re-surfacing, fireplaces). VAT: Stan/Spec.

Past & Present
16a The Fairland. NR9 4HN. (C. George). Est. 1970. Open by apppointment. SIZE: Medium. *STOCK: Furniture, £25-£1,500; smalls, 18th-19th C, £10-£500.* LOC: B1108. PARK: Easy. TEL: 01953 851400; home - same; fax - 01953 851010. SER: Valuations. FAIRS: Swinderby, Newark, Staffordshire. VAT: Stan.

HOLKHAM, Nr. Wells-next-the-Sea

The Potting Shed
Main Rd. (Bill Jellings). Est. 1993. Open Sat. afternoons only, trade mid-week by appointment. SIZE: Medium. *STOCK: English and French gardenalia.* LOC: On north Norfolk coast road (A149) by entrance to Holkham Hall. PARK: Easy. TEL: 01692 402424; home - same.

HOLT

Baron Art
9 Chapel Yard, Albert St. NR25 6HG. (Anthony R. Baron and Michael J. Bellis). Est. 1992. Open 9.30-5.30, Sun. by appointment. SIZE: Medium. *STOCK: Paintings, 19th-20th C, £50-£5,000; prints and lithographs, 19th-20th C, £5-£500; collectables, 1830-1940, £5-£500.* PARK: Easy. TEL: 01263 713906; home - 01263 588227. SER: Valuations; buys at auction (paintings). VAT: Stan/Spec.

Collectors Cabin
7 Cromer Rd. NR25 6HA. (J.M.E. Codling). Est. 1983. Open 10-1 and 2-4.30. CL: Thurs. pm. SIZE: Small. *STOCK: Bric-a-brac, bygones, toys, 19th C, £5-£25.* LOC: Near Post Office. PARK: Bull St. TEL: 01263 712241.

Cottage Collectables
8 Fish Hill and 3 Chapel Yard. NR25 6BD. (Philip & Linda Morris). Est. 1984. Open 10-5, Sun. 11-5. SIZE: Medium. *STOCK: Collectables, 18th-20th C, £5-£250; furniture, 18th-20th C, £50-£300; jewellery, from Victorian, £5-£50; linen.* PARK: Limited. TEL: 01263 711707/712920. SER: Valuations; restorations (furniture and ceramics); buys at auction (furniture and collectables). FAIRS: Swinderby, Peterborough, Newark and others.

Anthony Fell
Chester House, 47 Bull St. NR25 6HP. (A.J. and C.R. Austin-Fell). LAPADA. CINOA. Est. 1976. Open 9.30-1 and 2-5 - prior telephone call advisable if travelling long distance. CL: Mon. SIZE: Medium. *STOCK: English and Continental furniture, 16th-18th C, £1,000-£50,000; works of art, 16th C to contemporary, £1,000-£20,000.* PARK: Easy. TEL: 01263 712912; fax - same. SER: Valuations. FAIRS: Olympia (Feb., June and Nov.). VAT: Spec.

Simon Gough Books
5 Fish Hill. NR25 6BD. Est. 1976. Open 10-5. *STOCK: Antiquarian and secondhand books; bindings.* TEL: 01263 712650.

Heathfield Antiques & Country Pine
The Warehouse, 39 Hempstead Rd. NR25 6DL. (J.E., H.B. and S.M. Heathfield). Est. 1990. Open 8-5. SIZE: Large. *STOCK: Pine furniture, £50-£1,500.* LOC: Follow signs to Hempstead. PARK: Own. TEL: 01263 711122/711609; website - www.antique-pine.net. VAT: Stan/Global.

Judy Hines of Holt - The Gallery
3 Fish Hill. NR25 6BD . *STOCK: Modern British paintings, from 1900 - and the unusual; British 20th C prints (can be viewed in card index form).* TEL: 01263 713000; fax - same. SER: Framing.

Holt Antique Centre
Albert Hall, Albert St. NR25. (David Attfield). Est. 1980. Open 10-5, Sat. 10-5.30 (Sun. Easter-October). SIZE: Large. *STOCK: Pine and country furniture, china, glass, lighting, silver plate and kitchenalia, jewellery, clothes, soft furnishings, 18th-20th C, £1-£1,500.* LOC: Turn right from Chapel Yard car park, 100 yards. PARK: Easy. TEL: 01263 712097; home - 01263 860347.

Mews Antique Emporium
17B High St. Est. 1998. Open 10-5. SIZE: Large - 12 dealers. *STOCK: 18th-20th C furniture, collectables, £1-£1,000.* PARK: Nearby. TEL: 01263 713224.

Past Caring
6 Chapel Yard. NR25 6HG. (L. Mossman). Est. 1988. Open 11-5. CL: Thurs. SIZE: Medium. *STOCK: Period clothes, linen and textiles, Victorian to 1950, £5-£100; jewellery and accessories, Victorian to 1960, £2-£75.* PARK: Easy. TEL: 01263 713771; home - 01362 683363; e-mail - pstcaring@aol.com. SER: Valuations; restorations (christening gowns and some beadwork). FAIRS: Alexandra Palace, Stand W60.

Richard Scott Antiques
30 High St. NR25 6BH. Est. 1967. Open 10-5. CL: Thurs. SIZE: Large. *STOCK: Pottery, porcelain, glass, furniture, contemporary ceramics, oil lamps and spares, general antiques.* LOC: On A148. PARK: Easy. TEL: 01263 712479. SER: Valuations; conservation advice.

Delawood Antiques
10 Westgate. PE36 5AL. (R.C. Woodhouse). Resident. Est. 1975. Open Mon., Wed., Fri., Sat. 10-5 and most Sun. afternoons, other times by chance or appointment. SIZE: Small. *STOCK: General antiques, furniture, jewellery, collectors' items, books, £1-£1,000.* LOC: Near town centre and bus station. PARK: Easy. TEL: 01485 532903; home and fax - same. SER: Valuations; commission sales.

Le Strange Old Barns Antiques, Arts & Craft Centre
Golf Course Rd., Old Hunstanton. PE36 6JG. (E. Maloney). TEL: 01485 533402.

R.C. Woodhouse (Antiquarian Horologist)
10 Westgate. PE36 5AL. MBHI and BWCG. Resident. Est. 1975. Open Mon., Wed., Fri, Sat. and usually Sun. afternoons, other times by chance or appointment. SIZE: Small. *STOCK: Georgian, Victorian and Edwardian longcase, dial, wall and mantel clocks; some watches and barometers.* LOC: Near town centre and bus station. PARK: Easy. TEL: 01485 532903; home and fax - same. SER: Valuations; restorations (longcase, bracket, chiming, carriage, French, wall clocks, dials, barometers); small locks repaired and lost keys made - postal service if required.

Baron Art
The Old Reading Room. NR25 7EL. (Anthony R. Baron and Michael J. Bellis). Est. 1994. Open 10-5.30 including Sun. Easter to Oct. SIZE: Large. *STOCK: Paintings and prints, 19th-20th C, £5-£5,000; modern, first editions, poetry, art and children's books, £1-£500; furniture and collectables, 1830-1940, £5-£2,000.* LOC: A149 coast road between Weybourne and Cley, at war memorial in village. PARK: Easy. TEL: 01263 588227; home - 01263 588435. SER: Valuations; buys at auction (paintings and books). VAT: Stan/Spec.

Tim Clayton Jewellery & Antiques
21-23 Chapel St. PE30 1EG. Open 9-5. *STOCK: Silver, jewellery, clocks, furniture, china and pictures.* TEL: 01553 772329; fax - 01553 776583. SER: Bespoke jewellery; repairs; picture framing.

James K. Lee
Nicholson House, 29 Church St. (A.J. and J.K. Lee). Est. 1950. Open 9-6 including Sun. SIZE: Small. *STOCK: Furniture including desks, chests of drawers and tables, 18th-19th C, £800-£4,500.*

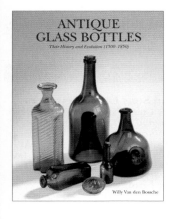

ANTIQUE
GLASS BOTTLES
Their History and Evolution (1500-1850)

Willy Van den Bossche

- ● *The first major reference book on utility bottles in Europe & America*

- ● *Destined to become the indispensable reference work on the subject*

- ● *A superb visual history of the evolution of the bottle over 350 years*

- ● *368 stunning new colour photographs of 773 bottles and seals*

- ● *Includes examples from Great Britain, Italy, Germany, Belgium, The Netherlands, France, Spain, Portugal, Scandinavia, Austria, Switzerland and America*

Antique Collectors' Club is privileged to present a book written for all antique glass bottle collectors and enthusiasts. This major work is the first of its kind. It comprehensively charts the history and evolution of antique glass utility bottles between 1500 and 1850. Written by a leading collector and authority on the subject, who once worked in the bottle-making industry, this unmatched book is destined to become *the* indispensable reference work on this subject. An incredible visual history of the evolution of the glass bottle over a period of 350 years is presented here. The thorough text is

accompanied by 368 remarkable original colour photographs of 773 bottles and seals.

The author's achievement is staggering. He has succeeded in producing an accurate study of each and every main region of Europe that has produced glass utility bottles. The inter-relationships and influences are observed and a comparative guide covering almost all of the bottle-producing world has been created. In addition to this, the book boasts the most comprehensive bibliography on glass bottles ever produced, listing 1,150 titles. Almost all of the bottles illustrated in this volume have been carefully chosen from a variety of private collections. This truly magnificent book demonstrates that collecting antique glass bottles is one of the most rewarding of all hobbies.

This outstanding work will appeal to archaeologists, researchers, historians, writers, museums, libraries, bottle-makers, dealers and all others who have an interest, whether involved or remote, in collecting antiques.

ISBN 1 85149 337 9, 439pp., 368 col., 26 b.&w. line drawings   **£50.00/$99.50**

For a free copy of our catalogue, please contact

ANTIQUE COLLECTORS' CLUB

5 Church Street, Woodbridge, Suffolk, IP12 1DS, UK
Tel: (01394) 385501 Fax: (01394) 384434
Sales Office Direct Fax: (01394) 388994
Email: sales@antique-acc.com Website: www.antique-acc.com

―――――――――― *or* ――――――――――

Market Street Industrial Park, Wappingers' Falls, NY 12590, USA
Tel: (845) 297 0003 Fax: (845) 297 0068 ORDERS: (800) 252 5231
Email: info@antiquecc.com Website: www.antiquecc.com

LOC: In old town, through Southgates, by mini roundabout. PARK: Easy and NCP opposite. TEL: 01553 810681; fax - 01553 760128; home - 01553 811522. SER: Valuations; restorations including polishing; buys at auction (furniture). VAT: Stan/Spec.

Norfolk Galleries
Railway Rd. PE30 1PF. (B. Houchen and G.R. Cumbley). Open 8.30-5.30, Sat. 8.30-12.30. *STOCK: Victorian and Edwardian furniture.* PARK: Nearby. TEL: 01553 765060.

Old Curiosity Shop
25 St. James St. PE30 5DA. (Mrs R.S. Wright). Est. 1980. Open 10.30-5, Sat. 9.30-6. SIZE: Small. *STOCK: General collectable smalls, glass, clothing, linen, jewellery, lighting, Art Deco and Art Nouveau, furniture, prints, stripped pine and paintings, pre 1930, £1-£500.* LOC: Off Saturday market place towards London Rd. PARK: At rear or nearby. TEL: 01553 766591. FAIRS: Alexandra Palace, Newark and local.

The Old Granary Antiques and Collectors Centre
King Staithe Lane, Off Queen St. PE30 1LZ. Open 10-5. *STOCK: China, glass, books, silver, jewellery, brass, copper, postcards, linen, some furniture, and general antiques.* PARK: Easy. TEL: 01553 775509.

Jennifer and Raymond Norman Antiques
Henstead Lodge. IP20 9LA. Resident. Est. 1974. Open by appointment. *STOCK: Clocks, 1780-1900, £100-£5,000; longcase, 1720-1830, £1,000-£8,000.* LOC: A143 Harleston by-pass. At Harleston/Needham roundabout turn towards Harleston. Entrance to Henstead Lodge immediately on right. PARK: Easy. TEL: 0139 855124; fax - 01379 855134; mobile - 07774 887045; e-mail - rjn@longcase.co.uk.SER: Valuations; restorations (longcase clocks - cases and movements); buys at auction (clocks). VAT: Stan/Spec.

The Angel Bookshop
4 Aylsham Rd. NR28 0BH. Resident. Est. 1980. Open 9.30-5, Wed. 9.30-1, Sat. 9.30-4. SIZE: Small. *STOCK: Books, 1700 to date, £3-£500.* PARK: Nearby. TEL: 01692 404054. SER: Valuations; buys at auction. FAIRS: East Anglia PBFA.

Eric Bates and Sons
Melbourne House, Bacton Rd. NR28 0RA. Est. 1973. Open 8-5. SIZE: Large. *STOCK: Victorian and Edwardian furniture.* TEL: 01692 403221; fax

- 01692 404388. SER: Restorations (furniture); manufacturer of period-style furniture; upholstery; shipping and container packing. VAT: Stan/Spec.

Albrow and Sons Family Jewellers
10 All Saints Green. NR1 3NA. (R. Albrow). NAG Registered Valuer. Open 9.30-4.30. *STOCK: Jewellery, silver, plate, china, glass, furniture.* LOC: Opposite Bond's store. PARK: Behind Bond's store. TEL: 01603 622569; fax - 01603 766158. SER: Valuations; repairs.

Liz Allport-Lomax
t/a Corner Antiques. *STOCK: Porcelain, glass, silver, objects de vertue, sewing accessories, small furniture and collectors items - card cases, lace bobbins, snuff boxes, scent bottles.* TEL: 01603 737631; mobile - 07747 843074; website - www.lomaxantiques.fairs.co.uk. FAIRS: Organiser of Lomax Antiques Fairs at Langley School (May and Oct.); North Norfolk, Burnham Market (Easter); Norwich (Feb.)

Antiques & Interiors
31-35 Elm Hill. NR3 1HG. Est. 1976. Open 10-5. *STOCK: Furniture including Arts and Crafts, Victorian, £5-£5,000; bergere suites, 1880-1908, to £1,000+.* PARK: Nearby. TEL: 01603 622695; home and fax - 01603 632446. SER: Restorations.

The Bank House Gallery
71 Newmarket Rd. NR2 2HW. (R.S. Mitchell). LAPADA. Resident. Est. 1979. Open by appointment. *STOCK: English oil paintings especially Norwich and Suffolk schools, 19th C, £1,000-£50,000.* LOC: On A11 between city centre and ring road. PARK: Own. TEL: 01603 633380; fax - 01603 633387. SER: Valuations; restorations. VAT: Stan/Spec.

Arthur Brett and Sons Ltd   BADA
42 St. Giles St. NR2 1LW. Est. 1870. Open 9.30-1 and 2-5. CL: Sat. except by appointment. SIZE: Large. *STOCK: Antique furniture, mahogany, walnut and oak; sculpture and metalwork.* LOC: Near City Hall. PARK: Easy. TEL: 01603 628171; fax - 01603 630245. FAIRS: Olympia. VAT: Stan/Spec.

J & D Clarke Book and Print Dealers
St Michael at Plea Church, Redwell St. NR2 4SN. Est. 1988. Open 9.30-5. SIZE: Medium. *STOCK: Books and prints, £1-£1,000.* LOC: Twixt Elm Hill and city centre. PARK: 30mins. on street, multi-storey nearby. TEL: 01603 617700/619226. SER: Book repairs; print colouring and mounting.

Cloisters Antique & Collectors Fair
St. Andrew's and Blackfriars Hall, St. Andrew's Plain. NR3 1AU. (Norwich City Council). Est.

1976. Open Wed. only 9-3.30. SIZE: 21 dealers. *STOCK: Wide range of antiques and collectables.* PARK: Easy. TEL: 01603 628477; fax - 01603 762182; bookings - 01493 750981.

Country and Eastern
8 Redwell St. and 34/36 Bethel St. (Old Skating Rink Gallery). NR2 4SN. (J. Millward). Est. 1978. Open 9.30-5.30; Bethel St. - open Thurs. and Sat. - other times by appointment via shop. SIZE: Shop and gallery. *STOCK: Oriental rugs, kelims and textiles; Indian and S.E. Asian antiques - furniture, objects, ceramics and metalwork.* LOC: Top of Elm Hill. Gallery - next to fire station. PARK: Nearby. TEL: 01603 623107; gallery - 01603 663890. VAT: Stan/Spec.

Crome Gallery and Frame Shop
34 Elm Hill. NR3 1HG. (J. Willis). Est. 1971. Open 9.30-5. SIZE: Medium. *STOCK: Mainly 20th C watercolours, oils and prints; some 19th C.* LOC: Near cathedral. PARK: Free. TEL: 01603 622827. SER: Crome Gallery Conservation (oils, watercolours, prints, frames).

Peter Crowe, Antiquarian Book Seller
75-77 Upper St. Giles St. NR1 2AB. Open 10-5. *STOCK: Antiquarian books, 17th-18th C, calf, 19th C, cloth and fine bindings, travel, topography and Norfolk; maps and prints.* TEL: 01603 624800.

Clive Dennett Coins
66 St. Benedicts St. NR2 4AR. BNTA. Est. 1970. CL: Thurs. and lunchtime. SIZE: Small. *STOCK: Coins and medals, ancient Greek to date, £5-£5,000; jewellery, 19th-20th C; banknotes, 20th C; both £5-£1,000.* PARK: Easy. TEL: 01603 624315. SER: Valuations; buys at auction (as stock). FAIRS: London Coin; International Banknote, London and Maastricht.

The Fairhurst Gallery
Bedford St. NR2 1AR. Est. 1951. Open 9-5. CL: Sat. pm. SIZE: Medium. *STOCK: Oil paintings, £5-£5,000; watercolours, £5-£2,000, both 19th-20th C; frames, 18th-20th C; furniture, £500-*

£10,000. LOC: Behind Travel Centre. TEL: 01603 614214. SER: Valuations; restorations; cleaning; framemakers. VAT: Spec.

Nicholas Fowle Antiques   BADA
Websdale Court, Bedford St. NR2 1AR. Est. **1965. Open 9-5, Sat. 9-1. SIZE: Medium.** *STOCK: Furniture, £500-£10,000; works of art, £5-£1,000; both 17th-19th C.* **LOC: City centre pedestrian area (limited access for loading and unloading). PARK: St Andrews multi-storey. TEL: 01603 219964; fax - 01692 630378; e-mail - nfowleantiques@aol.com. SER: Valuations; restorations (furniture). VAT: Stan/Spec.**

Spectacularly whorled glass by American Sam Herman at Christie's sale included this vase from 1977 which sold for £300.

From an Auction Report by Christopher Wight on 20th Century British Decorative Arts at Christie's South Kensington, London, 4th May 2000 which appeared in the July/August issue of **Antique Collecting** magazine. For more details and to subscribe see page 147.

John Howkins Antiques
1 Dereham Rd. NR2 4HX. (J.G. Howkins). Est. 1973. Open 10-5, prior telephone call advisable. SIZE: Large. *STOCK: Furniture and smalls, 18th to early 20th C, £25-£15,000.* LOC: Inner ring road, junction of Dereham Road and Grapes Hill. PARK: Own at rear. TEL: 01603 627832; fax - 01603 666626; e-mail - howkinsantiques@ clara.co.uk; website - www.antiques-antiques. co.uk. SER: Valuations; restorations (furniture, clocks, upholstery); buys at auction. VAT: Stan/Spec.

Leona Levine Silver Specialist   BADA
35 St. Giles St. NR2 1JN. Est. 1865. Open 9.30-5. CL: Thurs. *STOCK: Silver and Sheffield plate.* TEL: 01603 628709; fax - same. SER: Valuations; engraving; restorations. VAT: Stan/Spec.

Maddermarket Antiques
18c Lower Goat Lane. NR2 1EL. Est. 1955. Open 9.30-4.30. *STOCK: Jewellery, silverware.* TEL: 01603 620610. SER: Part exchange.

Mandell's Gallery   BADA
Elm Hill. NR3 1HN. Est. 1964. Open 9-5.30. SIZE: Large. *STOCK: Oils and watercolours, especially English and Continental works and Norwich and Suffolk painters, 19th-20th C.* LOC: Near shopping centre, close to cathedral. PARK: Easy. TEL: 01603 626892/629180; fax - 01603 767471. SER: Conservation; framing. VAT: Spec.

The Movie Shop
Antiquarian and Nostalgia Centre, 11 St. Gregory's Alley. NR2 1ER. Open 11-5. SIZE: Large. *STOCK: Books, magazines and movie ephemera; telephones, pre-1940 clothes and textiles, collectables and general antiques.* TEL: 01603 615239.

Oswald Sebley
20 Lower Goat Lane. NR2 1EL. (P.H. Knights). Est. 1895. Open 9-5.15. CL: Thurs. SIZE: Small. *STOCK: Silver, 18th-20th C, £15-£2,000; jewellery, Victorian, £10-£4,000.* LOC: 150yds. to right of City Hall, down paved street. PARK: Nearby. TEL: 01603 626504. SER: Valuations; restorations (silver and gold jewellery). VAT: Stan/Spec.

St. Michael at Plea Antiques and Book Centre
Bank Plain. NR2 4SN. Est. 1984. Open 9.30-5. SIZE: Medium - 30 dealers. *STOCK: General antiques and collectables, pre-1960, £1-£1,000; antiquarian prints.* LOC: Between Elm Hill and city centre. PARK: 30 minutes roadside, multi-storey nearby. TEL: 01603 618989. SER: Valuations; restorations.

Stiffkey Bathrooms
89 Upper St. Giles St. NR2 1AB. *STOCK: Victorian, Edwardian and French bathroom fittings.* PARK: Easy. TEL: 01603 627850; fax - 01603 619775. SER: Mail order period bathroom accessories.

Tombland Antiques Centre
Augustine Steward House, 14 Tombland. NR3 1HF. (Mrs Betty Godsafe). Est. 1974. Open 10-5. SIZE: Large. *STOCK: Furniture, 18th-20th C, £50-£1,000; china, porcelain, antiquities, dolls, Art Deco, Art Nouveau, collectables, curios, militaria, clocks and watches, pens, silver, pictures, postcards, jewellery, cranberry and other glass.* LOC: City centre, opposite cathedral. PARK: Elm Hill. TEL: 01603 619129. SER: Valuations; restorations (furniture, caning).

The Tombland Bookshop
8 Tombland. NR3 1HF. (J.G. and A.H. Freeman). Open 9.30-5. *STOCK: Antiquarian and secondhand books.* TEL: 01603 490000; fax - 01603 760610.

Tombland Jewellers & Silversmiths

12/13 Tombland. NR3 1HF. LAPADA. Est. 1972. Open 9-5, Sat. 9-4.30. *STOCK: English silver, flatware and jewellery, from 17th C; mustard pots, collectors' items, barometers, barographs, from 18th C.* LOC: Opposite Erpingham Gate, Norwich Cathedral and Maid's Head Hotel. TEL: 01603 624914; fax - 01603 764310. SER: Valuations; restorations; export facilities. VAT: Stan/Spec.

Malcolm Turner

15 St. Giles St. NR2 1JL. Open 9-5. CL: Thurs. SIZE: Small. *STOCK: Bronzeware, coins, Oriental ceramics, silver, Staffordshire, Imari, mostly 19th C, £50-£1,000.* PARK: Nearby. TEL: 01603 627007. SER: Valuations. VAT: Stan.

POTTER HEIGHAM

Times Past Antiques

Station Rd. NR29 5AD. (P. Dellar). Open Tues - Sun. 10-5 in summer. CL: Mon. (and Tues. in winter). *STOCK: Barometers, clocks, furniture including reproduction, china, bric-a-brac.* LOC: A149 village centre. PARK: Easy. TEL: 01692 670898.

RAVENINGHAM

M.D. Cannell Antiques

Castell Farm, Beccles Rd. NR14 6NU. Resident. Open Fri., Sat., Sun. and Mon. 10-6 or by appointment. SIZE: Large. *STOCK: Oriental rugs, carpets, kilims, furniture, metalwork and decorative items.* LOC: On B1140. PARK: Easy. TEL: 01508 548441. VAT: Stan/Spec.

REEPHAM

Echo Antiques

Church Hill. NR10 4JL. (Ms M. Stiefel and N. Bundock). Est. 1986. Open 10-5. CL: Thurs. SIZE: Medium. *STOCK: Furniture, 1650-1900, £10-£2,000; pine, 1800-1900, £50-£1,000; small items, 1650-1900, £10-£1,000.* Not Stocked: Jewellery. PARK: Market Sq. TEL: 01603 873291; home - 01603 872068. SER: Valuations; restorations (furniture); buys at auction.

SCRATBY, Nr. Gt. Yarmouth

Keith Lawson Antique Clocks

Scratby Garden Centre, Beach Rd. NR29 3AJ. LBHI. Est. 1979. Open seven days 9-6. SIZE: Large. *STOCK: Clocks and barometers.* LOC: B1159. PARK: Easy. TEL: 01493 730950. SER: Valuations; restorations. VAT: Stan/Spec.

SEETHING, Nr. Brooke

Country House Antiques

NR15 1AL. Est. 1979. Open by appointment. SIZE: Large trade warehouses. *STOCK: Mahogany, oak, walnut furniture, 17th-19th C; interesting china and porcelain.* LOC: Village centre. PARK: Easy. TEL: 01508 558144; mobile - 07860 595658. *Trade only.*

John Anster Fitzgerald, 'Fairies attacking a Bat'. Watercolour and bodycolour on paper, 11in. x 17in. (Sotheby's, London)

From an article entitled 'Victorian Fairy Painting' by Christopher Wood which appeared in the December 2000/January 2001 issue of **Antique Collecting** magazine. For more details and to subscribe see page 147.

SHARRINGTON, Nr. Holt

Sharrington Antiques
NR24 2PQ. (P. Coke). Est. 1944. Open by chance 9.30-5.00 or by appointment. CL: Jan.-Mar. SIZE: Medium. *STOCK: Small and interesting items, £5-£1,500; china, pictures, embroideries, treen, papier mâché.* LOC: 3 miles west of Holt. PARK: Easy. TEL: 01263 861411; home - 01263 860719.

SHERINGHAM

R.L. Cook
12 Sycamore Grove. NR26 8PG. Est. 1950. Open by appointment. *STOCK: Antiquarian books.* TEL: 01263 822050.

Dorothy's Antiques
23 Waterbank Rd. NR26 8RB. (Mrs D.E. Collier). Est. 1975. *STOCK: Cranberry glass, Royal Worcester, Royal Dux, commemorative and other china; small furniture.* TEL: 01263 822319; home - 01263 823018.

Parriss
20 Station Rd. NR26 8RE. (J.H. Parriss). Est. 1947. Open 9-5.30. CL: Wed. SIZE: Medium. *STOCK: Jewellery, £30-£2,500; silver, £40-£2,000; clocks, £100-£3,000.* LOC: A1082, in main street. PARK: Within 150yds. TEL: 01263 822661. SER: Valuations; restorations (jewellery, silver, clocks). VAT: Stan.

The Westcliffe Gallery
2-8 Augusta St. NR26 8LA. (Richard and Sheila Parks). Resident. Est. 1979. Open 9.30-1 and 2-5.30, Sat. 9.30-5.30, Sun. 10-4. SIZE: Medium. *STOCK: Oils, watercolours and drawings, 19th-20th C, £100-£15,000; furniture.* LOC: Town centre. PARK: Easy. TEL: 01263 824320. SER: Valuations; restorations (oils, watercolours, prints); gilding. VAT: Stan/Spec.

SOUTH WALSHAM

Leo Pratt and Son
Old Curiosity Shop. NR13 6EA. (R. and E.D. Pratt). LAPADA. Est. 1890. Open 9-5.30 or by appointment. SIZE: Large. *STOCK: Furniture, from 1700; porcelain, glass, pottery, 1830; shipping furniture, metalware.* PARK: Easy. TEL: 01603 270204. SER: Restorations (furniture); buys at auction. FAIRS: Norwich; Langley; Luton; NEC. VAT: Stan/Spec.

STALHAM

Stalham Antique Gallery
High St. NR12 9AH. (M.B. Hicks). LAPADA.

Est. 1970. Open 9-1 and 2-5. CL: Sat pm. SIZE: Medium. *STOCK: Furniture, 17th C to 19th C; pictures, china, glass, brass.* Not Stocked: Reproductions. PARK: Easy. TEL: 01692 580636. SER: Valuations; restorations. VAT: Spec.

STIFFKEY

Stiffkey Antiques
The Old Methodist Chapel. NR23 1AJ. Open 10-5 including Sun. CL: Thurs. *STOCK: Victorian and Edwardian bathroom fittings, door furniture, window fittings, bric-a-brac.* PARK: Easy. TEL: Bathrooms - 01328 830084; door and window fittings - 01328 830690; toys - 01328 830460; fax - 01328 830005.

The Stiffkey Lamp Shop
Townshend Arms. NR23 1AJ. (R. Belsten and D. Mann). Est. 1976. Open 10-5 including Sun. SIZE: Medium. *STOCK: Lamps, gas, electric and oil, 1800-1920, £25-£2,000; rare lamp fittings.* LOC: Coast road near Wells-next-the-Sea. PARK: Easy. TEL: 01328 830460; fax - 01328 830005. VAT: Stan.

STOKE FERRY, Nr. King's Lynn

Farmhouse Antiques
White's Farmhouse, Barker's Drove. PE33 9TA. (P. Philpot). Resident. Est. 1969. Open by appointment. *STOCK: General antiques.* TEL: 01366 500588. SER: Restorations; furniture made to order in old timber.

SWAFFHAM

Cranglegate Antiques
Market Place. PE37 7LE. (Mrs R.D. Buckie). Resident. Est. 1965. Open Tues., Thurs. and Sat. 10-1 and 2-5.30. SIZE: Small. *STOCK: Small furniture, general antiques and collectors items, 17th-20th C.* LOC: A47. PARK: In square opposite or in passage at rear. TEL: Home - 01760 721052; e-mail - rbuckie@buckie-antiques.com; website - www.buckie-antiques.com.

Swaffham Antiques Supplies
66/68 London St. PE37. (M. and R. Cross). Est. 1959. Open Thurs.-Sat. 10-4 (warehouse by appointment only). SIZE: Large + warehouse at The Old Cold Store Buildings, 7 Cley Road. *STOCK: General antiques, 18th-19th C; shipping furniture, £100-£5,000.* LOC: Off Market Place. PARK: Easy. TEL: 01760 721697/725418; home - 01760 721697.

SWAFIELD, Nr. North Walsham

Staithe Lodge Gallery
Staithe Lodge. NR28 0RQ. (M.C.A. Foster).
Resident. Est. 1976. Open 9-5, Sun. by
appointment. CL: Wed. pm. SIZE: Medium.
*STOCK: Watercolours, paintings and prints, 1800-
1950, £50-£500.* LOC: On B1145 at the Mundesley
end of the North Walsham by-pass. PARK: Easy.
TEL: 01692 402669. SER: Restorations; framing;
buys at auction (mainly watercolours).

TACOLNESTON, Nr. Norwich

Freya Antiques
St. Mary's Farm, Cheneys Lane. NR16 1DB.
Usually open but appointment advisable;
evenings by appointment. SIZE: Large. *STOCK:
General antiques, especially pine and country
furniture; upholstery.* TEL: 01508 489252;
mobile - 07880 737161. SER: Valuations;
restorations; re-upholstery.

THETFORD

The Antique Shop
8 Whitehart St. IP24 1AD. (Mr. and Mrs.
Hodgson). Est. 1997. Open 6 days. SIZE: Small.
*STOCK: Furniture, collectables, porcelain, coins,
badges, crested ware, jewellery and pictures,
19th C.* LOC: Town centre. PARK: Easy. TEL:
01842 755511.

TOTTENHILL, Nr. King's Lynn

Jubilee Antiques
Coach House, Whin Common Rd. PE33 0RS.
(Mr and Mrs A.J. Lee). Est. 1953. Open daily
including Sun. SIZE: Medium. *STOCK:
Furniture especially Victorian chairs, £50-
£4,000; interesting items.* LOC: Between King's
Lynn and Downham Market, adjacent to A10.
PARK: Easy. TEL: 01553 810681; home - same.
SER: Valuations; restorations (furniture).

TWYFORD, Nr. Fakenham

Norton Antiques
(T. and N. Hepburn). Est. 1966. Open by
appointment only. *STOCK: Furniture 1680-1900,
£25-£3,500; oils and watercolours, 19th to early
20th C, £25-£2,500; clocks, 18th-19th C, £40-
£3,500; woodworking and craftsman's hand
tools.* TEL: 01362 683331. SER: Valuations.

WATTON

Clermont Antiques
Clermont Hall. IP25 6LY. (P. Jones). Resident.
Est. 1983. Open daily. SIZE: Large. *STOCK:
Furniture, decorative items, 18th to early 19th C.*
LOC: Down farm track, off B1108. PARK: Easy.
TEL: 01953 882189. VAT: Spec.

WELLS-NEXT-THE-SEA

Church Street Antiques
2 Church St. NR23 1JA. (Paula Ford and Lesley
Ann Irons). Open 10-4 including Sun. (winter -
Thurs.-Sun.), Mon. by appointment. SIZE: Small.
*STOCK: Textiles, lace, costume jewellery, hat
pins, kitchenalia, ephemera, collectables, £1-
£500.* LOC: A149 main coast road, opposite
church. PARK: Easy. TEL: 01328 711698.

Wells Antique Centre
The Old Mill, Maryland. NR23 1LY. Open 10-5
(10-4 winter) including Sun. SIZE: 15 dealers.
STOCK: General antiques and collectables.
PARK: Easy. TEL: 01328 711433.

WROXHAM

T.C.S. Brooke   BADA
**incorporating The Ruth Lowe Gallery of
Contemporary Art, The Grange. NR12 8RX.
(S.T. Brooke). Est. 1952. Open 9.30-1 and 2.15-
5.30. CL: Mon. STOCK: English porcelain,
18th C; furniture, mainly Georgian; silver, glass,
works of art, Oriental rugs. PARK: Easy. TEL:
01603 782644. SER: Valuations. VAT: Spec.**

WYMONDHAM

King
Market Place. NR18 0AX. (M. King). Est. 1969.
Open 9-4. CL: Mon. and Wed., except by appoint-
ment. *STOCK: General antiques, furniture, copper,
brass, silver, jewellery, porcelain.* PARK: Easy.
TEL: 01953 604758; evenings - 01953 602427.

M.E. and J.E. Standley
"Acorns", 23 Norwich Rd. NR18 0NT. Open by
appointment. *STOCK: Furniture, 17th-19th C
and Victorian.* TEL: 01953 602566.

Turret House
27 Middleton St. NR18 0AB. (Dr and Mrs D.H.
Morgan). PBFA. Resident. Est. 1972. SIZE:
Small. *STOCK: Antiquarian books especially
science and medical; occasional scientific
instruments.* LOC: Corner of Vicar St., adjacent
to War Memorial. TEL: 01953 603462. SER:
Buys at auction. FAIRS: London Scientific &
Medical Instrument Fairs. VAT: Stan/Spec.

A period roomset at our showroom.

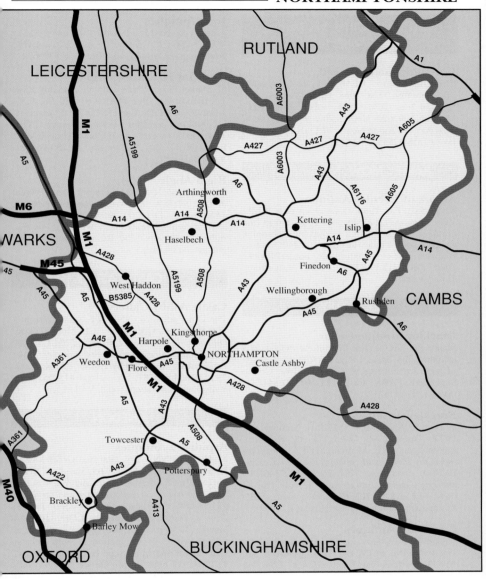

NORTHAMPTONSHIRE

ARTHINGWORTH, Nr. Market Harborough (Leics)

Coughton Galleries Ltd
The Old Manor. LE16 8JT. (Lady Isabel Throckmorton). Est. 1968. Open Wed., Thurs., Sat. and Sun. 10.30-5 or by appointment. SIZE: Medium. *STOCK: Modern British and Irish oil paintings and watercolours.* TEL: 01858 525436; fax - 01858 525535. VAT: Spec.

BARLEY MOW, Nr. Brackley

Amors of Evenley Antiques
NN13 5SB. Est. 1960. Open seven days. SIZE: Very large. *STOCK: Furniture, paintings and pictures, pottery.* LOC: Period barn complex adjacent A43 4 miles junction 10 M40, towards Brackley, just over Oxfordshire border. PARK: Own. TEL: 01869 811342. SER: Valuations. *Mainly trade.*

BRACKLEY

Brackley Antique Cellar
Manor Rd. NN13. (Jim Broomfield). Open 10-5 including Sun. SIZE: Large. *STOCK: Wide range of general antiques.* LOC: Below Co-op Superstore. PARK: Easy. TEL: 01280 841841; fax - 01280 841851.

Brackley Antiques
69 High St. NN13 7BW. (Mrs B.H. Nutting). Est. 1977. Open 10-6, Wed. 10-12, Sun. by appointment. SIZE: Medium. *STOCK: Furniture especially traditionally upholstered, 19th C, £50-£2,000; ceramics, 18th-20th C, £2-£400; interesting and unusual items.* LOC: A43. PARK: Easy. TEL: 01280 703362; home - same. SER: Restorations (furniture and upholstery).

Courtyard Antiques
Market House Courtyard. NN13 7AB. (Peter G. Titterton). FIMI, FCIM. Est. 1996. Open 10-6, Sat. 10-5. SIZE: Three showrooms. *STOCK: 17th-20th C furniture and effects including Oriental.* LOC: Close to Town Hall. PARK: Easy. TEL: 01280 703631; fax/home - same. SER: Valuations; restorations (furniture); buys at auction.

Peter Jackson Antiques
3 Market Place. NN13 7AB. Open 10.30-1 and 2-5. *STOCK: English and Continental porcelain and pottery, 18th-19th C; furniture, paintings, silver, jewellery, glass, watercolours and prints.* TEL: Mobile - 07702 230074. SER: Valuations; restorations.

Juno Antiques
4 Bridge St. NN13 7EP. Open 10-1 and 2-5. CL: Wed. *STOCK: General antiques.* LOC: Northampton/Oxford road. TEL: 01280 700639.

The Old Hall Bookshop
32 Market Place. NN13 7DP. (J. and Lady Juliet Townsend). Est. 1977. Open 9.30-5.30, Sat. 9.30-1 and 2-5.30. SIZE: Large. *STOCK: Antiquarian, secondhand and new books and maps.* LOC: Town centre on east side of Market Place. PARK: Easy. TEL: 01280 704146; fax - 01280 705131. VAT: Stan.

Right Angle
24 Manor Rd. NN13 6AJ. Open 9.30-5.30, Wed. 9.30-1. *STOCK: Drawings, British etchings, 1880-1940.* TEL: 01280 702462; e-mail - chris@rightangleart.com; website - www.rightangleart.com. SER: Restorations (frames); gilding and framing.

CASTLE ASHBY

Castle Ashby Gallery
The Old Farmyard. NN7 1LF. (G.S. Wright - Fine Paintings). Open 10-5. CL: Mon. *STOCK: Oil paintings - British, 1850-1950, £200-£20,000; significant Contemporary artists; furniture.* LOC: Adjacent to Castle Ashby House. PARK: Easy. TEL: 01604 696787; fax - 01604 415055. SER: Valuations; restorations (oils). VAT: Spec.

FINEDON

Aspidistra Antiques
51 High St. NN9 5JN. (Pat and Geoff Moss). Resident. Est. 1993. Open 10-5, Sun. 11-5. SIZE: Large. *STOCK: Arts & Crafts, Art Nouveau and Art Deco metal, ceramics, plaster and furniture, £25-£1,000; general antiques, £1-£500; 1950's, 1960's, 1970's memorabilia.* LOC: Off A14 junction 10 - turn right just before roundabout in village centre. From junction 11, turn right at roundabout and immediate left. PARK: Easy. TEL: 01933 680196; mobile - 07768 071948. SER: Valuations; restorations (furniture); buys at auction. FAIRS: NEC; Earls Court; Newark; Alexander Palace.

Simon Banks Antiques
28 Church St. NN9 5NA. Est. 1984. SIZE: Medium. *STOCK: 17th-20th C furniture, £30-£3,000; glass, silver, ceramics, prints, copper, decorative and collectable items.* TEL: 01933 680371; mobile - 07976 787539. VAT: Stan/Spec.

M.C. Chapman
11-25 Bell Hill. NN9 5ND. LAPADA. Est. 1967. Open 9-5.30, Sun. 11-5. SIZE: Large. *STOCK: Furniture, clocks, decorative items, 18th-20th C, £100-£4,000.* LOC: 400 yds. off A510. PARK: Easy. TEL: 01933 681260; fax - 01933 681779. SER: Container facilities. VAT: Stan/Spec/ Global.

Robert Cheney Antiques
11-13 High St. NN9 5JN. Est. 1991. Open 9-5.30, Sun. 11-4. SIZE: Medium. *STOCK: 18th-20th C furniture, china and glass, £5-£5,000.* LOC: A6. PARK: Easy. TEL: 01933 681048; home - 01933 680085. SER: Valuations.

E.K. Antiques
37 High St. NN9 5NB. Est. 1967. Open 9.30-5, Sun. 11-4. SIZE: Medium- several dealers. *STOCK: Furniture, china, silver, glass, pictures, needlework, clocks and decorative items, 1680-1950, £5-£8,000.* PARK: Easy. TEL: 01933 681882; home - 01933 410245. SER: Restorations (furniture); French polishing; valuations.

Finedon Antiques (Centre)
11-25 Bell Hill. NN9 5ND. Est. 1973. Open 9-5.30, Sun. 11-5. SIZE: Large - 35 dealers. *STOCK: Furniture, decorative items, collectables, silver, ceramics, soft furnishings, 18th to mid-20th C.* LOC: 400 yds. off A510. PARK: Easy. TEL: 01933 681260/682210; fax - 01933 681779; e-mail - sales@finedonantiques.com; website - www.finedonantiques.com. SER: Search service; export facilities; nationwide delivery. VAT: Stan/Spec/Global.

Huntershield Antiques and Granary Antiques
The Huntershields. NN7 4LZ. (Mrs. C. Madeira and Richard Sear). Est. 1968. Open 9-6, Sun. and other times by appointment. SIZE: Large. *STOCK: Furniture, 17th-19th C, £50-£5,000; early metalware specialist; decorative and period items, 19th C, £50-£2,000.* LOC: Off M1, junction 16, into Flore, last turning on left at bollard, premises on right. PARK: Easy. TEL: 01327 340718; home - same; fax - 01327 349263. VAT: Stan/Spec.

Christopher Jones Antiques
Flore House, The Avenue. NN7 4LZ. Est. 1977. Open 10-5, Sat. 11-4.30, Sun. by appointment. SIZE: Large. *STOCK: Period and decorative furniture, lighting, porcelain, glass and objects,* *18th-20th C.* PARK: Easy. TEL: 01327 342165; e-mail - florehouse@msn.com. SER: Interior decor advice. FAIRS: Olympia. VAT: Spec.

Inglenook Antiques
23 High St. NN7 4DH. (T. and P. Havard). Est. 1971. Open 9-7. SIZE: Small. *STOCK: General antiques, £1-£500.* LOC: In main street. PARK: Easy. TEL: 01604 830007.

Savage Fine Art
R.S.J. Savage & Son, The Gate House. NN6 9LQ. (Michael Savage). LAPADA. Est. 1905. Open by appointment only. *STOCK: Oils and watercolours, 19th and 20th C; work by local artists past and present.* TEL: 01604 686232; fax - 01604 686378. SER: Valuations; restorations (paintings and frames); framing. FAIRS: LAPADA; World of Drawings & Watercolours, Park Lane; Buxton; Snape.

John Roe Antiques
The Furnace Site, Kettering Rd. NN14 3JW. Est. 1968. Open 9-5.30, Sat. 10-4. *STOCK: General antiques; Continental and American shipping goods.* TEL: 01832 732937. VAT: Stan.

Dragon Antiques
85 Rockingham Rd. NN16 8LA. Open 10-4. CL: Thurs. *STOCK: Pictures, Oriental items, militaria and general antiques.* TEL: 01536 517017. SER: Framing.

Laila Gray Antiques
25 Welford Rd. NN2 8AQ. Open 9-5.30. *STOCK: Pine.* TEL: 01604 715277. SER: Waxing; stripping.

The Old Brigade
10a Harborough Rd. NN2 7AZ. (S.C. Wilson). Est. 1978. Open by appointment. SIZE: Medium. *STOCK: Military items, 1850's to 1945, £5-*

Cave's
111, KETTERING ROAD
NORTHAMPTON
(TEL: 01604 - 638278)

Hidden away in our Basement showroom is a large stock full of delightful surprises, mainly 18th and 19th Century Furniture in all woods and in condition worthy of high-class homes.

DEALERS SHOW CARD AND ASK FOR TRADE FACILITIES

Loop off M1 Exits 15 and 16 or short detour from A5

OPEN MON/TUES/WED/FRI/SAT 9AM – 5.30PM.

£5,000. LOC: Junction 15, M1. PARK: Easy. TEL: 01604 719389; fax - 01604 712489. SER: Valuations; illus. catalogue (£5 + SAE). VAT: Stan/Spec.

NORTHAMPTON

F. and C.H. Cave
111 Kettering Rd. NN1 4BA. Est. 1879. Open 9-5.30. CL: Thurs. SIZE: Large. *STOCK: Furniture - Georgian, Victorian and decorative; general antiques.* LOC: Near town centre, quarter mile outside pedestrianised area. PARK: Adjoining side streets. TEL: 01604 638278. VAT: Spec.

Michael Jones Jeweller
1 Gold St. NN1 1SA. Est. 1919. *STOCK: Silver, gold and gem jewellery, French carriage clocks.* TEL: 01604 632548. VAT: Margin.

Occultique
30 St Michael's Avenue. NN1 4JQ. (M.J. Lovett). Est. 1973. SIZE: Small. *STOCK: Books and artifacts, 50p-£500.* TEL: 01604 627727; fax - 01604 603860. SER: Catalogue available. VAT: Stan. *Mail Order only.*

Penny's Antiques
83 Kettering Rd. NN1 4AW. (Mrs P. Mawby). Est. 1976. Open Mon., Wed., Fri. and Sat. 11-4. SIZE: Small. *STOCK: Shipping goods, kitchen chairs, pictures, army badges, furniture, china, smalls, glass and brass, Victorian to 1940, £5-£100.* LOC: On A43 near town centre. PARK: Easy. TEL: 01604 632429.

POTTERSPURY, Nr. Towcester

Reindeer Antiques Ltd   BADA
43 Watling St. NN12 7QD. LAPADA. Est. 1959. Open 9-6, Sat. 10-5, Sun. by appointment. SIZE: Large. *STOCK: Fine English furniture, 17th-19th C; caddies, clocks, smalls, paintings.* LOC: A5. TEL: 01908 542407/ 542200; fax - 01908 542121. VAT: Stan/Spec.

RUSHDEN

Magpies
1 East Grove. NN10 0AP. (Jim and Janet Ward). Est. 1993. Open 10-5, Sun. 12-4. SIZE: Large. *STOCK: Furniture, £20-£1,000; china, glass, kitchenalia and bric-a-brac, £1-£25; all 19th-20th C.* LOC: A6 south on one-way system, first left after passing old station. PARK: Easy. TEL: 01933 411404.

D.W. Sherwood Antiques Ltd
59 Little St. NN10 0LS. Est. 1960. *STOCK: General antiques.* TEL: 01933 353265.

TOWCESTER

Clark Galleries
215 Watling St. NN12 6BX. (A. Clark). FABPR. Est. 1964. Open 9-5, Sat. 9-4. SIZE: Medium. *STOCK: Landscape paintings, 18th-19th C, £500-£15,000; portraits, 17th-18th C, £500-£5,000.* LOC: M1, junction 15A, on A5. PARK: Easy and at rear. TEL: 01327 352957; website - www.clarkgalleries.com. SER: Valuations; restorations and re-lining (oil paintings); picture hire. VAT: Stan/Spec.

Ron Green
227-239 Watling St. West. NN12 6DD. Est. 1952. Open 9-6, Sun. by appointment. SIZE: Large. *STOCK: English and Continental furniture, paintings and decorative items, £30-£30,000.* TEL: 01327 350387/350615; fax - 01327 350615; e-mail - ron@green227.freeserve.co.uk.

The World of Simon Drew

Simon Drew is an unusual combination of artist and wordsmith He combines these two talents with an inventive and quirky sense of humour in his range of books and invites us to look at the world through the magic of Drewsian spectacles. A new perspective unfolds on the world: the familiar becomes unfamiliar, the known becomes unknown, the serious becomes humorous, reality becomes nonsense. It is a topsy-turvy world of visual and verbal puns that never fail to delight. Simon Drew shakes us out of complacency in the most enjoyable of ways. For those who are not already addicted there is only one thing to suggest – read them all!

This book is the definitive manual for all people who love eating but want someone else to cook for them. This book has everything you never wanted to know about food and drink. Dieticians will run screaming from the building. Nutritionists will want to starve. Add a pinch of nonsense to a dessert spoon of language bending and three gallons of hidden meanings and you will end up with page after page of currant puns.
ISBN 1 85149 410 3, 48pp., c.70 col. illus.
8½ x 6in./210 x 148mm. **£7.50/$14.95**

All titles below are 48pp., and measure 8¼ x 6in./210 x 152mm. Colour illustrated throughout and priced at £7.50/$12.95 each unless otherwise indicated.

Dogsbodies –
a book of canine nonsense
ISBN 1 85149 271 2
Great Mistakes of Civilisation-
Mankind's Mistakes and Faux
Pas
ISBN 1 85149 246 1
Camp David – Nonsense in Art
ISBN 1 85149 162 7
Bird Dropping
Simon Drew's Best of Birds
ISBN 1 85149 245 3
Handel's Warthog Music
Nonsense in Music
ISBN 1 85149 186 4

Still Warthogs Run Deep and
Other Free Range Nonsense
ISBN 1 85149 087 6
Cat with Piano Tuna and
Other Feline Nonsense
ISBN 1 85149 138 4
The Very Worst of Simon Drew
£8.50/$12.95
ISBN 1 85149 331 X
Simon Drew's Beastly Address
Book for Beastly Friends
£9.95/$13.95
ISBN 1 85149 188 0
Simon Drew's Beastly Birthday
Book **£9.95/$13.95**
ISBN 1 85149 220 8

Simon Drew's offering is a collection of nonsensical puzzles. This is a book to exasperate and annoy: the only way to solve the puzzle drawings is either to start with a warped mind or put yourself through such gymnastic mental contortions that your mind ends up warped and twisted as a result. To offset these mind-blowing drawings light relief is provided by other pointless pictures accompanied, in many cases, by truly agonising verse.
ISBN 1 85149 356 5
8¼ x 6in/210 x 148mm., 48pp., colour drawings throughout. **£7.50/$14.95**

For a free copy of our catalogue, please contact

ANTIQUE COLLECTORS' CLUB

5 Church Street, Woodbridge, Suffolk, IP12 1DS, UK
Tel: (01394) 385501 Fax: (01394) 384434
Sales Office Direct Fax: (01394) 388994
Email: sales@antique-acc.com Website: www.antique-acc.com

or

Market Street Industrial Park, Wappingers' Falls, NY 12590, USA
Tel: (845) 297 0003 Fax: (845) 297 0068 ORDERS: (800) 252 5231
Email: info@antiquecc.com Website: www.antiquecc.com

R. and M. Nicholas

161 Watling St. NN12 6BX. Open 9.30-5. SIZE: Small. *STOCK: 18th-19th C porcelain, silver and glass.* TEL: 01327 350639.

WEEDON

Heart of England Antiques

23 High St. NN7 4QD. (Mrs M.R. Wain). Est. 1970. Open 10-5 including Sun. CL: Thurs. SIZE: Large. *STOCK: French pine armoires, 1800-1900; clocks.* PARK: Easy. TEL: 01327 341928; home - same; fax - 01327 342524; e-mail - myrawain@btconnect.com; website - www. heartofenglandantiques.com. VAT: Stan/Spec.

Helios & Co (Antiques)

25/27 High St. NN7 4QD. (J. Skiba and B. Walters). Open 9-6 including Sun. SIZE: Large. *STOCK: English and Continental furniture especially dining tables; decorative accessories.* PARK: Easy. TEL: 01327 340264; fax - 01327 342235. SER: Suppliers and restorers to H. M. Govt. VAT: Spec.

Rococo Antiques and Interiors

5 New St., Lower Weedon. NN7 4QS. (N.K. Griffiths). Resident. Usually available. *STOCK: Architectural goods and furnishings.* LOC: 3 miles junction 16, M1, quarter mile off A5. PARK: Easy. TEL: 01327 341288; mobile - 07721 836302. VAT: Stan/Spec.

The Village Antique Market

62 High St. NN7 4QD. (E.A. and J.M. Saunders). Est. 1967. Open 10.30-5.15 including Sun. and Bank Holidays. SIZE: Large - 40 dealers. *STOCK: General antiques and interesting items.* LOC: Off junction 16, M1. PARK: In front yard. TEL: 01327 342015.

Weedon Bec Antiques

66 High St. NN7 4QD. (N.M. Astbury). Est. 1990. Open Thurs. 10.30-4, Fri. and Sat. 10.30-4.30, Sun. 11.30-3.30, other days by appointment. SIZE: Small. *STOCK: Pine country furniture, £100-£4,000.* LOC: A45/A5 crossroads. PARK: Easy. TEL: 01327 349910/361614; fax - 01327 361463. VAT: Stan/Spec.

WELLINGBOROUGH

Antiques and Bric-a-Brac Market

Market Sq. NN8 1AF. Open Tues. 9-4. SIZE: 135 stalls. *STOCK: General antiques and collectables.* LOC: Town Centre.

Park Gallery & Bookshop

16 Cannon St. NN8 5DJ. (Mrs J.A. Foster). Est. 1979. Open 10-5.30. SIZE: Medium. *STOCK: Books, maps and prints, 18th-19th C, £2-£300.* LOC: Continuation of A510 into town. PARK: Easy. TEL: 01933 222592.

Bryan Perkins Antiques

Finedon Rd. NN8 4DJ. (J., B.H. and S.C. Perkins). Est. 1971. Open 9-5. CL: Sat. pm. SIZE: Large. *STOCK: Furniture and paintings, 19th C, £100-£2,000; small items.* PARK: Easy. TEL: 01933 228812; home - 01536 790259. SER: Valuations; restorations (furniture). VAT: Spec. *Trade Only.*

WEST HADDON

Barber Antiques

8 High St. NN6 7AP. (Miss Alison Barber). Est. 1994. Open 12-5, Sat. 10-5. CL: Mon. SIZE: Medium. *STOCK: Furniture, 18th-19th C, £100-£5,000; ceramics, 19th-20th C, £5-£300; country pine, collectables, 19th C, £5-£1,000.* LOC: A428. PARK: Easy. TEL: 01788 510315; e-mail - sales@barberantiques.co.uk; website - www. barberantiques.co.uk. SER: Valuations; restorations (furniture).

The Country Pine Shop

The Romney Building, Northampton Rd. NN6 7AS. (Ryan and Dodd). Est. 1985. Open 8-5. SIZE: Large. *STOCK: English and Continental stripped pine, £30-£1,200.* LOC: A428. TEL: 01788 510430.

Paul Hopwell Antiques   BADA

30 High St. NN6 7AP. LAPADA. Est. 1974. Open 10-6. CL: Sun. and Mon. a.m. except by appointment. SIZE: Large. *STOCK: 17th-18th C oak and walnut country furniture, longcase clocks, metalware: oil paintings and prints mainly sporting and country pursuits.* LOC: A428. PARK: Easy. TEL: 01788 510636; fax - 01788 510044; e-mail - PaulHopwell@ antiqueoak.co.uk; website - www.antiqueoak. co.uk. SER: Valuations; restorations (furniture and metalware); buys at auction. VAT: Spec.

Mark Seabrook Antiques

9 West End. NN6 7AY. Open 10-5.30. SIZE: Medium. *STOCK: Country furniture, period metalware, brass and copper, treen and other domestic items.* LOC: A428. PARK: Easy. TEL: 01788 510772; mobile - 07770 721931.

Oriental Rugs Volume 1: Caucasian

Caucasian rugs, with their warm natural colours and their strong designs, are a common sight in discriminating homes throughout the world. This is possibly the most useful book on the subject as it does not restrict itself to museum pieces but looks at rugs readily available to today's collector through dealers and auction houses. Colour illustrations feature hundreds of rugs of varying quality from dealers and auction rooms enabling the reader to identify and classify the varying types, as well as consider dates and areas of production.

ISBN 0 902028 58 8, 376pp., 336 col., 155 b.&w. illus. 10 x 8½in./254 x 216mm. **£45.00/$89.50**

Oriental Rugs Volume 2: Persian

Persia is famous for its carpets, some with abstract and geometric designs, some representational, in a palette as rich as a Renaissance painting, each in its own frame, with its own subtlety and complexity. This important reference provides the collector with clear and reliable information to assess a wide variety of pieces that pass through shops and auctions. Each area of carpet manufacture is divided into the towns and villages whose carpets display individual characteristics and these are studied under the headings: size, colours, patterns, foundation, knots, pile and quality.

ISBN 0 907462 12 X, 266pp., 141 col., 15 line drawings. 10 x 8½in./254 x 216mm. **£39.50/$89.50**

Oriental Rugs Volume 3: The Carpets of Afghanistan

This volume, fourth in the highly successful Oriental Rugs series, serves as a detailed introduction to the fascinating range of carpets and rugs from Turkey. The history of the region and the art of carpet weaving and knotting are explained whilst the various types and styles of rug are traced through the traditions and differing techniques found in the Anatolian peninsula. The pictorial catalogue has comprehensive captions with examples which range from antique and rare to modern and fake pieces.

ISBN 1 85149 091 4, 260pp., 210 col., 15 b.&w. illus. 10 x 8½in./254 x 216mm. **£35.00/$69.50**

Oriental Rugs Volume 4: Turkish

This fully revised edition, updated to include the carpets portraying the recent war and the resultant changes within the country's carpet industry as well as in the refugee camps, is the most detailed analysis of the Afghanistan rug production ever published. Additional colour plates illustrate and guide the new and established collector and the first-time buyer through the labyrinth of fascinating choices. Afghan rugs, which are instantly appealing due to traditional colours and bold designs, open up a whole new vista for the collector, from sumptuous piled purdahs to flat woven prayer rugs.

ISBN 1 85149 144 9, 196pp., 154 col., 90 b.&w. illus. 10 x 8½in./254 x 216mm. **£29.95/$59.50**

Oriental Rugs Volume 5: Turkoman

This is a detailed introduction to the extraordinary range of carpets and rugs made by the nomadic Turkoman tribes who inhabited the former soviet republics of Turkmenistan and Uzbekistan, north east Iran and the northern frontier region of Afghanistan. This English language edition of the classic German work is unrivalled in its coverage of a complex subject. Surprisingly, this is the first major monograph to have appeared on Turkoman Rugs for nearly a decade and is perhaps unrivalled in its comprehensiveness.

"…this book is certainly a winner in its class" **The Art Book**

ISBN 1 85149 136 8, 318pp., 299 col., 100 line drawings. 10 x 8½in./254 x 216mm. **£35.00/$69.50**

Tribal Rugs

Covered in this book is the weaving history of the nomadic tribes of central Asia from earliest times to the present day. It explores different tribal groups and illustrates the rugs, carpets, kilims and utilitarian bags attributed to their weavers. Most of the rugs shown are illustrated here for the first time and there are many revealing close-ups of the structure of the rugs. Particular attention is paid to the decline in use of natural dyes.

"The book is illustrated throughout with examples of the finest work of each tribe and close-ups of the structure of their rugs. Most of the illustrations are previously unpublished"

Antique Dealers and Collectors' Guide

ISBN 1 85149 268 2, 302pp., 220 col. illus. **£39.50/$89.50**

For a free copy of our catalogue, please contact

ANTIQUE COLLECTORS' CLUB

5 Church Street, Woodbridge, Suffolk, IP12 1DS, UK
Tel: (01394) 385501 Fax: (01394) 384434
Sales Office Direct Fax: (01394) 388994
Email: sales@antique-acc.com Website: www.antique-acc.com

or

Market Street Industrial Park, Wappingers' Falls, NY 12590, USA
Tel: (845) 297 0003 Fax: (845) 297 0068 ORDERS: (800) 252 5231
Email: info@antiquecc.com Website: www.antiquecc.com

ALNWICK

G.M. Athey
Castle Corner, Narrowgate. NE66 0NP. *STOCK: English oak, mahogany furniture, glass, china and brass, 18th-19th C.* TEL: 01665 604229; website - www.atheysantiques.com.

Bailiffgate Antique Pine
22 Bailiffgate. NE66 1LX. (S. Aston). Est. 1994. Open Thurs.-Sat. 10-4.30. SIZE: Large. *STOCK: Country pine furniture.* LOC: Opposite the castle. PARK: Easy. TEL: 01665 603616. SER: Valuations; restorations; buys at auction.

Barter Books
Alnwick Station. NE66 2NP. (Stuart & Mary Manley). Est. 1990. Open daily including Sun. SIZE: Large. *STOCK: Antiquarian books, £10-£5,000.* LOC: Off A1, on left on town approach. PARK: Easy. TEL: 01665 604888; fax - 01665 604444. SER: Valuations; book-binding and repair.

Gordon Caris
30 Fenkle St. NE66 1HR. Open Thurs. and Fri. 10-4. *STOCK: Clocks and watches.* TEL: 01665 510820. SER: Restorations (clocks and watches).

Tamblyn
12 Bondgate Without. NE66 1PP. (Mrs S.M. Hirst). Est. 1981. Open 10-4.30. SIZE: Medium. *STOCK: General antiques including country furniture, pottery, pictures, antiquities, glass, to 20th C, £5-£1,500.* LOC: Diagonally opposite war memorial at southern entrance to town. PARK: Easy. TEL: 01665 603024; home - same. SER: Valuations.

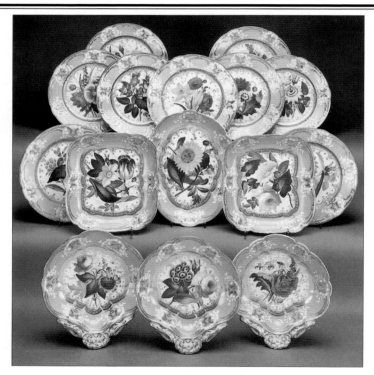

A John Rose part dessert service with low relief floral wreaths reserved against a duck-egg blue ground and superbly painted with flowers. Plates 9⅜in., red printed 'Feltspar Porcelain' and name, impressed '2'. About £400-£600 a pair of plates; pair of dishes £700-£1,000.

From an article entitled 'Factory Fact File: Coalport/Coalbrookdale' by David Battie which appeared in the November 2000 issue of **Antique Collecting** magazine. For more details and to subscribe see page 147.

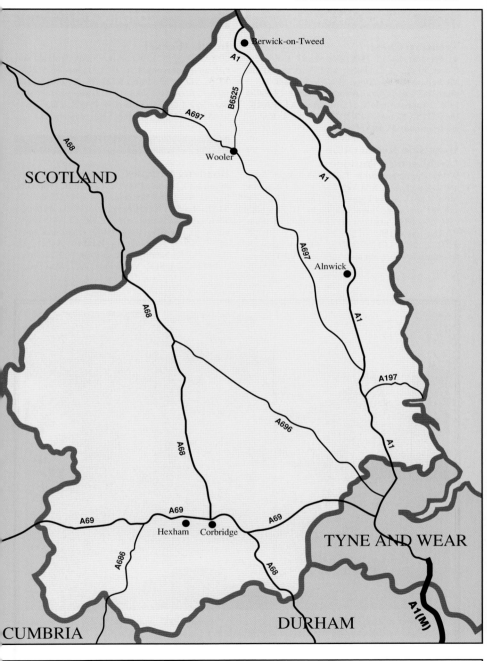

Dealers and Shops in Northumberland

Alnwick	5	Corbridge	1	Wooler	2
Berwick-on-Tweed	2	Hexham	6		

NORTHUMBERLAND

BERWICK-ON-TWEED

Treasure Chest
53 West St. TD15 2DX. (Y. Scott). Est. 1988. Open 11-4. CL: Tues. and Thurs. SIZE: Medium. *STOCK: China, jewellery, glass, silver plate and small furniture, from 1860, £1-£400.* LOC: Approximately 1 mile from A1. PARK: Easy. TEL: Home - 01289 307736. SER: Restorations (china). FAIRS: Local.

Woodside Reclamation (Architectural Antiques)
Woodside, Scremerston. TD15 2SY. (Keith Allan and Lynne Gray). SALVO. Est. 1990. Open 9-5, Mon. 9.30-5. SIZE: Large. *STOCK: Architectural salvage including fireplaces, baths, kitchen pine, 19th C.* LOC: Adjacent A1, just south of town. PARK: Easy. TEL: 01289 331211; fax - 01289 330274; home - 01289 302658. SER: Valuations; restorations (stripping and finishing). VAT: Spec.

CORBRIDGE

Judith Michael
20A Watling St. NE45 5AH. (Judith Troldahl and Gillian Anderson). Est. 1970. Open 10-5, Sun. 12-5. SIZE: Medium. *STOCK: China, glass, silver, furniture, mirrors, light fittings and jewellery.* LOC: Just off A69. PARK: Easy. TEL: 01434 633165; fax - same. SER: Valuations.

HEXHAM

Boadens Antiques
29 and 30 Market Place. NE46 3PB. (Richard, Sandra and Chris Boaden). Est. 1948. Open 9-5. SIZE: Large. *STOCK: Furniture - antique, Victorian and secondhand, £100-£3,000; silver, paintings, jewellery, £50-£1,500; china and glass, £5-£2,000.* LOC: Opposite Hexham Abbey, off A69. PARK: Nearby. TEL: 01434 603187; fax - 01434 603474. SER: Valuations. VAT: Stan/Spec.

Watercolour and pencil, 7in. x 10½in. Sold for £357, February 2000. A dependable but slow-moving artist, good for collectors but not so promising for investors.

From an article entitled 'British Watercolours' by Richard Kay which appeared in the July/August 2000 issue of **Antique Collecting** magazine. For more details and to subscribe see page 147.

Millers Antiques of Wooler

In Wooler we have 2 shops containing a large stock of good quality Georgian and Victorian furniture, mainly bookcases, dining furniture, tallboys, linen presses, long case clocks, burr walnut and marquetry furniture.

Also nearby we have a 10,000 sq ft warehouse with a stock of Victorian - 1930s mahogany, oak, walnut and pine furniture.

Tel: 01668 281500 Fax: 01668 282383

Established 1947

Gordon Caris
16 Market Place. NE46 1XQ. Est. 1972. Open 9-5. CL: Thurs. *STOCK: Clocks and watches.* TEL: 01434 602106. SER: Restorations (clocks and watches).

Hedley's of Hexham
3 St. Mary's Chare. NE46 1NQ. (P. Torday). Est. 1819. Open Mon.10-4, Tues.-Sat. 9.30-5. SIZE: Medium. *STOCK: Furniture, 18th-20th C; porcelain, silver, glass, jewellery, prints and collectables.* LOC: Off Market Place. PARK: 200 yds. TEL: 01434 602317. SER: Valuations; restorations. VAT: Stan/Spec.

Priest Popple Books
9B Priest Popple. NE46 1PF. (John B. Patterson). Est. 1997. Open 9-5. SIZE: Medium. *STOCK: Books - second-hand non-fiction, first editions, antiquarian, £5-£1,500.* LOC: From A69 to town centre, premises top of bus station. PARK: Easy. TEL: 01434 607773. SER: Valuations; book-binding.

Renney Antiques
6 Rear Battle Hill. NE46 1BB. SIZE: Large. *STOCK: Decorative lighting, antique furniture, garden and architectural items, decorative pieces and textiles.* LOC: Main shopping street, opposite NatWest Bank. PARK: 400 metres. TEL: 01434 607964. SER: Valuations; buys at auction.

The Violin Shop
27 Hencotes. NE46 2EQ. (D. Mann). Est. 1970. Open 10-5 or by appointment. *STOCK: Violins, violas, cellos, basses and bows.* TEL: 01434 607897.

WOOLER

Hamish Dunn Antiques
17 High St. NE71 6BU. Est. 1986. Open 9.30-12 and 1-4.30, Thurs. 9.30-12. SIZE: Medium. *STOCK: Curios and collectables, 19th-20th C, £5-£500; antiquarian and secondhand books, 18th-20th C, £1-£200; small furniture, 19th-20th C, £15-£1,000.* LOC: Off A697. PARK: Easy. TEL: 01668 281341; home - 01668 282013. VAT: Stan/Spec.

James Miller Antiques
1-5 Church St. NE71 6BZ. LAPADA. Est. 1947. Open Mon.-Fri. 9.30-5. SIZE: Large and warehouses. *STOCK: Georgian-Edwardian furniture and clocks.* LOC: A697. PARK: Nearby. TEL: 01668 281500; fax - 01668 282383; home - 01668 217281. VAT: Stan/Spec.

391

ASLOCKTON, Nr. Nottingham

Jane Neville Gallery
Elm House, Abbey Lane. NG13 9AE. (R. Repetto-Wright and J. Neville). Resident. Est. 1979. Open 10-4. SIZE: Medium. *STOCK: Paintings and prints including sporting, 19th-20th C, £50-£5,000.* LOC: A52. PARK: Easy. TEL: 01949 850220. SER: Valuations; restorations; framing; research; print publishers; buys at auction (sporting paintings). VAT: Stan/Spec.

BALDERTON

Blacksmiths Forge
74 Main St. NG24 3NP. (K. and J. Sheppard). Est. 1982. Open every day by appointment. SIZE: Small. *STOCK: Mainly architectural - specialising in fireplaces, Georgian to 1930's, £50-£600; beds, mainly Victorian, £100-£650.* LOC: Off A1, follow signs to village, turn right at traffic lights, shop on right next to church. PARK: Easy. TEL: 01636 700008; home - same. SER: Valuations; restorations; stripping; polishing; buys at auction (furniture).

Highlight of the commemoratives at Phillips Bayswater was this press-moulded saltglaze Jacobite dish, c.1748, which raised £2,000.

From an Auction Report by Christopher Wight which appeared in the March 2001 issue of **Antique Collecting** magazine on The Hacking Collection of Davenport, dry-bodied stoneware and other British ceramics which was held at Phillips Bayswater, 23rd January 2001. For more details and to subscribe see page 147.

DARLTON

A.J. O'Sullivan Antiques
Whimpton House, Dunham Rd. NG22 0TA. Resident. Est. 1977. Open 9-5, Sat. 9-1. SIZE: Medium. *STOCK: Furniture, 18th-19th C, £200-£4,000; decorative items.* LOC: From A1 take A57 (Lincoln road) at Markham Moor roundabout through Darlton, premises 1/4 mile on left. PARK: Easy. TEL: 01777 228626; fax - same; e-mail - tonyos@talk21.com. SER: Valuations; restorations (furniture). FAIRS: Newark. VAT: Stan/Spec/Global.

DUNHAM-ON-TRENT

R. G. Antiques
Main St. NG22 0TY. (R.G. and D.C. Barnett). Est. 1975. Open 10-6 including Sun. SIZE: Small. *STOCK: Arms, armour and militaria, general antiques, 18th-20th C, £5-£1,000.* PARK: Easy. TEL: 01777 228312. SER: Buys at auction (arms and armour). FAIRS: Newark.

LANGFORD, Nr. Newark

T. Baker
Langford House Farm. NG23 7RR. Est. 1966. CL: Sun. except by appointment and Sat. SIZE: Medium. *STOCK: Victoriana, period furniture and oak.* LOC: A1133. PARK: Own. TEL: 01636 704026. *Trade Only.*

MANSFIELD

The Book Shelf
7A Albert St. NG18 1EA. (S. Payton). Open 9.30-5. CL: Wed. SIZE: Medium. *STOCK: Antiquarian and secondhand books.* LOC: Town centre. TEL: 01623 648231; home - 01623 458077; e-mail - frank@bookshelf7a.freeserve .co.uk; website - www.bookshelf-online.co.uk. SER: Book search.

Fair Deal Antiques
138 Chesterfield Rd. North. NG19 7JD. (D. Lowe). Est. 1972. Open 9.30-5.30. CL: Sat. pm. and Sun. except by appointment. SIZE: Large. *STOCK: Shipping goods, £50-£100; furniture, mainly mahogany, Victorian, £100-£1,000; period furniture, metalware and small items.* PARK: Easy. TEL: 01623 653768/512419. VAT: Stan. *Trade Only.*

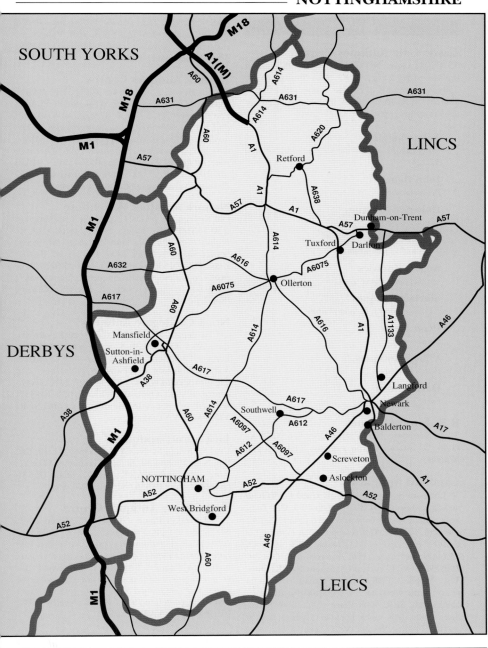

Dealers and Shops in Nottinghamshire

Aslockton	1	Langford	1	Ollerton	1	Sutton-in-Ashfield	1
Balderton	1	Mansfield	2	Retford	2	Tuxford	1
Darlton	1	Newark	9	Screveton	1	West Bridgford	2
Dunham-on-Trent	1	Nottingham	21	Southwell	1		

NOTTINGHAMSHIRE

NEWARK

Castle Gate Antiques Centre
55 Castle Gate. NG24 1BE. Est. 1985. Open
9.30-5. SIZE: Large. LOC: A46 through town,
250yds. from castle. PARK: Easy. TEL: 01636
700076. SER: Restorations. Below are listed the
dealers at this centre.

& Barrington
Fine antique and modern silver. TEL: 07850
577724.

John Dench
Period furniture.

Dukeries Antiques
Period furniture.

Vivienne Flint
Town and country furniture.

Angela Knowles
Jewellery, decorative items.

Sinclair Antiques
Furniture, pottery, decorative items.

Peter Straw
Furniture.

Village Antiques
Period furniture.

David Walsh
Early pottery.

R.R. Limb Antiques
31-35 Northgate. NG24 1HD. Open 9-6. *STOCK:
General antiques and pianos.* TEL: 01636
674546.

Lombard Antiques
35 Lombard St. NG24 1XG. (Bernard J. McGrath
and Ann Mason). Est. 1980. Open 10-5. CL: Tues.
and Sun. except Newark Fair times. SIZE:
Medium. *STOCK: Collectables, 18th-19th C, £5-
£1,000; longcase clocks, 18th-19th C, £1,500-
£15,000; furniture, 17th to early 20th C, £50-
£10,000.* LOC: Corner of Castlegate. PARK: Own.
TEL: Mobile - 07989 047547; e-mail - mcgrathbl
@aol.com; website - www.quality-antique-
clocks.com. SER: Valuations; restorations (clock
movements, dials, cases; porcelain repairs); buys at
auction. FAIRS: Newark. VAT: Spec.

M B G Antiques, Fine Art & Jewellery
41B Castlegate. NG24 1BE. (Margaret Begley-
Gray DGA). Est. 1982. Open 11-4. CL: Mon. and
Tues. SIZE: Small. *STOCK: Jewellery, paintings,
miniatures, 19th to early 20th C, to £4,000.*

PARK: Nearby. TEL: 01636 650790; fax - 01636
679586; mobile - 07702 209808. SER: Valuations;
restorations (jewellery and paintings). FAIRS:
NEC; Robert Bailey Fairs.

Newark Antiques Centre
Regent House, Lombard St. NG24 1XP. (Marks
Tinsley). Open 9.30-5, Sun. 11-4. SIZE: 55 units
and 46 cabinets. *STOCK: Georgian, Victorian
and period furniture, pottery, porcelain, glass,
textiles, militaria, clocks, pictures, books, silver,
antiquities, jewellery, paintings, coins, Oriental,
pine, oil lamps.* TEL: 01636 605504; fax - 01636
605101. SER: Upholstery, fabrics, metal
cleaning, valuations, porcelain, restorations.

Newark Antiques Warehouse
Old Kelham Rd. NG24 1BX. Open 8.30-5.30, Sat.
9.30-4. SIZE: 30+ dealers, 80+ cabinets. *STOCK:
Mainly 17th-20th C furniture and decorative items,
smalls and collectables.* LOC: Just off A1. PARK:
Easy. TEL: 01636 674869; fax - 01636 612933; e-
mail - enquiries@newarkantiques. co.uk; website -
www.newarkantiques.co.uk. FAIRS: Newark
(Sundays).

No. 1 Castlegate Antiques
1-3 Castlegate. NG24 1AZ. (Christine Kavanagh).
Est. 1985. Open 9.30-5, Sat.9.30-5.30. SIZE:
Large - 12 dealers. *STOCK: 17th-19th C English
oak, mahogany and walnut furniture and
decorative objects; all £100-£5,000.* LOC: Town
centre. PARK: Opposite. TEL: 01636 701877;
website www.castlegateantiques.com. SER:
Valuations. VAT: Stan/Spec.

Jack Spratt Antiques
Unit 5, George St. NG24 1LU. Open 8-5.30, Sat.
8-4, Sun. 10.30-3.30. SIZE: Warehouse. *STOCK:
Pine and oak.* PARK: Easy. TEL: 01636
681666/7; fax - 01636 681670. VAT: Stan.

Tudor Rose Antiques Centre
12-13 Market Place. NG24 1DU. Open 10-5.
SIZE: 35 cabinets + 4 floors. *STOCK: Furniture
including oak and country, pine, mahogany and
fine; metalware, copper, brass and silver,
militaria, clocks, English, Continental and
Oriental porcelain, pottery, glass, decorative
items and soft furnishings, treen, toys, pictures
and linen, (dateline 1940).* PARK: Nearby. TEL:
01636 610311. VAT: Stan/Spec.

NOTTINGHAM

Acanthus Antiques & Collectables
140 Derby Rd., Off Canning Circus. NG7 1LR.
(Trak E. and Mrs Smith). Est. 1980. Open 10-3,
Thurs. 10-2, Sat. 12-4. CL: Mon. SIZE: Small.

394

STOCK: *Ceramics and glass, 19th-20th C, £5-£1,000; collectors' items, mainly 20th C, £5-£800; period furniture, 18th-19th C, £200-£1,500.* LOC: Derby Rd. exit from Queens Medical Centre traffic island, continue for 1 mile, shop on left. PARK: Nearby. TEL: 0115 924 3226; e-mail - trak.e.smith@btinternet.com; website - www.acanthusantiques.co.uk. SER: Valuations; restorations (furniture and ceramics); buys at auction. FAIRS: Newark, Swinderby, Donington.

Antiques across the World
James Alexander Building, BR Goods Yard, London Rd./Manvers St. NG2 3AE. (A.R. Rimes). LAPADA. Est. 1993. Open 9-5, Sat. 10-2. SIZE: Large. STOCK: *Furniture, 18th C to Edwardian, £300-£3,000.* PARK: Easy. TEL: 0115 979 9199; fax - 0115 958 8314; home - 0116 239 3119; e-mail - tonyrimes@btinternet.com. SER: Valuations; buys at auction (furniture); finder; courier. FAIRS: Newark. VAT: Stan/Spec.

Dave Buckley Antique Exports
Nottingham Antique Centre, London Rd. NG2 3AE. Open by appointment. SIZE: Warehouse. STOCK: *Shipping furniture for USA, European and Japanese Markets.* LOC: Old British Rail goods yard, off London Road, by Hooters restaurant. PARK: Easy. TEL: 0115 9504504 (Ants Centre) e-mail - dave@nottsantiques. fsnet.co.uk. SER: Container packing; export facilities. *Trade Only.*

Castle Antiques
78 Derby Rd. NG1 5FD. Open 9.30-5. STOCK: *Maps, prints and general antiques.* TEL: 0115 947 3913.

Collectors World
188 Wollaton Rd., Wollaton. NG8 1MJ. (M. T. Ray). Est. 1975. Open 10.30-5. CL: Mon. SIZE: Small. STOCK: *Ancient and modern coins and banknotes, 20th C cigarette and postcards, 19th C medals and accessories, all £1-£100.* LOC: Ring road at A609 Crown Island/Raleigh Island. PARK: Easy. TEL: 0115 928 0347; fax - same. SER: Valuations; buys at auction (coins and banknotes). FAIRS: Newark, Birmingham MSCF and various specialist.

The Golden Cage
99 Derby Rd., Canning Circus. NG1 5BB. (J. Pearson and D. Walker). Open 10-5. STOCK: *Formal wear and period clothing from Victorian to1970's; costume jewellery.* TEL: 0115 9411600/9476478. SER: Hire (including 20's-40's and period costume); clothes copied to order.

Figure 1. (Left to right) Tankard, 1748, 30½oz, £2,300; tankard, 1746, 28¼oz, £2,530. Both Thomas Whipham. Inkstand, John Luff, 1738, 38oz, £7,130. Sold 4th June 1998.

ENGLISH SILVER

Peter Waldron

Last year I said it would be difficult to imagine prices going through the roof now that New Labour is in power as they had done in the late 1960s. There has certainly been little change, but what are the prospects for the future?

Taking a look at the market from a different angle, it is twenty years since we bought our house and having embarked on yet another round of refurbishment and decoration I was set to thinking about the value of the property. Today's valuation is in excess of ten times our original cost and although we have spent a fair amount on minor alterations and decoration in that time it made me wonder what would have happened had I put the same amount of money into a basket of silver. The resulting findings were quite an eye opener; pessimists will say never buy silver for investment while optimists will reflect that silver is at a low ebb and now is the time to put money into a market which must surely improve. There are areas of the silver market that have performed well and there is no doubt that some small collectors' items – card cases to novelties, and vinaigrettes to wine related pieces – are worth well in excess of their real value of twenty years ago. I have talked about these areas in my past articles and this year I feel it is time to look at those

pieces which seem to lack lustre and may be ready for a move.

When looking through Sotheby's catalogues produced in London in 1978 it is noticeable that the standard of pieces offered for sale today is better than it was then. In turnover terms the market appears to be buoyant today and when

Figure 2. A large cup, Hancocks & Co, 1889, 356oz, £14,375. Sold 5th March 1998.

comparing sale totals (now slightly over nine times what it was in 1978), values have held up well compared with the value of my house. In 1978 our important summer sale on 4th May made £245,547 for 185 lots with 7% by value unsold (buyer's premium was a straight 10% in those days); this year's sale on 4th June totalled £2,226,563 for 140 lots with just under 12% unsold by value. The top three lots in 1978 were the Paul Storr Rutland gold salver (£66,000), a pair of Paul Storr wine coolers, 1827 (£11,000) and Sir Edward Hasell's Lamerie coffee pot of 1738 (£12,100) which produced 36.3% of the sale total. This year the top three lots were the Drury-Lowe Lamerie tureen (£639,500), the Coote candelabra, B. Smith, 1812 (£265,500) and eighteen dinner plates, A. Nelme, 1698 (£221,500) producing 50.6% of the sale total. This illustrates that the top end of the market is performing well and delivering higher and higher prices. The proportion of sale total delivered by middle market items is consequently less and less by value.

There are clear comparisons which illustrate the poor performance of the middle market. It can be slightly dangerous doing this as it is not possible to be certain that objects sold so long ago were in the same condition as those sold today, but here goes. Two tankards sold on 5th June this year for £2,300 and £2,530 (figure 1) made less than five times the price achieved twenty years ago. Tankards of similar type and weight made between £700 and £900 in 1978. The other item in the illustration, a mid 18th century silver inkstand, sold for £7,130, having been bought in July 1990 for £7,700 where £3,000-£4,000 would have been the selling price in 1978. A set of three Samuel Wood caddies, 1766, sold for £6,325 or just over six times a similar set which made £935 in 1978. An Augustin Courtauld coffee pot, 1737, made £4,600 which is less than three times the price that a David Willaume pot of similar quality and weight, 1726, made two decades ago at £2,090. A pair of candlesticks, 1730, went for £5,175 as compared with the average price of between £1,000 and £1,250 twenty years ago. A dessert basket, William Pitts, 1801, made £6,325 having been bought from Sotheby's on 22nd March 1979 for £638. This is one area, along with epergnes, candelabra and wine related pieces, where prices have climbed steadily and kept up with the top of the market. Other items sold in the last year which can be compared are as follows (with 1978 prices in brackets): James I shell spice box, £25,300 (£3,960); George II cake basket of 50-60oz, £14,375 (£3,530); a set of four Paul Storr 340oz entrée dishes, $123,500 or £78,000 (£13,200); a 30oz 1770s cake basket, £2,300 (£440), a 1780s bright-cut tea caddy, $7,475 or £4,600 (£638). In short, nothing seems to have performed as well as bricks and mortar and some areas of traditional 18th/19th century silver have performed atrociously.

A brief look at Paul de Lamerie prices is necessary as one of the main events of the last year was the sale of the Patino Collection at Sotheby's New York in April. Some recent purchases did not show much movement (the Walpole inkstand, for instance, making roughly what it was bought for in 1988) but a cake basket in superb condition bought for £94,600 in 1985 made £662,500 (£410,000). On the other hand a vendor in a various owners' sale at Christie's in March made a thumping loss on a set of six Lamerie candlesticks bought in 1986 for £143,000 and sold for £106,000. After deduction of commission and premium the owner would have received about half of his original investment.

What is popular this year? Following a period in the doldrums early spoons are avidly sought after once more – apostles, maidenheads, lion sejants, seal tops, etc. This was aptly demonstrated by the sale of the Swaythling spoons (figure 4) although when looked at as a price per spoon there was no particular premium for a set. Single Henry VIII apostles have sold for in excess of £20,000 in the last two years. Candelabra have continued their

Figure 3. (Left to right) Four wine coasters, Paul Storr for Rundell, Bridge & Rundell, 1814, £27,600; a pair of silver-gilt snuffers' trays and two pairs of snuffers, maker's mark 'I W' and Thomas Radcliffe, 1820, £2,300. Sold 6th November 1997.

strong rise, a pair of 27 inch high corinthian five-light examples of 1886 made £10,350. Sculptural 19th century pieces are back in vogue although the Hancocks cup illustrated in figure 2 did not sell at an exceptional level as it was slightly out of period – i.e. made twenty years later than the style suggests. These objects should be bringing good prices when the cost of making reproductions is taken into account. We recently sold a 226oz Warwick vase for £9,200 and the buyer thought he would have it copied to make up a pair. We looked round for quotes to do this and the cost was going to be in the region of £13,000-£14,000! Sets of four George III column candlesticks still seem to be the most popular variety of the readily available types. In good condition they are making around £10,000 per set against estimates of £6,000-£8,000 but they have to have a good strong classic line. Fussiness with too many masks and swags and the price is down to half this level.

Finally, if you need to sell something then the novelty end of the market is still booming – an 1898 tortoise table bell made £1,955 and an 1806 ivory and silver cucumber slicer £943 (both at the end of May), whilst a 1905 elephant pin cushion, 3½in. long (with trunk raised of

course!) sold for £483 in April. If you are buying then take a careful look at those pieces that have performed badly, some of them must be due for an increase.

All photographs courtesy of Sotheby's.

Peter Waldron is a Senior Director of Sotheby's and Head of their Silver Departments throughout Europe.

*This article appeared in the July/August 1998 issue of **Antique Collecting** magazine. For more details and to subscribe see page 147.*

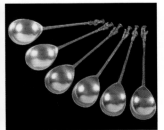

Figure 4. Six apostle spoons from the Swaythling spoons, maker's mark a heart, 1524, £254,500. Sold 5th March 1998.

Figure 5. Cake basket, Samuel Courtauld, 1747, 66oz, £17,825. Sold 5th March 1998.

Granny's Attic

308 Carlton Hill, Carlton. NG4 1GD. (Mrs A. Pembleton). Open Tues., Thurs., Fri. and Sat. 9-5. *STOCK: Dolls, miniatures, general antiques and furniture.* TEL: 0115 9265204.

Harlequin Antiques

79-81 Mansfield Rd., Daybrook. NG5 6BE. (P.R. Hinchley). Est. 1992. Open daily, Sun. by appointment. SIZE: Medium. *STOCK: 18th-19th C pine furniture, £300-£1,200; oak and mahogany, 18th to early 19th C, £300-£1,000.* LOC: A60 Mansfield road, north from Nottingham. PARK: Easy. TEL: 01159 674590; home - 01159 654197. SER: Valuations; restorations (oak and mahogany). FAIRS: Newark. VAT: Stan/Spec.

D.D. and A. Ingle

380 Carlton Hill. NG4 1JA. Est. 1968. Open 9-5, Sun. 10-12. SIZE: Small. *STOCK: Coins and medals, from Roman, £50-£100; jewellery and watches, £50-£1,000.* PARK: Nearby. TEL: 0115 987 3325; fax - same. SER: Valuations; restorations.

Ivory Gate Antiques

106 Derby Rd. NG1 5FB. (B. Orridge). Est. 1975. Open 9.45-4.45. SIZE: Medium. *STOCK: Furniture, 18th-19th C, £500-£4,000; clocks, 19th C, £200-£2,000; porcelain and glass, 18th-20th C, £10-£1,500.* LOC: A52 near city centre. PARK: Easy. TEL: 0115 947 3054; home - 0115 963 2734. SER: Valuations; restorations (furniture including upholstery, and clocks). FAIRS: Keddleston Hall, Lamport; Derby University.

Melville Kemp Ltd

79-81 Derby Rd. NG1 5BA. LAPADA. Est. 1900. Open 9-5.30. CL: Thurs. SIZE: Small. *STOCK: Jewellery, Victorian; silver, Georgian and Victorian, both £5-£10,000; ornate English and Continental porcelain, Sheffield plate.* LOC: From Nottingham on main Derby Rd. PARK: Easy. TEL: 0115 941 7055; fax - 0115 941 3075. SER: Valuations; restorations (silver, china, jewellery); buys at auction. VAT: Stan/Spec.

Lights, Camera, Action.

6 Western Gardens, Aspley. NG8 5GP. UACC. Est. 1996. Open by appointment. SIZE: Small. *STOCK: Autographs - film, television, sport, historical.* LOC: Off Nutall Rd. PARK: Easy. TEL: 0115 913 1116. SER: Valuations; buys at auction. FAIRS: NEC and local.

Michael D. Long

96-98 Derby Rd. NG1 5FB. Est. 1970. Open 9.30-5, Sat. 10-4. SIZE: Large. *STOCK: Arms and armour of all ages and nations.* LOC: From

city centre take main Derby Rd., shop on right. PARK: Easy. TEL: 0115 9474137; fax - 0115 9414199; website - www.michaeldlong.com. VAT: Stan/ Spec.

Luna

23 George St. NG1 3BH. (Paul Rose). Est. 1992. Open 10-5.30. SIZE: Small. *STOCK: Design items - glass, ceramics and furniture, 1940's-1970's, from £5.* LOC: Near Market Sq. PARK: Easy. TEL: 0115 924 3267; website - www.luna-online.co.uk. SER: Valuations.

Anthony Mitchell Fine Paintings

Sunnymede House, 11 Albemarle Rd., Woodthorpe. NG5 4FE. (M. Mitchell). Est. 1965. Open by appointment. *STOCK: Oil paintings, £2,000-£100,000; watercolours, £500-£30,000.* LOC: North on Nottingham ring road to junction with Mansfield road, turn right, then 3rd left. PARK: Easy. TEL: 0115 9623865; fax - same. SER: Valuations; restorations. VAT: Spec.

NSE Medal Dept.

97 Derby Rd. NG1 5BB. (Dennis Henson). Est. 1983. Open 8.30-3.30. SIZE: Medium. *STOCK: Medals, badges and coins, £5-£1,000+.* PARK: Easy. TEL: 0115 950 1882. SER: Valuations; medal mounting and framing.

Pegasus Antiques

62 Derby Rd. NG1 5FD. (P. and J. Clewer). Est. 1985. Open 9.30-5. *STOCK: English furniture and decorative antiques, mainly Georgian and Victorian; brass, copper, silver, jewellery and Staffordshire figures, 19th C.* TEL: 0115 9474220. SER: Stockist of Liberon Restoration products.

S. Pembleton

306 Carlton Hill, Carlton. NG4 1JB. Open Tues., Thurs. and Fri. 9-5, Sat. 10-5. *STOCK: General antiques.* TEL: 0115 9265204.

David and Carole Potter Antiques

76 Derby Rd. NG1 5FD. LAPADA. Est. 1966. Open by appointment only. SIZE: Medium. *STOCK: Clocks, 18th-19th C, £50-£8,000; period furniture, 17th-19th C, £500-£20,000; pottery, porcelain and glass, 18th-19th C, £20-£10,000; trade goods.* LOC: From Nottingham centre, take main Derby Rd., shop on right. PARK: Easy. TEL: 0115 9417911; mobile - 07973 689962. VAT: Stan/Spec.

Top Hat Antiques Centre

70-72 Derby Rd. NG1 3EN. (Top Hat Exhibitions). Est. 1978. Open 9.30-5. SIZE: Large. *STOCK: Furniture, Georgian to Edwardian; small porcelain and metal items, to Art Deco; oils, watercolours and prints, 19th-*

20th C, £30-£1,000. LOC: A52 town centre. PARK: Easy. TEL: 0115 9419143; website - www.tophat-antiques.co.uk. VAT: Stan/Spec.

Vintage Wireless Shop
The Hewarths, Sandiacre. NG10 5NQ. (Mr Yates). *STOCK: Early wireless and pre-war televisions, crystal sets, horn speakers, valves, books and magazines.* TEL: 0115 9393139; fax - 0115 9490180; mobile - 07989 102976.

OLLERTON

Hamlyn Lodge
Station Rd. NG22 9BN. (N., J.S. and M.J. Barrows). Open Tues.-Sat. 10-5. SIZE: Small. *STOCK: General antiques, 18th-19th C, £100-£3,000.* LOC: Off A614. PARK: Easy. TEL: 01623 823600; website - www.hamlynlodge. co.uk. SER: Restorations (furniture).

RETFORD

Stanley Hunt Jewellers
19 Exchange St. *STOCK: Antique jewellery.* TEL: 01777 703144.

Ranby Hall
Barnby Moor. DN22 8JQ. (Paul Wyatt). LAPADA. Est. 1980. Open Sat. and Sun. 10-7, other days by appointment. SIZE: Large. *STOCK: Furniture, 18th-20th C, £300-£25,000; mirrors, 19th C to 1930, £500-£15,000; oil paintings, 17th-20th C, £1,500-£10,000; garden urns and furniture, from 19th C, £500-£8,000.* LOC: Take Barnby Moor turning off A1, travel 1/4 mile - drive to house on right. PARK: Easy. TEL: 01777 860696; fax - 01777 701317; e-mail - paul.wyatt4 @virgin.net. SER: Buys at auction (furniture and oils). FAIRS: DMG Newark, LAPADA; Bailey, Tatton Park; RDS Dublin. VAT: Stan/Spec.

SCREVETON

Red Lodge Antiques
Fosseway. (L. Bradford). Resident. Est. 1999. Open 9-5 or by appointment, Sat. and Sun. appointment only. SIZE: Large. *STOCK: Shipping furniture, 1900-1930s, £25-£1,000.* LOC: A46 approx. 10 miles from Nottingham and 5 miles from Newark. PARK: Own. TEL: 01949 20244; home - same. SER: Container facilites available. *Trade & Export Only.*

SOUTHWELL

Strouds (of Southwell Antiques)
3-7 Church St. NG25 0HQ. (V.N. and J. Stroud). Est. 1972. Open 9.30-5 or by appointment. SIZE: Large. *STOCK: Furniture, clocks, metalware and decorative items, 17th-19th C, £10-£50,000.* LOC: Town centre. PARK: Easy. TEL: 01636 815001. VAT: Stan/Spec.

SUTTON-IN-ASHFIELD

Yesterday and Today
82 Station Rd. NG17 5HB. (John and Chris Turner). Resident. Est. 1990. Open 9-5, Sat. 9-4, other times by appointment. SIZE: Small. *STOCK: Furniture, 1920's-1930's oak and walnut, £50-£500; clocks, 19th C, £100-£2,000.* LOC: A38. PARK: Easy. TEL: 01623 442215. FAIRS: Swinderby.

TUXFORD

Sally Mitchell's Gallery
9 Eldon St. NG22 0LB. FATG. Est. 1976. Open Tues.-Sat. 10-5, Sun. and Mon. by appointment. SIZE: Medium. *STOCK: Contemporary sporting and animal paintings, £200-£5,000; limited edition sporting and animal prints, 20th C, £20-£350; sporting paintings.* LOC: 1 minute from A1, 14 miles north of Newark. PARK: Easy. TEL: 01777 838 234/655; e-mail - info@sallymitchell. com; website - www.sallymitchell.com. FAIRS: CLA Game and Burghley Horse Trials. VAT: Stan/Spec.

WEST BRIDGFORD

Bridgford Antiques
2A Rushworth Ave. NG2 7LF. Open 10-5. SIZE: Small. *STOCK: General antiques, collectables, pictures, books and postcards.* LOC: Opposite County Hall. TEL: 0115 9821835; home - 0115 9817161.

Joan Cotton (Antiques)
5 Davies Rd. NG2 5JE. Est. 1969. Open 9-4.30. CL: Wed. *STOCK: General antiques, Victoriana, jewellery, silver, china, glass and bygones.* LOC: 1/2 mile along Bridgford Rd. from Trent Bridge, in town centre. PARK: On forecourt. TEL: 0115 9813043.

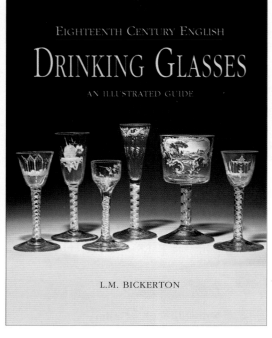

EIGHTEENTH CENTURY ENGLISH

DRINKING GLASSES

AN ILLUSTRATED GUIDE

L.M. BICKERTON

- *New digitally enhanced photographs*

- *A wealth of illustrations which facilitate identification of individual pieces*

- *The standard work on the subject, long out of print, and much sought after*

Firmly established as the standard textbook on the subject it is unique for two reasons: it contains a wealth of illustrations and includes an extensive bibliography by Robert Elleray – the most detailed ever produced on the subject. There is a continuing interest in 18th century drinking glasses which is fuelled by the enormous variety of bowls and stems. They are an eloquent testimony to the ingenuity and craftsmanship of glass workers of the time.

In the last revision the author had extended the illustrations to over one thousand. This made the book particularly valuable, since it was obviously impossible to show every minor variation although the sheer number of examples included provided a very good representation of what collectors were likely to find. A chapter was also included giving much fuller definitions of the classes of drinking glasses, avoiding the necessity of constant reference to other authorities. Special coverage of baluster-stemmed and engraved glasses was also included. Collectors, dealers, auction houses and anyone interested in this fascinating facet of the 18th century decorative arts will welcome this timely reprint.

Leonard Bickerton built up a collection of drinking glasses in Worthing Museum. In 1968 he mounted an exhibition of 500 18th century glasses including many important specimens from many private collections in the south-east. The catalogue for that exhibition was the basis of *An Illustrated Guide to Eighteenth Century English Drinking Glasses* published in 1971, of which this volume is a revised edition

ISBN 1 85149 351 4, 431pp., 1,220 b.& w. illus. **£49.50/$99.50**

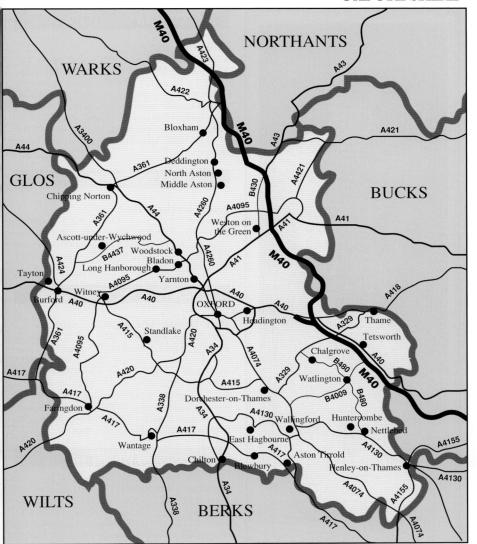

Dealers and Shops in Oxfordshire

Ascott-under-Wychwood	1	East Hagbourne	2	Taynton	1
Aston Tirrold	1	Faringdon	3	Tetsworth	2
Bladon	1	Headington	1	Thame	1
Blewbury	1	Henley-on-Thames	8	Wallingford	9
Bloxham	1	Huntercombe	1	Wantage	1
Burford	17	Long Hanborough	1	Watlington	2
Chalgrove	1	Middle Aston	1	Weston-on-the-Green	1
Chilton	1	Nettlebed	1	Witney	6
Chipping Norton	9	North Aston	1	Woodstock	6
Deddington	2	Oxford	16	Yarnton	1
Dorchester-on-Thames	2	Standlake	1		

A fine Silesian covered goblet, c.1700. Its Hochschnitt engraving, attributed to Friedrich Winter, features an eagle holding a ribbon in its beak, within strapwork and acanthus leafscroll, and the reverse, a sunflower and pendant tassel. Minor chip to rim. 12in. £109,000. (Sotheby's)

From an article on glass by Andy McConnell which appeared in the July/August 2000 issue of **Antique Collecting** magazine. For more details and to subscribe see page 147.

ASCOTT-UNDER-WYCHWOOD

William Antiques
Manor Farm. OX7 6AL. (Robert Gripper). Est. 1982. Open Mon.-Fri. 9-5. SIZE: Medium. *STOCK: Victorian and Georgian furniture, mainly mahogany, to £1,000.* LOC: Left turn off A361 from Chipping Norton, turn left between river bridge and level crossing. PARK: Easy. TEL: 01993 831960; home - same; fax - 01993 831395. SER: Valuations; restorations. VAT: Margin.

ASTON TIRROLD, Nr. Didcot

John Harrison Fine Art
Skirmers, Aston St. OX11 9DQ. (J.M.C. Harrison). TVADA. Strictly by appointment. *STOCK: Drawings and watercolours, 18th-19th C.* TEL: 01235 850260. SER: Commissions undertaken.

BLADON, Nr. Woodstock

Park House Tearoom & Antiques
26 Park St. OX20 1RW. (H.R. and T. Thomas). Resident. Open daily. *STOCK: Small furniture and decorative smalls.* LOC: On A4095 Woodstock to Witney road. PARK: Own. TEL: 01993 812817; fax - 01993 812912; e-mail - hughthomas@htshipping.com; website - www.htshipping.com. SER: Valuations; restorations; buys at auction; monthly shipping service to USA (check website for rate details).

BLEWBURY

Blewbury Antiques
London Rd. OX11 9NX. (S. and E. Richardson). Est. 1971. Open 10-6 including weekends. CL: Tues. *STOCK: General antiques, books, bric-a-brac, country and garden items, oil lamps and oil lamp parts.* PARK: Easy. TEL: 01235 850366.

BLOXHAM, Nr. Banbury

H.C. Dickins
High St. OX15 4LT. (P. and H.R. Dickins). Open 10-5.30, Sat. 10-1. *STOCK: 19th-20th C British sporting and landscape paintings, watercolours, drawings and prints.* TEL: 01295 721949.

BURFORD

Burford Antique Centre
Cheltenham Rd., At the Roundabout. OX18 4JA .
(G. Viventi). Est. 1979. Open 10-6 including Sun.
SIZE: Large. *STOCK: Furniture, 18th-19th C,
£100-£5,000; china and pictures.* LOC: A40.
PARK: Easy. TEL: 01993 823227. SER:
Restorations (furniture including re-leathering).

The Burford Gallery
Classica House, High St. OX18 4QA. (B.
Etheridge). Est. 1976. Open 9.30-5.30. SIZE:
Medium. *STOCK: British and Continental
watercolours, 18th-20th C, £40-£6,000.* LOC:
400yds. from A40 roundabout. PARK: Easy.
TEL: 01993 822305; fax - 01993 824148. SER:
Valuations; framing and mounting; buys at
auction (watercolours). VAT: Spec.

Bygones
29 High St. OX18 4RN. (C.B. Jenkins). Est.
1986. Open 10-1 and 2-5, Sat. 10-5, Sun. 12-5.
SIZE:Small. *STOCK: Prints and pictures, 1900's,
£5-£50; china and glass, curios, 1880-1950, £5-
£250.* LOC: A40. PARK: Easy. TEL: 01993
823588; fax - 01993 704338.

*David Roberts,
East end of the
church of St
Pierre, Caen;
inscribed l.r.
'St Pierre',
watercolour and
pencil
heightened with
bodycolour and
scratching out,
14½in. x 10in.
£2,070 in 1998.
(Sotheby's)*

From an article
entitled 'David
Roberts, R.A.
(1796-1864)' by
Charles Hind
which appeared
in the October
2000 issue of
**Antique
Collecting**
magazine. For
more details and
to subscribe see
page 147.

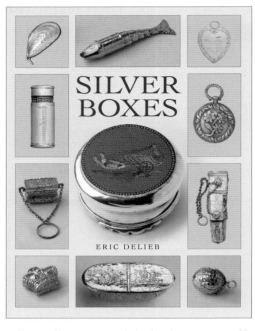

Jonathan Fyson Antiques

50 High St. OX18 4QF. (J.R. Fyson). CADA. Est. 1970. Open 9.30-1 and 2-5.30. SIZE: Medium. *STOCK: English and Continental furniture, decorative brass and steel including lighting and fireplace accessories; club fenders, mirrors, porcelain, glass, jewellery.* LOC: At junction of A40/A361 between Oxford and Cheltenham. PARK: Easy. TEL: 01993 823204; fax - same; home - 01367 860223. SER: Valuations. VAT: Spec.

Gateway Antiques

Cheltenham Rd., Burford Roundabout. OX18 4JA. (M.C. Ford and P. Brown). CADA. Est. 1986. Open 10-5.30 and Sun. pm. SIZE: Large. *STOCK: English and Continental furniture, 18th-early 20th C; decorative accessories.* LOC: On roundabout (A40) Oxford/Cheltenham road. PARK: Easy. TEL: 01993 823678; fax - 01993 823857; website www.gatewayantiques.co.uk. SER: Valuations. VAT: Stan/Spec.

Horseshoe Antiques and Gallery

97 High St. OX18 4QA. (B. Evans). Open 9-5.30, Sun. by appointment only. SIZE: Medium. *STOCK: Clocks including longcase (all fully restored); early oak and country furniture; oil paintings and watercolours; copper and brass, horse brasses.* LOC: East side of High St. PARK: Easy. TEL: 01993 823244; fax - 01993 822429. VAT: Spec.

Hubert's Antiques

Burford Roundabout, Cheltenham Rd. OX18 4JA. (Michael R. Hinds). LAPADA. Est. 1987. Open 10-5.30. SIZE: Large. *STOCK: Furniture, £150-£10,000; oils, £50-£5,000; clocks, £250-£5,000; all 17th-19th C.* LOC: A40 half way between Oxford and Cheltenham. TEL: 01993 822151; fax - same.

Lucy Johnson   BADA

LAPADA. CINOA. Est. 1982. Showroom open by appointment. SIZE: Medium. *STOCK: 17th to early 18th C furniture, Delftware and interiors.* PARK: Easy. TEL: 01993 823726; fax - 01993 824799; e-mail - lucy-johnson@lucy-johnson.com. FAIRS: BADA; Olympia.

Anthony Nielsen Antiques

80 High St. OX18 4QF. Est. 1977. Open 9.30-1 and 2-5.30. SIZE: Large. *STOCK: Furniture, mahogany, walnut, rosewood, oak, William and Mary to Edwardian, £200-£20,000; copper, brass, £20-£500.* PARK: Easy. TEL: 01993 822014; fax - same; after hours - 01451 821710.

Old George Inn Antique Galleries

104 High St. OX18 44QF. (E. Lyle-Cameron). Est. 1992. Open 10-5, Sun. 12-5. SIZE: Large. *STOCK: General antiques including china, furniture, textiles, silver, plate, books, glass, pictures, early 18th C to 1930's.* LOC: Main road. PARK: Around corner. TEL: 01993 823319.

David Pickup   BADA

115 High St. OX18 4RG. CADA. Est. 1977. Open 9.30-1 and 2-5.30, Sat. 10-1 and 2-4. SIZE: Medium. *STOCK: Fine furniture, works of art, from £500+; decorative objects, from £100+; all late 17th to mid 20th C, specialising in Arts & Crafts.* **PARK: Easy. TEL: 01993 822555. FAIRS: Olympia. VAT: Spec.**

Richard Purdon Antique Carpets BADA

158 The Hill. OX18 4QY. CADA. Open 10-6. SIZE: Medium. *STOCK: Antique Eastern and European carpets, village and tribal rugs, needlework, textiles and related items.* **TEL: 01993 823777; fax - 01993 823719; e-mail - rp@richardpurdon.demon.co.uk; website - www.purdon.com. SER: Valuations; restorations. VAT: Stan/Spec.**

Manfred Schotten Antiques

109 High St. OX18 4RH. CADA. Est. 1974. Open 9.30-5.30 or by appointment. *STOCK: Sporting antiques and library furniture.* TEL: 01993 822302; fax - 01993 822055; website - www. schotten.com. SER: Restorations.

The Stone Gallery

93 High St. OX18 4QA. (Mrs Phyllis M. and Simon Marshall). Est. 1918. Open 9.15-6. SIZE: Medium. *STOCK: Pre-Raphaelite and modern British pictures, 1840-1980, £120-£30,000; paperweights, from 1845, £50-£15,000; enamel boxes, from 1760, £50-£1,000.* LOC: Halfway down High St. PARK: Easy. TEL: 01993 823302; fax/home - same; e-mail - mail@stonegallery. co.uk; website - www.stonegallery.co.uk. SER: Valuations (paperweights); buys at auction (pictures and paperweights). VAT: Stan/Spec.

Swan Gallery

High St. OX18 4RE. (D. Pratt). LAPADA. CADA. Est. 1966. Open 10-5.30. SIZE: Large. *STOCK: Country furniture in oak, yew, walnut and fruitwood, 17th-19th C, £300-£12,000; Staffordshire figures and small decorative items, 18th-20th C, £50-£800.* PARK: Easy. TEL: 01993 822244. VAT: Mainly Spec.

Walkers

101 High St. OX18 4RH. (A.E. Walker). Est. 1954. Open 9-5. SIZE: Large. *STOCK: 18th-19th C English furniture.* TEL: 01993 823284. VAT: Stan/Spec.

Wren Gallery

4 Bear Court, High St. OX18 4RR. (S. Hall and G. Mitchell). Est. 1986. Open 10-5.30. SIZE: Medium. *STOCK: 19th-20th C watercolours and drawings.* TEL: 01993 823495. SER: Valuations; restorations (watercolours); buys at auction (watercolours). VAT: Spec.

CHALGROVE, Nr. Oxford

Rupert Hitchcox Antiques

Warpsgrove Lane. OX44 7RW. (P. and R. Hitchcox). Est. 1957. Open Mon.-Sat. 10-5 (Trade), Sun. 2-5 (Trade and public). SIZE: Large - 6 barns. *STOCK: Georgian, Victorian, Edwardian and 1920's furniture.* LOC: Halfway between Oxford and Henley, just off the B480, 6 miles from junction 6 M40. TEL: 01865 890241; fax - same. VAT: Stan/Spec.

CHILTON, Nr. Didcot

Country Markets Antiques and Collectables

at Country Gardens Garden Centre, Newbury Rd. OX11 0QN. Est. 1991. Open 10-5.30, Mon. 10.30-5.30, Sun. 10.30-4.30. SIZE: Large - 30 dealers. *STOCK: Wide variety of general antiques including furniture, books, jewellery, porcelain, militaria, cased fish and fishing tackle, £5-£5,000.* LOC: Off A34 near Harwell, 10 mins. from junction 13, M4, 20 mins. from Oxford. PARK: Easy. TEL: 01235 835125; fax - 01235 833068; e-mail - country.markets.antiques@breathemail.net; website - www.countrymarkets.co.uk. SER: Restorations (furniture and ceramics).

CHIPPING NORTON

Antique English Windsor Chairs - Michael Harding-Hill

at Bugle Antiques 9 Horse Fair. OX7 5AL. CINOA, CADA. Est. 1971. Open 10-5. *STOCK: 18th-19th C Windsor chairs, including sets.* TEL: 01608 643322; fax - 01608 644322; e-mail - antique-windsor-chairs@dial.pipex.com; website - www.antique-english-windsor-chairs.co.uk. VAT: Stan/Spec.

Chipping Norton Antique Centre

Ivy House, 1 Market Place and 21/44 West St. OX7 5NH. (G.Wissinger). Open 10-5.30 including Sun. SIZE: 20 dealers. *STOCK: A wide variety of smalls and furniture.* PARK: Own. TEL: 01608 644212.

Georgian House Antiques

21 West St. OX7 5EU. LAPADA. Open 9-6. *STOCK: 17th-19th C furniture and paintings.* TEL: 01608 641369.

Jonathan Howard

21 Market Place. OX7 5NA. (J.G. Howard). Est. 1979. Open by appointment or ring bell. SIZE: Small. *STOCK: Clocks - longcase, wall and carriage, 18th-19th C.* PARK: Easy. TEL: 01608 643065. SER: Valuations; restorations (movement, dials and cases).

Key Antiques

11 Horse Fair. OX7 5AL. (J. Riley). LAPADA, CADA. Open 10-5.30 or by appointment. CL: Mon. and Tues. SIZE: Medium. *STOCK: English period oak and country furniture, 17th-19th C; domestic metalware, pottery and associated items.* LOC: On main road. PARK: Easy. TEL: 01608 644992. VAT: Spec.

The Quiet Woman Antiques Centre

Southcombe. OX7 5QH. (David Belcher and Ann Marriott). Est. 1998. Open 10-7, Sat. 10-5.30, Sun. 11-4. SIZE: Large - several dealers. *STOCK: Wide variety of general antiques.* PARK: Own. TEL: 01608 646262; fax - same.

Station Mill Antiques Centre

Station Mill, Station Rd. OX7 5HX. (M.T. Langer). Est. 1994. Open 10-5 including Sun. SIZE: Large. *STOCK: Furniture, fine art, bric-a-brac and collectables, 17th-20th C, £2-£2,000.* LOC: Just out of town off A44 towards Moreton in Marsh. PARK: Easy. TEL: 01608 644563; fax - 01327 860952; e-mail - info@stationmill.com; website - www.stationmill.com. SER: Valuations; restorations.

TRADA

21 High St. OX7 5AD. Open 9-5. *STOCK: Antiquarian maps and engravings, 1600-1900.* TEL: 01608 644325. SER: Print renovation; colouring; picture frame making.

Peter Wiggins

Raffles Farm, Southcombe. OX7 5QH. Est. 1969. Usually available. *STOCK: Barometers.* LOC: 1 mile from Chipping Norton on A34. TEL: 01608 642652; home - same. SER: Valuations; restorations (barometers, clocks, automata); clock repairs; buys at auction.

DEDDINGTON

Castle Antiques Ltd

Manor Farm, Clifton. OX15 0PA. (J. and J.

Carriage clocks continue to sell keenly and advance in price, hardly bearing out the mantra about the middle market. (Left to right) These sold in March 2000 for £941 (by Garnier, retailed by Dent); £823 (strike/repeat, ivorine rings in gilt mask); £706 (silver and tortoiseshell miniature); £2,823 (grande sonnerie and three-colour gilt mask); £882 (hammered silver miniature); £1,176 (gorge by Jacot). (Phillips)

From an article on clocks by Richard Garnier which appeared in the July/August 2000 issue of **Antique Collecting** magazine. For more details and to subscribe see page 147.

Vaughan). LAPADA. Est. 1968. Open 10-5, Sun. 10-4. SIZE: Large. *STOCK: Furniture, £25-£3,000; silver, metalware, £10-£1,000; pottery, porcelain, £10-£2,000; kitchenalia.* LOC: B4031 (Aynho Road), 6 miles from junction 10, M40. PARK: Easy. TEL: 01869 338688. VAT: Stan/Spec.

Deddington Antiques Centre
Laurel House, Bull Ring, Market Sq. OX15 0TT. (Mrs B. J. Haller). TVADA. Est. 1972. Open 10-5, including Sun. SIZE: 27 dealers. *STOCK: Furniture, Georgian to 1930's, £40-£4,000; porcelain, silver, pictures, jewellery, 1700-1930, £5-£5,000; collectables, £10-£200.* LOC: Off A4260 Oxford-Banbury road at Deddington traffic lights. PARK: Easy, free. TEL: 01869 338968; fax - 01869 338916. SER: Valuations. FAIRS: NEC.

DORCHESTER-ON-THAMES

Dorchester Antiques
The Barn, 3 High St. OX10 7HH. (J. and S. Hearnden). LAPADA. TVADA. Est. 1992. Open Tues.-Sat. 10-5. SIZE: Medium. *STOCK: Furniture including chairs and decorative country pieces, 18th-19th C.* PARK: Easy. TEL: 01865 341373. SER: Restorations; finder.

Hallidays (Fine Antiques) Ltd
The Old College, High St. OX10 7HL. LAPADA. TVADA. Est. 1950. Open 9-5, Sat. 10-1 and 2-4. SIZE: Large. *STOCK: Furniture, 17th-19th C, £100-£40,000; paintings, 18th-19th C, £100-£20,000; decorative and small items, pine and marble mantelpieces, firegrates, fenders, 18th-20th C; room panelling.* PARK: At rear. TEL: 01865 340028; fax - 01865 341149. FAIRS: Olympia. VAT: Stan/Spec.

EAST HAGBOURNE

Craig Barfoot
Tudor House. OX11 9LR. (I.C. Barfoot). Est. 1993. Open any time by appointment. SIZE: Medium. *STOCK: Longcase clocks, £2,000-£12,000; bracket and lantern clocks.* LOC: Just off A34 halfway between Oxford and Newbury. PARK: Easy. TEL: 01235 818968; home - same; mobile - 07710 858158. SER: Restorations (clocks); buys at auction (clocks, English oak furniture). VAT: Spec.

E.M. Lawson and Co
Kingsholm. OX11 9LN. (W.J. and K.M. Lawson). Est. 1921. Usually open 10-5 but appointment preferred. CL: Sat. *STOCK: Antiquarian and rare books, 1500-1900.* PARK: Easy. TEL: 01235 812033. VAT: Stan.

409

Aston Pine Antiques
16-18 London St. SN7 7AA. (P. O'Gara). Est. 1982. Open Tues.-Sat. 9-5. *STOCK: Victorian and Continental pine; Victorian fireplaces, doors and bathrooms.* TEL: 01367 243840.

The Faringdon Antique Centre
35 Marlborough St. SN7 7JL. Open 10-5, Sun. 11-5. CL: Mon. except Bank Holidays. SIZE: Large. *STOCK: Mahogany, oak, walnut and pine furniture, Georgian to Edwardian, £500-£1,000+.* LOC: Off A420 at Faringdon roundabout, signposted A417 Lechlade, opposite Peugeot garage. PARK: Easy. TEL: 01367 243650. SER: Valuations; restorations (furniture, clocks, porcelain and china).

Oxford Architectural Antiques
16-18 London St. SN7 7AA . (M. O'Gara). Open Tues.-Sat. 9-5. *STOCK: Fireplaces, fixtures and fittings, doors.* TEL: 01367 242268; mobile - 07973 922393.

Barclay Antiques
107 Windmill Rd. OX3 7BT. (C. Barclay). Est. 1979. Open 10-5.30. CL: Wed. SIZE: Small. *STOCK: Porcelain, silver and jewellery, 18th-19th C, £50-£100; period lamps, 20th C, £50-£500.* PARK: Easy. TEL: 01865 769551. SER: Valuations.

Bromlea & Jonkers
24 Hart St. RG9 2AU. (Christiaan Jonkers). Est. 1990. SIZE: Medium. *STOCK: Fine and rare books, 1800-1950, £50-£50,000.* LOC: Main road. PARK: Easy. TEL: 01491 576427; fax - 01491 573805. SER: Valuations; buys at auction (rare books). FAIRS: Olympia.

Easystrip
Old Manor Farm, Bix. RG9 6BX. (R.J. Cain). Est. 1973. Open by apointment only. *STOCK: Victorian doors.* LOC: A4130 right at top of dual carriageway. PARK: Easy. TEL: 01491 577289; mobile - 07785 938580. SER: Restorations (stripping).

Friday Street Antique Centre (The Ferret)
4 Friday St. RG9 1AH . Open 10-5.30, Sun. 12-5. SIZE: 6 dealers. *STOCK: Furniture, china, silver,* *books, pictures, musical instruments, unusual items.* LOC: First left after Henley bridge, then first right, business on left. PARK: Easy. TEL: 01491 574104.

The Barry Keene Gallery
12 Thameside. RG9 1BH. (B.M. and J.S. Keene). FATG. Est. 1971. Open 9.30-5.30 and by appointment. *STOCK: Antique, 20th C and modern paintings, watercolours, drawings, etchings and prints; modern sculpture.* LOC: Junction 8/9 M4, over Henley bridge, left along riverside, 5th building on right. TEL: 01491 577119. SER: Restorations; framing, cleaning, relining, gilding, export. VAT: Stan/Spec.

Richard J. Kingston   BADA
95 Bell St. RG9 2BD. Open 9.30-5 or by appointment. SIZE: Medium. *STOCK: Furniture, 17th to early 19th C; silver, porcelain, glass, paintings, antiquarian and secondhand books.* PARK: Easy. TEL: 01491 574535; home - 01491 573133. SER: Restorations. FAIRS: Surrey, Buxton. VAT: Stan/Spec.

The Old French Mirror Company Ltd
Nightingales, Rotherfield Greys. RG9 4QQ. (Roger and Bridget Johnson). Resident. Est. 1999. Open by appointment only. *STOCK: French mirrors, 18th to early 20th C.* LOC: 3 miles from Henley-on-Thames. PARK: Easy. TEL: 01491 628080; fax - same; e-mail - bridget@ frenchmirrors.com; website - www. oldfrench mirrors.com. SER: Restorations; gilding. VAT: Spec.

Thames Oriental Rug Co
Thames Carpet Cleaners Ltd, 48/56 Reading Rd. RG9 1AG. (D. Benardout and C. Aigin). Resident. Est. 1955. Open 9-12.30 and 1.30-5, Sat. 9-12.30. SIZE: Medium. *STOCK: Oriental rugs, mid-19th C to modern.* PARK: Easy. TEL: 01491 574676. SER: Valuations; restorations and cleaning (carpets). VAT: Stan.

Richard Way Bookseller
54 Friday St. RG9 1AH. (Diana Cook and Richard Way). ABA. Est. 1977. Open 10-5.30. SIZE: Small. *STOCK: Rare and secondhand books, 1600-1999, £5-£1,000.* LOC: Over Henley bridge, turn immediately left behind Angel public house, follow river, turn right, shop past Anchor public house. PARK: Easy. TEL: 01491 576663; fax - 01491 576663. SER: Valuations; restorations. VAT: Stan.

The Country Seat
Huntercombe Manor Barn. RG9 5RY. (Harvey Ferry and William Clegg). LAPADA. TVADA.

Est. 1965. Open 9-5.30, Sun. by appointment. SIZE: Large. *STOCK: Furniture - signed and designed, 1700-1970; garden and architectural/ panelling; art pottery and metalwork, lighting.* LOC: 200 yds down right-hand turn off A4130 Nettlebed-Wallingford. PARK: Easy. TEL: 01491 641349; fax - 01491 641533; e-mail - ferry&clegg@the countryseat. com; website - www.thecountryseat. com. SER: Restorations. VAT: Spec.

LONG HANBOROUGH

Hanborough Antiques
125A-127 Main Rd. OX29 8JX. Open 11-5 (Sun. 1-4 from Easter through summer). CL: Mon. SIZE: Medium. *STOCK: Furniture, country and period; pottery, porcelain, Victoriana, rural and domestic bygones, brass and copper, collectors' items.* LOC: Going north from Oxford on A34 turn left before Woodstock on to A4095 near Witney. PARK: Easy. TEL: 01993 882767.

MIDDLE ASTON, Nr. Bicester

Cotswold Pine & Associates
The Old Poultry Farm. OX25 5QL. (R.J. Prancks). Est. 1980. Open 9-6, Sun. 10-4.30. SIZE: Large. *STOCK: Furniture, 18th-20th C.* LOC: Off A4260, 15 mins. from M40. PARK: Easy. TEL: 01869 340963. SER: Restorations (stripping, polishing and repairs). VAT: Stan/Spec.

NETTLEBED, Nr. Henley-on-Thames

Willow Antiques and the Nettlebed Antique Merchants
The Barns, 1 High St. RG9 5DA. (Willow Bicknell, Michael Plummer and Laurie Brunton). TVADA. Open 10-5.30, Sun. 11-4, other times by appointment. SIZE: Large. *STOCK: Decorative, fine and unusual furniture, objects and decorations, including architectural and garden items, 17th C to 1970s, including Gothic, Aesthetic, Arts & Crafts and Art Deco.* LOC: Between Wallingford and Henley on A4074. PARK: Easy. TEL: 01491 642062/628811; mobile - 07770 554559. SER: Finder; copy and design; advice on period design for house and garden.

NORTH ASTON

Elizabeth Harvey-Lee
1 West Cottages, Middle Aston Lane. OX25 5QB. Est. 1986. Open by appointment. *STOCK:*

Original prints, 15th-20th C; artists' etchings, engravings, lithographs, £100-£6,000. LOC: 6 miles from junction 10, M40, 15 miles north of Oxford. TEL: 01869 347164. SER: Illustrated catalogue available twice yearly (£20 p.a.). FAIRS: London Original Print, Royal Academy; Olympia (June and Nov); Art on Paper, Royal College of Art. VAT: Spec.

OXFORD

Antiques on High Ltd
85 High St. OX1 4BG. (Paul Lipson and Sally Young). TVADA. Est. 1962. Open 10-5, Sun. 11-5. SIZE: Large - 35 dealers. *STOCK: Small antiques and collectables including jewellery, silver and plate, ceramics, glass, clocks and watches, books, 17th-20th C.* PARK: St Clements, Westgate, Seacourt/Thornhill Park and Ride. TEL: 01865 251075. SER: Valuations; restorations (jewellery, silver including replating). FAIRS: TVADA.

Blackwell's Rare Books
48-51 Broad St. OX1 3BQ. Est. 1879. Open 9-6, Tues. 9.30-6, Sun. 11-5. *STOCK: Antiquarian and rare modern books.* TEL: 01865 333555; fax - 01865 794143; e-mail - rarebooks@blackwells bookshops.co.uk; website - www.rarebooks. blackwell.co.uk/. SER: Buys at auction. VAT: Stan/Spec.

The Corner Shop
29 Walton St. OX2 6AA. (P. Hitchcox and D. Florey). Est. 1978. Open 10-5. *STOCK: Pictures, china, glass, silver, small furniture and general items.* LOC: Central north Oxford. TEL: 01865 553364.

Reginald Davis Ltd   BADA
34 High St. OX1 4AN. Est. 1941. Open Tues.-Sat. 9-5. *STOCK: Silver, English and Continental, 17th to early 19th C; jewellery, Sheffield plate, Georgian and Victorian. Not Stocked: Glass, china, pewter.* LOC: On A40. PARK: Easy. TEL: 01865 248347. SER: Valuations; restorations (silver, jewellery). VAT: Stan/Spec.

Jeremy's (Oxford Stamp Centre)
98 Cowley Rd. OX4 1JE. Open 10-12.30 and 2-5. *STOCK: Stamps, postcards and cigarette cards.* TEL: 01865 241011; website - www.postcard. co.uk/jeremys.

Jericho Books
48 Walton St. OX2 6AD. (Frank Stringer). PBFA. Est. 1980. Open 10.30-6, Sun. 11-6. SIZE: Medium. *STOCK: Secondhand and antiquarian books.* PARK: Easy. TEL: 01865 511992. SER: Valuations; buys at auction (antiquarian books). FAIRS: Royal National Hotel. VAT: Stan.

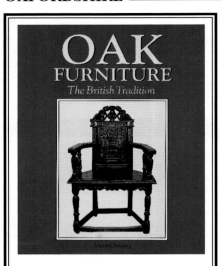

OAK FURNITURE
The British Tradition

This is the definitive book on the history and development of oak furniture in the British Isles and New England. Victor Chinnery concentrates on three fundamental characteristics of furniture: construction, function and decoration which cannot exist separately, but have to be analysed separately. The huge number of illustrations reflect the enormous scope of this pioneering study. It is the first major book on this subject for over 50 years.

ISBN 1 85149 013 2
620pp., 22 col., 2,000 b.&w. illus.
£49.50/$99.50

Christopher Legge Oriental Carpets
25 Oakthorpe Rd., Summertown. OX2 7BD. (C.T. Legge). Est. 1970. SIZE: Medium. *STOCK: Rugs, various sizes, 19th to early 20th C, £100-£6,000.* LOC: Near shopping parade. PARK: Easy. TEL: 01865 557572; fax - 01865 554877. SER: Valuations; restorations; re-weaving; handcleaning. VAT: Stan.

Laurie Leigh Antiques
36 High St. OX1 4AN. (L. and D. Leigh). LAPADA. Est. 1963. Open 10.30-5.30. CL: Thurs. *STOCK: Glass and keyboard musical instruments.* TEL: 01865 244197. VAT: Stan/Spec.

Magna Gallery
41 High St. OX1 4AP. (Martin J. Blant). Est. 1969. Open 10-5.30. SIZE: Medium. *STOCK: Maps especially English counties, general topography especially Oxford, prints including botanical, caricatures, 1550-1895.* TEL: 01865 245805. SER: Valuations; framing. VAT: Stan.

Oriental Rug Gallery Ltd
15 Woodstock Rd. OX2 6HA. (Richard Mathias and Julian Blair). BORDA. *STOCK: Russian, Afghan, Turkish and Persian carpets, rugs and kelims; Oriental objets d'art.* TEL: +44 (0) 1865 316333; fax - same; e-mail - rugs@oriental ruggallery.com; website - www.oriental ruggallery.com.

Payne and Son (Goldsmiths) Ltd BADA
131 High St. OX1 4DH. (E.P., G.N. and J.D.Payne, P.J. Coppock, A. Salmon and D. Thornton). Est. 1790. Open weekdays 9-5. SIZE: Medium. STOCK: British silver, antique, modern and secondhand; jewellery, all £50-£10,000+. LOC: Town centre near Carfax traffic lights. PARK: 800yds. TEL: 01865 243787; fax - 01865 793241; e-mail - silver@payneandson.co.uk; website - www.payneandson.co.uk. SER: Restorations (English silver). VAT: Stan/Spec.

Sanders of Oxford Ltd
Salutation House, 104 High St. OX1 4BW. Open 10-6. SIZE: Large. *STOCK: Prints, especially Oxford; maps and Japanese woodcuts.* TEL: 01865 242590; fax - 01865 721748; e-mail - info@sanders-oxford.co.uk; website - www. oxlink.co.uk/antiques/sanders.html. VAT: Stan/Spec.

A.J. Saywell Ltd. (The Oxford Stamp Shop)
15 Hollybush Row. OX1 1JH. (I.H. and H.J. Saywell). Est. 1943. Open 10-5.30, Thurs. 10-1. SIZE: Small. *STOCK: Stamps, accessories, coins and some medals.* LOC: Off Park End St. near railway station. PARK: Easy. TEL: 01865 248889. SER: Valuations. VAT: Stan.

St. Clements Antiques
93 St. Clements St. OX4 1AR. (Giles Power). Est. 1998. Open 10.30-5. SIZE: Medium. *STOCK: Oak and country items, 18th-19th C, £50-£5,000; interesting curios, 18th-20th C, £5-£500.* LOC: Close to city centre, next to Magdalen Bridge. PARK: Easy, opposite. TEL: 01865 727010; home - 01865 200359. SER: Valuations. VAT: Stan/Spec.

Thorntons of Oxford Ltd
11 Broad St. OX1 3AR. Open 9-6. SIZE: Large. *STOCK: Antiquarian books, prints and cards.* TEL: 01865 242939; fax - 01865 204021; e-mail - Thorntons@booknews.demon.co.uk; website - www.demon.co.uk/Thorntons.

Waterfield's
52 High St. OX1 4AS. Open 9.45-5.45. *STOCK: Antiquarian and secondhand books, all subjects, especially academic in the humanities; literature, history, philosophy, 17th-18th C English books.* TEL: 01865 721809.

Manor Farm Antiques
Manor Farm. OX8 7RL. (C.W.Leveson-Gower). Est. 1964. Open daily, Sun. by appointment. SIZE: Large. *STOCK: Victorian brass and iron beds.* PARK: Easy, in farmyard. TEL: 01865 300303.

Wychwood Antiques
Upper Farm Cottage. OX18 4UH. Open by appointment only. *STOCK: English country furniture, Mason's Ironstone, treen, metalware and decorative items.* TEL: 01993 822860.

Quillon Antiques of Tetsworth
Old Stores, High St. OX9 7AS. Open Tues.-Thurs. 10-5, Sat. 10-6, Sun. 12-5. SIZE: Medium.

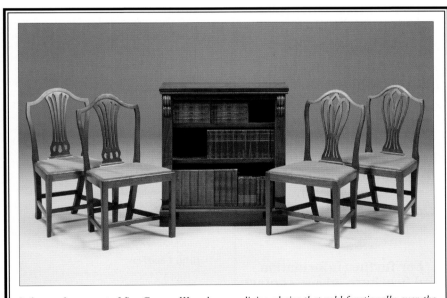

Left: two from a set of five George III mahogany dining chairs that sold fractionally over the mid-estimate for around £1,025, the set of six similar George III chairs (two shown on the right) also sold at mid-estimate for £1,550, the value of the sixth chair in the latter set at around £525 perhaps reflects the cost of having a modern copy made for the former set of five.

From an article entitled 'Furniture at Auction from £25' by William Lorimer which appeared in the May 2001 issue of **Antique Collecting** magazine. For more details and to subscribe see page 147.

THE SWAN

AT TETSWORTH

BRITAIN'S PREMIER ANTIQUES CENTRE

Over 40 rooms of Town, Country & Decorative Antiques

70 Quality Dealers
Rapid Turnover of Stock
Delivery & Shipping Arranged
Professional Sales Staff
Listed Elizabethan Building
Acclaimed Restaurant
5 mins Junct. 6/8 M40 Motorway
Calendar of Events
Ample Parking
Open 7 Days inc. Bank Hols.
10.00am to 6.00pm

For further information and brochure, please contact

The Swan at Tetsworth
High Street, Tetsworth, Thame
Oxfordshire OX9 7AB
Tel: 01844 281777
Fax: 01844 281770
www.theswan.co.uk
antiques@theswan.co.uk

STOCK: 17th-19th C oak and country furniture, including oak and pine refectory tables; period armour, muskets, armorial and medieval items. LOC: A40 between exits 6 and 7, M40. PARK: Easy. TEL: 01844 281636. SER: Valuations; restorations.

The Swan at Tetsworth
High St. OX9 7AB. TVADA. Est. 1995. Open 7 days 10-6. SIZE: 40+ rooms. LOC: A40, 5 minutes from junctions 6 and 8, M40. PARK: Own large. TEL: 01844 281777; fax - 01844 281770; website - www.theswan.co.uk; e-mail - antiques@theswan.co.uk. SER: Restorations (clocks, cabinet work and gilding). Below are listed the dealers at this centre.

Deborah Abbot
Jewellery and objets d'art.

Jason Abbot
Sporting guns.

Acanthus Design
Arts & Crafts and Art Nouveau furniture and accessories.

S.J. Allison
Decorative ceramics, small furniture and silver.

Beagle Antiques
Fine watercolours and oils

Bespoke Chair Company
Victorian and Edwardian upholstered wing chairs, sofas and footstools.

David Binns
Books and paperweights.

Peter Bond
Prints, watercolours. SER: Gilding.

S. Bond & Sons
Fine period furniture.

Ann Casey
Antique textiles, ceramics, fashion accessories and small furniture.

Caversham Antiques
Furniture and collectables.

John Chaffer
Framed antiquarian prints and maps.

David Collins
Fine oil paintings.

Audrey Cooper
Kitchenalia and country items.

Jenny Corkhill-Callin
Textiles, including cushions, curtains, braids and quilts.

S. and K. Cullup
Linens and textiles.

D. & R. Antiques
Regency, Victorian and Edwardian furniture. SER: *Restorations.*

Jacqueline Ding
Oriental antiques.

Rodney and Helen Dodson
Fine furniture and decorative items.

Sally Forster
Costume jewellery and antique accessories.

Mavis Foster-Abbott
20th C glass, specialising in Latticinio.

Framed Antiques
Collectable framed cigarette cards.

Gillian Gould
Maritime antiques. TEL: E-mail - gillgould@ dealwith.com.

Grate Expectations
Fireplaces, Cornish ranges, tiles, garden items and architectural salvage.

Le Grenier
Fine quality mirrors.

Harpers Jewellers
Vintage watches.

Hen's Teeth Antiques
(Martin Murray). TVADA. *Period furniture and decorative items.* TEL: Mobile - 07970 625359.

John Howkins Antiques
Late 18th to early 20th C furniture and decorative items.

Martin Isenberg
Period/decorative furniture, treen and ceramics.

Nigel Johnston
Furniture and small clocks.

Susan Ling
Small furniture, brass and copper.

Shelagh Lister
Fine English and decorative furniture.

Loire Valley Antiques
French furniture.

J. MacNaughton-Smith
TVADA. *Mainly 18th-19th C English furniture including desks, writing tables, chiffoniers, chests of drawers; small decorative items, 19th C watercolours.*

Market Square Antiques
18th-19th C china, silver, blue & white, sewing items and small decorative antiques.

Marquetry Antiques
Chinese antiques and objets d'art.

Eddie McCourt
Period furniture and decorative items.

Sarah McKean
French country furniture, textiles and decorative items.

Millroyal Antiques
Fine furniture and smalls.

Nicholas Mitchell
Unusual period furniture and smalls.

Old Chair Company

Orient Carpets
Persian rugs, kelims and textiles.

Peter Phillips
Ceramics, especially blue & white transferware; small period furniture.

T.H.A. & F.M. Sharland
Frames, prints and watercolours.

Gail Spence Antiques
Small decorative, collectables and gift antiques.

Steeple Antiques
LAPADA. *Large period furniture and chandeliers.*

Jackie Stewart-Jones
Desk and writing accessories.

E. Stone Associates
Antique and secondhand jewellery. SER: Restorations.

Tartan Antiques
Objets d'art, pictures and toys.

Geoff and Coral Taylor-Robinson
French provincial furniture and decorative accessories.

Paul Templeton
Silver, jewellery and small objets d'art.

Touchwood Antiques
English country furniture, specialising in oak.

Duncan Webster
Fine 18th-19th C furniture and paintings.

Jinny Wright
French country furniture including garden and kitchen.

Wright Associates
Jewellery, glass, silver, boxes and small furniture.

Caroline Wyatt
Fine English oak furniture, pine and silver collectables.

THAME

Rosemary and Time
42 Park St. OX9 3HR. Open 9-6. CL: Mon.
STOCK: Clocks and barometers. TEL: 01844
216923. SER: Valuations; restorations; old spare
parts. VAT: Stan/Spec.

WALLINGFORD

de Albuquerque Antiques
12 High St. OX10 0BP. Est. 1982. Open 10-5.
SIZE: Medium. *STOCK: Furniture and objects,
18th-19th C.* PARK: At rear. TEL: 01491 832322;
fax - same; e-mail - janedea@lineone.net. SER:
Framing; gilding.

Toby English
10 St Mary's St. OX10 0EL. PBFA. Est. 1980.
Open 9.30-5. SIZE: Medium. *STOCK: Books,
19th-20th C, £5-£500, prints, 19th-20th C, £20-
£200; maps, 19th C, £30-£500.* LOC: Town
centre. PARK: Cattle Market. TEL: 01491
836389; fax - same; e-mail - toby@tobyenglish.
com; website - www.tobyenglish.com. SER:
Valuations; restorations; buys at auction. FAIRS:
PBFA London.

The Lamb Arcade
83 High St. OX10 0BX. TVADA. Open 10-5,
Sat. 10-5.30. *STOCK: As below plus books, crafts
and ephemera.* TEL: 01491 835166. SER:
Restorations (furniture). Below are listed some of
the dealers at this centre.

Alicia Antiques
(A. Collins). *China, silver and collectors' items.*
TEL: 01491 33737.

Anne Brewer Antiques
Furniture, china, jewellery and objets d'art. TEL:
01491 38486.

Pat Hayward
Furniture, light fittings and decorative items.

OTT
*Tin toys, motoring and aviation memorabilia,
pictures.* TEL: 01491 832023.

Phoenix Antiques
*Victorian furniture, Continental and English pine,
lighting.*

Precious Antiques
*Art Nouveau and Arts & Crafts furniture, china and
glass, specialising in Noritake.*

Stag Antiques & Gallery
*Jewellery, furniture, pictures, Staffordshire figures,
Clarice Cliff and Belleek.* TEL: 01491 834516.

416

Gretel Stone
Small furniture, porcelain, silver, pictures and objets d'art.

Tags
(T. and A. Green). *Collectors' items, curios, dolls' house furniture, jewellery, militaria, scientific instruments and furniture.* TEL: 01491 35048; home - 01491 872962.

Waters Violins
Old violins, violas and cellos. TEL: 01491 25616. SER: Valuations; restorations.

MGJ Jewellers Ltd.
1A St. Martins St. OX10 0AQ. (Mrs M. Jane). Est. 1971. Open 10-4.30, Sat. 10-5. SIZE: Small. *STOCK: Jewellery, Victorian and secondhand, £100-£2,500.* LOC: Town centre. PARK: Nearby. TEL: 01491 834336. VAT: Stan/Spec.

Chris and Lin O'Donnell Antiques
26 High St. OX10 0BU. Open 9.30-1 and 2-5. SIZE: Large. *STOCK: Furniture, 18th C to Edwardian, to £3,000; rugs, to £500; unusual objects, Oriental antiques, taxidermy.* LOC: Into town over Wallingford Bridge, 150yds. along High St. on left-hand side. PARK: Thames St. TEL: 01491 839332. VAT: Spec.

Otter Antiques
20 High St. OX10 0BP. (P. and B. Otter). Open 9.30-5.30, Sun. 10.30-5. SIZE: Medium. *STOCK: Furniture, writing boxes, etc.* PARK: Easy, rear of shop. TEL: 01491 825544; fax - 01865 407396; website - www.otterantiques.co.uk. SER: Restorations (boxes). VAT: Stan/Spec.

Mike Ottrey Antiques
16 High St. OX10 0BP. (M.J. Ottrey). Est. 1955. Open 9.30-5.30. CL: Sat. SIZE: Large. *STOCK: Furniture, 17th-19th C; oil paintings, copper and brass, decorative and unusual items.* LOC: A429. PARK: At rear. TEL: 01491 836429. VAT: Spec.

Summers Davis Antiques Ltd
Calleva House, 6 High St. OX10 0BP. (Graham Wells). LAPADA. CINOA. TVADA. Est. 1917. Open 9-5.30, Sat. 9-5, Sun. 11-5. SIZE: Large. *STOCK: English and Continental furniture, decorative items and objects.* Not Stocked: Silver, shipping goods. LOC: From London, shop is on left, 50yds. from Thames Bridge. PARK: Opposite, behind castellated gates. TEL: 01491 836284; fax - 01491 833443; e-mail - summers davisantiques@msn.com; website - www.sd-antique-furniture.com. VAT: Spec.

W. R. Harvey & Co (Antiques) Ltd.

FINE ANTIQUE FURNITURE
& WORKS OF ART,
CONSERVATION &
CONSULTANCY

86 Corn Street, Witney,
Oxfordshire OX28 6BU.

Tel: 01993 706501
Fax: 01993 706601

Web Site:
www.wrharvey.co.uk
e-mail:
antiques@wrharvey.co.uk

A superb Regency Period Mahogany extending Dining Table Ca: 1815. Height: 27½" Width: 47" Length:(Closed) 52½" (Fully extended) 141"

Tooley Adams & Co
P O Box 174. OX10 0YT. (S. Luck). ABA IMCOS. Est. 1979. *STOCK: Antiquarian maps and atlases; travel and map related reference books.* TEL: 01491 838298; fax - 01491 834616; e-mail - Steve@tooleys.co.uk; website - www.tooleys.co.uk. SER: Valuations; restorations. FAIRS: Worldwide.

WANTAGE

The Arbery Centre
Market Place. OX12 8AB. (Tapecrown Ltd). Est. 2000. Open 9.30-5, Sun. 10-4. SIZE: Large. *STOCK: Wide range of general antiques and collectables.* PARK: Behind premises. TEL: 01235 769325; fax - 01235 765242.

WATLINGTON, Nr. Oxford

Cross Antiques
37 High St. OX9 5PZ. (R.A. and I.D. Crawley). Est. 1986. Open 10-6, Sun. and Wed. by appointment. SIZE: Small. *STOCK: Furniture, £100-£5,000; decorative smalls, clocks and garden items, £50-£2,000; all 1600-1900.* LOC: Off B4009 in village centre. PARK: Easy and at rear. TEL: 01491 612324; home - same.

Stephen Orton Antiques
The Antiques Warehouse, Shirburn Rd. OX49 5BZ. TVADA. Open Mon.-Fri. 9-5, other times by appointment. SIZE: Warehouse. *STOCK: 18th-19th C furniture, some decorative items.* LOC: 2 mins. from exit 6, M40. TEL: 01491 613752; e-mail - Orton.Antiques@virgin.net. SER: Supply and pack containers; valuations; restorations; buying agent. VAT: Stan/Spec.

WESTON-ON-THE-GREEN

Julie Strachey
Southfield Farm, North Lane. OX6 8RG. TVADA. Open by appointment only. *STOCK: Decorative 18th-19th C farm and country furniture, especially tables, dressers, chests, wrought iron and unusual garden items.* LOC: 5 minutes from junction 9, M40 or off A34 on to B430. TEL: 01869 350833; mobile - 07711 249939.

WITNEY

The Clock Work Shop
79 Corn St. OX8 7DH. (Steve Fletcher). Est. 1973. Open Tues.-Fri. 9-12 and 1-5, Sat. 9-4. CL:

Mon. SIZE: Small. *STOCK: Clocks, furniture, £30-£10,000; treen, £30-£150; all 18th-19th C.* PARK: Easy. TEL: 01993 772123. SER: Valuations; restorations (clock movements, furniture). VAT: Stan/Spec.

Colin Greenway Antiques
90 Corn St. OX8 7BU. CADA Resident. Est. 1975. Open 9.30-5, Sat. 10-4, Sun. by appointment. SIZE: Large. *STOCK: Furniture, 17th-20th C; metalware, decorative and unusual items.* LOC: Along High St. to town centre, turn right, shop 400yds. on right. PARK: Easy. TEL: 01993 705026; mobile - 07831 585014. VAT: Stan/Spec.

W.R. Harvey & Co (Antiques) Ltd
BADA
86 Corn St. OX8 7BU. CADA. GMC. Open 9.30-5.30, and by appointment. SIZE: Large. *STOCK: Fine English furniture, £500-£50,000; clocks, mirrors, objets d'art, £250-£20,000; all 1680-1830.* LOC: 300 yds. from Market Place. PARK: Easy. TEL: 01993 706501; fax - 01993 706601; e-mail - antiques@wrharvey.co.uk; website - www.wrharvey.co.uk. SER: Valuations; restorations; consultancy. FAIRS: BADA; Chelsea (March & Sept.); Olympia (June). VAT: Stan/Spec.

Barbara Radman
Westfield House 2G Westfield Rd. OX8 5JG . Est. 1976. Open by appointment only. SIZE: Medium. *STOCK: Orders, medals, badges, decorations, specialist in miniature orders, medals and decorations of the world; military books, police and fire brigade memorabilia, postal history, paper money, maps and books.* PARK: Easy and nearby. TEL: 01993 772705; fax - same; e-mail - radman@tinyonline.co.uk. SER: Valuations; buys at auction.

Joan Wilkins Antiques
158 Corn St. OX8 7BY. (Mrs J.Wilkins). Est. 1973. Open 10-5. *STOCK: Furniture, 18th-19th C, £150-£3,500; 19th C glass, metalware, £10-£1,500.* LOC: Town centre. PARK: Easy. TEL: 01993 704749. VAT: Spec.

Witney Antiques
BADA
96/100 Corn St. OX28 6BU. (L.S.A. and C.J. Jarrett and R.R. Jarrett-Scott). LAPADA, CADA. Est. 1962. Open 10-5. SIZE: Large. *STOCK: English furniture, 17th-18th C; bracket and longcase clocks, mahogany, oak and walnut, metalware, needleworks and works of art.* LOC: From Oxford on old A40 through Witney via High St., turn right at T-junction, 400yds. on right. PARK: Easy. TEL: 01993 703902/703887; fax - 01993 779852. SER: Restorations. FAIRS: BADA; Grosvenor House. VAT: Spec.

Witney Antiques

WOODSTOCK

Antiques of Woodstock
18/20 Market Place. OX20 1TA. (Allan James and Andrew Hennell). Est. 1975. Open 10.30-5.30, Sun. 10.30-5. SIZE: Large. *STOCK: Fine Georgian and Regency dining room furniture, long sets of period chairs, early 17th-19th C oak and country furniture, period silver and glass.* LOC: Opposite The Bear Hotel. PARK: Easy. TEL: 01993 811818; fax - 01993 811831. SER: Valuations; restorations; consultations; interior decor advice; buys at auction; search; commission sales. VAT: Stan.

Chris Baylis Country Chairs
16 Oxford St. OX20 1TS. TVADA. Open 10.30-5.30, Sun. 11-5, appointment advisable to view stock. *STOCK: English country chairs, from 1780; sets of rush seated chairs including ladder and spindle backs, Windsors and kitchen chairs.* TEL: 01993 813887; fax - 01993 812379; e-mail - rwood@mcmail.com; website - www.realwoodfurniture.co.uk.

Bees Antiques
30 High St. OX20 1TG. (Jo and Jim Bateman). TVADA. Est. 1991. Open 10-1 and 1.30-5, Sun. 11-5. CL: Tues. SIZE: Small. *STOCK: Pottery, porcelain and glass, 18th-20th C, £30-£1,500; small furniture, 19th to early 20th C, £50-£2,000; metalware, 19th C, £30-£200; jewellery, 19th-20th C, £30-£1,000.* LOC: Just off A3440 Oxford/Stratford-on-Avon road, in town centre. PARK: Opposite. TEL: 01993 811062; home - 01993 771593. SER: Valuations; buys at auction (as stock). FAIRS: TVADA.

The Chair Set - Antiques
18-20 Market Place. OX20. (Allan James). Est. 1982. Open 10.30-5.30, including Sun. SIZE: Large. *STOCK: Sets of chairs, £1,000-£20,000; single and pairs of chairs, £200-£3,000; dining tables and accessories, £800-£15,000; all early 18th to late 19th C.* LOC: Opposite Bear Hotel. PARK: Easy. TEL: 01993 811818; fax - 01428 707435. SER: Valuations; restorations (woodwork and upholstery); buys at auction (sets of chairs). VAT: Spec.

Robin Sanders and Sons
11 Market St. OX20 1SU. LAPADA. CINOA. *STOCK: English and some French furniture, 17th-19th C; Staffordshire and Masons ironstone pottery, brass, treen and English glass pictures.* TEL: 01993 813930.

Span Antiques
6 Market Place. OX20 1TA. TVADA. Est. 1978. Open 10-1 and 2-5, Sun 1-5. SIZE: Medium. LOC: Near Town Hall. PARK: Easy. Below are listed some of the dealers selling from these premises. TEL: 01993 811332.

> **Doreen Caudwell**
> *Textiles and porcelain.*
>
> **Diana Clark**
> *Old and interesting books.*
>
> **Francoise Daniel**
> *Boxes, porcelain and collectables.*
>
> **Liz Hall-Bakker**
> *Art Nouveau and Deco.*
>
> **Jasper Antiques**
> *Silver and decorative items.*
>
> **Rebecca Stuart-Mobey**
> *Furniture and glass.*

YARNTON

Yarnton Antiques Centre
Yarnton Nurseries Garden Centre, Sandy Lane. OX5 1PA. Open 10-4.30 including Sun. SIZE: 50 dealers. *STOCK: General antiques.* TEL: 01865 379600.

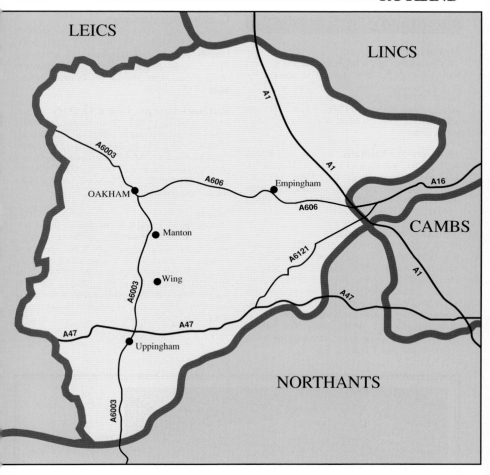

Dealers and Shops in Rutland

Empingham	1	Oakham	6	Wing	1
Manton	1	Uppingham	8		

EMPINGHAM, Nr. Oakham

Churchgate Antiques
13 Church St. LE15 8PN. (R.Wheatley). Open Wed., Fri., Sat. and Sun. 12-6, other times by appointment. SIZE: Medium. *STOCK: Furniture, mainly 18th-19th C, £50-£4,000; paintings and prints, £25-£1,000; plate, 19th-20th C, £5-£300.* LOC: Opposite church, off A606. PARK: Easy. TEL: 01780 460528.

MANTON

David Smith Antiques
Old Cottage, 20 St. Mary's Rd. LE15 8SU. Est. 1953. Open 9-5. CL: Sun., except by appointment. *STOCK: Furniture, glass, silver.* PARK: Easy. TEL: 01572 737244/737607.

Decorum

18 Church St. LE15 6AA. (Gina and Gilbert Flach). Est. 1996. Open Tues., Wed. and Fri. 10-5, Sat. 9-5, other days by appointment. SIZE: Small. *STOCK: 19th C clocks, china, jewellery, furniture and linen, £5-£1,500.* PARK: 100 yds. TEL: 01572 771775. SER: Valuations; restorations (china).

Fine Art of Oakham   BADA

4 High St. LE15 6AL. (Dr A.J. Smith). LAPADA. Open 10-5. CL: Mon. *STOCK: Continental oils and watercolours, Victorian and 19th C.* **TEL: 01572 755221; fax - 01572 770047.**

The Old House Gallery

13-15 Market Place. LE15 6DT. (R.A. Clarke). Est. 1979. Open 10-1 and 2-5. CL: Thurs. SIZE: Medium. *STOCK: Oil paintings, £50-£3,500; art studio pottery, 1850-1990, £5-£500; watercolours, £25-£2,000; prints and objets d'art, £5-£500; antiquarian county maps, £15-£250; contemporary paintings, sculpture and three-dimensional works.* PARK: Easy. TEL: 01572 755538. SER: Valuations; restorations (oils, watercolours, prints, frames); framing.

C. Reynolds Antiques

The East Lodge, Burley Mansion House, Burley-on-the-Hill. LE15 7TE. Est. 1972. Resident. Usually available but telephone call advisable. SIZE: Large. *STOCK: Early verge watches, repeater and other unusual clocks and watches.* TEL: 01572 771551.

Rutland Antique Clock Gallery

37 Trent Rd. LE15 6HE. (K.G. Neale). Est. 1986. Open by appointment only. SIZE: Small. *STOCK: 17th C clocks, £45-£2,000.* LOC: A606, Oakham High St., Mill St., corner plot between Trent Rd. and Spey Rd. PARK: Easy. TEL: 01572 723375; home - same. SER: Valuations; restorations.

Swans

17 Mill St. LE15 6EA. (P.W. Jones). Est. 1988. Open 9.30-5.30, Sun. 2-5.30. SIZE: Large. *STOCK: French and English beds and associated furniture; 18th-19th C antiques, mainly decorative and upholstered.* LOC: 150yds. from High St. PARK: Easy. TEL: 01572 724364; home - 01572 757252. SER: Manufactures new bases and mattresses; valuations; restorations. VAT: Stan/Spec.

This mid-19th century oak writing table is estimated to realise £2,000-£3,000 at Phillips Bond Street on 22nd May.

From an Auction Preview which appeared in the May 2001 issue of **Antique Collecting** magazine. For more details and to subscribe see page 147.

JOHN GARNER
51-53 High Street East, Uppingham, Rutland, LE15 9PY

Fine 18th & 19th Century Furniture, Paintings, Clocks, Bronzes, Garden Statuary Some 20th Century Furniture.

Very large selection of period prints

Tel: **01572 823607** Fax: **01572 821654**
Website: **www.johngarnerantiques.com**

Clutter
14 Orange St. LE15 9SQ. (M.C. Sumner). Est. 1982. Open 10-5. *STOCK: Victorian linen and lace; textiles including Durham quilts, chenilles; interesting silver, porcelain, glass, small furniture, kitchenalia, 10p-£1,000.* LOC: Take old A47 from by-pass, shop 25yds. from traffic lights. PARK: Nearby. TEL: 01572 823745; home - 01572 717243. SER: Valuations; restorations (furniture, brass, copper, silver, bronze, ivory, lacquer, shibayama and associated materials, ceramics); hire (christening gowns and Victorian wedding dress and accessories).

John Garner
51-53 High St. East. LE15 9PY. LAPADA. Est. 1966. Open 9-5.30, Sun. 2-5, prior telephone call advisable. SIZE: Large + warehouse. *STOCK: 18th-19th C furniture, paintings, prints, clocks, bronzes, mirrors, garden statuary, some 20th C furniture.* LOC: Just off A47, 80 yards from market place. PARK: Easy. TEL: 01572 823607; fax - 01572 821654; mobile - 07850 596556; e-mail - johngarner@aol.com; website - www.johngarnerantiques.com. SER: Valuations; restorations (furniture, paintings, prints); framing (trade); courier; export. VAT: Stan/Spec.

Gilberts of Uppingham
Ayston Rd. LE15 9RL. (M. Gilbert). Open 9.30-5, Mon. and Tues. 9.30-1 and 2-5. *STOCK: General antiques.* TEL: 01572 823486.

Goldmark Books
14 Orange St. LE15 9SQ. (Mike Goldmark). Open 9.30-5.30 and Sunday afternoons. *STOCK: Antiquarian and secondhand books.* LOC: Between Market Sq. and traffic lights. PARK: Nearby. TEL: 01572 822694.

Marc Oxley Fine Art
10 Orange St. LE15 9SQ. Resident. Est. 1981. Open 9.30-5.30, Sat. 10-6, Sun. by appointment. *STOCK: Original watercolours and drawings, 1700-1950, £5-£850; oils, 19th-20th C, £100-£1,500; prints, mainly 19th C, £5-£50; maps, 17th-19th C, £10-£375.* LOC: From A47 on main road into town, just before Market Sq. PARK: Market Sq. TEL: 01572 822334; home - same. SER: Valuations; restorations (oils).

T.J. Roberts
39/41 High St. East. LE15 9PY. Resident. Open 9.30-5.30. *STOCK: Furniture, porcelain and pottery, 18th-19th C; Staffordshire figures, general antiques.* PARK: Easy. TEL: 01572 821493. VAT: Stan/Spec.

Tattersall's
14b Orange St. LE15 9SQ. (J. Tattersall). Est. 1985. Open 9.30-5. CL: Mon. SIZE: Small. *STOCK: Persian rugs, 19th-20th C.* PARK: Easy, 200yds. TEL: 01572 821171. SER: Restorations (rugs, carpets).

Woodman's House Antiques
35 High St. East. LE15 9PY. (Mr. and Mrs. James Collie). Est. 1991. SIZE: Small. *STOCK: Furniture, 17th-18th C.* PARK: Easy. TEL: 01572 821799; fax - same; website - www.rutnet.co.uk/woodmans. SER: Valuations; restorations; buys at auction.

Robert Bingley Antiques
Home Farm, Church St. LE15 8RS. Open Wed.-Sat. 10-5, Sun.-Tues. by appointment. SIZE: Large. *STOCK: Furniture, 17th-19th C, £50-£5,000; glass, clocks, silver and plate, pictures and porcelain.* LOC: Next to church. PARK: Own. TEL: 01572 737725; home - 01572 737314. SER: Valuations; restorations. VAT: Spec.

ATCHAM, Nr. Shrewsbury

Mytton Antiques

Norton Cross Roads. SY4 4UH. (M.A., E.A., J.M. and S. Nares). Est. 1972. Open 9.30-5.30 or by appointment. SIZE: Medium. *STOCK: General antiques, furniture, 1700-1900, £50-£3,000; clocks, all types, £35-£2,000; smalls, £15-£1,000.* LOC: On B5061 (the old A5) between Shrewsbury and Wellington. PARK: Own. TEL: 01952 740229 (24hrs.); fax - 01952 461154; mobiles - 07860 575639/07711 205503; e-mail - nares@myttonantiques.freeserve.co.uk. SER: Buys at auction; suppliers of reference books and restoration materials. VAT: Stan/Spec.

BISHOP'S CASTLE

Ark Antiques

9 Market Square. (Jill Thomas). Est. 1974. Open 10.30-4.30 and Bank Holidays. CL: Mon. and Wed. SIZE: Small. *STOCK: Oak and pine country furniture, 18th-19th C; country and rural tools, brass and iron beds.* PARK: Easy. TEL: Home - 01588 638608. SER: Valuations; restorations (metal and wood); buys at auction (cottage furniture and artifacts).

Decorative Antiques

47 Church St. SY9 5AD. (Evelyn Bowles and Richard Moulson). Est. 1996. Open seven days. SIZE: Small. *STOCK: Ceramics and glass, jewellery and metalware, small furniture, 20th C, £5-£1,000.* PARK: Easy. TEL: 01588 638851; fax/home - same. SER: Valuations. FAIRS: Warwick Deco; Chester Deco.

BRIDGNORTH

Bridgnorth Antiques Centre

Whiteburn St. WV16 4QT. (R.G. Lewis). Est. 1992. Open 10-5.30, Sun. 10.30-4.30. SIZE: Large. *STOCK: Clocks, furniture, collectables.* PARK: Easy. TEL: 01746 768055. SER: Restorations (clocks).

English Heritage

2 Whitburn St., High Town. WV16 4QN. (P.J. Wainwright). Open 10-5. CL: Thurs. SIZE: Medium. *STOCK: Jewellery, silverware and general antiques, militaria, coins.* LOC: Just off High St. PARK: Easy. TEL: 01746 762097. VAT: Stan/Spec.

Malthouse Antiques

The Old Malthouse, 6 Underhill St. WV16 4BB. (Susan and William Mantle). Est. 1980. Open 10-

A selection of Siebe Gorman 12-bolt diving helmets. (Left to right) 1950s helmet – £3,200; 1960s helmet – £1,700; c.1910 helmet – £6,500.

From an Auction Report by Christopher Wight on Maritime and Naval Battles at Christie's South Kensington on 9th November 2000. This sale was featured in the February 2001 issue of **Antique Collecting** magazine. For more details and to subscribe see page 147.

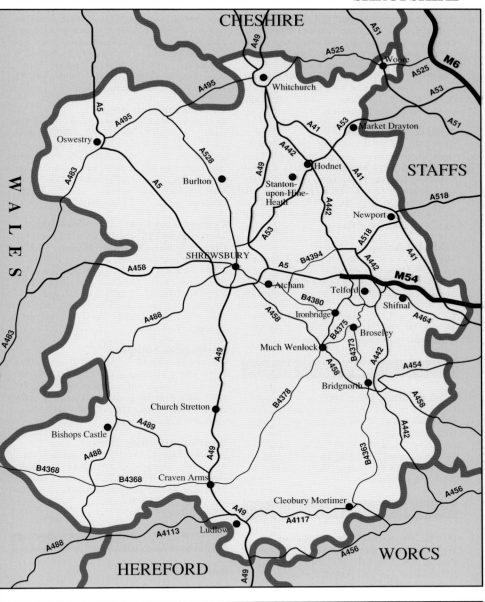

Dealers and Shops in Shropshire

Atcham	1	Craven Arms	1	Oswestry	1
Bishop's Castle	2	Hodnet	1	Shifnal	1
Bridgnorth	5	Ironbridge	1	Shrewsbury	15
Broseley	1	Ludlow	11	Stanton upon Hine Heath	1
Burlton	1	Market Drayton	3	Telford	2
Church Stretton	5	Much Wenlock	4	Whitchurch	2
Cleobury Mortimer	2	Newport	1	Woore	1

6, Sun. by appointment. CL: Wed. SIZE: Medium. *STOCK: Victorian and Edwardian furniture, French beds and armoires, £100-£1,500; upholstered chairs and sofas, from 19th C, £300-£1,800; china and decorative items, 19th-20th C, £5-£150.* LOC: Main road into town from Wolverhampton. PARK: Nearby. TEL: 01746 763054; fax/home - same. SER: Valuations; restorations (furniture).

Micawber Antiques
64 St. Mary's St. WV16 4DR. (N. Berthoud). Open 10-5, other days by appointment. CL: Mon. and Thurs. SIZE: Medium. *STOCK: English porcelain and pottery, decorative items, £5-£500; small furniture, £100-£1,000.* LOC: 100yds. west of town hall in High St. PARK: Easy. TEL: 01746 763254; home - same. SER: Buys at auction (English porcelain).

Old Mill Antique Centre
Mill St. WV15 5AG. (D.A. and J.R. Ridgeway). Est. 1996. Open 10-5 including Sun. SIZE: Large - 90 dealers. *STOCK: Wide range of general antiques including period furniture, porcelain and silver, jewellery, prints and watercolours, collectables.* LOC: Main road. PARK: Own. TEL: 01746 768778; fax - 01746 762248. SER: Valuations; restorations. VAT: Stan.

BROSELEY

John Boulton Fine Art
6 Church St. TF12 5DG. Resident. Est. 1983. Open 9-5, Sun. 2-5. SIZE: Medium. *STOCK: Oils, watercolours and prints, late 19th C to contemporary, £100-£2,500.* LOC: Junction 4, M54, take A442. PARK: Easy. TEL: 01952 882860. FAIRS: Buxton; NEC Birmingham; Shrewsbury; Edinburgh.

BURLTON, Nr. Shrewsbury

North Shropshire Reclamation
Wackley Lodge Farm. SY4 5TD. (A. and J. Powell). SALVO. Est. 1997. Open 7 days 9-5. SIZE: Large. *STOCK: Wide range of reclaimed materials.* LOC: A528. PARK: Easy. TEL: 01939 270719; home/fax - 01939 270895.

CHURCH STRETTON

Cardingmill Antiques
1 Burway Rd. SY6 6DL. (Mrs P. A. Benton). Est. 1976. Open Thurs., Fri. and Sat. 11-5 or by appointment. *STOCK: 18th-19th C longcase and

wall clocks, furniture, £250-£2,000; Measham teapots, £90-£450; original horsebrasses and martingales (NHB Soc.); Victorian oil lamps with original shades, £200-£650; 18th-19th C metalware. LOC: A49. TEL: 01694 724555; home - 01584 877880; mobile - 07802 194253; website - www.churchstretton.co.uk.

Church Stretton Books
48 High St. SY6 6BX. (Roger Toon). PBFA. Est. 1992. Open 10-5, Wed. 10-1. SIZE: Small. *STOCK: Books - mainly secondhand, some antiquarian.* LOC: Off A49 at traffic lights, after 300 yards turn left at bank, shop 150 yards on right. PARK: Nearby. TEL: 01694 724337; fax - same. SER: Valuations. FAIRS: PBFA, Birmingham; Haydock Park; Bristol.

Cobwebs Antiques & Collectables
13-15 High St. SY6 6BX. (S. Thomas). Est. 1991. Open 10-5, Sun. 11-4. SIZE: Medium. *STOCK: Porcelain and furniture, 19th C to 1940, £20-£750; collectables, 20th C, £10-£80; interesting items, from 19th C, £10-£100.* LOC: A49. PARK: Easy. TEL: 01694 723090; home - same. SER: Valuations; buys at auction. FAIRS: Newark, Stafford Showground, Prestwood Centre, Ardingly. VAT: Stan.

Longmynd Antiques
Crossways. SY6 6PG. (David Coomber). Est. 1994. Open 10.30-5. SIZE: Large. *STOCK: Furniture, 17th C to Edwardian, £100-£10,000.* LOC: A49. Premises immediately south of traffic lights. PARK: Own. TEL: 01694 724474; fax - same. VAT: Spec.

Stretton Antiques Market
36 Sandford Ave. SY6 6BH. (T. and L. Elvins). Est. 1986. Open 9.30-5.30, Sun. and Bank Holidays 10.30-4.30. SIZE: Large - 55 dealers. *STOCK: General antiques, shipping items and collectables.* LOC: Town centre. PARK: Easy. TEL: 01694 723718.

CLEOBURY MORTIMER, Nr. Kidderminster

Antique Centre
Childe Rd. DY14 8PA. Open 10-5, Sun. by appointment. SIZE: Large. *STOCK: Georgian, Victorian, Edwardian, old pine and French furniture, period beds, garden statuary and architectural items.* PARK: Own. TEL: 01299 270513; fax - 01299 270513; e-mail - antique centre@supanet.com.

M. and M. Baldwin
24 High St. DY14 8BY. Est. 1978. Open mainly by appointment. SIZE: Medium. *STOCK: 19th-

20th C books, to £500. LOC: A4117. PARK: Easy. TEL: 01299 270110; fax/home - same. SER: Valuations; buys at auction (books). FAIRS: Crick Boat Show; IWA National Festival, Milton Keynes. VAT: Stan.

CRAVEN ARMS

Portcullis Furniture
Ludlow Rd. SY7 9QL. (Sally Allen and John Cox). Est. 980. Open 10-5.30, Sun. 10.30-4.30. SIZE: Large. *STOCK: Victorian, Edwardian, shipping and reproduction furniture, £5-£2,000.* LOC: A49. PARK: Easy. TEL: 01588 672263; fax - 01588 673321; home - 01588 673007. SER: Buys at auction (furniture). FAIRS: Newark; Swinderby. VAT: Stan/Spec.

HODNET, Nr. Market Drayton

Hodnet Antiques
13a Shrewsbury St. TF9 3NP. (Mrs J. Scott). Est. 1976. Open Tues.-Thurs. 2-5.30, other times by appointment. SIZE: Small. *STOCK: General antiques - china, glass, silver, jewellery, pictures, brass and copper, collectables and unusual decorative items, £5-£1,000; 18th-20th C furniture, £100-£5,000.* LOC: A53. PARK: Outside shop. TEL: Home - 01630 638591. SER: Valuations; buys at auction.

IRONBRIDGE

Tudor House Antiques
11 Tontine Hill. TF8 7AL. (Peter Whitelaw). Open 10-5. *STOCK: General antiques, especially porcelain including Coalport and Caughley .* LOC: Opposite bridge. TEL: 01952 433783; e-mail - tudoriron@aol.com; website - www. tudorhouse.co.uk.

LUDLOW

Bayliss Antiques
22-24 Old St. SY8 1NP. Resident. *STOCK: 18th-19th C furniture.* TEL: 01584 873634.

R.G. Cave and Sons Ltd   BADA
17 Broad St. SY8 1NG. LAPADA. Resident. Est. 1962. Open 9.30-5.30. *STOCK: Furniture, 1630-1830; clocks, barometers, metalwork, fine art and collectors' items.* **PARK: Easy. TEL: 01584 873568; fax - 01584 875050. SER: Valuations. VAT: Spec.**

Claymore Antiques
18 Broad St. SY8 1NG. Est. 1995. Open 10-5, Fri. and Sat. 10-5.30, Sun. by appointment. *STOCK: English furniture, 18th-19th C, £200-£10,000; English giltwood mirrors, 18th-19th C.* PARK: Easy. TEL: 01584 875851; fax - 01885 400278; mobile - 07801 627235. SER: Valuations; buys at auction.

A subtle French lithograph in pristine condition which brought £350.

From an Auction Report by Christopher Wight on Cycles and Cycling Memorabilia held at Phillips, Bayswater, London on 19th August 2000 which appeared in the October 2000 issue of **Antique Collecting** magazine. For more details and to subscribe see page 147.

John Clegg
12 Old St. SY8 1NP. Resident. Est. 1960. Open 8.30-5. *STOCK: Country and other period furniture, metalware and decorative items.* TEL: 01584 873176.

Garrard Antiques
139a Corve St. SY8 2PG. (Caroline Garrard). Est. 1985. Open 10-1 and 2-5, Sat. 10-5. SIZE: Medium. *STOCK: Pine and country furniture, 18-19th C, to £950; French provincial furniture, 19th to early 20th C, to £900; books, linen, textiles, silver and treen, porcelain.* LOC: 200 yards below Feathers Hotel. PARK: Opposite. TEL: 01584 876727; fax - 01584 781277. SER: Valuations. FAIRS: NEC. VAT: Spec.

G. & D. Ginger Antiques
5 Corve St. SY8 1DA. Resident. Open 9-5. SIZE: Large. *STOCK: Oak dressers and farmhouse tables, Welsh cupboards and presses, country and mahogany furniture; decorative and associated items.* TEL: 01584 876939; fax - 01584 876456; mobile - 07970 666437.

Robert Miller
The Angel, Broad St. SY8 1NG. Est. 1996. Open 9.30-5.30, Sun. by appointment. SIZE: Large. *STOCK: English and Continental furniture, 1680-1940; paintings and drawings, 17th-20th C; ceramics, silver, works of art; all £50-£25,000.*

PARK: Easy. TEL: 01584 877788; home - 01584 831221. SER: Valuations; restorations (furniture and oil paintings); buys at auction. FAIRS: Olympia. VAT: Spec.

Mitre House Antiques
Corve Bridge. SY8 1DY. (L. Jones). Open 9-5.30. SIZE: Shop + trade warehouse. *STOCK: Clocks, pine and general antiques. Warehouse - unstripped pine and shipping goods.* TEL: 01584 872138.

M. & R. Taylor Antiques
Sarah Taylor Interiors
1 Pepper Lane. SY8 1PX. (M. Taylor). Est. 1977. Open 10-4. SIZE: Medium. *STOCK: Furniture, mahogany, oak and walnut, brass and copper, 17th-19th C.* PARK: Nearby. TEL: 01584 874169; home - 01299 832352. VAT: Stan/Spec.

Teme Valley Antiques
1 The Bull Ring. SY8 1AD. (C.S. Harvey). Est. 1979. Usually open 10-5.30, Sun. by appointment. SIZE: Medium. *STOCK: English and Continental porcelain, 18th to early 20th C, £25-£2,500; furniture, oil and watercolour paintings, £50-£2,500; jewellery, silver, plate, metalware and glass, £10-£3,500; both 17th to early 20th C. Not Stocked: Militaria, coins and carpets.* LOC: Town centre opposite Lunn Poly. PARK: Easy. TEL: 01584 874686. SER: Valuations; buys at auction (porcelain). VAT: Stan/Spec.

G. & D. GINGER
ANTIQUE DEALERS

Known as a good trade call for
Welsh dressers and associated
oak and fruitwood country furniture.

*We also stock period
mahogany and
decorative items*

**5 Corve Street
Ludlow
Shropshire
SY8 1DA
Tel. 01584 876939
Fax. 01584 876456
Mobile: 07970 666437**

Valentyne Dawes Gallery
Church St. SY8 1AP. (B.S. McCreddie). Open
10-5.30. SIZE: Medium. *STOCK: Paintings, 19th
to early 20th C, £200-£40,000; furniture, 17th-
19th C, £50-£4,000; porcelain, 19th C, £5-£500.*
LOC: Town centre near Buttercross. PARK:
Nearby. TEL: 01584 874160; fax - 01384
455576; e-mail - sales@gallery.wyenet.co.uk;
website - www. starmark.co.uk/valentyne-dawes/.
SER: Valuations; restorations (oil paintings,
watercolours, furniture). VAT: Spec.

MARKET DRAYTON

Arty Faherty
Honeypots Farm, Rosehill. (McNulty Wholesalers). Est. 1983. Open 11-5. *STOCK: Painted
pine, mahogany; small interesting items.* PARK:
Easy. TEL: 01630 639562. VAT: Stan.

Deppner Antiques
The Towers Lawn. TF9 3EB. (J. Deppner). Est.
1985. Open 9.30-5.30, Wed. 9.30-3.30, Thurs.
and Sun. by appointment. SIZE: Small. *STOCK:
Stripped pine, general antiques, 19th C, £20-
£1,000.* LOC: From A53 towards town centre
(Cheshire St.). PARK: Easy. TEL: 01630 654111.
SER: Valuations. FAIRS: Newark, Ardingly.

Peter Wain   **BADA**
Glynde Cottage, Longford. TF9 3PW. Open by
appointment only. SIZE: Medium. *STOCK:
Oriental ceramics and works of art, £100-
£10,000.* TEL: 01630 638358; fax - 01630
639613; e-mail - peter.wain@ukonline.co.uk.
SER: Valuations; buys at auction.

MUCH WENLOCK

Cruck House Antiques
23 Barrow St. TF13 6EN. (B. Roderick Smith). Est.
1985. Open 9.30-5.30. CL: Wed. SIZE: Small.
*STOCK: Silver and watercolours, 19th-20th C,
£25-£300; furniture, 19th C, £50-£500; general
antiques.* Not Stocked: Weapons and gold. LOC:
Near Square. PARK: Easy. TEL: 01952 727165.

Myra's Antiques
5 High St. TF13 6AA. (M. Mullard). Open Wed.-
Sat. 10-4. *STOCK: Collectables, small antiques
and furniture, Carlton Ware.* TEL: 01952 727596.
SER: Clock repairs; polishing; restorations.

Raynalds Mansion   **BADA**
**Raynalds Mansion. TF13 6AE. (John King).
Resident. Est. 1970. Open Mon., Tues. and Fri.
10-2, prior 'phone call advisable. SIZE:**

Medium. *STOCK: Period furniture and associated items, £500-£15,000.* **PARK: Easy. TEL: 01952 727456; fax/home - same. FAIRS: Olympia (June, Nov.). VAT: Spec.**

Wenlock Fine Art
3 The Square. TF13 6LX. (P. Cotterill). Est. 1990. Open Wed.-Sat. 10-5. SIZE: Medium. *STOCK: Modern British paintings, mainly 20th C, some late 19th C.* PARK: Nearby. TEL: 01952 728232; home - 01952 252376. SER: Valuations; restorations (cleaning); mounting; framing; buys at auction (as stock). VAT: Spec.

NEWPORT

Amanda's Secondhand Hypermarket
Newport Business Park, Audley Rd. TF10 7DP. (Amanda Sutton). Est. 1992. Open 10-4, Sun. 12-4. SIZE: Large. *STOCK: General antiques.* LOC: Off A41 Wolverhampton-Whitchurch. PARK: 50 yds. TEL: 01952 820364.

OSWESTRY

Arcadia
6 Upper Brook St. SY10 2TB. (Joyce & Rod Whitehead). Est. 1980. Open 9.30-5. *STOCK: Fine art, 18th C to contemporary applied artists, £5-£1,000; contemporary pottery, glass and country furniture.* LOC: Near parish church. PARK: Easy. TEL: 01691 655622. SER: Buys at auction.

SHIFNAL

Corner Farm Antiques
Weston Heath, Sheriffhales. TF11 8RY. (Tim Dams). Est. 1994. Open 10-5 including Sun. SIZE: Large. *STOCK: Georgian to Edwardian furniture, £100-£4,000; clocks including longcase, Victorian, £250-£5,000; Victorian fireplaces, £350-£750; collectables, £5-£500.* LOC: A41 between Tong and Newport. PARK: Own large. TEL: 01952 691543; home/fax - same; website - www. antiques.uk.ws. SER: Valuations; restorations (furniture and clocks); buys at auction. VAT: Stan.

SHREWSBURY

Candle Lane Books
28-29 Princess St. SY1 1LW. (J. Thornhill). Open 9.30-5. *STOCK: Antiquarian and secondhand books.* TEL: 01743 365301.

Juliet Chilton Antiques and Interiors
69 Wyle Cop. SY1 1UX. Open 9.30-6. SIZE: Large. *STOCK: Furniture and smalls, mainly 1700's-1920's and some reproduction.* TEL: 01743 358699/366553; fax - 01743 366563. SER: Shipping and packing.

Collectors' Gallery
Central Hall, Castle Gates. SY1 2AD. Open 9-5.30. SIZE: Large. *STOCK: Coins and medals, stamps, postal history, bonds and share certificates; related books and accessories.* TEL: 01743 272140; fax - 01743 366041; e-mail - enquiries@collectors-gallery.co.uk; website - www.collectors-gallery.co.uk.

Collectors' Place
29a Princess St., The Square. SY1 1LW. (Keith Jones). Open Wed-Sat. 9.30-5. *STOCK: Collectables especially Prattware potlids and bottles, 1700-1900.* TEL: 01743 246150.

Adrian Donnelly Antique Clocks
7 The Parade, St Mary's Place. SY1 1DL. BHI, BWCG. Est. 1985. Open 10-5, Sat. 10-1. SIZE: Medium. *STOCK: Longcase and bracket clocks and barometers, 17th-19th C, £250-£12,000.* LOC: Town centre. PARK: Easy. TEL: 01743 361388; fax - same. SER: Valuations; restorations (clocks and barometers). FAIRS: NEC. VAT: Stan/Spec.

Expressions
17 Princess St. SY1 1LP. Open 10.30-4.30. CL: Thurs. *STOCK: Art Deco originals, ceramics, furniture, jewellery, lighting, mirrors, prints.* TEL: 01743 351731.

Hutton Antiques
18 Princess St. SY1 1LP. (Mrs C. Brookfield). Est. 1978. Open 9.30-12.30 and 1.30-4. CL: Mon. SIZE: Medium. *STOCK: Silver, porcelain and glass, 18th-19th C, £25-£500; small furniture, £100-£2,000; Victorian jewellery.* LOC: Off square, near Music Hall. PARK: Easy. TEL: 01743 245810. SER: Valuations.

The Little Gem
18 St. Mary's St. SY1 1ED. (M.A. Bowdler). Est. 1969. Open 9-5.30. CL: Thurs. (except Dec.). SIZE: Medium. *STOCK: Georgian and Victorian jewellery; unusual gem stones, watches; handmade jewellery.* Not Stocked: Weapons, coins, medals, furniture. LOC: Opposite St. Mary's Church along from G.P.O. PARK: In side road (St. Mary's Place) opposite shop. TEL: 01743 352085; e-mail - mbowdler@littlegem. freeserve.co.uk. SER: Repairs; valuations.

F.C. Manser and Son Ltd
53/54 Wyle Cop. SY1 1XJ. LAPADA. Est. 1944. Open 9-5. SIZE: Large. *STOCK: Furniture, 17th-20th C, £250-£40,000; silver, plate, copper, 18th-*

20th C, £5-£6,000; jewellery, 19th-20th C, £50-£6,000. Not Stocked: Coins, books. LOC: 150yds. town side of English bridge. PARK: Own. TEL: 01743 351120/245730; fax - 01743 271047. SER: Valuations; restorations. VAT: Stan/Spec.

Princess Antique Centre
14a The Square. SY1. (J. Langford). Open 9.30-5.30. SIZE: 35 dealers. *STOCK: General antiques and collectables.* TEL: 01743 343701.

Quayside Antiques
9 Frankwell. (Jean and Chris Winter). Open Tues. and Wed. 10-4, Fri. and Sat. 10-5. SIZE: Large. *STOCK: Victorian and Edwardian furniture, especially dining tables and sets of chairs, desks, bookcases, beds, wardrobes.* LOC: Near Halls Saleroom. PARK: Own. TEL: 01743 360490; workshop - 01948 665838; home - 01948 830363. SER: Restorations (furniture).

Raleigh Antiques of Hanwood Hall
Hanwood. SY5 8LY. (Ruth and Greville Handbury-Madin). Open 7 days. *STOCK: Furniture, small antiques and collectables.* TEL: 01743 860489.

Shrewsbury Antique Centre
15 Princess House, The Square. SY1 1JZ. (J. Langford). Est. 1978. Open 9.30-5.30. SIZE: Large - 50 dealers. *STOCK: General antiques and collectables.* LOC: Town centre just off the Square. PARK: Nearby. TEL: 01743 247704.

Shrewsbury Antique Market
Frankwell Quay Warehouse. SY3 8LG. (J. Langford). Open 9.30-5. SIZE: Large - 45 units. *STOCK: General antiques and collectors' items, £1-£2,000.* LOC: Alongside Frankwell Quay car park. PARK: Easy. TEL: 01743 350916.

Tiffany Antiques
Shrewsbury Antique Centre, 15 Princess House, The Square. SY1 1JZ. (A. Wilcox). Est. 1988. Open 9.30-5.30. *STOCK: Metalware, collectables, curios, china and glass.* LOC: Town centre. PARK: Multi-storey. TEL: Home - 01270 257425; mobile - 07970 419263. SER: Buys at auction.

STANTON UPON HINE HEATH, Nr. Shrewsbury

Marcus Moore Antiques
Booley House, Booley. SY4 4LY. (M.G.J. and M.P. Moore). Est. 1980. Usually open but prior telephone call advisable. SIZE: Medium. *STOCK: Oak and country furniture, late 17th to 18th C; Georgian mahogany furniture, 18th to early 19th C; all £50-£7,000; some Victorian*

furniture; associated items. LOC: Half a mile north of Stanton on right. PARK: Easy. TEL: 01939 200333; website - www.marcusmoore-antiques.com. SER: Restorations (furniture); polishing; search; shipping. VAT: Stan/Spec.

TELFORD

Haygate Gallery
40 Haygate Rd., Wellington. TF1 1QT. (Mrs M. Kuznierz). Open 9-5, Sat. 9-1. CL: Wed. *STOCK: Chandeliers, lighting and decorative antiques.* LOC: One mile from junction 7, M54. PARK: Easy. TEL: 01952 248553. SER: Framing.

Brian James Antiques
Old Maltings, The Lawns, Wellington. TF1 3AF. Est. 1985. Open 9-6, Sat. 9.30-12.30, Sun. by appointment. SIZE: Large. *STOCK: Chests of drawers, Georgian to Victorian, £50-£1,500.* LOC: Off M54, junction 6. Follow signs for Telford Hospital then Wellington Centre, turn right at Red Lion. PARK: Easy. TEL: 01952 256592/243906. SER: Restorations and conversions; linen presses, sideboards and chests made to order. VAT: Stan. *Trade Only.*

WHITCHURCH

Age of Elegance
54 High St. SY13 1BB. (Mike and Janet Proudlove). Est. 1988. Open 10-4. CL: Wed. SIZE: Small. *STOCK: Collectables including china and glass; Victorian and Edwardian furniture.* LOC: Midway between Shrewsbury and Chester. PARK: Easy. TEL: 01948 666145; fax - same.

Dodington Antiques
7 Sherrymill Hill. SY13 1BN. (G. MacGillivray). Resident. Est. 1978. By appointment. SIZE: Large. *STOCK: Oak, fruitwood, walnut country and 18th to early 19th C mahogany furniture, longcase clocks, barometers, £10-£6,000.* LOC: On fringe of town centre. PARK: Easy. TEL: 01948 663399. SER: Buys at auction. VAT: Stan/Spec.

WOORE, Nr. Crewe

The Mount
12 Nantwich Rd. CW3 9SA. Est. 1978. Open most afternoons and weekends (prior telephone call advisable). *STOCK: Watercolours, oils and drawings, Victorian to 20th C; maps, prints and topographical items, from 17th C; all £2-£500.* LOC: Junction of A51 and A525. PARK: Easy. TEL: 01630 647274; home - same. SER: Framing; finder (maps and topography).

SOMERSET

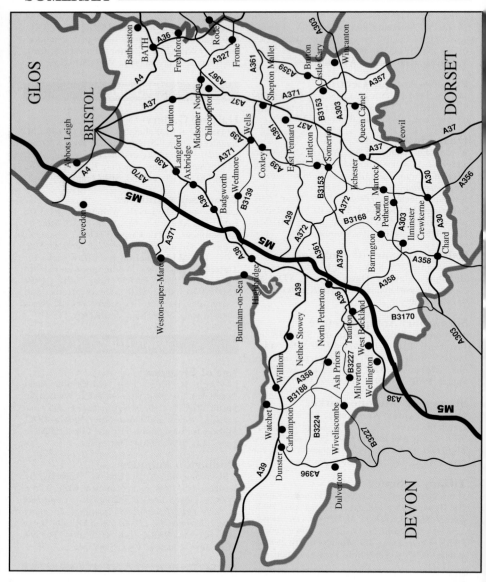

Dealers and Shops in Somerset

Abbots Leigh	1	Castle Cary	1	Freshford	2	Nether Stowey	2	Wellington	1
Ash Priors	1	Chard	1	Frome	2	North Petherton	1	Wells	3
Axbridge	1	Chilcompton	1	Highbridge	3	Queen Camel	1	West Buckland	1
Badgworth	1	Clevedon	3	Ilchester	1	Rode	1	Weston-Super-	
Barrington	1	Clutton	1	Ilminster	1	Shepton Mallet	1	Mare	3
Bath	51	Coxley	2	Langford	1	Somerton	3	Williton	2
Batheaston	1	Crewkerne	4	Littleton	1	South Petherton	1	Wincanton	1
Bruton	3	Dulverton	5	Martock	1	Taunton	5	Wiveliscombe	2
Burnham-on-Sea	4	Dunster	1	Midsomer Norton	1	Watchet	2	Yeovil	1
Carhampton	1	East Pennard	1	Milverton	1	Wedmore	1		

ABBOTS LEIGH, Nr. Bristol

David and Sally March Antiques

Oak Wood Lodge, Stoke Leigh Woods. BS8 3QB. (D. and S. March). LAPADA. Est. 1981. Open by appointment. *STOCK: 18th to early 19th C English porcelain especially figures and Bristol.* PARK: Easy. TEL: 01275 372422; fax - same; mobile - 07774 838376. SER: Valuations; buys at auction (as stock). FAIRS: Olympia; LAPADA (London and NEC); NEC. VAT: Spec.

ASH PRIORS, Nr. Taunton

The Granary Galleries

Court House. TA4 3NQ. (R. and J. Hall). Est. 1969. Open 8.30-5.30. SIZE: Large. *STOCK: Period items, general antiques, 18th-19th C furniture, some shipping goods.* PARK: Easy. TEL: 01823 432402. VAT: Stan/Spec.

AXBRIDGE

The Old Post House

Weare, Bridgewater Rd. BS26 2JF. (Ray and Mollie Seaman). *STOCK: General antiques and country furniture.* TEL: 01934 732372.

BADGWORTH, Nr. Axbridge

John Hawley (MBHI) Antique Clocks

Court Barn, Church Lane. BS26 2QP. Est. 1972. Open by appointment. *STOCK: Clocks especially longcase, bracket, wall and carriage; horological books and tools.* TEL: 01934 733444. SER: Valuations; restorations; repairs.

BARRINGTON, Nr. Ilminster

Stuart Interiors (Antiques) Ltd

Barrington Court. TA19 0NG. LAPADA. Open 9-5, Sat. 10-5. SIZE: Large. *STOCK: Oak furniture, £100-£10,000; accessories, £50-£2,500; both pre-1720.* Not Stocked: 18th C mahogany. LOC: Between A303 and M5, 5 miles north-east of Ilminster. House is National Trust property, signposted in area. PARK: Easy. TEL: 01460 240349. SER: Valuations; buys at auction (early oak furniture and accessories, interior design and architectural items including oak panelling). VAT: Spec.

BATH

A J Antiques

13 Broad St. BA1 5LJ. (Patrick Anketell-Jones).

BABAADA. Open 10-6 or by appointment. *STOCK: Furniture, Georgian to Art Deco.* TEL: 01225 447765.

Abbey Galleries

9 Abbey Churchyard. BA1 1LY. (R.Dickson). Est. 1930. Open 10.30-5.30. *STOCK: Jewellery and Oriental items, 18th-19th C; silver, 18th C.* Not Stocked: Furniture. TEL: 01225 460565. SER: Valuations; restorations (jewellery and clocks); buys at auction. VAT: Stan.

Adam Gallery

13 John St. BA1 2JL. (P. and P. Dye). Open 9.30-5.30 or by appointment. *STOCK: 20th C and contemporary paintings, especially St Ives, Nicholson, Piper, Lanyon, Moore, Picasso, Braque, Hitchens, Hilton, Heron and Scott, £500-£30,000.* TEL: 01225 480406; fax - same. SER: Contemporary exhibitions.

Alderson   BADA

2 Princes Buildings, George St. BA1 2ED. (C.J.R. Alderson). BABAADA. Est. 1976. Open 9.30-1 and 2-5.30, Sat 9.30-1 or by appointment. *STOCK: Furniture and accessories, 17th-18th C.* LOC: Central. TEL: 01225 421652; fax - same. VAT: Spec.

Antique Linens and Lace

11 Pulteney Bridge. BA2 4AY. (Mrs R. Mellor). BABAADA. Est. 1971. Open 10-5.30 including Sun. SIZE: Small. *STOCK: Quality linens and lace, bedspreads, sheets, tablecloths, pillow cases, christening gowns, baby bonnets, beaded bags, veils, shawls, quilts and textiles, 1850-1920, £10-£600.* LOC: City centre. PARK: Great Pulteney St.- 100 yards. TEL: 01225 465782; fax - 01225 754067. VAT: Stan/Spec.

Antique Textiles & Lighting

34 Belvedere, Lansdown Rd. BA1 5BN. (Joanna Proops). BABAADA. Open Tues.-Fri. 10-5 or by appointment. *STOCK: Chandeliers, wall lights, tapestries, paisleys, beadwork, fans, samplers, bellpulls, linen and lace, tapes, ties.* TEL: 01225 310795.

Antiques of Bath

12 Margarets Buildings, Brock St. BA1 2LP. BABAADA. Open 10.30-5.30 including Sun. or by appointment. SIZE: Medium. *STOCK: 19th-20th C furniture, paintings, silver and decorative items.* LOC: Off Brock St. between The Circus and Royal Crescent. PARK: Nearby. TEL: 01225 448432; e-mail - sales@antiques-of-bath.co.uk; website - www.antiques-of-bath.co.uk.

The Antiques Warehouse

57 Walcot St. BA1 5BN. BABAADA. Open 10.30-5.30. SIZE: Medium. *STOCK: 19th C mahogany furniture, £300-£2,000 and decorative objects, £20-£200.* LOC: From junction 18, M4 along A46 then A4, at first mini-roundabout veer

left into Walcot St. Shop 300yds on right. PARK: Easy. TEL: 01225 444201; mobile - 07990 690240. VAT: Stan/Spec.

Arkea Antiques
10A Monmouth Place. BA1 2AX. (G. Harmandian). Est. 1969. *STOCK: Furniture and china.* TEL: 01225 429413/835382. SER: Repairs (antiques); traditional French polishing; desk leathering.

Assembly Antiques Centre
5/8 Saville Row. BA1 2QP. Open 10-5, Wed. 8-5. *STOCK: 18th-19th C furniture, scent bottles, Art Deco items, tea caddies, boxes, pictures, lighting and decorative effects.* LOC: Rear of the Assembly Rooms. TEL: 01225 426288; fax - 01225 429661.

Bartlett Street Antiques Centre
5-10 Bartlett St. BA1 2QZ. BABAADA. Open 9.30-5, Wed. 8-5. SIZE: 50+ dealers and 150 display cases. *STOCK: Wide range of general antiques.* TEL: 01225 466689; stallholders - 01225 310457/446322; fax - 01225 444146.

Bath Galleries
33 Broad St. BA1 5LP. (J. Griffiths). BABAADA. Open 9.30-5. SIZE: Medium. *STOCK: Clocks, furniture, paintings, porcelain, barometers, silver.* LOC: 50yds. from Central Post Office. PARK: Walcot St. multi-storey, 30yds. TEL: 01225 462946. SER: Valuations; restorations; buys at auction. VAT: Stan/Spec.

Bath Saturday Antiques Market
Walcot St. BA1 5B. (J. Whittingham). Est. 1978. Open Sat. 7-5. SIZE: 100 stalls. *STOCK: Wide variety of general antiques, £1-£4,000.* LOC: Close to Hilton Hotel. PARK: Multi-storey. TEL: Mobile - 07836 534893.

Bath Stamp and Coin Shop
Pulteney Bridge. BA2 4AY. (H. and A. Swindells). Est. 1946. Open 9.30-5.30. *STOCK: Coins - Roman, hammered, early milled, G.B. gold, silver and copper, some foreign; literature and accessories; banknotes, medals, stamps and postal history.* PARK: Laura Place; Walcot multi-storey. SER: Valuations. VAT: Stan.

George Bayntun
Manvers St. BA1 1JW. (E.W.G. Bayntun-Coward). BABAADA. Est. 1894. Open 9-1 and 2-5.30, Sat. 9.30-1. SIZE: Large. *STOCK: Rare books. First or fine editions of English literature, standard sets, illustrated and sporting books, poetry, biography and travel, mainly in new leather bindings; antiquarian books in original bindings.* LOC: By railway and bus stations. PARK: 50 yds. by station. TEL: 01225 466000; fax - 01225 482122. SER: Restorations (rare books). VAT: Stan.

Bedsteads
BADA
2 Walcot Buildings, London Rd. BA1 6AD.

(Mark and Nikki Ashton). **Est. 1991. Open Tues.-Sat. 10-6.** *STOCK: Brass, iron and wooden bedsteads, 1840-1920, £500-£4,500; bedroom suites, 1880-1920, £2,000-£5,500.* LOC: 200 yds. before traffic lights, end of London Road. **TEL: 01225 339182; fax - same; home - 01275 464114. SER: Valuations; restorations (bedsteads). VAT: Stan/Spec.**

Bladud House Antiques
8 Bladud Buildings. BA1 5LS. (Mrs E. Radosenska). Open 9.30-1 and 2-4.30. CL: Mon. and Thurs. *STOCK: Jewellery and small items.* Not Stocked: Furniture. TEL: 01225 462929.

Lawrence Brass
Apple Studio, Ashley. BA1 3SD. BAFRA: UKIC. Est. 1973. Open by appointment. SIZE: Small. *STOCK: Furniture, 16th-19th C, £50-£5,000.* Not Stocked: Ceramics, silver, glass. LOC: A4 towards Chippenham. PARK: Easy. TEL: 01225 852222; fax - 01225 851050. SER: Restorations (furniture, clocks and barometers). VAT: Stan/Spec.

Geoffrey Breeze
6 George St. BA1 2EH. LAPADA. BABAADA. Open 10-5. *STOCK: Furniture, 18th-20th C.* TEL: 01225 466499; e-mail - gebreeze@aol.com.

David Bridgwater
Heather Cottage, Lansdown. BA1 9BL. Open by appointment. *STOCK: Architectural and garden sculpture, decorative and practical items for the period garden.* TEL: 01225 463435.

Bryers Antiques
Entrance to the Guildhall Market, High St. BA1 1JQ. (S. Bryers). Est. 1940. *STOCK: Furniture, decorative items, porcelain, glass, silver and Victorian plate.* TEL: 01225 466352/460535.

Camden Books
146 Walcot St. BA1 5BL. (Victor and Elizabeth Suchar). PBFA. Est. 1984. Open 10-5. *STOCK: Books - architecture, philosophy, economics, science, 18th-20th C; general, 19th-20th C.* LOC: From east on to London Rd., then Walcot St. PARK: Easy. TEL: 01225 461606; fax - same; website - www.camdenbooks.com. SER: Valuations; buys at auction. FAIRS: Bath PBFA; London PBFA.

Brian and Caroline Craik Ltd
8 Margaret's Buildings. BA1 2LP. *STOCK: Decorative items, mainly 19th C; metalwork, treen, glass and pewter.* TEL: 01225 337161.

Mary Cruz
5 Broad St. BA1 5LJ. LAPADA. BABAADA. CINOA. Est. 1974. Open 10-6.30, Sun. by appointment. SIZE: Medium. *STOCK: 18th-19th C furniture and decorative items; 19th-20th C*

paintings and sculpture. PARK: Easy. TEL: 01225 334174; fax - 01225 423300. SER: Valuations; restorations. VAT: Stan/Spec.

Andrew Dando   BADA
4 Wood St., Queen Sq. BA1 2JQ. (A.P. and J.M. Dando). LAPADA, BABAADA. Est. 1915. Open 10-5.30, Sat. 10-1. CL: Some Mondays. SIZE: Large. *STOCK: English, Continental, Oriental porcelain and pottery, 17th to mid-19th C; local topographical and decorative antique prints; some furniture, 18th to mid-19th C.* LOC: 200yds. from bottom of Milsom St. towards Queen Sq. TEL: 01225 422702; website - www.andrewdando.co.uk. SER: Valuations. VAT: Stan/Spec.

D. and B. Dickinson   BADA
22 New Bond St. BA1 1BA. (S.G., D. and N.W. Dickinson and Mrs E.M. Dickinson). BABAADA. Est. 1917. Open 9.30-1 and 2-5. SIZE: Small. *STOCK: Jewellery, 1770-1900, £20-£2,000; silver, 1750-1900, £25-£3,000; Sheffield plate, 1770-1845, £50-£1,000.* LOC: Next to Post Office. PARK: 100yds. at bottom of street, turn left then right for multi-storey. TEL: 01225 466502. VAT: Stan/Spec.

£473 is a high price for a single piece of black basalt, but an impressed 'Herculaneum' mark identifies this as a rare Liverpool creamjug, c.1805.

From an article entitled 'Not So Potty After All – Early English Pottery' by John Sandon which appeared in the July/August 2000 issue of **Antique Collecting** magazine. For more details and to subscribe see page 147.

Frank Dux Antiques
33 Belvedere, Lansdown Rd. BA1 5HR. (F. Dux and M. Hopkins). Resident. BABAADA. Open Tues.-Sat. 10-6. SIZE: Medium. *STOCK: 18th C and later English glass, some 19th and 20th C Venetian; furniture (mainly oak) and unusual decorative items including glass paintings.* LOC: From Broad St. up Lansdown Hill, on right 100yds. past Guinea Lane. PARK: Easy. TEL: 01225 312367; fax - same; website - www. antique-glass.co.uk; e-mail - antique.glass @bath.co.uk.

Fountain Antiques Market
6 Bladud Buildings, The Paragon. BA1 5LS. (Maggie Adams and Ken Jones). BABAADA. Open 10-5, Wed. 8-5. SIZE: Medium. *STOCK: General antiques including jewellery, furniture, clocks, porcelain, collectables, vintage and antique clothing, textiles, linen, lace, costume jewellery and toys and games.* LOC: At the crossroads with the Paragon, George St. PARK: Nearby. TEL: 01225 428731/471133.

George Gregory
Manvers St. BA1 1JW. (C.A.W. Bayntun-Coward). Est. 1845. Open 9-1 and 2-5.30, Sat. 9.30-1. SIZE: Large. *STOCK: Secondhand books, engraved views and portraits.* LOC: By rail station. PARK: By rail station. TEL: 01225 466055; fax - 01225 482122.

Haliden Oriental Rug Shop
98 Walcot St. BA1 5BG. (Andrew Lloyd, Craig Bale and Owen Parry). BABAADA. Est. 1963. Open 10-5. SIZE: Medium. *STOCK: Caucasian, Turkish, Persian, Chinese, Afghan, Turcoman and tribal rugs and carpets, 19th C, £50-£3,000; some Oriental textiles - coats, embroideries, wall hangings, 19th C, £50-£750.* LOC: Off main London road, into town by Walcot Reclamation. PARK: Walcot St. or multi-storey. TEL: 01225 469240. SER: Valuations; cleaning; restorations (as stock); buys at auction (as stock).

Anthony Hepworth Fine Art Dealers
1 Margarets Buildings, Brock St. BA1 2LP. Open during exhibitions Wed.-Sat. 11-5 other times by appointment. *STOCK: Mainly 20th C British paintings and sculpture; also African tribal art.* LOC: Off Brock St. between Royal Crescent and Circus. PARK: Brock St. TEL: 01225 447480/ 442917; fax - 01225 442917; mobile - 07970 480650 (during fairs only). SER: Exhibitions Bath and London. FAIRS: Olympia; 20th/21st C British Art.

Helena Hood and Co
3 Margarets Buildings, Brock St. BA1 2LP. (Mrs L.M. Hood). BABAADA. Est. 1973. Open 9.30-1 and 2.15-5.30, Sat. 10.30-1. CL: Mon. SIZE: Medium. *STOCK: Decorative items - furniture, prints, paintings and porcelain, 18th-19th C, £50-*

£2,500. LOC: Pedestrian walkway running north from Brock St. PARK: Easy. TEL: 01225 424438. SER: Restorations. VAT: Stan/Spec.

Jadis Ltd

14, 15 & 17 Walcot Buildings, London Rd., BA1 6AD. (S.H.Creese-Parsons and N.A. Mackay). BABAADA. Est. 1970. Open 9.30-6, Sun. by appointment. SIZE: Medium. *STOCK: English and European furniture, 18th-19th C; decorative items.* LOC: On left hand side of A4 London Rd., entering Bath. PARK: At rear. TEL: 01225 338797; fax - same; 01225 333130; mobiles - 07768 232133/07879 692371; e-mail - Jadpalad@aol.com. and NamJadis@aol.com; website - www.Jadis-Ltd.com. SER: Design service, murals and trompe l'oeil. VAT: Stan/Spec.

Kembery Antique Clocks (inc. K & D Antique Clocks)

Bartlett Street Antique Centre, 5 Bartlett St. BA1 2QZ. (E. Kembery). Est. 1993. Open 10-5. *STOCK: Longcase, bracket, mantel, wall and carriage clocks and barometers, 18th-19th C, £200-£10,000.* TEL: 0117 956 5281; website - www.kdclocks.co.uk. SER: Valuations; restorations. VAT: Spec.

Ann King

38 Belvedere, Lansdown Rd. BA1 5HR. Est. 1977. Open 10-5. SIZE: Small. *STOCK: Period clothes, 19th C to 1960; baby clothes, shawls, bead dresses, linen, lace, curtains, cushions, quilts and textiles.* LOC: Around corner from Guinea Lane Antique Market. PARK: Easy. TEL: 01225 336245.

Lansdown Antiques

23 Belvedere, Lansdown Rd. BA1 5ED. (Chris and Ann Kemp). BABAADA. Open 9.30-5.30, Sun. by appointment. *STOCK: Painted pine and country furniture, 17th-19th C; metalware, unusual and decorative items.* LOC: From A4/A46 roundabout across 2 sets of traffic lights, right at mini roundabout, right at next traffic lights, shop 350yds. on left. PARK: Easy. TEL: 01225 313417; home - same; mobile - 07801 013663; e-mail - lansdown-antiques@lineone.net. VAT: Stan/Spec.

Looking Glass of Bath

94-96 Walcot St. BA1 5BG. (Anthony Reed). Est. 1972. Open 9-6. SIZE: Small. *STOCK: Large mirrors and picture frames, 18th-19th C, £50-£5,000; decorative prints, 18th-20th C.* PARK: Easy. TEL: 01225 461969; fax - 01225 316191; home - 01275 333595; website - www. lookinglassofbath.co.uk. SER: Valuations; restorations (re-gilding, gesso and compo work, re-silvering and bevelling glass); manufactures arched top overmantel, pier, convex and triptych mirrors; old mirror plates supplied; simulated mercury silvered mirror glass; buys at auction (mirrors and pictures). VAT: Stan/Spec.

E.P. Mallory and Son Ltd **BADA**

1-4 Bridge St. and 5 Old Bond St. BA2 4AP. BABAADA. Est. 1856. Open 10-5. *STOCK: Period silver and Sheffield plate, jewellery, objets de vertu, £50-£5,000.* TEL: (0044) 0 1225 788800; fax - (0044) 0 1225 442210; e-mail - mail@mallory-jewellers.com; website - www.mallory-jewellers.com. VAT: Stan/Spec.

Montague Antiques

16 Walcot Buildings, London Rd. BA1 6AD. (A. R. Schlesinger and D.K. Moore). BABAADA. Resident. Est. 1986. Open 10-6, Sun.11-4. CL: Thurs. SIZE: Medium. *STOCK: Furniture, 17th C to 1920, £50-£1,000; collectables, Oriental rugs, ceramics, glass, £1-£500; glass light shades and fittings, to 1939, £5-£1,500.* Not Stocked: Weapons and jewellery. LOC: A4. Shop 100m west of Safeway supermarket. PARK: Own at rear, via Bedford St. TEL: 01225 469282; home - same. SER: Valuations.

Nick Kuhn: 4 Miles Buildings

4 Miles Buildings, Off George St. BA1 2QS. (Nick Kuhn and Alexandra Fane). BABAADA. Est. 1992. Always open Sat. 10-5, other times by appointment. SIZE: Small. *STOCK: 20th C furniture and modern design, British fine art, naïve art, hooked rugs, £30-£3,000.* LOC: City centre, near Bartlett Street Antiques Centre. PARK: Nearby. TEL: 01225 425486. FAIRS: BABAADA.

Paragon Antiques and Collectors Market

3 Bladud Buildings, The Paragon. BA1 5LS. (T.J. Clifford and Son Ltd). Est. 1978. Open Wed. 6.30-3.30. SIZE: Large. LOC: Milsom St./Broad St. PARK: 50yds. TEL: 01225 463715.

Patterson Liddle

10 Margaret's Buildings, Brock St. BA1 2LP. ABA, PBFA. Open 10-5.30. *STOCK: Antiquarian books and prints especially art and architecture, illustrated and transport history, travel, English literature, maps.* PARK: Nearby. TEL: 01225 426722; fax - same; e-mail - patlid@cwcom.net; website - www.pattersonliddle.mcmail.com. SER: Transport History catalogues issued.

Quiet Street Antiques

3 Quiet St. and 14/15 John St. BA1 2JS. (K.

The English pursue the Spanish Fleet east of Plymouth (31st July-1st August)', engraved and published by John Pine. The names of the English commanders are inscribed in the borders. Drake's capture of the Rosario is shown in the lower left-hand corner, and is depicted as a desperate boarding action – in reality, the ship surrendered without firing a shot. (Private collection)

From an article entitled 'Marine Painting – Part I' by James Taylor which appeared in the October 2000 issue of **Antique Collecting** magazine. For more details and to subscribe see page 147.

Hastings-Spital). BABAADA. Est. 1985. Open 10-6. SIZE: Large - 8 showrooms. *STOCK: Furniture especially English mahogany, 1750-1870, £250-£8,000; objects including bronzes, caddies, boxes, mirrors, £50-£2,000; Royal Worcester porcelain, £30-£2,000; clocks including longcase, wall, bracket and carriage, 1750-1900, £150-£6,000.* LOC: 25yds. from Milsom St. PARK: Nearby. TEL: 01225 315727; fax - 01225 448300; website - www.quietstreet antiques.co.uk. SER: Buys at auction (furniture and clocks); upholstery; free delivery service 100 mile radius of Bath.

Sarah Russell Antiquarian Prints

5 Margaret's Buildings, Brock St. BA1 2LP. BABAADA. *STOCK: Unusual antiquarian prints - architecture, flowers, portraits, landscapes and Bath views, many in original frames.* TEL: 01225 466335; fax - same; e-mail - bathprint@aol.com.

Michael and Jo Saffell

3 Walcot Buildings, London Rd. BA1 6AD. BABAADA. Est. 1975. Open 9.30-5, Sat. by appointment. SIZE: Small. *STOCK: British tins and other advertising material including showcards and enamels, 1870-1939; decorative items; all £5-£5,000.* LOC: A4 - main road into city from M4. PARK: Side streets opposite. TEL: 01225 315857; fax - same; home - same; mobile - 07941 158049; e-mail - michael.saffell@ virgin.net.

Tim Snell Antiques

5 & 6 Cleveland Terrace, London Rd. BA1 5DF. BABAADA. Open 10-6 including Sun. *STOCK: Fully restored golden oak, mahogany and walnut furniture, late 19th to early 20th C.* TEL: 01225 423045.

Source

93-95 Walcot St. BA1 3SD. (Roderick I. Donaldson). BABAADA. *STOCK: Period architectural materials, church and bar fittings, mirrors, lighting, decorative items, metalware, ironwork and garden furniture, 20th C metal fitted kitchens.* PARK: Nearby and limited. TEL: 01225 4692000; website - www.source-antiques. co.uk. SER: Worldwide search and supply.

Susannah

25 Broad St. BA1 5LW. (Sue Holley). BABAADA. Open 10-5. *STOCK: Decorative textiles and antiques.* TEL: 01225 445069; fax - 01225 339004.

James Townshend Antiques

1 Saville Row. BA1 2QP. BABAADA. *STOCK: Trade furniture, china, unusual decorative items.* PARK: Easy. TEL: 01225 332290. SER: Deliveries arranged.

Trimbridge Galleries

2 Trimbridge. BA1 1HE. (Mr and Mrs A. Anderson). BABAADA. Est. 1973. SIZE: Medium. *STOCK: Watercolours and drawings, £50-£3,000; prints and oil paintings; all 18th to early 20th C.* LOC: Just off lower end of Milsom St. PARK: Easy. TEL: 01225 466390.

Walcot Reclamation

108 Walcot St. BA1 5BG. BABAADA. Est. 1977. Open 8.30-5.30, Sat. 9-5. SIZE: Large. *STOCK: Architectural items - chimney pieces, ironwork, doors, fireplaces, garden statuary, period baths and fittings and traditional building materials.* PARK: Own and multi-storey nearby. TEL: 01225 444404/335532; e-mail - rick@ walcot.com and colin@reproshop.com; websites - www.walcot.com and www.reproshop.com. SER: Valuations; restorations; brochure available. VAT: Stan.

PICCADILLY ANTIQUES
(Opening 4 June, 2001)

1 MILE EAST OF BATH CITY CENTRE ON A4

Well established group of four
dealing in country furniture and
decorative accessories.
(formerly part of Pennard House Associates)

**JOHN DAVIES, ROBIN COLEMAN,
GENE FOSTER, MIKE HOLT.**

Over 25 years combined experience
in dealing with the American
export market

280 High Street, Batheaston,
Bath, BA1 7RA
Tel:01225 851494
Email: piccadillyantiques@ukonline.co.uk

*AN ECLECTIC SELECTION OF THE
RARE AND UNUSUAL*

BATHEASTON, Nr. Bath

Piccadilly Antiques
280 High St. BA1 7RA. BABAADA. Est. 1990.
Open 9.30-5.30, Sun. 10.30-4.30 or by appointment.
SIZE: Large. *STOCK: Country furniture, decorative
accessories, £100-£5,000.* LOC: A4, 1 mile east of
Bath. PARK: Easy. TEL: 01225 442215/852103; fax
- 01225 448196; e-mail - piccadillyantiques
@ukonline.co.uk. SER: Valuations; restorations
(country furniture). FAIRS: Bath and Patricia Harvey
Decorative. VAT: Stan/Spec. Below are listed the
dealers trading from these premises.

Robin Coleman Antiques
BABAADA. *Interesting and decorative items.*
VAT: Stan/Spec.

John Davies
*18th-19th C furniture especially country and Gothic
oak, and decorative smalls.* TEL: Home - 01225
852103.

Gene Foster (Antiques)
BABAADA. *Decorative and unusal items, 17th-
19th C; Continental and English painted furniture,
paintings, needlework, prints and metalware, £25-
£2,500.* VAT: Stan/Spec.

Mike Holt
BABAADA. *19th C decorative metalware.*

BRUTON

The Antique Shop
5 High St. BA10 0AB. (D.L. Gwilliam and M.J.
Wren). Open Tues.-Sat. 10-5.30 or by
appointment. SIZE: Medium. *STOCK: Furniture,
jewellery, silver, china, copper, brass, general
collectables, decorative art and antiques,
Georgian to Art Deco, £5-£1,500.* PARK: Easy.
TEL: 01749 813264.

Michael Lewis Gallery - Antiquarian
Maps & Prints
17 High St. BA10 0AB. Open 9.30-5.30 or by
appointment. CL: Thurs. pm. SIZE: Large.
STOCK: Maps, 17th-19th C; prints. LOC: A359.
PARK: High St. TEL: 01749 813557; home -
same. SER: Picture framing.

M.G.R. Exports
Station Rd. BA10 0EH. BABAADA. Open Mon.-
Fri. 8.30-5.30 or by appointment. SIZE: Large.
*STOCK: Georgian, Victorian, Edwardian and
decorative items, carved oak, barley twist and
shipping goods, Continental furniture.* PARK:
Easy. TEL: 01749 812460; fax - 01749 812882;
e-mail - antiques@mgr.exports.co.uk. SER:
Packing and shipping.

THE PARIS SALONS 1895-1914

From 1895 through to the First World War, the Paris Salons were a showcase for all that was innovative and exciting in the world of the decorative arts. They embraced both individual works from artist-craftsmen as well as mass-produced designs from manufacturing industries. The items displayed were all recorded in individual catalogues. Alastair Duncan, a leading expert in the field and author of many books on the period, has exhaustively researched these catalogues and reassembled the material in them into subject areas catalogued by individual artists. The resultant volumes are a mine of easily accessible images, each one prefaced by a scholarly and informative essay.

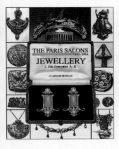 

Vol.I and II: Jewellery. The catalogues of the Paris Salons from the turn of the century provide a unique archive of illustrations of the decorative arts at a pivotal time in their development. These volumes contain over 5,500 illustrations of items of jewellery by leading designers such as Boucheron, Chaumet and Lalique. The pictures have been sourced and re-photographed from the original and often rare catalogues. They have been re-arranged alphabetically by artist designer thus providing an indispensable and practical reference for this seminal twenty year period. They are a unique source for identification and authentication and an invaluable key both to design ideas and the jewellery of the period.

ISBN 1 85149 159 7 Vol. I A-K: 350pp., 15col., 3,000 b.&w. illus.
ISBN 1 85149 168 6 Vol. II L-Z: 306pp., 8 col., 2,500 b.&w. illus. **£45.00/$89.00 each volume**

Vol.III Furniture: The works of hundreds of furniture designers, cabinet makers and partnerships clearly illustrate the revolution in design that took place in France from the emergence of Art Nouveau to the early manifestations of Art Deco at the turn of the last century. The illustrations taken from the many original Salon catalogues, have been rearranged for easy reference and become a unique source of readily accessible reference for furniture design at the crucial end of the 19th and start of the 20th century.
ISBN 1 85149 190 2 576pp., 25 col.,1,200 b.&w. illus. **£49.50/$99.50**

Vol.IV: Ceramics. The French word *orfèvrerie* defines both the art of the goldsmith and the silversmith as well as that of the artist craftsman who works in precious metals. The industry received a huge impetus in the early 1890s with the decision to expand membership of two of the Paris Salons to include jewellery and *orfèvrerie*. Metalware, in the context of this volume, covers the works of both the sculptor and the metalworker, at a time when the growing prosperity of the bourgeoisie came to be reflected in the quality of objets d'art.
ISBN 1 85149 304 2 566pp., 39 col., 2,000 b.&w. illus. **£49.50/$99.50**

Vol.V: Objets d'art & Metalwork. At the turn of the century there was an enormous and diverse output of works from both the independent artists-craftsmen and the commercial manufactories. For the former each piece was a work of art in its own right, for the latter standardisation was paramount. Both are illustrated and categorised in this survey based on the catalogues from the Paris Salons.
ISBN 1 85149 229 1 464pp., 27 col., 1,500 b.&w. illus. **£49.50/$99.50**

For a free copy of our catalogue, please contact

ANTIQUE COLLECTORS' CLUB

5 Church Street, Woodbridge, Suffolk, IP12 1DS, UK
Tel: (01394) 385501 Fax: (01394) 384434
Sales Office Direct Fax: (01394) 388994
Email: sales@antique-acc.com Website: www.antique-acc.com

or

Market Street Industrial Park, Wappingers' Falls, NY 12590, USA
Tel: (845) 297 0003 Fax: (845) 297 0068 ORDERS: (800) 252 5231
Email: info@antiquecc.com Website: www.antiquecc.com

BURNHAM-ON-SEA

Adam Antiques
30 Adam St. TA8 1PQ. (R. Coombes). Open 9-5. SIZE: Large. *STOCK: Furniture, clocks, brass, porcelain and shipping goods.* PARK: Easy. TEL: 01278 783193.

Burnham Collectors Shop
Unit 6 Victoria Court, 5 Victoria St. TA8 1AL. (W.I. Loudon). Est. 1993. Open 9.30-5. SIZE: Small. *STOCK: Postcards, pre-1945, 50p-£100; models, old and new issues.* LOC: Just off High St., behind Lloyds Bank. PARK: Limited. TEL: 01278 780066; fax - same. SER: Valuations. FAIRS: Yeovil (Feb.)

Castle Antiques
(T.C. Germain). Open by appointment. *STOCK: Jewellery, silver, 18th-19th C furniture, porcelain, clocks.* TEL: 01278 785031; website - www. castleantiquesjewellery.com.

Heape's Antiques
39 Victoria St. TA8 1AN. (Mrs M.M. Heap). FATG. Open 10-1 and 2.30-4.30. *STOCK: Small furniture, fine arts, porcelain, glass, memorabilia.* TEL: 01278 782131.

CARHAMPTON, Nr. Minehead

Chris's Crackers
Townsend Garage. Open 11-5.30 including Sun. SIZE: Large warehouses. *STOCK: Mainly 18th-19th C furniture, stripped pine, architectural antiques, iron and stone-work, general building reclamation materials and country artefacts.* LOC: A39 coast road. TEL: 01643 821873/01984 623703. SER: Pine-stripping.

CASTLE CARY

Cary Antiques
2 High St. BA7 7AW. (Mrs. J.A. Oldham). Est. 1977. Open 10.30-5. CL: Mon. and Wed. SIZE: Small. *STOCK: Furniture, Victorian and Edwardian, £30-£500; china, brass and copper, glass, bric-a-brac, pictures, 18th-19th C, £5-£150.* LOC: Town centre, B3152. PARK: Easy. TEL: 01963 350437. SER: Valuations; picture framing; caning and rushing.

CHARD

Chez Chalon
Field Bars House, Shepherds Lane. TA20 1QX. (Jake and Nick Chalon). Est. 1973. Open by appointment. *STOCK: French and English country furniture, £100-£10,000.* PARK: Easy. TEL: 01460 68679; fax - 01460 239005; e-mail - antiques@chezchalon.freeserve.co.uk. SER: Restorations (country furniture). VAT: Stan.

CHILCOMPTON, Nr. Bath

Billiard Room Antiques
The Old School, Church Lane. BA3 4HP. (Mrs J. McKeivor). LAPADA. BABAADA. Est. 1992. Open by appointment. SIZE: Medium. *STOCK: Billiard, snooker and pool tables and accessories, 19th C, £100-£40,000.* PARK: Easy. TEL: 01761 232839; home and fax - same. SER: Valuations; restorations; buys at auction; search.

CLEVEDON

Beach Antiques
Adelaide House, 13 The Beach. BS21 7QU. (D.A. Coles). Open 2-5, Sat. and Sun. 11-5. CL: Mon. and Fri. *STOCK: Jewellery, silver frames, china, brass, glass, mainly small items.* PARK: Easy. TEL: 01275 876881.

The Collector
14 The Beach. BS21 7QU. (Mrs Tina Simmonds). Est. 1993. Open 10-5, Sun. 2-5. CL: Thurs. (Jan.-Feb. open weekends only). SIZE: Small. *STOCK: Small items and collectables, from 1880, £5-£200; postcards and emphemera, 1900-1960, £1-£30; Beatrix Potter and Bunnykins figures, from 1960, £16-£300.* LOC: On sea front, near pier. PARK: Easy. TEL: 01275 875066; home - same. FAIRS: Malvern 3 Counties; Temple Meads, Brunel, Bristol.

Nostalgia
65a Hill Rd. BS21 7PD. (Mrs Wendy Moore). Est. 1985. Open Wed.-Fri. 10-1 and 2-5, Tues. 10-1 and 2-4.30, Sat. 10-1 and 2-5.30. SIZE: Medium. *STOCK: Furniture, Victorian, £200-£600; china and linen, 1930's and earlier, £3-£100.* PARK: Easy. TEL: 01275 342587.

CLUTTON

Ian McCarthy
Arcadian Cottage, 112 Station Rd. BS39 5RA. Resident. Est. 1958. Open by appointment. SIZE: Medium. *STOCK: Lamps - oil, gas, electric for domestic, industrial, shipping and transport usage; unusual candle lamps; copper and brassware, 17th C to 1920, £5-£2,000.* PARK: Easy and opposite. TEL: 01761 453188. SER: Valuations; restorations (metalware); cleaning; spares and lamp-shades.

COXLEY, Nr. Wells

Courtyard Antiques
Main Rd. BA5 1QZ. (Mr and Mrs M. J. Mitchell). Est. 1985. Open 9-5, Sun by appointment. SIZE: Medium. *STOCK: Furniture, £100-£300; smalls, £10-£50; both 19th-20th C.* TEL: 01749 679533. SER: Valuations; restorations (upholstery, cane and rush work, china and furniture).

Wells Reclamation Company
BA5 1RQ. (H. Davies). Est. 1984. Open 9-5.30. SIZE: Large. *STOCK: Architectural items, 18th-19th C.* LOC: A39 towards Glastonbury from Wells. PARK: Easy. TEL: 01749 677087. SER: Valuations. VAT: Stan.

CREWKERNE

Antiques and Country Pine
14 East St. TA18 7AG. (M.J. Wheeler). Open Tues.-Sat. 10-5 or by appointment. *STOCK: Country pine and decorative items.* TEL: 01460 75623.

Julian Armytage
Open by appointment only. *STOCK: Fine sporting, marine and decorative prints, 18th-19th C.* TEL: 01460 73449; fax - same.

Crewkerne Antique Centre
16 Market St. TA18 7LA. (F. Martin). Est. 1987. Open 9.30-4.30. CL: Mon. SIZE: Large. *STOCK: Furniture, £25-£3,000; collectables, £5-£1,000; pictures, £5-£2,000; all 18th-20th C.* LOC: A303 westward, A359 to Crewkerne, Chard road through town. PARK: Easy. TEL: 01460 77111. SER: Valuations; restorations.

Hennessy
42 East St. TA18 7AG. (Carl Hennessy). Est. 1977. Open 10-5. SIZE: Large. *STOCK: Furniture - pine, country, painted and French provincial; related decorative items.* LOC: A30 from Yeovil. PARK: Easy. TEL: 01460 78600; fax - same; workshop - 01460 78060; mobile - 07768 286455; e-mail - carl@veryold.co.uk; website - www.veryold.co.uk. VAT: Stan/Spec.

DULVERTON

Acorn Antiques
39 High St. TA22 9DW. (P. Hounslow). Est. 1988. Open 9.30-5.30. SIZE: Medium. *STOCK: Decorative antique furniture, period and reproduction upholstery, sofas, fine art, textiles,*

country furniture. LOC: Town centre. PARK: Nearby. TEL: 01398 323286; home - same. SER: Interior design.

Guy Dennler Antiques
The White Hart, 23 High St. TA22 9HB . Open 10-1 and 2-5. *STOCK: Fine 18th to early 19th C English furniture and decorative objects.* TEL: 01398 324300; fax - 01398 324301; e-mail - guydennler@btconnect.com.

Faded Elegance
39 High St. TA22 9DW. (M. Delbridge). Open 9.30-5.30. *STOCK: 18th-19th C decorative antiques, textiles, upholstery.* TEL: 01398 323286.

Rothwell and Dunworth
2 Bridge St. TA22 9HJ. (Mrs C. Rothwell and M. Rothwell). ABA. Est. 1975. Open 10.30-1 and 2.15-5, including Sun. (excluding Nov-Feb). SIZE: Medium. *STOCK: Antiquarian and secondhand books especially on hunting and horses and military history.* LOC: 1st shop in village over River Barle. PARK: 100yds. TEL: 01398 323169; fax - 01398 331161; e-mail - rothwellm@aol.com. SER: Valuations.

The Longton Hall, Liverpool printed (by Sadler) Brandenburg mug which rated £900 because of extensive damage.

From an Auction Report by Christopher Wight on The Hacking Collection of Davenport, dry-bodied stoneware and other British ceramics which was held at Phillips Bayswater, 23rd January 2001. This sale was featured in the March 2001 issue of **Antique Collecting** magazine**.** For more details and to subscribe see page 147.

Anthony Sampson Antiques
Holland House, Bridge St. TA22 9HJ. Open 9.30-5.30, Sun. by appointment. SIZE: Medium. *STOCK: Town and country furniture, 17th to early 19th C, £500-£10,000+; porcelain, pottery, silver, glass, pictures and garden ornaments.* LOC: Main road, prominent position near bridge. PARK: Nearby. TEL: 01398 324247; fax - 01398 324027; e-mail - anthony.sampson@virgin.net. SER: Valuations. VAT: Spec.

DUNSTER

The Crooked Window
7 High St. TA24 6SF. (Robert Ricketts). Est. 1984. SIZE: Small. *STOCK: Chinese ceramics, 3000BC-19th C, £50-£5,000; English furniture, 17th-18th C, £500-£10,000; maps and prints, 16th-18th C, £50-£2,000.* PARK: Easy. TEL: 01643 821606; home - same. SER: Valuations; restorations (walnut and mahogany 'problem' surface); buys at auction. FAIRS: Wilton House.

EAST PENNARD, Nr. Shepton Mallet

Pennard House Antiques
BA4 6TP. (Martin Dearden). Resident. Est. 1979.

Open 9.30-5.30 or by appointment. SIZE: Large. *STOCK: French and English country furniture, £300-£5,000.* LOC: From Shepton Mallet, 4 miles south off A37. One hour from Bath. PARK: Easy. TEL: 01749 860731; home - 01749 860266; fax - 01749 860732. SER: Valuations; restorations; export. VAT: Stan/Spec.

FRESHFORD, Nr. Bath

Janet Clarke
3 Woodside Cottages. BA3 6EJ. Open by appointment. *STOCK: Antiquarian books on gastronomy, cookery and wine.* TEL: 01225 723186; fax - 01225 722063. SER: Catalogue issued.

Freshfords
High St. BA3 6EF. LAPADA. CINOA. Est. 1973. Open 10-5, Sat. 10-1, Sat. pm. and Sun. by appointment. SIZE: Large. *STOCK: English Regency furniture, 18th-19th C, £2,000-£50,000; Victorian oil paintings, £2,000-£12,000; decorative accessories, 18th-19th C, £2,000-£5,000.* LOC: 4 miles from Bath towards Warminster, just off A36. PARK: Easy. TEL: 01225 722111; fax - 01225 722991; mobile - 07970 517332. SER: Valuations; restorations; buys at auction. FAIRS: Olympia; Harrogate, Chelsea. VAT: Spec.

FROME

Antiques & Country Living
43-44 Vallis Way, Badcox. BA11 3BA. (Mrs D.M. Williams). Open 9.30-5.30 including Sun. SIZE: Medium. *STOCK: Furniture including country, 19th-20th C, £15-£1,000; porcelain, 18th-19th C, £5-£500.* LOC: A362 Frome to Radstock road. PARK: Free opposite. TEL: 01373 463015.

Frome Reclamation
Station Approach. BA11 1RE. (S.J., K.R., R.L. and J.B. Horler). Est. 1987. Open 8-5. SIZE: Large + yard. *STOCK: Architectural reclamation.* LOC: From A361 follow signs for railway station. PARK: Easy. TEL: 01373 463919/453122; fax - 01373 453122. SER: Valuations. VAT: Stan.

HIGHBRIDGE

C.W.E. Dyte
The Old Bacon Factory, Huntspill Rd. TA9 3DE. Open 8-6 or by appointment. SIZE: Large - 3 dealers. *STOCK: 18th-20th C shipping goods.* PARK: Easy. TEL: 01278 788590/788603. SER: Packing; transport; documentation.

John Dyte Antiques
Four Winds, Huntspill Rd. TA9 3DE. *STOCK: Longcase clocks, 18th-20th C, furniture.* TEL: 01278 788603; fax - 01278 788604.

T.M. Dyte Antiques
9 Gass Close, Isleport Business Park. TA9 4JT. Open 8.30-5.30. CL: Sat. *STOCK: Shipping goods.* TEL: 01278 786495.

ILCHESTER

Gilbert & Dale
The Old Chapel, Church St. BA22 8LN. Est. 1965. Open 9-5.30 or by appointment. SIZE: Large. *STOCK: English and French country furniture and accessories.* LOC: Centre of village on A37. PARK: Easy. TEL: 01935 840464; fax - 01935 841599; home - 01458 250193.

ILMINSTER

County Antiques
Rear of 21 West St. TA19 0DU. (Mrs J.P. Barnard). Resident. Est. 1981. Open by appointment only. SIZE: 6 dealers. *STOCK: 18th-19th C pottery, porcelain, metalwork, furniture and decorative antiques.* TEL: 01460 54151; home - 01460 52269; mobile - 07803 362327. SER: Upholstery.

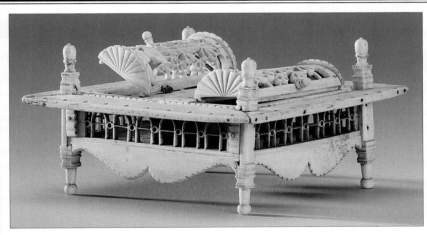

This early 19th century French prisoner of war bone model of a grasshopper table cage raised £2,200.

From an Auction Report by Christopher Wight on the sale of Maritime and Naval Battles held at Christie's South Kensington on 9th November 2000. This was featured in the February 2001 issue of **Antique Collecting** magazine. For more details and to subscribe see page 147.

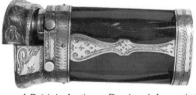

LANGFORD, Nr. Bristol

Richard Essex Antiques
BS40 5BP. Est. 1969. *STOCK: General antiques
from mid-18th C.* TEL: 01934 863302.

LITTLETON, Nr. Somerton

Westville House Antiques
TA11 6NP. (D. and M.Stacey). Est. 1986. Open
daily, Sun. by appointment. SIZE: Large. *STOCK:
18th-19th C pine, mahogany and oak furniture;*
LOC: B3151 approximately 1.5 miles north of
Somerton. PARK: Own. TEL: 01458 273376; fax -
same; e-mail - antique@westville.co.uk; website -
www.westville.co.uk; SER: Valuations; buys at
auction. VAT: Stan/Spec.

MARTOCK

Castle Reclamation
Parrett Works. TA12 6AE. (T.A.B. Dance and
A.J. Wills). Est. 1986. Open daily, Sat. 10-1.
SIZE: Large. *STOCK: Architectural antiques.*
LOC: 2 miles off A303 between Martock and
South Petherton. PARK: Easy. TEL: 01935

826483; fax - 01935 826791; website -
www.castlereclamation.com. SER: Restorations
(stone). FAIRS: Bath and West. VAT: Stan.

MIDSOMER NORTON

Somervale Antiques   BADA
6 Radstock Rd. BA3 2AJ. (Wing Cdr.R.G.
Thomas). BABAADA, LAPADA, CINOA.
Resident. Open by appointment only. *STOCK:
English drinking glasses, decanters, cut and
coloured; "Bristol" and "Nailsea"glass;
bijouterie; glass scent bottles, 18th to early 19th
C.* LOC: On A362. PARK: Easy. TEL: 01761
412686 (24hrs); fax - same; mobile - 07885
088022; e-mail - ronthomas@somervale
antiquesglass.co.uk; website - www.somervale
antiquesglass.co.uk. SER: Valuations; buys at
auction; trains to Bath met by arrangement.
VAT: Stan/Spec.

MILVERTON, Nr. Taunton

J.C. White
The Granary, Fitzhead. TA4 3JT. Est. 1960.
STOCK: Country furniture and clocks. TEL:
01823 400427.

JOHN GARDINER ANTIQUES

Dealer in 18th - 19th Century Antiques

Monteclefe House	20 minutes from M5	Tel: 01458 272238
Somerton, Somerset	20 minutes from Bruton	Fax & A/Phone: 01458 274329
TA11 7NL	5 minutes from A303	Mobile: 07831 274427

NETHER STOWEY, Nr. Bridgwater

The Court Gallery
2 Lime St. TA5 1NG. (John Wilcox). Est. 1990. Open during exhibitions or by appointment. SIZE: Medium. *STOCK: British paintings, 1880-1939, especially Newlyn, St Ives and London Group, £50-£15,000.* LOC: Bridgwater turn off M5, then A39 towards Minehead. PARK: Easy. TEL: 01278 732539; home - same. SER: Valuations; restorations; buys at auction.

House of Antiquity
St. Mary St. TA5 1LJ. (M.S. Todd). Est. 1967. Open 10-5 or by appointment. SIZE: Medium. *STOCK: Philatelic literature, world topographical, maps, handbooks, postcards, ephemera, postal history.* LOC: A39. PARK: Easy. TEL: 01278 732426; fax - same; e-mail - mstodd@lineone.net. SER: Valuations; buys at auction. VAT: Stan.

NORTH PETHERTON, Nr. Taunton

Harrison House Antiques
60 Fore St. TA6 6QA. (James Yarrow). Open by appointment. SIZE: Large. *STOCK: Architectural features, furniture and furnishings.* LOC: Off junction 24, M5. PARK: Own. TEL: 01278 662535. *Trade Only.*

QUEEN CAMEL, Nr. Yeovil

Steven Ferdinando
The Old Vicarage. BA22 7NG. Open by appointment. *STOCK: Antiquarian and secondhand books.* TEL: 01935 850210.

RODE

Domain Interiors Ltd
The Chapel, 16a High St. BA3 6NZ. BABAADA. Open 10-5 or by appointment. *STOCK: English and Continental furniture; fabrics; decorative items.* LOC: A36 between Bath and Warminster. PARK: Easy. TEL: 01373 830531; fax - 01373 830792; mobile - 07802 884133; e-mail - domaininteriors@hotmail.com. SER: Interior design.

SHEPTON MALLET

Edward Marnier Antiques
Old Bowlish House, Forum Lane, Bowlish. BA4 5JA. (E.F. Marnier). Resident. BABAADA. Est. 1989. Open 7 days, prior telephone call advisable. *STOCK: English and Continental furniture, pictures, rugs, carpets and interesting decorative objects, 17th-20th C, £5-£10,000.* LOC: Quarter mile from Shepton Mallet on A371 Wells Road, turn right into Forum Lane. PARK: Easy. TEL: 01749 343340. SER: Valuations; buys at auction. VAT: Spec.

SOMERTON

John Gardiner Antiques
Monteclefe House. TA11 7NL. Appointment advisable. *STOCK: General antiques; decorative Edwardian, Georgian and quality old reproduction furnishings.* LOC: A303, close to M5. TEL: 01458 272238; fax/answerphone - 01458 274329; mobile - 07831 274427.

The London Cigarette Card Co. Ltd
West St. TA11 6NB. (I.A. and E.K.Laker, F.C.Doggett and Y.Berktay). Est. 1927. Open daily. SIZE: Medium. *STOCK: Cigarette and trade cards, 1885 to date; sets from £1.50; other cards, from 15p; frames for mounting cards and special albums.* PARK: Easy. TEL: 01458 273452; e-mail - cards@londoncigcard.co.uk; website - www.londoncigcard.co.uk. SER: Publishers of catalogues, reference books and monthly magazine; mail order.

Somerton Antiques Centre
Market Place. TA11 7NB. Est. 1998. Open 10-5. Sun. by appointment. SIZE: Large - 26 dealers. *STOCK: General antiques, £5-£1,200.* PARK: Own. TEL: 01458 274423. SER: Valuations; repair and restoration (furniture). FAIRS: Shepton Mallet.

SOUTH PETHERTON

Rostrum Antiques
The Old Flaxmill, Flaxdrayton Farm, Drayton. TA13 5LR. Open by appointment. *STOCK: 18th-19th C English and Continental furniture, objets d'art, £100-£20,000*. TEL: 01460 249249. SER: Valuations; gilding; French polishing; restorations (antique furniture and musical instruments only); replica dining tables and other furniture designed and hand-made to order; interior decoration.

TAUNTON

T.J. Atkins
East Criddles Farm, Tolland, Lydeard St. Lawrence. TA4 3PW. Est. 1958. Open by appointment only. SIZE: Medium. *STOCK: Porcelain and pottery including Prattware, 18th-19th C.* TEL: 01984 667310.

Lords Antiques
8 East Reach. TA1 3EN. (J.R. and A.A. Lord). Open 10-4. SIZE: Medium. *STOCK: Furniture and metalware, 18th-19th C, £50-£1,000*. PARK: Easy. TEL: 01823 275641. VAT: Global.

Selwoods
Queen Anne Cottage, Mary St. TA1 3PE. Est. 1927. Open 9.30-5. SIZE: Large. *STOCK: Furniture, including Victorian and Edwardian*. TEL: 01823 272780.

Taunton Antiques Market - Silver Street
25/29 Silver St. TA1 3DH. (Bath Antiques Market Ltd.). Est. 1978. Open Mon. 9-4 including Bank Holidays. SIZE: 100+ dealers. *STOCK: General

This Arts and Crafts cigarette box enamelled with St. George made an unexpected £3,000.

From an Auction Report by Tim Ford on the Autumn Fine Art Sale held at Bearne's, Exeter on 20th and 21st October, 1998. This feature appeared in the December 1998/January 1999 issue of **Antique Collecting** magazine. For more details and to subscribe see page 147.

antiques and collectables, including specialists in most fields. LOC: 2 miles from M5, junction 25, to town centre, 100yds. from Sainsburys car park across lights. PARK: Easy - Sainsburys (town centre branch). TEL: 01823 289327; fax - same; enquiries - 020 7969 1500. SER: Valuations.

M.G. Welch Jeweller
1 Corporation St. TA1 4AJ. (Mark and Liz Welch). NAG. Est. 1978. Open 9.30-5. SIZE: Medium. *STOCK: Antique and secondhand jewellery, £100-£10,000; antique and secondhand silver, £100-£1,000*. LOC: Town centre, corner of High St. PARK: Nearby. TEL: 01823 270456; fax - same. SER: Valuations; restorations (jewellery); buys at auction (jewellery). VAT: Stan/Spec.

WATCHET

Clarence House Antiques
41 Swain St. TA23 0AE. Est. 1970. Open 10.30-5.30. CL: Sun. in winter. SIZE: Medium. *STOCK: General antiques, pine, brass, copper, bric-a-brac, upholstered furniture, books (including specialist and antiquarian).* TEL: 01984 631389. VAT: Stan.

Nick Cotton Fine Art
Beachstone House, 46/47 Swain St. TA23 0AG. Est. 1970. Open 10-6. SIZE: Large. *STOCK: Paintings, 1850-2000; some period furniture.* TEL: 01984 631814. SER: Restorations; conservation; research. VAT: Spec.

WEDMORE

R. Tincknell
Shop One, The Borough and Ebenezer Hall, Combe Batch. Open 10-4 or by appointment. *STOCK: Antique and country furniture, decorative accessories.* TEL: 01934 713773/713338.

WELLINGTON

Michael and Amanda Lewis Oriental Carpets and Rugs
8 North St. TA21 8LT. LAPADA. UKIC. Est. 1982. Open 10-1 and 2-5.30, Mon. and weekends by appointment. SIZE: Medium. *STOCK: Oriental carpets and rugs, mainly 19th-20th C, £25-£25,000*. PARK: 100yds. TEL: 01823 667430. SER: Valuations; restorations; repairs and cleaning; courses; tapestry restoration and conservation.

WELLS

Bernard G. House
Market Place. BA5 2RF. Est. 1963. Open 9.30-5.30. SIZE: Medium. *STOCK: Barometers and

scientific instruments, barographs, telescopes, tripod and hand held; furniture including miniatures and apprentice pieces, 18th-19th C; longcase and bracket clocks, metalware, decorative and architectural items. PARK: Opposite shop. TEL: 01749 672607. SER: Repairs; restorations. VAT: Stan/Spec.

Edward A. Nowell   BADA
12 Market Place. BA5 2RB. Est. 1952. Open 9.15-5. SIZE: Large. *STOCK: Furniture, clocks, barometers, 17th to early 19th C; jewellery, silver, porcelain, English and Continental, all prices.* Not Stocked: Victoriana, bric-a-brac, curios, weapons, books. LOC: From any direction, turn left into Market Place (one-way system). PARK: 20yds. facing shop. TEL: 01749 672415; fax - 01749 673519; e-mail - antiques@eanowell.demon.co.uk. SER: Valuations; restorations (furniture, silver, clocks and jewellery); re-upholstery. VAT: Stan/Spec.

Sadler Street Gallery,
7a Sadler St. BA5 2RR. Open 10-5.30. CL: Mon. *STOCK: Watercolours and oils, mainly contemporary.* TEL: 01749 670220.

WEST BUCKLAND, Nr. Taunton

Everett Fine Art
Budleigh Studios, Budleigh. (Tim and Karen Everitt). Open by appointment. *STOCK: 18th-20th C paintings and sculpture, £200-£5,000.* PARK: Easy. TEL: 01823 421710; e-mail - info@everett-art.co.uk; website - www.everett-art.co.uk. SER: Restorations; conservation (paintings and frames); framemakers. VAT: Stan/Spec.

WESTON-SUPER-MARE

D.M. Restorations
3 Laburnum Rd. BS23 3LL. (D. Pike). Open 9-5. *STOCK: Small mahogany furniture.* PARK: Easy. TEL: 01934 811120.

Sterling Books
43A Locking Rd. BS23 3DG. Est. 1966. Open 10-5.30. CL: Mon. and Thurs. p.m. *STOCK: Books, antiquarian and secondhand, some new; ephemera and prints.* TEL: 01934 625056. SER: Bookbinding and picture framing.

Winter's Antiques
62 Severn Rd. BS23 1DT. (R.N. and E.P. Winters). LAPADA. Open 9-12 and 2-3.30. CL: Sat. pm. and Thurs. SIZE: Large. *STOCK: Furniture, clocks, smalls and fine art, all periods.* Not Stocked: Coins, stamps. LOC: Off sea front. PARK: Easy. TEL: 01934 620118/814610.

WILLITON

Courtyard Antiques
Home Farm Holiday Centre, St. Audries. TA4 4DP. (Nick Wass and Liz Cain). Open Tues., Thurs., Fri. 9-4, Sat. and Sun. 10-4. SIZE: Medium. *STOCK: English vernacular furniture - oak, elm and pine, upholstered chairs, gilded frames, mostly 18th-20th C, £100-£2,000.* LOC: Off the A39 at West Quantoxhead. PARK: Easy. TEL: 01984 633701; fax - same; home - 01984 640314. SER: Restorations. VAT: Stan/Spec.

Edward Venn
Unit 3, 52 Long St. TA4 4QU. Est. 1979. Open 10-5. *STOCK: Furniture, clocks.* TEL: 01984 632631; fax - same. SER: Restorations (furniture, barometers and clocks).

WINCANTON

Green Dragon Antiques Centre
24 High St. BA9 9JF. (Mrs Sally Denning). Est. 1991. Open 10-5 including Sun. SIZE: 112 dealers. *STOCK: Wide variety of general antiques and collectables, £1-£1,000.* TEL: 01963 34111/34702. SER: Valuations.

WIVELISCOMBE

J.C. Giddings
TA4 2SN. Open by appointment only. SIZE: Large warehouses. *STOCK: Mostly 18th-19th C furniture, iron-work and general building reclamation materials.* TEL: 01984 623703. VAT: Stan. *Mainly Trade.*

Heads 'n' Tails
Bournes House, 41 Church St. TA4 2LT. (D. McKinley). Resident. Open by appointment. *STOCK: Taxidermy including Victorian cased and uncased birds, mammals and fish, £5-£2,000; decorative items, glass domes.* LOC: Opposite church. PARK: Easy. TEL: 01984 623097; fax - 01984 624445. SER: Taxidermy; restorations; commissions; hire. VAT: Spec.

YEOVIL

John Hamblin
Unit 6, 15 Oxford Rd., Penn Mill Trading Estate. BA21 5HR. (J. and M. A. Hamblin). Est. 1980. Open 8.30-5. CL: Sat. SIZE: Small. *STOCK: Furniture, 1750-1900, £300-£3,000.* PARK: Easy. TEL: 01935 471154; home - 01935 476673. SER: Restorations (furniture); cabinet work. VAT: Stan.

ALRESWAS, Nr. Burton-on-Trent

Poley Antiques
5 Main St. DE13 7AA. (D.T. and A.G. Poley). Est. 1977. Open Thurs., Fri. 10-5.30, Sat. 10-5, other times by arrangement. SIZE: Small. *STOCK: General antiques, furniture, silver, china, glass, copper, brass.* Not Stocked: Stamps, coins and militaria. LOC: 20yds. from A38, between Lichfield and Burton. PARK: Own. TEL: 01283 791151; home - same; fax - same; e-mail - dennis.poley@which.net.

BRERETON, Nr. Rugeley

Rugeley Antique Centre
161/3 Main Rd. WS15 1DX. Open 9-5, Sun. 12-4.30. SIZE: Large - 40 units. *STOCK: China, glass, pottery, pictures, furniture, pine, treen, linen and shipping goods.* LOC: A51, one mile south of Rugeley town, opposite Cedar Tree Hotel. PARK: Own. TEL: 01889 577166; e-mail - info@rugeleyantiquecentre.co.uk; website - www.rugeleyantiquecentre.co.uk. VAT: Stan/Spec.

BREWOOD

Passiflora
25 Stafford St. ST19 9DX. (David and Paula Whitfield). Est. 1988. Usually open 10-4ish, prior 'phone call advisable. SIZE: Medium. *STOCK: General antiques, collectables and curios, copper and brass, Victorian to 1950's, £1-£300; early childrens books and Mabel Lucie Attwell corner; garden statuary.* LOC: Off A5 and A49 near Gailey roundabout, village on Shropshire Union canal. PARK: Free opposite. TEL: 01902 851557 (answerphone); e-mail - paula.whitfield@uk online.co.uk. SER: Valuations. FAIRS: Bingley Hall.

BURTON-ON-TRENT

Burton Antiques
1-2 Horninglow Rd. DE14 2PR. (C.H. Armett). Est. 1977. Open 10-5 every day. SIZE: Large. *STOCK: Shipping and pine furniture.* LOC: A511. PARK: Nearby. TEL: 01283 542331. SER: Valuations; pine stripping; buys at auction.

(Left and centre) Two vases designed by Fulvio Bianconi in 1951, with fused green, blue, red and clear panels. Acid-stamped 'Venini, Murano, Italia'; left, 8½in., centre, 9½in. Each sold for £4,600. (Right) A vase designed by Dino Martens, c.1960, for Aureliano Toso, with panels of opaque yellow, red, white and blue, copper aventurine inclusions, an asymmetric pinwheel of white and amethyst, and 'zanfirico' panels. 11¼in. Sold for £3,450. (Christie's South Kensington)

From an article on glass by Andy McConnell which appeared in the July/August 2000 issue of **Antique Collecting** magazine. For more details and to subscribe see page 147.

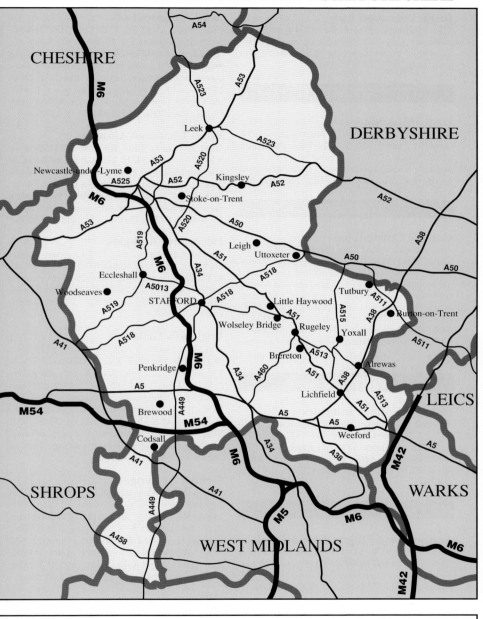

Dealers and Shops in Staffordshire

Alrewas	1	Leek	15
Brereton	1	Leigh	1
Brewood	1	Lichfield	7
Burton-on-Trent	2	Little Haywood	1
Codsall	1	Newcastle-under-Lyme	3
Eccleshall	1	Penkridge	1
Kingsley	1	Rugeley	1

Stafford	2
Stoke-on-Trent	4
Tutbury	3
Uttoxeter	1
Weeford	1
Wolseley Bridge	1
Woodseaves	1
Yoxall	1

Justin Pinewood Ltd
The Maltings, Wharf Rd. DE14 1PZ. (S. Silvester). Open 9-5.30, including Sun. *STOCK: Stripped pine furniture and decorative accessories.* TEL: 01283 510860.

CODSALL

Dam Mill Antiques
Birches Rd. WV8 2JR. (H. Bassett). Est. 1977. Open 10-1 and 2.30-5.30. CL: Tues. and Thurs. SIZE: Small. *STOCK: General antiques, small furniture, china, glass, copper, brass, silver and jewellery.* PARK: Easy. TEL: 01902 843780.

ECCLESHALL

Cottage Collectibles
The Old Bakery, 62 High St. ST21 6BZ. (Mrs Sheila Kettle). Est. 1995. Open by appointment. SIZE: Small. *STOCK: English and Continental kitchenalia, 19th C, £10-£250; pine and painted furniture, £100-£1,000; garden and rural artefacts, £10-£250.* LOC: Village centre. PARK: Easy. TEL: 01785 850210; fax - 01785 850757. SER: Restorations (metalwork and furniture). FAIRS: Shepton Mallet; Antiques for Everyone (NEC).

KINGSLEY, Nr. Leek

Country Cottage Interiors
Newhall Farmhouse, Hazels Crossroads. ST10 2AY. (L. Salmon). Resident. Est. 1972. Open 10-5. SIZE: Medium. *STOCK: Pine, £5-£500; kitchenalia, 25p-£100.* LOC: Off A52. PARK: Own. TEL: 01538 754762; mobile - 07855 584790.

LEEK

Antiques and Objets d'Art of Leek
70 St. Edwards St. ST13 5DL. Est. 1955. Open 10-6. CL: Thurs. *STOCK: English and Continental furniture; porcelain, silver, glass, oil paintings.* TEL: 01538 382587. VAT: Spec.

Antiques Within Ltd
Ground Floor, Compton Mill. ST13. (R. and K. Hicks). Est. 1992. Open 10-5.30. Sun. (Oct.to April) 1-5.30. SIZE: Stan. *STOCK: Pine, oak and mahaogany, £50-£3,000; bric-a-brac, £5-£500; all 19th C.* LOC: A520 towards Cheddleton, opposite Catholic church. PARK: Easy. TEL: 01538 387848. SER: Restorations; courier, packing and shipping. FAIRS: Newark. VAT: Stan.

Anvil Antiques Ltd
Cross Mills, Cross St. ST13 6BL. (J.S. Spooner and N.M. Sullivan). Est. 1975. Open 9-5, Sat. 10-5, Sun. 12-4. SIZE: Large. *STOCK: Stripped pine, old and reproduction; oak, mahogany, bric-a-brac and decorative items, architectural items.* LOC: Ashbourne Rd., from town centre roundabout, turn first left, Victorian mill on right. PARK: Easy. TEL: 01538 371657. VAT: Stan.

Sylvia Chapman Antiques
56 St. Edward St. ST13 5DL. Est. 1983. Open 10-5.30. CL: Thurs. SIZE: Medium. *STOCK: Small oak, mahogany and country furniture; general antiques and collector's items, especially 19th to early 20th C pottery and porcelain, Staffordshire jugs, Victorian coloured glass, copper, brass and kitchenalia.* PARK: Outside. TEL: 01538 399116.

Decorative Antiques
60B St Edward St. ST13 5DL. (Joan Smith-Gamble). Est. 1985. Open 10-5. SIZE: Small. *STOCK: French and English decorative items, 19th C to 1920's, £50-£300.* PARK: Limited. TEL: 01538 372202; fax/home - 01538 381939. FAIRS: Newark.

England's Gallery
Ball Haye House, 1 Ball Haye Terr. ST13 6AP. (F.J. and S. England). Est. 1968. Open 10-5.30. CL: Mon. SIZE: Large. *STOCK: Oils and water-colours, 18th-19th C, £500-£10,000; etchings, engravings, lithographs, mezzotints, £50-£4,000.* LOC: Towards Ball Haye Green from A523 turn at lights. PARK: Nearby. TEL: 01538 373451. SER: Valuations; restorations (cleaning, relining, regilding); framing, mount cutting; buys at auction (paintings). VAT: Stan.

Gemini Trading
Limes Mill, Abbotts Rd. ST13 6EY. (T.J. Lancaster and Mrs Y.A. Goldstraw). Est. 1981. Open Mon.-Fri. 9-5, other times by appointment. SIZE: Large. *STOCK: Antique pine, £25-£1,000; decorative items, £10-£75.* LOC: Turn off A53 along Abbotts Rd. before town centre. PARK: Easy. TEL: 01538 387834; fax - 01538 399819; e-mail - geminitrading@lineone.net. VAT: Stan.

Gilligans Antiques
59 St. Edward St. ST13 5DN. (M.T. Gilligan). Est. 1977. *STOCK: Victorian and Edwardian furniture.* TEL: 01538 384174.

Grosvenor Clocks
71 St Edwards St. ST13 5DN. Open 9-4.30. *STOCK: Clocks, watches and barometers; some furniture.* TEL: 01538 385669.

Roger Haynes - Antiques Finder
31 Compton. ST13 5NJ. Open by appointment. *STOCK: Pine, smalls and decorative items.* TEL: 01538 385161.

Jewel Antiques
'Whitegates', 63 Basford Bridge Lane, Cheddleton. ST13 7EQ. (B. and D. Jeacott-Smith). Est. 1967. Open by appointment. *STOCK: Paintings, prints, jewellery, oil lamps, small furniture and clocks, 18th-19th C, £25-£2,000.* PARK: Easy. TEL: 01538 360744/361247; fax - same.

Johnson's
120 Mill St. ST13 8HA. Est. 1976. Open 8-5, Sat. and Sun. by appointment. SIZE: Large. *STOCK: 18th-19th C English, Irish and French country furniture, £50-£2,000; decorative accessories, £10-£500.* PARK: At rear and side. TEL: 01538 386745; fax - same.

The Leek Antiques Centre (Barclay House)
4-6 Brook St. ST13 5JE. Est. 1977. Open 10-5, Sun. by appointment. SIZE: 3 floors - 13 showrooms. *STOCK: Extending dining tables, sets of chairs, chests of drawers, bedroom furniture, pine, pottery, watercolours and oils, upholstered furniture.* TEL: 01538 398475. SER: Valuations; restorations (furniture). FAIRS: Bowman's and West Midland, Staffordshire Showground. VAT: Stan/Spec.

Molland Antique Mirrors
40 Compton. ST13 5NH. (John Molland). Est. 1980. Open 8-5. SIZE: Medium. *STOCK: Mirrors - gilt, painted and wooden, 19th C, £500-£3,500.* LOC: On A53 from Stoke-on-Trent, right at 1st traffic lights, shop 200 yards on right. PARK: Easy. TEL: 01538 372553; fax - 01538 387072; e-mail - sales@mollandmirrors.co.uk. SER: Export packing. FAIRS: NEC; Earls Court. VAT: Stan/Spec. *Mainly Trade.*

Odeon Antiques
76-78 St. Edward St. ST13 5DL. (Steve Ford). Open 10-5. *STOCK: Lighting, beds, pine and general antiques.* TEL: 01538 387188; fax - same. SER: Restorations (lighting).

John Nicholls
Open by appointment only. *STOCK: Oak furniture and related items, 17th-18th C.* LOC: 2 miles from Uttoxeter, just off A50 towards Stoke-on-Trent. TEL: 01889 502351; mobile - 07836 244024.

Mike Abrahams Books
9 Burton Old Rd., Streethay. WS13 8LJ. Est. 1975. Open by appointment. SIZE: Large. *STOCK: Books and ephemera especially Midlands topography, sport, transport, childrens, illustrated, military and antiquarian, 17th C to date, £2-£1,000.* LOC: Last but one right turn A5127 Lichfield to Burton-on-Trent before road joins A38 by-pass, house on left near corner. PARK: Easy. TEL: 01543 256200; home - same. SER: Valuations. FAIRS: Stafford, Bingley Hall and Pavillion; Midland Antiquarian Book (organiser).

Cordelia and Perdy's Antique Junk Shop
53 Tamworth St. WS13 6JW. (C.R.J. and P.J. Mellor). *STOCK: General antiques and trade shipping goods.* TEL: 01543 263223.

Images - Peter Stockham
at The Staffs Bookshop, 4 & 6 Dam St. WS13 6AA. Open 9.30-5. *STOCK: Early children's books, art and illustrated books, printed ephemera; antique toys, mainly wooden; games and associated items; fine printing; prints and wood engravings.* TEL: 01543 264093.

James A. Jordan
7 The Corn Exchange. WS1 36. CMBHI. Open 9-5. *STOCK: Clocks, longcase, barometers, jewellery and small furniture.* TEL: 01543 416221. SER: Restorations (clocks and chronometers).

Milestone Antiques
5 Main St., Whittington. WS14 9JU. (H. and E. Crawshaw). LAPADA. Resident. Est. 1988. Open Thurs.-Sat. 10-6, Sun. 11-3, other times by appointment. *STOCK: Furniture, porcelain, pottery, pictures, brass and copper, mirrors, 18th-19th C.* LOC: A51 Lichfield/Tamworth road, turn north at Whittington Barracks, shop 50yds. past crossroads in village. PARK: Outside. TEL: 01543 432248. VAT: Stan/Spec.

L. Royden Smith
Church View, Farewell Lane, Burntwood. WS7 9DP. Est. 1972. Open Sat. and Sun. 10-4 or by appointment. *STOCK: Secondhand books, general antiques, bric-a-brac.* TEL: 01543 682217.

The Staffs Bookshop
4 & 6 Dam St. WS13 6AA. Open 9.30-5. *STOCK: Rare, secondhand, antiquarian and collectors books, especially 18th-19th C.* TEL: 01543 264093.

18th Century
English Porcelain

Simon Spero

Throughout the 1990s, the market for early English porcelain has been increasingly polarised between what is seen as most desirable in terms of rarity, early period and fine quality, and the substantial portion of the market which has been perceived, for one reason or another, as out of fashion. Yet all fashions are cyclic and the current price levels in some sections of the porcelain market may perhaps offer rewarding opportunities to the collector with the discrimination and the initiative to buck the trend.

Nowhere is this polarisation more apparent than in coloured **Worcester** of the early 1750s. This has become the exclusive focus of interest to many collectors in recent years, forcing prices steadily upwards, to levels far beyond all other categories of Worcester. Delightful and evocative though these early wares are, there will surely be an eventual reassessment of these comparative price levels. Even within this tiny section of the market there are cross currents, with a clear preference for smaller objects and a premium for absolute perfection of condition. Yet in so strong a market, rarity can outweigh such factors. Thus, the rare and superbly painted bell-shaped mug in figure 4 was sold for £7,130 despite having the handicap of a chip to its thumbrest and a height of 4½ inches.

New books tend to stimulate fresh interest in their subject and English porcelain has been well served in this respect during the past ten or fifteen years. If the market for

Worcester has been animated by the publication of a recent monograph[1], the long-awaited appearance of Dr. Bernard Watney's book on **Liverpool**[2] has had an even more galvanising effect on collectors. As with Worcester, it is the earlier, finer quality and rarer pieces which are climbing fastest in price. The demand is strongest for the factories of Gilbody and Chaffers', yet a pre-occupation with wares of the 1750s is not always synonymous with good value. A comparison between two pieces of Liverpool, both in perfect condition, sold at provincial auctions within the last six months, might serve to illustrate this view. A Chaffers' coffee can of about 1760, painted in underglaze blue with the 'Jumping Boy' pattern sold for £1,650. By contrast, a John Pennington coffee pot and cover of about 1775, painted in colour with exotic birds, fetched £858. Although some fifteen years later in period, the coffee pot was by far the more unusual shape and the decoration, too, was rarer. In the 1970s, the coffee pot would certainly have been worth twice the price of the little coffee can. Yet if this comparison seems a distortion of the

price levels of twenty years ago, it is echoed in such factories as **Bow**, **Lowestoft** and **New Hall**. Here too, a massive premium exists for the earlier examples of each factory. Significantly, though, for these factories, perfect condition need not be a prerequisite. Rarity of shape or pattern will also determine price levels, but 'early period' is the decisive factor. Thus, a rare piece of late Bow is met with comparative indifference whereas a more common example of fifteen years earlier remains desirable. This extreme emphasis on period will surely be diluted as collecting fashions change.

There is still a formidable focus of interest on **Limehouse** and **Vauxhall**, the two 'new' factories whose output has been reallocated from Liverpool to London. Prices for Limehouse, fuelled by scarcity and early period, rise progressively year by year and will almost certainly continue to do so. Vauxhall is neither quite so scarce, nor so early in period, and consequently price levels are less coherent. The fortunes of a portion of Dr. Bernard Watney's collection of blue and white Vauxhall, sold at Phillips in March, demonstrate an intriguing paradox. The 40 or so lots were not fully representative of the factory's production, as Dr. Watney chose to retain his favourite pieces, including all his sauceboats. Yet a distinct and somewhat surprising profile of prices emerged from the sale. With two exceptions, all of the larger scale pieces, such as plates, mugs, teapots, vases and large jugs, fetched prices which seemed moderate in view of their rarity (figure 3). By contrast, the small objects, such as odd saucers, tea bowls, pickle leaves and coffee cups, far less rare, seemed very expensive. It almost defies logic, for example, that an extremely rare plate should fetch barely twice as much as a fairly ordinary odd

Above. Figure 2. One of a pair of Longton Hall peony dishes, £1,495 the pair; Worcester salt, £748; and one of a pair of Longton Hall cos lettuce leaf dishes, £1,093 the pair. Sotheby's, 21st April 1998.

Left. Figure 1. A rare red anchor period Chelsea creamboat finely painted with flowers, c.1752-53, £4,370. Christie's, 7th July 1997.

saucer. Not so long ago, the plate would have been worth at least ten times as much as the saucer.

Recent prices for **Chelsea** have been fickle, reflecting a lack of the devotees who support so many other factories. This is in part due to an erroneous perception that all Chelsea porcelain is expensive. This was perhaps true 30 years ago, today it is emphatically not so. Then, a typical red anchor period Chelsea plate might cost around £15, roughly the same as a blue and white Worcester 'scratch cross' tankard. Today, the tankard is worth seven times as much as the plate. Neither red anchor nor gold anchor period Chelsea has altered much in price for several years, and is consequently excellent value. Only certain categories have advanced in price, including botanical plates, O'Neale's fable decoration, triangle period wares of the 1740s and some rarer shapes incorporating Kakiemon and floral themes (figure 1).

Bow prices are even more polarised, roughly in terms of period. The market for pre-1755 wares is firm, but almost any pieces dating from the 1760s or beyond are more or less ignored by the majority of collectors. No factory should be judged solely by its first few years of production and, in time, Bow collectors will surely revert to aspiring to a more balanced overall view of the factory's output.

The preoccupation with 'early period' which so defines the market for 18th century English porcelain at present, does not apply to **Derby**. Here, the concentration of collecting and the highest prices pertain to the final decades of the century, with the landscape artists such as 'Jockey Hill', Boreman and Complin, and the floral subjects associated with Quaker Pegg and Billingsley. This market is very strong and prices are generally far higher than for wares of the 1750s and 1760s. Yet perhaps the most undervalued and sparsely collected era of the factory is the elegant Chelsea–Derby period of the 1770s.

Whilst prices continue to rise for Lowestoft, Liverpool and New Hall, with only later examples faltering, the picture is far less buoyant in several other factories. **Longton Hall**, for example, is generally less

Figure 3. Vauxhall porcelain sold at Phillips on 4th March 1998. The bell-shaped mug (lower row, second from right) fetched £8,625 – it was in perfect condition. Prices for the other pieces ranged from £667 to £2,175.

expensive than it was in the late 1980s, when it was palpably overpriced. The leaf-shaped dishes in figure 2, for example, would have commanded at least twice their current prices in those heady days which culminated in the Rous Lench sale at Christie's in 1990. That sale was in many respects a watershed in the market for early English porcelain. Only a proportion of the often staggering prices achieved then could be exceeded today.

Yet, of course, much depends upon the perspective from which the market is viewed. Generally, the more poorly a class of porcelain has performed over a decade or so, the more likely it is to have become undervalued. Amongst the factories which fall into this category are Longton Hall, good quality Bow and Derby figures of the 1760s, red and gold anchor period Chelsea, Christian's Liverpool, Chelsea–Derby and Champion's Bristol. All these classes of porcelain, if collected with discernment and perhaps expert guidance, would represent excellent value.

Worcester, perhaps the most widely collected of all the early English factories, mirrors the wider state of the porcelain market. The current taste is for the chinoiserie idioms of the 1750s and for the Giles atelier patterns. The colourful blue grounds and 'Japan' patterns of the 1770s have hardly shifted in

price since the late 1980s and now compare favourably with prices for early 19th century porcelain. Now might also be an ideal moment to collect the floral designs and the overglaze transfer prints of the 1760s. Current price levels are almost certain to be reassessed in a factory which offers the widest variety of shapes and styles, and the richest literature, of all 18th century English porcelain.

1. Simon Spero and John Sandon, *Worcester Porcelain, The Zorensky Collection.*
2. Bernard M. Watney, *Liverpool Porcelain.*

*This article appeared in the July/August 1999 issue of **Antique Collecting** magazine. For more details and to subscribe see page 147.*

Figure 4. A superb early Worcester mug c.1752-53, sold at Phillips on 17th September 1997 for £7,130.

LITTLE HAYWOOD, Nr. Stafford

Jalna Antiques
Coley Lane. ST18 0UP. Resident. Est. 1974. Open most times. *STOCK: Furniture, pre-1900.* Not Stocked: Shipping goods. LOC: 1/2 mile off A51, 12 miles north of Lichfield. TEL: 01889 881381. SER: Restorations; re-upholstery. VAT: Spec.

NEWCASTLE-UNDER-LYME

Antique Forum
The Stones. ST5 2AG. Every Tues. 9-4. SIZE: 70 tables. *STOCK: General antiques.* TEL: 01782 595805.

Richard Midwinter Antiques
31 Bridge St. ST5 2RY. (Mr and Mrs R. Midwinter). Est. 1987. Open 10-5, Thurs. by appointment. SIZE: Medium. *STOCK: Furniture, oak, walnut, mahogany, 17th-19th C, £50-£10,000; textiles, samplers and embroideries; longcase, mantel and wall clocks, £150-£4,000; paintings, £35-£3,000, both 18th-19th C; ceramics and watercolours, 19th C, £15-£1,500.* Not Stocked: Pine and ephemera. LOC: Close to Sainsburys and the Magistrates Courts. TEL: 01782 712483; home - 01630 672289. SER: Valuations; restorations (gilding, clock repair). VAT: Spec.

Windsor House Antiques
5a King St. ST5 1EH. (Paul Barker and Shelagh Teahan). Est. 1990. Open 10-5. SIZE: Large. *STOCK: Furniture, 18th-20th C, £200-£800; silver, paintings and ceramics, 19th-20th C, £30-£300.* LOC: A53 Hanley road, 200 yards out of Newcastle. PARK: Easy. TEL: 01782 633111; mobile - 07946 761081. SER: Valuations; buys at auction. FAIRS: Bingley Hall, Stafford; Prestwood Centre, Stafford. VAT: Margin.

PENKRIDGE, Nr. Stafford

Golden Oldies
1 and 5 Crown Bridge. ST19 5AA. (W.A. and M.A. Knowles). Open 9.30-5.30, Mon. 9.30-1.30. *STOCK: Victorian, Edwardian and later furniture; paintings, decorative items.* PARK: Easy. TEL: 01785 714722.

RUGELEY

Eveline Winter
1 Wolseley Rd. WS15 2QH. (Mrs E. Winter). Est. 1962. Open Thurs.-Sat. 10.30-5 appointment advisable. SIZE: Small. *STOCK: Staffordshire figures, pre-Victorian, from £90; Victorian, £30-£500; copper, brass, glass and general antiques.* Not Stocked: Coins and weapons. LOC: Coming from Lichfield or Stafford stay on A51 and avoid town by-pass. PARK: Easy and at side of shop. TEL: 01889 583259.

STAFFORD

Browse
127 Lichfield Rd. ST17 4LF. (H. Barnes). Est. 1981. Open 10-5, Sun. 12-4. CL: Wed. SIZE: Large. *STOCK: Furniture, 1860-1940 and reproduction.* LOC: Outskirts of town. PARK: Easy. TEL: 01785 241097; home - 01785 660336. SER: Valuations; restorations.

Windmill Antiques
9 Castle Hill, Broadeye. ST16 2QB. Open 10-5. SIZE: Medium - several dealers. *STOCK: General antiques and decorative items.* PARK: Easy. TEL: 01785 228505.

STOKE-ON-TRENT

Ann's Antiques
24/26 Leek Rd., Stockton Brook. ST9 9MN. Open 10-5. CL: Wed. and Thurs. *STOCK: Victorian furniture, brass, copper, jewellery, paintings, pottery and unusual items.* TEL: 01782 503991. VAT: Stan.

The Potteries Antique Centre Ltd
271 Waterloo Rd., Cobridge. ST6 3HR. (W. Buckley). Est. 1972. Open 9-5.30, Sun. 10-4.30. SIZE: Large + trade and export warehouse. *STOCK: Furniture including pine and shipping, 18th-20th C; pottery and porcelain including Doulton, Moorcroft, Beswick, Wedgwood, Coalport, Shelley, 19th-20th C; collectors' items, silver plate, clocks, brass, jewellery, pictures, 18th-20th C; all £1-£5,000.* LOC: Off M6, junction 15 or 16 on to A500, follow signs for Festival Park or Potteries Shopping Centre. PARK: Easy. TEL: 01782 201455; fax - 01782 201518; 01782 286622 (auctions). SER: Valuations; export facilities - supply and packing; buys at auction (pottery and collectors' items); Potter. VAT: Stan/Spec.

The Pottery Buying Centre
535 Etruria Road, Basford. ST4 6HT. (Paul Hume). Est. 1989. Open 10-4, incl. Sun. SIZE: 2 floors. *STOCK: Pottery and porcelain, 19th-20th C; collectables, 20th C; furniture, 18th-20th C; all £10-£1,000.* PARK: Easy. TEL: 01782 635453; home - same. SER: Valuations; restorations.

Top of the Hill (Ceramic Search)
12/14/14a Nile St., Burslem. ST6 2AF. (A. and J. Phillips). Est. 1980. Open 9.30-5, Sun. by appointment. SIZE: Large. *STOCK: Ceramics, antique and collectable, £50-£100; curios, antique and reproduction furniture, £50-£1,000.* LOC: Follow Royal Doulton signs from A500, premises opposite factory shop. PARK: Easy. TEL: 01782 834506; fax - same. SER: Valuations; restorations (ceramics); buys at auction (ceramics).

TUTBURY, Nr. Burton-on-Trent

R.A. James - The Clock Shop
1 High St. DE13 9LP. (Rob and Alison James). MBHI. Est. 1988. Open 10-5. SIZE: Medium. *STOCK: Longcase, bracket and wall clocks, £500-£10,000.* LOC: 2 miles from A38/A50 junction. PARK: Easy. TEL: 01283 814596; fax - 01283 814594. SER: Valuations; restorations (clocks). VAT: Stan/Spec.

Old Chapel Antique & Collectables Centre
High St. DE13 9LP. Open 10-5 including Sun., other times by appointment. *STOCK: China, glass, furniture.* PARK: Easy. TEL: 01283 815255; mobiles - 07721 438803/07774 238775.

Tutbury Mill Antiques Centre
Tutbury Mill Mews, Lower High St. DE13 9LU. . Open 10.30-5.30, Sun. 12-5. SIZE: Large. *STOCK: General antiques including collectables, china and pine, from 18th C, £10-£2,500.* PARK: Easy. TEL: 01283 520074. SER: Valuations. VAT: Stan/Spec.

UTTOXETER

White House Antiques
50-52 Bridge St. ST14 8AP. (Christopher White). Est. 1983. Open 10-4.30. CL: Mon. SIZE: Medium. *STOCK: Victorian and Edwardian furniture, £100-£500; Beswick pottery, £10-£700; Beatrix Potter figures, £15-£450.* LOC: Next to Wheatsheaf public house, on Market Sq. PARK: Nearby. TEL: 01889 569344; home/fax - 01889 500380. SER: Valuations; restorations (pottery); buys at auction (Beswick, furniture). FAIRS: Castle Donington.

WEEFORD, Nr. Lichfield

Blackbrook Antiques Village
London Rd. WS14 0PS. Open Tues.-Sun. 10-

5.30. SIZE: Large. *STOCK: Architectural antiques including fireplaces, lighting, garden statuary, stained glass, furniture.* LOC: A38. PARK: Own. TEL: 01543 481450; fax - same.

WOLSELEY BRIDGE, Nr. Rugeley

Jalna Antiques
The Old Barn. ST18 0XY. (G. and D. Hancox). Open 10-5. *STOCK: Furniture and smalls.* LOC: Junction A51/A513. TEL: 01889 882125.

WOODSEAVES

AD Antiques
P O Box 1623. ST20 0SF. (Alison Davey). Open by appointment. *STOCK: British Art pottery, Arts & Crafts, Art Nouveau, Art Deco, £50-£2,000.* TEL: Mobile - 07939 508171. SER: Valuations; buys at auction. FAIRS: NEC; Bingley Hall; Gaydon; Coopers.

YOXALL, Nr. Burton-on-Trent

H.W. Heron and Son Ltd
The Antique Shop, 1 King St. DE13 8NF. (H.N.M., J. and P.D. Heron). LAPADA. Est. 1949. Open 9-6, Sat. 9-5.30, Sun. 2-6, Bank Holidays 10.30-5.30. SIZE: Medium. *STOCK: 18th-19th C furniture, ceramics and decorative items.* LOC: A515 village centre, opposite church. PARK: Easy. TEL: 01543 472266; home - same; fax - 01543 473800. SER: Valuations. VAT: Spec.

A Tudric rosebowl, the design claimed by Rex Silver, c.1903, 5¾in. diameter. £250- £350.

From an article entitled 'Tudric Pewter by Liberty & Co' by Jeremy Morrison which appeared in the November 2000 issue of **Antique Collecting** magazine. For more details and to subscribe see page 147.

458

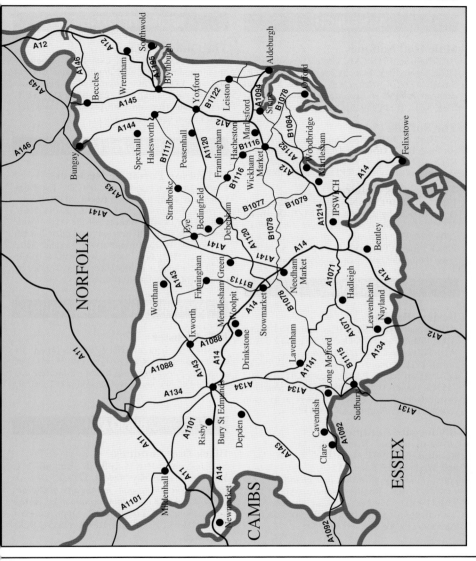

Dealers and Shops in Suffolk

				Leavenheath	1	Snape	1
				Leiston	2	Southwold	6
Aldeburgh	3	Drinkstone	1	Long Melford	18	Spexhall	1
Beccles	4	Eye	3	Marlesford	1	Stowmarket	1
Bedingfield	1	Felixstowe	1	Martlesham	2	Stradbroke	1
Bentley	1	Finningham	1	Mendlesham Green	1	Sudbury	5
Blythburgh	1	Framlingham	5	Mildenhall	1	Wickham Market	2
Bungay	4	Hacheston	1	Nayland	2	Woodbridge	13
Bury St. Edmunds	6	Hadleigh	2	Needham Market	3	Woolpit	1
Cavendish	1	Halesworth	1	Newmarket	3	Wortham	1
Clare	4	Ipswich	8	Orford	1	Wrentham	3
Debenham	2	Ixworth	1	Peasenhall	1	Yoxford	2
Depden	1	Lavenham	4	Risby	1		

ALDEBURGH

Mole Hall Antiques
102 High St. IP15 5AB. (Peter Weaver). Est. 1976. Open 10-5, Sun. by appointment. SIZE: Small. *STOCK: Paintings, prints, unusual decorative items and country furniture.* PARK: Easy. TEL: 01728 452361; home - same.

The Suffolk
152 High St. IP15 5AX. Open Thurs., Fri. and Sat. and Bank Holidays 10.30-4, Sun. 10.30-1. *STOCK: 18th-19th C ceramics. silver and plate, pictures and objets d'art.* TEL: 01728 454508.

Thompson's Gallery
175 High St. IP15 5AN. (J. and S. Thompson). Open 10-5 or by appointment. SIZE: Medium. *STOCK: Oils, watercolours, pastels, 19th-20th C, £300-£20,000; furniture, 18th to early 20th C.* PARK: Easy. TEL: 01728 453743; website - www.thompsonsgallery.co.uk. VAT: Spec.

BECCLES

Besleys Books
4 Blyburgate. NR34 9TA. (P.A. and P.F. Besley). ABA, PBFA. Est. 1978. Open 9.30-1 and 2-5. CL: Wed. SIZE: Medium. *STOCK: Books, 50p-£1,000; prints, £7-£50; maps, £3-£100; all 17th-20th C.* LOC: Town centre. PARK: Nearby. TEL: 01502 715762; home - 01502 675649. SER: Valuations; restorations (book binding); buys at auction (books). FAIRS: Various ABA and PBFA.

Blyburgate Antiques
27-29 Blyburgate. NR34 9TB. (Mrs. K. Lee). Resident. Est. 1997. Open 10-4.30. CL: Mon. and Wed. SIZE: Small. *STOCK: 19th-20th C china, jewellery, furniture and metalware, £5-£1,000.* PARK: Rainbow supermarket at rear. TEL: 01502 711174; fax/home - same. SER: Valuations; restorations (china). FAIRS: Alexandra Palace.

Fauconberges
8 Smallgate. NR34 9AD. Open Mon.-Fri. 10-5. *STOCK: Furniture, 1700-1900; pictures, clocks, glass, porcelain, silver.* TEL: 01502 716147.

Saltgate Antiques
11 Saltgate. NR34 9AN. (A.M. Ratcliffe). Resident. Est. 1971. Open 10-5. CL: Wed. pm. SIZE: Medium. *STOCK: Furniture, 17th-19th C, £100-£4,500; clocks, collectors' items, brass, copper, Staffordshire figures, paintings and prints, 19th C bric-a-brac, £5-£300.* LOC: Town centre opposite bus station. PARK: Easy. TEL: 01502 712776.

BEDINGFIELD, Nr. Eye

The Olde Red Lion
The Street. IP23 7LQ. Est. 1973. Open by appointment. *STOCK: Furniture and general antiques.* LOC: 3 miles from Eye, 2 miles from Debenham. TEL: 01728 628491. SER: Restorations (furniture, oil paintings, ceramics, snuff boxes, wood carvings).

BENTLEY, Nr. Ipswich

P. Dawson Furniture Restorers
Unit O, Dodnash Priory Farm. IP9 2DF. Est. 1996. Open by appointment. SIZE: Small. *STOCK: Furniture, 17th-20th C, £50-£3,000.* LOC: Take Bentley turning off the A12 outside Ipswich, 1st right into Bergholt road, then 2nd left and follow the road round to farm estate. TEL: 01473 462397; fax - same; workshop - 01473 311947; e-mail - Paul@Dawson 21.freeserve. co.uk. SER: Restorations (furniture).

BLYTHBURGH, Nr. Halesworth

E.T. Webster
Westwood Lodge. IP19 9NB. Open by appointment. *STOCK: Ancient oak beams, oak ceilings, panelling, quality reproduction oak furniture, doors, mullioned windows.* TEL: 01502 478539.

BUNGAY

Black Dog Antiques
51 Earsham St. NR35 2PB. (K. Button). Est. 1986. Open seven days a week. *STOCK: General antiques including oak, mahogany and pine, china, linen and collectables, antiquities, Saxon and Roman, £1-£1000.* LOC: Opposite Post Office. PARK: Easy. TEL: 01986 895554. SER: Valuations.

Cork Brick Antiques
6 Earsham St. NR35 1AG. (G. and K. Skipper). Open 10.30-5.30. CL: Mon. *STOCK: Country and decorative antiques; architectural decoration.* PARK: Easy. TEL: 01986 894873; home - 01502 712646.

Friend or Faux
28 Earsham St. NR35 1AQ. (Kim Sisson and Jane Cudlipp). Resident. Est. 1993. Open Fri. and Sat. 10-5.30 (prior phone call advisable on Fri.), other days by appointment. *STOCK: Porcelain, 1800-1900, £50-£100; lighting, late 1800's to*

1950, £100-£500; Victorian watercolours, £100-£200. PARK: Nearby. TEL: 01986 896170; fax - 01502 714246. SER: Restorations (painted furniture, gilded pieces, porcelain).

One Step Back
4a Earsham St. NR35 1AQ. (Ian and Diane Wells). Est. 1970. Open 10-5. CL: Wed. SIZE: Medium. *STOCK: Furniture, from 17th C; porcelain, rugs, from 18th C; both £50-£1,000.* TEL: 01986 896626; home - 01508 550988. SER: Valuations; restorations. FAIRS: Halesworth, Bungay, Norwich.

BURY ST. EDMUNDS

Corner Shop Antiques
1 Guildhall St. IP33 1PR. Open 10-4.30. CL: Mon. and Thurs. *STOCK: Victoriana, porcelain, jewellery, silver, glass and collectors' items.* LOC: Corner of Abbeygate St., opposite Corn Exchange. TEL: 01284 701007.

The Enchanted Aviary
Lapwings, Rushbrooke Lane. IP33 2RS. (C.C.Frost). Est. 1970. Open by appointment only. *STOCK: Cased and uncased mounted birds, animals and fish, mostly late Victorian, £15-£800.* PARK: Easy. TEL: 01284 725430.

Guildhall Street Antiques
27 Guildhall St. IP33 1QD. (Mrs T. Cutting). Est. 1965. Open 9-5. CL: Thurs. SIZE: Medium. *STOCK: General antiques, bric-a-brac and books, £25-£2,500.* LOC: From town centre down Guildhall St. to below Churchgate St. junction. TEL: 01284 703060/735278.

Peppers Period Pieces
23 Churchgate St. IP33 1RG. (M.E. Pepper). Est. 1975. Open 10-5. *STOCK: Furniture, oak, elm, yew, fruitwood, mahogany, 16th-19th C; English domestic implements in brass, copper, lead, tin, iron, pewter and treen, 16th to early 20th C; some pottery and porcelain, bygones and collectables, late 19th to early 20th C.* Not Stocked: Reproductions. PARK: Easy. TEL: 01284 768786; home - 01359 250606. SER: Valuations; repairs and polishing.

Talisman 2
18 Out Westgate. IP33 3NZ. (Shirley and David McNaught). Est. 1980. Open 10-1 and 2-5, Sat. 10-3, Thurs. by appointment. CL: Tues. SIZE: Small. *STOCK: Small antiques and decorative collectables, some period furniture, 18th-20th C, £5-£1,500.* LOC: Just outside town centre on A143 Haverhill road. PARK: Nearby. TEL: 01284 725712; fax - 01284 724660; website -

www.talisman2.co.uk. SER: Valuations; restorations (ceramics, furniture, metalwork); upholstery.

Winston Mac (Silversmith)
65 St. John's St. IP33 1SJ. (E.W. McKnight). Est. 1978. Open 9-5. CL: Sun. except by appointment and Sat. SIZE: Small. *STOCK: Silver tea services, creamers, salts.* PARK: Easy. TEL: 01284 767910. SER: Restorations (silver and plating). VAT: Stan/Spec.

CAVENDISH

Cavendish Rose Antiques
High St. CO10 8AF. (T. Patterson). Est. 1972. Open 10.30-5. SIZE: Large. *STOCK: Furniture, 18th-19th C mahogany, £150-£5,000.* PARK: Easy. TEL: 01787 282133. VAT: Spec.

CLARE, Nr. Sudbury

Robin Butler
The Old Bank House, Market Hill. CO10 8NN. Resident. Open by appointment. *STOCK: Furniture, 18th-19th C, £200-£20,000; silver, 18th C, £80-£8,000; glass, 18th C, £20-£5,000; wine associated antiques, 17th-20th C, £50-£5,000.* PARK: Easy. TEL: 01787 279111; fax - same. SER: Valuations. VAT: Spec.

Clare Antique Warehouse
The Mill, Malting Lane. CO10 8NW. Est. 1989. Open 9.30-5, Sun. 1-5. SIZE: Large - over 80 dealers. *STOCK: 17th-20th C furniture, textiles, pictures, porcelain, glass, silver, decorative items.* LOC: 100yds. from High St. Follow signs for Clare Castle, Country Park. PARK: Easy. TEL: 01787 278449. SER: Valuations; restorations. VAT: Stan/Spec.

F.D. Salter Antiques
1-2 Church St. CO10 8NN. Est. 1959. Open 9-5. CL: Wed. pm. SIZE: Medium. *STOCK: 18th to early 19th C English furniture, porcelain and glass.* LOC: A1092. PARK: Easy. TEL: 01787 277693. SER: Valuations; restorations (furniture). FAIRS: Harrogate (April); West London. VAT: Stan/Spec.

Trinders' Fine Tools
Malting Lane. CO10 8NW. (P. and R. Trinder). Est. 1975. Open 10-1 and 2-5 - prior phone call advisable. CL: Wed. SIZE: Medium. *STOCK: Hand tools for craftsmen, engineers and collectors, woodworking and metalworking books including furniture reference and clocks, other art and antiques reference books.* PARK: Easy.

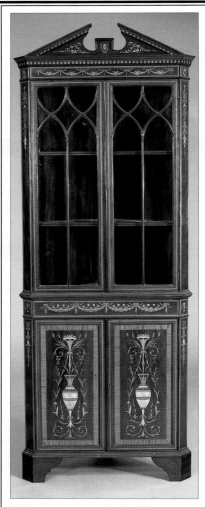

Mahogany corner cupboard with marquetry inlay, 1900-10. £4,500-£6,000.

The light, highly decorative 'Edwardian Sheraton' furniture made in the first ten years of this century is becoming increasingly popular. Ideal for displaying collections, prices reflect the craftsmanship involved. From an article entitled 'Edwardian Exuberance' by John Andrews which appeared in the December 1998/January 19099 issue of **Antique Collecting** magazine. For more details and to subscribe see page 147.

TEL: 01787 277130; home - same; fax - 01787 277677; e-mail - peter@trindersfinetools.co.uk; website - www.trindersfinetools.co.uk/.

DEBENHAM

Debenham Antiques
73 High St. IP14 6QS. Est. 1969. Open 9.15-5.30. SIZE: Large. *STOCK: 17th-19th C furniture and paintings, £50-£10,000.* PARK: Easy. TEL: 01728 860707; fax - 01728 860333. VAT: Stan/Spec.

Quercus
4 High St. IP14 6QH. (Peter Horsman and Bill Bristow-Jones). Resident. Est. 1972. Open by appointment. SIZE: Medium. *STOCK: Oak furniture, 17th-18th C, £1,000-£5,000.* PARK: Easy. TEL: 01728 860262; home - same. SER: Valuations; restorations (17th C oak furniture). VAT: Spec.

DEPDEN, Nr. Bury St. Edmunds

Coblands Farm Antiques
Bury Rd. IP29 4BT. (Mrs Janet Harding). Open 10-5.30, Sun. 2-5. SIZE: Large. *STOCK: Antique pine and other furniture, especially wing chairs and sofas, £5-£2,000.* LOC: A143 between Haverhill and Bury St. Edmunds. PARK: Easy. TEL: 01440 820007; home - same; fax - 01440 821165. SER: Restorations (upholstery).

DRINKSTONE, Nr. Bury St. Edmunds

Denzil Grant Antiques   BADA
Drinkstone House. IP30 9TG. LAPADA. Est. 1979. Open anytime by appointment. *STOCK: Furniture, 16th to early 19th C; speciality French farm tables.* LOC: Off A14 between Bury St. Edmunds and Ipswich. PARK: Easy. TEL: 01449 736576; fax - 01449 737679; e-mail - denzil@denzilgrant.com; website - www. denzilgrant.com.

EYE

Bramley Antiques
4 Broad St. 1P23 7AF. (C. Grater). Open Wed.-Sat. 9.30-5, other times by appointment. SIZE: Medium. *STOCK: Furniture, £20-£5,000; glass, £5-£500; boxes, pictures, general antiques, all 18th to early 20th C.* PARK: Easy. TEL: 01379 871386. SER: Valuations; restorations.

This is the classic reference work on British antique silver hallmarks. The original 1905 Jackson's has been revised by a distinguished team of experts to take into account the vast store of information which has been unearthed in the intervening years as a result of detailed and wide-ranging research. It contains literally thousands of corrections in addition to new material making dating and attribution more accurate than ever. There are not many standard reference works which survive for eighty years without being displaced; it remains a 'bible' for all antique silver enthusiasts and a key reference for dealers, scholars and collectors.

ISBN 0 907462 63 4
768pp., 400 b.&w. illus., approx. 15,000 marks. **£49.50/$99.50**

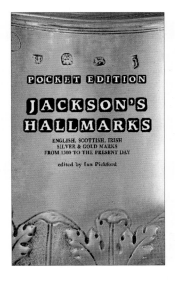

Extremely compact but at the same time packed with information and marks, this book has been described as 'the ideal travelling and buying companion.' This is the most accurate and up to date guide of its kind on the market.
Edited by Ian Pickford, it contains over 1,000 makers whose work is of especial interest. This is the most accurate, complete, and up-to-date guide on the market.
Ian Pickford is the author of *Starting to Collect Antique Silver* (see pages 7 and 28).

ISBN 1 85149 128 7
£12.50/$25.00 hb
ISBN 1 85149 169 4
£6.95/$14.50 pb
8½ x 4¼in./215 x 120mm.
172pp., over 1,000 marks.

English and Continental Antiques
1 Broad St. IP23. (Roger Ford and Steve Harmer). Est. 1977. Open 10-5. CL: Mon. SIZE: Medium. *STOCK: Furniture, 17th-19th C, £50-£5,000.* PARK: Easy. TEL: 01379 871199.

Laburnum Cottage Antiques
Laburnum Cottage, 2 Broad St. IP23 7AF. (S. Grater). Resident. Est. 1978. Open Wed.-Sun. 9.30-5, other times by appointment. SIZE: Small. *STOCK: Porcelain and glass, £5-£250; silver and plate, £30-£100; linen, jewellery, £2.50-£100; all 18th-20th C.* PARK: Easy. TEL: 01379 871386. SER: Valuations.

FELIXSTOWE

John McCulloch Antiques
1a Hamilton Rd. IP11 7HN. Open 9.30-5, Wed. 9.30-1. *STOCK: Furniture, copper, brass, pictures, clocks and bric-a-brac.* LOC: Main street, sea front end at top of Bent Hill. PARK: Around corner. TEL: 01394 283126.

FINNINGHAM

Abington Books
Primrose Cottage, Westhorpe Rd. IP14 4TW. (J. Haldane). Est. 1971. By appointment only. SIZE: Small. *STOCK: Books on Oriental rugs, from 1877, £1-£5,000; books on classical tapestries, from 17th C, £1-£3,000.* PARK: Easy. TEL: 01449 780303; fax - 01449 780202. SER: Valuations; book binding.

FRAMLINGHAM

Abbott & Fisk
Church St. IP13 9BQ. (Paul Abbott). Est. 1999. Open from 10, Sun. from 11. CL: Wed pm. *STOCK: 19th C Eastern European pine, to £1,000.* PARK: Easy. TEL: 01728 724758; fax - same. VAT: Stan/Spec.

Antiques Warehouse
The Old Station. IP13 9EE. (Bed Bazaar and Richard Goodbrey). Est. 1992. Open 10-5, Sun. 2-5. *STOCK: Decorative furniture and Victorian brass and iron bedsteads.* PARK: Easy. TEL: 01728 723756; fax - 01728 724626. SER: Restorations (beds); mattresses and bases made-to-measure.

Dix-Sept
17 Station Rd. IP13. (S. Goodbrey and M. Cluzan). Est. 1996. Open Sat. 10-1 and 2-5, other times by appointment. *STOCK: French country furniture and decoration, pottery, garden furniture, mirrors.* LOC: On approach road from A12. PARK: Easy. TEL: 01728 621505. VAT: Global.

Goodbreys
29 Double St. IP13 9BN. (R. and M. Goodbrey). Est. 1965. Open Sat. 9-5.30, other times by appointment. SIZE: Large. *STOCK: Decorative items including sleighbeds, upholstery, Biedermeier, simulated bamboo, painted cupboards, garden furniture, country pieces; pottery, glass, textiles, mirrors, bric-a-brac.* LOC: Up Church St. towards Framlingham Castle. Opposite church gates turn right into Double St. PARK: Easy. TEL: 01728 621191; fax - 01728 724626. VAT: Mainly Spec. *Mainly Trade.*

The Green Shed
26 Fore St. IP13 9DF. (J.G. Mulligan). Est. 1988. Open 9.30-5.30. SIZE: Large. *STOCK: Furniture, 18th C, £500-£1,000; French country, 18th-19th C, £500-£1,000; country pine, 19th C, £100-£500; objets d'art, £50-£100.* LOC: Main road through town. PARK: At rear. TEL: 01728 621069; home - 01986 784553. SER: Valuations; restorations. VAT: Spec.

HACHESTON, Nr. Wickham Market

Joyce Hardy Pine and Country Furniture
IP13 0DS. Resident. Open 9.30-5.30, Sun. 9.30-12. *STOCK: Pine - dressers, corner cupboards, butcher's blocks, old French farmhouse tables.* LOC: B1116, Framlingham Rd. PARK: Easy. TEL: 01728 746485. SER: Hand-made furniture from old pine.

HADLEIGH, Nr. Ipswich

Randolph   BADA
97 and 99 High St. IP7 5EJ. (B.F. and H.M. Marston). Est. 1921. Open by appointment only. SIZE: Medium. *STOCK: Furniture, 1600-1830, £50-£25,000; brass, copper, porcelain, delftware, treen.* Not Stocked: Silver. PARK: Easy. TEL: 01473 823789; fax - 01473 823867. VAT: Spec.

Tara's Hall
Victoria House, Market Place. IP7 5DL. (B. O'Keefe). Est. 1977. Open by appointment. SIZE: Medium. *STOCK: Textiles and linen, jewellery, Art Nouveau and Art Deco, small items.* PARK: Easy. TEL: 01473 824031. SER: Valuations; buys at auction (jewellery, Art Nouveau objects).

HALESWORTH

Halesworth Antiques Market
3A Bridge St. IP19 8AB. (Sue Hull and Alida Saunders). Est. 1994. Open 10-5, Thurs. 10-1. SIZE: Medium. *STOCK: Victorian furniture and country pine, £50-£1,000, china, £5-£150; general small antiques and gifts.* PARK: Easy. TEL: 01986 875599.

IPSWICH

A. Abbott Antiques
757 Woodbridge Rd. IP4 4NE. (C. Lillistone). Est. 1965. Open 10.30-5. CL: Wed. SIZE: Medium. *STOCK: Small items, especially clocks and jewellery; Victorian, Edwardian and shipping furniture, £5-£5,000.* PARK: Easy. TEL: 01473 728900; fax - same; mobile - 07771 533413.

Tony Adams Wireless & Bygones Shop
175 Spring Rd. IP4 5NG. Open 10-5. CL: Wed. and Thurs. *STOCK: Bygones, especially wireless sets; toy trains, cameras.*

Bridge Collectables
425 Norwich Rd. IP1 5DN. (A.A. and S.J. Creasey). Est. 1988. Open 10-5. SIZE: Small. *STOCK: Mechanical bygones, 19th-20th C, £10-£100; cameras, bakelite, postcards, 20th C, £1-£150.* PARK: Easy. TEL: 01473 421316.

Claude Cox at College Gateway Bookshop
3 Silent St. IP1 1TF. Open Wed.-Sat. 10-5. SIZE: Medium. *STOCK: Books, from 1470; some local maps and prints.* LOC: Leave inner ring road at Novotel double roundabout, turn into St. Peters St. PARK: Cromwell Square and Buttermarket Centre. TEL: 01473 254776; fax - same; e-mail - books@ claudecox.co.uk; website - www. claudecox.co.uk. SER: Valuations; restorations (rebinding); buys at auction; catalogue available.

The Edwardian Shop
556 Spring Rd. IP4 4NT. Est. 1979. Open 9-5. *STOCK: Victorian, Edwardian and 1920's shipping goods, £10-£400.* LOC: Half-mile from hospital. PARK: Own. TEL: 01473 716576.

Hubbard Antiques
16-18 St. Margarets Green. IP4 2BS. Est. 1964. Open 9.30-5.30 and by appointment. SIZE: Large. *STOCK: Furniture and decorative items, 18th-19th C.* PARK: Easy. TEL: 01473 226033/233034; fax - 01473 253639. SER: Valuations; restorations. VAT: Stan/Spec. *Trade & Export.*

Orwell Pine Co Ltd
Halifax Mill, 427 Wherstead Rd. IP2 8LH. (M.Weiner). Open 8.30-5.30, Sat. 8.30-4. *STOCK: Pine.* TEL: 01473 680091. SER: Restorations; stripping; pine furniture and kitchens made to order from old wood.

Thompson's
418 Norwich Rd. IP1 5DX. (D. Thompson). Est. 1977. Open 9-5. CL: Sun. except by appointment. SIZE: Medium. *STOCK: Furniture, mainly late Victorian and shipping, 1870 to date, £10-£1,000.* LOC: 1 mile from town centre, on corner at traffic lights next to railway bridge. PARK: Own, at side of premises. TEL: 01473 747793; fax - same; e-mail - thompsonsantiques@ yahoo.com. SER: Valuations; buys at auction (shipping items). VAT: Stan/Spec.

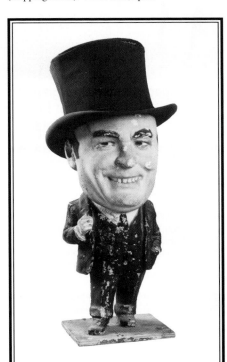

This 1920s advertising figure for a tailor's shop should arouse some interest around the £100 mark at Edgar Horn's sale on 20th September.

From an Auction Preview which appeared in the September issue of **Antique Collecting** magazine. For more details and to subscribe see page 147.

E.W. COUSINS AND SON

Established since 1910

Main Warehouse: The Old School, Thetford Road, Ixworth, Near Bury St. Edmunds, Suffolk

Tel: (01359) 230254   Fax: (01359) 232370

E.Mail: john@ewcousins.co.uk   Website: www.ewcousins.co.uk

Monday-Friday 8.30-5.00. Saturday 8.30-1.00 or by appointment

Specialists in Georgian, Victorian & Edwardian Furniture. 20,000 sq. ft. of furniture in various showrooms. Wholesale, Retail & Export Trade Welcome.

IXWORTH, Nr. Bury St. Edmunds

E.W. Cousins and Son
27 High St. and The Old School. IP31 2HJ. LAPADA. CL: Sat. pm. SIZE: Large and warehouse. *STOCK: General antiques, 18th-19th C, £50-£6,000; shipping items.* LOC: A143. PARK: Easy. TEL: 01359 230254; fax - 01359 232370; e-mail - john@ewcousins.co.uk; website - www.ewcousins.co.uk. SER: Valuations; restorations. VAT: Stan/Spec.

LAVENHAM, Nr. Sudbury

R.G. Archer (Books)
7 Water St. CO10 9RW. Est. 1970. Open 10-5 including Sun. CL: Wed. *STOCK: Antiquarian and secondhand books.* TEL: 01787 247229.

J. and J. Baker
12-14 Water St. and 3a High St. CO10 9RW. (C.J. and Mrs B.A.J. Baker). Est. 1960. Open 9-1 and 2-5.30. SIZE: Medium. *STOCK: Oak and mahogany furniture, 1680-1900, £100-£10,000; oils and watercolours, 19th C, £150-£5,000; English porcelain and metalware, 18th-19th C, £20-£1,000; collectors' items, £20-£1,000.* LOC:

Below Swan Hotel at T junction of A1141 and B1071. PARK: Easy. TEL: 01787 247610. VAT: Stan/Spec.

One Bell
46 High St. CO10 9PY. (J.F. and M.A. Tinworth). Open 11-4.30, Sat. 10.30-5, Sun. 11-5. CL: Wed. and Thurs. SIZE: Small. *STOCK: Militaria and collectables.* LOC: A134. PARK: Easy. TEL: 01787 248206; home - same.

The Timbers Antique & Collectables Centre
High St. CO1 9PY . (B.A. Preece and A.M. Trodd). Resident. Est. 1996. CL: Wed. SIZE: Medium. *STOCK: Smalls and furniture, £5-£500.* PARK: Easy. TEL: 01787 247218; home - same.

LEAVENHEATH

Clock House
Locks Lane. CO6 4PF. (A.G. Smeeth). Est. 1983. Open by appointment. SIZE: Small. *STOCK: English clocks, 17th to early 19th C, £1,500-£6,000; French and English clocks, Victorian and Edwardian, £300-£2,000.* PARK: Easy. TEL: 01206 262187; home - same. SER: Valuations; restorations (clocks and furniture); buys at auction (clocks and furniture).

LEISTON

Leiston Trading Post
13a High St. IP16 4EL. (L.K. Smith). Est. 1967. Open 10-1 and 2-5, other times by appointment. CL: Wed. pm. *STOCK: Bric-a-brac, Victoriana, Victorian and Edwardian furniture.* PARK: Easy. TEL: 01728 830081; home - 01728 831488. VAT: Stan.

Warrens Antiques Warehouse
High St. IP16 4EL. (J.R. Warren). Est. 1980. CL: Wed. and Sat. pm. except by appointment. SIZE: Medium. *STOCK: Furniture, Georgian, Victorian, Edwardian and shipping oak, £20-£2,000.* LOC: Off High St., driveway beside Geaters Florists. PARK: Easy. TEL: 01728 831414; home - same; mobile - 07989 865598. SER: Valuations; restorations (furniture). VAT: Stan/Spec.

LONG MELFORD

Antique Clocks by Simon Charles
Little St Mary's Court, Hall St. CO10 9LQ. Est. 1970. Open 11-5.30. SIZE: Medium. *STOCK: Clocks - especially longcase, lantern and early bracket, 17th-19th C, £150-£10,000; barometers, 18th-19th C, £150-£1,000.* LOC: Opposite fire station on main road. PARK: Easy. TEL: 01787 880040; home and fax - 01787 375931; e-mail - simon.charles@virgin.net; website - www. go.to/antiqueclocks. SER: Valuations; restorations (clock movements and cases); buys at auction (clocks). VAT: Stan/Spec.

Ashley Gallery
Belmont House, Hall St. CO10 9JF. Est. 1965. Open 9.30-5.30 or by appointment. SIZE: Medium. *STOCK: Paintings, watercolour drawings, furniture, porcelain.* LOC: A134, opposite Crown Hotel. PARK: Easy. TEL: 01787 375434.

Karen Bryan Antiques
Little St. Mary's Court. CO10 9LQ. Est. 1975. Open 10.30-5. SIZE: Medium. *STOCK: Mahogany, walnut and satinwood furniture, 18th-19th C, £200-£8,000; prints, paintings, mirrors and lighting, 19th C, £30-£700; objects of vertu, 19th to early 20th C, £20-£400.* PARK: Easy. TEL: 01787 312613. SER: Valuations. VAT: Spec.

Sandy Cooke Antiques
Hall St. CO10 9JQ. Est. 1982. Open Fri., Sat. and Mon. 10-5. SIZE: Large. *STOCK: Furniture, 17th to early 19th C, £100-£40,000.* Not Stocked: Silver and glass. LOC: A134. PARK: Easy. TEL: 01787 378265; fax - 01284 830935; mobile - 07860 206787; e-mail - sandycooke@ englishfurniture. co.uk; website - www.english furniture.co.uk. SER: Valuations; restorations; buys at auction (furniture). VAT: Stan/Spec.

Country Antiques
10 Westgate St. CO10 9DS. (Mr and Mrs G. Pink). Est. 1984. Open 11-5. CL: Mon. and Thurs. SIZE: Small. *STOCK: Objects, jewellery; metalware and small furniture, £50-£2,000; unusual objects, £50-£500.* LOC: Outskirts of village, on Clare road. PARK: Easy. TEL: 01787 310617; fax - same; e-mail - countrypink @supanet.com.

The presence of Apollo, painted above the label of this English delft drug jar, encouraged one dealer to spend as much as £2,900.

From an Auction Report by Christopher Wight on the Three Ceramics Collections held at Vost's, Newmarket on 28th June 2000. This sale was featured in the September 2000 issue of **Antique Collecting** magazine. For more details and to subscribe see page 147.

Long Melford Antiques Centre

Large selection of quality antique furniture,
silver, pictures, clocks, objets d'art,
and decorator accessories.

Open Mon-Sat 9.30am-5.30pm
Chapel Maltings, Long Melford
Suffolk. Phone: SUDBURY 01787 379287

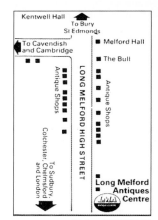

**At the SUDBURY
end of the town.**

Long Melford Antiques Centre
Chapel Maltings. CO10 9HX. (Baroness V.von Dahlen). Est. 1984. Open 9.30-5.30 or by appointment. SIZE: Large - 42 dealers. *STOCK: Furniture - oak, Georgian, Edwardian and Victorian; silver, china, glass, clocks and decorators' items.* LOC: A134, Sudbury end of village. TEL: 01787 379287. SER: Packing and shipping. VAT: Stan/Spec.

Alexander Lyall Antiques
Belmont House, Hall St. CO10 9JF. (A.J. Lyall). Est. 1977. Open 9.30-5.30. SIZE: Medium. *STOCK: Furniture, 18th-19th C.* LOC: A134 opposite Crown Hotel. PARK: Easy. TEL: 01787 375434; home - same; website - www. lyallantiques.com. SER: Restorations (furniture); buys at auction (English furniture). VAT: Stan/Spec.

Magpie Antiques
Hall St. CO10 9JT. (Mrs P. Coll). Est. 1985. Open 10.30-1 and 2.15-5, Sat. 11-5. CL: Mon. and Wed. SIZE: Small. *STOCK: Smalls including hand-painted china; furniture, Victorian and stripped pine.* LOC: Main street. PARK: Easy. TEL: 01787 310581; home - same.

Patrick Marney
The Gate House, Melford Hall. CO10 9AA. Est. 1964. Open by appointment. SIZE: Small. *STOCK: Fine barometers, 18th-19th C, £1,000-£5,000; pocket aneroids, 19th C, £150-£1,000; scientific instruments, 18th-19th C, £250-£2,000; all fully restored.* LOC: A134. PARK: Easy. TEL: 01787 880533. SER: Valuations; restorations (mercury barometers). VAT: Stan.

Melford Antique Warehouse
Hall St. CO10 9JG. (D. Edwards and J. Tanner). Open 9.30-5, Sun. 1-5. SIZE: 150 dealers exhibiting. *STOCK: 18th-20th C furniture and decorative items.* TEL: 01787 379638; e-mail - patrick@worldwideantiques.co.uk; website - www.worldwideantiques.co.uk.

Noel Mercer Antiques
Aurora House, Hall St. CO10 9RJ. Est. 1990. Open 10-5. SIZE: Large. *STOCK: Early oak, walnut and country furniture, incl. refectory and gateleg tables, sets of chairs and dressers; works of art, £500-£30,000.* LOC: Centre of Hall St. PARK: Easy. TEL: 01787 311882.

The Persian Carpet Studio
The Old White Hart. CO10 9HX. Est. 1990. Open 10-5.30. SIZE: Medium. *STOCK: Antique and*

decorative Oriental carpets and rugs, from 1860, from £50. LOC: Sudbury end of Long Melford. PARK: Own. TEL: 01787 882214; fax - 01787 882213; e-mail - sarabarber@persian-carpet-studio.net; website - www.persian-carpet-studio.net. SER: Valuations; repairs and hand-cleaning (Oriental rugs); buys at auction (Oriental carpets, rugs and textiles). Exhibitions held. VAT: Stan/Spec.

Seabrook Antiques
Hall St. CO10 9JG. (J. Tanner). Est. 1965. Open 9.30-5.30, Sun. 1-5. SIZE: Large - 10 showrooms. STOCK: Furniture, £500-£15,000; objects, £100-£2,000; both 17th-18th C. LOC: A134 near Bull Hotel. TEL: 01787 375787; fax - same; home - 01787 311788. SER: Valuations; restorations (17th-18th C furniture); buys at auction (17th-18th C furniture). FAIRS: International.

Suthburgh Antiques
Red House, Hall St. CO10 9JQ. (R.P. Alston). Est. 1977. Open by appointment. SIZE: Medium. STOCK: Furniture, 17th C oak, 18th C walnut and mahogany, £500-£5,000; portraits, 17th-19th C, £2,000-£10,000; Georgian barometers and clocks, £400-£15,000; small collectors' items, boxes, glass, brass, copper, oak carvings and panels, £50-£600; English county maps and prints, £40-£500. Not Stocked: Victorian furniture and later items. LOC: Opposite Bull Hotel. PARK: Easy. TEL: 01787 374818; fax - same; home - same. SER: Valuations; restorations (furniture, barometers); buys at auction. VAT: Stan/Spec.

Trident Antiques
2 Foundry House, Hall St. CO10 9JR. (Thomas McGlynn). LAPADA. Est. 1989. Open 10-5.30, Sat. 10-6, Sun. by appointment. SIZE: Medium. STOCK: Oak furniture, 17th C, £250-£10,000; barometers, 19th C, £450-£2,500; paintings, 17th-18th C, £2,000-£6,000; objects including bottles, spoons and carvings, 17th-18th C, £100-£600. LOC: Next to Cock and Bell Inn. PARK: Easy. TEL: 01787 883388; fax - 01787 378850; home - 01787 371867; e-mail - tridentoak@aol.com; website - www.earlyoak.com. SER: Valuations; restorations (early English oak); buys at auction (oak furniture). FAIRS: LAPADA (NEC and London). VAT: Spec.

Tudor Antiques
Little St. Marys. CO10 9HY. (S.J. Denton-Ford). Est. 1974. Open 10-5, Sun. 2-4.30 (usually). SIZE: Large + art gallery. STOCK: General antiques, £5-£5,000; curios, silver, objets d'art, furniture, bygones, books on antiques. LOC: Sudbury end of Long Melford, shop with yellow blind. PARK: Easy. TEL: 01787 375950; mobile - 07968 201654;

e-mail - sford@antiqueand silver.demon.co.uk. SER: Valuations; metal polishing; repairs (metal, silver, china, barometers); mail-order catalogue. VAT: Stan/Spec.

Village Clocks
Little St. Mary's. CO10 9LQ. (J.C. Massey). Est. 1975. Open 10-5, Sat. 9.30-5. CL: Wed. SIZE: Small. STOCK: Clocks - longcase, bracket, wall and mantel, 18th-19th C, £500-£5,000+; carriage, 19th C, £500-£2,000+. PARK: Easy. TEL: 01787 375896. SER: Valuations; restorations (as stock); buys at auction (clocks). FAIRS: Uxbridge Horological, Brunel University.

Vintage Pine
Hall St. CO10 9JL. (Nikki Hamilton and Irene Fielding). Open 10-5. CL: Mon. SIZE: Medium. STOCK: Victorian stripped pine, brass and copper, china and country implements. PARK: Easy. TEL: 01787 377523; home - 01787 247771.

MARLESFORD

Antiques Warehouse (incorporating The Woodbridge Trading Co.)
The Old Mill, Main Rd. IP13 0AG. (John M. Ball). Est. 1979. Open 8-4.30, Sat. 10-4.30, Sun. by appointment. SIZE: Large. STOCK: Furniture including fine country, 18th-20th C, £50-£5,000; mirrors and decorative items, 18th-20th C, £10-£2,000. LOC: A12 7 miles north of Woodbridge. PARK: Easy. TEL: 01728 747438; fax - 01728 747627; home - 01394 382426. SER: Valuations; buys at auction.

MARTLESHAM, Nr. Woodbridge

Martlesham Antiques
The Thatched Roadhouse. IP12 4RJ. (R.F. Frost). Est. 1973. Open Mon.-Fri., Sat. and Sun. by appointment. SIZE: Large. STOCK: Furniture and decorative items, 17th-20th C, £25-£3,000. LOC: A1214 opposite Red Lion public house. PARK: Own. TEL: 01394 386732; fax - 01394 382959.

John Read
29 Lark Rise, Martlesham Heath. IP5 3SA. Est. 1992. By appointment. STOCK: Pre 1840 Staffordshire figures, animals and English pottery, including Delft, salt glaze, creamware and pearlware, coloured glazed, underglazed (Pratt) and enamel decoration, 1750-1840, £100-£8,000. LOC: A12 Ipswich bypass, opposite B.T. tower. PARK: Easy. TEL: 01473 624897; home - same. SER: Valuations; restorations (as stock).

Dent, London, no. 1774: a Victorian mahogany and burr walnut wall regulator with jewelled deadbeat escapement and invar pendulum, sold in March 2000 for £18,820, considerably more than its estimated £4,000-£6,000, but in fact in line with previous prices for good wall regulators. (Phillips)

From an article on clocks by Richard Garnier which appeared in the July/August 2000 issue of **Antique Collecting** magazine. For more details and to subscribe see page 147.

MENDLESHAM GREEN

Frank Collins Antiques
Green Farm. IP14 5RE. Open by appointment only. *STOCK: Furniture, mainly mahogany and oak, 17th-18th C; decorative works of art.* TEL: 01449 766135; mobile - 07802 492153.

MILDENHALL

Mildenhall Antiques
10 North Terrace. IP28 7AA. Open 11-5. SIZE: Large. *STOCK: Restored antique pine, Victorian and 1920's oak furniture, bric-a-brac.* TEL: 01638 718025.

NAYLAND

Maria Cass Interiors
15 High St. CO6 4JF. (Mrs Bettina Maria Stevens). Resident. Est. 1998. Open Tues.-Fri. 10-3, Sat. 9-1, Sun. by appointment. SIZE: Small. *STOCK: Longcase clocks, George III, £2,500; chests, drawers, Georgian-Victorian, £400-£1,000; ornate mirrors, Georgian, Regency, Victorian, £200-£1,250; chairs and upholstered furniture, 20th C pictures.* LOC: Village centre, on A134 towards Sudbury. PARK: Easy. TEL: 01206 263929; fax - same. SER: Restorations including upholstery; FAIRS: Newark.

Watermill Antiques
The Mill. CO6 4HU. (N. and A. Warren-Thomas). Open 10-1 and 1.30-5 including Sun., Tues. 11-4. *STOCK: Furniture and paintings, 17th-20th C, £200-£1,000; porcelain, rugs, silver, gardening and farming implements.* LOC: A134 midway between Colchester and Sudbury. PARK: Easy. TEL: 01206 262621; fax/home - 01206 263069. SER: Valuations; restorations. VAT: Stan.

NEEDHAM MARKET

Roy Arnold
77 High St. IP6 8AN. Est. 1974. Open 10-6 appointment advisable, Sun. by appointment. SIZE: Medium. *STOCK: Woodworkers' and craftsmen's tools; scientific instruments; books - new, secondhand and antiquarian - on tools and trades; all £10-£5,000.* LOC: A14, centre of High St. PARK: Easy. TEL: 01449 720110; fax - 01449 722498; e-mail - ra@royarnold.com. VAT: Stan.

The Old Town Hall Antique Centre
High St. IP6 8AL. (S. and R. Abbott). Open 10-5. SIZE: Several dealers. *STOCK: General antiques.* TEL: 01449 720773. SER: Repairs (jewellery).

The Tool Shop
78 High St. IP6 8AW. (Tony Murland).
LAPADA. Est. 1988. Open 10-5. SIZE: Small.
*STOCK: Antique and usable woodworking tools,
from 19th C.* PARK: Easy. TEL: 01449 722992;
fax - 01449 722683. SER: Valuations; buys at
auction; tool auctions held. FAIRS: All major
Woodworking Shows, Woodmex, Axminster,
Harrogate. VAT: Stan.

NEWMARKET

Derby Cottage Antiques
Fordham Rd. CB8 7LG. (V. Cole). Open 9-6
including Sun. SIZE: Medium. *STOCK: Furniture
and ceramics especially Derby porcelain, 19th to
early 20th C, £5-£1,500; bygones and collectors'
items, £1-£300.* LOC: Just off A14 Newmarket by-
pass on A142 to Ely. PARK: Easy. TEL: 01638
578422; home - same.

Jemima Godfrey
5 Rous Rd. CB8 8DH. (Miss A. Lanham). Est.
1968. Open Thurs. and Fri. 10-1 and 2-4.30.
SIZE: Small. *STOCK: Small antiques, jewellery
and linen, 19th C.* LOC: Just off High St., near
clock tower. PARK: Easy. TEL: 01638 663584.

R.E. and G.B. Way
Brettons, Burrough Green. CB8 9NA. Open 8.30-5
appointment advisable. *STOCK: Antiquarian and*
*secondhand books on shooting, fishing, horses,
racing and hunting and small general section.*
TEL: 01638 507217; fax - 01638 508058.

ORFORD

Castle Antiques
Market Sq. IP12 2LH. (S. Simpkin). Est. 1969.
Open daily including Sun. 11-4.30. SIZE:
Medium. *STOCK: Furniture, general small
antiques, bric-a-brac, glass, china, clocks.* TEL:
01394 450100.

PEASENHALL, Nr. Saxmundham

Peasenhall Art and Antiques Gallery
The Street. IP17 2HJ. (A. and M. Wickins).
Resident. Est. 1972. Open every day. *STOCK:
19th C watercolours and oils; some furniture;
walking sticks.* TEL: 01728 660224; home -
same. SER: Restorations (oils, watercolours,
furniture).

RISBY, Nr. Bury St. Edmunds

The Risby Barn
IP28 6QU. (R. and S. Martin). Open 9-5.30, Sun.
and Bank Holidays 10-5. SIZE: 24 dealers.
STOCK: Furniture, porcelain, metalware, tools,

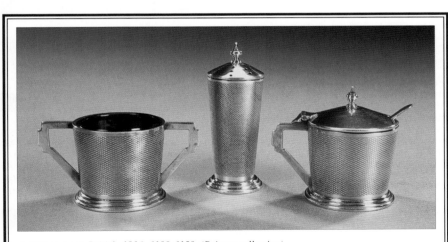

Art Deco cruet, British, 1936, £100-£150. (Private collection)

Once the Art Deco style had been accepted in Britain, designers produced some stylish pieces in
silver. From an article entitled 'Art Deco Silver' by Christopher Parker which appeared in the
December 2000/January 2001 issue of **Antique Collecting** magazine. For more details and to
subscribe see page 147.

pine, Art Deco. LOC: Just off A14 west of Bury St. Edmunds. TEL: 01284 811126; fax - 01284 810783.

SNAPE

Snape Antiques and Collectors Centre
Snape Maltings. IP17 1SR. Est. 1992. Open 7 days 10-6 or until dusk in winter. SIZE: 40 dealers. *STOCK: Antiques and collectables, especially smalls - cutlery, pens, sewing, silver, jewellery, ceramics from 18th C, Doulton, Deco, Studio, glass, maps, prints, paintings, textiles, country, decorative and useful furniture, stamps, costume jewellery.* LOC: Next to the Concert Hall. PARK: Easy. TEL: 01728 688038.

SOUTHWOLD

Cannonbury
Bridgefoot Corner, Reydon. IP18 6NF. (D. Brinsmead). Est. 1975. Open 10-5, Sun. 11-4. SIZE: Medium. *STOCK: General antiques and furniture, 1800-1950's, £5-£500+.* LOC: A1095 to Southwold from A12. PARK: Easy. TEL: 01502 722133. SER: Valuations; restorations; buys at auction. FAIRS: Newark; Stoneleigh.

The Emporium Antiques and Collectors Centre
70 High St. IP18 6DN. (Michael Brown). Est. 1992. Open 10-5, Sun. 11-4. SIZE: Over 40 dealers. *STOCK: Wide range of general antiques and collectables.* PARK: Nearby. TEL: 01502 723909; website - www.emporium-antiques. co.uk; e-mail - enquiry@emporium-antiques.co. uk.

Farleigh House Antiques
Basement, 39 High St. IP18 6AB. (Sharon Munday). Est. 1996. Open 10-5, Sun. by appointment. CL: Wed. SIZE: Small. *STOCK: Porcelain - Lowestoft, Worcester, etc; glass and silver, jewellery, coins, medals, militaria, brass, copper and antiquities, decorative furniture.* PARK: Easy. TEL: 01502 722630.

Puritan Values at the Dome
The Art and Antiques Centre, Southwold Business Centre, St. Edmunds Rd. IP18 6BZ . (A.F. Geering). Resident. Est. 1984. Open 10-6, Sun. 11-5. SIZE: Large. *STOCK: Arts & Crafts, Gothic Revival, Aesthetic, decorative arts and Art Nouveau, £50-£20,000.* PARK: Easy. TEL: 01502 722211; mobile - 07966 371676; website - www.puritanvalues.com. SER: Valuations; restorations; buys at auction. FAIRS: Earls Court; Newark. VAT: Stan/Spec.

T. Schotte Antiques
The Old Bakehouse, Black Mill Rd. IP18 6AQ. (T. and J. Schotte). Open 10-1 and 2-4. CL: Wed. SIZE: Small. *STOCK: Small furniture, £25-£500; decorative objects, £5-£250; both 18th-19th C. Unusual collectables, £5-£100.* LOC: Turn right at the King's Head, then first left. TEL: 01502 722083. FAIRS: Long Melford monthly; Adams, Horticultural Hall, London.

S. J. Webster-Speakman   BADA
Open by appointment only. *STOCK: English furniture, clocks, Staffordshire pottery, general antiques.* **TEL: 01502 722252. SER: Valuations; restorations (clocks, furniture, ceramics). FAIRS: Various.**

SPEXHALL, Nr. Halesworth

P & R Antiques Ltd
Fairstead Farm Buildings, Wash Lane. IP19 0RF. (Pauline and Robert Lewis). Est. 1997. Open by appointment. SIZE: Large. *STOCK: Chests of drawers, £900-£1,200, dining and drawing room furniture, £500-£1,500, all 18th-19th C.* LOC: From A12, take Halesworth turning, through town, turn left into Wissett Road, then right after half mile into Wash Lane, farm is half mile on right. PARK: Easy. TEL: 01986 873232; home - same; fax - 01986 874682. FAIRS: Snape. VAT: Spec.

STOWMARKET

Trench Puzzles
Three Cow Green, Bacton. IP14 4HJ. *STOCK: Antique, old jigsaw and mechanical puzzles.* TEL: 01449 781178. *Mail Order Only.*

STRADBROKE, Nr. Eye

Mary Palmer Antiques
The Cottage Farm, New St. IP21 5JG. (Mrs M. Palmer Stones). Resident. Est. 1980. Open 9-5, Sun. by appointment. SIZE: Small. *STOCK: English glass, 1750-1850; furniture, 1700-1900.* LOC: B1117. PARK: Easy. TEL: 01379 388100.

SUDBURY

Antique Clocks by Simon Charles
The Limes, 72 Melford Rd. CO10 1LT. Est. 1970. Open by appointment only. *STOCK: Interesting clocks especially English longcase, lantern and unusual skeleton clocks, 17th-19th C.* TEL: 01787 375931; fax - same; e-mail - simon.charles@

virgin.net; website - www.go.to/antiqueclocks. SER: Valuations; free estimates; restorations; repairs.

Gainsborough Antiques
36 Cross St. CO10 2DR. (Anthony and William Robison-Smith). Est. 1984. Open 10-1 and 2-5. CL: Wed. SIZE: Medium. *STOCK: Furniture, 18th-19th C, £150-£3,500.* LOC: A131 towards Chelmsford, on left before bridge. PARK: Nearby. TEL: 01787 315800; fax - same. SER: Valuations; restorations (furniture); buys at auction. VAT: Spec.

Napier House Antiques
Church St. CO10 6BJ. Est. 1977. Open 10-4.30 and by appointment. SIZE: Large. *STOCK: 18th-19th C mahogany furniture, especially larger items - linen presses, wardrobes, desks, bureaux, bookcases, dining tables, sideboards, wing chairs, £350-£5,000.* PARK: Easy. TEL: 01787 375280; fax - 01787 478757. SER: Free delivery (UK).

Neate Militaria & Antiques
P O Box 3794, Preston St Mary. CO10 9PX . (Gary C. Neate). OMRS, OMSA, MMSSA. MCCofC. Open Mon.-Fri. 9-6. *STOCK: Orders, decorations and medals of the world, £5-£15,000.* TEL: 01787 248168; fax - 01787 248363; e-mail - gary@neatemedals.co.uk; website - www. neatemedals.co.uk. SER: Valuations; 4 catalogues p.a. FAIRS: Brittania Medal; Aldershot Medal & Militaria; OMRS Convention. VAT: Spec. *Mail order only.*

Sitting Pretty Antiques
16 Friars St. CO10 2AA. (Mrs Susan Fletcher). Est. 1982. Open 9.30-12.45 and 1.45-5 or by appointment. SIZE: Large. *STOCK: Re-upholstered period furniture, small tables and mirrors, 18th C to 1930, £50-£2,000.* LOC: Through Market Square, branch left at bottom fork. PARK: Further down street. TEL: 01787 880908. SER: Valuations; restorations; re-upholstery; buys at auction.

WICKHAM MARKET

Ashe Antiques Warehouse
The Old Engine Shed, Station Rd., Campsea Ashe. IP13. (Graham Laffling). Est. 1986. Open 10-5 including Sun. SIZE: Large. *STOCK: Furniture, 18th-20th C, £100-£5,000; collectables, pictures and prints, 19th C, £50-£500.* LOC: 1.5 miles from A12 Wickham Market by-

pass, signposted Orford and Tunstall. PARK: Easy. TEL: 01473 747255; 01394 460490. SER: Valuations; restorations (ceramics, furniture repairs, re-polishing, upholstery); buys at auction. FAIRS: Newark.

Roy Webb
179 & 181 High St. IP13 0RQ. Open Mon., Thurs. and Sat. 10-6 or by appointment. *STOCK: Furniture, 18th-19th C; clocks.* TEL: 01728 746077; home - 01394 382697. VAT: Stan.

At Bonhams & Brooks Knightsbridge on 16th May this George I wooden doll carries a pre-sale estimate of £10,000-£15,000.

From an Auction Preview which appeared in the May 2001 issue of **Antique Collecting** magazine. For more details and to subscribe see page 147.

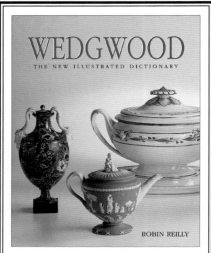

WEDGWOOD
THE NEW ILLUSTRATED DICTIONARY

ROBIN REILLY

When it was first published in 1980, this dictionary was the first of its kind. In this revised edition, Robin Reilly discusses the entire range of wares, the manufacturing processes, the subjects and styles of decoration and their sources as well as the men and women who played an important part in the firm's direction. Also covered are the firm's policies and designs, the distinguishing marks used in every period are illustrated and a bibliography provides invaluable details for those wishing to study the subject in even greater depth. This reference work is essential for identifying and dating Wedgwood with accuracy, and is of exceptional value to anyone interested in Wedgwood, English pottery or ceramic history.
ISBN 1 85149 209 7
516pp., 133 col., 1,080 b.&w. illus.
£45.00/$89.50

For a free copy of our catalogue, please contact

ANTIQUE COLLECTORS' CLUB
5 Church Street, Woodbridge
Suffolk, IP12 1DS, UK
Tel: (01394) 385501 Fax: (01394) 384434
Sales Office Direct Fax: (01394) 388994
Email: sales@antique-acc.com
Website: www.antique-acc.com
————— *or* —————
Market Street Industrial Park, Wappingers'
Falls, NY 12590, USA
Tel: (845) 297 0003 Fax: (845) 297 0068
ORDERS: (800) 252 5231
Email: info@antiquecc.com
Website: www.antiquecc.com

WOODBRIDGE

Antiques & Desirables
32 Church St. IP12 1DH. (C.L. and J.B.L. Buckley). Open 10-5, Wed. 10-1. SIZE: Medium. *STOCK: General antiques, 18th-20th C, £25-£1,000.* LOC: Within the market square. PARK: 200 yds. TEL: 01394 389500; fax - same; mobile - 07881 628514.

Bagatelle
40 Market Hill. IP12 4LU. (N. Lambert). Est. 1990. Open 10-3.30, Wed. 10.30-1. CL: Thurs. SIZE: Medium. *STOCK: Orientalia, water-colours, oils and engravings, furniture, china, glass, 18th-20th C, £10-£2,000.* PARK: Nearby. TEL: 01394 380204.

Brightwell Antiques
at Woodbridge Gallery Antique Centre, 23 Market Hill. IP12. (Angela and Martin Riley). Est. 1972. CL: Wed pm. SIZE: Small. *STOCK: Chinese export porcelain, 18th C, £25-£500; silhouttes, 18th-19th, £100-£300; watercolours and pastel portraits, 18th-19th C, £250-£1,000; small decorative items and silver, 18th-19th C, £25-£500.* LOC: Opposite Shire Hall. PARK: Easy. TEL: 01394 386500; fax - same. FAIRS: Snape (July); Loddon (October).

Church Street Centre
6E Church St. IP12 1DH. (M. Brown). Est. 1994. Open 10-5, Sat. 10-5.30. SIZE: Medium. *STOCK: General antiques, 18th-19th C, £25-£150; collectables, 20th C, £5-£100; some linen, £5-£25.* LOC: Town centre, just off Thoroughfare. PARK: Nearby. TEL: 01394 388887.

David Gibbins Antiques   BADA
21 Market Hill. IP12 4LX. Est. 1964. Open 9.30-5.30, Wed. 9.30-1. *STOCK: English furniture, late 16th to early 19th C, £300-£15,000; English pottery and porcelain, metalwork.* PARK: Own in Theatre St. TEL: 01394 383531; fax - same; home - 01394 382685; mobile - 07702 306914. SER: Valuations; buys at auction. VAT: Spec.

Hamilton Antiques
5 Church St. IP12 1DH. (H.T. and R.E. Ferguson). LAPADA. Est. 1976. Open 10-5. *STOCK: Furniture - mahogany and walnut, especially inlaid, rosewood and some oak.* TEL: 01394 387222; fax - 01394 383832. VAT: Stan/Spec.

Anthony Hurst Antiques
13 Church St. IP12 1DS. (C.G.B. Hurst). LAPADA. Est. 1957. Open 9.30-1 and 2-5.30. CL: Wed. and Sat. pm. SIZE: Large. *STOCK: English furniture, oak, walnut and mahogany,*

1600-1900, £100-£5,000. PARK: Easy. TEL: 01394 382500. SER: Valuations; restorations (furniture); buys at auction. VAT: Stan/Spec.

Lambert's Barn

24A Church St. IP12 1DH. Open 9.30-1 and 2-5. CL: Wed. pm. SIZE: Large. *STOCK: Mainly Victorian and 20th C furniture, miscellaneous items.* PARK: Easy. TEL: 01394 382380.

Edward Manson (Clocks)

8 Market Hill. IP12 4LU. Open 10-5.30, Wed. 10-1. *STOCK: Clocks.* TEL: 01394 380235. SER: Restorations (clocks).

Melton Antiques

Kingdom Hall, Melton Rd., Melton. IP12 1NZ. (A. Harvey-Jones). Est. 1975. Open 9.30-5. CL: Wed. pm. SIZE: Small. *STOCK: Silver, collector's items, £5-£500; decorative items and furniture, £15-£500; both 18th-19th C; Victoriana and general antiques, 19th C, £5-£500.* LOC: On right hand-side coming from Woodbridge. PARK: Easy. TEL: 01394 386232.

Sarah Meysey-Thompson Antiques

10 Church St. IP12 1DH. Est. 1962. Open 10-5, Wed. 10-1, Sun. by appointment. SIZE: Medium. *STOCK: Small furniture, late 18th to early 19th C; china, glass, decorative items, 19th C; textiles and curtains.* PARK: Easy. TEL: 01394 382144. VAT: Spec.

Isobel Rhodes

10-12 Market Hill. IP12 4LU. *STOCK: Furniture, oak, country, mahogany; brassware.* PARK: Easy. TEL: 01394 382763. VAT: Spec.

Woodbridge Pine & Collectables

6 Market Hill. IP12. (S. Tallowin). Est. 1996. Open 10-5. SIZE: Small. *STOCK: Smalls items, collectables, £5-£100.* PARK: Easy. TEL: 01394 383831. SER: Valuations.

WOOLPIT, Nr. Bury St. Edmunds

J.C. Heather

The Old Crown. IP30 9SA. Est. 1946. Open every day 9-8. SIZE: Large. *STOCK: Furniture,*

Gerald Ackerman (1876-1960), 'Low Tide', signed, watercolour and pencil, 9½in. x 13¾in. Sold for £940, November 1999. A highly collectable East Anglian artist. Augurs well for investment.

From an article entitled 'British Watercolours' by Richard Kay of Phillips which appeared in the July/August 2000 issue of **Antique Collecting** magazine. For more details and to subscribe see page 147.

18th-19th C, £20-£1,000. Not Stocked: China. LOC: Near centre of village on right. PARK: Easy. TEL: 01359 240297. VAT: Stan/Spec.

WORTHAM, Nr. Eye

The Falcon Gallery

Honeypot Farm. IP22 1PW. (N. Smith). Est. 1974. Open by appointment seven days. SIZE: Small. *STOCK: Watercolours and oils especially animal paintings and primitives, 19th C.* LOC: South side of A143 in village centre, overlooking village green, 4 miles west of Diss. PARK: Easy. TEL: 01379 783312; fax - same; e-mail - falcongallery@talk21.com. SER: Valuations; restorations (oils, watercolours); framing.

WRENTHAM, Nr. Beccles

Bly Valley Antiques

The Old Reading Rooms, 7 High St. NR34 7HD. Open 11-5, including Sun. SIZE: *STOCK: 18th-19th C furniture, ceramics, silver and plate, pictures, objets d'art.* TEL: 01502 675376.

Wren House Antiques

1 High St. NR34 7HD. (Valerie and Tony Kemp). Open Thurs.-Sat. 10.30-5, Sun. 11-4 or by appointment. SIZE: Medium. *STOCK: Furniture, china and collectables.* LOC: A12 village centre, Fiveways junction. TEL: 01502 675276.

Wrentham Antiques

40-44 High St. NR34 7HB. (B. Spearing). Open Mon.-Sat. SIZE: Large. *STOCK: Victorian, Georgian, Edwardian and decorative furniture.* LOC: A12. PARK: Easy. TEL: 01502 675583; fax - 01502 675707; home - 01502 562495. SER: Buys at auction. VAT: Stan/Spec.

YOXFORD

Red House Antiques

The Red House, Old High Rd. IP17 3HW. (J. and Mrs M. Trotter). Est. 1987. Open Fri. and Sat. 9.30-5, other times by appointment. *STOCK: 18th and early 19th C ceramics, £20-£1,000.* Not Stocked: Stamps, arms, silver and clocks. LOC: Off either A1120 or A12, opposite churchyard. PARK: Easy. TEL: 01728 668615.

Suffolk House Antiques   BADA

High St. IP17 3EP. (A. Singleton). Open 10-1 and 2.15-5.15. CL: Wed. SIZE: Large. *STOCK: 17th-18th C oak and country furniture, works of art, paintings, clocks, delftware and metalware.* LOC: A1120, just off A12. PARK: Easy. TEL: 01728 668122; fax - same; mobile - 07860 521583; e-mail - andrew.singleton@ suffolk-house-antiques.co.uk; website - www. suffolk-house-antiques.co.uk.

A section of the Atlantic cable laid by the SS Great Eastern in 1866 which made £400.

From an Auction Report by Christopher Wight on Maritime and Naval Battles, Christie's South Kensington, 9th November 2000. This sale was featured in the February 2001 issue of **Antique Collecting** magazine. For more details and to subscribe see page 147.

ABINGER HAMMER

Abinger Bazaar
Guildford Rd. RH5 6SA. Est. 1978. Open Wed.-Fri. 10.30-4.30, Sat. and Sun. 12-5.30. SIZE: Medium. *STOCK: Antiques, collectables, books and bric-a-brac.* LOC: A25 next to Drake's on the Pond Restaurant. PARK: By shop or nearby. TEL: 01306 730756.

Stirling Antiques
Aberdeen House. RH5 6RY. (V.S. Burrell). Est. 1968. Open 9.30-6.30. CL: Thurs. *STOCK: Stained glass, furniture, copper, brass, jewellery, silver, curios, dolls.* PARK: Easy. TEL: 01306 730706. VAT: Stan.

ASH VALE, Nr. Aldershot (Hants)

House of Christian
5-7 Vale Rd. GU12 5HH. (A. Bail). Est. 1978. Open 10-5, Sat. 12-3. SIZE: Medium. *STOCK: Pine, 19th-20th C, £30-£1,500; some mahogany, oak, 19th-20th C.* LOC: On B3411 between Ash and Ash Vale. From Ash Wharf over canal bridge, shop (bright green) on left on hill. PARK: Easy - opposite. TEL: 01252 314478. SER: Valuations; restorations (including stripping, waxing, staining); stockists of Briwax and Liberon wax/stain, etc.

ASHTEAD

Bumbles
90 The Street. KT21 1AW. (Barbara Kay). Open 10.30-5.30. *STOCK: General antiques.* PARK: Easy. TEL: 01372 276219. SER: Restorations (furniture including upholstery); oil lamp spare parts.

Temptations
88 The Street. KT21 1AW. (Pauline Watson). FGA, NAG. Open 10-5. *STOCK: Jewellery and silver.* LOC: Main street. PARK: Easy. TEL: 01372 277713. SER: NAG registered valuer; security photography; lecturer. VAT: Stan/Spec.

BAGSHOT

Country Antiques
Pantiles, London Rd. GU19 5HN. (S. Sommers and C. Martin). Est. 1990. Open 10-5 including Sun. SIZE: Large. *STOCK: Victorian and Edwardian, some Georgian, furniture, £50-£3,000; china and glass, collectables including lace and prints, Victorian to 1930's, £2-£100.* TEL: 01276 489499.

BETCHWORTH, Nr. Dorking

Stoneycroft Farm
Reigate Rd. RH3 7EY. (J.G. Elias). Open Mon.-

Fri. 8-5.30, evenings and weekends by appointment. *STOCK: Large oak and country furniture, library bookcases, dining tables and chairs, special writing furniture.* TEL: 01737 845215; website - www.desk.uk.com.

BLETCHINGLEY

Cider House Galleries Ltd
Norfolk House, 80 High St. RH1 4PA. (T. Roberts). Est. 1967. Open 10-5.30. CL: Sat. pm. and Sun. except by appointment. SIZE: Large. *STOCK: Paintings, 17th-20th C, from £350.* LOC: A25, behind F.G. Lawrence Auctioneers. PARK: Own. TEL: 01883 742198; fax - 01883 744014; e-mail - tony.roberts@virgin.net; website - www.ciderhousegalleries.com. SER: Valuations. VAT: Stan/Spec.

John Anthony Antiques
71 High St. RH1 4LJ. (J.A. and N. Hart). Resident. Open by appointment only. *STOCK: 18th to early 19th C furniture.* TEL: 01883 743197; fax - 01883 742108.

Simon Marsh
The Old Butchers Shop, High St. RH1 4PA. Est. 1970. Open by appointment. *STOCK: Grandfather clocks; 18th-19th C furniture.* PARK: Easy. TEL: 01883 743350; fax - 01883 744844. SER: Restorations (furniture and clocks).

Post House Antiques
32 High St. RH1 4PE. (P. and V. Bradley). Open daily, Sun. by appointment. *STOCK: Antique lighting, fenders, mirrors.* LOC: A25. PARK: Easy. TEL: 01883 743317; website - www.antique lightinguk.co.uk. VAT: Stan/Spec.

Quill Antiques
86 High St. RH1 4PA. (Mrs J. Davis). Est. 1971. Open 10-1 and 2-5.30, other times by appointment. *STOCK: Farm and agricultural bygones and cottage antiques including copper, brass, china, kitchenalia, linen and lace.* LOC: A25. PARK: Easy. TEL: 01883 743755; home - same.

BRAMLEY, Nr. Guildford

Memories
High St. GU5 0HB. (P. Kelsey). Est. 1984. Open 10-5. SIZE: Small - 7 dealers. *STOCK: Victorian and Edwardian furniture, china and glass, silver, linen and lace, collectables and bygones, kitchenalia, stripped pine furniture, Art Deco.* LOC: South of Guildford on A281. PARK: Easy. TEL: 01483 892205.

The Old Works
24 High St. GU5 0HB. (A. Sutherland). Est. 1994. Open 9-5.30, Sat. 9.30-5, Sun. 10.30-4.

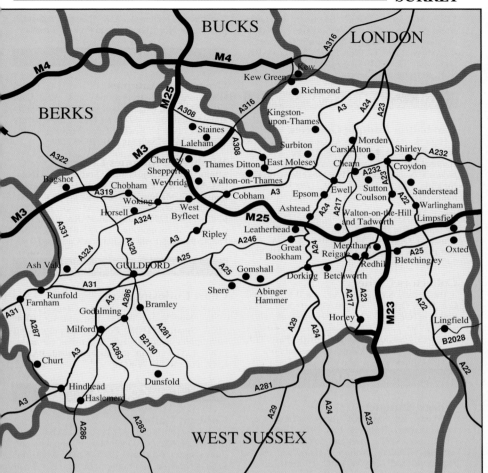

Dealers and Shops in Surrey

SIZE: Medium. *STOCK: Furniture including chests of drawers, wardrobes, tables, cupboards, dressers, coffers, chairs, bookcases, Georgian to Victorian, £100-£1,000.* LOC: A281. PARK: Opposite. TEL: 01483 894648; home - same. SER: Restorations (carpentry).

CARSHALTON

Carshalton Antique Galleries
5 High St. SM5 3AP. (B.A. Gough). Est. 1968. Open 9-4. CL: Wed. SIZE: Large. *STOCK: General antiques, furniture, clocks, glass, china, pictures.* Not Stocked: Silver, jewellery, bronze, firearms. PARK: Nearby. TEL: 020 8647 5664; home - 01306 887187. VAT: Stan/Spec.

Cherub Antiques
312-314 Carshalton Rd. SM5 3QB. (M. Wisdom). Open 9-5.30, Sat. 10-6. *STOCK: Pine and general antiques.* TEL: 020 8643 0028/8661 7427. VAT: Spec.

Collectors Corner
3 The Square. SM5 3BN. (A.J. and B.M. Wilton). Est. 1975. Open 11.30-3.30, Sat. 10-5.30. SIZE: Small. *STOCK: Collectors items, china, glass, 1780-1980, £50-£100; stamps, coins, medals, postcards, 19th-20th C, £5-£25.* PARK: Easy. TEL: 020 8669 7377. SER: Valuations; restorations.

CHEAM

Village Antiques
16 Malden Rd. SM3 8QF. (Rebecca Fownes and Sandy Jenner). Resident. Est. 1970. Open 11-5. CL: Thurs. SIZE: Medium. *STOCK: General antiques including furniture, lighting and smalls, 19th-20th C, £5-£1,000.* LOC: 10 mins. off A3 towards Worcester Park. PARK: Easy. TEL: 020 8644 8567. FAIRS: Kempton Racecourse.

CHERTSEY

Chertsey Antiques
10 Windsor St. KT16 8AS. Open 8-5, Sun 11-4. SIZE: Medium. *STOCK: Furniture, jewellery, glass, pottery and porcelain, silver, silver plate, pictures, kitchenalia, memorabilia, books, linen, clocks.* TEL: 01932 563313; fax - 01753 682082.

D'Eyncourt
21 Windsor St. KT16 8AY. (Mr and Mrs Davies). Est. 1968. Open 10-5.15, Sat. 7-5.30, Sun. 11-5. SIZE: Medium. *STOCK: Furniture, Victorian to Art Deco, £50-£500; china, £5-£50; lighting and fireplaces, Victorian to present day, £25-£500.* PARK: Easy and Guildford St. TEL: 01932 563411. SER: Valuations; restorations; buys at auction

(furniture and paintings). FAIRS: London Photograph (Bonnington Hotel, Southampton Row). VAT: Stan.

CHOBHAM

Greengrass Antiques
Hookstone Farm, Hookstone Lane, West End. GU24 9QP. (D. Greengrass). LAPADA. Open by appointment only. *STOCK: Decorative items; furniture, 19th C; works of art; shipping goods.* TEL: 01276 857582; fax - 01276 855289.

Mimbridge Antiques Centre
Mimbridge Garden Centre, Station Rd. GU24. (F.C.M. Scott). Est. 1998. Open 10-5 including Sun. SIZE: Medium. *STOCK: Collectors' items, furniture, prints, watercolours and maps, 18th-20th C, £5-£2,500.* LOC: Main road. PARK: Easy. TEL: 01276 855736; mobile - 07771 862284. SER: Picture framing. FAIRS: Kempton; Oatlands Hotel.

CHURT, Nr. Farnham

Churt Curiosity Shop
Crossways. GU10 2JE. (Mrs G. Gregory). Est. 1996. Open Tues., Thurs., Fri. and Sat. 10-4. SIZE: Small. *STOCK: Pottery, porcelain and collectables, Victorian and Edwardian furniture.* LOC: A287 Farnham to Hindhead road. PARK: Easy. TEL: 01428 714096.

COBHAM

Cobham Galleries
65 Portsmouth Rd. KT11 1JQ. (Mrs Jerry Burkard). LAPADA. Open Mon. by appointment, Tues.-Sat. 10-5, Sun. 11-5. SIZE: Medium. *STOCK: Period and country furniture, 19th to early 20th C oils and watercolours.* LOC: South off A3, on second roundabout. 5 minutes from M25. PARK: Driveway beside shop. TEL: 01932 867909; mobile - 07850 651743. SER: Buys at auction; searches.

Village Antiques
38 Portsmouth Rd. KT11 1HZ. (N. Tsangari & Son). Resident. Est. 1965. Open 10-6, Sat. and Sun. by appointment. SIZE: Small. *STOCK: Oil paintings, watercolours, chairs, brass, wood, mainly 19th C.* LOC: Just off A3. PARK: Easy. TEL: 01932 589841. SER: Restorations (oil paintings). VAT: Stan.

COULSDON

Decodream
233 Chipstead Valley Rd. CR5 3BY. Open by appointment only. *STOCK: Pottery - Clarice Cliff,*

Shorter, Shelley, Foley, F. and C. Rhead and Carlton ware. PARK: Free. TEL: 020 8668 5534.

D. Potashnick Antiques
7 Stoats Nest Parade, 73 Stoats Nest Rd. CR5 2JJ. Open 9-5.30, Sat. 9-12 or by appointment. *STOCK: General antiques.* TEL: 020 8660 8403. SER: Restorations (furniture).

CROYDON

Oscar Dahling Antiques
87 Cherry Orchard Rd. CR0 6BE. (Oscar Dahling and Liz Lancaster). Est. 1988. Open Mon.-Fri. 10.30-6, Sun. 10.30-3.30, other times by appointment. SIZE: Medium. *STOCK: Furniture, £50-£2,500; ceramics, £10-£250; jewellery and costume, £10-£500; all 18th-20th C.* LOC: Ist left after leaving East Croydon B.R. station. shop 300 yards, near Grouse and Claret public house. PARK: Easy. TEL: 020 8681 8090; home - same. SER: Valuations.

G.E. Griffin
43a Brighton Rd., South Croydon. CR2 6EB. (E.J.H. Robinson). Est. 1896. Open 8-5.30, Sat. 10-4.30. SIZE: Large. *STOCK: General antiques.* TEL: 020 8688 3130; e-mail - ted@gegriffin. freeserve.co.uk; website - www.griffinantiques. co.uk. SER: Restorations; upholstery.

The Whitgift Galleries
77 South End. CR0 1BF. FATG. Est. 1945. *STOCK: 20th C paintings.* TEL: 020 8688 0990; fax - 020 8760 0522; e-mail - info@whitgif tgalleries.co.uk; website - www.whitgiftgalleries. co.uk. SER: Restorations; conservation, framing. VAT: Spec.

DORKING

Antique Clocks by Patrick Thomas
62A West St. RH4 1BS. Open 9.30-5.30, Sun. 11-4. SIZE: Medium. *STOCK: Clocks, 18th-19th C, £50-£5,000; optical antiques, 19th-20th C, £50-£3,000; paintings, 19th-20th; sporting memorabilia, 19th-20th C, £50-£1,000.* TEL: 01306 743661; fax - 01483 715289; website - www.antiqueclockshop.co.uk. SER: Valuations; restorations (clock and furniture). VAT: Spec.

G. D. Blay Antiques   BADA
56 West St. RH4 1BS. Open 10-5 and by appointment. CL: Thurs. SIZE: Medium. STOCK: Fine 18th to early 19th C furniture, £500-£50,000. TEL: 01306 743398; mobile - 07785 767718. FAIRS: Olympia (summer, winter, spring). VAT: Spec.

T. M. Collins
70 High St. RH4 1AY. Est. 1963. SIZE: Medium. *STOCK: Jewellery, 1800-1900, £25-£3,000.*

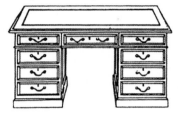

LOC: Opposite Boots chemist. PARK: Behind shop. TEL: 01306 880790. SER: Valuations; restorations (jewellery). VAT: Stan.

J. and M. Coombes
44 West St. RH4 1BU. Est. 1965. Open 9-5, Sun. 11-4. *STOCK: General antiques.* TEL: 01306 885479. VAT: Stan.

Dolphin Square Antiques
42 West St. RH4 1BU. (Mr and Mrs N. James). Est. 1995. Open 10-5.30. *STOCK: Furniture, clocks, china and glass, bronzes, Staffordshire, 17th to early 20th C, £50-£15,000.* LOC: Western end of High St. PARK: Nearby. TEL: 01306 887901. SER: Valuations; shipping.

Dorking Desk Shop
41 West St. RH4 1BU. (J.G. Elias). LAPADA. Est. 1969. Open 8-1 and 2-5.30, Sat. 10.30-1 and 2-5. SIZE: Large. *STOCK: Desks, especially partners, cylinder bureaux, davenports, kneehole and pedestal, 18th to mid-20th C, £100-£60,000.* PARK: Nearby. TEL: 01306 883327; fax - 01306 875363; e-mail - dorkingdesks@aol.com; website - www.desk.uk.com. VAT: Stan/Spec.

Dorking House Antiques
17/18 West St. RH4 1BS. (Mrs G.D. Emburey). Est. 1989. Open 10-5. SIZE: 30 dealers. *STOCK: Period and pine furniture, silver, porcelain,*

longcase, wall and table clocks, jewellery, copper and brass, pictures and prints, decorative and collectors' items. LOC: Continuation of High St. into one-way system. PARK: Opposite. TEL: 01306 740915. SER: Restorations.

Gallery Eleven

11 West St. RH4 1BL. Open 10-5, Sun. 11.30-4 Oct.-April. SIZE: Large. *STOCK: Furniture, 1650-1920; pictures and smalls.* PARK: Opposite. TEL: 01306 887771; fax - same. SER: Valuations.

Hampshires of Dorking

50-52 West St. RH4 1BU. LAPADA. CINOA. Open 9.30-1 and 2.15-5.30. SIZE: Large. *STOCK: Fine English walnut, mahogany, rosewood and satinwood furniture, 18th-19th C, £500-£70,000.* PARK: Own. TEL: 01306 887076; fax/ansaphone - 01306 881029; e-mail - nicholas@ hampshires. co.uk; website - www. hampshires.co. uk. VAT: Spec.

Harman's Antiques

19 West St. RH4 1QH. (Paul and Nicholas Harman). LAPADA. Est. 1956. Open 10-5. SIZE: Large. *STOCK: Furniture including tables, linen presses, sideboards, bookcases, 18th-19th C, £100-£15,000.* PARK: Nearby. TEL: 01306 743330; home - same; fax - 01306 742593. SER: Restorations (polishing and repairs); upholstery; valuations. VAT: Stan/Spec.

Hebeco

47 West St. RH4 1BU. Est. 1982. Open 10.30-5. SIZE: Small. *STOCK: 18th-20th C silver and plate, £5-£6,000, glass, £5-£300; 17th-19th C pewter; 18th-19th C blue and white printed earthenware.* LOC: A25. PARK: Nearby. TEL: 01306 875396 (answerphone); e-mail - hebeco@mcmail.com. SER: Valuations. FAIRS: Country Houses. VAT: Stan/Spec/Global.

Holmwood Antiques

Norfolk Rd., South Holmwood. RH5 4LA. (R. Dewdney). Open 9-6.30, evenings and weekends by appointment. *STOCK: Georgian and Victorian furniture.* TEL: 01306 888174/888468.

The House of Bulow Antiques

5 West St. RH4 1BL. (Karen E. von Bülow). Est. 1989. Open 10.30-5. SIZE: Medium. *STOCK: Furniture, 19th C, £1,000-£5,000; British Victorian porcelain and pottery, especially jugs, £10-£500; paintings, £100-£500; small collectibles, £5-£200.* LOC: Town centre. PARK: Nearby. TEL: 01306 877767; website - www.antiques-in-dorking.com.

King's Court Galleries

54 West St. RH4 1BS. (Mrs J. Joel). Open 9.30-5.30. *STOCK: Antique maps, engravings, decor-*

ative and sporting prints. TEL: 01306 881757; website - www.kingscourtgalleries.co.uk. SER: Framing.

Malthouse Antiques

49 West St. RH4 1BU. Open 10-5, Sat. 10-5.30. SIZE: Large. *STOCK: 18th-19th C mahogany, rosewood and walnut, 17th-19th C oak and country, £100-£5,000; metalware, 19th C, £25-£1,000; giltwood mirrors, 18th-19th C, £500-£3,000.* PARK: Pay and display behind shop. TEL: 01306 886169. VAT: Spec.

Mayfair Antiques

43 West St. RH4 1BU. Est. 1963. Open 9-1 and 2-5. SIZE: Large. *STOCK: Furniture, mainly 18th-19th C, to £500+.* LOC: Opposite Junction Rd. PARK: Nearby. TEL: 01306 885007. VAT: Spec.

Norfolk House Galleries

48 West St. RH4 1BU. Open 10-5. *STOCK: 18th-19th C furniture, especially dining tables and sets of chairs.* TEL: 01306 881028.

The Olde Bakehouse Antiques

1A West St. RH4 1BL. (Mrs S.M. and D.E. Kenny). Est. 1982. Open 10-5. SIZE: Medium. *STOCK: 18th-19th C furniture; British ceramics including Art Deco, Clarice Cliff, Shelley; objets d'art, £20-£5,000.* LOC: A25. PARK: Nearby. TEL: 01306 876646.

Pilgrims Antique Centre

7 West St. RH4 1BL. Est. 1974. Open 10-5.30. SIZE: 10 dealers. *STOCK: Furniture, 18th to early 20th C, glass, books, barometers, Art Deco and Nouveau, paintings, smalls, copper and brass, silver.* LOC: A25 through town, just off High St. PARK: Easy. TEL: 01306 875028.

Elaine Saunderson Antiques   BADA.

18/18a Church St. RH4 1DW. (Mrs E.C. Saunderson). Est. 1988. Open 10-1 and 2-5.30, Sat. 9.30-6, other times by appointment. SIZE: Medium. STOCK: Furniture, late 18th to early 19th C, £50-£10,000; decorative items. Not Stocked: Silver and jewellery. LOC: Turn left into North St. at end of West St. one-way. 100yds. up North St., opposite junction with Church St. PARK: Easy. TEL: 01306 881231; fax - 01306 502120; mobile - 07836 597485. SER: Valuations; restorations (furniture). VAT: Spec.

Thorpe and Foster Ltd

51 West St. RH4 1BU. LAPADA. CINOA. Open 9.30-1 and 2.15-5.30. SIZE: Large. *STOCK: Fine English walnut, mahogany, rosewood and satinwood furniture, 18th-19th C, £500-£70,000.* LOC: On A24. PARK: Own. TEL: 01306

887076; fax - 01306 881029; e-mail - nicholas@hampshires.co.uk; website - www.hampshires.co.uk. VAT: Spec.

Victoria and Edward Antiques Centre
61 West St. RH4 1BS. Est. 1972. Open 9.30-5.30. SIZE: Medium - 28 dealers. *STOCK: General antiques.* PARK: Nearby. TEL: 01306 889645.

The Vinery
55 West St. RH4 1BS. (Pauline Schwarz and Cindy King). Resident. Est. 1980. Open 10.30-5, Mon. and Sun. by appointment. SIZE: Medium. *STOCK: Mahogany and walnut furniture, 18th-19th C, £500-£10,000; small Edwardian inlaid furniture and display cabinets, £300-£3,000; French furniture, late 19th to early 20th C £500-£2,500.* LOC: Town centre. PARK: West St. TEL: 01306 743440; fax - same. SER: Valuations; restorations (polishing and repairs). VAT: Margin.

Pauline Watson
Old King's Head Court. RH4 1AR. FGA, NAG. Est. 1960. Open 9.30-5. SIZE: Small. *STOCK: Jewellery and silver especially Victorian.* LOC: In the High Street at the top of West Street. PARK: Behind shop in North St. TEL: 01306 885452. SER: NAG registered valuer; lecturer. VAT: Stan/Spec.

West Street Antiques
63 West St. RH4 1BS. (J.G. Spooner, R.A. Ratner and P.J. Spooner). Est. 1980. Open 9.30-1 and 2.15-5.30. SIZE: Medium. *STOCK: Furniture, 17th to early 20th C, £100-£10,000; arms and armour, 17th-19th C, £100-£20,000; brass and copper, ceramics, paintings and collectors' items.* Not Stocked: Jewellery and carpets. LOC: A25, one-way system. PARK: Nearby. TEL: 01306 883487; fax - same; home - 01306 730182 or 01372 452877; e-mail - weststant@aol.com; website - www.antiquearmsandarmour.com. VAT: Spec.

The Westcott Gallery
4 Guildford Rd., Westcott. RH4 3NR. (Anthony Wakefield). Open 9-5, Sat. 10-5. *STOCK: Specialist in contemporary paintings and ceramics by Surrey artists.* TEL: 01306 876261; fax - 01306 740770; e-mail - westcottgallery@cs.com; website - www.westcottgallery.co.uk.

DUNSFOLD, Nr. Godalming

Antique Buildings Ltd
GU8 4NP. (Peter Barker). Resident. Est. 1975. Open daily, Sat. and Sun. by appointment. SIZE: Large. *STOCK: Oak timbers, 17th C, £25-£1,000; architectural items, 15th-18th C, £25-£500; barn frames, 17th C, £2,000-£50,000.* LOC: From Sun public house 500 yards down Alford road, row of white posts, premises up tarmac drive between last two. PARK: Easy. TEL: 01483 200477; fax - 01483 200752. SER: Valuations; restorations (ancient oak framed buildings); buys at auction (buildings and architectural items). VAT: Stan.

EAST MOLESEY

The Antiques Centre at Hampton Court
77 Bridge Rd., Hampton Court. KT8 9HH. (Stuart James). Open 10-5. SIZE: 10 dealers. *STOCK: 18th to early 20th C furniture, silver, ceramics, glass, prints, jewellery and decorative antiques.* LOC: Turn down Creek Rd., opposite Hampton Court station, into Bridge Rd. TEL: 020 8979 7954.

Elizabeth R. Antiques
39 Bridge Rd., Hampton Court. KT8 9ER. Est. 1988. Open 10-4.30, Sun. 11-3.30. SIZE: Medium. *STOCK: Furniture, 19th C, £500-£2,000; silver, 18th-20th C, £75-£300; toys, 20th C, £35-£600; jewellery, 19th-20th C, £40-£700.* PARK: Easy. TEL: 020 8979 4004; fax - same. SER: Valuations; restorations (French polishing, waxing; clock, glass and china repairs). FAIRS: Sandown; Alexandra Palace.

Hampton Court Emporium
52-54 Bridge Rd., Hampton Court. KT8 9HA. Open 10-5.30, Sun 11-5.30. SIZE: Medium. *STOCK: Furniture, paintings, silver, jewellery, mirrors, books, clocks, brass and copper, objets d'art, lamps, china and porcelain, collector's cameras, Art Deco.* PARK: Palace Rd. station. TEL: 020 8941 8876. SER: Valuations; restorations. VAT: Stan/Spec.

Hampton Court Palace Antiques
16 Bridge Rd., Hampton Court. KT8 9HA. (J. Clark). Est. 1980. Open 10-6 including Sun. *STOCK: Furniture, oils, watercolours, prints, 18th-19th C, £35-£6,000.* PARK: Easy. TEL: 020 8941 2212. SER: Export facilities; valuations; repairs (furniture, art).

Howard Hope Phonographs and Gramophones
21 Bridge Rd., Hampton Court. KT8 9EU. Open Sat. 10-5 (prior 'phone call advisable) and by appointment. *STOCK: Mechanical and musical items.* LOC: Close by Hampton Court Palace. TEL: 020 8941 2472/8398 7130; mobile - 07713 901995; e-mail - phonoking@hotmail.com; website - www.gramophones.uk.com. SER: Spare parts.

Nicholas Antiques
31 Bridge Rd., Hampton Court. KT8 9ER. Open 9.30-5. *STOCK: Furniture, general antiques and decorative items.* TEL: 020 8979 0354. VAT: Stan/Spec.

The Nostradamus Centre
30-32 Bridge Rd., Hampton Court. KT8 9HA. (Heather Ferri). Est. 1998. Open 10-5.30, Sun. 11-6. CL: Mon. SIZE: Medium. *STOCK: Furniture, 18th-19th C; Art Deco, £25-£1,000; Victorian jewellery and silver, £100-£1,000; brass, lighting, cameras.* LOC: 5 mins. walk from Hampton Court railway station, 10 mins from the Palace. PARK: Easy. TEL: 020 8979 6766. SER: Valuations; restorations. VAT: Stan.

Nostradamus II
53 Bridge Rd., Hampton Court. KT8 9HA. (Heather Ferri). Est. 1998. Open 10-5.30, Sun. 11-6. CL: Mon. SIZE: Medium. *STOCK: Furniture, 18th-19th C; Art Deco, £25-£1,000; Victorian jewellery and silver, £100-£1,000; brass, lighting, cameras.* LOC: 5 mins walk from Hampton Court railway station, 10 mins from the Palace. PARK: Easy. TEL: 020 8783 0595. SER: Valuations; restorations. VAT: Stan.

EPSOM

Vandeleur Antiquarian Books
6 Seaforth Gdns. KT19 0NR. (E.H. Bryant). By appointment only. *STOCK: Antiquarian and secondhand books on all subjects; prints including rowing, and maps.* TEL: 020 8393 7752; fax - same. SER: Valuations; subject lists on request. FAIRS: Various book. VAT: Stan.

EWELL

A. E. Booth & Son
9 High St. KT17 1SG. (David J. and Mrs Ann Booth). BAFRA, Assn. Master Upholsterers. Est. 1934. Open 9.30-4.30. SIZE: Large. *STOCK: Furniture, 1700-1900, £200-£2,000; porcelain, from 1800, £20-£200.* LOC: A24 to Ewell village. PARK: Own - through gates beside shop. TEL: 020 8393 5245; fax - same. SER: Restorations (furniture including polishing, repairs and upholstery). VAT: Stan/Spec.

J.W. McKenzie
12 Stoneleigh Park Rd. KT19 0QT. Est. 1971. Appointment advisable. *STOCK: Old and new books on cricket.* TEL: 020 8393 7700; e-mail - jwmck@netcomuk.co.uk; website - www. mckenzie-cricket.co.uk.

FARNHAM

Annie's Antiques
1 Ridgway Parade, Frensham Rd. GU9 8UZ. Est. 1982. Open 9.30-5.30, Fri. 10.30-5.30, Sun. by appointment. SIZE: Medium. *STOCK: Furniture, bric-a-brac, jewellery, 19th to early 20th C, £5-£1,000; general antiques.* LOC: 1 mile out of Farnham on A287 towards Hindhead. PARK: Easy. TEL: 01252 713447; home - 01252 723217.

The Antiques Warehouse
Badshot Farm, St George's Rd., Runfold. GU9 9HY. (Hilary Burroughs). Est. 1995. Open 10-5.30, including Sun. *STOCK: Furniture, 18th C to 1930's, £75-£2,000; china, glass, silver, jewellery, paintings, prints and interesting collectables, 18th C to 1940's, £5-£500.* LOC: A31 from Farnham towards Guildford, 1st exit (signed Runfold), left at end of slip road towards Badshot Lea, premises 200 yds on left. PARK: Easy. TEL: 01252 317590; fax - 01252 879751. SER: Restorations (woodwork including dipping, veneering, caning).

Bits and Pieces Antiques
82 West St. GU9 7EN. (Mrs C.J. Wickins). *STOCK: Victoriana, chandeliers, furniture, Art Nouveau, Art Deco and costume.* TEL: 01252 722355/715043.

Bourne Mill Antiques
39-43 Guildford Rd. GU9 9PY. Est. 1960. Open 10-5.30 every day. SIZE: Large - 83 dealers. *STOCK: Antique and reproduction furniture in oak, walnut, mahogany, yew and pine; china, glass, pictures, jewellery, fireplaces, beds, kitchenalia, bespoke furniture, collectors' items, books, bric-a-brac; garden ornaments, furniture and buildings.* PARK: Own. TEL: 01252 716663.

Casque and Gauntlet Militaria
55/59 Badshot Lea Rd., Badshot Lea. GU9 9LP. (R. Colt). Est. 1957. Open 11-5. SIZE: Large. *STOCK: Militaria, arms, armour.* LOC: On Aldershot to Farnham road. PARK: Easy. TEL: 01252 320745; fax - same. SER: Restorations (metals); re-gilding.

Childhood Memories
57 Downing St. GU9 7PN. (Miss M.A. Stanford). *STOCK: Teddy bears, dolls, Dinky and Britains toys, games and childhood collectables.* PARK: 100 yds. TEL: 01252 793704; e-mail - maureen@ childhood-memories.co.uk; website - www. childhood-memories.co.uk.

Christopher's Antiques
Sandford Lodge, 39a West St. GU9 7DX. (Mr and Mrs C.M. Booth). Resident. Est. 1972. Open 8-1 and 2-5.30, weekends by appointment. SIZE: Large. *STOCK: Fruitwood country and*

mahogany furniture, 18th-19th C; walnut furniture, 17th-18th C. LOC: From Guildford on the A31, turn right at second roundabout. PARK: Easy. TEL: 01252 713794; fax - 01252 713266; e-mail - cbooth7956@aol.com. SER: Valuations; restorations (furniture). VAT: Stan/Spec.

Farnham Antique Centre
57A Downing St. GU9 7PN. (Miss M.A. Stanford). Est. 1976. Open 9.30-5. SIZE: 6 dealers. *STOCK: General antiques including silver, jewellery, porcelain, brass and copper, clocks, small furniture and collectors' items.* LOC: On the one-way system into Farnham. PARK: 100 yds. TEL: 01252 724475.

Heytesbury Antiques   BADA
P.O. Box 222. GU10 5HN. (Ivor and Sally Ingall). LAPADA. Est. 1974. Open by appointment only. SIZE: Medium. *STOCK: 18th-19th C Continental and English furniture, statuary, bronzes and decorative items, £1,000-£15,000.* TEL: 01252 850893; mobile - 07836 675727; fax - 01252 850828. FAIRS: Olympia; Decorative Antiques & Textiles. VAT: Spec.

Maltings Monthly Market
Bridge Sq. GU9 7QR. Est. 1969. First Sat. monthly. SIZE: 200+ stalls. *STOCK: 60% of the dealers sell a wide variety of antiques, postcards, bric-a-brac and collectables.* LOC: Follow signs to Wagon Yard car park, Maltings over footbridge. TEL: 01252 726234; stalls - 01252 717434; fax - 01252 718177; e-mail - FarnMalt@aol.com; website - www.farnham maltings.com.

Karel Weijand Fine Oriental Carpets
BADA
Lion and Lamb Courtyard. GU9 7LL. LAPADA. Est. 1975. Open 9.30-5.30. SIZE: Large. *STOCK: Fine antique and contemporary Oriental rugs and carpets, from £150.* LOC: Off West St. PARK: Easy. TEL: 01252 726215. SER: Valuations; restorations; cleaning. VAT: Stan/Spec.

GODALMING

The Antique Shop
72 Ockford Rd. GU7 1RF. (G. Jones). Open 10.30-4.30, Sat. 10.30-5. SIZE: 6 dealers. *STOCK: General antiques including furniture, light fittings.* PARK: Opposite. TEL: 01483 414428.

Church Street Antiques
10 Church St. GU7 1EH. (L.Bambridge). Est. 1985. Open 10-5, Wed. 10-1. SIZE: Medium. *STOCK: British ceramics, 1800-1930, £5-£1,000; glass, 1800-1930, £5-£200; silver, 1750-1930, £20-£500.* LOC: Off A3. PARK: Easy and behind shop. TEL: 01483 860894. SER: Valuations; commission buying. VAT: Stan/Spec.

Heath-Bullocks   BADA
8 Meadrow. GU7 3HN. (Roger, Mary and Charlotte Heath-Bullock). Est. 1926. Open Fri. and Sat. 10-5 (some Sundays - phone for dates) and by appointment. SIZE: Large. *STOCK: English and Continental furniture.* LOC: A3100. From Guildford on the left side approaching Godalming. PARK: Own. TEL: 01483 422562; fax - 01483 426077. SER: Valuations; restorations. FAIRS: BADA; exhibitors at and organisers of Buxton and Surrey.

Priory Antiques
29 Church St. GU7 1EL. (P. Rotchell). Open 10-4. CL: Wed. *STOCK: General antiques.* TEL: 01483 421804.

GOMSHALL, Nr. Guildford

The Coach House Antiques
60 Station Rd. GU5 9NP. (P.W. and L. Reeves). Resident. Est. 1985. Open 9-5.30, Sun. 11-5. SIZE: Small. *STOCK: Longcase clocks, 1780 to 19th C, £4,000-£20,000; furniture, 1790 to late 19th C, £1,000-£20,000.* LOC: Between Guildford and Dorking on the Shere by-pass. PARK: Easy. TEL: 01483 203838; fax - 01483 202999; e-mail - coach_house.antiques@virgin.net; website - www.coachhouseantiques.com. SER: Valuations; restorations (clocks and furniture); buys at auction (as stock). FAIRS: Guildford. VAT: Spec.

The Studio
Station Rd. GU5 9LQ. (Mrs M. Ellenger). Est. 1985. Open 12-5, Sat. and Sun. 10.30-5. SIZE: Small. *STOCK: General antiques.* LOC: A25 midway between Guildford and Dorking. PARK: Easy. TEL: 01483 202449. SER: Valuations. VAT: Stan.

GREAT BOOKHAM, Nr. Leatherhead

Roger A. Davis Antiquarian Horologist
19 Dorking Rd. KT23 4PU. Est. 1971. Open Tues., Thurs. and Sat. 9.30-12.30 and 2-5, other times by appointment. SIZE: Small. *STOCK: Clocks, 18th-19th C, £150-£5,000.* LOC: From Leatherhead A246 to centre of village, turn left at sign for Polesden Lacey, shop 1/4 mile along Dorking Rd. PARK: Easy. TEL: 01372 457655; home - 01372 453167. SER: Valuations; restorations (mechanical and case work).

Memory Lane Antiques
30 Church Rd. KT23 3PW. (J. Westwood). Est. 1984. Open 10-5. CL: Wed. *STOCK: Toys and general antiques, pre-1920, £5-£1,000.* PARK: Easy. TEL: 01372 459908.

Cry for the Moon
17 Tunsgate. GU1 3QT. (J.L. Ackroyd). Est. 1977. Open 9.30-5.30. SIZE: Medium. *STOCK: Mainly jewellery and certificated diamonds, £30-£50,000; silver and objets d'art.* TEL: 01483 306600; fax - 01483 306300. SER: Valuations; repairs; jewellery commissions undertaken. VAT: Stan/Margin.

Denning Antiques
1 Chapel St. GU1 3UA. Open 10-5. *STOCK: Silver, jewellery, lace, linen, and collectors' items.* LOC: Off High St. PARK: Nearby. TEL: 01483 539595.

Horological Workshops   BADA
204 Worplesdon Rd. GU2 9UY. (M.D. Tooke). Est. 1968. Open Tues.-Fri. 8.30-5.30, Sat. 9-12.30 or by appointment. *STOCK: Clocks, watches, barometers.* TEL: 01483 576496.

Oriental Rug Gallery
230 Upper High St. GU1 3JD. (R. Mathias and J. Blair). *STOCK: Russian, Afghan, Turkish and Persian carpets, rugs and kelims; Oriental objets d'art.* TEL: + 4 (0) 1483 457600; fax - same; e-mail - rugs@orientalruggallery.com; website - www.orientalruggallery.com.

Thomas Thorp Bookseller
170 High St. GU1 3HP. Est. 1883. Open 9-5, 5.30 on Sat. SIZE: Large. *STOCK: Books including antiquarian and out-of-print.* LOC: At traffic lights at top of High St. PARK: Road running parallel High St. 200yds. away. TEL: 01483 562770. SER: Buys at auction (antiquarian books); private collections bought.

Charles W. Traylen
Castle House, 49/50 Quarry St. GU1 3UA. Est. 1945. Open 9-5. CL: Mon. SIZE: Large. *STOCK: Fine books and manuscripts, 13th C to date.* PARK: 200yds. TEL: 01483 572424; fax - 01483 450048. SER: Valuations; restorations (bindings); catalogues issued. VAT: Stan.

Allen Avery Interiors
1 High St. GU27 2JZ. Est. 1971. Open 9-1 and 2.15-5. CL: Sat. pm. and Wed. *STOCK: English furniture.* TEL: 01428 643883.

Haslemere Antique Market
1A Causewayside, High St. GU27 2JZ. Est. 1990. Open 9.30-5. SIZE: Large. *STOCK: Wide variety of general antiques.* LOC: Off High St. (A286). PARK: Easy. TEL: 01428 643959. SER: Valuations; restorations; buys at auction.

Serendipity Antiques & Crafts
7 Petworth Rd. GU27 2JB. (E.J. Moore). Est. 1995. Open 10-5 (Sun. 11-4 summer and Christmas). SIZE: Medium. *STOCK: Furniture, £400-£600, books, £20-£100, both 19th C; china, late 19th to early 20th C, glass, silver, metalware, clocks, £5-£1,000.* LOC: East at base of High Street, 100 yds on right. PARK: High St. TEL: 01428 642682. SER: Restorations (clocks).

Surrey Clock Centre
3 Lower St. GU27 2NY. (J.P. Ingrams and S. Haw). Est. 1962. Open 9-1 and 2-5. SIZE: Large. *STOCK: Clocks and barometers.* PARK: Easy. TEL: 01428 651313. SER: Restorations; hand-made parts; shipping orders; clocks made to order. VAT: Stan/Spec.

Wood's Wharf Antiques Bazaar
56 High St. GU27 2LA. SIZE: 12 dealers. *STOCK: A wide selection of antiques.* TEL: 01428 642125; fax - same.

Albany Antiques Ltd
8-10 London Rd. GU26 6AF. (T. Winstanley). Est. 1965. Open 9-6. CL: Sun. except by appointment. *STOCK: Furniture, 17th-18th C, £20-£400; china including Chinese, £5-£400; metalware, £7-£50; both 18th-19th C.* Not Stocked: Silver. LOC: A3. PARK: Easy. TEL: 01428 605528. VAT: Stan/Spec.

M. J. Bowdery   BADA
12 London Rd. GU26 6AF. Est. 1970. Always available, prior telephone call advisable. *STOCK: Furniture, 18th-19th C.* TEL: 01428 606376; mobile - 07774 821444. VAT: Stan/Spec.

Drummonds Architectural Antiques
The Kirkpatrick Buildings, 25 London Rd. GU26 6AB. Est. 1988. Open 9-6 including Sun. SIZE: Very large. *STOCK: Architectural and decorative antiques, garden statuary and furniture, period bathrooms.* TEL: 01428 609444; fax - 01428 609445. SER: Restorations (stonework and gates); handmade cast iron baths and fittings, cast iron conservatories; vitreous re-enamelling of baths. VAT: Stan/Spec.

Second Hand Rose
Crossways Rd., Grayshott. GU26 6HG. (S.J. Ridout). Est. 1980. Open 10-5.30 and by appointment. SIZE: Medium. *STOCK: Furniture, paintings, bric-a-brac, 18th-20th C.* LOC: Village centre. PARK: Opposite. TEL: 01428 604880; home - same. VAT: Stan/Spec.

HORLEY

Surrey Antiques
3 Central Parade, Massetts Rd. RH6 7PP. (Michael Bradnum). Est. 1990. Open 10-5, Sat. 10-4. SIZE: Small. *STOCK: China, pottery and glass, £5-£50, furniture, all 19th-20th C.* LOC: On left by traffic lights. PARK: Public behind shop. TEL: 01293 775522. FAIRS: Ardingly; Croydon Hilton.

HORSELL, Nr. Woking

Philip Gilbert
77 High St. GU21 4UA. Est. 1974. Open 10-5. SIZE: Small. *STOCK: Brown furniture, 18th-19th C, £100-£3,000.* LOC: From A322 along Knaphill High St. At roundabout turn right into Horsell High St. PARK: High St. TEL: 01483 756807. SER: Restorations (French polishing, cabinet work, upholstery); buys at auction (furniture). VAT: Spec.

KEW

Lloyds of Kew
9 Mortlake Terrace. TW9 3DT. (C. Patterson). Open 10.30-6. *STOCK: Out-of-print and antiquarian books including gardening, film, childrens.* LOC: Junction of Kew and Mortlake Roads, 10 mins walk from Kew Gardens Station (District line). PARK: Easy. TEL: 020 8940 2512; fax - same; mobile - 07941 592141; e-mail - books@lloydsofkew.co.uk; website - www.loydsofkew.co.uk. SER: Quarterly catalogues.

KEW GREEN

Andrew Davis
6 Mortlake Terrace. TW9 3DT. Resident. Est. 1969. *STOCK: Decorative and functional items of all periods, including furniture, ceramics, glass, pictures, clocks, garden and architectural items.* TEL: 020 8948 4911. SER: Valuations.

KINGSTON-UPON-THAMES

Glencorse Antiques
321 Richmond Rd., Ham Parade, Ham Common. KT2 5QU. (M. Igel and B.S. Prydal). LAPADA. Open 10-5.30. *STOCK: 18th-19th C furniture; 19th C oils and modern British oils and watercolours.* PARK: Own. TEL: 020 8541 0871.

Glydon and Guess Ltd
14 Apple Market. KT1 1JE. Est. 1940. Open 9.30-5. *STOCK: Jewellery, small silver, £100-£5,000.* LOC: Town centre. TEL: 020 8546 3758. SER: Valuations; restorations.

Kingston Antique Market
29-31 London Rd. KT2 6ND. Est. 1995. Open 9.30-6, Thurs. 9.30-7, Sun. 10-6. SIZE: 100 dealers. *STOCK: General antiques including period furniture, porcelain, collectables and jewellery.* LOC: Off Clarence St. PARK: Easy. TEL: 020 8549 2004; e-mail - webmaster@ antiquesmarket.co.uk; website - www.antique market.co.uk.

LALEHAM, Nr. Staines

Laleham Antiques
23 Shepperton Rd. TW18 1SE. (E. Potter). Est. 1970. Open 10.30-5. SIZE: Medium. *STOCK: Furniture, porcelain, mirrors, antique lighting, silver, general and trade antiques.* LOC: B376. PARK: Easy. TEL: 01784 450353.

LEATHERHEAD

Alan's Antiques
1-3 Church St. KT22 8DN. (Michael Laikin). Est. 1960. Open 9-5.30. SIZE: Medium. *STOCK: Furniture, £500+, porcelain, £100-£300, silver, £100+, all late 19th to early 20th C.* LOC: Town centre. PARK: Opposite. TEL: 01372 360646. SER: Valuations; restorations (porcelain and furniture). FAIRS: Sandown Park. VAT: Stan/Spec.

LIMPSFIELD

Limpsfield Watercolours
High St. RH8 0DT. (Mrs C. Reason). FATG. Est. 1985. Open Tues.-Fri. 10.30-4, Sat. 9.30-4. SIZE: Small. *STOCK: Watercolours, £15-£5,000; prints and etchings, £5-£200; all 1850-1940 and contemporary.* Not Stocked: Oils. LOC: From junction 6 M25 follow A25 towards Westerham, village is left on B269. PARK: Easy. TEL: 01883 717010. SER: Valuations; restoration and cleaning of watercolours, prints and oils; framing including conservation. VAT: Spec.

LINGFIELD

Browsers
7 East Grinstead Rd. RH7 6EU. (S. Robbins). Open 10-5. SIZE: Small. *STOCK: Collectables including stamps, books.* LOC: Between East Grinstead and Lingfield Race Course. PARK: Easy. TEL: 01342 834881. SER: Valuations.

Elm House Antiques

3 High St. RH1 3BA. (Robert Black). Est. 1995.
Open 10.30-5.30. SIZE: Medium. *STOCK:
Georgian to Edwardian town and country
furniture, mahogany, oak and decorative items,
£50-£5,000; country furniture, pine, kitchenalia,
decorative items, textiles, £5-£500; brass and
copper, £5-£100; period cabinet fittings.* LOC:
A23 just past beginning of M23. PARK: Own.
TEL: 01737 643983. SER: Valuations; restorations
(textiles, boxes, inlay, gesso work, furniture
including French polishing, upholstery).

Geoffrey Van-Hay Antiques

The Old Smithy, 7 High St. RH1 3BA. Open 9-5.
SIZE: Medium. *STOCK: 18th-19th C furniture,
£500-£1,000.* PARK: Easy. TEL: 01737 645131;
fax - same. SER: Valuations; restorations. VAT:
Spec.

Michael Andrews Antiques

Portsmouth Rd. GU8 5AU. Est. 1974. Open
daily, Thurs. and Sun. by appointment. SIZE:
Medium. *STOCK: Furniture, 18th-19th C.* LOC:
Corner of Cherry Tree Rd. (on traffic lights, from
A3 slip road to Petworth). PARK: Own. TEL:
01483 420765; home - same.

E. Bailey

Portsmouth Rd. GU8 5DR. (Eric Bailey). Est.
1979. Open 9-5. CL: Thurs. SIZE: Small.
*STOCK: Furniture and tools, from Victorian, £5-
£100; china, £5-£25.* LOC: Main road. PARK:
Easy. TEL: 01483 422943.

A. Burton-Garbett

35 The Green. SM4 4HJ. Est. 1959. By appointment only. Prospective clients met (at either
Morden or Wimbledon tube station) by car.
*STOCK: Books on Latin American and Caribbean
travel, arts and antiquities.* TEL: 020 8540 2367;
fax - 020 8540 4594. SER: Buys at auction (books,
pictures, fine arts, ethnographica). VAT: Stan.

Secondhand Bookshop

56 Station Rd. West. RH8 9EU. (David Neal). Est.
1985. Open 10-5. SIZE: Small. *STOCK: Books,
18th C to present day, £1-£500.* LOC: Adjacent to
station. PARK: Safeway immediately behind shop.
TEL: 01883 715755; home - 01883 723131. SER:
Valuations; buys at auction (books). FAIRS: Book
- in south-east. VAT: Stan.

Wagstaffs

80-84 Station Rd. East. RH8 0PG. (Mrs J.
Wagstaff). Est. 1992. Open 9.30-5.30. SIZE:
Medium. *STOCK: General antiques and
collectables including china and porcelain,
silver, glass, pictures and small furniture, £1-
£1,000; second-hand book basement.* LOC: 3
miles south junction 6, M25; off A25. PARK:
Easy and at rear. TEL: 01883 712806.

Wagstaffs

Books in the Basement, 80-84 Station Rd. East.
RH8 0PG. (David Neal). Est. 1985. Open 9.30-5.30.
SIZE: Medium. *STOCK: 20th C books, £1-£100
(plus antiques and collectables upstairs).* LOC:
Opposite Station Parade. PARK: Behind row of
shops. TEL: 01883 717183; home - 01883 723131.
SER: Valuations; buys at auction. VAT: Stan.

F.G. Lawrence and Sons

89 Brighton Rd. RH1 6PS. Est. 1891. Open 9-5,
Sat. 9-1. SIZE: Large. *STOCK: Edwardian,
Victorian and Georgian furniture.* LOC: On A23.
PARK: Own. TEL: 01737 764196. SER: Valu-
ations. VAT: Stan.

Bourne Gallery Ltd

31/33 Lesbourne Rd. RH2 7JS. (J. Robertson).
LAPADA. Est. 1970. Open 10-1 and 2-5. CL:
Mon. SIZE: Large. *STOCK: 19th-20th C oils and
watercolours, £250-£25,000.* PARK: Easy. TEL:
01737 241614; website- www.bournegallery.com.
SER: Restorations (oil paintings). VAT: Spec.

The Gallery

3/5 Church St. RH2 0AA. (Jeffrey S. Cohen).
LAPADA. Open 10-6. SIZE: Medium. *STOCK:
19th-20th C oil paintings and watercolours,
especially Modern British artists post 1850,
£250-£15,000; 18th-19th C furniture and
mirrors, especially small decorative pieces, £500-
£10,000.* LOC: Town centre. PARK: Easy and
opposite. TEL: 01737 242813; fax - 01737
362819. SER: Valuations; restorations (paintings
and furniture). VAT: Stan/Spec.

Bertram Noller (Reigate)

14a London Rd. RH2 9HY. (A.M.Noller). Est.
1970. Open Tues., Thurs., Sat. 9.30-1 and 2-5.30.

SIZE: Small. *STOCK: Collectors' items, furniture, grates, fenders, mantels, copper, brass, glass, pewter, £1-£500.* LOC: West side of one-way traffic system. Opposite Upper West St. car park. PARK: Opposite. TEL: 01737 242548. SER: Valuations; restorations (furniture, clocks, bronzes, brass and copper, marble).

Reigate Galleries
45a Bell St. RH2 7AQ. (J.S. Morrish). Est. 1958. Open 9-5.30, Wed. 9-1. SIZE: Large. *STOCK: Old prints, engravings, antiquarian books.* PARK: Opposite. TEL: 01737 246055. SER: Picture framing. VAT: Stan.

M. & M. White Antique & Reproduction Centre
57 High St. RH2 9AE. Est. 1993. Open 10-5.30. SIZE: Medium. *STOCK: Mahogany, £100-£2,500, pine, £60-£1,500, both 18th C; reproduction, 1920-1970, £40-£1,000.* PARK: Easy. TEL: 01737 222331; fax - 01737 215702. SER: Valuations; restorations. FAIRS: Newark; Ardingly; Kempton Park. VAT: Spec.

RICHMOND

Antique Mart
72-74 Hill Rise. TW10 6UB. (G. Katz). Open Thurs., Fri., Sat. and Sun. 2-6, otherwise by appointment. SIZE: Large. *STOCK: Furniture, 18th-19th C; French and English oils and watercolours, 19th-20th C.* TEL: 020 8940 6942; mobile - 07775 626423; e-mail - katz.george@ hotmail.com. SER: Buys at auction. VAT: Stan/Spec.

Mollie Evans
82 Hill Rise. TW10 6UB. Est. 1965. Open by appointment only. SIZE: Medium. *STOCK: Early country and painted furniture, interesting bygones, unusual bold decorative items, original works of art, bronzes and sculpture, £50-£5,000.* LOC: Town centre, take A307 towards Kingston (Petersham Rd.). Fork left up hill immediately after passing Richmond Bridge on right. PARK: Meters. TEL: 020 8948 0182; fax/answerphone - same. SER: Buys at auction. VAT: Spec.

The Gooday Gallery
14 Richmond Hill. TW10 6QX. (Debbie Gooday). Est. 1971. Open Thurs.-Sat. 11-5. SIZE: Medium. *STOCK: Decorative and applied design, 1880-1980, Arts & Crafts, Art Nouveau - especially Liberty pewter, Art Deco, furniture, pictures, ceramics, metalwork, jewellery; African and oceanic tribal artefacts; all £50-£5,000.* LOC: 100yds. from Richmond Bridge. PARK: Easy. TEL: 020 8940 8652; mobile - 07710 124540; e-mail - GoodayGallery.uk. SER: Buys at auction.

Roland Goslett Gallery
139 Kew Rd. TW9 2PN. Est. 1974. Open Thurs. and Fri. 10-6, Sat. 10-2 or by appointment. SIZE: Small. *STOCK: English watercolours and oil paintings, 19th to early 20th C, £100-£5,000.* PARK: Meters. TEL: 020 8940 4009. SER: Valuations; restorations (oils, watercolours and frames); framing. VAT: Spec.

Hill Rise Antiques
26 Hill Rise. TW10 6UA. (P. Hinde and D. Milewski). LAPADA. Est. 1978. Open 10.30-5.30, Sun. 2.30-5.30. CL: Wed. SIZE: Large. *STOCK: 18th-19th C walnut and mahogany furniture, £100-£10,000; silver and plate, mirrors, boxes and glassware.* LOC: 1 mile from A316 (M3). PARK: At rear by arrangement. TEL: 020 8332 2941; home - same; e-mail - antiques@ hillrisehouse.com. VAT: Stan/Spec.

Horton
2 Paved Court, The Green. TW9 1LZ. (D. Horton). LAPADA. FGA. *STOCK: Jewellery and silver, 18th-20th C, £500-£2,000.* TEL: 020 8332 1775; fax - 020 8332 1994; website - www. horton london.co.uk.

Lionel Jacobs
16 Brewers Lane. TW9 1HH. Open 9-5. *STOCK: Silver and jewellery.* TEL: 020 8940 8069.

Robin Kennedy
P.O Box 265. TW9 1UB. Open by appointment. *STOCK: Japanese prints, £50-£5,000.* TEL: 020 8940 5346; fax - same; e-mail - robin@ japaneseprints.co.uk.

F. and T. Lawson Antiques
13 Hill Rise. TW9 6UQ. Resident. Est. 1965. Open 10-5.30, Sat. 10-5. CL: Wed. and Sun. am. SIZE: Medium. *STOCK: Furniture, 1680-1870; paintings and watercolours; both £30-£1,500; clocks, 1650-1930, £50-£2,000; bric-a-brac, £5-£300.* LOC: Near Richmond Bridge at bottom of Hill Rise on the river side, overlooking river. PARK: Limited and further up Hill Rise. TEL: 020 8940 0461. SER: Valuations; buys at auction.

Marryat
88 Sheen Rd. TW9 1AJ. (Marryat (Richmond) Ltd.). LAPADA. Est. 1990. Open 10-5.30. SIZE: Large. *STOCK: English and Continental furniture, watercolours and oils, £150-£5,000; porcelain, pottery, glass, silver, objets and decorative antiques, £10-£1,000; all 18th-19th C.* LOC: Follow M3/A316 towards Richmond, first left into Church Rd. then left again. Close to underground station. PARK: Easy. TEL: 020 8332 0262. SER: Restorations. VAT: Stan/Spec.

Ripley Antiques

Heather Denham

LAPADA
MEMBER

Specialising in 18th and 19th Century Furniture and Decorative Items for Trade and Export

67 High Street, Ripley, Surrey GU23 6AN

Telephone Guildford (01483) 224981 Fax (01483) 224333

2 mins. from Junction 10 on the M25 and 30 mins. from London on the A3

Palmer Galleries
10 Paved Court. TW9 1LZ. (C.D. and V.J. Palmer). Est. 1984. Open 10-5. SIZE: Medium. *STOCK: Prints, watercolours and engravings, 19th-20th C, £50-£1,000.* PARK: Richmond Green. TEL: 020 8948 2668; website - www. palmergalleries.co.uk. VAT: Stan.

Piano Nobile Fine Paintings
26 Richmond Hill. TW10 6QX. (Dr. Robert A. Travers). SLAD. Est. 1986. Open Tues.-Sat. 10-5.30. SIZE: Medium. *STOCK: Fine 19th C Impressionist and 20th C Post-Impressionist and Modernist British and Continental oil paintings and sculpture, especially Les Petit Maitres of the Paris Schools, £500-£100,000.* PARK: Easy. TEL: 020 8940 2435; fax - same; e-mail - art@pianonobile.freeserve.co.uk; website - www.piano-nobile.com. SER: Valuations; restorations (paintings and sculpture); framing; buys at auction (19th-20th C oil paintings). FAIRS: Grosvenor; 20th C British Art & London Contemporary; BADA; Olympia; Art London. VAT: Stan/Spec.

Succession
18 Richmond Hill. TW10 6QX. (Michael John and William Camp). Est. 1974. Open Fri. and Sat. 10-6, Sun. 1-6, other days by appointment. SIZE: Small. *STOCK: Art Nouveau, Art Deco, avant garde design paintings, sculpture, ceramics and glass, to £20,000.* PARK: Easy. TEL: 020 8940 6774; fax - 020 8940 9801. SER: Valuations; buys at auction (20th C works of art). FAIRS: Olympia; Chelsea. VAT: Spec

Town & Country Decorative
24 Hill Rise. TW10 6UA. Open 10.30-5.30, Sun. 2-5. CL: Wed. *STOCK: Decorative antiques.* TEL: 020 8948 4638.

Cedar House Gallery
High St. GU23 6AE. LAPADA. Resident. Est. 1987. *STOCK: Watercolours and oils, 19th to early 20th C, £500-£10,000.* LOC: 1/2 mile M25/A3 junction. PARK: Easy. TEL: 01483 211221. SER: Restorations.

J. Hartley Antiques Ltd
186 High St. GU23 6BB. LAPADA. Est. 1949. Open 8.45-5.45, Sat. 9.45-4.45. *STOCK: Queen Anne, Georgian and Edwardian furniture.* TEL: 01483 224318. VAT: Stan.

Ripley Antiques
67 High St. GU23 6AN. (H. Denham). LAPADA. Est. 1960. Open 9.30-5.30, Sun. by appointment.

Anthony Welling

Specialising in C17th and C18th Period Oak Furniture

Broadway Barn, High Street, Ripley, Surrey, GU23 6AL

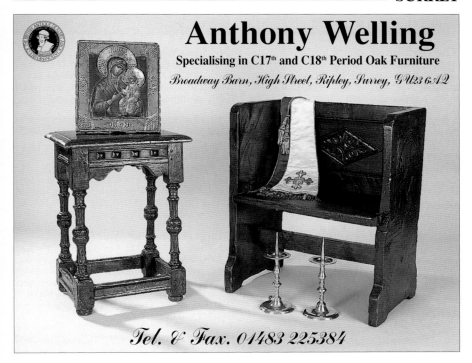

Tel. & Fax. 01483 225384

SIZE: Large. *STOCK: Furniture, English and French, 18th-19th C; decorative items - mirrors and chandeliers.* LOC: 2 mins. from junction 10 at M25/A3 interchange. Between Heathrow and Gatwick Airports. PARK: Easy. TEL: 01483 224981; fax - 01483 224333. SER: Valuations; restorations. VAT: Stan/Spec.

Sage Antiques and Interiors

High St. GU23 6BB. (H. and C. Sage). LAPADA. GMC. Est. 1971. Open 9.30-5.30. SIZE: Large. *STOCK: Furniture, mahogany, oak, walnut, 1600-1900, £150-£8,000; oil paintings, £100-£5,000; watercolours, £50-£1,000, china, £2-£500, all 18th-19th C; silver, Sheffield plate, brass, pewter, decorative items, 18th-19th C, £50-£1,000.* LOC: Village centre, on main road. PARK: Easy. TEL: 01483 224396; fax - 01483 211996. SER: Restorations (furniture, pictures); interior furnishing. VAT: Stan.

Sweerts de Landas   BADA

Dunsborough Park, Newark Lane. GU23 6AL. (A.J.H. and A.C. Sweerts de Landas). Est. 1979. Open by appointment only. SIZE: Large. *STOCK: Garden ornaments and statuary, 17th-20th C, £250-£150,000.* LOC: From High St. turn into Newark Lane (between estate agent and Suzuki garage), continue 400 yds, go through archway on right, follow drive to gate. PARK: Easy. TEL: 01483 225366; home - same. SER: Valuations; restorations (stone, lead, cast iron, marble); buys at auction (as stock). FAIRS: Olympia; Maastricht; Grosvenor House. VAT: Stan/Spec.

Talbot Walk Antique Centre

The Talbot Hotel, High St. GU23 6BB. (P. Skellett). Est. 1999. Open 10-5, Sun. 11-4. SIZE: Large. *STOCK: English furniture, 1750-1920, £100-£5,000+; glass and ceramics, 1800-1940, £10-£3,000+; lighting, 1850-1940, £50-£2,000+; general antiques, 1850-1920, £10-£1,000+.* LOC: B2215 to Ripley, 400yds on left after entering village. PARK: Own at rear of premises. TEL: 01483 211724; fax - 01483 213009. VAT: Stan/Spec.

Anthony Welling Antiques   BADA

Broadway Barn, High St. GU23 6AQ. Est. 1970. Open 9.30-1 and 2-5. Sun. and evenings by appointment. SIZE: Large. *STOCK: English oak, 17th-18th C, £250-£8,000; country furniture, 18th C, £200-£6,000; brass, copper, pewter, 18th C, £100-£750. Not Stocked: Glass, china, silver.* LOC: Turn off A3 at Ripley, shop in village centre on service road. PARK: Easy. TEL: 01483 225384; fax - same. VAT: Spec.

RUNFOLD, Nr. Farnham

The Packhouse
Hewetts Kilns, Tongham Rd. GU10 1PQ. (Mr and Mrs P. Hewett). Est. 1991. Open 10.30-5.30 including Sun. SIZE: Large. *STOCK: Furniture including period, 1930's and country pine; garden statuary, architectural items.* LOC: Off A31 (Hogs Back). PARK: Easy. TEL: 01252 781010; fax - 01252 783876.

SANDERSTEAD

Raymond Slack FRSA & Shirley Warren
STOCK: Reference books on glass collecting. TEL: 020 8657 1751. FAIRS: London and Birmingham Glass Fairs. *Mail Order.*

SHEPPERTON

Rickett & Co. Antiques
The Summer House, 40 Mulberry Trees. TW17 8JN. (A.L. Spencer). Est. 1968. Open by appointment. *STOCK: Brass and copper, 18th-19th C, £100-£300; fenders and fire tools, oil lamps, inkwells, chandeliers, grandfather clocks.* LOC: 10 mins. from London airport. TEL: 01932 243571; home - 01932 222508; e-mail - rickett@freenetname; website - www.rickett-antiques.co.uk. SER: Restorations (metal repairs and polishing).

SHERE, Nr. Guildford

Helena's Collectables
Shops 1 and 2, Middle St. GU5 9HF. (Mrs. K. White and Ms. H. White). Est. 1995. Open 9.30-4.30, Sat. 9.30-5, Sun. 10.30-4.30. SIZE: Medium. *STOCK: Royal Doulton, from 1930's, £100-£2,500; Beswick, from 1950's, from £50+; miscellaneous, from 50p.* LOC: A24. PARK: Behind sports ground. TEL: 01483 203039; fax - same; e-mail - helen@collectables.demon.co.uk. SER: Valuations; restorations; search; buys at auction. FAIRS: DMG. VAT: Stan.

Shere Antiques Centre
Middle St. GU5 9HL. (Jean Watson). Est. 1986. Open 10-5, Sun. 11-5. SIZE: Large. *STOCK: Mid-Georgian, Victorian and Edwardian clocks, silver, copper, brass, English and Continental porcelain, maps and prints.* LOC: A25 - between Dorking and Guildford. PARK: Easy. TEL: 01483 202846; fax - 01483 830761; e-mail - jean.watson@glenturret.co.uk; website - www.glenturret.co.uk.shereantiques. VAT: Stan/Spec.

SHIRLEY

Norman Witham
217 Wickham Rd. CR0 8TG. Est. 1959. Open Mon.-Sat. *STOCK: Porcelain, glass, small furniture, mainly Victorian, £5-£500.* TEL: 020 8655 4445; evenings - 020 8650 4651. SER: Valuations.

STAINES

K.W. Dunster Antiques
23 Church St. TW18 4EN. Open 9-4.30. CL: Thurs. SIZE: Medium. *STOCK: Clocks, furniture, general antiques, interior decor, jewellery, nautical items.* TEL: 01784 453297; fax - 01784 483146. VAT: Stan/Spec.

Margaret Melville Watercolours
11 Colnebridge, Market Sq. TW18 4RZ. LAPADA. TVADA. Est. 1980. Open by appointment only. *STOCK: Watercolours, 1850-1950, £200-£7,000.* TEL: 01784 455395; fax - same. SER: Valuations; commissions. FAIRS: LAPADA; NEC (Jan.); Chester (Feb.); Penman Fairs; TVADA (May, Oct.). VAT: Spec.

SURBITON

Cockrell Antiques
278 Ewell Rd. KT6 7AG. (Sheila and Peter Cockrell). Resident. Est. 1982. Open most Fri., Sat., Sun. and evenings - prior telephone call advisable. SIZE: Medium. *STOCK: Furniture including Art Deco, from 18th C, £50-£3,000+; decorative items, £50-£500.* LOC: Off A3 at Tolworth Tower on A240. PARK: Easy. TEL: 020 8390 8290; home - same; e-mail - antiques@cockrell.co.uk; website - www.cockrell. co.uk. FAIRS: DMG and Kempton Park. VAT: Stan/Spec.

Maple Antiques
4 Maple Rd. KT6 4AB. (Geoff and Lynda Morris). Resident. Est. 1965. Open every day except Tues. am and Thurs. am. SIZE: Small. *STOCK: Pine, oak, mahogany, lights and mirrors, garden statuary and urns, cast iron benches, 19th-20th C, £25-£1,000.* PARK: Easy. TEL: 020 8399 6718. SER: Valuations. FAIRS: Ardingly.

B. M. and E. Newlove
139-141 Ewell Rd. KT6 6AL. Est. 1958. Open 9.30-5.30, Sat. by appointment. CL: Wed. SIZE: Medium and store. *STOCK: Furniture especially early oak and Georgian mahogany, 17th-19th C, £500-£10,000; china, 18th-19th C, £75-£200; paintings, all periods, £50-£2,000; longcase clocks, Georgian barometers.* Not Stocked: Pot-lids,

SURREY

fairings. LOC: Down Kingston by-pass at Tolworth underpass, turn right into Tolworth Broadway, then into Ewell Rd. Shop one mile on. PARK: Easy. TEL: 020 8399 8857. VAT: Stan/Spec.

Laurence Tauber Antiques
131 Ewell Rd. KT6 6AL. Open 10-5. CL: Wed. pm. *STOCK: General antiques, especially for Trade.* PARK: Easy. TEL: 020 8390 0020. VAT: Stan/Spec.

SUTTON

S. Warrender and Co
4 and 6 Cheam Rd. SM1 1SR. (F.R. Warrender). Est. 1953. Open 9-5.30. CL: Wed. SIZE: Medium. *STOCK: Jewellery, 1790 to date, £10-£1,500; silver, 1762 to date, £10-£1,000; carriage clocks, 1860-1900, £115-£800.* TEL: 020 8643 4381. SER: Valuations; restorations (jewellery, silver, quality clocks). VAT: Stan.

THAMES DITTON

Clifford and Roger Dade
Boldre House, Weston Green. KT7 0JP. LAPADA. Resident. Est. 1937. Open 9.30-6. SIZE: Large. *STOCK: Mahogany furniture, 18th to early 19th C, £500-£5,000.* LOC: A309 between Esher and Hampton Court, near Sandown Park Racecourse. PARK: Outside shop. TEL: 020 8398 6293; fax - same; mobile - 07702 014222. VAT: Spec.

WALTON-ON-THAMES

Antique Church Furnishings
Rivernook Farm, Sunnyside. KT12 2ET. (L. Skilling and S. Williams). Est. 1989. Open Mon.-Fri. 10-6. SIZE: Large. *STOCK: Church chairs and pews, £10-£750; altar tables and screens, pulpits, lecterns, reredos, pine and architectural items, £20-£2,000; all late 19th C to early 20th C.* LOC: Between A3050 and River Thames. PARK: Easy. TEL: 01932 252736; fax - same. SER: Valuations; buys at auction (church fixtures and furnishings, stained glass). FAIRS: Newark. VAT: Stan/Spec.

Susan Becker
P O Box 160. KT12 3HJ. (S. Becker Fleming). LAPADA. Est. 1959. Open by appointment only. *STOCK: English (especially Royal Worcester), and Continental porcelain, 18th-20th C, £200-£25,000; glass and fine objects.* LOC: 10 minutes A3, M25, M4. PARK: Easy. TEL: 01932 227820. SER: Valuations. VAT: Spec.

Boathouse Gallery
The Towpath, Manor Rd. KT12 2PG. (B.E. Clark). CL: Mon. *STOCK: Oil paintings, watercolours, engravings.* TEL: 01932 242718. SER: Picture framing, mounting and restorations. VAT: Stan.

WALTON-ON-THE-HILL & TADWORTH

Ian Caldwell
9a Tadworth Green, Dorking Rd. KT20 5SQ. LAPADA. Est. 1978. Open 10-5. CL: Wed. SIZE: Medium. *STOCK: Oak, walnut and mahogany furniture especially Georgian.* LOC: 2 miles from M25, 1/4 mile from A217 on B2032 in Dorking direction. PARK: Easy. TEL: 01737 813969; e-mail - caldwell.antiques@virgin.net. SER: Valuations; restorations. VAT: Stan/Spec.

WARLINGHAM

Trengove
397 Limpsfield Rd, The Green. CR6 9LA. Est. 1890. SIZE: Small. *STOCK: General antiques, pictures.* TEL: 01883 624422.

WEST BYFLEET

Academy Billiard Company
5 Camphill Industrial Estate. KT14 6EW. (R.W. Donnachie). Est. 1975. Open anytime by appointment. SIZE: Large warehouse and showroom. *STOCK: Period and antique billiard/snooker tables, all sizes, 1830-1920; combined billiard/dining tables, period accessories including other games-room equipment and lighting.* LOC: On A245, 2 miles from M25/A3 junction. PARK: Easy. TEL: 01932 352067; mobile - 07860 523757; fax - 01932 353904. SER: Valuations; restorations; removals; structural advice. VAT: Stan/Spec.

WEYBRIDGE

Ariel
89 Queens Rd. KT13 9UQ. (Mrs. P. Harvey and Mrs. G. Rees). Est. 1993. Open 10-5. SIZE: Small. *STOCK: Furniture, Georgian-Edwardian, £50-£1,500; clocks, jewellery and silver, 19th C, £100-£500.* PARK: Easy. TEL: 01932 850135. SER: Valuations; restorations; clock repairs.

Brocante
120 Oatlands Drive, Oatlands Village. KT13 9HL. (Barry Dean and Ray Gwilliams). Est. 1988. Open 10-5.30, Sun. 10-5. CL: Mon. and Wed. SIZE: Small. *STOCK: Furniture, 19th C,*

£300-£1,500; porcelain, 19th C, £10-£250; Sheffield plate, 18th-19th C, £10-£300. PARK: Easy. TEL: 01932 857807; home - 01932 345524. SER: Valuations. FAIRS: Oatlands Park Hotel; Seven Hills Hilton, Cobham.

Church House Antiques
42 Church St. KT13 8DP. (M.I. Foster). LAPADA. Est. 1886. Open Thurs., Fri., Sat. 10-5.30. SIZE: Medium. *STOCK: Furniture, 18th-19th C, £95-£7,000; jewellery, 18th-19th C, some modern, £30-£5,000; pictures, silver, plate, decorative items.* Not Stocked: Coins and stamps. PARK: Behind library. TEL: 01932 842190. VAT: Stan/Spec.

The Clock Shop Weybridge
64 Church St. KT13 8DL. Est. 1970. Open 10-6. CL: Wed. SIZE: Medium. *STOCK: Clocks, 1685-*

A large early George III oval brass-bound mahogany wine cooler on its original neo-classical stand, c.1770. When not in use for cooling wine, these were sometimes used to hold plants.

From an article entitled 'The 18th Century British Interior Part II' by Christopher Claxton Stevens which appeared in the October 2000 issue of **Antique Collecting** magazine. For more details and to subscribe see page 147.

1900, from £500; French carriage clocks, from £300. LOC: Opposite HSBC bank on corner. PARK: Easy. TEL: 01932 840407/855503. SER: Valuations; restorations (clocks). VAT: Stan/Spec.

Edward Cross - Fine Paintings
128 Oatlands Drive. KT13 9HL. Est. 1973. Open Fri. 10-3, Sat. 10-12.30. SIZE: Medium. *STOCK: Fine paintings and bronzes, 19th-20th C, £500-£30,000.* LOC: A3050. PARK: Opposite. TEL: 01932 851093. SER: Valuations; restorations (watercolours and oil paintings); buys at auction (pictures). VAT: Spec.

Not Just Silver
16 York Rd. KT13 9DT. (Mrs S. Hughes). Est. 1969. Open 9.30-5.30, Sun. by appointment. *STOCK: Silver, Georgian to modern.* LOC: Opposite car park, just off Queens Rd. TEL: 01932 842468; fax - 01932 830054; mobile - 07774 298151. SER: Valuations.

Village Antiques
39 St Mary's Rd., Oatlands Village. KT13 9PT. (B. Mulvany). Est. 1976. Open 10-4.30. CL: Wed. SIZE: Small. *STOCK: Furniture, small silver and china, 19th-20th C, £50-£100.* LOC: Off Oatlands Drive. PARK: Easy. TEL: 01932 846554. SER: Valuations; restorations (French polishing, small furniture repairs). FAIRS: Ardingly.

Weybridge Antiques
43 Church St., The Quadrant. KT13 8XD. (P. Pocock). Est. 1974. Open 10-5.30. SIZE: Large. *STOCK: Furniture, 18th-19th C; paintings, objects.* LOC: From M25 into town, Church St. is first right. PARK: Opposite in Mayfield Road. TEL: 01932 852503. SER: Restorations (oil paintings, porcelain, furniture, leathering). VAT: Spec.

Willow Gallery   BADA
75 Queens Rd. KT13 9UQ. (Andrew and Jean Stevens and Alick Forrester). LAPADA. Est. 1987. Open 10-6, Sun. by appointment. SIZE: Large. *STOCK: British and European oil paintings, 19th C, £3,000-£200,000.* LOC: Near town centre. PARK: Easy and nearby. TEL: 01932 846095/6. SER: Valuations; restorations; conservation; framing; catalogue available. FAIRS: BADA; LAPADA; NEC; Olympia. VAT: Spec.

WOKING

Keith Baker
42 Arnold Rd. GU21 5JU. (K.R. Baker). *STOCK: General antiques.* TEL: 01483 767425.

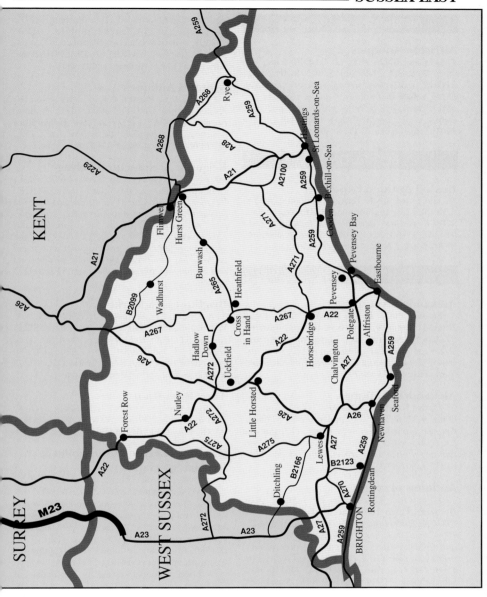

Dealers and Shops in East Sussex

Alfriston	1	Ditchling	1	Horsebridge	1	Pevensey Bay	1
Bexhill-on-Sea	1	Eastbourne	15	Hurst Green	3	Polegate	2
Brighton	46	Flimwell	1	Lewes	14	Rottingdean	1
Burwash	1	Forest Row	1	Little Horsted	1	Rye	5
Chalvington	1	Hadlow Down	1	Newhaven	1	Seaford	4
Cooden	1	Hastings	6	Nutley	1	St. Leonards-on-Sea	7
Cross in Hand	1	Heathfield	1	Pevensey	1	Uckfield	1
						Wadhurst	1

ALFRISTON, Nr. Polegate

Alfriston Antiques
The Square. BN26 5UD. (J. Tourell). Est. 1967. Open Wed.-Sat. 11-5, Sun. 2.30-5. SIZE: Small. *STOCK: Collectors' items, vinaigrettes, snuff boxes, caddy spoons, silver, plate, carriage and other clocks, jewellery, paintings, pot-lids, copper, brass, books.* PARK: Easy. TEL: 01323 870498; fax - same. VAT: Stan/Spec.

BEXHILL-ON-SEA

Bexhill Antique Exporters
56 Turkey Rd. BN40 2HA. (K. Abbott). Open 8-5.30, Sun. by appointment. SIZE: Warehouse. *STOCK: Antique and shipping furniture.* TEL: 01424 225103; fax - 01424 731430; mobile - 07702 006982. SER: Container packing.

BRIGHTON

Alexandria Antiques
3 Hanover Place, Lewes Rd. BN2 2SD. (A.H. Ahmed). Open 9.30-6, Sat. by appointment. *STOCK: Georgian and Victorian furniture; Oriental and European porcelain; oil and watercolour paintings; Oriental carpets, objets d'art.* TEL: 01273 688793; fax - same.

Alexandria Antiques
33 Upper North St. BN1 3FG. (A.H. Ahmed). Open 9.30-6, Sat. by appointment. *STOCK: Georgian and Victorian furniture, Oriental and European porcelain; oil and watercolour paintings; Oriental carpets, objets d'art.* TEL: 01273 328072.

Antiques et cetera
190 Portland Rd., Hove. BN3 5QN. (Ken Bomzer). Open 10-4, Sat. 10-1. SIZE: Small. *STOCK: Porcelain, £5-£1,000; glassware, £5-£500; small furniture, £50-£2,000; costume, silver and gold jewellery, £5-£1,000; watercolours, prints and oils, £10-£500; silver and plate, £10-£500; 19th C to date.* TEL: 01273 746159; fax - same; mobile - 07747 666343. SER: Valuations; restorations (porcelain, jewellery).

Art Deco Etc.
73 Upper Gloucester Rd. BN1 3LQ. (John Clark). Est. 1979. Open 12-5.30, Sun. and other times by appointment. SIZE: Medium. *STOCK: Pottery, especially Poole; Scandinavian ceramics and glass; glass, lighting, mirrors, pictures and collectors' items, Art Deco, Art Nouveau, Arts and Crafts, 1950's, £5-£2,000.* LOC: From Brighton station down Queens Rd., first on right. PARK: Easy. TEL: 01273 329268; mobile - 07971 268302; e-mail - johnclark@artdeco etc.co.uk. SER: Valuations. FAIRS: Art Deco, Battersea; Alexandra Palace; Ardingly and Newark.

Ashton's Antiques
1-3 Clyde Rd., Preston Circus. BN1 4NN. (R. Ashton). Open 10-4. CL: Wed. SIZE: 4 showrooms. *STOCK: Victorian and Edwardian furniture, upholstery and decorative items.* TEL: 01273 605253; fax - same. VAT: Stan/Spec.

Brighton Architectural Salvage
33-34 Gloucester Rd. BN1 4AQ. (R.L. Legendre). Open Tues.-Sat. 10-5. *STOCK: Restored architectural items including pine furniture; fireplaces and surrounds - marble, pine, mahogany, cast-iron, Victorian tiled and cast inserts and over-mantels; doors, stained glass, panelling; cast-iron balcony and street railings, gas coal fires, light fittings; garden seats and ornaments, reclaimed flooring.* TEL: 01273 681656.

Brighton Flea Market
31A Upper St. James's St. BN2 1JN. (A. Wilkinson). Est. 1990. Open seven days. SIZE: Large. *STOCK: Bric-a-brac, furniture and collectables, 19th-20th C, £5-£1,000.* LOC: 50 yards from coast road, Kemp Town. TEL: 01273 624006; e-mail - arwilkinsn@aol.com.

Tony Broadfoot
39 Upper Gardner St. BN1 4AN. SIZE: *STOCK: Furniture, from 17th C.* LOC: Off North Rd. PARK: Easy. TEL: 01273 695457.

C.A.R.S. (Classic Automobilia & Regalia Specialists)
4-4a Chapel Terrace Mews, Kemp Town. BN2 1HU. (G.G. Weiner). *STOCK: Collectors' car badges, mascots and associated automobilia and related motoring memorabilia; children's pedal cars, electric cars, collectors' veteran and vintage pedal cars, 1930's-1970's.* TEL: 01273 601960; fax - same; e-mail - cars@kemptown-brighton.freeserve.co.uk; website - www.carsofbrighton.co.uk; website for The Pedal Car Collectors' Club - www.eurosurf.co.uk and www.brmmbrmm.com/pedalcars. SER: Catalogue/price list on receipt of SAE.

Connoisseur Antique Gallery
113 Church Rd., Hove. BN3 2AF. *STOCK: General antiques.* TEL: 01273 777398.

Harry Diamond and Son
9 Union St., The Lanes. BN1 1HA. (R. and H. Diamond). Est. 1937. Open 9-5. *STOCK: Diamond*

jewellery, antique silver, £50-£20,000. Not Stocked: Coins, furniture. TEL: 01273 329696. VAT: Stan.

James Doyle Antiques
10 Union St., The Lanes. BN1 1HA. (J.R. Doyle). Est. 1975. Open 9.30-6. *STOCK: Jewellery, silver.* TEL: 01273 323694; fax - 01273 324330.

Faques Gallery
32 Upper St James's St., BN2 1JN. Est. 1962. Open 10-5.30. SIZE: Large. *STOCK: Repro-duction oil paintings.* LOC: Kemp Town area. PARK: Side roads. TEL: 01273 624432; fax - 01273 683692. VAT: Stan.

Alan Fitchett Antiques
5-5A Upper Gardner St. BN1 4AN. Est. 1969. Open 9-5.30. CL: Sat. SIZE: Large. *STOCK: Furniture, 18th-20th C, £50-£10,000; works of art.* LOC: North Laines (Station area). PARK: Easy. TEL: 01273 600894; fax - same. SER: Valuations; restorations. VAT: Stan.

Paul Goble
44 Meeting House Lane, The Lanes. BN1 1HB. Est. 1965. Open 9-5.30, Sat. 9-6, Sun. 10-6. *STOCK: Jewellery, watches, silver, pictures and prints, teddy bears and dolls.* TEL: 01273 202801; fax - 01273 202736. SER: Trade/export valuation. VAT: Stan/Spec.

Douglas Hall Ltd
23 Meeting House Lane. BN1 1HB. (K.J. Longthorne). Est. 1968. Open 9.30-5. *STOCK: Silver, jewellery.* TEL: 01273 325323. VAT: Stan.

Hallmark Jewellers
4 Union St., The Lanes. BN1 1HA. (J. Hersheson). Est. 1966. Open 9-5. SIZE: Small. *STOCK: Diamond and gem set jewellery; antique and modern silver.* TEL: 01273 725477; fax - same. VAT: Stan/Spec.

Mark and David Hawkins The Lanes Armoury
26 Meeting House Lane, The Lanes. BN1 1HB. Open 10-5.15. *STOCK: Militaria, arms, armour and books, from 500BC to WWII.* TEL: 01273 321357; website - www.thelanesarmoury.co.uk.

Heritage Antiques   BADA
P O Box 2974. BN1 3QG. (Anjula Daniel). LAPADA. CINOA. Est. 1975. Open by appointment. SIZE: Large. *STOCK: Metal-ware, £50-£5,000; interesting and decorative items.* TEL: 01273 326850; fax - same; e-mail - anjie@heritage-antiques-uk.com. VAT: Stan/Spec.

The House of Antiques
39 Upper North St. BN1 3FH. (A. Margiotta). LAPADA. Open 10-5.30. *STOCK: Jewellery and silver, general antiques.* TEL: 01273 327680; fax - 01273 324961. VAT: Stan.

Dudley Hume
46 Upper North St. BN1 3FH. Est. 1973. CL: Sat. pm. and Sun., except by appointment. SIZE: Medium. *STOCK: Period and Victorian furniture, metal, light fittings, decorative items.* LOC: Parallel to the Western Rd., one block to the north. TEL: 01273 323461; fax - same. VAT: Stan/Spec.

Jezebel
14 Prince Albert St. BN1 1HE. (Amanda Davis). Est. 1989. Open 11-5.30, Sun. by appointment. SIZE: Medium. *STOCK: Art Deco ceramics, furniture, lighting, chrome, collectables including Bakelite jewellery, £20-£2,000.* LOC: Just off Ship Street, near the Lanes. PARK: Easy. TEL: 01273 206091; fax - same; home - 01273 675616. SER: Valuations; restorations; buys at auction (Art Deco/Nouveau). FAIRS: Newark.

Leoframes
70 North Rd. BN1 1YD. (S. Round). Open 9-5.30. *STOCK: Prints and maps.* TEL: 01273 695862. SER: Restorations; framing.

Harry Mason
P O Box 687, Hove. BN3 6JY. Est. 1954. Open by appointment. *STOCK: Silver and plate, 18th-20th C; jewellery, 19th-20th C.* TEL: 01273 500330; fax - 01273 553300; e-mail - mason@ fastnet.co.uk. SER: Valuations; restorations (silver and jewellery); buys at auction (as stock); buyers of scrap silver and gold. FAIRS: Sunday London Hotel. VAT: Stan/Spec.

Patrick Moorhead Antiques
Spring Gardens, 76 Church St. BN1 1RL. Open 9.30-5.30 or by appointment. SIZE: Large trade warehouse - showrooms at 15b Prince Albert St. *STOCK: Victorian, Georgian and Continental furniture; Oriental, Continental and English porcelain, clocks, pictures, decorative objects and bronzes.* TEL: 01273 779696; fax - 01273 220196; showrooms - 01273 774227; fax - same.

Michael Norman Antiques Ltd   BADA
Palmeira House, 82 Western Rd., Hove. BN3 1JB. Est. 1965. Open 9-1 and 2-5.30, other times by appointment. *STOCK: English furniture.* TEL: 01273 329253 or 01273 326712; fax - 01273 206556; e-mail - antiques@ michael norman.com; website - www.michael norman. com. VAT: Stan/Spec.

Starting to Collect Series

The *Starting to Collect Series* is intended to fill a need for inexpensive practical books which will answer the needs of the beginner who is interested in exploring possible new collecting areas. They give the historical and geographical background to their subjects together with a wealth of factual information on individual representative pieces. They offer guidance on where and how to buy as well as advice on how not to be taken in by fakes and copies. A key feature of all the books in the series are the suggestions for further reading for those who wish to study particular aspects of collecting in more depth. The series is extensively illustrated in colour. The books are compact yet comprehensive.

Praise for *Starting to Collect Antique Silver*:
"…this well illustrated guide…is a mine of information for anyone wanting to know about silver and is designed to help collectors get the most out of their hobby" **Irish Independent**

Praise for *Starting to Collect Antique Furniture*:
"…this book is small enough to be toted around the auction room and galleries. Like all Antique Collectors' Club offerings, it is chock full of splendid photographs and illustrations, with a huge amount of information expressed in an invitingly readable manner on its well laid out pages" **Furniture & Cabinetmaking**

Praise for *Starting to Collect Antique Porcelain*:
"Altogether this is a very special kind of reference book; its readable and knowledgeable yet compact presentation will be appreciated by commited collectors and enthusiasts whilst giving the novice the confidence to follow in thier footsteps" **Antique Dealers and Collectors Guide**

Praise for *Starting to Collect Antique Glass*:
"Illustrated with all the finesse of a specialist book three times its price, this excellent publication tells you where to hunt for bargains and how to add varieties to a growing collection" **Birmingham Post**

Forthcoming 2002 titles in the *Starting to Collect Series*:
STC Oriental Rugs ISBN 1 85149 406 5
STC Antique Jewellery ISBN 1 85149 407 3
STC Antique Clocks ISBN 1 85149 408 1
STC Blue & White Pottery ISBN 1 85149 409 X

Starting to Collect Antique Silver
This book provides in compact but readable form the essential background knowledge of silver and the technique of silversmithing which are necessary for an intelligent understanding of the subject. Suggestions for further reading for those who wish to pursue specific areas of interest are included. Over fifty types of silver object are discussed and there is useful information on marks. Many of the photographs have not been published in book form before.
ISBN 1 85149 244 5, 192pp., colour throughout. 8 x 5½in./203 x 140mm.
£12.50/$25.00

Starting to Collect Antique Furniture
A concise yet wide-ranging survey of collectable antique furniture, illustrated throughout in full colour, guides the new collector through almost three centuries of Western Furniture with clarity and authority. Existing collectors will find all titles in the series act as a handy and portable reference, and beginners will welcome a reliable, accessible starting point from which their interests can develop.
ISBN 1 85149 241 0, 192pp., colour throughout. 8 x 5½in./203 x 140mm. **£12.50/$25.00**

Starting to Collect Antique Porcelain is a compact but fact filled book including porcelain from both the West and the Far East and covers comprehensively all price ranges and sources of purchase with advice on fakes and caring for a collection. Answering the basic questions of what, where and how to buy, this is an ideal reference work for the collector or an enthralling introduction for the beginner.
ISBN 1 85149 242 9, 192pp. colour throughout. 8 x 5½in./203 x 140mm. **£12.50/$25.00**

Starting to Collect Antique Glass
In this book John Sandon tells the whole story of glass from its discovery in Ancient Egypt to the advanced designs and forward looking techniques of the 20th century. He looks beyond just the valuable rarities. Carefully chosen illustrations focus on available and affordable specimens, offering practical advice to novice collectors keen to get started in the exciting world of glass collecting. John Sandon is also the author of *The Dictionary of Worcester Porcelain Vol. I.*
ISBN 1 85149 286 0, 192pp., colour throughout. 8 x 5½in./203 x 140mm. **£12.50/$25.00**

For a free copy of our catalogue, please contact
ANTIQUE COLLECTORS' CLUB
5 Church Street, Woodbridge, Suffolk, IP12 1DS, UK
Tel: (01394) 385501 Fax: (01394) 384434
Sales Office Direct Fax: (01394) 388994
Email: sales@antique-acc.com Website: www.antique-acc.com

or

Market Street Industrial Park, Wappingers' Falls, NY 12590, USA
Tel: (845) 297 0003 Fax: (845) 297 0068 ORDERS: (800) 252 5231
Email: info@antiquecc.com Website: www.antiquecc.com

Oasis Antiques
39 Kensington Gdns. BN1 4AL. (I. and A. Stevenson). Est. 1970. Open 10-5, Mon. 11-5, Sat. 8-5. SIZE: Medium. *STOCK: Lighting and furniture, to 1970, £1-£5,000; European and Oriental items including bronzes, art glass, period clothes, linen and lace, gramophones, radios, telephones, collectable modern design, Art Nouveau, Art Deco.* LOC: Off North Road from railway station, centre of North Laines. PARK: Nearby. TEL: 01273 683885. SER: Restorations (radios, telephones, furniture, metals); polishing.

Odin Antiques
43 Preston St. BN1 2HP. (Audun Sjovold). Resident. Est. 1981. Open 10.30-5.30. SIZE: Medium. *STOCK: Furniture, 18th-19th C; telescopes, scientific instruments, 19th-20th C, £500-£1,500; maritime instruments, 19th-20th C, £500-£1,000.* LOC: Off Kings Rd. (seafront) near West Pier.PARK: Regency Sq. TEL: 01273 732738; home - same. VAT: Stan/Spec.

The Old Furniture Store
5 Boundary Rd., Hove. BN3 4EH. *STOCK: 1930's and older furniture.* TEL: 01273 705004; fax - 01273 705005; e-mail - peter.furn@ FSBDial.co.uk.

Colin Page Antiquarian Books
36 Duke St. BN1 1AG. (John Loska). Est. 1971. Open 9.30-5.30. *STOCK: Antiquarian and secondhand books, especially topography, travel, natural history, illustrated and leather bindings, 16th-20th C, £1-£5,000.* LOC: Town centre. PARK: Multi-storey nearby. TEL: 01273 325954; fax - 01273 746246; e-mail - cpage@pavilion. co.uk.

Brian Page Antiques
18 Regent Arcade, East St. BN1 1HR. Open 10-5.30. *STOCK: Oriental antiques, 3000 BC to 20th C.* LOC: Adjacent to Town Hall. TEL: 01273 723956; fax - 01273 719228; e-mail - brianpage @pavilion.co.uk; website - www.trocadero. com/paha.

Dermot and Jill Palmer Antiques
7-8 Union St., The Lanes. BN1 1HA. Resident. Est. 1968. Open 9-6, Sun. by appointment. *STOCK: French and English furniture, objects, pictures, mirrors, screens, garden furniture and ornamental pieces, textiles, £50-£5,000.* TEL: 01273 328669 (2 lines); fax - 01273 777641. FAIRS: Olympia; Decorative Antique & Textile. VAT: Stan/Spec.

Sue Pearson
13 1/2 Prince Albert St. BN1 1HE. Open 10-5. SIZE: Small. *STOCK: Antique dolls, teddy bears,* *dolls' house miniatures.* LOC: Lanes area. PARK: NCP. TEL: 01273 329247. SER: Valuations; restorations; buys at auction (dolls and bears). FAIRS: Major London Doll and Bear. VAT: Stan/Spec.

Ben Ponting Antiques
53 Upper North St. BN1 3FH. Open 9.30-5.30. CL: Sat. *STOCK: Furniture, 18th-19th C.* TEL: 01273 329409.

Recollections
1a Sydney St. BN1 4EN. (B. Bagley). Est. 1973. Open Tues., Thurs., Fri. and Sat. 10.30-4.30. SIZE: Small. *STOCK: Antique and reproduction firebaskets, firebacks, fenders, scuttles, firetools in sets or loose, spark guards, architectural salvage items, décor pieces.* LOC: From railway station down Trafalgar St., last turning on right. PARK: Opposite in Belmont St. TEL: 01273 681517. SER: Metal polishing; repairs.

Savery Antiques
257 Ditchling Rd., (Fiveways). BN1 6JH. (A. and M. Savery). Resident. Est. 1968. Open Mon. 10.30-5, Thurs.-Sat. 9.30-5. *STOCK: China, glass, metalware and collectables.* LOC: Near HSBC Bank. TEL: 01273 564899. FAIRS: Ardingly; Sandown Park.

Shirley Ann's Antiques International Interiors
69 New Church Rd., Hove. BN3 2BB. (Shirley Ann Downes). Est. 1985. Open 10-5.30. SIZE: Medium. *STOCK: General antiques, Victorian, Georgian, French reproduction, especially mirrors.* PARK: Easy. TEL: 01273 770045. SER: Valuations; restorations (polishing, upholstery, silver and brass repair). VAT: Stan.

S.L. Simmons
9 Meeting House Lane, The Lanes. BN1 1HB. NAG. Est. 1948. Open 9.30-5.30. *STOCK: Jewellery and silver, 19th C.* TEL: 01273 327949. VAT: Stan.

Sleeping Beauty Antique Beds
212 Church Rd., Hove. BN3 2DT. (Mr and Mrs Roberts). Est. 1975. Open 10-5 including Sun. SIZE: Medium. *STOCK: Brass, iron and French wooden beds, 19th C, £500-£1,000.* LOC: Continuation of Western Rd. PARK: Nearby. TEL: 01273 205115; home - same; e-mail - info@antiquebeds.com; website - www. antiquebeds.com. SER: Valuations; restorations; buys at auction (beds).

Wardrobe
51 Upper North St. BN1 3FH. (Clive Parks and Philip Parfitt). Est. 1984. Open 10-5, Mon. and

Tues. by appointment. SIZE: Small. *STOCK: Vintage clothing, '20's to '30's, £300-£700; Art Deco plastics/Bakelite, 20's-40's, £20-£100; Art Deco furniture, £400-£800.* PARK: On street - vouchers. TEL: 01273 202201; fax - same. FAIRS: Alexandra Palace; Sandown Park; Royal Horticultural Hall, Vincent Square.

Graham Webb
59A Ship St. BN1 1AE. Est. 1961. Open 10-5, prior telephone call advisable. SIZE: Small. *STOCK: Cylinder and disc musical boxes, all mechanical musical instruments, £650-£45,000.* LOC: Close to the Lanes. PARK: Middle St. TEL: 01273 321803; fax - same; home - 01273 772154. VAT: Stan/Spec.

E. and B. White
43 & 47 Upper North St. BN1 3FH. Est. 1962. Open 9.30-5. CL: Sat. pm. SIZE: Medium. *STOCK: Oak and country furniture and decorative items, £50-£2,000.* LOC: Upper North St. runs parallel to and north of Western Rd. (main shopping street). TEL: 01273 328706; fax - 01273 207035. VAT: Spec.

Wilkinsons
11 Church St. BN1 1US. Est. 1985. Open Mon.-Sat. SIZE: Small. *STOCK: Furniture, lighting, decorative accessories and collectables, 18th-20th C, £10-£5,000.* LOC: 200 metres north of Brighton Pavilion. PARK: NCP adjacent. TEL: 01273 328665; fax - same; e-mail - arwilkinsn. @aol.com.

Wish
101 Gloucester Rd. BN1 4AP. (Greg Wish). Open 11-6, Sun. pm. SIZE: Small. *STOCK: Stripped light oak, Arts & Crafts to early 20th C.* LOC: North Lanes area. TEL: 01273 628444. SER: Valuations; restorations; hand oak stripping.

The Witch Ball
48 Meeting House Lane. BN1 1HB. (Mrs Gina Daniels). Est. 1967. Open 10.30-6. *STOCK: 18th-19th C topographical and decorative engravings; 16th-19th C maps.* TEL: 01273 326618. VAT: Stan/Spec.

Yellow Lantern Antiques Ltd
34 Holland Rd., Hove. BN3 1JL. (B.R. and E.A. Higgins). LAPADA. Est. 1950. Open 10-1 and 2.15-5.30, Sat. 10-4. SIZE: Medium. *STOCK: Mainly English furniture, £50-£3,000; French and English clocks; both to 1850; bronzes, 19th C, £100-£1,500; Continental porcelain, 1820-1860, £50-£1,000.* Not Stocked: Pottery, oak, 18th C porcelain. LOC: From Brighton seafront to Hove, turn right after parade of Regency houses, shop 100yds. on left past traffic lights, opposite Michael

Norman Antiques. PARK: Easy. TEL: 01273 771572; mobile - 07860 342976; home - 01273 455476. SER: Valuations; restorations; buys at auction. FAIRS: Buxton; Harrogate; NEC; Olympia; Guildford; Kensington; Chester. VAT: Spec.

Chateaubriand Antiques Centre
High St. TN19 7ES. Open 10-5.30, Sun. 12-5.30. SIZE: 8 dealers. *STOCK: Linen, furniture, country oak, glass, paintings, smalls.* LOC: A265. PARK: Nearby. TEL: 01435 882535; e-mail - chateauframe@hotmail.com. SER: Shipping; picture framing.

Sussex Antiques
Open by appointment only. SIZE: Medium. *STOCK: Victorian lamps, china, glass, furniture, clocks, silver and plate.* PARK: Easy. TEL: 01825 872222.

Annies
4 Bixlea Parade, Little Common Rd. TN39 4SD. (P.A. Rose). Est. 1990. Open 10-5, Wed. and Sun. by appointment. SIZE: Small. *STOCK: China, glass, porcelain and linen, 1800-1930, £5-£500; furniture, from 1880, £50-£750; silver plate, kitchenalia, copper, brass and clocks, from 1800, £5-£150.* LOC: A259 between Bexhill and Eastbourne by Little Common roundabout. PARK: Easy. TEL: 01424 846966. SER: Valuations; buys at auction. FAIRS: De La Warr, Bexhill. VAT: Stan/Spec.

Colonial Times
Lewes Rd. TN21 0TA. (A.P. Skinner). Open 10-5. SIZE: Medium + barns. *STOCK: Colonial furniture, Victorian and Edwardian, £50-£2,500; china, including Staffordshire, £20-£300; clocks, Edwardian, £40-£125.* LOC: A267 from Tunbridge Wells to Eastbourne, opposite Esso garage. PARK: Easy. TEL: 01435 866442; fax and home - 01435 862962. FAIRS: Newark. VAT: Stan.

DITCHLING

Dycheling Antiques
34 High St. BN6 8TA. (E.A. Hudson). Est. 1977. Open 10.30-5.30. CL: Mon. and Wed. SIZE: Large - shop and showroom. *STOCK: Georgian, Victorian and Edwardian furniture, especially dining and armchairs, £25-£5,000.* LOC: Off A23 on A273-B2112 north of Brighton. PARK: Easy. TEL: 01273 842929; home - same; fax - 01273 841929; mobile - 07885 456341; website - www.antiquesweb.co.uk. VAT: Spec.

EASTBOURNE

Bell Antiques
47 South St. BN21 4UT. (Mrs. M.J. Everett). Open 10-1 and 2-4.30. SIZE: Small. *STOCK: Porcelain and small bijou items, 18th-19th C, £10-£300; furniture, Victorian and Edwardian, £50-£400; paintings and prints, to 1930, £10-£150.* LOC: Road opposite Town Hall. PARK: Easy. TEL: 01323 641339. SER: Valuations.

W. Bruford
11/13 Cornfield Rd. BN21 3NA. Est. 1883. Open 9.30-5.15. SIZE: Medium. *STOCK: Jewellery, Victorian, late Georgian; some silver, clocks (bracket, carriage).* Not Stocked: China, glass, brass, pewter, furniture. TEL: 01323 725452. SER: Valuations; restorations (clocks and silver). VAT: Stan/Spec.

Camilla's Bookshop
57 Grove Rd. BN21 4TX. (C. Francombe and S. Broad). Est. 1976. Open 10-5.30. *STOCK: Books including antiquarian and on art, antiques and collectables, and especially naval, military, aviation, technical, needlework, broadcasting.* LOC: Next to police station. TEL: 01323 736001; e-mail - camillas.books@virgin.net. SER: Valuations; book search; postal service; own book tokens.

John Cowderoy Antiques
The Clock and Musical Box Centre, 42 South St. BN21 4XB. (D.J. and R.A. Cowderoy). LAPADA. GMC. Est. 1973. Open 8.30-5. CL: Wed. pm. SIZE: Large. *STOCK: Clocks, musical boxes, furniture, porcelain, silver and plate, jewellery, copper, brass.* LOC: 150yds. from Town Hall. PARK: Easy. TEL: 01323 720058; website - www.cowderoyantiques.co.uk. SER: Restorations (clocks, barometers, music boxes and furniture). VAT: Stan/Margin.

Crest Collectables
54 Grove Rd. BN21 4UD. (C. Powell). Open 10-6. *STOCK: General antiques and collectables.* TEL: 01323 721185.

An early German 'flat' Botanical Garden, c.1820, £1,100. Sold 3rd December 1998.

From an article on toys by Hugo Marsh of Christie's South Kensington which appeared in the July/August 1999 issue of **Antique Collecting** magazine. For more details and to subscribe see page 147.

John Day of Eastbourne Fine Art
9 Meads St. BN20 7QY. Est. 1964. Open during exhibitions, 9.30-1 and 2-5, otherwise by appointment. SIZE: Medium. *STOCK: English, especially East Anglian, and Continental paintings and watercolours, 19th C.* LOC: Meads village, west end of Eastbourne. PARK: Easy. TEL: 01323 725634; mobile - 07860 466197. SER: Restorations; framing (oils and watercolours).

Roderick Dew
10 Furness Rd. BN21 4EZ. Est. 1971. *STOCK: Antiquarian books, especially on art and antiques.* TEL: 01323 720239. *Postal Only.*

Eastbourne Antiques Market
80 Seaside. BN22 7QP. Est. 1969. Open 10-5.30, Sat. 10-5. SIZE: Large - 30+ stalls. *STOCK: A wide selection of general antiques and collectables.* PARK: Easy. TEL: 01323 642233.

Elliott and Scholz Antiques
12 Willingdon Rd. BN21 1TH. (C.R. Elliott and K.V. Scholz). Est. 1981. Open 9.30-4.30, Wed. and Sat. 9.30-1. SIZE: Small. *STOCK: Small furniture, £100-£500; clocks, £20-£300; bric-a-brac, £10-£100; all 19th-20th C.* LOC: A22. PARK: Easy. TEL: 01323 732200. SER: Valuations.

Enterprise Collectors Market
The Enterprise Centre, Station Parade. BN21 1BE. Est. 1989. Open 9.30-5. SIZE: Medium. *STOCK: Wide range of general antiques and collectables.* LOC: Next to railway station. PARK: Easy. TEL: 01323 732690. SER: Valuations.

A. & T. Gibbard
30 South St. BN21 4XB. Open 9.30-5.30. SIZE: Large. *STOCK: Secondhand and antiquarian books, 16th-20th C, £1-£1,000.* LOC: 200yds. east of Town Hall. TEL: 01323 734128. SER: Valuations. VAT: Stan.

The Old Town Antiques Centre
52 Ocklynge Rd. BN21 1PR. (V. Franklin). Est. 1990. Open 10-5. SIZE: Medium. *STOCK: General antiques.* LOC: East Dean coast road. PARK: Easy. TEL: 01323 416016. FAIRS: Ardingly.

Timothy Partridge Antiques
46 Ocklynge Rd. BN21 1PP. Open 10-1. *STOCK: Victorian, Edwardian and 1920's furniture.* LOC: In old town, near St. Mary's Church. PARK: Easy. TEL: 01323 638731.

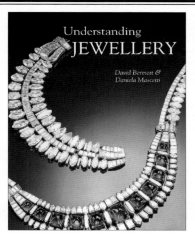

Pharoahs Antiques Centre
28 South St. BN21 4UJ. (W. and J. Pharoah). Est. 1973. Open 10-5. SIZE: Medium. 14 stallholders. *STOCK: A wide range of antiques including jewellery, pine, kitchenalia, china, curios, lace, linen, Victorian furniture, original light fittings and lamps.* LOC: Near Town Hall. PARK: Easy. TEL: 01323 738655. FAIRS: Ardingly.

Stewart Gallery
25 Grove Rd. BN21 4TT. (Gallery Laraine Ltd.). Est. 1970. Open 9-5.30. SIZE: Large. *STOCK: Paintings and ceramics, 19th-20th C, £5-£25,000.* LOC: Next to library, 150yds. from station. PARK: Easy. TEL: 01323 729588; fax - 01323 412900. SER: Valuations; restorations (paintings and frames). VAT: Stan/Spec.

FLIMWELL

Graham Lower
Stonecrouch Farmhouse. TN5 7QB. Open by appointment. *STOCK: English and Continental 17th-18th C oak furniture.* LOC: A21. TEL: 01580 879535. SER: Valuations. VAT: Spec.

FOREST ROW

J. Markies Ltd - Antiques
16 Hartfield Rd. RH18 5DN. (Trudy and Jeroen Markies). Est. 1980. Open 9.30-5.30. *STOCK: Fine 18th-19th C furniture, £500-£8,000; silver, European and Oriental ceramics, £20-£2,000.* LOC: 3 miles south of East Grinstead on A22, left at roundabout down Hartfield Rd. PARK: Behind shop. TEL: 01342 824980; fax - 01342 823677; e-mail - sales@markies.co.uk; website - www. markies.co.uk.

HADLOW DOWN, Nr. Uckfield

Hadlow Down Antiques
Hastingford Farm, School Lane. TN22 4DY. (Adrian Butler). Est. 1989. Open 10-5 including Sun., Wed. by appointment. SIZE: Large. *STOCK: General antiques, country and formal furniture, 17th-20th C, £25-£2,500; decorative accessories, £5-£500.* LOC: 2 mins. down School Lane from A272 in village. PARK: Easy. TEL: 01825 830707; home - same; e-mail - hdantiques @talk21.com. SER: Valuations; restorations (furniture).

HASTINGS

Coach House Antiques
42 George St. TN34 3EA. (R.J. Luck). Est. 1972. Open 10-5 including Sun. SIZE: Medium. *STOCK: Longcase clocks, 18th-19th C, £1,000+; furniture, 19th C, £100+; collectables including Dinky toys, trains, dolls houses.* PARK: Nearby. TEL: 01424 461849. SER: Valuations; restorations (clocks and furniture); buys at auction (clocks and furniture). VAT: Spec.

George Street Antiques Centre
47 George St. TN34 3EA. (F. Stanley and H. Stallybrass). Est. 1969. Open 10-5, Sun. 11-4. SIZE: Medium - 10 dealers. *STOCK: Small items, 19th-20th C, £5-£500.* LOC: In old town, parallel to seafront. PARK: Seafront. TEL: 01424 429339; home - 01424 813526/428105.

Howes Bookshop
Trinity Hall, Braybrooke Terrace. TN34 1HQ. ABA. Est. 1920. Open 9.30-5. *STOCK: Antiquarian and academic books in literature, history, arts, bibliography.* TEL: 01424 423437; fax - 01424 460620; e-mail - rarebooks@howes. co.uk. FAIRS: ABA.

Nakota Curios
12 Courthouse St. TN35 3AU. (D.H. Brant). Est. 1964. Open 10.30-1 and 2-5. SIZE: Medium. *STOCK: General trade items, decorative china, Victoriana, jewellery, pictures, lighting.* Not Stocked: Coins, medals. PARK: Easy. TEL: 01424 438900.

J. Radcliffe
5 Claremont. TN34 1HA. Open 10-1 and 2-5. CL: Wed. pm. *STOCK: General antiques, trade goods.* TEL: 01424 426361.

Spice
Samphire House, 75 High St., Old Town. TN34 3EL. (S. Dix). Open by appointment. *STOCK: Early furniture and decorative items.* TEL: Mobile - 07710 209556.

HEATHFIELD

John Botting Antiques & Others
Forty One Antiques, High St. Open 9.30-5 or by appointment. *STOCK: Victorian and Edwardian furniture and effects; French furniture.* TEL: 01435 863656/813553.

HORSEBRIDGE, Nr. Hailsham

Horsebridge Antiques Centre
1 North St. BN27 4DJ. (R. Lane). Resident. Est. 1978. Open 10-1 and 1.30-5. SIZE: Large. *STOCK: General antiques including furniture, silver, glass, pottery, brass and copper.* LOC: A271. PARK: Easy. TEL: 01323 844414; fax - 01323 844000. SER: Valuations.

HURST GREEN

Delmar Antiques
77 London Rd. TN19 7PN. (Harry and Sara Nicol). Est. 1973. Open 10-6, Sun. by appointment. CL: Mon. STOCK: Fine furniture, paintings and antiquarian books. TEL: 01580 860345.

Lawson Antiques Limited
Silver Hill Farm, Silver Hill. TN19 7PU. (M.P. Baldwin). Est. 1735. Open 10-5 including Sun. SIZE: Large. STOCK: Furniture, pictures, collectables, £5-£5,000. LOC: North end of High St. PARK: Public at rear. TEL: 01580 860177.

Libra Antiques
81 London Rd. TN19 7PN. (Janice Hebert). Resident. Est. 1976. Open 9.30-6, Sun. and Mon. by appointment. SIZE: Medium. STOCK: Lighting, 19th to early 20th C, £100-£500; pine furniture, £50-£500; decorative items, £10-£200; both 18th-19th C. LOC: A21. PARK: Easy. TEL: 01580 860569; home - same.

LEWES

John Bird and Annette Puttnam Antiques
Norton House, Iford. BN7 3EJ. Est. 1970. Open anytime by appointment. STOCK: Furniture - country, pine, oak, fruitwood, mahogany, painted, architectural, garden and upholstered. TEL: 01273 483366; mobiles - 07973 421070/07970 683949.

Bow Windows Book Shop
175 High St. BN7 1YE. (A. and J. Shelley). Open 9.30-5. SIZE: Large. STOCK: Books including natural history, English literature, travel, topography. LOC: Off A27. TEL: 01273 480780; fax - 01273 486686. FAIRS: Antiquarian Book.

Castle Antiques
163a High St. BN7 1XU. (C. J. Harris). Est. 1984. Open 10-5, Sun. 11-5. SIZE: Medium. STOCK: Pine furniture, late 19th C, £80-£300; kitchenalia, late 19th C, £5-£25; bric-a-brac, late 19th to early 20th C, £5-£25. LOC: Top part of High St., down a twitten, opposite Lloyds Bank. TEL: 01273 475176.

Church-Hill Antiques Centre
6 Station St. BN7 2DA. (S. Miller and S. Ramm). Est. 1970. Open 9.30-5. SIZE: 60 stalls and cabinets. STOCK: Wide range of general antiques including furniture, china, silver, jewellery, clocks, lighting, paintings and decorative items. LOC: From railway station, in town centre. PARK: Easy, own. TEL: 01273 474842; fax - 01273 846797. VAT: Stan.

Cliffe Antiques Centre
47 Cliffe High St. BN7 2AN. Est. 1984. Open 9.30-5. SIZE: Medium - 16 dealers. STOCK: General antiques, £5-£1,000. LOC: Follow town centre signs, turning left 200 yds. past Safeways. PARK: Easy. TEL: 01273 473266.

Cliffe Gallery Antiques
39 Cliffe High St. BN7 2AN. (Grimes & Hayward). Open 9.30-5. STOCK: 18th-20th C furniture and objects, including pine, mahogany, oak, china and lighting. TEL: 01273 471877.

A. & Y. Cumming
84 High St. BN7 1XN. Est. 1976. Open 10-5, Sat. 10-5.30. STOCK: Antiquarian and out of print books. TEL: 01273 472319. SER: Buys at auction.

The Emporium Antique Centre
42 Cliffe High St. BN7 2AN. (Doyle and Madigan). Open 9.30-5, Sun. (Easter-Christmas) 11-4. SIZE: 48 dealers. STOCK: Furniture, pictures, clocks, collectables, books, jewellery, Art Nouveau and Deco, decorative arts, vintage and collector's toys, Royal Winton. TEL: 01273 486866.

Fifteenth Century Bookshop
99 High St. BN7 1XH. (S. Mirabaud). Est. 1938. Open 10-5.30. STOCK: Antiquarian and general secondhand books, especially children's and illustrated; prints and teddies. TEL: 01273 474160.

Bob Hoare - Pine Antiques
Unit Q, Phoenix Place, North St. BN7 2DQ. Open 8-6, Sat. 9-2. STOCK: Pine. TEL: 01273 480557; fax - 01273 471298; website - www.antiques-index.com.

Lewes Antique Centre
20 Cliffe High St. BN7 2AH. (Jamie Pettit). Est. 1968. Open 9.30-5. SIZE: Large - 75 stallholders. STOCK: Furniture, china, copper and metalware, glass, clocks, architectural salvage. LOC: A27 from Brighton, 2nd roundabout into Lewes, end of tunnel turn left, then next left, next right into Phoenix car park. 100m. walk to Cliffe High Street. PARK: Easy. TEL: 01273 476148/472173. SER: Shipping; stripping; restorations; valuations.

Lewes Flea Market
14a Market St. BN7 2NB. Est. 1995. Open daily including Sun. SIZE: Large. STOCK: Bric-a-brac, furniture, collectables, 18th-20th C, £5-£1,000. LOC: 50 metres north of monument. TEL: 01273 480328.

Pastorale Antiques
15 Malling St. BN7 2RA. (O. Soucek). Open 9.30-6 or by appointment. SIZE: Large. STOCK: Pine and European country furniture, Georgian

and Victorian mahogany and decorative items and garden items. TEL: 01273 473259; home - 01435 863044; fax - 01273 473259.

Southdown Antiques
48 Cliffe High St. BN7 2AN. (Miss P.I. and Mr. K.A. Foster). Est. 1969. Open by appointment. SIZE: Medium. *STOCK: Small antiques, especially 18th-19th C English, Continental and Oriental porcelain, objets d'art, works of art, glass, papier mâché trays, silver plate, £50-£350,000; reproduction and interior decor items.* LOC: A27. One-way street north. PARK: Easy. TEL: 01273 472439. VAT: Stan/Spec.

LITTLE HORSTED, Nr. Uckfield

Pianos Galore
Worth Farm. TN22 5TT. Est. 1922. Open 9-5, Sun. 10-12. SIZE: Large. *STOCK: Over 150 pianos, upright and grands especially Steinway and Bechstein grands, £250-£20,000; piano stools.* LOC: From A22 Uckfield by-pass take A26 at Little Horsted roundabout. After 1 mile, opposite Wicklands Residential Home, turn right (opposite piano sign), down lane. PARK: Easy. TEL: 01825 750567; fax - 01825 750566. SER: Valuations; restorations (piano repolishing and reconditioning); buys at auction (pianos). VAT: Margin/Stan.

NEWHAVEN

Newhaven Flea Market
28 South Way. BN9 9LA. (R. Mayne). Est. 1971. Open every day 10-5.30 except 25th Dec. *STOCK: Victoriana, Edwardian, bric-a-brac.* TEL: 01273 517207/516065.

NUTLEY

Nutley Antiques
Libra House, High St. TN22 3NF. (Liza Hall and Anne-Marie Dickinson). Open 10-5, Sun. and Bank Holidays 1.30-5. SIZE: Small. *STOCK: Country and cottage furniture, £10-£1,000; decorative items, £1-£400; prints, oils, watercolours, £5-£500; all 19th C to 1930.* LOC: A22 between East Grinstead and Uckfield. PARK: Easy. TEL: 01825 713220. VAT: Stan.

PEVENSEY

The Old Mint House
High St. BN24 5LF. (J.C. and A.J. Nicholson). Est. 1901. Open 9-5.30, Sat. 10.30-4.30, otherwise by appointment. SIZE: Large + export warehouse. *STOCK: Furniture - Georgian,*

Victorian, Edwardian; porcelain, clocks, barometers and decorative items, 18th C-1920's, £50-£10,000. LOC: A27, 1 mile from Eastbourne. PARK: Easy. TEL: 01323 762337; fax - same; e-mail - antiques@minthouse.co.uk; website - www.minthouse.co.uk. SER: London trains met at local station (Polegate). VAT: Stan/Spec.

PEVENSEY BAY

Murray Brown
The Studio, Norman Rd. BN24 6JE. (G. Murray-Brown). Open by appointment only. *STOCK: Paintings and prints.* TEL: 01323 764298. SER: Valuations; restorations; cleaning; conservation.

POLEGATE

Graham Price Antiques Ltd
Applestore, Chaucer Industrial Estate. BN26 6JF. Open 9-5. SIZE: Large. *STOCK: Mainly furniture - country, decorative, French, Irish, painted, some formal and shipping.* LOC: Between Hastings and Brighton on A27. TEL: 01323 487167; fax - 01323 483904. SER: Export, packing, shipping and courier; restorations.

E. Stacy-Marks Limited   BADA
The Flint Rooms, P O Box 808. BN26 5ST. Est. 1889. SIZE: Large. *STOCK: Paintings, English, Dutch and Continental schools, 18th-20th C.* TEL: 01323 482156; fax - 01323 482513. VAT: Stan.

ROTTINGDEAN

Trade Wind
15A Little Crescent. BN2 7GF. (R. Morley Smith). Est. 1974. Open by appointment only. *STOCK: Caddy and sifter spoons, wine labels and other interesting items, including coloured glass, Bristol blue, green and amethyst.* TEL: 01273 301177.

RYE

Bragge and Sons
Landgate House. TN31 7LH. (N.H. and J.R. Bragge). Est. 1840. Open 9-5. CL: Tues. *STOCK: 18th C furniture and works of art.* LOC: Entrance to town - Landgate. TEL: 01797 223358. SER: Valuations; restorations. VAT: Spec.

East Street Antiques
Apothecary House, 1 East St. TN31 7JY. (Mr and Mrs Bloomfield). Est. 1988. Open 10.30-5 including Sun. SIZE: Medium. *STOCK: Furniture, 18th-19th C, £500-£1,000.* LOC: Just off High St. PARK: Easy. TEL: 01797 229266; home - same. SER: Buys at auction. FAIRS: Newark and Ardingly.

Herbert Gordon Gasson
The Lion Galleries, Lion St. TN31 7LB. (T.J. Booth). Est. 1909. Open 10-5.30. CL: Tues. pm. SIZE: Large. *STOCK: 17th-19th C oak, walnut and mahogany furniture; decorative items.* Not Stocked: Silver and glass. PARK: Easy. TEL: 01797 222208; fax - same; e-mail - hggassonantiques@hotmail.com. SER: Restorations. VAT: Stan/Spec.

(Left to right) A pottery elephant's head, £280. An enamelled pottery bottle, £500. A strawberry and a raspberry novelty scent bottle, £320.

From an Auction Report by Christopher Wight on 'A Private Collection of Scent Bottles' held at Bonhams, Chelsea on 7th November 2000. This sale was featured in the December 2000/January 2001 issue of **Antique Collecting** magazine. For more details and to subscribe see page 147.

ANN LINGARD

Rope Walk Antiques, Rye, Sussex
Telephone: Rye (01797) 223486
Fax: (01797) 224700

Large selection of hand finished Antique
English Pine furniture. Complementary
Accessories and Garden tools etc.
Separate Kitchen Shop.

SHIPPERS WELCOME

Ann Lingard - Rope Walk Antiques

18-22 Rope Walk. TN31 7NA. LAPADA. Est.
1972. SIZE: Large. *STOCK: English antique pine
furniture, accessories; kitchen shop; garden
tools and accessories, some architectural items.*
Not Stocked: Jewellery, silver and plate. PARK:
Own, and public next door. TEL: 01797 223486;
fax - 01797 224700. VAT: Stan.

Rye Antiques

93 High St. TN31 7JN. (Mrs D. Turner). Est.
1966. Open 9.30-5.30. CL: Sun. except by
appointment. SIZE: Small. *STOCK: Small oak,
walnut and mahogany furniture, 17th-19th C,
£50-£1,000; metalware, jewellery, silver and
plate, 18th-19th C, £5-£1,000.* Not Stocked:
Coins, bric-a-brac. PARK: Easy. TEL: 01797
222259.

Wish Barn Antiques

Wish St. TN31 7DA. (Joe Dearden and Robert
Wheeler). Est. 1993. Open 10-5 including Sun.
SIZE: Medium. *STOCK: 19th C furniture
including oak, mahogany and pine, £50-£1,500;
silver plate.* LOC: Just off A259. PARK: Easy.
TEL: 01797 226797; home 01580 881485.

SEAFORD

Colonial Times II

25/27 High St. Open 9.30-5.30. SIZE: Large.
*STOCK: Colonial furniture and Chinese antique
furniture, £50-£2,500; clocks, £40-£125.* PARK:
Easy. TEL: 01323 492200.

The Courtyard Antiques Market

15 High St. BN25 1PD. (Mrs V.E. Finch). Open
9-5, Wed. 9-1. SIZE: Medium - 13 dealers.
STOCK: General antiques and collectables. TEL:
01323 892091.

The Old House

15/17 High St. BN25 1PD. (S.M. Barrett). Est.
1928. Open 9-5, Wed. 9-1. SIZE: Large. *STOCK:*

18th-20th C furniture, china and glass, £5-£5,000.
LOC: Near railway station. PARK: Opposite in
Pelham Yard. TEL: 01323 892091/893795. SER:
Valuations; restorations (furniture); shippers.
VAT: Stan/Spec.

Seaford's "Barn Collectors' Market" and Studio Bookshop

The Barn, Church Lane. BN25 1HL. Est. 1967.
Open 9.30-5. SIZE: Several dealers. *STOCK:
Collectables, ephemera, books, post and cigarette
cards.* LOC: Off High St. TEL: 01323 890010.

ST. LEONARDS-ON-SEA

Aarquebus Antiques

37 & 46 Norman Rd. TN38 0EJ. (Mr and Mrs G.
Jukes). Resident. Est. 1957. Open 9.30-5, Sat.
9.30-1. CL: Wed. SIZE: Medium. *STOCK:
Furniture, 18th C, £500-£1,000; shipping goods,
Victorian to 1930, £5-£500; glass, gold and
silver, 18th-19th C, £5-£1,000.* LOC: Take
A2100 to St. Leonards-on-Sea, turn right after
main P.O. PARK: Easy. TEL: 01424 433267.
SER: Valuations.

The Book Jungle

24 North St. TN38 0EX. (M. Gowen). Est. 1988.
Open 10-5. CL: Wed. SIZE: Medium. *STOCK:
Secondhand books.* LOC: Just off seafront.
PARK: Nearby. TEL: 01424 421187.

Nicholas Cole Antiques

7 Grand Parade. TN38 0DA. Est. 1973. Open
seven days by appointment only. SIZE: Medium.
*STOCK: Mainly French decorative furniture and
accessories.* LOC: A259 junction with A21.
PARK: Easy. TEL: Home - 01424 461031;
mobile - 07931 508913. SER: Valuations;
restorations. VAT: Stan.

Gensing Antiques

70 Norman Rd. TN38 0EJ. (Peter Cawson). Open
normal shop hours and by appointment. *STOCK:*

General antiques especially early Chinese furniture and other Oriental items. TEL: 01424 424145/714981.

The Hastings Antique Centre

59-61 Norman Rd. TN38 0EG. (R.J. Amstad). Open 10-5.30, Sun. by appointment. TEL: 01424 428561. Below are listed some of the dealers at this centre.

R.J. Amstad
Furniture.

Fred Bourne
French decorative antiques.

Pascal Bourne
French furniture.

Jenny Brown
Decorative wares.

Bruno Antiques
French furniture.

Dee's Antiques
Decorative items.

P. Few
Decorative French items.

P. Grant
French furniture, decorative items and pine.

K. Gumbrell
Decorative items.

Bridget Howett
Decorative items.

Clare Kinloch
Dolls.

G. Mennis
Sporting, leather goods.

Mick Neale
Oak.

Robert Paul Antiques
Furniture and shipping goods.

Pat Robbins
Furniture.

Monarch Antiques

19 Grand Parade. TN38 0DD. (J.H. King). Est. 1983. Open Mon.-Fri. 8.30-5 or by appointment. SIZE: Large + warehouse (371 Bexhill Road). *STOCK: General furniture, especially 1930's oak furniture for the Japanese, Korean, American and European markets.* LOC: A259. PARK: Own. TEL: 01424 445841; fax - 01424 204142; home - 01424 214158/720821; mobiles - 07802 217842/213081 and 07809 027930; warehouse - 01424 204141; e-mail - monarch.antiques@ virgin.net.

John H. Yorke Antiques

Filsham Farmhouse, 111 Harley Shute Rd. TN38 8BY. Open 9-5.30. *STOCK: Furniture for trade, export and shipping.* TEL: 01424 433109. VAT: Stan.

Ringles Cross Antiques

Ringles Cross. TN22 1HF. (C. and J. Dunford). Resident. Est. 1965. Open 10-5 or by appointment. *STOCK: English furniture, 17th-18th C, and accessories; Oriental items.* LOC: 1 mile north of Uckfield. PARK: Own. TEL: 01825 762909.

Park View Antiques

High St., Durgates. TN5 6DE. (B. Ross). Est. 1985. Open 10-4. CL: Mon. SIZE: Medium. *STOCK: Pine, oak and country furniture, 17th-19th C, £100-£1,500; decorative items, 1930's, £25-£150; iron and metalware, 17th-19th C, £25-£250.* LOC: On B2099 Frant-Hurst Green road. PARK: Easy. TEL: 01892 783630; fax - 01892 740264; home - 01892 740264; website - www.parkviewantiques.co.uk. SER: Valuations; restorations (furniture).

Wriggled work narrow rimmed plate depicting a pelican in her piety, c.1690, 8⅝in. (£1,200, June 1998.)

From an article by Mark Stephen entitled 'British Pewter Plates, Dishes and Chargers: A Guide to Identification' which appeared in the September 2000 issue of **Antique Collecting** magazine. For more details and to subscribe see page 147.

Old House Antique Centre
Old House. RH14 9JJ. Open daily including Sun. SIZE: 30+ stallholders. *STOCK: General antiques and collectors' items.* PARK: Easy. TEL: 01403 782186/783594.

Bygones
The Square. BN16 4EQ. (R.A. and Mrs L.R. Whittaker). Est. 1965. Open Tues. and Thurs. 10-1 and 2.15-5, Sat. 10-12. SIZE: Medium. *STOCK: Furniture, £50-£2,500; china, £5-£750; silver, £10-£250; linen, £5-£75; all 1790-1940.* LOC: A280. PARK: Easy. TEL: 01903 786152; home - same. SER: Valuations; buys at auction (furniture).

Antiquities
5/7 Tarrant St. BN18 9DG. (Ian and Christina Fenwick). Est. 1990. Open 10-5 or by appointment. SIZE: Large + displayed warehouses. *STOCK: Decorative and unusual - including 19th C English and French furniture, some mahogany and fruitwood, painted items, Staffordshire, majolica, metalware, French mirrors, pond yachts, luggage.* LOC: Just off town square.

PARK: Nearby. TEL: 01903 884355; fax - same; e-mail - antiquities@montal-internet.co.uk. SER: Shipping. VAT: Stan/Spec.

Arundel Clocks
Lasseters Corner, High St. BN18 9AB. (F.M. Henderson). Open 9.30-1 and 2-5. *STOCK: Clocks - longcase, £1,500-£6,000; dial, £300-£4,000; mantel and bracket, £250-£5,000; carriage, £200-£2,000.* LOC: Corner of High St. and Mill Lane. PARK: Easy. TEL: 01903 884525; fax - same. SER: Valuations; restorations (dials, movements and cases). VAT: Spec.

Baynton-Williams
37A High St. BN18 9AG. (R.H. and S.C. Baynton-Williams). Est. 1946. Open 10-6. *STOCK: Maps, views, sporting, marine and decorative prints.* TEL: 01903 883588; fax - same; e-mail - gallery@baynton-williams. freeserve.co.uk; website - www.baynton-williams. com. SER: Valuations; cataloguing. VAT: Stan/Spec.

Faringdon Gallery
27 Tarrant St. BN18 9DG. (Mr and Mrs G.E. Lott). Est. 1970. Open Wed.-Sun. 10.30-5, Mon. and Tues. by appointment. SIZE: Small. *STOCK: Watercolours and etchings, late 19th C to contemporary, £100-£3,000.* LOC: From A27, first right down High St. hill. PARK: 100 yards at rear. TEL: 01903 882047; home - 01243 554572. SER: Valuations; restorations; buys at auction (watercolours and etchings).

Two lots of Minton majolica which confounded predictions despite some damage to both lots. The pair of cock and hen spill vases fetched £7,200 (estimate £2,000-£3,000), while the George Jones game pie dish took £3,800 (estimate £800-£1,200).

From an Auction Report by Tim Ford on the Autumn Fine Art Sale held at Bearne's, Exeter on 20th and 21st October, 1998. This sale featured in the December 1998/January 1999 issue of **Antique Collecting** magazine. For more details and to subscribe see page 147.

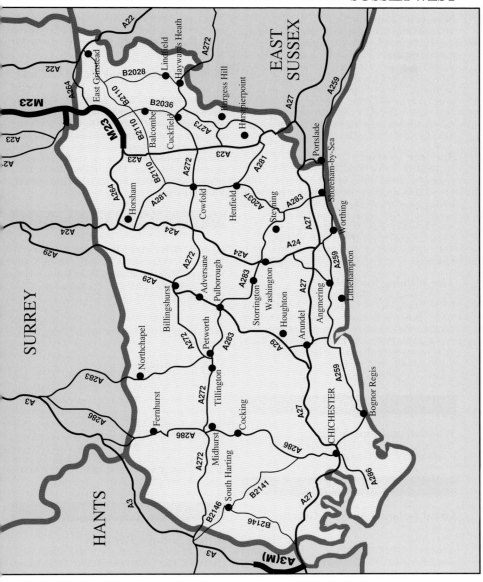

Dealers and Shops in West Sussex

Adversane	1	Cocking	1	Houghton	1	Pulborough	2
Angmering	1	Cowfold	1	Hurstpierpoint	2	Shoreham-by-Sea	1
Arundel	7	Cuckfield	2	Lindfield	3	South Harting	1
Balcombe	1	East Grinstead	1	Littlehampton	3	Steyning	2
Billingshurst	3	Fernhurst	1	Midhurst	2	Storrington	1
Bognor Regis	2	Haywards Heath	1	Northchapel	1	Tillington	1
Burgess Hill	2	Henfield	2	Petworth	27	Washington	1
Chichester	13	Horsham	1	Portslade	1	Worthing	5

Nineveh House
The Old Chapel Antiques and Collector's Centre, Tarrant St. BN18 9DG. (P. Jarrett). Open 10-5, Sun. 11-5. SIZE: Large - 12 dealers. *STOCK: Wide range of general antiques including Edwardian and Victorian, country and pine furniture, jewellery and silver, paintings and prints, china and glass, luggage and Oriental rugs.* LOC: Off A27 and A29 into town then second left off High St. PARK: Own forecourt. TEL: 01903 884307. SER:

Spencer Swaffer
30 High St. BN18 9AB. LAPADA. Est. 1974. Open 9-6, other times by appointment. SIZE: Large. *STOCK: Quirky decorative and traditional items, English, French, brown and painted furniture, dinner services, chandeliers, lighting, marble tables, iron low tables, bamboo, shop fittings, majolica, garden furniture.* PARK: Easy. TEL: 01903 882132; fax - 01903 884564. VAT: Stan/Spec.

The Walking Stick Shop
Stuart Thompson (Fine Canes), 39 Tarrant St. BN18 9DG. Est. 1981. Open 8.30-5.30, Wed. 8.30-1, Sun. pm. by appointment. SIZE: Medium. *STOCK: Walking sticks and canes, 1620 to date, £10-£2,000.* LOC: Off High St. PARK: Easy. TEL: 01903 883796; home - 01903 882713; fax - 01903 884491. SER: Valuations; buys at auction (canes). VAT: Stan.

BALCOMBE

Woodall and Emery Ltd
Haywards Heath Rd. RH17 6PG. Est. 1884. TEL: 01444 811608. VAT: Stan.

BILLINGSHURST

Great Grooms Antique Centre
Great Grooms, Parbrook. RH14 9EU. Est. 1983. Open Mon.-Sat. 9.30-5.30, Sun. 10-6. SIZE: 50 dealers. *STOCK: Wide variety of specialist dealers in 18th-19th C English and Continental town and country furniture, pottery and porcelain, silver (including Scottish) and plate, tortoiseshell, works of art, metalware, glass, clocks, Oriental, oils and watercolours, prints, books, clocks and watches.* LOC: Old A29 south of Billingshurst. PARK: Easy. TEL: 01403 786202; fax - 01403 786224. SER: Valuations; restorations (furniture, pictures, silver and jewellery). VAT: Spec.

Lannards Gallery
Okehurst Lane. RH14 9HR. (Mr and Mrs Derek Sims). Open by appointment; open every day during exhibitions. *STOCK: Watercolours, oils and furniture, from 1850.* TEL: 01403 782692. SER: Exhibitions held, please telephone for details.

Michael Wakelin and Helen Linfield
BADA
P.O Box 48. RH14 0YZ. LAPADA. Est. 1968. Open any time by appointment only. *STOCK: Fine English and Continental formal and country furniture - walnut, fruitwoods, faded mahogany and other exotic woods; early brass, bronze, iron and steel; wood carvings, treen, needlework, naïve pictures and lighting.* TEL: **01403 700004; fax - same; e-mail - wakelin_linfield@lineone.net.** VAT: Stan/Spec.

BOGNOR REGIS

Gough Bros. Art Shop and Gallery
71 High St. PO21 1RZ. (S. Neal). Est. 1916. CL: Wed. pm. SIZE: Medium. *STOCK: Watercolours, £50-£1,000; oils, £100-£1,500; miniatures, £150-£400; all 19th-20th C.* LOC: Off High St., behind Unicorn public house. PARK: Nearby. TEL: 01243 823773. SER: Valuations; restorations (oils and watercolours, frames and gilding). VAT: Stan/Spec.

V. & A. Antiques
65 Hawthorn Rd. PO21 2BW. (Mr. A. T. and Mrs. V. M. Kitching). Open by appointment. SIZE: Small. *STOCK: Edwardian furniture, £5-£10,000; pottery and porcelain including Susie Cooper, Clarice Cliff, Charlotte Rhead, £50-£1,000; Art Deco mirrors, china, jewellery, furniture, £2-£1,000.* LOC: Off A259 before junction with A29, at the end of a precinct of shops on left. PARK: Own. TEL: 01243 870847; home - 01243 870827. FAIRS: Ardingly.

BURGESS HILL

British Antique Replicas
School Close, Queen Elizabeth Ave. RH15 9RX. LAPADA. Est. 1962. Open 9-5.30. SIZE: Large. *STOCK: Furniture, £100-£20,000.* LOC: 3 miles west A23. PARK: Easy. TEL: 01444 245577. SER: Bespoke furniture. VAT: Stan.

Recollect Dolls Hospital
17 Junction Rd. RH15 0HR. (P. Jago). Est. 1970. Open 10-4. CL: Mon. and Sat. *STOCK: Dolls, dolls house miniatures, doll restoration materials.* TEL: 01444 871052; e-mail - dollshopuk@aol.com. SER: Restorations (dolls); catalogues available (£2.75 cash/stamps).

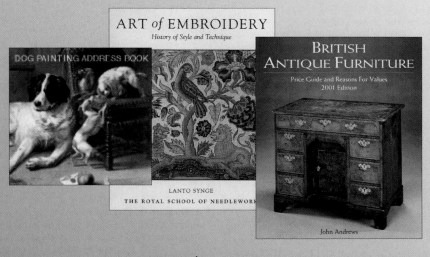

Almshouses Arcade

19 The Hornet. PO19 4JL. (Mrs V. Barnet). Est. 1983. Open 9.30-4.30. LOC: 200yds. from Cattle Market at eastern end of city. On one-way system (A286) just before traffic lights at Market Ave. PARK: Easy. Below are listed the dealers at these premises. TEL: 01243 528089.

Antics

(P. German). *General antiques and collectables.* TEL: 01243 786327.

Autodrome

Motoring, tin plate and ephemera. TEL: 01243 778126.

R .K. Barnett

Antiques and collectables, furniture. TEL: 01243 528089.

Collectors Corner

Small collectables and antiques. TEL: 01243 778126

Overlord

(D. Rowe). *Militaria, toys and general antiques, £5-£100.* TEL: 01243 774613.

Yesteryears

(J.A. Cook). *Lighting (oil), general antiques and collectables.* TEL: 01243 771994.

Antiques & Bygones

24 The Old Butter Market, North St. PO19 1LO. (Mrs. Maureen Haydon). Est. 1975. Open Tues.-Sat. 9.30-4. SIZE: Small. *STOCK: General collector's items, mainly porcelain and glass, Doulton, Beswick, small pieces of furniture.* LOC: City centre precinct opposite Woolworth's. TEL: 01243 788071. SER: Valuations.

Canon Gate Bookshop

28 South St. PO19 1EL. (Philip and Wendy Pegler). PBFA. Est. 1980. Open 10.30-5. SIZE: Small. *STOCK: Books, mainly 19th-20th C, £1-£1,000.* LOC: Town centre. PARK: Nearby. TEL: 01243 778477. SER: Valuations.

Chichester Antiques Centre

46-48 The Hornet. PO19 4JG. (Mike Carter). Est. 1994. Open 10-5, Sun. 11-5. SIZE: 50 stalls. *STOCK: General antiques and collectables, 50p to £10,000.* LOC: M27 onto A27 to town. PARK: Loading only and nearby. TEL: 01243 530100; website - www.antiqueschichester.com. SER: Clock restoration on premises.

Chichester Gallery

8 The Hornet. PO19 4JG. (Tom McHale). Est. 1988. Open Tues., Wed. and Fri. 10-4. SIZE: 5 rooms. *STOCK: Victorian oils, watercolours, etchings and engravings, £250-£2,500.* PARK: Nearby. TEL: 01243 779821. SER: Cleaning and restorations; commission sales.

The Delightful Muddle

82 Fishbourne Rd. West. PO19 3JL. Open Thurs.-Sat. 11-4, Sun. 1-4 (5.30 in summer). *STOCK: China, glass, objets d'art, Victorian and Edwardian, £1-£100; lace £1-£50; linen, general antiques and bric-a-brac, £3-£65.* LOC: 1 mile west of Chichester on A259, opposite Fishbourne P.O & Stores. PARK: Easy.

Frensham House Antiques

Hunston. PO20 6NX. (J. and M. Riley). Est. 1966. Open 9-6. *STOCK: English furniture, 1700-1830, £500-£6,000; clocks, paintings, copper.* LOC: One mile south of Chichester by-pass on B2145. PARK: Easy. TEL: 01243 782660.

Gems Antiques

39 West St. PO19 1RP. Open 10-1 and 2.30-5.30. CL: Mon. *STOCK: Period furniture, Staffordshire and porcelain figures, glass and pictures.* TEL: 01243 786173.

Peter Hancock Antiques

40-41 West St. PO19 1RP. Articles on coins. Est. 1950. Open 10.30-1 and 2.30-5.30. CL: Mon. SIZE: Medium. *STOCK: Silver, jewellery, porcelain, furniture, £20-£2,000; pictures, glass, clocks, books, £5-£500; all 18th-19th C; enthnographica, Art Nouveau, Art Deco, 19th-20th C, £5-£500.* LOC: From Chichester Cross, 17 doors past Cathedral. PARK: Easy. TEL: 01243 786173. SER: Valuations. VAT: Stan/Spec.

Heritage Antiques

84 St. Pancras. PO19 4NL. (D.R. Grover). Open 9.30-5.30. *STOCK: Furniture and decorative items.* TEL: 01243 783796.

Rathbone Law

59 North St. PO19 1NB. (Mr and Mrs R. Law). Open 9.30-5. CL: Some Mon. *STOCK: Victorian and Edwardian fine jewellery, silver, designer pieces in gold and silver, objets d'art, fine gems.* TEL: 01243 787881.

W.D. Priddy Antiques

Unit 6 Terminus Mill, Terminus Rd. PO19 2UN. Open 10-4, Sun. 11-4, or by appointment. SIZE: Large. *STOCK: Oak, mahogany, walnut and pine furniture, mid-19th C to pre-war and shipping, £20-£3,000.* LOC: Runs off A27 Chichester bypass. PARK: Easy. TEL: 01243 783960; fax - same; home - 023 9266 7436; website - www.priddyantiques.co.uk. FAIRS: Newark; Ardingly. VAT: Stan./Spec.

St. Pancras Antiques
150 St. Pancras. PO19 1SH. (R.F. and M. Willatt).
Est. 1980. Open 9.30-1 and 2-5. CL: Thurs. pm.
SIZE: Small. *STOCK: Arms and armour, militaria,
medals, documents, uniforms and maps, 1600-
1914, £5-£3,000; china, pottery and ceramics,
1800-1930, £2-£500; small furniture, 17th-19th C,
£20-£1,000; coins, ancient to date.* Not Stocked:
Silver and carpets. TEL: 01243 787645. SER:
Valuations; restorations (arms and armour); buys
at auction (militaria).

COCKING, Nr. Midhurst

The Victorian Brass Bedstead Company
Hoe Copse. GU29 0HL. (David Woolley).
Resident. Est. 1970. Open by appointment. SIZE:
Large. *STOCK: Victorian and Edwardian brass
and iron bedsteads, bases and mattresses, 19th-
20th C, £300-£3,500.* LOC: Right behind village
Post Office, 3/4 mile left turning to Hoe Copse.
PARK: Easy. TEL: 01730 812287. SER: Valu-
ations; restorations (brass and iron bedsteads).
VAT: Stan.

COWFOLD

Squire's Pantry Pine and Antiques
Station Rd. RH13 8DA. (B. Holmes). Open 10-1
and 2-5. *STOCK: Pine.* TEL: 01403 864869.
VAT: Stan/Spec.

CUCKFIELD

David Foord-Brown Antiques   BADA
**High St. RH17 5JU. LAPADA. Est. 1988.
Open 10-5.30. SIZE: Medium. *STOCK:
Furniture, 1750-1880, £500-£25,000; decorative
objects.* Not Stocked: Country furniture. LOC:
A272. PARK: Easy. TEL: 01444 414418.**

Richard Usher Antiques
23 South St. RH17 5LB. Est. 1978. Open 10-5.30
and at other times by appointment. CL: Wed. pm.
and Sat. pm. SIZE: Medium. *STOCK: Furniture,
17th-19th C, £50-£3,000; decorative items.* LOC:
A272. PARK: Easy. TEL: 01444 451699. SER:
Valuations; restorations.

EAST GRINSTEAD

The Antique Print Shop
11 Middle Row. RH19 3AX. (A.A.W.Daszewski
and Mrs A.C. Keddie). Est. 1988. Open 9.30-5.
CL: Mon. SIZE: Small. *STOCK: Prints, pre-
1880, £10-£200; maps, especially British county,
1500-1870, £20-£1,000; English watercolours
and drawings, 1700-1880, £100-£1,000.* LOC:
On island in middle High St., opposite St.
Swithins church. PARK: Lewes Rd. TEL: 01342
410501; fax - 01342 410795. SER: Restorations;
framing. FAIRS: Park Lane Hotel, London
(Sundays); NEC. VAT: Stan.

FERNHURST, Nr. Haslemere

Sheelagh Hamilton
9b Midhurst Rd. GU27 3EE. Open 9-5, Sat. 9-1,
Sun. by appointment. *STOCK: Period furniture,
pictures.* LOC: A286 village centre. TEL: 01428
653253.

HAYWARDS HEATH

Roundabout Antiques Centre
7 Commercial Sq. RH16 1DW. (Angie Craik).
Open 10-5. SIZE: Medium. *STOCK: Ceramics,
glass and silver, jewellery, £50-£1,000; furniture,
£50-£2,000; all 19th-20th C. Musical instruments,
20th C, £50-£2,000.* LOC: Across roundabout
from railway station. PARK: On forecourt. TEL:
01273 835926; fax - 01273 835659.

HENFIELD

Alexander Antiques
Post House, Small Dole. BN5 9XE. (Mrs J.A.
Goodinge). Est. 1971. CL: Sun. except by
appointment. SIZE: Medium. *STOCK: Country
furniture, brass, copper, pewter, samplers, small
collectors' and decorative items, treen.* LOC:
A2037. PARK: Easy. TEL: 01273 493121; home
- same. VAT: Stan/Spec.

Ashcombe Coach House   BADA
P O Box 2527. CINOA. Open strictly by appointment only. *STOCK: Furniture and objects, 17th to
early 19th C.* TEL: 01273 491630; mobile - 07803
180098.

HORSHAM

Gubbins
74 Park St. (W. Gent). GMC: FSB. Open 10-5.
SIZE: Large. *STOCK: Furniture, china and
glass, general antiques, 19th-20th C, £1-£2,000.*
LOC: From A23 or A24 towards station, then to
town centre - on left hand side, opposite Sun
Alliance building. PARK: Waitrose. TEL: 01403
268801. VAT: Spec.

HOUGHTON, Nr. Arundel

Stable Antiques at Houghton
The Old Church, Main Rd. BN18 9LW. (Ian. J. Wadey). Open Tues.-Sat. 11-4. *STOCK: General antiques and furniture, £20-£1,000.* LOC: On B2139 5 miles between Storrington and Arundel. PARK: Own. TEL: 01798 839555; fax - same; website - www.stableantiques.co.uk.

HURSTPIERPOINT

The Clock Shop
34-36 High St. BN6. LAPADA. Open 9-6 including Sun., or by appointment. *STOCK: 18th-19th longcase and table clocks.* TEL: 01273 832081; mobile - 07860 230888. SER: Restorations (clocks and furniture).

Julian Antiques
124 High St. BN6 9PX. Est. 1964. Open by appointment only. *STOCK: French 19th C mirrors, fireplaces, fenders, furniture, etc.* TEL: 01273 832145.

LINDFIELD

Lindfield Galleries - David Adam
BADA
62 High St. RH16 2HL. Est. 1972. Open 9.30-5.30. *STOCK: Oriental carpets.* TEL: 01444 483817. VAT: Stan/Spec.

Spongs Antiques Centre
102 High St. RH16 2HS. (Ashley and Karen Richardson). Est. 1999. Open 10-5. SIZE: Medium. *STOCK: Porcelain and pottery, 18th-20th C, £10-£100; oak and mahogany furniture, 17th-20th C, £50-£700; silver, 17th-20th C, £30-£200.* PARK: At rear. TEL: 01444 487566. SER: Valuations.

Stable Antiques
98A High St. RH16 2HP. (Adrian Hoyle). Est. 1987. Open 10-5.30, Mon. 1.30-5.30, Sun. 11.30-5.30. SIZE: Medium. *STOCK: Furniture including mahogany and rosewood bookcases, chests of drawers, sofas, Regency dining tables; oak desks, bookcases, roll-tops, dropleaf, Georgian to 1940's; pine including dressers, mule chests and wardrobes, 1870-1900.* LOC: Off A272 on B2028, 2 miles south of Ardingly. PARK: Easy and free. TEL: 01444 483662; fax - 01444 482274; mobile - 07768 900331; e-mail - a.hoyle@cwcom.net. SER: Valuations. VAT: Spec.

LITTLEHAMPTON

Joan's Antiques
1 New Rd. BN17 5AX. (J. Walkden and M. Hill). Est. 1976. Open Thurs.-Sat. 10.30-4.30. SIZE: Small. *STOCK: China and collectables, Victorian to 1930's, £5-£100.* LOC: From Woolworths, Surrey St, keep left and turn into New Road. PARK: Easy. TEL: 01903 722422; home - 01903 784495. FAIRS: Goodwood.

Magic of Quimper
Faux Cottage, 4A Selborne Rd. BN17 5NN. (John Haynes and Kay Meader). Usually available but prior telephone call advisable. *STOCK: Over 200 pieces of Quimper faience, Desvres and other French faience.* PARK: Easy. TEL: 01903 714261.

The Round Pond
Faux Cottage, 4a Selborne Rd. BN17 5NN. (John Haynes and Kay Meader). Est. 1962. Open by appointment. SIZE: Small. *STOCK: Vintage model boats especially yachts, 19th C to 1950's, £50-£2,000.* PARK: Easy. TEL: 01903 714261; home - same. SER: Valuations.

MIDHURST

Churchill Clocks
Rumbolds Hill. GU29 9BZ. (W.P. and Dr. E. Tyrrell). Open 9-5, Wed. 9-1. *STOCK: Clocks and furniture.* LOC: Main street. TEL: 01730 813891; fax - same; website - www.churchillclocks .article7.co.uk. SER: Clock restoration.

The Old Town Hall Antique Centre
Market Square. GU29 9NJ. (P.B. Baker). Open 10-5. SIZE: Medium. *STOCK: Furniture, porcelain, decorative items.* PARK: Easy. TEL: 01730 817166.

NORTHCHAPEL, Nr. Petworth

Callingham Antiques
GU28 9HL. Est. 1979. Open 9-5.30. CL: Wed. SIZE: Medium. *STOCK: Furniture, 1700-1900, £10-£10,000.* LOC: London Road 5 miles north of Petworth. PARK: Easy. TEL: 01428 707379. SER: Valuations; restorations.

PETWORTH

Angel Antiques
Church St. GU28 0AD. (Nick and Barbara Swanson). Resident. Open 10-5.30, Sun. by appointment. SIZE: Medium. *STOCK: English and French 17th-19th C country furniture and associated items, £80-£15,000.* LOC: Opposite Petworth House and war memorial. TEL: 01798 343306; fax - 01798 342665; e-mail - swan189@ aol.com. VAT: Spec.

Antiquated
10 New St. GU28 0AS. (Vicki Emery). PAADA. Open 10-5.30 or by appointment. *STOCK: 18th-19th C original painted furniture, decorative items, garden furniture; 19th C rocking horses.* TEL: 01798 344011; fax - same.

Bacchus Gallery
Lombard St. GU28 0AG. (R. and A. Gillett). Est. 1988. Open 10-1 and 2.30-5. SIZE: Small. *STOCK: Wine related items.* LOC: Cobbled street leading off town square. PARK: Town square. TEL: 01798 342844; fax - 01798 342634. SER: Buys at auction (as stock). VAT: Stan/Spec.

Baskerville Antiques   BADA
Saddlers House, Saddlers Row. GU28 0AN. (A. and B. Baskerville). PAADA. Est. 1978. Open Tues.-Sat. 10-6, or by appointment. SIZE: Medium. *STOCK: English clocks, barometers and furniture, £1,000-£40,000; decorative items and instruments, £500-£10,000; all 17th-19th C.*

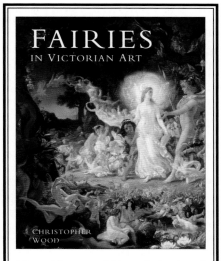

The golden age of fairy painting lasted between 1840 and 1870 when fairies found expression in most of the Victorian arts – from illustration to ballet. Fairies represented another way for the Victorians to escape the intolerable reality of living in an unromantic, materialistic and scientific age. In this atmosphere, fairy painting flourished; between the artist and his public there was a common ground, an area of escapism in which both sides were prepared to believe.

ISBN 1 85149 336 0
11 x 9½in./280 x 240mm.
192pp., 150 col., 20 b.&w. illus.
£30.00/$59.50

LOC: Town centre. PARK: Public, adjoining shop. TEL: 01798 342067; home - same; fax - 01798 343956. VAT: Spec.

Bradley's Past & Present

21 High St. GU28 0AU. (M. and A. Bradley). Est. 1975. CL: Mon. SIZE: Small. *STOCK: Furniture, 19th-20th C, £50-£500; china and decorative items, £5-£100; metalware, phonographs, gramophones and records.* PARK: Nearby. TEL: 01798 343533. SER: Restorations; repairs.

Lesley Bragge Antiques

Fairfield House, High St. GU28 0AU. LAPADA. PAADA. Est. 1974. Open 10-1 and 2-5.30. SIZE: Medium. *STOCK: Decorative furniture, 18th-19th C; silver and plate, porcelain, textiles, ormolu, brass, copper, objets d' art, garden furniture.* LOC: Off Golden Square. PARK: Nearby. TEL: 01798 342324; fax - 01798 344988. SER; Valuations; restorations; upholstery. VAT: Stan/Spec.

The Canon Gallery   BADA

New St. GU28 0AS. (Jeremy Green and James Fergusson). LAPADA, PAADA. Open 10-5.30. SIZE: Medium. *STOCK: Oils and water-colours, 18th-20th C, £500-£25,000.* LOC: Main road. PARK: Easy. TEL: 01798 344422. SER: Valuations; restorations. FAIRS: World of Watercolours; NEC; Harrogate; Olympia; New York; BADA. VAT: Spec.

Ronald G. Chambers Fine Antiques

Market Sq. GU28 0AH. LAPADA. CINOA. PAADA. Open 10-5.30 including Sun. *STOCK: Fine 18th-19th C furniture and objets d' art.* TEL: 01798 342305; fax - 01798 342724; mobile - 07932 161968; website - www.ronaldchambers. com; e-mail - Jackie@ronaldchambers.com.

J. Du Cros Antiques

1 Pound St. GU28 0DX. (J. and P.Du Cros). PAADA. Est. 1982. Open 10-5.30, sometimes closed Wed. pm. SIZE: Medium. *STOCK: English furniture, 1660-1900, £100-£5,000; treen, metalware, some glass.* LOC: Corner of Sadlers Row. PARK: Nearby. TEL: 01798 342071. VAT: Stan/Spec.

Elliott's

East St. GU28 0AB. PAADA. Open 10-5. *STOCK: 18th-20th C furniture, fine art and decorative items.* TEL: 01798 343408.

The French Room

5 & 6 High St. GU28 0AU. PAADA. Open 10-5.30, Sun. by appointment. *STOCK: 19th-20th C French furniture and decorative antiques.* TEL: 01798 344454.

Richard Gardner Antiques

Swan House, Market Sq. GU28 0AN. (Richard and Janice Gardner). LAPADA. PAADA. Resident. Est. 1992. Open 10-5.30 including Sun. SIZE: Large. *STOCK: Fine period furniture and works of art, up to £75,000; English and Continental porcelain, Victorian Staffordshire figures, bronzes, silver, paintings, 17th-19th C; associated items.* PARK: 50 yards. TEL: 01798 343411/344463; website - www.richardgardner antiques.co.uk. VAT: Spec.

Granville Antiques   BADA

High St. GU28 0AU. (I.E.G. Miller). Est. 1979. Open 10-5.30 or by appointment. SIZE: Medium. *STOCK: Period furniture, pre-1840, £50-£15,000; accessories and pictures.* Not Stocked: Militaria and jewellery. LOC: 100yds. from market square. PARK: Nearby. TEL: 01798 343250; mobile - 07966 279761. SER: Valuations (furniture); restorations (furniture). FAIRS: BADA; Chelsea. VAT: Spec.

William Hockley Antiques

East St. GU28 0AB. (D. and V. Thrower). LAPADA. PAADA. Est. 1974. *STOCK: Fine 18th to early 19th C furniture and decorative items; early English pottery.* TEL: 01798 343172.

The Madison Gallery

Swan House, Market Sq. GU28 0AH. (G.W. Mott). PAADA. Open 10-5 including Sun. SIZE: Large. *STOCK: Furniture - oak, country, formal and decorative; pictures, silver, porcelain and accessories.* PARK: Easy. TEL: 01798 343638. SER: Restorations; upholstery. VAT: Stan/Spec.

Octavia Antiques

East St. GU28 0AB. (Aline Bell). PAADA. Est. 1973.Open 10.30-5.30. CL: Fri. SIZE: Small. *STOCK: Decorative items - blue and white china, lamps, mirrors, chairs, small sofas, mainly 19th C.* PARK: Easy. TEL: 01798 342771.

Persian Carpet Gallery of Petworth

Church St. GU28 0AD. LAPADA. Open 9.30-5. *STOCK: Old and new Oriental rugs and carpets.* LOC: A272. PARK: Nearby. TEL: 01798 343344; fax - 01798 342673. SER: Valuations; restorations; hand cleaning; insurance claims.

Petworth Antique Market

East St. GU28 0AB. (D.M. Rayment). PAADA. Est. 1968. Open 10-5.30. SIZE: Large - 36 dealers. *STOCK: General antiques, books, furniture, brass, copper, pictures, textiles.* LOC: Near church. PARK: Adjoining. TEL: 01798 342073. VAT: Stan/Spec.

PETWORTH
WEST SUSSEX

Antiques Centre of the South

For Brochure –
Tel: (01798) 343411

Annette Puttnam
2 Leppards High St. GU28 0AU. Open 10.15-5.15. *STOCK: Furniture - country, pine, oak, fruitwood, mahogany, painted, architectural, garden and upholstery.* TEL: 01798 343933; mobile - 07973 421070.

Red Lion Antiques
New St. GU28 0AS. (R. Wilson and D. Swanson). PAADA. Est. 1981. Open 10-5.30. SIZE: Large. *STOCK: Antiques for the country home, oak, walnut and pine furniture, 17th-19th C, £100-£20,000.* LOC: Town centre. PARK: Easy. TEL: 01798 344485; fax - 01798 342367; website - www.redlion-antiques.com. VAT: Spec.

Riverbank
High St. GU28 0AU. (Linda Burke-White). PAADA. Open 10-5.30. *STOCK: Antiques for the house and garden.* TEL: 01798 344401; fax - 01798 343135.

Ruddy Antiques
10A New St. GU28 0AS. (Robin and Paula Ruddy). Est. 1994. Open 10.30-5 or by appointment. SIZE: Medium. *STOCK: Eclectic Continental and English furniture, 18th-19th C.* TEL: 01798 344622.

H. G. Saunders
Market Sq. GU28 0AH. LAPADA. Open 7 days 10-5.30. *STOCK: Fine antique furniture and objets d'art.* TEL: 01798 344333.

Sayer Antiques - The French Room
5 & 6 The High St. Est. 1971. Open 10-5.30, also private viewing of separate trade stock. *STOCK: 19th-20th C French and Italian furniture, lighting and mirrors.* TEL: 01798 344454/01293 852515; e-mail - sayerantiques@lasource.freeserve.co.uk. VAT: Margin.

Stewart Antiques
High St. GU28 0AU. (John and Sandra Moore). Est. 1984. Open 10-5.30, Sun. by appointment. SIZE: Medium. *STOCK: Victorian stripped pine and fruitwood, £30-£3,000; kitchenalia and Continental decorative items.* LOC: Town centre. PARK: Easy. TEL: 01798 342136. SER: Valuations. VAT: Spec.

J.C. Tutt Antiques
Angel St. GU28 0BQ. Open 10-5. CL: Some Mon. SIZE: Large. *STOCK: Mahogany and country furniture and accessories.* PARK: Nearby. TEL: 01798 343221.

T.G. Wilkinson Antiques Ltd   BADA
Lombard St. GU28 0AG. (T. and S. Wilkinson). **PAADA. Est. 1979. Open 10-5.30. SIZE:** Medium. *STOCK: English and Continental furniture, paintings and works of art, 17th-19th C, £500-£25,000.* PARK: Town centre. TEL: 01798 344443. VAT: Stan/Spec.

PORTSLADE

J. Powell (Hove) Ltd
20 Wellington Rd. BN4 1DN. LAPADA. Est. 1949. Open 7.30-5.30. CL: Sun. and Sat. pm. except by appointment. SIZE: Large. *STOCK: Bookcases, display cabinets, £110-£1,500; writing tables and desks, £120-£1,200; longcase and bracket clocks, £50-£2,000; general furniture, shipping goods, 18th-20th C, £5-£1,500.* Not Stocked: Porcelain, jewellery, silver. LOC: 150yds. west of Boundary Rd., on seafront. PARK: Easy. TEL: 01273 411599; fax - 01273 421591; e-mail - j-powell-hove-ltd@cwcom.net. SER: Restorations (furniture). VAT: Stan.

PULBOROUGH

Georgia Antiques
The Barn, Broomershill Farm. RH20 2HZ. (Georgia Hicks). LAPADA. CINOA. Est. 1979. Open by appointment. SIZE: Medium. *STOCK: English furniture, pictures and fine art, 18th-19th C; decorative lighting, 19th C.* TEL: 01798 872348; fax - 01798 875200; e-mail - georgia@ georgia-antiques.com; website - www.georgia-antiques.com. VAT: Spec.

Thakeham Furniture
Marehill Rd. RH20 2DY. (T. and B. Chavasse). Est. 1988. Open Mon.-Fri. 9-5. SIZE: Medium. *STOCK: 18th-19th C English furniture, £100-£8,000; clocks.* LOC: 1 mile east of Pulborough next to White Horse Inn on A283. PARK: Easy. TEL: 01798 872006. SER: Restorations (furniture). VAT: Spec.

SHOREHAM-BY-SEA

Rodney Arthur Classics
Unit 6 Riverbank Business Centre, Old Shoreham Rd. BN43 5FL. (Rodney Oliver). Est. 1979. Open 9.30-5, Sat. and Sun. by appointment. SIZE: Large. *STOCK: Furniture, 1800-1920, £100-£2,500.* LOC: From A27 take A283 exit near Shoreham Airport, then south towards sea, shop opposite Swiss Cottage pub. TEL: 01273 441606; fax - 01273 441977. SER: Restorations; French polishing. VAT: Stan/Spec.

Julia Holmes Antique Maps and Prints

South Gardens Cottage. GU31 5QJ. By appointment only. SIZE: Medium. *STOCK: Maps, 1600-1850, £10-£1,000; prints, especially sporting, to £500.* LOC: End of main street, on the Chichester road. PARK: Opposite. TEL: 01730 825040. SER: Valuations; restorations (cleaning and colouring maps and prints); framing; buys at auction; catalogues. FAIRS: Local and major sporting events. VAT: Stan.

David R. Fileman

Squirrels, Bayards. BN44 3AA. Open daily. *STOCK: Table glass, £20-£1,000; chandeliers, candelabra, £500-£20,000; all 18th-19th C. Collectors' items, 17th-19th C, £25-£2,000; paperweights, 19th C, £50-£5,000.* LOC: A283 to north of Steyning village. TEL: 01903 813229. SER: Valuations; restorations (chandeliers and candelabra). VAT: Stan/Spec.

Phyllis Gordon

Est. 1972. Open by appointment only. *STOCK: Georgian and Victorian furniture; button back chairs, porcelain, silver, glass and clocks.* TEL: 01903 810058.

Stable Antiques

46 West St. RH20 4EE. (Ian J. Wadey). Est. 1993. Open 10-6 including Sun. SIZE: Large. *STOCK: General antiques, furniture and bric-a-brac, £1-£1,000.* LOC: A283 west of A24 towards Pulborough, just before Amberley turn. PARK: Easy. TEL: 01903 740555; fax - 01903 740441; website - www.stableantiques.co.uk.

Loewenthal Antiques

Tillington Cottage. GU28 0RA. CL: Wed. *STOCK: 18th C furniture and objets d'art.* LOC: A272, 1 mile west of Petworth. TEL: 01798 342969.

Chanctonbury Antiques

Clematis Cottage. RH20 4AP. (G. D. Troche). Est. 1961. Open by appointment only. SIZE: Small. *STOCK: Pottery, porcelain, needlework, small furniture and collectables.* LOC: Just off A24. PARK: Easy. TEL: 01903 892233.

Acorn Antiques

91 Rowlands Rd. BN11 3JX. (Henry Nicholls). Est. 1992. Open 9-5.30, Mon. and Wed. 9-4. SIZE: Small. *STOCK: Furniture, china and porcelain, 18th-19th C.* LOC: Off Heene Road near seafront. PARK: Easy. TEL: 01903 216926. SER: Restorations; polishing. FAIRS: Ardingly; Goodwood.

Chloe Antiques

61 Brighton Rd. BN11 3EE. (Mrs D. Peters). Est. 1960. Open 10-12.30 and 1.30-4.30. CL: Wed. SIZE: Small. *STOCK: General antiques, furniture, jewellery, china, glass, bric-a-brac.* LOC: From Brighton, on main rd. just past Beach House Park on corner. PARK: Opposite. TEL: 01903 202697.

Corner Antiques

9/10 Havercroft Buildings, North St. BN11 1DY. (R.A. Mittok). Est. 1992. Open 10-5. SIZE: Small. *STOCK: Pine and country furniture, 19th C, £200-£500; objets d'art, 50p-£150, furniture, £100-£1,000; all 19th-20th C.* LOC: Top end of High Street, turn right at the roundabout. PARK: Loading only, otherwise Connaught NCP. TEL: 01903 537669; fax - 01903 206881. SER: Restorations (furniture including French polishing, upholstering and repairs); buys at auction. FAIRS: Charmandean Centre.

Robert Warner and Son Ltd

1-13 South Farm Rd. BN14 7AB. Est. 1940. CL: Wed. pm. SIZE: Large. *STOCK: Furniture.* TEL: 01903 232710; fax - 01903 217515; website - www.rewarner.co.uk. VAT: Stan.

Wilsons Antiques

45-47 New Broadway, Tarring Rd. BN11 4HS. (F. Wilson). LAPADA. Est. 1936. Open 10-5. SIZE: Large. *STOCK: Period furniture, 18th-19th C, £100-£10,000; Edwardian furniture, £50-£4,000; decorative items, 19th C, £10-£750; watercolours and oil paintings, 19th-20th C.* Not Stocked: Pine. PARK: Easy. TEL: 01903 202059; mobile - 07778 813395; e-mail - Frank@Wilsons_Antiques.com; website - www.wilsons-antiques.com. SER: Valuations. FAIRS: Olympia (June); Goodwood House; NEC. VAT: Stan/Spec/Global.

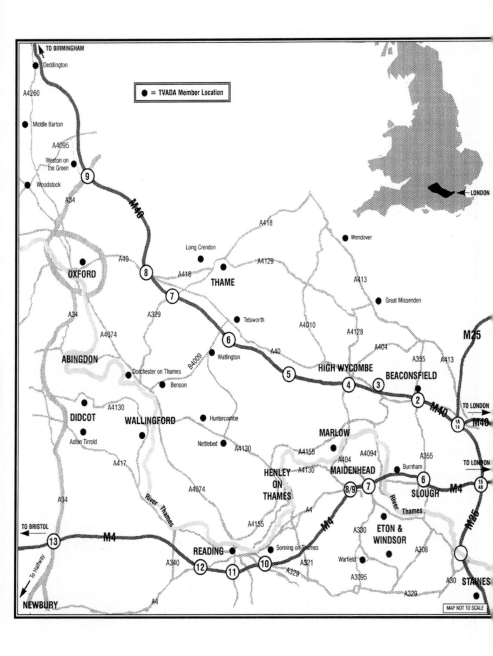

● = TVADA Member Location

TO BIRMINGHAM

Deddington

A4260

Middle Barton

A4095

Weston on the Green

Woodstock

A34

M40

9

Long Crendon

A418

Wendover

OXFORD

A40

8

A418

THAME

A4129

A413

7

Great Missenden

A34

A329

Tetsworth

A4010

A4128

M25

A4074

6

A40

A404

A413

M40

ABINGDON

B4009

Watlington

5

HIGH WYCOMBE

A355

BEACONSFIELD

Dorchester on Thames

4

3

2

Benson

A4130

Huntercombe

M40

1A 14

TO LONDON

M40

DIDCOT

WALLINGFORD

Nettlebed

A4130

MARLOW

TO LONDON

Aston Tirrold

A417

A4074

A4155

A404

A4094

A355

Burnham

15 4B

A34

HENLEY ON THAMES

A4130

MAIDENHEAD

6

SLOUGH

M4

TO BRISTOL

M4

A4

River Thames

A4155

7

8/9

M4

A4

ETON & WINDSOR

M25

13

Sonning on Thames

A380

To Halfway

READING

A340

12

11

10

A321

A329

Warfield

A308

A30

STAINES

NEWBURY

A4

A3095

A329

LONDON

MAP NOT TO SCALE

THAMES VALLEY
ANTIQUE DEALERS ASSOCIATION

TVADA

Meander through the beautiful Thames Valley and you embark on a journey through the history of these islands. From the great Norman castle at Windsor, symbol of royal power, to ancient Oxford and one of the world's greatest seats of learning, you will discover institutions that have served this country well. The area is also home to knowledge-based industries, many at the cutting edge of modern day technology.

The FIFTY members of the Thames Valley Antiques Dealers Association (TVADA) like to think of themselves as not just representing all that is best of the old but also embracing the modern. A tour of the Association's antiques shops and centres in the Thames Valley will provide an awareness of the finest examples of English art and craftmanship. As well as beautiful Queen Anne walnut and elegant Georgian mahogany furniture, there are 19th century country chairs that transcend fashion. You will also discover the work of the Arts and Crafts Movement and Ray Eames chairs which represent the best in post-war design. For buyers of ceramics the choice is just as rich and varied. Early oriental pieces, elegant and ornate 19th century porcelain and the best designed, signed work of the 20th century are all on sale in our members' premises. There is plenty for the serious collector in all fields but for the casual buyer, particularly in our centres, you will find those inexpensive and often amusing curiosities that make modern, mass-produced souvenirs look tame by comparison. Indeed, just as there is something for everyone in the tourist attractions along the river, up to the edge of the beautiful Cotswolds, so there are antiques for everyone in our members' premises.

As well as a comprehensive list of the names and addresses of the fifty members in the Thames Valley Antique Dealers Association, we have also devised three fascinating day long tourist trails. These are available, free of charge, by writing to :

The Secretary, TVADA, The Old College, Queen St., Dorchester on Thames, Oxon., OX10 7HL. Tel/Fax: 01865 341639 Email: antiques@tvada.co.uk

  Look out for **OLD FATHER THAMES,** named after the Roman God **TAMESIS** who is our **LOGO** and is on the door of our shops and centres.

FOR OUR FRIENDS FROM OVERSEAS

We are conveniently situated only 20 miles west of London and served by three major roads out of that city — the M4, M25 and M40. Heathrow Airport is within sight of Windsor. Rail links and public transport to the major towns are good, this being the London commuter belt. We can arrange courier services and shipping and have many associate members who specialise in restoring just about anything.

The Association runs TWO vetted Fairs, one in the spring at Sonning on Thames near Reading, the other in the autumn at Radley College near Oxford. Details from the Secretary.

WE LOOK FORWARD TO SEEING YOU SOON

ASTON TIRROLD, Nr. Didcot

John Harrison Fine Art
Skirmers, Aston St. OX11 9DQ. (J.M.C. Harrison). TVADA. Strictly by appointment. *STOCK: Drawings and watercolours, 18th-19th C.* TEL: 01235 850260. SER: Commissions undertaken.

BEACONSFIELD

Period Furniture Showrooms
49 London End. HP9 2HW. (R.E.W. Hearne and N.J. Hearne). TVADA. Est. 1965. Open Mon.-Sat. 9-5.30. SIZE: Large. *STOCK: Furniture, 1700-1900, £50-£5,000.* LOC: A40 Beaconsfield Old Town. PARK: Own. TEL: 01494 674112; fax - 01494 681046; e-mail - Sales@period-furniture-showrooms.co.uk; website - www.periodfurniture.net. SER: Restorations (furniture). VAT: Stan/Spec.

CAVERSHAM, Nr. Reading

The Clock Workshop
17 Prospect St. RG4 8JB. (J. M. Yealland FBHI). LAPADA. TVADA. Est. 1980. Open 9.30-5.30, Sat. 10-1. SIZE: Small. *STOCK: Clocks, late 17th to late 19th C, £350-£60,000; barometers, 18th-19th C, £500-£12,000.* LOC: Prospect St. is the beginning of main Reading to Henley road. PARK: North St. TEL: 0118 9470741. SER: Valuations; restorations (clocks, barometers, chronometers, barographs); buys at auction. FAIRS: TVADA; LAPADA; Olympia. VAT: Stan/Spec.

DEDDINGTON

Deddington Antiques Centre
Laurel House, Bull Ring, Market Sq. OX15 0TT. (Mrs B. J. Haller). TVADA. Est. 1972. Open 10-5, including Sun. SIZE: 27 dealers. *STOCK: Furniture, Georgian to 1930's, £40-£4,000; porcelain, silver, pictures, jewellery, 1700-1930, £5-£5,000; collectables, £10-£200.* LOC: Off A4260 Oxford-Banbury road at Deddington traffic lights. PARK: Easy, free. TEL: 01869 338968; fax - 01869 338916. SER: Valuations. FAIRS: NEC.

DORCHESTER-ON-THAMES

Dorchester Antiques
The Barn, 3 High St. OX10 7HH. (J. and S. Hearnden). LAPADA. TVADA. Est. 1992. Open Tues.-Sat. 10-5. SIZE: Medium. *STOCK: Furniture including chairs and decorative country pieces, 18th-19th C.* PARK: Easy. TEL: 01865 341373. SER: Restorations; finder.

Hallidays (Fine Antiques) Ltd
The Old College, High St. OX10 7HL. LAPADA. TVADA. Est. 1950. Open 9-5, Sat. 10-1 and 2-4. SIZE: Large. *STOCK: Furniture, 17th-19th C, £100-£40,000; paintings, 18th-19th C, £100-£20,000; decorative and small items, pine and marble mantelpieces, firegrates, fenders, 18th-20th C; room panelling.* PARK: At rear. TEL: 01865 340028; fax - 01865 341149. FAIRS: Olympia. VAT: Stan/Spec.

HALFWAY, Nr. Newbury

Alan Walker   BADA
Halfway Manor. RG20 8NR. TVADA. Open by appointment. *STOCK: Fine barometers and weather instruments.* TEL: 01488 657670; mobile - 07770 728397. SER: Restorations.

HUNTERCOMBE

The Country Seat
Huntercombe Manor Barn. RG9 5RY. (Harvey Ferry and William Clegg). LAPADA. TVADA. Est. 1965. Open 9-5.30, Sun. by appointment. SIZE: Large. *STOCK: Furniture - signed and designed, 1700-1970; garden and architectural/panelling; art pottery and metalwork, lighting.* LOC: 200 yds down right-hand turn off A4130 Nettlebed-Wallingford. PARK: Easy. TEL: 01491 641349; fax - 01491 641533; e-mail - ferry&clegg@the countryseat.com; website - www.the countryseat.com. SER: Restorations. VAT: Spec.

MARLOW

Marlow Antique Centre
35 Station Rd. SL7 1NW. TVADA. SIZE: 30+ dealers. *STOCK: 18th-20th C furniture, collectors' china from Worcester to Clarice Cliff, Staffordshire figures and dogs, chandeliers, silver, decorative glass, writing slopes, tea caddies, postcards, pens, cuff-links, equestrian items, cameras, jewellery.* TEL: 01628 473223; fax - 01628 478989.

NETTLEBED, Nr. Henley-on-Thames

Willow Antiques and the Nettlebed Antique Merchants
The Barns, 1 High St. RG9 5DA. (Willow

Bicknell, Michael Plummer and Laurie Brunton). TVADA. Open 10-5.30, Sun. 11-4, other times by appointment. SIZE: Large. *STOCK: Decorative, fine and unusual furniture, objects and decorations, including architectural and garden items, 17th C to 1970s, including Gothic, Aesthetic, Arts & Crafts and Art Deco.* LOC: Between Wallingford and Henley on A4074. PARK: Easy. TEL: 01491 642062/628811; mobile - 07770 554559. SER: Finder; copy and design; advice on period design for house and garden.

OXFORD

Antiques on High Ltd
85 High St. OX1 4BG. (Paul Lipson and Sally Young). TVADA. Est. 1962. Open 10-5, Sun. 11-5. SIZE: Large - 35 dealers. *STOCK: Small antiques and collectables including jewellery, silver and plate, ceramics, glass, clocks and watches, books, 17th-20th C.* PARK: St Clements, Westgate, Seacourt/Thornhill Park and Ride. TEL: 01865 251075. SER: Valuations; restorations (jewellery, silver including replating). FAIRS: TVADA.

PANGBOURNE

Rita Butler
4a Station Rd. RG8 7AN. TVADA. Open 10-5. *STOCK: General antiques including brass and bronze, early 19th C to early 20th C especially Art Deco; glass, early 1800's.* TEL: 0118 984 5522; mobile - 07752 936327.

READING

Rupert Landen Antiques
Church Farm, Reading Rd., Woodcote. RG8 0QX. TVADA. Open by appointment only. *STOCK: Late 18th to early 19th C furniture.* TEL: 01491 682396; mobile - 07974 732472.

SONNING-ON-THAMES

Cavendish Fine Arts
The Dower House. RG4 6UL. (Janet Middlemiss and Guy Hazel). LAPADA. TVADA. Open by appointment only. *STOCK: Fine Queen Anne and English Georgian furniture, glass and porcelain.* TEL: 01189 691904; mobile - 07831 295575. VAT: Stan/Spec.

STAINES

Margaret Melville Watercolours
11 Colnebridge, Market Sq. TW18 4RZ.

LAPADA. TVADA. Est. 1980. Open by appointment only. *STOCK: Watercolours, 1850-1950, £200-£7,000.* TEL: 01784 455395; fax - same. SER: Valuations; commissions. FAIRS: LAPADA; NEC (Jan.); Chester (Feb.); Penman Fairs; TVADA (May, Oct.). VAT: Spec.

TETSWORTH

The Swan at Tetsworth
High St. OX9 7AB. TVADA. Est. 1995. Open 7 days 10-6. SIZE: 40+ rooms. LOC: A40, 5 minutes from junctions 6 and 8, M40. PARK: Own large. TEL: 01844 281777; fax - 01844 281770; website - www.theswan.co.uk; e-mail - antiques@theswan.co.uk. SER: Restorations (clocks, cabinet work and gilding).

WALLINGFORD

The Lamb Arcade
83 High St. OX10 0BX. TVADA. Open 10-5, Sat. 10-5.30. *STOCK: As below plus books, crafts and ephemera.* TEL: 01491 835166. SER: Restorations (furniture).

Summers Davis Antiques Ltd
Calleva House, 6 High St. OX10 0BP. (Graham Wells). LAPADA. CINOA. TVADA. Est. 1917. Open 9-5.30, Sat. 9-5, Sun. 11-5. SIZE: Large. *STOCK: English and Continental furniture, decorative items and objects.* Not Stocked: Silver, shipping goods. LOC: From London, shop is on left, 50yds. from Thames Bridge. PARK: Opposite, behind castellated gates. TEL: 01491 836284; fax - 01491 833443; e-mail - summersdavisantiques@msn.com; website - www.sd-antique-furniture.com. VAT: Spec.

WARFIELD

Moss End Antique Centre
Moss End Garden Centre. RG12 6EJ. TVADA. Open 10.30-5. CL: Mon. SIZE: Large - 25 dealers. *STOCK: General antiques and collectables.* LOC: A3095. PARK: Own. TEL: 01344 861942.

WATLINGTON

Stephen Orton Antiques
The Antiques Warehouse, Shirburn Rd. OX49 5BZ. TVADA. Open Mon.-Fri. 9-5, other times by appointment. SIZE: Warehouse. *STOCK: 18th-19th C furniture, some decorative items.* LOC: 2 mins. from exit 6, M40. TEL: 01491

613752; e-mail - Orton.Antiques@virgin.net.
SER: Supply and pack containers; valuations;
restorations; buying agent. VAT: Stan/Spec.

WESTON-ON-THE-GREEN

Julie Strachey
Southfield Farm, North Lane. OX6 8RG. TVADA.
Open by appointment only. *STOCK: Decorative
18th-19th C farm and country furniture, especially
tables, dressers, chests, wrought iron and unusual
garden items.* LOC: 5 minutes from junction 9,
M40 or off A34 on to B430. TEL: 01869 350833;
mobile - 07711 249939.

WINDSOR AND ETON

Eton Gallery
(Josephine Smith). LAPADA. TVADA. By
appointment only. *STOCK: Fine 18th to early
19th C furniture.* TEL: 01753 860963.

Marcelline Herald Antiques
41 High St., Eton. SL4 6BD. TVADA. Est. 1993.
Open Tues.,Thurs., Fri. and Sat. 10-5, other days by
appointment. SIZE: Medium. *STOCK: Furniture
including beds, £500-£5,000; mirrors, pelmets and
screens, £200-£2,500; ceramics, lamps and prints,
£50-£1,000; all 18th to early 19th C.* PARK:
Loading only. TEL: 01753 833924; fax - 0118 971
4683; home - same. FAIRS: TVADA; Decorative
Antiques and Textiles. VAT: Spec.

Peter J. Martin
40 High St., Eton. SL4 6BD. TVADA. Est. 1963.
Open 9-1 and 2-5. CL: Sun. SIZE: Large and
warehouse. *STOCK: Period, Victorian and
decorative furniture and furnishings, £50-£20,000;
metalware, £10-£500, all from 1800.* PARK:
50yds. opposite. TEL: 01753 864901; home -
01753 863987. SER: Restorations; shipping
arranged; buys at auction. VAT: Stan/Spec.

*Ivory toilet comb with fretted heading and
handle, probably British, 1890-1910. 7¼in.
long, 1⅝in. wide. (Private collection)*

From an article entitled 'Combs as Love-
Tokens' by Jen Cruse and Robert Watts which
appeared in the December 2000/January 2001
issue of **Antique Collecting** magazine. For
more details and to subscribe see page 147.

WOOBURN, Nr. High Wycombe

Lafleure Antiques & Decoration
Endsleigh, Town Lane. HP10 0JP. (Peter Lane).
TVADA. Open 10-5, Sun. by appointment. CL:
Mon. and Wed. *STOCK: Gilded, walnut and
marble French furniture, soft furnishings, mirrors
and objects, 19th C; paintings and unusual items,
curtain accessories, lighting and decorative
objects.* LOC: Off M4 on main road between
Beaconsfield and Bourne End. TEL: 01628
530461.

WOODSTOCK

Chris Baylis Country Chairs
16 Oxford St. OX20 1TS. TVADA. Open 10.30-
5.30, Sun. 11-5, appointment advisable to view
stock. *STOCK: English country chairs, from
1780; sets of rush seated chairs including ladder
and spindle backs, Windsors and kitchen chairs.*
TEL: 01993 813887; fax - 01993 812379; e-mail
- rwood@mcmail.com; website - www.windsor
chairs.co.uk.

Bees Antiques
30 High St. OX20 1TG. (Jo and Jim Bateman).
TVADA. Est. 1991. Open 10-1 and 1.30-5, Sun.
11-5. CL: Tues. SIZE: Small. *STOCK: Pottery,
porcelain and glass, 18th-20th C, £30-£1,500;
small furniture, 19th to early 20th C, £50-£2,000;
metalware, 19th C, £30-£200; jewellery, 19th-
20th C, £30-£1,000.* LOC: Just off A3440
Oxford/Stratford-on-Avon road, in town centre.
PARK: Opposite. TEL: 01993 811062; home -
01993 771593. SER: Valuations; buys at auction
(as stock). FAIRS: TVADA.

Span Antiques
6 Market Place. OX20 1TA. TVADA. Est. 1978.
Open 10-1 and 2-5, Sun 1-5. SIZE: Medium.
LOC: Near Town Hall. PARK: Easy. TEL:
01993 811332.

WRAYSBURY, Nr. Staines

Clive Rogers Oriental Rugs
TW19 5PE. TVADA Est. 1974. Open by
appointment. SIZE: Medium. *STOCK: Oriental
rugs, carpets, textiles; Oriental and Islamic works
of art.* LOC: On B376, 10 minutes from Heathrow
Airport. PARK: Own. TEL: 01784 481177/
481100; fax - 01784 481144; mobile - 07747
114757; e-mail - info@orient-rug.com; website -
www.orient-rug.com. SER: Valuations; restorations
(as stock); historical analysis commission agents;
buys at auction. VAT: Stan/Spec.

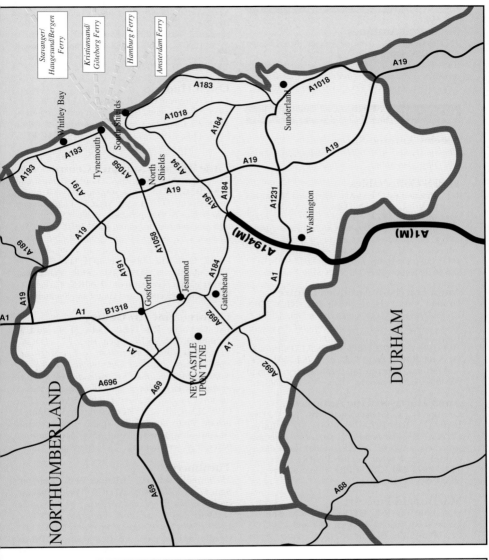

Dealers and Shops in Tyne and Wear

				Sunderland	1
Gateshead	1	Newcastle-upon-Tyne	8	Tynemouth	1
Gosforth	5	North Shields	1	Washington	2
Jesmond	5	South Shields	1	Whitley Bay	3

Sovereign Antiques
35 The Boulevard, Antique Village, Metrocentre. NE11 9YN. Open Mon.-Wed. 10-8, Thurs. 10-9, Sat. 9-6. STOCK: Fine antique and modern jewellery, diamonds, silver, prints and maps. TEL: 0191 460 9604; fax - 0191 460 7600.

Causey Antique Shop
Causey St. NE3 4DL. STOCK: Silver, Victoriana and collectors' items.

H & S Collectables
1-3 Ashburton Rd. NE3 4XN. (Harry and Mrs Sheila Shorrick). Est. 1986. Open 10-5, Sun. by appointment. SIZE: Small. STOCK: China, porcelain, figurines, Tyneside Malingware, spelter, silver, Sheffield plate, Cranberry glass, prints, armchairs and small occasional furniture, all £5-£900. LOC: On corner with Salters Road. TEL: 0191 284 6626; home - 0191 285 5543. SER: Valuations.

Anna Harrison Antiques Centre
Grange Park, Great North Rd. NE3 2DQ. LAPADA. Est. 1976. Open 10-5, Sat. 10.30-5. SIZE: Large. STOCK: Furniture and porcelain, 18th-20th C, £20-£2,000; paintings and prints, 19th-20th C, £50-£2,000. LOC: B1318 through Gosforth. PARK: Easy. TEL: 0191 284 3202. SER: Valuations; restorations (upholstery, French polishing, cabinet making, china). VAT: Stan/Spec.

Anna Harrison Fine Antiques
Grange Park, Great North Rd. NE3 2DQ. LAPADA. Est. 1976. Open 9-5. SIZE: Large. STOCK: English furniture, porcelain, oils and watercolours. LOC: A6125, 3 miles north of city centre, near Regent Centre. PARK: Forecourt. TEL: 0191 284 3202. SER: Valuations; restorations. VAT: Stan/Spec.

MacDonald Fine Art
8 Ashburton Rd. NE3 4XN. (T. and C. MacDonald). Est. 1976. Open 10-1 and 2.30-5.30. CL: Wed. SIZE: Medium. STOCK: Watercolours and oils, mainly north-eastern artists, English and Scottish, 18th-20th C. LOC: 1 mile west of A1. PARK: Easy. TEL: 0191 284 4214; home - 0191 285 6188. SER: Valuations; restorations (watercolours and oils); framing; buys at auction (watercolours and oils). VAT: Spec.

Cradlewell Antiques
4 Churchill Gardens. NE2 1LD. (Steve Bardy). Est. 1979. Open Thurs.-Sat. 11-5, Sun. 12-4., Tues. and Wed. by appointment. SIZE: Medium. STOCK: Small furniture, lighting, Art Nouveau, Art Deco, 20th C modern design, £50-£500; ceramics, bakelite telephones and radios, £20-£200. LOC: Left off A1058 coast road to shops at lights just before Cradlewell bypass. PARK: Easy. TEL: 0191 212 1500; mobile - 07966 246101.

Owen Humble
11-12 Clayton Rd. NE2 4RP. LAPADA. Est. 1958. Open 6 days. SIZE: Large and warehouse. STOCK: Furniture, general antiques. PARK: Easy. TEL: 0191 281 4602; fax - 0191 281 9076. SER: Restorations. VAT: Stan/Spec.

Little Theatre Antiques Centre
75-79 Fern Ave. NE2 2RA. (Louise Bennett and John Bell). Est. 1994. Open 10-5.30 or by appointment. SIZE: Large. STOCK: Victorian and Edwardian British furniture, £200-£500; north-east England pressed glass, 1860-1930, £20-£250; French furniture 1900's, £500-£1,500. LOC: Follow city centre motorway to Jesmond exit. PARK: Own. TEL: 0191 209 4321; fax - 0191 209 4320; mobile - 07951 035038. SER: Valuations; restorations (furniture). FAIRS: Caygill - Newcastle Racecourse and Gateshead Stadium.

Osborne Fine Art Gallery
18c Osborne Rd. NE2 2AD. (F.T. and J. Jackman). Est. 1974. Open 10-5.15. STOCK: Victorian and Edwardian oil paintings, watercolours, drawings and sketches - especially Northumbrian and Tyneside artists; topographical engravings and antiquarian maps, etchings including marine, 19th-20th C. TEL: 0191 281 6380. SER: Restorations (oil paintings, ornate Victorian frames); paper conservation (watercolours, maps, etchings, documents); bespoke picture-framing. VAT: Stan/Spec.

Turnburrys
257 Jesmond Rd. NE2 1LB. Est. 1995. Open 9-6, Sun. 12-3. SIZE: Large. STOCK: Period, antique and bespoke fireplaces; original and bespoke vestibule doors: radiators, Victorian to 1920's, £100-£500; over mantel mirrors. LOC: Off Cradlewell by-pass, next to Jesmond Dene. PARK: Easy. TEL: 0191 281 1770; fax - 0191 240 2569. SER: Valuations; restorations (doors, furniture and fireplaces). FAIRS: Traditional Homes & Period Living, London. VAT: Stan.

Davidson's The Jewellers Ltd
94 and 96 Grey St. NE1 6AG. Open 9-5.30. STOCK: Jewellery, silver. TEL: 0191 232 2551/232 2895.

The Dean Gallery Ltd
42 Dean St. NE1 1PG. Est. 1970. Open 10-5. CL: Sat. pm. SIZE: Large. *STOCK: Oils, water-colours, local and national, 18th to early 20th C, £500-£10,000.* LOC: Going north over Tyne Bridge, turn left, and left again. PARK: Easy. TEL: 0191 232 1208. SER: Valuations; restorations; framing. VAT: Stan/Spec.

Dog Leap Antiques
61 Side. NE1 3JE. Est. 1950. Open 9.15-1 and 2-5, Sat.9.30-1. SIZE: Small. *STOCK: Antique engravings and reproduction prints.* LOC: Bottom of Dean St. PARK: Easy. TEL: 0191 232 7269.

Intercoin
103 Clayton St. NE1 5PZ. Open 9-4.30. *STOCK: Coins and items of numismatic interest; jewellery, silver.* LOC: City centre. TEL: 0191 232 2064.

Steve Johnson Medals & Militaria
P O Box 1SP. NE99 1SP. *STOCK: Medals and militaria.* TEL: Fax - 01207 547073; e-mail - steve@wwmeinc.com; website - www.wwmeinc.com. *Mail Order and Online.*

Owen's Jewellers
14 and 153 Shields Rd., Byker. NE6 1DR. (D.W. Robertson). Est. 1968. Open 9-5. *STOCK: Jewellery.* TEL: 0191 265 4332/8699.

Shiners, Snobs Knobs
81 Fern Avenue, Jesmond. NE2 2RA. (B. and A. Lawson). Open 10-5. SIZE: Large. *STOCK: Fireplaces, door furniture, pine and vestibule doors, lighting, fenders.* PARK: Easy. TEL: 0191 281 6474; fax - 0191 281 9041.

R.D. Steedman
9 Grey St. NE1 6EE. Est. 1907. CL: Sat. pm. *STOCK: Rare books.* TEL: 0191 232 6561.

Maggie May's
(Incorporating Tynemouth Fine Art) 49 Kirton Park Terrace. NE29 0LJ. (Miss M.L. Hayes). Est. 1960. Open Thurs.-Sat. 11-5.30. SIZE: Medium. *STOCK: General antiques and collectors' items, Art Deco, Victorian and Edwardian furniture, china, glass; paintings and watercolours, especially North-umbrian artists, 1800-1950; Continental furniture, glassware, porcelain, decorative items, gramo-phones.* LOC: Opposite The Gunner Inn. TEL: 0191 237 6933. SER: Valuations; restorations; framing; French polishing; buys at auction.

The Curiosity Shop
16 Frederick St. NE33 5EA. Est. 1969. CL: Wed. *STOCK: General antiques, paintings, jewellery, furniture, Royal Doulton.* TEL: 0191 456 5560.

Peter Smith Antiques
12-14 Borough Rd. SR1 1EP. LAPADA. Est. 1968. Open 9.30-4.30, Sat. 10-1, other times by appointment. SIZE: Warehouse. *STOCK: Georgian, Victorian, Edwardian longcase clocks, shipping goods, £5-£15,000.* LOC: 10 miles from A1(M); towards docks/Hendon from town centre. PARK: Easy. TEL: 0191 567 3537/567 7842; fax - 0191 514 2286; home - 0191 514 0008; e-mail - petersmithantiques@btinternet.com. SER: Valuations; restorations; some shipping; containers packed; buys at auction. VAT: Stan/Spec.

Ian Sharp Antiques
23 Front St. NE30 4DX. LAPADA. Open 10-5.30 or by appointment. *STOCK: Furniture, 19th*

to early 20th C; British pottery including northern especially Maling and Sunderland lustreware, 18th to early 20th C. TEL: 0191 296 0656; fax – same; e-mail – iansharp@sharpantiques. demon. co.uk; website – www.sharpantiques. demon.co.uk.

WASHINGTON

Harold J. Carr Antiques
Field House, Rickleton. NE38 9HQ. LAPADA. Open by appointment. *STOCK: General antiques and furniture.* TEL: 0191 388 6442. SER: Shippers.

Grate Expectations (Fireplaces)
Unit 6, Lee Close, Pattinson North Industrial Estate. NE38 8QF. (Geoffrey Moore). Est. 1983. Open 9-5. SIZE: Large. *STOCK: Fireplaces, £95-£650; fireplace accessories, £10-£125; both 19th C.* LOC: Close to A1 and A19. PARK: Easy. TEL: 0191 416 0609. SER: Restorations (cast-iron refurbishment, repair and welding). VAT: Stan.

WHITLEY BAY

Northumbria Pine
54 Whitley Rd. NE26 2NF. (C. and V. Dowland). Est. 1979. Open 9-5.30. SIZE: Small. *STOCK: Stripped pine and reproduction items.* LOC: Cullercoats end of Whitley Rd., behind sea front. PARK: Easy. TEL: 0191 252 4550. VAT: Stan.

Oliver's Bookshop
48A Whitley Rd. NE26 2NF. (J. Oliver). Est. 1986. Open 11-5. CL: Tues. and Wed. SIZE: Small. *STOCK: Antiquarian and secondhand books, some postcards, 50p to £50.* PARK: Easy. TEL: 0191 251 3552. SER: Valuations. FAIRS: Tynemouth Book.

Treasure Chest
2 and 4 Norham Rd. NE26 2SB. Est. 1974. Open 10.30-1 and 2-4. CL: Wed. and Thurs. SIZE: Small. *STOCK: General antiques.* LOC: Just off main shopping area of Park View, leading to Monkseaton Railway Station. PARK: Easy. TEL: 0191 251 2052.

A set of six salts engraved with the crests of Proctor-Beauchamp, Wakelin & Taylor, 1789, £2,070. A salver on panel supports, Langlands & Robertson, Newcastle, 1786, 7in. diameter, £483. All sold at Gleneagles on 31st August 1999. Newcastle marked silver is one example of provincial silver where the prices rarely exceed similar London pieces. (Sotheby's)

From an article on silver by Peter Waldron which appeared in the July/August 2000 issue of **Antique Collecting** magazine. For more details and to subscribe see page 147.

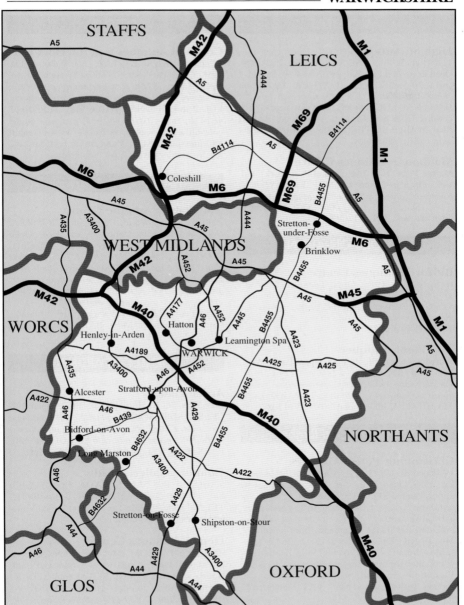

Dealers and Shops in Warwickshire

			Shipston-on-Stour	5
Alcester	2	Hatton	1	Stratford-upon-Avon	11
Bidford-on-Avon	2	Henley-in-Arden	3	Stretton-on-Fosse	1
Brinklow	2	Leamington Spa	4	Stretton-under-Fosse	1
Coleshill	1	Long Marston	1	Warwick	18

ALCESTER

High St. Antiques
11A High St. B49 5AE. (B.J. Payne). Est. 1979. Open Tues. and Fri. 11-1 and 2.30-4.30, Sat. 11-1 and 2.30-5. SIZE: Small. *STOCK: Glass and china, 18th-20th C, £5-£200; postcards and Art Deco china.* LOC: On left-hand side near church coming from Stratford-on-Avon road. PARK: Rear of High St. TEL: 01789 764009; home - same. SER: Valuations.

Malthouse Antiques Centre
Market Place. B49 5AE. (J. and P. Allcock). Est. 1982. Open 10-5, Sun. 1-4. SIZE: Large. *STOCK: Furniture, china, silver, collectables and objets d'art, 18th-20th C, £1-£2,000.* LOC: Adjacent to town car park. TEL: 01789 764032.

BIDFORD-ON-AVON

Bidford Antiques Centre
High St. Est. 1983. Open Tues. 10-6, Wed., Thurs., Sat. 10-5, Fri. 10-4. SIZE: 12 dealers. *STOCK: Furniture, china, glass, jewellery, pictures, books, linen, collectables.* PARK: Easy. TEL: 01789 773680.

Top Floor Antiques
Warwick House, 96 High St. Open Tues., Wed., Fri. and Sat. 10-4. *STOCK: Toby jugs, Torquayware, collectables, curios, china, glass, pictures, jewellery, bric-a-brac.* PARK: Easy. TEL: 01789 773680; mobile - 07855 913087.

BRINKLOW, Nr. Rugby

Christopher Peters Antiques
19 Broad St. CV23 0LS. (Chris and Jill Peters). Est. 1987. Open Thurs.-Sat. 10-5, other times by appointment. SIZE: Large. *STOCK: Country antiques, dressers, housekeepers' cupboards, decorative items. 18th C French provincial tables and armoires.* LOC: 10 minutes from junction 2, M6. PARK: Easy. TEL: 01788 832673; fax - same; home - 01926 632517; website - www.christopherpetersantiques.co.uk. SER: Valuations; restorations and repairs; buys at auction (period oak and pine). VAT: Stan/Spec.

The Victorian Ironmonger
The Old Garage, 70 Broad St. CV23 0LN. (Marlene and Dave Thompson). SALVO. Est. 1993. Open Fri. and Sat. 10-5, Sun. 11-3. SIZE: Medium. *STOCK: Door furniture, 17th to early 20th C, £2-£500; fireplaces, 19th C, £150-£1,500; architectural items, 17th to early 20th C, £25-£2,000.* PARK: Easy. TEL: 01788 832292; home - same. VAT: Spec.

COLESHILL

Coleshill Antiques and Interiors Ltd
12 and 14 High St. B46 1AZ. (A.J. Webster). Est. 1958. Open Tues.-Sat. 9.30-5 or by appointment. SIZE: Large. *STOCK: Continental porcelain, furniture, jewellery, silver and decorative items.* LOC: 1 mile from NEC. PARK: Easy. TEL: 01675 467416; fax - 01675 462931; e-mail - enq@coleshillantiques-com; website - www.coleshill antiques-com. SER: Valuations; restorations; repairs; interior design. VAT: Stan/Spec.

HATTON, Nr. Warwick

The Stables Antique Centre
Hatton Country World, Dark Lane. CV35 8XA. (John and Margaret Colledge). Est. 1990. Open 10-5 including Sun. SIZE: Large - 25 units. *STOCK: Furniture, 18th-19th C, £50-£3,000; china, 19th-20th C, £5-£200; clocks, 18th-19th C, £200-£4,000; linen, glass, brass and copper, paintings and prints, jukeboxes, radios, gramophones, kitchenalia and jewellery.* LOC: Just off A4177 Solihull-Warwick road, 5 minutes from junction 15, M40. PARK: Own. TEL: 01926 842405. SER: Valuations.

HENLEY-IN-ARDEN

Arden Gallery
B95 5AN. (G.B. Horton). Est. 1963. Open 1-6. CL: Sat. SIZE: Medium. *STOCK: Oil paintings, Victorian, £20-£1,000; watercolours, all periods, to £1,500; portrait miniatures.* LOC: A3400. PARK: Easy. TEL: 01564 792520. VAT: Spec.

Colmore Galleries Ltd
52 High St. B95 5AN. LAPADA. Open 11-5.30, Sat. 11-4.30. *STOCK: Pictures, 19th-20th C.* TEL: 01564 792938; fax - same. SER: Valuations; restorations; framing.

Henley Antiques Centre
92 High St. B95 5DM. (Mrs Rosie Montague, Gill Rayso, Gill Duse). Open 10.30-5, Sun. and Bank Holidays 11-4. CL: Mon. SIZE: Large. *STOCK: Furniture, 19th to early 20th C, £100-£200; porcelain, 20th C, £50-£100; collectables, 19th-20th C, £50-£100.* PARK Nearby. TEL: 01564 795979; mobile - 07950 324262. SER: Valuations.

LEAMINGTON SPA

David & Karol Hooper Antiques
The Elephant House, 38-40 Morton St. CV32 5SY. Open by appointment only. *STOCK:*

General antiques, fairground, circus and unusual items. TEL: 01926 429679; mobile - 07831 241284; 07775 850219.

The Incandescent Lighting Company
36 Regent St. CV32 5EG. (Mrs Patricia Cunningham). Est. 1988. Open 9.30-5.30, Sat. 9-6. SIZE: Medium. *STOCK: Lighting and especially glass shades, 19th to early 20th C, £25-£2,500; reproduction period-style lighting, shades and components, £2-£1,000.* LOC: Town centre. PARK: Easy. TEL: 01926 422421. SER: Valuations. VAT: Stan.

King's Cottage Antiques
4 Windsor St. CV32 5EB. (G. and A. Jackson). LAPADA. Open 9.30-5. *STOCK: Early oak and country furniture, 16th-18th C.* TEL: 01926 422927.

Yesterdays
21 Portland St. CV32 5EY. (Shona Caldwell). Est. 1986. Open Tues.-Sat. 10-5. SIZE: Medium. *STOCK: Furniture, George III to Edwardian, £75-£3,500; china, prints, 1850-1910, £10-£200.* Not Stocked: Pine. LOC: Parallel to The Parade. PARK: Easy. TEL: 01926 450238.

LONG MARSTON
Nr. Stratford-upon-Avon

Barn Antiques Centre
Station Rd. CV37 8RB. (Bev and Graham Simpson). Open every day 10-5. SIZE: Very large - over 35 dealers. *STOCK: Georgian, Victorian, Edwardian and later furniture, collectables, silver, porcelain, china, kitchenalia, fireplaces, linen, pictures, 18th C to 1950, £5-£2,000.* LOC: Take B4632 from Stratford-upon-Avon to Mickleton, brown tourist signs en route. PARK: Easy. TEL: 01789 721399; fax - 01789 721390.

SHIPSTON-ON-STOUR

Fine-Lines (Fine Art)
The Old Rectory Lodge, West St. CV36 4HD. (L.W. and R.M. Guthrie). LAPADA. Est. 1975. Open seven days by appointment only. SIZE: Medium. *STOCK: British and European water-colours, pastels, drawings and selected oils, from 1850, £300-£20,000.* PARK: Easy and nearby. TEL: 01608 662323 (answerphone). SER: Valuations; restorations, cleaning and framing; buys at auction (paintings, watercolours and drawings). VAT: Spec.

The Grandfather Clock Shop
2 Bondgate House, West St., Granville Court. CV36 4AL. (M.S. Chambers). Est. 1978. Open 9.30-5. CL:

Mon. and Thurs. pm. SIZE: Medium. *STOCK: Clocks - longcase, pre-1800, £2,500-£7,500; wall, £250-£1,000; mantel and bracket, 1790-1890, £200-£2,000; barometers, 1790-1860, £350-£2,000; furniture including oak, 17th-18th C.* PARK: Easy. TEL: 01608 662144; home - 01926 857487.

Halford Bridge Antiques
Halford Bridge. CV36 5BN. Open Tues., Thurs. and Sat. 2.30-5 or by appointment. SIZE: Small. *STOCK: Furniture, paintings, silver and EPNS, clocks, rugs, prints, copper, brass, pewter, ivory, statuary, garden ornaments, watercolours and etchings, 18th-20th C.* LOC: On Fosse Way A429, near Tredington roundabout. PARK: Fairly easy. TEL: 01789 740377.

Pine and Things
Portobello Farm, Campden Rd. CV36 4PY. (Richard Wood). Est. 1991. Open 9-5. SIZE: Large. *STOCK: Pine, 18th-19th C, £50-£2,000.* LOC: A429. PARK: Easy. TEL: 01608 663849; home - same; website - www.pineandthings.net. VAT: Stan/Spec.

'Time in Hand'
11 Church St. CV36 4AP. (F.R. Bennett). Open 9-1 and 2-5.30 or by appointment. SIZE: Large. *STOCK: Longcase, carriage and wall clocks, barometers.* PARK: Free - Banbury Road. TEL: 01608 662578. SER: Restorations (clocks, watches, barometers and mechanical instruments).

STRATFORD-UPON-AVON

The Antique Shop
30 Henley St. (Margaret Clift). Est. 1969. Open 10-5.30, Sun. 11-5.30. *STOCK: 19th C jewellery, collectables and furniture, £10-£100.* LOC: Opposite Shakespeare's birthplace. PARK: Windsor St. TEL: 01789 292485. SER: Valuations.

Arbour Antiques Ltd
Poet's Arbour, Sheep St. CV37 6EF. (R.J. Wigington). Est. 1952. Open 9-5, Sat. by appointment. *STOCK: Arms and armour.* LOC: From town centre towards Theatre and River, behind Lamb's Café through archway at right. TEL: 01789 293453. VAT: Spec.

Bow Cottage Antiques
At 30 Henley St. CV37 6QW. (R. Harvey-Morgan). Open 10-5.30. *STOCK: English porcelain, glass, silver, paintings, engravings, maps, books; general antiques, all 18th-20th C, £5-£150+.* TEL: 01789 205883. FAIRS: Classic.

Burman Antiques
34 College St. CV37 6BW. (J. and J. Burman Holtom). Est. 1973. Open by appointment only. *STOCK: Ruskin ware, pot-lids, fishing tackle.* TEL: 01789 295164. SER: Restorations (clocks).

TEXTILES

Patricia Frost

The past year has seen a consolidation of the market for antique textiles and costumes, with some very high prices for exceptional items and a marked lack of enthusiasm for the lower end of the market. Collectors and dealers are now international, but the market is really centred in London, despite local high spots such as strong prices for French textiles in France, and enthusiasm for Oriental textiles in New York.

Specialist sales did well, seeing a steeper rise in interest than general sales, as auction houses and fairs targeted clients with particular collecting fields. Many watched with interest the inauguration at Olympia in June of the Hali Antique Carpet and Textile Art Fair. This was generally pronounced successful and is intended to be an annual event. It seems that mid range carpets and European textiles were the most sought after, with other more specialist areas such as Chinese textiles not as popular.

The core of the London market is, of course, European textiles. The last twelve months have seen the auction houses offering some spectacular pieces which have had collectors dipping deep into their piggy-banks. Sotheby's, for instance, twice broke the world record for a 17th century sampler, proving that these embroideries have a big following, particularly in America. However, decorative samplers have also been selling well, firming middle market prices. Late or damaged pieces have not been finding homes so easily.

Large-scale embroideries and pictures have been selling well with some high prices for tapestry fragments and 18th century embroidered hangings of the kind which work well in 18th century interiors. Arts and Crafts textiles, particularly William Morris, are now rare but keenly disputed; a screen with embroidered panels sold in November at Christie's South Kensington for £5,750.

Early laces have been difficult to find in the last twelve months, unlike the ever-popular Brussels Point de Gaze needlelace, for which the market appears to have an insatiable appetite. Large-scale pieces, particularly shawls and wedding veils, are the most popular. Phillips sold a large stole in May for £2,500 and a wedding gown of Brussels lace for £4,000, with smaller flounces still being affordable. Collectors might consider avoiding the '3Bs' (Big Bits of Brussels) and concentrate

A fine and important long sampler, English, c.1660, £80,700. (Sotheby's).

on snapping up 17th and 18th century fragments for a comparatively small outlay.

Prices for European shawls have settled to a more realistic level after a prolonged period of high prices in the mid 1990s buoyed up by interest from interior decorators. Most decent 1860s shawls can now be bought for between £200-£500, with only the exceptional shawl, such as the Duché Ainé shawl sold at Christie's South Kensington in January (£13,800) scaling the heights. Indian Kashmir shawl prices fluctuate in a unpredictable manner so that it is possible to find beautiful shawls at reasonable prices; a Kashmir shawl is, however, still roughly three times as expensive as its French or Scottish counterpart.

Costume collectors have been offered some very interesting 18th century pieces this year. Men's coats, usually without the matching breeches, from the second half of

Ottoman embroidery, late 17th century, £21,850. (Christie's, South Kensington)

Pair of 17th century mules, £10,400. (Phillips)

Rare chintz open robe decorated with coloured silks and silver metal thread, late 18th century. Because it was virtually unaltered it made £20,700. (Christie's, South Kensington)

the 18th century, are the most common survivors. Women's costume is more frequently altered to suit later generations, prices varying according to the silk they are made of and the extent of the alterations. Because virtually unaltered, a rare chintz open robe of the late 18th century, offered by Christie's South Kensington in November, sold for £20,700.

Islamic and Indian textiles, particularly classic Mughal and Ottoman textiles, are the focus of the non-European market, with all the auction houses offering good pieces, either in the context of decorative art sales or in specialist sales. High prices were paid for classical Ottoman textiles in Sotheby's Turkish sale and Christie's South Kensington's Islamic & Indian textile sales. Early Chinese textiles, a relatively new field of interest for the art market, have been selling for six figure sums on a regular basis both at fairs and from specialist dealers. These textiles are now coming on to the auction market as well, as seen when Spink offered an interesting selection at Christie's South Kensington in June.

Textiles to watch are those from North Africa, particularly Morocco and Tunisia, where there are serious collectors waiting for the right pieces. Quilts are still relatively cheap, especially in comparison to US prices, although the best are rising in price.

The message of the past year seems to be that the market responds to specialist auctions, dealers and fairs. This to me indicates that the market is becoming more sophisticated. Better quality catalogues and presentation encourage the general buying public to look at textiles as works of art. This can only be good news for those of us who collect textiles.

Patricia Frost is a specialist in antique textiles at Christie's South Kensington.

*This article appeared in the July/August 1998 issue of **Antique Collecting** magazine. For more details and to subscribe see page 147.*

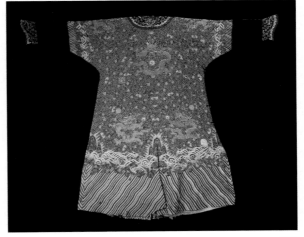

Imperial robe, kesi, 19th century, £10,350. (Christie's South Kensington)

Howards Jewellers
44a Wood St. CV37 6JG. (Howards of Stratford Ltd). Est. 1985. Open 9.30-5.30. *STOCK: Jewellery, silver, objets d'art, 19th C.* LOC: Town centre. PARK: Nearby. TEL: 01789 205404. SER: Valuations; restorations (as stock). VAT: Stan/Spec.

The Loquens Gallery
The Minories, Rother St. CV37 6NF. (S. and J. Loquens). Est. 1980. Open 9.30-5, Sun. by appointment. SIZE: Medium. *STOCK: English watercolours, some oil paintings, late 18th to early 20th C, to £5,000.* LOC: From island in town centre, follow Wood St. to Rother St. junction, entrance to Minories is on right. PARK: Easy. TEL: 01789 297706. SER: Valuations; restorations (cleaning watercolours, relining oils); framing. VAT: Stan/Spec.

George Pragnell Ltd
5 & 6 Wood St. CV37 6JA. *STOCK: Jewellery and silver.* TEL: 01789 267072; fax - 01789 415131; e-mail - enquiries@pragnell.co.uk; website - www.pragnell.co.uk.

Stratford Antique Centre
Ely St. CV37 6LN. (N. Sims). Open 10-5.30 every day. SIZE: 60 dealers. *STOCK: General antiques.* TEL: 01789 204180.

The Stratford Antiques and Interiors Centre Ltd
Dodwell Industrial Park, Evesham Rd. CV37 9ST. (Andrew and Suszanna Kerr). Est. 1980. Open 10-5 including Sun., evenings by appointment. SIZE: 25+ dealers. *STOCK: Georgian, Victorian, Edwardian and shipping furniture, £100-£8,000; china and smalls, 19th-20th C, £5-£300; reclaimed pine, £50-£2,000.* LOC: B439. PARK: Easy. TEL: 01789 297729; fax - 01789 297710; website - www.stratfordantiques.co.uk. SER: Valuations; restorations; buys at auction. FAIRS: Newark and Ardingly.

The Stratford Bookshop
45A Rother St. CV37 6LT. (J. and S. Hill). Est. 1993. Open 10-6. SIZE: Medium. *STOCK: Secondhand and out-of-print books.* LOC: From island in town centre follow Wood St., shop opposite police station. PARK: Easy. TEL: 01789 298362.

Robert Vaughan
20 Chapel St. CV37 6EP. (C.M. Vaughan). ABA. Est. 1953. Open 9.30-5.30. SIZE: Medium. *STOCK: Antiquarian and out-of-print books, maps and prints.* LOC: Town centre. PARK: Easy. TEL: 01789 205312. SER: Valuations; buys at auction (books). VAT: Stan.

Astley House - Fine Art
The Old School. GL56 9SA. (David, Nanette and Caradoc Glaisyer). LAPADA. CADA. Est. 1973. Open by appointment. SIZE: Large. *STOCK: Large decorative oil paintings, 19th-21st C.* LOC: Village centre. PARK: Easy. TEL: 01608 650601; fax - 01608 651777; e-mail - astart333@aol.com; website - www.art-uk.com. SER: Exhibitions; mailing list. VAT: Spec.

The Old Forge
29 Main St. CV23 0PF. (A. Blackburn). Est. 1991. Open Fri., Sat. and Sun. 11-4 pm. SIZE: Large. *STOCK: Hardwood furniture, £50-£5,000; pine, £50-£1,000; ceramics, £5-£300; glass, £5-£100.* LOC: Half mile from The Fosse Way, 2 miles north of Brinklow and 8 miles north east of Coventry. PARK: Easy. TEL: 01788 832191; e-mail - r.black2330@aol.com; website - www. oldforge. antiques.co.uk. SER: Buys at auction (furniture).

Duncan M. Allsop
68 Smith St. CV34 4HS. ABA. Est. 1965. Open 9.30-5.30. SIZE: Medium. *STOCK: Antiquarian and modern books.* PARK: Nearby. TEL: 01926 493266; fax - same; mobile - 07770 895924.

Apollo Antiques Ltd
The Saltisford, Birmingham Rd. CV34 4TD. (R.H. Mynott). LAPADA. Est. 1968. Open 9-6, Sat. 9.30-12.30. SIZE: Large. *STOCK: English furniture, 18th-19th C; Continental and gothic revival furniture, sculpture, paintings, Arts and Crafts and decorative items.* PARK: Easy. TEL: 01926 494746; fax - 01926 401477; e-mail - mynott@apolloantiques.com; website - www. apolloantiques.com. VAT: Stan/Spec

William J. Casey Antiques
9 High St. CV34. (William and Pat Casey). LAPADA. Est. 1970. Open 10-5, Sun. by appointment. SIZE: Large. *STOCK: Furniture, 18th-20th C, £750-£7,500.* LOC: Town Centre. PARK: Nearby. TEL: 01926 499199; home - 01562 777507. VAT: Spec.

Castle Antiques
24 Swan St. CV34 4BJ. (Julia Reynolds). Est. 1979. Open 10-5, Sun. by appointment. SIZE: Medium. *STOCK: China including Shelley, and linen, 19th-20th C, £5-£500; furniture, 19th to early 20th C, £100-£3,000.* LOC: Town centre.

PARK: Easy - at rear. TEL: 01926 401511; fax - 01926 492469. SER: Restorations (ceramics). FAIRS: Heritage Museum, Gaydon. VAT: Spec.

English Antiques
3 High St. CV34 4AP. (Cadport Ltd). Est. 1959. Open 10-5.30, Sun. by appointment. SIZE: Very large. *STOCK: 18th-19th C furniture especially dining tables, £1,000-£15,000; decorative smalls.* PARK: Nearby. TEL: 01926 408656; fax - same. VAT: Stan/Spec.

John Goodwin and Sons
20-22 High St., CV34 4AP. Open 9.30-5.30. SIZE: Shop (+ warehouse on request - 20 mins. away). *STOCK: Furniture, clocks, ceramics, oil paintings, collectables.*TEL: 01926 853332. SER: Restorations (furniture).

Russell Lane Antiques
2-4 High St. CV34 4AP. (R.G.H. Lane). Open 10-5. *STOCK: Fine jewellery and silver.* TEL: 01926 494494.

Patrick and Gillian Morley Antiques
62 West St. CV34 6AW. LAPADA. Est. 1968. Open 9-5.30, Sat. and Sun. by appointment. SIZE: Large. *STOCK: Furniture, 17th to late 19th C; unusual and decorative items, sculpture, carvings and textiles; all £50-£20,000.* LOC: Almost opposite Warwick Castle 2nd car park. PARK: Easy. TEL: 01926 494464; home - 01926 854191; mobile - 07768 835040; fax - 01926 400531. SER: Valuations; buys at auction. VAT: Mainly Spec.

Patrick and Gillian Morley Antiques Warehouse
Unit 7 Cape Industrial Estate, Cattell Rd. Est. 1968. Open 9-5.30, Sat. and Sun. by appointment. SIZE: Large. *STOCK: 17th to late 19th C fine furniture, unusual and decorative items, sculpture, carvings, £50-£50,000.* TEL: 01926 498849; fax - 01926 400531.

The Old Cornmarket Antiques Centre
70 Market Place. CV34 4SO. (Jonathan Lysaght). Est. 1993. Open 10-5, Sat. 9.30-5.30. LOC: Town centre. TEL: 01926 419119. FAIRS: Below are listed the dealers at this Centre:

Cliffe Antiques
Est. 1973. *Antique jewellery, silver and porcelain.*

P.M. Haddow
Military and sports items.

J & S Antiques
(J. Lysaght). *Clocks, from carriage to bracket.*

Midland Goss and Commemoratives
Est. 1978. *Ceramics especially Goss and crested ware.*

Richmond Antiques
(Terry Hare-Walker). Est. 1981. *Period jewellery, wooden boxes, barometers and porcelain.*

The Saltisford, Warwick CV34 4TD
Tel: 01926 494746   Fax: 01926 401477
email: mynott@apolloantiques.com

Fine English and Continental Furniture and Works of Art. Also Arts & Crafts & Gothic Revival.

1½ hrs from central London via M40 (J15).

VISIT OUR WEBSITE
www.apolloantiques.com

WARWICK

JAMES REEVE

9 Church Street
Warwick
Tel 01926-498113

Antique English furniture of the 17th, 18th and 19th centuries. All items are sold in the finest condition.

Established over 100 years

James Reeve

at Quinneys of Warwick, 9 Church St. CV34 4AB. Est. 1865. Open 9.30-5.30. CL: Sat. pm. *STOCK: Furniture, mahogany, oak, and rosewood, 17th-18th C, £80-£30,000; furniture, 19th C, £50-£10,000; glass, copper, brass, pewter, china.* TEL: 01926 498113. VAT: Stan/Spec.

A Safari chair by Kaare Klint for Rud Rasmussens Snedkerier, Denmark, c.1960. Sold for £391 in March 2000.

From an article entitled 'Scandinavian Furniture 1930-1975' by Dan Tolson which appeared in the December 2000/January 2001 issue of **Antique Collecting** magazine. For more details and to subscribe see page 147.

Don Spencer Antiques

36a Market Place. CV34 4SH. Est. 1963. Open daily. SIZE: Large. *STOCK: Desks, 1850-1920, £500-£5,000; dining furniture and bookcases, 1800-1920, £500-£3,000.* PARK: Easy. TEL: 01926 499857/407989; home - 01564 775470; website - www.antique-desks.co.uk. VAT: Stan/Spec.

Summersons

172 Emscote Rd. CV34 5QN. (Peter Lightfoot). CMBHI. Open 10-5, Sat. 10-1. *STOCK: Clocks and barometers.* TEL: 01926 400630; fax - same; mobile - 07770 300695; e-mail - clocks@ summersons. com; website - www.summersons. com. SER: Restorations; repairs; materials and parts.

Tango Art Deco & Antiques

46 Brook St. CV34 4BL. (Jenny and Martin Wills). Open Thurs., Fri. and Sat. 10-5. SIZE: Medium. *STOCK: Art Deco and general including Clarice Cliff, Susie Cooper, Myott, Burleigh, Carlton, Crown Devon, small furniture, mirrors, £5-£1,000.* LOC: Town centre. PARK: Free nearby. TEL: 01926 496999; home/fax - 0121 704 4969; e-mail - info@tango-artdeco.co.uk; website - www.tango-artdeco.co.uk. FAIRS: NEC; Stafford; Deco at Warwick, Loughborough, Chester, Leeds, Syon Park. VAT: Spec.

Vintage Antiques Centre

36 Market Place. CV34 4SH. (Peter Sellors). Est. 1977. Open 10-5.30, Sun. 11.30-4.30. SIZE: 15 dealers + cabinets. *STOCK: Ceramics, glass, collectables and small furniture, 19th-20th C.* PARK: Easy. TEL: 01926 491527.

The Warwick Antique Centre

20-22 High St. CV34 4AP. Est. 1973. Open 10-5. SIZE: 25 dealers. *STOCK: Porcelain, silver and plate, jewellery, coins, militaria, books, furniture, stamps, metalware, toys, collectables, postcards, glass.* TEL: 01926 491382/495704.

Warwick Antiques

16-18 High St. CV34 4AP. (M. Morrison). Est. 1969. Open 9-5, Sat. 10-5. SIZE: Large and warehouses. *STOCK: Furniture, mahogany, oak, Chinese; metalware, copper, brass, pewter, glass, china, bygones, curios, statuary, garden furniture, shipping goods.* LOC: Midway between East and West Gate clock towers. PARK: At rear. TEL: 01926 492482; fax - 01926 492482. SER: Restorations (furniture). VAT: Stan/Spec.

West Rock Antiques

19 West Rock, Birmingham Rd., The Saltisford. CV34 4SG. (Christina Goodson). Est. 1974. Open 9.30-5.30, Sat. 10-4. SIZE: Medium. *STOCK: Furniture, £200-£5,000; decorative items, £5-£500; both 19th C; general antiques, to 1940, £50-£100.* PARK: At rear. TEL: 01926 411175; fax - 01926 411176. SER: Valuations.

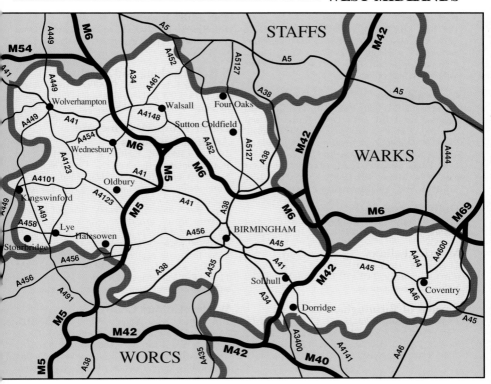

Dealers and Shops in the West Midlands

Birmingham	20	Kingswinford	1	Sutton Coldfield	4
Coventry	2	Lye	2	Walsall	3
Dorridge	1	Oldbury	1	Wednesbury	1
Four Oaks	2	Solihull	2	Wolverhampton	9
Halesowen	1	Stourbridge	3		

BIRMINGHAM

Peter Asbury Antiques
Greenfield House Farm, 6 Hales Lane, Smethwick, Warley. B67 6RS. Open 9.30-5. *STOCK: General antiques.* TEL: 0121 558 0579. SER: Doll repairs.

Paul Baxter
Open by appointment only. *STOCK: Oriental ceramics and general antiques.* TEL: 01564 824920.

The Birmingham Antique Centre
1403-1407 Pershore Rd., Stirchley. B30 2JR. Est. 1960. Open 9-5.30, Sun. 10-5. *STOCK: General antiques, collectables, shipping furniture, trade display cabinets.* TEL: 0121 459 4587/689 6565.

Carleton Gallery
91 Vivian Rd., Harborne. B17 0DR. (D. Dunnett). Open 9-5.30, Wed. 9-1. *STOCK: Maps and prints.* TEL: 0121 427 2487.

Chesterfield Antiques
181 Gravelly Lane. B23 5SG. (Mara Cirjanic). Est. 1977. Open 9.30-5.30. *STOCK: General antiques and fine art.* TEL: 0121 373 3876.

Peter Clark Antiques
36 St. Mary's Row, Moseley. B13 8JG. LAPADA. Open 9-5.30. SIZE: Medium. *STOCK: Furniture, mid-17th C to early 20th C, £175-£2,500; silver, early 19th C to early 20th C, £100-£500. LOC: Centre of Moseley. PARK: At rear. TEL: 0121 449 8245. SER: Valuations; restorations (furniture). VAT: Stan/Spec.*

R. Collyer
185 New Rd., Rubery. B45 9JP. Open 9-5.30. *STOCK: Clocks including longcase; watches, barometers, secondhand jewellery.* LOC: 1 mile from junction 4, M5. TEL: 0121 453 2332. SER: Valuations; restorations.

Cross's Curios
928 Pershore Rd., Selly Park. B29 7PY. (John and Valerie Cross). Est. 1972. Open Thurs., Fri. and Sat. 10-6, other times by appointment. SIZE: Small. *STOCK: Old toys, juvenalia, dolls, tinplate, teddies, furniture, china, jewellery and collectables.* LOC: From city centre, take Pershore Rd., shop just past Pebble Mill on left. PARK: Easy. TEL: 0121 415 4866. SER: Valuations; buys at auction.

Dolly Mixtures
Open by appointment. *STOCK: Dolls and teddies.* TEL: 0121 422 6959. SER: Restorations.

Maurice Fellows
21 Vyse St., Hockley. B18 6LE. *STOCK: Objets d'art, jewellery.* TEL: 0121 554 0211. SER: Valuations; restorations.

Format of Birmingham Ltd
18 Bennetts Hill. B2 5QJ. (G. Charman and D. Vice). Open 9.30-5. CL: Sat. *STOCK: Coins, medals.* PARK: New St. station. TEL: 0121 643 2058. VAT: Stan/Spec.

Garratt Antiques
20 Great Western Arcade. Est. 1958. *STOCK: Jewellery, clocks, brass, silver, copper, pewter, silver plate, china, crystal, dolls and bric-a-brac.* TEL: 0121 212 9770; fax - 0121 200 1591. SER: Valuations; restorations - VAT: Stan/Spec.

A.W. Hone and Son Oriental Carpets
1486 Stratford Rd., Hall Green. B28 9ET. (Ian Hone). Est. 1949. Open 9.30-5.30, Sun. 11-4. SIZE: Medium. *STOCK: Persian rugs and carpets, late 19th C to date.* LOC: A34 south of city on Robin Hood Island. PARK: Own forecourt. TEL: 0121 744 1001; fax - same. SER: Valuations; restorations; finder service. VAT: Stan.

Rex Johnson and Sons
8 Corporation St. B2 4RN. (D. Johnson). Open 9.15-5.15. *STOCK: Gold, silver, jewellery, porcelain and glass.* TEL: 0121 643 9674.

F. Meeks & Co
197 Warstone Lane, Hockley. B18. (M.L. and S.R. Durham). Open 9-5, Sat. 9-12. *STOCK: Clocks especially longcase, mantel and wall; vintage wrist watches and antique pocket watches; all £100-£10,000.* TEL: 0121 236 9058. SER: Valuations; restorations (clocks); clock and watch parts supplied. VAT: Stan/Spec.

Piccadilly Jewellers
105 New St. B2 4HD. (R. and R. Johnson). Open 10-5. *STOCK: Jewellery, silver and objects.* TEL: 0121 643 5791.

S.R. Furnishing and Antiques
18 Stanley Rd., Oldbury. B68 0DY. (S. Willder). Est. 1975. *STOCK: General antiques and shipping furniture.* TEL: 0121 422 9788.

David Temperley Fine and Antiquarian Books
19 Rotton Park Rd., Edgbaston. B16 9JH. (D. and R.A. Temperley). Resident. Est. 1967. Open 9.30-5.30 by prior appointment. SIZE: Small. *STOCK: Fine antiquarian and rare books,16th-20th C especially fine bindings, illustrated and private press; fine colour plate books - natural history, costume, travel, British topography and atlases; early and rare English and European playing cards.* LOC: 150 yards off Hagley Rd. (A456) and under 2 miles from city centre. 4 miles junction 3, M5. PARK: Easy. TEL: 0121 454 0135; fax - 0121 454 1124. SER: Valuations; restorations (book binding and paper); buys at auction (antiquarian books).

Warley Antique Centre
146 Pottery Rd., Warley Woods. B68 9HD. (Angela Hamilton). Open six days. SIZE: 70 cabinets and 4 furniture showrooms. *STOCK: Antiques, furnishings and collectables including Ruskin, Worcester, Doulton, clocks, silver, mainly 19th-20th C.* LOC: Off the A456 or A4123, junctions 2/3, M5. PARK: Easy. TEL: 0121 434 3813; mobile - 07702 976759.

The Windmill Gallery
c/o Snell & Prideaux Ltd., 6 Ernest St., Holloway Head. B1 1NS. (M. and C. Ashton). Est. 1985. Open 9-5.30, Sat. and Sun. by appointment. SIZE: Medium. *STOCK: Watercolours and drawings, 18th-20th C, £100-£3,000+.* LOC: City centre. PARK: Easy. TEL: 0121 622 3986; fax - 0121 666 6630. SER: Valuations; restorations; mounting, framing. VAT: Spec.

COVENTRY

Coventry Antique Centre
Rugby Rd., Binley Woods. (N. and J. Green). Open 10-4.45, including Sun. SIZE: 10 dealers. *STOCK: Furniture including shipping, and effects.* LOC: Close to M6, M69, A46 and M1. PARK: Easy. TEL: 024 7645 3878. VAT: Stan.

Luckmans Antiques
40 Far Gosford St. CV1 5DW. (K. Harris). Est. 1977. Open 12.30-6. CL: Tues. SIZE: Small. *STOCK: Bric-a-brac, books, medals, post and cigarette cards.* PARK: Easy. TEL: 02476 223842.

DORRIDGE, Nr. Solihull

Dorridge Antiques & Collectables
7 Forest Court. (M. Kentish and C. Swift). SIZE: Medium. *STOCK: Furniture, £5-£1,500 ;ceramics, £5-£1,100; arms and armour, £5-£750; all from 18th C.* PARK: Easy. TEL: 01564 779336; home - 01564 779768.

FOUR OAKS, Nr. Sutton Coldfield

M. Allen Watch and Clockmaker
76A Walsall Rd. B74 4QY. (M.A. Allen). Est. 1969. Open 9-5.30, Sun. by appointment. SIZE: Small. *STOCK: Vintage wristwatches - Omega, Longines, Girard, Perregaux and Jaeger le Coultre; clocks - Vienna regulators, 1820-1880, mantel and wall clocks.* LOC: By Sutton Park, close to television mast. PARK: Easy. TEL: 0121 308 6117; home - 0121 308 8134. SER: Valuations; restorations (clocks and watches). VAT: Stan/Spec.

Robert Taylor
Windy Ridge, Worcester Lane. B75 5QS. Est. 1983. Open 9-6.30 including Sun., by appointment only. *STOCK: Old collectable toys, including Dinky, Corgi, clockwork, tinplate, £5-£1,000.* PARK: Easy. TEL: 0121 308 4209; fax - 0121 323 3473. SER: Valuations; buys at auction. FAIRS: NEC; Donington; Windsor.

HALESOWEN, Nr. Birmingham

Tudor House Antiques
68 Long Lane. B62 9LS. (D. Taylor). Open 9.30-5.30. *STOCK: Doors, fireplaces, pine including kitchens and furniture.* TEL: 0121 561 5563.

KINGSWINFORD

Unicorn Antiques & Reproductions
29-30 High St., Wall Heath. DY6 0JA. (J.C. Vaughan). Est. 1998. Open Tues. and Wed. 10.15-4.15, Sat.10.15-5. SIZE: Medium. *STOCK: 19th C and reproduction furniture, china and collectables, £5-£1,000.* LOC: A449. PARK: Easy. TEL: 01384 288122. SER: Restorations (furniture).

LYE, Nr. Stourbridge

Lye Antique Furnishings
High St. DY9 8LH. (Mr and Mrs P. Smith). Est. 1979. Open 9-5. SIZE: Medium. *STOCK: Furniture, china, glass, metalware and collectors' items.* PARK: Easy. TEL: 01384 897513; mobile - 07976 765142. SER: Valuations.

Retro Antiques
Antique Warehouse, The Yard, Star St. DY9 8TU. (M. McHugo). Est. 1980. Open 9.30-5. CL: Sat. SIZE: Large. *STOCK: Furniture - Victorian, Edwardian, garden and shipping, £5-£1,000; cast iron, metalwork, architectural items.* LOC: Off Stourbridge to Birmingham Rd. PARK: Easy. TEL: 01384 894042/442065; mobile - 07860 307446. FAIRS: Ardingly and Newark. VAT: Stan.

OLDBURY

The Glory Hole
431 Moat Rd., Warley. B68 8EJ. (Colin Dickens). Est. 1985. Open 9.30-5.30, Tues. 12-5.30, Sat.10-5.30. SIZE: Small. *STOCK: Furniture, 19th-20th C, £50-£100; china, 20th C, £5-£100.* PARK: Easy. TEL: 0121 544 1888; home - 0121 561 3573. SER: Valuations. FAIRS: Malvern Showground, Peterborough Festival, Norwich Sports Centre.

SOLIHULL

Renaissance
18 Marshall Lake Rd., Shirley. B90 4PL. (S.K. Macrow). MGMC. Est. 1981. Open 9-5. SIZE: Small. *STOCK: General antiques.* LOC: Near Stratford Rd. TEL: 0121 745 5140. SER: Restorations (repairs, re-upholstery and polishing).

Tilleys Antiques
(S.A. Alpren). GADAR. Open by appointment only. *STOCK: British glass, Oriental pottery, porcelain, shipping goods; silver, 19th C; Worcester.* TEL: 0121 704 1813. SER: Valuations; restorations (jewellery, silver); clock and watch repairs.

STOURBRIDGE

Oldswinford Gallery
106 Hagley Rd., Oldswinford. DY8 1QU. (A.R. Harris). Open 9.30-5. CL: Mon. and Sat. p.m. *STOCK: 18th-20th C oil paintings, watercolours, antiquarian prints and maps.* TEL: 01384 395577. SER: Restorations; framing.

Regency Antique Trading Centre
116 Stourbridge Rd. DY9 7BU. (D. Bevan). Open 9.30-5. SIZE: Several dealers. *STOCK: General antiques and collectables, fireplaces and pine.* TEL: 01384 868778.

Retro
48 Worcester St. DY8 1AS. (M. McHugo). Open Tues., Thurs., Sat. 9.30-5. *STOCK: Furniture.* TEL: 01384 442065.

SUTTON COLDFIELD

Thomas Coulborn and Sons BADA
Vesey Manor, 64 Birmingham Rd. B72 1QP. (P. Coulborn). Est. 1939. Open 9.15-5.30 (1hr. lunch). SIZE: Large. *STOCK: General antiques, 1600-1830; fine English and Continental furniture, 17th-18th C; paintings and clocks.* LOC: 3 miles from Spaghetti Junction. From Birmingham A5127 through Erdington, premises on main road opposite cinema. PARK: Easy. TEL: 0121 354 3974; fax - 0121 354 4614; e-mail - art@coulborn. com. SER: Valuations; restorations (furniture and paintings); buys on commission. VAT: Spec.

Driffold Gallery
78 Birmingham Rd. B72 1QR. (David Gilbert). Open 10.30-5.30. CL: Thurs. *STOCK: Oil paintings and watercolours, 19th C to contemporary.* TEL: 0121 355 5433.

Osborne Antiques
91 Chester Rd., New Oscott. B73 5BA. (C. Osborne). Est. 1976. Open 9-5, Sat. 9.15-1. CL: Mon. *STOCK: Barometers and clocks.* TEL: 0121 355 6667. SER: Restorations; spares (clocks, barometers); glass-blowers (barometers).

H. and R.L. Parry Ltd
23 Maney Corner. B72 1QL. (H. Parry). Est. 1925. Open 9.30-5.30. CL: Wed. SIZE: Medium. *STOCK: Porcelain, silver and jewellery, all periods; metalware, paintings.* LOC: A38 from Birmingham road into Sutton. Cinema on right, on corner of service road in which premises are situated. TEL: 0121 354 1178. SER: Valuations. VAT: Stan/Spec.

WALSALL

The Doghouse
309 Bloxwich Rd. WS2 7BD. Open 9-5.30, Sun. (Oct.-March) 2-5.30. SIZE: Large. *STOCK: General antiques.* TEL: 01922 630829. VAT: Stan.

Hardwick Antiques
317B Chester Rd., Aldridge. WS9 0PH. (P. Chatfield). Open 11-5. CL: Wed. am. *STOCK: Jewellery, silver, porcelain, furniture.* LOC: Opposite Ruby Rest. TEL: 0121 353 1489.

L.P. Antiques (Mids) Ltd
The Old Brewery, Short Acre St. WS2 8HW. (Pierre Farouz). Est. 1982. Open daily, Sun. by appointment. SIZE: Warehouse. *STOCK: French and Continental decorative furniture, period armoires, rustic furniture, parquet tables, reproduction chairs.* LOC: Junction 10, M6, take A34 towards Cannock. PARK: Easy. TEL: 01922 746764; fax - 01922 611316; mobile - 07860 249097; e-mail - pierre.farouz@virgin.net; website - www.lpantiques.co.uk. SER: Packing, shipping. VAT: Stan.

WEDNESBURY

Brett Wilkins Antiques
81 Holyhead Rd. WS10 7PA. (Brett Wilkins Ltd). Est. 1983. Open by appointment only. SIZE: Medium. *STOCK: Shipping, export and French furniture.* PARK: Easy. TEL: 0121 502 0720; mobile - 07860 541260. FAIRS: All major. VAT: Stan. *Export Only.*

WOLVERHAMPTON

Afantiques
Open by appointment only. *STOCK: Clocks, wrist and pocket watches.* TEL: 01902 731167.

Antiquities
75-76 Dudley Rd. Est. 1968. Open 10-6. *STOCK: General antiques.* TEL: 01902 459800.

Doveridge House Antiques BADA
P O Box 1856. WV3 9XH. LAPADA. CINOA. Open by appointment. *STOCK: 17th-19th C English and Continental furniture, fine art,*

I'M COMING ROMPING HOME.

Design no. 1233 from the Chloë Preston Series, pub: Valentine (1928). Artist: Chloë Preston (1928).

From an article entitled 'Little Treasures – Collecting Children's Postcards' by Dawn and Peter Cope which appeared in the June 2001 issue of **Antique Collecting** magazine. For more details and to subscribe see page 147.

clocks, decorative artifacts. TEL: 01902 312211. SER: Valuations; restorations (furniture and oils); interior design; export. FAIRS: Advisers to NEC Antiques for Everyone.

Martin-Quick Antiques
323 Tettenhall Rd. WV6 0JZ. LAPADA. Est. 1965. Open 9.30-5.30, Sat. 9.30-2. SIZE: Large. *STOCK: 18th-19th C English, French and upholstered furniture and shipping goods.* LOC: One mile from town centre on A41. PARK: Easy. TEL: 01902 754703; home - 01902 752908; fax - 01902 756889; e-mail - mqantiques@hotmail. com. SER: Packing and shipping. VAT: Stan/Spec.

Newhampton Road Antiques
184/184A Newhampton Rd. East, Whitmoreans. WV1 4PQ. (Robert and Linda Hill). Est. 1982. Open 10-3.30. SIZE: Small. *STOCK: General antiques and collectables, Victorian and Edwardian, £50-£1,500.* LOC: From A449 left at Wolverhampton football ground. PARK: Easy. TEL: 01902 712583. SER: Valuations. FAIRS: Newark, Swinderby.

No 9 Antiques
9 Upper Green, Tettenhall. WV6 8QQ. Open 10-5.30. CL: Mon. and Tues. SIZE: Medium. *STOCK: Furniture, 18th-19th C, £200-£1,000; ceramics, silver and prints, 19th C, £25-£500; works of art, £25-£100.* LOC: Corner of the Green. PARK: Easy. TEL: 01902 755333.

The Red Shop
7 Hollybush Lane, Penn. (B. Savage). Open 9.30-5.30. *STOCK: Furniture including pine.* TEL: 01902 342915.

Martin Taylor Antiques
140b Tettenhall Rd. WV6 0BQ. LAPADA. Est. 1967. Open 8.30-5.30, Sat. 9.30-4. SIZE: Large. *STOCK: Furniture, mainly 1800-1930, for the UK and USA market, £50-£10,000.* LOC: One mile from town centre on A41. PARK: Easy. TEL: 01902 751166; fax - 01902 746502; mobile - 07836 636524; home - 01785 284539; e-mail - enquiries@mtaylor-antiques.co.uk; website - www.mtaylor-antiques.co.uk. VAT: Stan/Spec

Wolverhampton Antiques and Collectors Market
Basement of Retail Market, Salop St. WV3 0SF. (Mrs B. Tonks). Open Tues., Wed. and Fri. 9-4, Sat. 9-5. SIZE: 20 units. *STOCK: China, glass, jewellery, militaria, books and comics, linen, football memorabilia, 19th C, £5-£1,000.* LOC: Wolverhampton ring road, exit Chapel Ash island, market signposted. PARK: Easy - Peel St. and Pitt St. TEL: 01902 55519; mobile - 07790 992357.

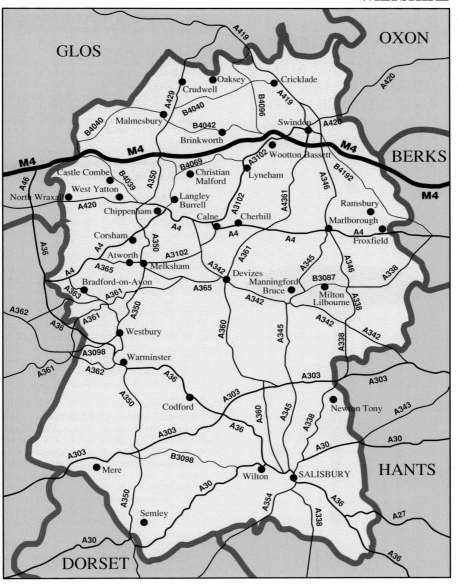

Dealers and Shops in Wiltshire

Atworth	1	Codford	1	Malmesbury	2
Bradford-on-Avon	7	Corsham	1	Manningford Bruce	1
Brinkworth	1	Cricklade	1	Marlborough	8
Calne	3	Crudwell	1	Melksham	3
Castle Combe	1	Devizes	2	Mere	1
Cherhill	1	Froxfield	1	Milton Lilbourne	1
Chippenham	2	Langley Burrell	1	Newton Tony	1
Christian Malford	1	Lyneham	1	North Wraxall	1
				Oaksey	1

Ramsbury	2
Salisbury	12
Semley	1
Swindon	5
Warminster	8
West Yatton	1
Westbury	1
Wilton	4
Wootton Bassett	1

AVON ANTIQUES
25-26-27 MARKET STREET
BRADFORD-ON-AVON
WILTSHIRE BA15 1LL
Tel. (01225) 862052
Fax: (01225) 868763

*Eight showrooms of 17th, 18th
and early 19th century furniture,
clocks, barometers, metalwork,
some textiles, painted and
lacquered furniture*

**Member of the British Antique
Dealers Association**

Peter Campbell Antiques
59 Bath Rd. SN12 8JY. (P.R. Campbell).
BABAADA. Est. 1976. Open 10-5, Sun. and
Thurs. by appointment. SIZE: Medium. *STOCK:
General antiques and decorative items, 18th-19th
C.* Not Stocked: Silver and jewellery. LOC:
Between Bath and Melksham on A350. PARK:
Easy. TEL: 01225 709742; home - same. VAT:
Stan/Spec.

Asylum House Antiques
5 Mount Pleasant. BA15 1SJ. (Peter Jacobs).
Resident. BABAADA. Est. 1986. Open by
appointment. SIZE: Small. *STOCK: English and
Irish drinking glasses, decanters and table glass,
Georgian and Regency, £50-£2,000; decorative
gilt mirrors, 18th-19th C, £500-£3,000.* LOC: Off
A363 from Bath. PARK: Easy. TEL: 01225
866043. SER: Valuations. VAT: Stan/Spec.

Audley House Antiques
5 Woolley St. BA15 1AD. (David, Joyce and
Richard Brown). BABAADA. Open 9-6 or by
appointment. *STOCK: Mainly Victorian and
Edwardian furniture; watercolours, prints, small
silver, porcelain and interesting small items.*
TEL: 01225 862476. SER: Framing.

Avon Antiques   BADA
**25, 26 and 27 Market St. BA15 1LL. (V. and
A. Jenkins BA). BABAADA. Est. 1963. Open
9.45-5.30, Sun. by appointment. SIZE: Large.
STOCK: English and some Continental
furniture, 1600-1880; metalwork, treen, clocks,
barometers, some textiles, painted and lacquer
furniture. LOC: A363, main street of town.
PARK: Ask at shop for key to private parking
opposite. TEL: 01225 862052; fax - 01225
868763. FAIRS: Grosvenor House. VAT: Spec.**

Mac Humble Antiques   BADA
**7-9 Woolley St. BA15 1AD. (W. Mc. A. and B.J.
Humble). BABAADA. Open 9-6. SIZE:
Medium. STOCK: 17th-19th C oak, mahogany,
fruitwoods, metalware, treen, samplers, silkwork
pictures, decorative objects. TEL: 01225 866329;
fax - same; e-mail - mac.humble@virgin.net;
website - www.machumbleantiques.co.uk. SER:
Valuations; restorations. VAT: Stan/Spec.**

Moxhams Antiques
17, 23 and 24 Silver St. BA15 1JZ. (R., J. and N.
Bichard). LAPADA. BABAADA. Est. 1967.
Open 9-5.30 or by appointment. SIZE: Large.

BRADFORD ON AVON

BATH
&
BRADFORD
ON
AVON
ANTIQUE
DEALERS
ASSOCIATION

Probably the best town for period antique furniture outside London

AVON ANTIQUES
Established 1963

25-26-27 MARKET STREET, BRADFORD ON AVON, WILTSHIRE BA15 1LL
TELEPHONE: (01225) 862052   ANDREW & VIBEKE JENKINS

Trevor Waddington OBE
ANTIQUE CLOCKS

★ Offering quality antique clocks, restored and fully guaranteed   ★ Showroom open by appointment   ★ Stock details on request/website

5 TROWBRIDGE RD., BRADFORD ON AVON
Tel: 01225 862351
www.antiques-uk.co.uk/waddington

MEMBER OF THE
BRITISH HOROLOGICAL
INSTITUTE

MOXHAMS ANTIQUES
17, 23 & 24 Silver Street, Bradford on Avon, Wiltshire BA15 1JZ
Tel: (01225) 862789 Fax: (01225) 867844 Home: (01380) 828677
Roger, Jill and Nicholas Bichard   Est. 1967

LAPADA
MEMBER

Period furniture, ceramics, metalware, needlework, decorative & garden items
E-mail: jill@moxhams-antiques.demon.co.uk
Website: www.moxhams-antiques.co.uk

AUDLEY HOUSE ANTIQUES
5 Woolley Street, Bradford-on-Avon, Wiltshire BA15 1AD
Tel: (01225) 862476
RICHARD, DAVID & JOYCE BROWN
Good quality 19th Century Furniture, Ceramics, Oils, Watercolours, Silver & Smalls

MAC HUMBLE ANTIQUES
EST. 1979

18th & 19th Century Furniture, Metalware, Treen and Needlework.
Decorative items. Valuations & Restorations.
7-9 Woolley Street, Bradford-on-Avon, Wiltshire BA15 1AD
Telephone: (01225) 866329 Facsimile: (01225) 866329
E-mail: mac.humble@virgin.net

An excellent place to stop for lunch with good pubs, cafes and restaurants in the centre of this beautiful Wiltshire town.

STOCK: English and Continental furniture, clocks, 1650-1850; European and Oriental pottery and porcelain, 1700-1850; decorative items, 1600-1900, all £50-£50,000. PARK: Own, at rear. TEL: 01225 862789; fax - 01225 867844; home - 01380 828677/01225 755026; e-mail - jill@moxhams-antiques.demon.co.uk. VAT: Spec.

Town and Country Antiques   BADA
34 Market St. BA15 1LL. (Rosemary Drewett and Michael Hughes). BABAADA. Open 10-5, Sat. 10-1, other times by appointment. SIZE: Large. *STOCK: Fine period furniture, metalware, caddies, boxes and period decorative items.* PARK: Nearby. TEL: 01225 867877; fax - same. VAT: Spec.

Trevor Waddington Antique Clocks
5 Trowbridge Rd. BA15 1EE. MBHI. BABAADA. Est. 1996. Strictly by appointment. SIZE: Small. *STOCK: 18th-19th C clocks - longcase, £3,000-£13,000; wall, £750-£2,000; carriage, bracket and mantel, £500-£5,000.* LOC: Quarter mile south of town bridge on A363. PARK: Easy. TEL: 01225 862351; home/fax - same; website - www.antiques-uk.co.uk/ waddington. SER: Valuations; restorations (BADA/West Dean Dip. conservator).

North Wilts Exporters
Farm Hill House. SN15 5AJ. (M. Thornbury). Est. 1972. Open Mon.-Sat. or by appointment.

STOCK: Imported Continental pine, 18th-19th C; shipping goods. LOC: Off M4, junction 16 Malmesbury road. TEL: 01666 510876; mobile - 07836 260730. SER: Valuations; shipping; import and export. VAT: Stan.

Calne Antiques
London Rd. SN11 0AB. (M. Blackford). Open 10-5 seven days. *STOCK: Antique pine and country furniture, Victorian to 1930's; mahogany, oak and walnut.* LOC: A4, next to White Hart Hotel. TEL: 01249 816311; fax - same. SER: Furniture made to order; free-standing kitchens.

Clive Farahar and Sophie Dupré - Rare Books, Autographs and Manuscripts
Horsebrook House, 15 The Green. SN11 8DQ. Open by appointment. SIZE: Medium. *STOCK: Rare books on voyages and travels, autograph letters and manuscripts, 15th-20th C, £5-£5,000.* LOC: Off A4 in town centre. PARK: Easy. TEL: 01249 821121; fax - 01249 821202; e-mail - post@faraharddupre.co.uk or farahar_dupre@compuserve.com; website - www.faraharddupre.co.uk. SER: Valuations; buys at auction (as stock). FAIRS: ABA; Universal Autograph Collectors' Club. VAT: Stan.

Hilmarton Manor Press
Hilmarton Manor. SN11 8SB. (H. Baile de Laperriere). Est. 1967. Open 9-6. SIZE: Medium. *STOCK: New and out-of-print art and photography reference books, some antiquarian.* LOC: 3 miles from Calne on A3102 towards Swindon. PARK: Easy. TEL: 01249 760208; fax - 01249 760379. SER: Buys at auction.

Combe Cottage Antiques
SN14 7HU. (B. and A. Bishop). Est. 1960. Appointment advisable. SIZE: Medium. *STOCK: Country furniture, £20-£5,000; metalware, £10-£2,000; both 17th to early 19th C; treen, pottery, 18th-19th C, £5-£500; early lighting devices.* Not Stocked: Mahogany furniture, glass, silver, Victoriana. LOC: A420 from Chippenham towards Bristol. After 3 miles bear right on B4039. PARK: 20yds. TEL: 01249 782250; fax - 01249 782250. SER: Valuations; specialists in cottage furnishings. VAT: Spec.

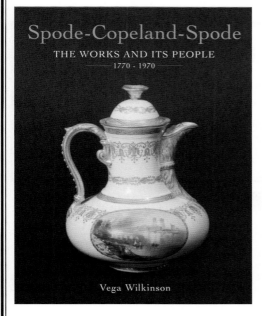

LUCY COPE LIMITED (LC) FOXHILL ANTIQUES

FOXHILL HOUSE • ALLINGTON • CHIPPENHAM • WILTSHIRE SN14 6LL

Telephone No. (01249) 650446   Fax No. (01249) 444936

Accessories, Antique and Period style lighting.
Specialist lampshade makers. Restoration of antique lamps and lampshades.

Trade by appointment   *Off A420 on the west side of Chippenham*

CHERHILL, Nr. Calne

P.A. Oxley Antique Clocks and Barometers
The Old Rectory, Main Rd. SN11 8UX.
LAPADA. Est. 1971. Open 9.30-5, other times by
appointment. CL: Wed. SIZE: Large. *STOCK:
Longcase, bracket, carriage clocks and
barometers, 17th-19th C, £500-£30,000.* LOC:
A4, not in village. PARK: Easy. TEL: 01249
816227; fax - 01249 821285; e-mail - info@
paoxley.com; website - www.british-antique
clocks.com. VAT: Spec.

CHIPPENHAM

Lucy Cope Ltd
Foxhill House, Allington. SN14 6LL. (G.E. and
L. Cope). Resident. Est. 1986. Open 7 days 9-6
by appointment. SIZE: Medium. *STOCK: Lamps,
small decorative accessories and paintings.* LOC:
Off A420 towards Bath, 2 miles from
Chippenham. PARK: Easy. TEL: 01249 650446;
fax - 01249 444936. SER: Restorations (period
lampshades); lampshade makers. *Trade Only.*

Cross Hayes Antiques
Unit 6 Westbrook Farm, Draycot Cerne. SN15
5LH. (D. Brooks). LAPADA. Est. 1975. Open 9-5
or by appointment. SIZE: Warehouse. *STOCK:
Furniture, 1850-1930, Victorian, Edwardian and
shipping oak.* TEL: 01249 720033; fax - same;
home - 01666 822062; website - www.crosshayes.
co.uk; e-mail - david@crosshayes.co.uk. SER:
Packing and shipping. VAT: Stan/Spec.

CHRISTIAN MALFORD, Nr. Chippenham

Harley Antiques
The Comedy. SN15 4BS. (G.J. Harley). Est.
1959. Open 9-6 including Sun. or later by
appointment. SIZE: Large. *STOCK: Furniture,*
*18th-19th C, £150-£3,000; decorative objects,
£30-£1,000.* LOC: B4069, 4 miles off M4,
junction 17. PARK: Own. TEL: 01249 720112;
home - same; fax - 01249 720553. SER: Colour
brochure available (export only). VAT: Stan.
Trade Only.

CODFORD, Nr. Warminster

Tina's Antiques
75 High St. BA12 0ND. (T.A. Alder). Open 9-6,
Sat. 9-1. *STOCK: General antiques.* TEL: 01985
850828.

CORSHAM

Matthew Eden
Pickwick End. SN13 0JB. Resident. Est. 1951.
SIZE: Large. *STOCK: Country house furniture
and garden items, 17th-19th C.* TEL: 01249
713335; fax - 01249 713644. VAT: Spec.

CRICKLADE, Nr. Swindon

Edred A.F. Gwilliam
Candletree House, Bath Rd. SN6 6AX. Est. 1976.
Open by appointment. SIZE: Medium. *STOCK:
Arms and armour, swords, pistols, long guns,
£50-£20,000+.* PARK: Easy. TEL: 01793
750241; fax - 01793 750359. SER: Valuations;
buys at auction. FAIRS: Major arms. VAT:
Stan/Spec.

CRUDWELL

Philip A. Ruttleigh Antiques incorporating Crudwell Furniture
Odd Penny Farm. SN16 9SJ. Est. 1990. Open 9-5
and by appointment. CL: Sat. SIZE: Small.
*STOCK: Furniture including pine in the paint, and
decorative items, £10-£2,000.* LOC: Next to RAF

Kemble on A429, 5 minutes from Cirencester, 15 mins from junction 17, M4. TEL: 01285 770970; website - www.crudwell furniture.co.uk. SER: Furniture restoration, including stripping; bead blasting for architectural antiques.

DEVIZES

Cross Keys Jewellers
The Ginnel, Market Pl. SN10 1HN. (D. and D. Pullen). Est. 1967. Open 9.15-5.15. *STOCK: Jewellery, silver*. LOC: Alley adjacent Nationwide Building Society. PARK: Easy. TEL: 01380 726293. VAT: Stan.

St Mary's Chapel Antiques
Northgate St. SN10 1JL. (Richard Sankey). BABAADA. *STOCK: Painted and Continental furniture, decorative accessories and gardens items*. TEL: 01380 721399; website - www.st-marys-chapel-Antiques.org.uk.

FROXFIELD

Blanchard
Bath Rd. LAPADA. Est. 1940. Open 9.30-6. SIZE: Large. *STOCK: 18th-20th C antiques and decorative pieces including garden furniture*. TEL: 01488 680666; fax - 01488 680668.

LANGLEY BURRELL, Nr. Chippenham

Harriet Fairfax Fireplaces and General Antiques
Langley Green. SN15 4LL. Open by appointment only. *STOCK: China, glass, dolls, furniture, fabrics and needlework; architectural items and fittings, brass and iron knobs, knockers; fireplaces, pine and iron, 1780-1950*. TEL: 01249 652030. SER: Design consultancy.

LYNEHAM, Nr. Chippenham

Pillars Antiques
10 The Banks. SN15 4NS. (K. Clifford). Resident. Est. 1986. Open 10-5, including Sun. CL: Thurs. *STOCK: Victorian and Edwardian pine, shipping oak*. LOC: B4069 Chippenham road, 1 mile from village. PARK: Easy. TEL: 01249 890632; home - same.

MALMESBURY

Antiques - Rene Nicholls
56 High St. SN16 9AT. (Mrs R. Nicholls). Est.

1980. Open 10-5.30, Sun. by appointment. SIZE: Small. *STOCK: English pottery and porcelain, 18th to early 19th C, £50-£900; small furniture*. PARK: Opposite. TEL: 01666 823089; home - same.

Andrew Britten Antiques
48 High St. SN16 9AT. (T.M. Tyler and T.A. Freeman). Est. 1975. Open 9.30-6, Sun. by appointment. SIZE: Medium. *STOCK: Furniture, 1700-1900, £100-£1,500; decorative brass, wood, glass and porcelain items, £15-£500*. PARK: Opposite. TEL: 01666 823376. VAT: Spec.

MANNINGFORD BRUCE

Indigo
Dairy Barn. SN9 6JW. (Richard and Marion Lightbown). Est. 1982. Open 9-1 and 2-5. CL: Sat. SIZE: Large. *STOCK: 19th C Indian and Chinese furniture, Chinese lacquer cabinets, £100-£2,000; Far Eastern architectural items, 18th-19th C, £500-£3,000*. LOC: A345 south of Marlborough. PARK: Easy. TEL: 01672 564722; fax - 01672 564733. VAT: Stan.

MARLBOROUGH

Bowmoore Gallery
4 London Rd. SN8 1PH. Est. 1968. Open Wed.-Sun. 10-6 or by appointment. *STOCK: 20th C oil paintings and watercolours, small collectables, interior design and garden items*. PARK: Easy. TEL: 01672 513593; e-mail - bowmoore@supanet.com. SER: Framing and restorations.

Brocante Antiques Centre
6 London Rd. SN8 1PH. (Robert Stenhouse, Peter Randall and David & Rosemary Barfield). Est. 1986. Open 10-5. SIZE: Large. *STOCK: Furniture including French, £50-£1,500; ceramics including Staffordshire, £5-£1,000; all 18th-20th C; collectables*. LOC: A4 entering Marlborough. PARK: Easy. TEL: 01672 516512; fax - same; e-mail - brocante@brocante antiques.co.uk; website - www.brocanteantiques. co.uk. SER: Valuations; restorations (furniture). VAT: Global.

Cook of Marlborough Fine Art Ltd
High Trees House, Savernake Forest. SN8 4NE. (W.J. Cook). LAPADA. BAFRA. Est. 1963. Open by appointment only. SIZE: Medium. *STOCK: Furniture, 18th to early 19th C; objets d'art, 18th-19th C*. LOC: 1.5 miles from Marlborough on A346 towards Burbage. PARK: Easy. TEL: 01672 513017; fax - 01672 514455. SER: Valuations; restorations (furniture including polishing and gilding); buys at auction (furniture). FAIRS: Olympia; Harrogate; Claridges; Chester; Tatton Park. VAT: Stan/Spec.

Katharine House Gallery
Katharine House, The Parade. SN8 1NE. (C.C. Gange). Est. 1983. Open 10-5.30. SIZE: Medium. *STOCK: Furniture, 17th-19th C, £200-£2,000; decorative items, £100-£1,000; Chinese, Roman and Greek antiquities, 2000BC-1000AD, £100-£1,000; paintings and prints, £10-£1,000; books, £5-£500.* PARK: Easy. TEL: 01672 514040; home - same. VAT: Stan/Spec.

Robert Kime Antiques
P O Box 454 SN8 3UR. Est. 1968. Open by appointment only. *STOCK: Decorative, period furniture.* TEL: 01264 731268. VAT: Spec.

The Marlborough Parade Antique Centre
The Parade. SN8 1NE. (T. Page and N. Cannon). Est. 1985. Open 10-5 including Sun. SIZE: 57 dealers. *STOCK: Good quality furniture, paintings, silver, porcelain, glass, clocks, jewellery, copper, brass and pewter, £5-£5,000.* LOC: Adjacent A4 in town centre. PARK: Easy. TEL: 01672 515331. SER: Valuations; restorations (furniture, porcelain, copper, brass). VAT: Spec.

The Military Parade Bookshop
The Parade. SN8 1NE. (G. and P. Kent). *STOCK: Military history books especially regimental histories and the World Wars.* LOC: Next to The Lamb. TEL: 01672 515470; fax - 01980 630150; e-mail - enquiry@militaryparadebooks.com; website - www.militaryparadebooks.com.

Annmarie Turner Antiques
22 Salisbury Rd. SN8 4AD. Resident. Est. 1960. Open 10-6, Sun. by appointment. SIZE: Small. *STOCK: British oak, fruitwood, pine and primitive country furniture, £50-£1,500; treen and kitchenalia, £5-£100; allied decorative items and the unusual, £20-£500, 17th C to 1920's.* Not Stocked: Mahogany, jewellery, silver, reproduction. LOC: Left side of first roundabout approaching town from Hungerford on A4. PARK: Easy and at rear. TEL: 01672 515396; home - same. SER: Valuations. VAT: Spec.

MELKSHAM

Dann Antiques Ltd
Unit 1, Avonside Enterprise Park, New Broughton Rd. SN12 8BS. BABAADA. Open 9-5.30, Sat. 9-1. SIZE: Large. *STOCK: 18th-19th C English furniture; French and decorative pieces, lighting, fenders, mirrors, pottery, porcelain.* TEL: 01225 707329; fax - 01225 790120; home - 01380 860255; e-mail - 113665.1341@compuserve.com.

Rupert Gentle

Dealer in Antiques and
Works of Art

The Manor House, Milton Lilbourne, Pewsey, Wiltshire SN9 5LQ

Telephone (01672) 563344
Fax (01672) 563563

Specialist in c.1700-1900 English and Continental domestic brass. Also stocks needlework, decorative items and domestic accessories of the period.

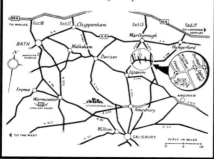

Alan Jaffray
16 Market Place. SN12 6EX. BABAADA. Est. 1956. Open Mon.-Fri. 9-5. SIZE: Large. *STOCK: Furniture and smalls, 18th-19th C, £50-£2,000.* LOC: Main Bath to Devizes Rd. PARK: On premises. TEL: 01225 702269; fax - 01225 790413; e-mail - jaffray.antiques@talk21.com. VAT: Stan/Spec.

King Street Curios
8 King St. SN12 6HD. Est. 1991. SIZE: 20 units. *STOCK: China, discontinued Denby, USSR, glass, jewellery, Art Deco, kitchenalia, furniture.* LOC: A350. PARK: Own at rear. TEL: 01225 790623. FAIRS: Oasis, Swindon; Neeld Hall, Chippenham; Templemeads (Brunel), Bristol.

MERE, Nr. Warminster

Louis Stanton   **BADA**
P O Box 2839. BA12 6BY. (L.R. and S.A. Stanton). CINOA. Est. 1965. Open by appointment only. *STOCK: Early English oak furniture, medieval sculpture and works of art, metalware, unusual decorative items.* TEL: 01747 860747; fax - same. SER: Valuations; buys at auction.

MILTON LILBOURNE, Nr. Pewsey

Rupert Gentle Antiques   **BADA**
The Manor House. SN9 5LQ. Est. 1954. Open 9.15-6. SIZE: Medium. *STOCK: English and Continental domestic metalwork, 1650-1850; treen, decorative objects, needlework and domestic accessories.* LOC: From Hungerford on A4 take A338 for Pewsey. PARK: Easy. TEL: 01672 563344; fax - 01672 563563. SER: Valuations; buys at auction. VAT: Stan/Spec.

NEWTON TONY, Nr. Salisbury

Ray Best Antiques
Owl Cottage SP4 0HF. LAPADA. Est. 1964. Open by appointment. *STOCK: 17th-18th C oak and mahogany furniture, pottery, textiles and metalware.* TEL: 01980 629528; mobile - 07831 766340; e-mail - raybestantiques@hotmail.com; website - www.raybestantiques.co.uk. *Trade Only.*

NORTH WRAXALL, Nr. Chippenham

Delomosne and Son Ltd   **BADA**
Court Close. SN14 7AD. (T.N.M. Osborne and M.C.F. Mortimer). BABAADA. Articles on chandeliers, glass and porcelain. Est. 1905. Open Mon.-Fri. 9.30-5.30, other times by appoint-

ment. SIZE: Large. *STOCK: English and Irish glass, pre-1830, £20-£20,000; glass chandeliers, English and European porcelain, needlework, papier mâché and treen.* LOC: Off A420 between Bath and Chippenham. PARK: Easy. TEL: 01225 891505; fax - 01225 891907; website - www.delomosne.co.uk. SER: Valuations; buys at auction. FAIRS: International Ceramic; Winter Olympia. VAT: Spec.

OAKSEY

Lyon Oliver Antiques
Laynes House. SN16 9SE. TADA. Prior telephone call advisable. *STOCK: English and Irish country house furniture, large mirrors, upholstery and decorative sculpture.* TEL: 01666 577603; e-mail - lyon@lyon-oliver.demon.co.uk.

RAMSBURY, Nr. Marlborough

Heraldry Today
Parliament Piece. SN8 2QH. Est. 1954. Open 9.30-4.30. CL: Sat. *STOCK: Heraldic and genealogical books and manuscripts, £3-£8,000.* TEL: 01672 520617; fax - 01672 520183; e-mail - heraldry@heraldrytoday.co.uk; website - www.heraldrytoday.co.uk.

Inglenook Antiques
59 High St. SN8 2QN. (Dennis White). Est. 1969. Open 10-1 and 2-5, prior telephone call advisable. CL: Mon. and Wed. except by appointment. SIZE: Small. *STOCK: Oil lamps, £50-£850; clocks, barometers and spare parts, £150-£4,000; some furniture.* LOC: 3 miles from A4 between Hungerford and Marlborough. PARK: Easy. TEL: 01672 520261; home - same. SER: Restorations (longcase clock movements only).

SALISBURY

Antique and Collectors Market
37 Catherine St. SP1 2DH. Open 10-5. SIZE: Large. *STOCK: Silver, plate, china, glass, toys, books, taxidermy, prints, pens and furniture.* TEL: 01722 326033.

The Avonbridge Antiques and Collectors Market
United Reformed Church Hall, Fisherton St. SP2 7RG. Open Tues. 9-3.30. SIZE: 15 dealers. *STOCK: General antiques.* TEL: 01202 669061.

The Barn Book Supply
88 Crane St. SP1 2QD. (J. and J. Head). Est. 1958. Open 9.30-5. CL: Sat. *STOCK: Antiquarian books on angling, shooting, horses, deerstalking.* TEL: 01722 327767; fax - 01722 339888.

Boston Antiques
223 Wilton Rd. and warehouse at Wilton. SP2 7JY. Est. 1964. Open 9.30-5. *STOCK: 18th-19th C furniture.* TEL: 01722 322682; home - 01722 324426. VAT: Stan/Spec.

Robert Bradley Antiques
71 Brown St. SP1 2BA. Est. 1970. Open 9.30-5.30. CL: Sat. *STOCK: Furniture, 17th-18th C; decorative items.* TEL: 01722 333677; fax - 01722 339922. VAT: Spec.

Ronald Carr
6 St. Francis Rd. SP1 3QS. (R.G. Carr). Est. 1983. Open by appointment. SIZE: Small. *STOCK: Modern British etchings, wood engravings and colour wood cuts, £5-£1,000.* LOC: 1 mile north of city on A345. PARK: Easy. TEL: 01722 328892; home - same. SER: Buys at auction.

Castle Galleries
81 Castle St. SP1 3SP. (John C. Lodge). Est. 1971. Open 9-4.30, Sat. 9-1. CL: Mon. and Wed. *STOCK: General antiques, coins and medals.* PARK: Easy. TEL: 01722 333734; mobile - 07890 225059; e-mail - johnlodge@bun.com.

Edward Hurst Antiques
The Garden Room, Netherhampton. SP2 8PU. Est. 1983. Open 9.30-5.30, Sat. by appointment. SIZE: Medium. *STOCK: English furniture and associated works of art, 1650-1820.* LOC: Just west of Salisbury. PARK: Easy. TEL: 01722 743042. VAT: Spec.

Pennyfarthing Antiques
52-54 Winchester St. SP1 1HG. (Mike and Bernadett Scott). Open 9-5.30, Sun. 11-4. SIZE: Medium. *STOCK: Country furniture including Windsor arm chairs, 18th to early 20th C, £50-£1,000.* PARK: Easy. TEL: 01722 505955. SER: Restorations (furniture).

Salisbury Antiques Warehouse
94 Wilton Rd. SP2 7JJ. (Chris Watts). LAPADA. Est. 1964. Open 9.30-5.30, Sat. and Sun. by appointment. SIZE: Large. *STOCK: Furniture, clocks and shipping goods, 18th-19th C, £50-£3,000; paintings, 19th C, £100-£2,000.* LOC: A36 Warminster-Southampton road. PARK: Easy. TEL: 01722 410634; mobile - 07802 635055. VAT: Stan/Spec.

William Sheppee
Old Sarum Airfield. SP4 6BJ. (W. Hiley and J. Hedges). Est. 1989. Open Mon.-Fri. by appointment only. SIZE: Large. *STOCK: Indian and Chinese antiques and antique replica mirrors.* TEL: 01722 334454; fax - 01722 337754; e-mail - custserv@williamsheppee.com. VAT: Stan. *Trade Only.*

Chris Wadge Clocks
83 Fisherton St. SP2 7ST. Open 9-4. CL: Mon. *STOCK: Clocks, movements and spare parts.* TEL: 01722 334467. SER: 400 day specialist.

SEMLEY

Dairy House Antiques
Station Rd. SP7 9AN. (Miss I. Moyes). Open 9.30-5.30. SIZE: Large. *STOCK: Furniture, paintings, decorative items, 1600-1900.* TEL: 01747 853317.

SWINDON

Antiques and All Pine
11 Newport St., Old Town. SN1 3DX. (J. and M. Brown). Open 10-5.30. CL: Wed. SIZE: Medium. *STOCK: Pine, traditional brass and iron beds, china, lace, linen and costume jewellery.* LOC: From M4, junction 15 or 16 follow signs to Old Town. PARK: 100yds. TEL: 01793 520259. VAT: Stan/Spec.

Penny Farthing Antiques Arcade
Victoria Centre, 138/9 Victoria Rd., Old Town. SN1 3BU. (Ann Farthing). Est. 1977. Open 10-5. SIZE: Large. *STOCK: Furniture, silver, porcelain, watches, clocks.* LOC: On left on hill between Old Town and college. PARK: Prospect Place. TEL: 01793 536668. VAT: Stan.

Sambourne House Antiques Ltd
50-51 The Arcade, Brunel Shopping Centre. SN1 1LL. (T. and Mrs K. Cove). Est. 1984. Open 10-5, Sun. 10-4. SIZE: Large. *STOCK: Restored 19th C pine, £120-£2,000; reclaimed 19th C pine, £50-£1,500; reproduction smalls, £2-£90.* LOC: 1.5 miles off junction 16, M4, towards Swindon. PARK: Easy. TEL: 01793 610855; fax - same. SER: Stripping; specialist pine importer. VAT: Stan/Global.

Allan Smith Antique Clocks
162 Beechcroft Rd., Upper Stratton. SN2 7QE. Est. 1988. Open by appointment. SIZE: Large. *STOCK: 50-60 longcase clocks including automata, moonphase, painted dial, brass dial, 30 hour, 8 day, London and provincial, £1,950-£33,000; occasionally stick and banjo barometers, mantel, wall, bracket, Vienna and lantern clocks.* LOC: Near Bakers Arms Inn. PARK: Own. TEL: 01793 822977; mobile - 07778 834342; e-mail - allansmithclocks@lineone.net; website - www.allan-smith-antique-clocks.co.uk. VAT: Spec.

Guanella, Bristol. Recorded circa 1830. Typical Bristol mahogany case of excellent quality & proportions. 89" (226cms.)

Brownless, Staindrop. Probably Robert born 1697 died 1744. This example circa 1725. Burr & figured walnut case quarter striking on 6 bells. Finned, ringed & knopped pillars (two latched). Moonphases to arch. 92" (234cms.)

A mahogany standing corner cabinet in the George III style – although glazed doors below would have been highly unusual in the 18th century. (Sotheby's)

At the end of last year, a decorated corner cupboard, estimated at £300-£500, was sold for £4,100. To learn more about the subject, Peter Philp pays a visit to Alice in an article entitled 'Cornering the Market' which appeared in the June 2001 issue of **Antique Collecting** magazine. For more details and to subscribe see page 147.

WARMINSTER

Bishopstrow Antiques
55 East St. BA12 9BZ. (J.M. Stewart Cox). BABAADA. Est. 1974. Open 10-1 and 2-5.30. SIZE: Medium. *STOCK: 18th-19th C mahogany, oak and painted furniture; pottery and porcelain, boxes, pictures and decorative items.* LOC: On left of old A36 leaving Warminster on Salisbury road, opposite Esso garage. PARK: Easy. TEL: 01985 212683; home - 01985 840877; e-mail - shop@bishopstrowantiques.com. VAT: Spec.

Cassidy's Antiques
7 Silver St. BA12 8PS. (M. Cassidy). BABAADA. Est. 1989. Open 9.30-5, Sat. 10-4.30. SIZE: Medium. *STOCK: Furniture, 17th-19th C, £200-£1,500.* PARK: Easy. TEL: 01985 213313. SER: Restorations (furniture and cabinet making).

Choice Antiques
4 Silver St. BA12 8PS. (Avril Bailey). Open 10-1 and 2-5.30. SIZE: Medium. *STOCK: General antiques and decorative items, 18th-19th C, £25-£2,000.* PARK: Easy. TEL: 01985 218924. VAT: Stan/Spec.

Emporium
33a Silver St. BA12 9LX. (Mrs Christine Dew). Est. 1963. Open 9-5.30. *STOCK: General antiques, £5-£1,000.* TEL: 01985 219614; fax - same; mobile - 07702 477517. *Trade only.*

Isabella Antiques
11 Silver St. BA12 8PS. (B.W. Semke). BABAADA. Est. 1990. Open 10-5. SIZE: Medium. *STOCK: Furniture, late 18th C to late 19th C, £100-£5,000; boxes and mirrors, 19th C, £50-£500.* LOC: Main road. PARK: Easy. TEL: 01985 218933. SER: Buys at auction (furniture). VAT: Spec.

Obelisk Antiques
2 Silver St. BA12 8PS. (P. Tanswell). LAPADA. BABAADA. Open 10-1 and 2-5.30. SIZE: Large. *STOCK: English and Continental furniture, 18th-19th C; decorative items, objets d'art.* TEL: 01985 846646; fax - 01985 219901.

Warminster Antiques Centre
6 Silver St. BA12 8TT. (P. Walton). BABAADA. Est. 1970. Open 10-5. SIZE: 15 dealers. *STOCK: Furniture, home embellishments, textiles, silver, jewellery, collectors' items.* TEL: 01985 847269; home - 01985 847021.

Victoria Bookshop
30 Wood St., Old Town. SN1 4AB. (S. Austin). Est. 1965. Open 9-5.30. SIZE: Large. *STOCK: Books, most subjects, old postcards.* LOC: Middle of Old Town shopping area. PARK: Nearby. TEL: 01793 527364.

K. and A. Welch

1A Church St. BA12 8PG. Est. 1967. Open 8-6, Sat. 9-1. SIZE: Large. *STOCK: Shipping furniture, 18th-19th C, £10-£2,000.* LOC: A36 west end of town. PARK: Own. TEL: 01985 214687; home - 01985 213433. VAT: Stan/Spec.

WEST YATTON, Nr. Chippenham

Heirloom & Howard Limited

Manor Farm. SN14 7EU. (D.S. Howard). BABAADA. Est. 1972. Open 9.30-5.30, Sat. 11-5 or by appointment. SIZE: Medium. *STOCK: Porcelain mainly Chinese armorial and export, 18th C, £100-£5,000; heraldic items, 18th-19th C, £10-£1,000; portrait engravings, 17th-19th C, £10-£50.* LOC: 10 miles from Bath, 1/4 mile off A420 Chippenham/Bristol road. Transport from Chippenham station (4 miles) if required. PARK: Own. TEL: 01249 783038; fax - 01249 783039. SER: Valuations; buys at auction (Chinese porcelain). VAT: Spec.

WESTBURY

Ray Coggins Antiques

1 Fore St. BA13 3AU. Open 9-5.30. *STOCK: Antique and decorative furniture and architectural fittings.* TEL: 01373 826574.

WILTON, Nr. Salisbury

Bay Tree Antiques

26 North St. SP2 0HJ. Open 9-5.30 or by appointment. SIZE: Medium. *STOCK: General antiques, specialising in period English furniture.* TEL: 01722 743392.

Hingstons of Wilton

36 North St. SP2 0HJ. Open 9-5, Sat. 10-4. SIZE: Large. *STOCK: 18th-20th C furniture and objects.* TEL: 01722 742263; home - 01722 714742; mobile - 07887 870569; website - www.hingstons -antiques.co.uk.

Carol Musselwhite Antiques

6 West St. SP2 0DF. Est. 1990. Open 10-5. CL: Jan.-Easter. SIZE: Medium. *STOCK: Porcelain and pottery especially discontinued Denby, pre 1980, linen and lace, £1-£300.* LOC: Village centre. PARK: 30 metres. TEL: 01722 742573.

A.J. Romain and Sons

The Old House, 11 and 13 North St. SP2 0HA. *STOCK: Furniture, mainly 17th-18th C; early*

William Wyld's watercolour 'A Merchant in Damask' is estimated at £1,800-£2,500 at Dreweatt Neate on 6th September.

From an Auction Preview which appeareed in our September issue of **Antique Collecting** magazine. For more details and to subscribe see page 147.

oak, walnut and marquetry; clocks, copper, brass and miscellanea. TEL: 01722 743350. VAT: Stan/Spec.

WOOTTON BASSETT, Nr. Swindon

Tubbjoys Antique Market

118 High St. SN4 7AU. (Charles and Bridget Tubb). Est. 1992. Open 10-5. SIZE: 15 units. *STOCK: Midwinter Poole pottery and Whitefriars glass.* LOC: 2 miles off M4, junction 16. PARK: Easy and at rear. TEL: 01793 849499; home - same; fax - same; e-mail - bridgett@tubbjoys. freeserve.co.uk; website - www.tubbjoys. freeserve.co.uk.

H. W. KEIL LTD

Telephone
01386 852408
Fax 01386 852069

TUDOR HOUSE
BROADWAY
WORCESTERSHIRE
WR12 7DP

Member of the
British Antique
Dealers' Association

17th & 18th Century Furniture - Works of Art

COME TO THE COTSWOLDS AND VISIT
TUDOR HOUSE AND

See our showrooms which have a fine range of furniture from the 17th, 18th & 19th Centuries. Particularly oak with walnut & mahogany, together with works of art, pewter, copper & brass and other interesting pieces.

Originators of the well known Keil's dark and light Wax Polish available in 6½oz and 2lb sizes

In association with H.W. Keil (Cheltenham) Ltd. 129-131 The Promenade, Cheltenham, Gloucestershire

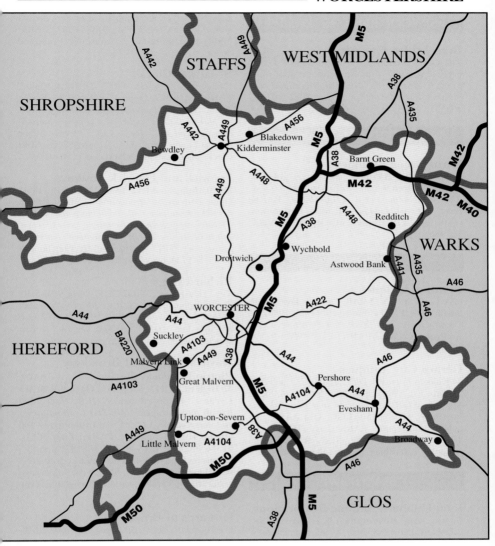

Dealers and Shops in Worcestershire

Astwood Bank	1	Evesham	2	Redditch	1
Barnt Green	1	Great Malvern	8	Suckley	1
Bewdley	2	Kidderminster	3	Upton-upon-Severn	1
Blakedown	1	Little Malvern	1	Worcester	13
Broadway	8	Malvern Link	2	Wychbold	1
Droitwich	2	Pershore	3		

Bracebridge Fine Art
The Old Bakehouse, 1242 Evesham Rd. B96
6AA. Est. 1987. Open by appointment only.
*STOCK: 18th-20th C oil paintings, and rare
signed limited edition prints.* TEL: 01527
893557.

Barnt Green Antiques
93 Hewell Rd. B45 8NL. (N. Slater). BAFRA.
Est. 1965. Open 9-5.30. SIZE: Medium. *STOCK:
Furniture, 17th-19th C, £100-£5,000.* PARK:
Easy. TEL: 0121 445 4942. SER: Restorations
(furniture, gilt frames, clocks, oils). VAT:
Stan/Spec.

Bewdley Antiques
62A Load St. DY12 2AP. Open 7 days. SIZE:
Small. *STOCK: 25 cabinets displaying 19th-20th
C collectables and decorative furniture.* LOC:
A456 town centre. PARK: Easy. TEL: 01299
405636.

Gerard Guy Antiques
24 Kidderminster Rd. DY12 1AG. (C.G. and P.G.
Mason). Est. 1990. Open 11-5, Sun. 12-4. SIZE:
Medium. *STOCK: Victorian and stripped pine
furniture, £250-£450.* LOC: Old A456, just
outside town centre. PARK: Easy. TEL: 01299
400032; home - same. SER: Restorations
(stripping, refinishing, repairs and upholstery).

John Hubbard Antique Restorations
Castle Ash, Birmingham Rd. DY10 3SE.
LAPADA. Est. 1968. Open by appointment only.
SIZE: Small. *STOCK: Furniture, 18th-19th C;
paintings and watercolours, all £50-£15,000;
lighting, silver, plate and decorative items.* TEL:
01562 701020; e-mail - jhantiques@aol.com;
website - www.antiquesbulletin.com/John
HubbardAntiques. SER: Valuations; restorations
(furniture including upholstery); leather linings.
VAT: Stan/Spec.

Broadway Bears & Dolls
76 High St. WR12 7AJ. (Janice Longhi). Open 7

days 10-5. *STOCK: Antique and modern artist's
dolls and teddy bears.* TEL: 01386 858323. SER:
Teddy bear museum; restorations (bears and
dolls).

Broadway Clocks
Kennel Lane, High St. WR12 7DP. (R.J. Kemp).
FBHI. Est. 1992. Open 10-1 and 2.15-5. CL:
Thurs. *STOCK: Longcase clocks, 17th-19th C,
£1,500-£6,000; also bracket, French mantel,
carriage and wall clocks.* LOC: 30 yds up lane
next to Lloyds Bank. TEL: 01386 852458. SER:
Clock restorations and repairs. VAT: Stan/Spec.

Fenwick and Fenwick Antiques
88-90 High St. WR12 7AJ. CADA. Est. 1980.
Open 10-6 or by appointment. SIZE: Large.
*STOCK: Furniture, oak, mahogany and walnut,
17th to early 19th C; samplers, boxes, treen,
Tunbridgeware, Delft, decorative items and
corkscrews.* TEL: 01386 853227; after hours -
01386 841724; fax - 01386 858504.

Richard Hagen
Yew Tree House. WR12 7DT. Open 9.30-5.30,
Sun. by appointment. *STOCK: 20th C oils, watercolours and bronzes.* TEL: 01386 853624/
858561; fax - 01386 852172; e-mail - fineart
@richardhagen.com. VAT: Spec.

Haynes Fine Art of Broadway
Picton House Galleries   BADA
**42 High St. WR12. LAPADA. Open 9-6. SIZE:
Large - 14 showrooms. STOCK: Over 2000
British and European 16th-21st C oil paintings
and watercolours. LOC: From Lygon Arms, 100
yds up High St. on left. PARK: Easy. TEL:
01386 852649; fax - 01386 858187; e-mail -
enquiries@haynes-fine-art.co.uk; website -
www.haynesfineart.com. SER: Free valuations;
restorations; framing; catalogue available (£10).
VAT: Spec.**

Howards of Broadway
27a High St. WR12 7DP. Open 9.30-5.30. SIZE:
Small. *STOCK: Jewellery, 1750 to modern, £20-
£5,000; silver, 1700 to modern, £20-£5,000;
objects of vertu, 1700-1900, £50-£500.* PARK:
Easy and nearby. TEL: 01386 858924. SER:
Valuations; restorations. VAT: Stan/Spec.

H.W. Keil Ltd   BADA
**Tudor House. WR12 7DP. CADA. Est. 1925.
Open 9.15-12.45 and 2.15-5.30. SIZE: Large.
STOCK: Walnut, oak, mahogany and rosewood
furniture; early pewter, brass and copper,
tapestry, glass and works of art, 17th-18th C.
LOC: By village clock. TEL: 01386 852408;
fax - 01386 852069. VAT: Spec.**

John Noott Galleries BADA
58 High St., 14 Cotswold Court and at The Lygon Arms, High St. WR12 7AA. LAPADA, CADA. Est. 1972. Open 9.30-1 and 2-5. SIZE: Large. *STOCK: Paintings, watercolours and bronzes, 19th C to Contemporary.* PARK: Easy. TEL: 01386 854868/858969; fax - 01386 854919. SER: Valuations; restorations; framing. VAT: Stan/Spec.

DROITWICH

Robert Belcher Antiques
128 Worcester Rd. WR9 8AN. (Robert & Wendy Belcher). Est. 1986. Open 9.30-5.30, Sun. by appointment. CL: Mon. SIZE: Large. *STOCK: Furniture, 18th-19th C, £500-£10,000; ceramics, silver, glass, paintings and prints, 19th-20th C, £50-£1,000.* PARK: Easy. TEL: 01905 772320. SER: Valuations; restorations; picture framing. FAIRS: NEC. VAT: Spec.

Grant Books
The Coach House, New Rd., Cutnall Green. WR9 0PQ. Est. 1976. Open 9-5 or by appointment. CL: Sat. SIZE: Small. *STOCK: Golfiana, books, prints, pictures, clubs, £5-£1,000.* TEL: 01299 851588; fax - 01299 851446; e-mail - golf@ grantbooks.co.uk; website - www. golf books-memorabilia.com.

EVESHAM

Bookworms of Evesham
81 Port St. WR11 6AF. (T.J. Sims). PBFA. Est. 1999. Open 10-5, Mon. by appointment. SIZE: Small. *STOCK: Books - Gloucestershire and Worcestershire, 19th-20th C, £5-£1,200; John Moore, 20th C, £5-£75; general books, 19th-20th C, from 50p.* PARK: Behind premises. TEL: 01386 45509. SER: Valuations; restorations; buys at auction. FAIRS: PBFA - Bath, Cheltenham, Gaydon, Cirencester and Churchdown. VAT: Stan.

Magpie Jewellers and Antiques and Magpie Arms & Armour
Manchester House 1 High St. WR11 4DA. (R.J. and E.R.Bunn). LAPADA. Est. 1975. Open 9-5.30. SIZE: Large. *STOCK: Silver, jewellery, furniture, general antiques, arms and armour, books, stamps and coins.* TEL: 01386 41631.

GREAT MALVERN

Carlton Antiques
43 Worcester Rd. WR14 4RB. (Dave Roberts). Open 10-5. *STOCK: Edwardian postcards and cigarette cards; Victorian and Edwardian furniture, stripped pine; oil paintings, watercolours and prints.* TEL: 01684 573092; e-mail - dave@carlton-antiques.com; website - www.carlton-antiques.com. SER: Valuations.

Foley Furniture
Foley Bank. WR14. (Dave Roberts). *STOCK: Furniture - shipping, modern and old; postcards, cigarette cards, books, pictures, sheet music and general collectables.* TEL: 01684 891255; website - www.carlton-antiques.com.

Great Malvern Antiques
Salisbury House, 6 Abbey Rd. WR14 3HG. (Leonard Sutton and Robert J. Rice). Est. 1966. Open by appointment. SIZE: Large. *STOCK: Decorative furniture and objects, 1800-1940, £250-£2,500.* LOC: Near theatres. PARK: Easy. TEL: 01684 575490; home - same; e-mail - gmantiques@dial.pipex.com. SER: Valuations. FAIRS: Decorative Antiques & Textile, Bath Decorative Antiques. VAT: Stan/Spec. *Trade Only.*

Malvern Bookshop
7 Abbey Rd. WR14 3ES. (Howard and Julie Hudson). Open 10-5. *STOCK: Antiquarian, secondhand books and remainders.* LOC: Near GPO by Priory steps. PARK: Short stay on road above. TEL: 01684 575915.

Malvern Studios
56 Cowleigh Rd. WR14 1QD. (L.M. Hall). BAFRA. Open 9-5.15, Fri. and Sat. 9-4.45. CL: Wed. *STOCK: Period, Edwardian painted and inlaid furniture, general furnishings.* TEL: 01684 574913; fax - 01684 569475. SER: Restorations; woodcarving; polishing; interior design. VAT: Stan/Spec.

Miscellany Antiques
20 Cowleigh Rd. WR14 1QD. (Ray and Liz Hunaban). Resident. Est. 1974. SIZE: Medium showroom + trade warehouse. *STOCK: Victorian, Edwardian and Georgian furniture, including shipping goods, £300-£20,000; some porcelain, silver, bronzes and jewellery.* LOC: B4219 to Bromyard. PARK: Own. TEL: 01684 566671; fax - 01684 560562; mobile - 07836 507954; e-mail - liz.hunaban@virgin.net; website - www.freespace.virgin.net/liz.hunaban/index.htm. SER: Valuations. VAT: Stan/Spec.

Promenade Antiques
41 Worcester Rd. WR14 4RB. (Mark Selvester). Open 10-5, Sun. 12-5. CL: Tues. *STOCK: General antiques, including Victorian and Edwardian furniture, bric-a-brac and books.* TEL: 01684 566876.

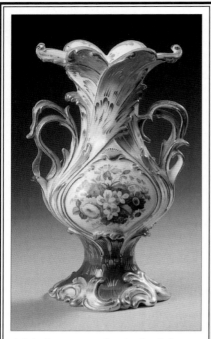

A John Rose vase, well painted with flowers, c.1825, 10¼in. £300-£400.

From an article entitled 'Factory Fact File: Coalport/Coalbrookdale' by David Battie which appeared in the November 2000 issue of **Antique Collecting** magazine. For more details and to subscribe see page 147.

Whitmore

Teynham Lodge, Chase Rd., Upper Colwall. WR13 6DT. *STOCK: British and foreign coins, 1700-1950, £1-£500; trade tokens, 1650-1900, £1-£200; commemorative medallions, 1600-1950, £1-£200.* TEL: 01684 540651. *Postal Only.*

KIDDERMINSTER

The Antique Centre

5-8 Lion St. DY10 1PT. (Vivien Bentley). Est. 1980. Open 10-5.30. SIZE: Large. *STOCK: Furniture, early 18th C to 1930's, £10-£2,000; collectables, to 1930's, £1-£1,000; Victorian, Edwardian and reproduction fireplaces.* LOC: Off Bromsgrove St. PARK: Easy. TEL: 01562 740389; fax - same; mobile - 07980 300660. SER: Valuations; restorations (furniture including stripping, jewellery repairs and commissions).

B.B.M. Jewellery and Antiques

8 and 9 Lion St. DY10 1PT. (W.V. and A. Crook). Est. 1977. Open 10-5. CL: Tues. SIZE: Medium. *STOCK: Jewellery, 19th C, £50-£3,000; coins, £5-£1,000; general antiques, £5-£500.* LOC: Adjacent Youth Centre, off ring road. PARK: Easy. TEL: 01562 744118. SER: Valuations; restorations (jewellery, porcelain, silver). VAT: Stan/Spec/Global.

Gemini Antiques & Gallery

152 Offmore Rd. DY10 1SB. (D.A. Southern). Resident. Est. 1985. Open 10-5.30.CL: Wed. SIZE: Medium. *STOCK: Furniture, 19th-20th C, £100-£500; porcelain, 18th-19th C, £50-£500; mirrors, 19th-20th C, £100-£300.* LOC: Off Birmingham to Chester road. PARK: Easy. TEL: 01562 824109. SER: Valuations; restorations (desk leathers, upholstery, polishing); buys at auction. FAIRS: Malvern and Birmingham. VAT: Stan.

LITTLE MALVERN

St. James Antiques

De Lys Wells Rd. WR14 4JL. (H. Van Wyngaarden). Open 10-5 or by appointment. *STOCK: Continental pine furniture.* PARK: Easy. TEL: 01684 563404. SER: Restorations. VAT: Stan.

MALVERN LINK

Kimber & Son

6 Lower Howsell Rd. WR14 1EF. Est. 1956. Open 9-5.30, Sat. 9-1. *STOCK: 18th-20th C antiques for English, Continental and American markets.* TEL: 01684 574339; home - 01684 572000. VAT: Stan/Spec.

Malvern Link Antiques Centre

154 Worcester Rd. WR14. (Trevor Guiver, Roger Hales, Charles Harries and Paul Shaw). Open 10-5.30, Sun. 11-5. SIZE: Large. *STOCK: General furnishings and beds, 19th to early 20th C, £100-£2,000; collectables, china, £5-£100; fireplaces, from 19th C, £75-£2,000.* LOC: A449 entering Malvern Link. PARK: Easy. TEL: 01684 575750; home - 01684 575904/572491. SER: Restorations; French polishing; buys at auction. VAT: Stan/Spec.

PERSHORE

The Drawing Room - Interiors & Antiques

9 Bridge St. WR10 1AJ. (Janet Davie). IDS. Est. 1980. Open 9.30-5, Sat. 9.30-1. CL: Thurs. SIZE: Medium. *STOCK: Decorative pieces including*

SCOTTISH
WILD FLOWERS

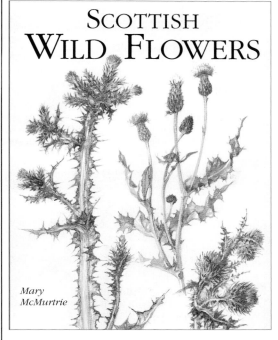

Mary McMurtrie

Scotland contains an interesting and varied flora with many areas of the country such as the Highlands, the mountains and moors of Central Scotland, the Islands of the West and the long and varied coastline remaining relatively wild and unspoilt. Numerous nature reserves serve to protect not just the many rare plants but also those which, although once common, are now becoming scarcer. This book is intended to delight and promote an interest in the native flora by presenting it in an attractive and aesthetically pleasing way. Mary McMurtrie, a leading botanical artist whose work also appears in the well received *Scots Roses*, employs her considerable artistic skills to educate and inform but above all delight her readers with the aid of more than 350 individual watercoloured drawings.

The book is not intended as a complete flora of Scottish wild flowers but is, nevertheless, exceedingly representative. It is set out for quick and easy identification, the recognition being made easier because of the use of the author's original paintings completed from live studies, rather than photographs. This use of individual painting allows the artist to emphasize important recognition features while minimising non-essential detail. To help the reader identify plants quickly and easily, they have been arranged, as far as possible, in groups according to colour – white, red/pink, yellow and blue/purple. There are always variations, however, and many flowers change colour as they age. The descriptions are placed opposite the illustrations and include the common name, the botanical name, the plant family, and the habit and time of flowering. Whenever possible, the plants of the same family are kept together within the particular colour section.

Born in 1902, Mary McMurtrie studied at Gray's School of Art in Aberdeen and for over 40 years had a nursery specialising in alpine and old garden flowers. She has collected and painted the wild flowers of Scotland, the Algarve and Kenya, specialising in watercolours, and exhibitions of her work have been seen in Scotland, England and France.

ISBN 1 870673 38 7, 9 x 6in./228 x 152mm., 272pp., 131 col. illus. **£25.00/$45.00**

antique and reproduction furniture, lighting, mirrors, framed prints and engravings, £50-£20,000. PARK: Easy (in main square or opposite). TEL: 01386 555747; fax - 01386 555071. SER: Valuations; interior design. VAT: Stan/Spec.

Hansen Chard Antiques
126 High St. WR10 1EA. (P.W. Ridler). BSc LBHI. Est. 1984. Open Tues., Wed., Fri. and Sat. 10-4.30 or by appointment. SIZE: Large. *STOCK: Clocks, barometers, models, tools, books, antique and secondhand, £5-£4,000.* LOC: On A44. PARK: Easy. TEL: 01386 553423; home - same. SER: Valuations; restorations (as stock); buys at auction (as stock). VAT: Spec.

S.W. Antiques
Abbey Showrooms, Newlands. WR10 1BP. (R.J. Whiteside). Est. 1978. Open 9-5, Sun. 10.30-4. SIZE: Large. *STOCK: 19th-20th C furniture including beds and bedroom furniture, to £4,000.* Not Stocked: Jewellery, small items. LOC: 2 mins. from Abbey. PARK: Own. TEL: 01386 555580; fax - 01386 556205; website - www.sw-antiques.co.uk. VAT: Stan/Spec.

Lower House Fine Antiques
Lower House, Far Moor Lane, Winyates Green. B98 0QX. (Mrs J.B. Hudson). Est. 1987. Usually open but prior appointment advisable. SIZE: Small. *STOCK: Furniture, 17th to early 20th C, £100-£4,000; silver and plate, 18th to early 20th C, £10-£1,000; oil lamps, 19th C, £50-£500.* Not Stocked: Pine furniture. LOC: 3 miles due east Redditch town centre and half a mile from Coventry Highway island, close to A435. PARK: Own. TEL: 01527 525117; home - same. SER: Valuations; restorations (including porcelain).

Holloways
Lower Court. WR6 5DE. (Edward and Diana Holloway). SIZE: Large. *STOCK: Garden ornaments and furniture, £20-£5,000.* LOC: A44 from Worcester towards Leominster, left at Knightwick, 3 miles, situated in front of village church. PARK: Easy. TEL: 01886 884665; website - www.holloways.co.uk. SER: Valuations; restorations; buys at auction. VAT: Stan/Spec.

The Highway Gallery
40 Old St. WR8 0HW. (J. Daniell). Est. 1969. Open 10.30-5, but appointment advisable. CL: Thurs. and Mon. SIZE: Small. *STOCK: Oils, watercolours, 19th-20th C, £100-£10,000.* Not Stocked: Prints. LOC: 100yds. from crossroads towards Malvern. PARK: Easy. TEL: 01684 592645; home - 01684 592909. SER: Valuations; restorations (reline and clean); buys at auction (pictures).

Antique Map and Print Gallery
61 Sidbury. WR1 2HU. (M. Nichols). Open 9-5.30. *STOCK: Antiquarian maps, prints and books, Baxter and Le Blond prints.* TEL: 01905 612926. SER: Greetings cards reproduced from original prints.

Antique Warehouse
Rear of 74 Droitwich Rd, Barbourne. WR3 8BW. (D. Venn). Open 9-5, Sat. 10-4.30. *STOCK: General antiques, shipping, restored pine and satin walnut, Victorian doors and fireplaces.* PARK: Easy. TEL: 01905 27493. SER: Stripping (wood and metalwork).

Antiques and Curios
50 Upper Tything. WR1 1JZ. Open 9.30-5.30. SIZE: Large - 6 dealers on three floors. *STOCK: 18th to early 20th C furniture, oak, mahogany, walnut, especially Victorian and Edwardian desks, dining and bedroom, decorative and upholstered, furnishings, mirrors, pictures, clocks, curios, treen, objects d'art.* LOC: From Birmingham A38 into Worcester on right-hand side. PARK: Easy. TEL: 01905 25412/764547. SER: Restorations; re-polishing; upholstery; valuations.

The Barber's Clock
37 Droitwich Rd. WR3 7LG. (Graham Gopsill). Est. 1990. Open 9-5, Mon. 10-5, Sun. 1-4. SIZE: Medium. *STOCK: Clocks, 19th C to Art Deco, £350-£1,000; gramophones and phonographs, 20th C, £250-£475+.* PARK: Own. TEL: 01905 29022; home - 01905 779011. SER: Valuations; restorations (clocks and gramophones).FAIRS: Swinderby, Stone Manor, Kidderminster.

Bygones by the Cathedral
Cathedral Sq. WR1. (Gabrielle Doherty Bullock). LAPADA. FGA DGA. Est. 1946. Open 9.30-5.30, Sat. 9.30-1 and 2-5.30. *STOCK: Furniture,*

17th-19th C; silver, Sheffield plate, jewellery, paintings, glass; English and Continental pottery and porcelain especially Royal Worcester. LOC: Adjacent main entrance to Cathedral. TEL: 01905 25388.

Bygones of Worcester

55 Sidbury. WR1 2HU. (Gabrielle Bullock). LAPADA. FGA. Est. 1946. Open 9.30-1 and 2-5.30. *STOCK: Walnut, oak, mahogany and exotic wood furniture, brass and copper, oil paintings, porcelain, pottery and glass.* LOC: Opposite car park near approach to the cathedral. TEL: 01905 23132. VAT: Stan/Spec.

Gray's Antiques

29 The Tything. WR1 1JL. (David Gray). Open 8.30-5.30. *STOCK: General antiques and soft furnishings.* TEL: 01905 724456; fax - 01905 723433; e-mail - enqs@grays-interiors.com.

Gray's Interiors

35 The Tything. WR1 1JL. Open 8.30-5.30. *STOCK: Chandeliers, chairs, sofas, soft furnishings.* TEL: 01905 21209; e-mail - enqs@grays-interiors.com.

Heirlooms

46 Upper Tything. WR1 1JZ. (D. Tarran and L. Rumford). Open 9.30-4.30. *STOCK: General antiques, objets d'art, Royal Worcester porcelain and prints.* TEL: 01905 23332.

Sarah Hodge

Peachley Manor, Hallow Lane, Lower Broadheath. WR2 6QL. Resident. Est. 1985. Open daily including Sun. SIZE: Large. *STOCK: General antiques, country bygones, pine and kitchenalia.* LOC: Off B4204, 3 miles N.W. Worcester. PARK: Easy. TEL: 01905 640255.

M. Lees and Sons

Tower House, Severn St. WR1 2NB. LAPADA. Resident. Est. 1955. Open 9.15-5.15, Sat. by appointment. CL: Thurs. pm. SIZE: Medium. *STOCK: Furniture, 1780-1880; porcelain, 1750-1920.* LOC: At southern end of Worcester Cathedral adjacent to Edgar Tower; near Royal Worcester Porcelain Museum and factory. PARK: Easy. TEL: 01905 26620; home - 01905 427142. VAT: Stan/Spec.

Round the Bend

1 Deansway. WR1 2JD. Open 10-5.30. *STOCK: Eccentricities, brocante-type goods and jolly junk.* LOC: Corner of Cathedral Square. TEL: 01905 616516.

Worcester Antiques Centre

15 Reindeer Court, Mealcheapen St. WR1 4DF. (Stephen Zacaroli). Est. 1992. Open 10-5. *STOCK: Pottery and porcelain, 1750-1950, £10-£2,000; silver, 1750-1940, £10-£3,000; jewellery, 1800-1940, £5-£2,000; furniture, 1650-1930, £50-£5,000.* PARK: Loading only or 50 yards. TEL: 01905 610680/1. SER: Valuations; restorations. FAIRS: NEC (April and Aug); East Berkshire (May and Oct).

WYCHBOLD

D & J Lines Antiques

Papermill Lane. WR9 0DE. (Derek and Jill Lines). By appointment only. SIZE: Medium. *STOCK: Oak and country furniture, 17th-18th C, £500-£8,000; metalware, 18th-19th C, £50-£500; Persian carpets, 19th-20th C, £50-£1,000.* TEL: 01527 861282. SER: Valuations; restorations; desk re-leathering.

Attributed to William Powell Frith, RA, Portrait of a young lady, oil on board, 7½in. x 5½in. £7,480. The Bristol Auction Rooms, Avon.

From a feature on Saleroom Prices which appeared in the March 2001 issue of **Antique Collecting** magazine. For more details and to subscribe see page 147.

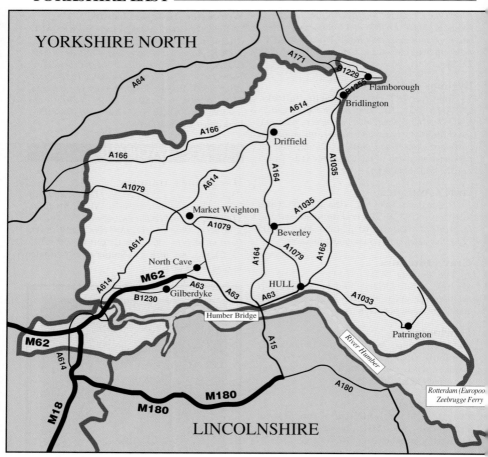

Dealers and Shops in Yorkshire East

Beverley	5	Flamborough	1	Market Weighton	3		
Bridlington	3	Gilberdyke	1	North Cave	1		
Driffield	3	Hull	7	Patrington	1		

BEVERLEY

Karen Guest Antiques
24 Saturday Market Place. HU17. NAG registered Valuer and Jeweller. HRD Dip. of Diamond Grading. Open 9.15-5. SIZE: Medium. *STOCK: Jewellery and silver, 18th-20th C, £50-£15,000.* PARK: Easy. TEL: 01482 882334; fax - same. SER: Valuations; restorations. VAT: Stan/Spec.

Hawley Antiques
5 North Bar Within. HU17 8AP. LAPADA. Open 10-4, Sat. 9.30-5. *STOCK: General antiques, furniture, pottery, porcelain, glass, oil paintings, watercolours, silver.* TEL: 01482 868193; mobile - 07850 225805. SER: Restorations (fine furniture). VAT: Stan/Spec.

St Crispin Antique Centre
11 Butcher Row. HU17 0AA. (Geoff and Helen Storr). Est. 1971. Open seven days. SIZE: 50+

dealers. *STOCK: Mainly ceramics - Moorcroft, Mason's, Doulton, 18th to late 19th C, £5-£1,000.* TEL: 01482 869583; home/fax - 01482 571935. SER: Valuations.

James H. Starkey Galleries

49 Highgate. HU17 0DN. Est. 1968. Open 9.30-4.30, Sat. by appointment. SIZE: Medium. *STOCK: Oil paintings, 16th-19th C; drawings and watercolours, 17th-19th C.* LOC: Opposite minster. PARK: Easy. TEL: 01482 881179; fax - 01482 861644. SER: Valuations; restorations (paintings); buys at auction. VAT: Stan/Spec.

Time and Motion

1 Beckside. HU17 0PB. (Peter A. Lancaster). FBHI. Est. 1977. Open 10-5. CL: Thurs. SIZE: Medium. *STOCK: English longcase clocks, 18th-19th C, £1,500-£8,000; English, German and French mantel and wall clocks, 19th C, £300-£3,500; aneroid and mercurial barometers, 18th-19th C, £150-£3,000.* LOC: .25 mile from town centre and minster, 300 yards from Army Museum of Transport. PARK: Easy. TEL: 01482 881574; home - same. SER: Valuations; restorations (clocks and barometers). VAT: Stan/Spec.

An early George III serpentine and bombé figured mahogany commode in French taste, c.1770. 46in. wide. This combines a rococo form with neo-classical swag handles.

From an article entitled 'The 18th Century British Interior – Part II' by Christopher Claxton Stevens which appeared in the September 2000 issue of **Antique Collecting** magazine. For more details and to subscribe see page 147.

BRIDLINGTON

C.J. and A.J. Dixon Ltd
1st Floor, 23 Prospect St. YO15 2AE. Est. 1969. Open 10-4.30. SIZE: Large. *STOCK: War medals and decorations, British and foreign.* LOC: Town centre. PARK: Easy. TEL: 01262 676877/603348; fax - 01262 606600. SER: Valuations; renovations. VAT: Stan/Spec.

Priory Antiques
47-49 High St. YO16 4PR. (P.R. Rogerson). Est. 1979. Open 10-5. CL: Thurs. *STOCK: Georgian and Victorian furniture.* TEL: 01262 601365.

Sedman Antiques
106 Cardigan Rd. YO15 3LR. (R.H.S. and M.A. Sedman). Est. 1971. Open 10-5.30, Sun. by appointment. *STOCK: General antiques, period and shipping furniture, Oriental porcelain, Victorian collectors' items.* TEL: 01262 675671.

DRIFFIELD

The Antique Pine & Country Furniture Shop
58A Middle St. North. YO25 6SU. (D. A. Smith). Est. 1977. Open 9.30-5.30, Sat. 9.30-5, Sun. by appointment. SIZE: Medium + warehouse. *STOCK: Furniture including pine and country, 18th to early 20th C, £50-£2,000; furniture designed and made to order, from £50+.* LOC: Main street. PARK: Easy. TEL: 01377 256321; home - same; fax - 01377 256070; e-mail - dave@pine-on-line.co.uk; website - www.pine-on-line.co.uk. SER: Restorations.

The Crested China Co
Station House. YO25 7PY. (D. Taylor). Est. 1978. Open Mon.-Fri. 9-5, other times by appointment or by chance. *STOCK: Goss and crested china.* PARK: Easy. TEL: 01377 257042 (24 hr.). SER: Sales catalogues.

Karen Guest Antiques
80A Middle St. South. YO25 7QE. NAG registered Valuer and Jeweller. HRD Diploma of Diamond Grading. Open 9.15-5. SIZE: Small. *STOCK: Jewellery and silver, 18th-20th C, £50-£1,000.* TEL: 01377 241467. SER: Valuations; restorations. VAT: Stan/Spec.

FLAMBOROUGH, Nr. Bridlington

Lesley Berry Antiques
The Manor House. YO15 1PD. (Mrs L. Berry). Resident. Est. 1972. Open 9.30-5.30, other times by appointment. SIZE: Small. *STOCK: Furniture, silver, jewellery, amber, Whitby jet, oils, watercolours, prints, copper, brass, textiles, fountain pens, secondhand and antiquarian books on-line.* Not Stocked: Shipping goods. LOC: On corner of Tower St. and Lighthouse Rd. PARK: Easy. TEL: 01262 850943; e-mail - lb@flamboroughmanor.co.uk; website - www.flamboroughmanor.co.uk. SER: Buys at auction.

GILBERDYKE

Lewis E. Hickson FBHI
Antiquarian Horologist, Sober Hill Farm. HU15 2TB. Est. 1965. Open by appointment only. SIZE: Small. *STOCK: Longcase, bracket clocks, barometers and instruments.* TEL: 01430 449113. SER: Restorations; repairs.

HULL

Grannie's Parlour
33 Anlaby Rd. HU1 2PG. (Mrs N. Pye). Open 11-5. CL: Thurs. *STOCK: General antiques, ephemera, Victoriana, dolls, toys, kitchenalia.* TEL: 01482 228258; home - 01482 341020.

Grannie's Treasures
1st Floor, 33 Anlaby Rd. HU1 2PG. (Mrs N. Pye). Open 11-5. CL.Thurs. *STOCK: Advertising items, dolls prams, toys, small furniture, china and pre-1940s clothing.* TEL: 01482 228258; home - 01482 341020.

David Hakeney Antiques
P O Box 65. HU10 7XT. Open by appointment only. *STOCK: Porcelain and silver; 19th C and Edwardian furniture, decorative items.* TEL: 01482 651177; fax - same; mobile - 07860 507774. FAIRS: NEC (April, Aug. and Dec.); Newark. *Trade Only.*

Hull Antique Centre
Anderson Wharf, Wincolmlee. HU2 8AH. (Melvin Anderson). Est. 1975. Open 9-5, Sat. and Sun. 10-4. SIZE: Large. *STOCK: Furniture, period, Victorian and Edwardian, 17th to early 20th C, £50-£3,000.* LOC: From M64 take Clive Sullivan Way. PARK: Easy. TEL: 01482 609958.

SER: Valuations. FAIRS: Newark, Swinderby, York, Ardingly, Harrogate, Birmingham. VAT: Stan/Spec.

Imperial Antiques
397 Hessle Rd. HU3 4EH. (M.Langton). Est. 1982. Open 9-5.30. *STOCK: British stripped pine furniture, antique, old and reproduction.* TEL: 01482 327439; fax - same. FAIRS: Newark, Ardingly. VAT: Stan.

Kevin Marshall's Antiques Warehouse
17-20A Wilton St., Holderness Rd. HU8 7LG. Est. 1981. Open 10-5 including Sun. SIZE: Large. *STOCK: Bathroom ware, architectural items, fires, lighting, furniture and reproductions, 19th C, £5-£5,000.* LOC: 1st right off Dansom Lane South. PARK: Easy. TEL: 01482 326559; fax - same; e-mail - kevinmarshall @antique warehouse.karoo.co.uk. SER: Valuations; restorations; boardroom tables made to order. VAT: Stan/Spec.

Sandringham Antiques
64a Beverley Rd. HU5 1NE. (P. and P. Allison). Est. 1968. *STOCK: General antiques.* TEL: 01482 847653/320874.

MARKET WEIGHTON, Nr. York

Garforth Gallery
57 Market Place. YO43 3AJ. Est. 1956. Open 10.30-4. CL: Thurs. SIZE: Small. *STOCK: Paintings, prints, maps, clocks, jewellery, silver, some porcelain, £20-£600.* LOC: On main road in town centre. TEL: 01430 803173. SER: Valuations; restorations.

Houghton Hall Antiques
Cliffe/North Cave Rd. YO43 3RE. (M.E. Watson). Est. 1965. Open daily 8-4, Sun. 11-4. SIZE: Large. *STOCK: Furniture, 17th-19th C, £5-£8,000; china, 19th C, £1-£600; paintings and prints, £20-£1,000; objets d'art.* Not Stocked: Coins, guns. LOC: Turn right on new by-pass from York (left coming from Beverley), 3/4 mile, signposted North Cave - sign on entrance. PARK: Easy. TEL: 01430 873234. SER: Valuations; restorations (furniture); buys at auction. FAIRS: New York. VAT: Stan/Spec.

Pieter Plantenga
49 Holme Rd. YO43 3EW. Open 9-4.30. *STOCK: Stripped pine, general furniture.* TEL: 01430 872473.

NORTH CAVE

Penny Farthing Antiques
Albion House, 18 Westgate. (C.E. Dennett). Est. 1987. Open 9.30-6. SIZE: Medium. *STOCK: 19th-20th C furniture, Victorian brass and iron bedsteads, £25-£2,000; linen, textiles and samplers, 18th-20th C, £5-£500; general collectables, china and glass, 19th-20th C, £5-£500.* LOC: Main road (B1230). PARK: Easy. TEL: 01430 422958. SER: Valuations; buys at auction. FAIRS: Newark.

PATRINGTON

Clyde Antiques
12 Market Place. HU12 0RB. (S. M. Nettleton). Est. 1978. Open 10-5. CL: Sun., Mon. and Wed. except by appointment. SIZE: Medium. *STOCK: General antiques.* PARK: Easy. TEL: 01964 630650; home - 01964 612471. SER: Valuations. VAT: Stan.

Circle of Angelica Kauffmann (1741 -1807), 'Tuccia, A Vestal Virgin'; oil on canvas, 37in. x 30in. Worth about £1,500-£2,000. An honourable period copy. Only an added signature or a full attribution to Kauffmann would turn this into a fake.

From an article entitled 'Guilty Until Proven Innocent' by Richard Kay which appeared in the October 2000 issue of **Antique Collecting** magazine. For more details and to subscribe see page 147.

George III Mahogany Bureau in original condition.

R. S. Wilson & Sons
Antiques

Good selection of 18th & 19th Century
Period Furniture & Accessories

4 HALL SQUARE,
BOROUGHBRIDGE, N. YORKS. YO51 9AN.

EST.
1917

TEL/FAX
01423 322417

BEDALE

Bennett's Antiques & Collectables
7 Market Place. DL8 1ED. (Paul and Kim Bennett). Est. 1996. Open 9-5, Sun. by appointment. SIZE: Large. *STOCK: Furniture, 18th to early 20th C, £100-£10,000; fine art, 19th to early 20th C, £100-£4,000; clocks, 19th to early 20th C, £200-£4,000; collectables, 19th-20th C, £20-£1,000; local works of art, 20th C, £100-£600.* PARK: Easy and free. TEL: 01677 427900; fax - 01677 426858; website - www. bennetts.uk.com. SER: Restorations; clock repairs. VAT: Spec.

BIRSTWITH, Nr. Harrogate

John Pearson Antique Clock Restoration
Church Cottage. HG3 2NG. Est. 1978. Open by appointment. *STOCK: Longcase, bracket and wall clocks, 18th C.* LOC: Off A59. PARK: Easy. TEL: 01423 770828; home - same. SER: Restorations (clocks, cases, movements and especially dials).

BOLTON ABBEY

The Grove Country Bookshop with Coopers of Ilkley
The Old Post Office. (Andrew and Janet Sharpe). LAPADA. PBFA. Open 10-5 (summer) including Sun. *STOCK: Antiquarian and rare books, maps, prints, country furniture, metalware, glass, clocks.* PARK: Own. TEL: 01756 710717; fax - 01943 817086. SER: Valuations; book-binding; restorations (furniture); buys at auction (as stock).

BOROUGHBRIDGE

Anthony Graham Antiques
Aberure, Bridge St. YO51 9LA. Resident. Est. 1985. Open 9.30-5 or by appointment. SIZE: Small. *STOCK: Period decorative antiques and accessories, pictures, furniture and collectors items, 18th-19th C, £5-£5,000.* LOC: Off A1. PARK: Easy. TEL: 01423 323952; fax - same; mobile - 07803 596410; website - www.anthony grahamantiques.co.uk. SER: Valuations.

St. James House Antiques
St. James Sq. YO51 9AR. (J.D. Wilson). LAPADA. Est. 1989. Open 9-5.30, Sun. by appointment. SIZE: Medium. *STOCK: Period and later furniture, brass, copper and china.* LOC: Town centre. PARK: Own. TEL: 01423 322508; home - same; mobile - 07720 544926. SER: Valuations; restorations; upholstery. VAT: Stan/Spec.

R.S. Wilson and Sons
4 Hall Square. YO51 9AN. Est. 1917. Open 9-5.30, Thurs. and Sun. by appointment. *STOCK: 17th-19th C furniture and accessories.* TEL: 01423 322417; fax - same. VAT: Stan/Spec.

BRANDSBY

L.L. Ward and Son
Bar House. YO61 4RQ. (R. Ward). Est. 1970. Open 8.30-5. *STOCK: Antique pine.* TEL: 01347 888651

BURNESTON, Nr. Bedale

W. Greenwood (Fine Art)
Oak Dene, Church Wynd. DL8 2JE. Est. 1978. Open by appointment. *STOCK: Paintings and watercolours, 19th-20th C, £100-£5,000; frames, £20-£500; mirrors.* LOC: Take B6285 left off A1

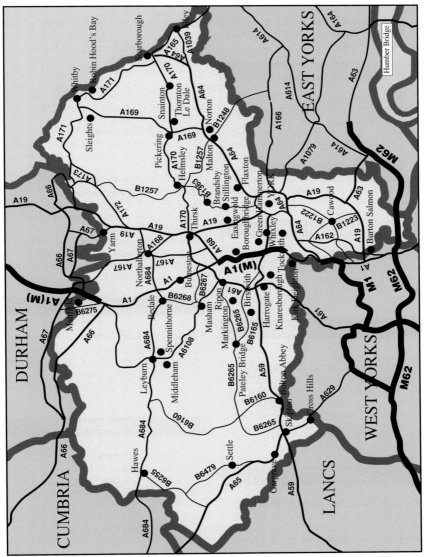

Dealers and Shops in North Yorkshire

Bedale	1	Flaxton	1	Manfield	1	Skipton	2
Birstwith	1	Gargrave	4	Markington	1	Sleights	1
Bolton Abbey	1	Green Hammerton	1	Masham	1	Snainton	1
Boroughbridge	3	Harrogate	27	Middleham	2	Spennithorne	1
Brandsby	1	Hawes	1	Northallerton	1	Stillington	2
Burneston	1	Helmsley	3	Norton	1	Thirsk	5
Burton Salmon	1	Kirk Deighton	1	Pateley Bridge	2	Thornton le Dale	1
Cawood	1	Knaresborough	5	Pickering	2	Tockwith	1
Cross Hills	1	Leyburn	1	Ripon	3	Whitby	5
Easingwold	5	Lythe	1	Robin Hood's Bay	1	Whixley	1
Filey	1	Malton	2	Scarborough	2	Yarm	1
				Settle	5	York	17

northbound, house 1/4 mile on right. PARK: Easy. TEL: 01677 424830; home - 01677 423217. SER: Valuations; restorations (paintings and frames); framing.

BURTON SALMON

Old Hall Antiques
Hall Farm, Main St. (J.T. and S.G. Fenteman). Resident. Open Tues.-Sun. 10-5, Mon. by appointment, SIZE: Large. STOCK: Country furniture, oak and pine, £50-£10,000; period metalwork, kitchenalia, pictures and prints; all 17th-19th C. LOC: 3 miles from junction 33 M62(A1) just off A162. PARK: Easy. TEL: 01977 607778; home/fax - 01977 672052. SER: Buys at auction (early oak). VAT: Spec.

CAWOOD, Nr. Selby

Cawood Antiques
Sherburn St. YO8 3SS. (J.E. Gilham). Open 8-5. STOCK: Furniture, copper, brass, weapons, medals, golfing memorabilia and collectors' items. PARK: Easy. TEL: 01757 268533.

CROSS HILLS, Nr. Keighley

Heathcote Antiques
Skipton Rd. Junction. BD20 7DS. (M. Webster). Resident. Est. 1979. Open 10-5.30, Sun. 12.30-4.30. CL: Mon. and Tues. SIZE: Very large showroom + trade warehouse. STOCK: Furniture, clocks, barometers, unstripped English pine, pottery, porcelain, brass and metal wares. PARK: Own. TEL: 01535 635250; fax - 01535 637205; mobile - 07836 259640.

EASINGWOLD

Fox's Old Pine & Country Furniture
108 Long St. YO61 3HY. (M.J. Fox). Est. 1958. Open 10.15-5. STOCK: Period pine and country furniture including kitchenalia and collectables. Not Stocked: Reproduction. PARK: Easy. TEL: 01347 822977.

Milestone Antiques
Farnley House, 101 Long St. YO61 3HY. (A.B. and S.J. Streetley). Open daily, Sun. by appointment. SIZE: Medium. STOCK: Mahogany and oak furniture, £100-£2,000; longcase and wall clocks, upholstered and pine furniture, pictures, prints, oils and watercolours, £100-£800; all 18th to early 20th C. LOC: A19, village centre. PARK: Easy. TEL: 01347 821608; home - same. SER: Valuations. VAT: Stan/Spec.

Old Flames
30 Long St. YO61 3HT. (P. Lynas and J.J. Thompson). Est. 1988. Open 10-5. SIZE: Medium. STOCK: Fireplaces, 18th-19th C, £100-£4,000; lighting, 19th C, £100-£3,000; architectural items, 18th-19th C, £50-£500. PARK: Easy. TEL: 01347 821188; website - www.salvoweb.com/dealers/old-flames. SER: Valuations. FAIRS: Newark. VAT: Stan/Spec.

Mrs B.A.S. Reynolds
42 Long St. YO61 3HT. STOCK: General antiques, Victorian. TEL: 01347 821078.

The White House Antiques & Architectural Reclamation
Thirsk Rd. YO61 3NF. (G. Hood). Resident. Est. 1960. Usually open but prior 'phone call advisable. STOCK: Rural and domestic bygones, stone troughs, architectural reclamation and garden ornaments. LOC: 1 mile north of Easingwold, 200 yds from northern junction of bypass (A19). PARK: Easy. TEL: 01347 821479.

FILEY

Cairncross and Sons
31 Bellevue St. YO14 9HU. (G. Cairncross). Open 9.30-12.45 and 2-4.30. CL: Wed. pm (April-Sept). STOCK: Medals, uniforms, insignia, cap badges. Not Stocked: Weapons. TEL: 01723 513287.

FLAXTON, Nr. York

Elm Tree Antiques
YO60 7RJ. (R. and J. Jackson). Est. 1975. Open 9-5, (winter - 4.30) Sun. 10-5 (winter - Sat. and Sun. 10-4). SIZE: Large. STOCK: Furniture, 17th C to Edwardian; small items, £5-£5,000, Staffordshire figures. LOC: 1 mile off A64. PARK: Easy. TEL: 01904 468462; home - same; fax - 01904 468728; website - www.elmtreeantiques.co.uk. SER: Valuations; restorations (cabinet making, polishing and upholstery).

GARGRAVE, Nr. Skipton

Antiques at Forge Cottage
22A High St. BD23 3RB. Est. 1979. Open Wed.-Sat. 10-5. STOCK: Pottery and porcelain. LOC: A65. PARK: Easy. TEL: 01756 748272; mobile - 07860 525579; e-mail - philina@carrol.fsnet.co.uk.

Bernard Dickinson
Estate Yard, West St. BD23 3PH. (H.H. and A.E. Mardall). Resident. Est. 1958. Open 9-5.30 or by appointment. *STOCK: Early English furniture.* LOC: Just off A65 Skipton-Settle road. PARK: Easy. TEL: 01756 748257. VAT: Spec.

Gargrave Gallery
48 High St. BD23 3RB. (B. Herrington). Appointment advisable. *STOCK: General antiques, oak, mahogany, metal, paintings, 18th to early 20th C.* PARK: Easy. TEL: 01756 749641.

R.N. Myers and Son   BADA
Endsleigh House, High St. BD23 3LX. Est. 1890. Open 9-5.30 or by appointment. SIZE: Medium. STOCK: Furniture, oak, mahogany, 17th to early 19th C; pottery, porcelain and metalware. Not Stocked: Victoriana, weapons, coins, jewellery. LOC: A65. Skipton-Settle road. PARK: Behind shop and opposite. TEL: 01756 749587. SER: Valuations. VAT: Spec.

The Main Pine Co
Grangewood, The Green. YO26 8BQ. (C. and K.M. Main). Est. 1976. Open 9-5. SIZE: Large. *STOCK: Pine furniture, 18th-19th C, £100-£1,500; reproductions from old pine.* LOC: Just off A59. PARK: Easy. TEL: 01423 330451; home - 01423 331078; fax - 01423 331278; e-mail - mainpine@onyxnet.co.uk; website - www.activ.co.uk/mainpine/. SER: Export; containers packed. VAT: Stan.

Nigel Adamson
Flat 1, 19 Park View. HG1 5LY. (N.J.G. Adamson). Est. 1863. Open by appointment only. *STOCK: Furniture, 17th to early 19th C; porcelain, Chinese, English and Continental.* TEL: 01423 528924; mobile - 07939 566391. SER: Valuations; restorations (furniture, porcelain). VAT: Spec.

Armstrong   BADA
10-11 Montpellier Parade. HG1 2TJ. (M.A. Armstrong). LAPADA. Est. 1976. Open 10-5.30. SIZE: Medium. STOCK: Fine English furniture, 18th to early 19th C; glasses and works of art, 18th C. PARK: Easy. TEL: 01423 506843. FAIRS: Olympia (June, Nov). VAT: Spec.

Bill Bentley
16 Montpellier Parade. HG1 2TG. Open 9.30-5.30 or by appointment. SIZE: Large. *STOCK:*

Oak furniture, 1600-1800; country furniture, 1700-1800; period metalwork and treen. PARK: Easy. TEL: 01423 564084; home - 01423 564564. VAT: Spec.

Bryan Bowden
Oakleigh, 1 Spacey View, Leeds Rd., Pannal. HG3 1LQ. Est. 1969. By appointment only. SIZE: Small. *STOCK: English pottery and porcelain, 1750-1850; small Georgian furniture.* LOC: 2.5 miles south of Harrogate on Leeds road. PARK: Easy. TEL: 01423 870007; home - same. SER: Valuations; restorations (pottery and porcelain); buys at auction (English pottery and porcelain). FAIRS: Northern; Buxton; Wakefield Ceramic. VAT: Spec.

Derbyshire Antiques Ltd
27 Montpellier Parade. HG1 2TG. (R.C. and M.T. Derbyshire). Est. 1960. Open 10-5.30. SIZE: Medium. *STOCK: Early oak and walnut, 16th-18th C; Georgian furniture to 1820; decorative items.* TEL: 01423 503115/564242. VAT: Spec.

Dragon Antiques
10 Dragon Rd. HG1 5DF. (P.F. Broadbelt). Resident. Est. 1954. Open 11-6. Always available. SIZE: Small. *STOCK: Victorian art glass, £30-£300; art pottery, postcards, G.B. and foreign.* LOC: 5 mins. from town centre, opposite Dragon Road car park. PARK: Easy. TEL: 01423 562037.

Garth Antiques
2 Montpellier Mews. HG1 2TQ. (I. Chapman). LAPADA. Open 10-5.30. SIZE: Small. *STOCK: Furniture, 18th-19th C, £50-£3,000; brass and copper, 19th C, £1-£500; oils and watercolours, £5-£3,000.* LOC: Turn left from Montpellier Parade at Montpellier public house. TEL: 01423 530573. VAT: Stan/Spec.

The Ginnel
Harrogate Antiques Centre, The Ginnel. HG1 2RB. (P. Stephenson). Open 9.30-5.30. *STOCK: All date-lined and vetted - see individual entries.* LOC: Off Parliament St. opposite Debenhams. PARK: Nearby. TEL: 01423 508857; website - www.ginnel.co.uk and www.ginnel.com. SER: Courier. Below are listed the specialist dealers at this centre.

Anglo-Scandinavian
Cutlery, silver plate, inkwells, collectors' and decorative items.

Appleton Antiques
19th-20th pottery including Carlton, Moorcroft, Linthorpe, Poole and crested china; drinking glasses, paintings, small furniture.

Discover in Harrogate's Premier Antique Centre, two floors housing 50 units offering a wide selection of Antiques and a Licensed Coffee Shop.

Open 9.30am-5.30pm Mon. to Sat.
The Corn Exchange Building, The Ginnel
Off Parliament Street, Opposite Debenhams
Harrogate HG1 2RB. Tel: 01423 508857
Websites: www.ginnel.co.uk www.ginnel.com

Fiona Aston
Objets d'art including porcelain and miniatures.

Beaver
19th C porcelain and glass.

M. Bedi
Fine 19th C furniture and paintings.

Elizabeth Bowden Antiques
19th C furniture and porcelain.

Brackmoor Antiques
Silver, porcelain and objets d'art.

P. Carrol
18th-19th C pottery and porcelain.

Catkins Jewellery
Victorian and Edwardian jewellery, Royal Worcester porcelain.

Mary Cooper
Antique costumes and textiles, to 1929, including lace, fans, shawls, linen, quilts, samplers, wool and beadwork. TEL: 01423 567182.

Cornmill Antiques
19th to early 20th C china, especially Royal Doulton.

Eve Antiques
Early 20th C pottery and porcelain.

Richard Freeman
British, Oriental and Continental ceramics, 18th to early 19th C. TEL: Mobile - 0421 645788.

Jeffrey and Pauline Glass
Porcelain and glass, objets d'art, 19th to early 20th C.

Harpers
Watches, 1920-40.

R. Himsworth
Silver and jewellery.

S. Judge
20th C pottery and china including Shelley, Doulton, Bretby, Charlotte Rhead, Moorcroft.

G. Kendall
Furniture and collectables.

Libra Antiques
Edwardian furniture, cranberry glass,

Brian Loomes
Longcase clocks, small period furniture.

E.R. Marris
19th C silver.

Sheila Morgan
Victorian collectables.

O'Flynn
19th-20th C prints and books.

Octavia Antiques
1920's, 1930's pottery and porcelain.

Parker Gallery
19th to early 20th C oils and watercolours, £100-£3,000.

Past Reflections
Victorian and Edwardian furniture, porcelain and silver.

Purr-fect Antiques
Silver and jewellery.

Paul Raine
19th C silver.

G.M. Ritchie
Porcelain, copper and brass, linen.

Rose Fine Art
19th to early 20th C prints and engravings.

Alan Sharp
English pottery and porcelain, 1750-1850.

Stella-Mar
Fine 19th C furniture and furnishings, wide variety of object d'art.

Tango Curios
19th-20th C collectables.

Terry's Art Co
18th-19th C Chinese works of art.

C.E. Tweedale
Victorian and Edwardian pottery.

Upstairs, Downstairs
19th to early 20th C kitchen furnishings and utensils.

E.H. Ward
Pottery, porcelain and glass.

Ann Wilkinson
Silver, porcelain and jewellery.

Michael Green Pine & Country Antiques
Library House, Regent Parade. HG1 5AN. Est. 1976. Open 8.30-5.30, Sat. 8.45-4, Sun. by appointment. SIZE: Medium. *STOCK: Oak, mahogany and pine furniture, from 17th C, £5-£3,000; treen, kitchenalia and collectors treasures.* LOC: Overlooking the Stray. PARK: Easy. TEL: 01423 560452. SER: Valuations; restorations; stripping. VAT: Stan/Spec.

Havelocks
13-17 Westmoreland St. HG1 5AY. (Philip Adam). Est. 1989. Open 10-5 including Sun. SIZE: Large. *STOCK: Original pine, oak, general antique furniture.* LOC: A59 towards Skipton, turn left into Westmoreland St. TEL: 01423 506721. SER: Valuations; restorations; stripping and finishing.

Haworth Antiques
26 Cold Bath Rd. HG2 0NA. (G. and J. White). Open 10-5 or by appointment. CL: Mon. SIZE: Medium. *STOCK: Clocks, 18th-19th C, £100-£3,000; small furniture, Georgian and Victorian, £50-£1,000.* LOC: 300yds. from Crown Hotel. PARK: Easy. TEL: 01423 521401; mobile - 07831 692263. SER: Restorations (clocks, dials re-painted and re-silvered). VAT: Stan/Spec.

London House Oriental Rugs and Carpets
9 Montpellier Parade. HG1 2TJ. Est. 1981. Open 10-5. SIZE: Medium. *STOCK: Persian, Turkish, Indian, Tibetan, Nepalese and Afghan rugs and carpets, 19th-20th C, £25-£5,000; kelims and camel bags, 19th-20th C, £25-£2,000.* LOC: Town centre on The Stray. PARK: Easy. TEL: 01423 567167; home - 01937 845123. SER: Valuations; restorations (handmade rugs). VAT: Stan.

Elegant Regency chairs with tapered reeded legs, c.1820. A set of eight, including two armchairs, were sold at Billingshurst in February for around £10,000. (Sotheby'South)

From an article entitled '19th Century Furniture' by John Andrews which appeared in the July/August 2000 issue of **Antique Collecting** magazine. For more details and to subscribe see page 147.

David Love
BADA
10 Royal Parade. HG1 2SZ. LAPADA. Est. 1969. Open 9-1 and 2-5.30. SIZE: Large. *STOCK: Furniture, English, 17th-19th C; pottery and porcelain, English and Continental; decorative items, all periods.* LOC: Opposite Pump Room Museum. PARK: Easy. TEL: 01423 565797. SER: Valuations; buys at auction. VAT: Stan/Spec.

Charles Lumb and Sons Ltd
BADA
2 Montpellier Gardens. HG1 2TF. (F. and A.R. Lumb). Est. 1920. Open 10-1 and 2-6. SIZE: Medium. *STOCK: Furniture, 17th to early 19th C; metalware, period accessories.* PARK: 20yds. immediately opposite. TEL: 01423 503776; home - 01423 863281; fax - 01423 530074. VAT: Spec.

McTague of Harrogate
17/19 Cheltenham Mount. HG1 1DW. (P. McTague). Open 9.30-1 and 2-5. SIZE: Medium. *STOCK: Prints, watercolours, some oil paintings, mainly 18th to early 20th C.* LOC: From Conference Centre on Kings Rd., go up Cheltenham Parade and turn first left. PARK: Easy. TEL: 01423 567086; fax - 01423 564539. VAT: Stan/Spec.

Montpellier Mews Antique Market
Montpellier St. HG1 2TG. Open 10-5. SIZE: Various dealers. *STOCK: General antiques - porcelain, jewellery, furniture, paintings, interior decor, cricket memorabilia, linen, glass and silver.* LOC: Behind Weatherells Antiques. TEL: 01423 530484.

Ogden of Harrogate Ltd
BADA
38 James St. HG1 1RQ. Est. 1893. Open 9.15-5. SIZE: Large. *STOCK: Jewellery, English silver and plate.* TEL: 01423 504123; fax - 01423 522283; e-mail - sales@ogden-of-harrogate. co.uk; website - www.ogden-of-harrogate.co. uk. VAT: Stan/Spec.

Paraphernalia
38A Cold Bath Rd. HG2 0NA. (P.F. Hacker). Open 10-5. *STOCK: Wallplates, crested and commemorative china, cutlery, glass including carnival, Mauchlineware, bric-a-brac, small furniture.* TEL: Evenings - 01423 567968.

Paul M. Peters Antiques
15a Bower Rd. HG1 1BE. LAPADA. Est. 1967. Open 10-5. CL: Sat. SIZE: Medium. *STOCK: Chinese and Japanese ceramics and works of art, 17th-19th C; European ceramics and glass, 18th-19th C; European metalware, scientific instruments and unusual objects.* LOC: Town centre, at bottom of Station Parade. PARK: Easy. TEL: 01423 560118. SER: Valuations. VAT: Stan/Spec.

Elaine Phillips Antiques Ltd
BADA
1 and 2 Royal Parade. HG1 2SZ. Open 9.30-5.30, other times by appointment. SIZE: Large. *STOCK: Oak furniture, 1600-1800; country furniture, 1700-1840; some mahogany, 18th to early 19th C; period metalwork and decoration.* LOC: Opposite Crown Hotel. TEL: 01423 569745; fax - 01977 620868; e-mail - ep@ heliscott.co.uk. VAT: Spec.

Smith's (The Rink) Ltd
Dragon Rd. HG1 5DR. Est. 1906. Open 9-5.30. SIZE: Large. *STOCK: General antiques, 1750-1820, £150; Victoriana, 1830-1900, £50.* LOC: From Leeds, right at Prince of Wales crossing, left at Skipton Rd. and left before railway bridge. PARK: Easy. TEL: 01423 567890. VAT: Stan/Spec.

Sutcliffe Galleries
BADA
5 Royal Parade. HG1 2SZ. Est. 1947. Open 10-5. CL: Mon. *STOCK: Paintings, 19th C.* LOC: Opposite Crown Hotel. TEL: 01423 562976; fax - 01423 528729. SER: Valuations; restorations; framing.

Thorntons of Harrogate
1 Montpellier Gdns. HG1 2TF. LAPADA. Open 9.30-5.30. *STOCK: 17th-19th C furniture, metalware, clocks, paintings, porcelain, scientific instruments.* TEL: 01423 504118; fax - 01423 528400; e-mail - info@harrogateantiques.com. VAT: Spec.

Walker Galleries Ltd
BADA
6 Montpellier Gdns. HG1 2TF. LAPADA. Est. 1972. Open 9.30-1 and 2-5.30. SIZE: Medium. *STOCK: Oil paintings and watercolours, 18th C furniture.* TEL: 01423 567933; fax - 01423 536664; e-mail - wgltd@aol.com; website - www.walkergalleries.com. SER: Valuations; restorations; framing. FAIRS: BADA, London; Harrogate: Olympia. VAT: Spec.

Weatherell's of Harrogate Antiques and Fine Arts
29 Montpellier Parade. HG1 2TG. LAPADA. Open 9-5.30. SIZE: Large. *STOCK: Period and fine decorative furniture.* TEL: 01423 507810/525004; fax - 01423 520005.

Chris Wilde Antiques
The Courtyard, Mowbray Sq., Westmoreland St. HG1 5AU. (C.B. Wilde). LAPADA. Est. 1996. Open Tues.-Sat. 10-5 or by appointment. SIZE:

Large. *STOCK: Furniture, 1680-1920, £300-£8,000; longcase clocks, 1720-1920, £500-£5,000.* LOC: North side of town. PARK: Easy. TEL: 01423 525855; mobile - 07831 543268; e-mail - chris@harrogate.com; website - www. antiques.harrogate.com. SER: Valuations. VAT: Stan/Spec.

Yorkshire Country Wines & Antiques
The Mill, Glasshouses. HG3 5QH. (Richard Brown). Est. 1980. Open Wed.-Sun. 11.30-4.30, (reduced hours Jan. and Feb) - most times by appointment. SIZE: Medium. *STOCK: Oak and country furniture, 17th-19th C, £50-£5,000.* LOC: 1/4 mile from crossroads of B6165. PARK: Easy. TEL: 01423 711947; fax - same; home - 01423 711223. VAT: Spec.

Sturman's Antiques
Main St. DL8 3QW. LAPADA. Open 10-5 including Sun. *STOCK: Georgian and Victorian furniture; porcelain, silver plate, paintings; longcase, wall and mantel clocks.* TEL: 01969 667742.

E. Stacy-Marks Limited
10 Castlegate. YO62 5BZ. Est. 1889. *STOCK: Paintings, English, Dutch and Continental schools, 18th-20th C.* TEL: 01439 771950; fax - 01439 771859.

Westway Pine
Carlton Lane. YO62 5HB. (J. and J. Dzierzek). Est. 1987. Open 9-5, Sat. 10-5, other times by appointment. SIZE: Medium. *STOCK: Pine furniture, 19th C, £20-£2,000.* LOC: From A170 from Scarborough, first right into town, first left, then left again 100m. PARK: Easy. TEL: 01439 771399. SER: Valuations; restorations (pine).

York Cottage Antiques
7 Church St. YO62 5AD. (G. and E.M. Thornley). LAPADA. Est. 1976. Open May-Oct. Thurs., Fri. and Sat.; Nov.-April Fri. and Sat. 10-4 or by appointment. *STOCK: Early oak and country furniture; 18th-19th C metalware; drinking glasses, pottery and porcelain especially ironstone, Staffordshire figures, lustre and blue and white; cranberry glass.* LOC: Opposite church. PARK: Adjacent. TEL: 01439 770833; home - same.

Elden Antiques
23 Ashdale View. LS22 4DS. (E. and D. Broadley). Est. 1970. Open 9-6, Sat. 12-5.30. SIZE: Medium. *STOCK: General antiques including furniture.* LOC: Main road between Wetherby and Knaresborough. PARK: Easy. TEL: 01937 584770; home - same.

Robert Aagaard & Co
Frogmire House, Stockwell Rd. HG5 0JP. Est. 1961. Open 9-5, Sat. 10-4. SIZE: Medium. *STOCK: Chimney pieces, marble fire surrounds and interiors.* LOC: Town centre. PARK: Own. TEL: 01423 864805. VAT: Stan.

Bowkett
9 Abbey Rd. HG5 8HY. (E.S. Starkie). Resident. Est. 1919. Open 9-6. SIZE: Medium. *STOCK: Chairs, small furniture, brass, copper, pot-lids, Goss, books.* LOC: By the river at the lower road bridge. PARK: Easy. TEL: 01423 866112. SER: Restorations (upholstery and small furniture).

Omar (Harrogate) Ltd
21 Boroughbridge Rd. Est. 1946. Open by appointment. *STOCK: Persian, Turkish, Caucasian rugs and carpets.* PARK: Easy. TEL: 01423 863199; fax - same. SER: Cleaning and restoration. VAT: Stan.

The Gordon Reece Gallery
24 Finkle St. HG5 8AA. Open 10.30-5, Sun. 2-5. CL: Wed. and Thurs. SIZE: Large. *STOCK: Flat woven rugs and nomadic carpets, tribal sculpture, jewellery, Chinese, Japanese and Indian furniture, decorative and non-European folk art especially ethnic and Oriental ceramics.* TEL: 01423 866219; fax - 01423 868165. SER: Restorations.

John Thompson Antiques
Swadforth House, Gracious St. HG5 8DT. LAPADA. Est. 1968. *STOCK: 18th-19th C furniture and related decorative objects.* TEL: 01423 864698. VAT: Spec.

Thirkill Antiques
Newlands, Worton. DL8 3ET. Est. 1963. *STOCK: Musicals, pottery, porcelain, small furniture, 18th-19th C.* TEL: 01969 650725.

LYTHE, Nr. Whitby

Lythe Cottage Antiques
High St. (Mrs. Lynne Robinson). *STOCK: Victorian, Edwardian, early oak and country cottage furniture.* LOC: Three miles from Whitby towards Staithes. PARK: Easy. TEL: Mobile - 07961 828679. SER: Valuations.

MALTON

Malton Antique Market
2 Old Maltongate. YO17 0EG. (Mrs M.A. Cleverly). Est. 1970. Open 9.30-12.30 and 2-5. CL: Thurs. SIZE: Medium. *STOCK: Furniture, Georgian to Victorian, to £1,500; glass, bric-a-brac, porcelain, pottery, copper, brass, silver and plate.* LOC: From York take A64, shop is at main traffic light junction in Malton. PARK: 20yds. further. TEL: 01653 692732.

Talents Fine Arts Ltd
7 Market Place. YO17 7LP. (L. Vaughan). Est. 1986. Open daily. SIZE: Medium. *STOCK: Oils, watercolours and prints, £500-£3,000; contemporary local artists.* LOC: A64 near church. PARK: Easy. TEL: 01653 600020. SER: Restorations; framing.

MANFIELD, Nr. Darlington

Joan and David White
Lucy Cross Cottage. DL2 2RJ. Est. 1975. Open after prior telephone call. *STOCK: Georgian, Victorian and export furniture.* LOC: B6275, Scotch Corner to Piercebridge road, on left 3 miles after leaving A1. PARK: Easy. TEL: 01325 374303; mobile - 07779 206036. VAT: Stan/Spec.

MARKINGTON, Nr. Harrogate

Daleside Antiques
Hinks Hall Lane. HG3 3NU. Est. 1978. Open 8-5, Sat. and Sun. by appointment. *STOCK: Pine furniture, decorative items, architectural features and fittings, 18th-19th C, £50-£3,500; Georgian mahogany furniture; Victorian shop fittings.*

'The Wimbledon Tennis Party', a lively lawn tennis party scene by E.F. Brewtnall (1846-1902). Signed and dated 1891, watercolour and bodycolour.

From an article entitled 'Lawn Tennis Memorabilia' by Gerald Gurney which appeared in the June 2001 issue of **Antique Collecting** magazine. For more details and to subscribe see page 147.

TEL: 01765 677888; fax - 01765 677886; e-mail - sales@daleside.net; website - www.daleside.net. SER: Containers; restorations. VAT: Stan.

MASHAM, Nr. Ripon

Aura Antiques

1-3 Silver St. HG4 4DX. (R. and R. Sutcliffe). Est. 1985. Open 9.30-5, Sun. by appointment. SIZE: Medium. *STOCK: Furniture especially period mahogany dining furniture, 18th to mid-19th C, £50-£5,000; metalware - brass and copper, fenders, £5-£250; china, glass, silver and decorative objects, £5-£1,000; all 18th-19th C.* LOC: Corner of Market Sq. PARK: Easy. TEL: 01765 689315; home - 01765 658192; e-mail - Robert@aura-antiques.co.uk; website - www.aura-antiques.co.uk. SER: Valuations; delivery throughout UK. VAT: Spec.

MIDDLEHAM, Nr. Leyburn

Castle Antiques Centre

34 Market Pl. DL8 4QW. (Derek and Joanne Jarvill). Est. 1994. Open 10-5.30 including Sun., Tues by appointment. SIZE: Medium (5 rooms). *STOCK: Georgian, Victorian and Edwardian furniture, pottery, porcelain, glass, clocks, metalware, treen, Art Nouveau, jewellery, general antiques and collectables.* LOC: Town centre. PARK: Easy. TEL: 01969 624655.

Middleham Antiques

The Corner Shop, Kirkgate. DL8 4PF. (Mike Pitman and Anji Walton). Est. 1984. Open 10-5.30 most days, Wed. by appointment - prior 'phone call advisable. *STOCK: Pre 1830 oak and country furniture, longcase clocks, curios, £20-£7,000.* PARK: Easy. TEL: 01969 622982; fax - same.

NORTHALLERTON

Collectors Corner

145/6 High St. DL7 8SL. (J. Wetherill). Est. 1972. Open 10-4 or by appointment. CL: Thurs. *STOCK: General antiques, collectors' items.* LOC: Opposite GPO. TEL: 01609 777623; home - 01609 775199.

NORTON, Nr. Malton

Northern Antiques Company

2 Parliament St., Scarborough Rd. YO17 9HE. (Sara Ashby-Arnold). Est. 1991. Open 9-1 and 2-5, Sat. 9.30-12.30, Sun. and evenings by

BRIAN LOOMES

Specialist dealer in antique British clocks. Internationally recognised authority and author of numerous books on antique clocks. Large stock of longcase clocks with a number of lantern clocks and bracket clocks.

Restoration work undertaken

EST'D 36 YEARS (2002)

Resident on premises. Available six days a week but strictly by prior telephone appointment. *Copies of my current books always in stock.*

CALF HAUGH FARMHOUSE, PATELEY BRIDGE, NORTH YORKS. Tel: (01423) 711163.

(On B6265 Pateley-Grassington road.)

www.brianloomes.com

appointment. SIZE: Medium. *STOCK: Country oak furniture, from 17th C, £200-£2,000; pine, Georgian to Victorian, to £1,000; upholstered sofas and chairs, cast-iron and wooden beds, decorative items and prints, from 19th C, to £800; some contemporary interior design items.* LOC: From Malton town centre on old Scarborough Rd., through Norton, shop on right above Aga shop. PARK: Easy. TEL: 01653 697520.

PATELEY BRIDGE

Brian Loomes

Calf Haugh Farm. HG3 5HW. (Author of clock reference books). Est. 1966. Open strictly by appointment. SIZE: Medium. *STOCK: British clocks especially longcase, wall, bracket and lantern, pre-1840, £500-£15,000. Not Stocked: Foreign clocks.* LOC: From Pateley Bridge, first private lane on left on Grassington Rd. (B6265). PARK: Own. TEL: 01423 711163; home and fax - same; website - www.brianloomes.com. VAT: Spec.

Pateley Bridge Antiques

The Apothecary's House, 35 High St. HG3 5JZ. (A.D. Gora). Est. 1995. Open 10-5.30, Sat. 11-5, or by appointment. SIZE: Medium. *STOCK: Oak and country furniture, 17th-18th C, £100-£10,000; longcase clocks, £1,000-£3,000; metalware including copper and pewter, 17th-19th C, £30-£500.* LOC: Ripon-Grassington road. PARK: Almost opposite. TEL: 01423 711004; e-mail - info@earlyoak.co.uk; website - www.earlyoak.co.uk. SER: Valuations.

PICKERING

Country Collector
11-12 Birdgate. YO18 7AL. (G. and M. Berney). Est. 1991. Open 10-5. CL: Wed. SIZE: Small. *STOCK: Ceramics, including blue and white and Art Deco pottery, and collectables, 1800-1940, £10-£1,000.* LOC: Top of the Market Place, at crossroads of A169 and A170. PARK: Eastgate. TEL: 01751 477481. SER: Valuations; buys at auction (ceramics). VAT: Stan.

C.H. Reynolds Antiques
The Old Curiosity Shop, 122 Eastgate. YO18 7DW. Est. 1947. Open 9.30-5.30, Sun. by appointment. *STOCK: General antiques.* TEL: 01751 472785.

RIPON

Milton Holgate   BADA
P O Box 77. HG4 3XX. Est. 1972. By appointment only. STOCK: Fine English furniture and accessories, 17th-19th C. TEL: 01765 620225.

Sigma Antiques and Fine Art
The Old Opera House, Water Skellgate. HG4 1BH. (D. Thomson). Est. 1963. Open 10.30-5, other times by appointment. *STOCK: 17th-20th C furniture, furnishing items, pottery, porcelain, objets d'art, paintings, jewellery and collectors' items.* PARK: Nearby. TEL: 01765 603163; fax - same.

Skellgate Curios
2 Low Skellgate. HG4 1BE. (J.I. Wain and P.S. Gyte). Est. 1974. Open 11-5. CL: Wed. *STOCK: Furniture, decorative antiques, period jewellery, silver, brass, copper and collectors items.* TEL: 01765 601290; home - 01765 635336/635332.

ROBIN HOOD'S BAY

John Gilbert Antiques
King St. YO22 4SH. Est. 1990. Open Sat. 10-1 and 2-5, Sun. 10-1 and 2-4, other days by appointment. SIZE: Small. *STOCK: Country furniture, 18th-19th C, £100-£500; oak furniture from 1650, £250-£1,000; Victorian furniture, £50-£500; treen, £5-£150.* LOC: At bottom of old village, between Bay and Dolphin Hotels. PARK: Top of hill. TEL: Home - 01947 880528. SER: Valuations; restorations (furniture).

SCARBOROUGH

Hanover Antiques & Collectables
33 St Nicolas Cliff. YO11 2ES. Est. 1976. Open 10-4.30. CL: Wed. pm. *STOCK: Small collectables, medals, badges, toys, 50p-£500.* PARK: Nearby. TEL: 01723 374175.

Shuttleworths
7 Victoria Rd. YO11 1SB. (L.R. Shuttleworth). Open 10-4. CL: Wed. *STOCK: General antiques.* TEL: 01723 366278.

SETTLE

Mary Milnthorpe and Daughters Antique Shop
Market Place. BD24 9DX. Est. 1958. Open 9.30-5. CL: Wed. SIZE: Small. *STOCK: Antique and 19th C jewellery and English silver.* LOC: Opposite Town Hall. PARK: Easy. TEL: 01729 822331. VAT: Stan/Spec.

Nanbooks
Roundabout, 41 Duke St. BD24 9DJ. (J.L. and N.M. Midgley). Resident. Est. 1955. Open Tues., Fri. and Sat. 11-12.30 and 2-5.30. CL: Nov.-Feb. SIZE: Small. *STOCK: English pottery, porcelain including Oriental, glass, general small antiques, 17th-19th C, to £500.* Not Stocked: Jewellery. LOC: A65. PARK: Easy. TEL: 01729 823324.

Roy Precious Antiques & Fine Art
King William House, High St. BD24 9EX. Resident. Est. 1972. Open 10-5.30 or by appointment. CL: Wed. SIZE: Large. *STOCK: Oak, walnut, mahogany and country furniture, 17th-19th C, £200-£10,000; oil paintings, especially portraits, 17th-19th C, £600-£20,000; pottery and prints; textiles, needlework pictures and tapestries, 17th-19th C.* LOC: Near the Talbot Inn on the old High St. PARK: Easy. TEL: 01729 823946; e-mail - roy@preciousantiques.co.uk: website - www.antiqnet.co.uk/rprecious. SER: Valuations. VAT: Stan/Spec.

Anderson Slater Antiques
6 Duke St. BD24 7DW. (K.C. Slater). Est. 1962. Open 10-1 and 2-5. CL: Wed. SIZE: Medium. *STOCK: Furniture, 18th-19th C, £200-£4,000; porcelain, 18th-19th C, £25-£500; pictures, 19th-20th C, £200-£1,500.* LOC: Main street out of Market Place. PARK: Nearby. TEL: 01729 822051. SER: Valuations; restorations (furniture and porcelain); buys at auction. VAT: Stan/Spec.

E. Thistlethwaite
The Antique Shop, Market Sq. BD24 9EF. Est. 1972. Open 9-5. CL: Wed. SIZE: Medium. *STOCK: Country furniture and metalware, 18th-19th C.* LOC: Town centre, A65. PARK: Forecourt. TEL: 01729 822460. VAT: Stan/Spec.

SKIPTON

Adamson Armoury
Otley Rd. BD23 1ET. (J.K. Adamson). Est. 1975. Open by appointment only. SIZE: Medium. *STOCK: Weapons, 17th-19th C, £10-£1,000.* LOC: A65, 200yds. from town centre. PARK: At rear. TEL: 01756 791355. SER: Valuations. FAIRS: London.

Corn Mill Antiques
High Corn Mill, Chapel Hill. BD23 1NL. (Mrs M. Hawkridge). Est. 1984. Open 10-4. CL: Tues. and Wed. SIZE: Medium. *STOCK: Oak, mahogany and walnut furniture, £100-£2,000; porcelain, silver plate, prints, pictures, brass and copper, £5-£500; all Georgian to 1920's.* Not Stocked: Jewellery, gold and silver. LOC: From town centre take Grassington Road, Chapel Hill is first right. PARK: Easy. TEL: 01756 792440; home - 01729 830489. SER: Valuations. VAT: Spec.

SLEIGHTS, Nr. Whitby

Eskdale Antiques
164 Coach Rd. YO22 4BH. (Philip Smith). Est. 1978. Open 9-5.30 including Sun. SIZE: Medium. *STOCK: Pine furniture and farm bygones, 19th-20th C, £50-£500.* LOC: Main Pickering road. PARK: Easy. TEL: 01947 810297; home - same. SER: Valuations; buys at auction.

SNAINTON, Nr. Scarborough

Antony, David & Ann Shackleton
19 & 72 High St. YO13 9AE. Resident. Est. 1984. Open every day. SIZE: Medium. *STOCK: Longcase clocks, Victorian rocking horses, Georgian and Victorian furniture, collectables, £1-£3,500.* LOC: A170, equidistant Scarborough and Pickering. PARK: Easy. TEL: 01723 859577/850172. SER: Restorations (furniture, longcase clocks, rocking horses).

SPENNITHORNE, Nr. Leyburn

N.J. and C.S. Dodsworth
Thorney Hall. DL8 5PW. Est. 1973. Open by appointment. SIZE: Medium. *STOCK: Furniture, clocks and small items, 17th-19th C.* LOC: Off A684. TEL: 01969 622277. VAT: Margin.

STILLINGTON

Pond Cottage Antiques
Brandsby Rd. YO61 1NY. (C.M. and D. Thurstans). Resident. Est. 1972. *STOCK: Pine, kitchenalia, country furniture, treen, metalware, brass, copper.* TEL: 01347 810796.

Rose Fine Art and Antiques
Fox Inn Farm, Easingwold Rd. YO61 1LS. (Mr and Mrs S. Rose). Est. 1984. Open by appointment. *STOCK: Pictures, 18th to early 20th C, £5-£2,000.* PARK: Easy. TEL: 01347 810554. SER: Valuations; restorations (pictures). *Trade Only.*

THIRSK

Classic Rocking Horses
from Windmill Antiques. (B. and J. Tildesley). Est. 1980. Open by appointment only. *STOCK: Restored antique rocking horses and authentic replicas of Victorian rocking horses, £1,500-£5,000.* TEL: 01845 501330; fax - 01845 501700; e-mail - info@classicrockinghorses.co.uk; website - www.classicrockinghorses.co.uk.

Cottage Antiques and Curios
1 Market Place. YO7 1HQ. (Mrs E.H. and S.R. Ballard). Est. 1970. Open 9-4. CL: Wed. *STOCK: Victorian porcelain and glass, £5-£500; paintings, £20-£1,000, furniture, from 1750, £20-£1,000; brass, copper, silver and plated ware, £5-£500.* PARK: Easy. TEL: 01845 522536/523212.

Kirkgate Fine Art & Conservation
18 Kirkgate. YO7 1PQ. (Richard Bennett). Est. 1979. Open by appointment. SIZE: Small. *STOCK: Oil paintings, £50-£2,000; water-colours, £50-£500; both 19th to mid-20th C.* LOC: Joins Market Place. PARK: Nearby. TEL: 01845 524085; home - same. SER: Restorations (oil paintings and framing); buys at auction.

Millgate Pine & Antiques
12 Millgate. YO7 1AA. (T.D. and M. Parvin). Open 10-5, Sun. 10-5. SIZE: Large + warehouse. *STOCK: English and European pine.* TEL: 01845 523878. SER: Repairs; stripping; restorations.

Potterton Books
The Old Rectory, Sessay. YO7 3LZ. (Clare Jameson). Open 9-5. SIZE: Large. *STOCK: Classic reference works on art, architecture,*

interior design, antiques and collecting. TEL: 01845 501218; fax - 01845 501439; e-mail - potterton.books@sagehost.co.uk; website - www.pottertonbooks.co.uk. SER: Book search; catalogues. FAIRS: London; Frankfurt; Paris; New York; Milan; Dubai.

THORNTON DALE, Nr. Pickering

Stable Antiques
4 Pickering Rd. YO18 7LG. (Mrs S. Kitching Walker). Open 2-5, mornings by appointment. CL: Mon. SIZE: Medium. *STOCK: Porcelain, £5-£500; furniture, £20-£700; silver, glass, brass, plate, copper, collectors' items, £5-£150, all 19th C to 1930's.* LOC: A170. PARK: Easy. TEL: 01751 474332; home - 01751 474435; e-mail - yvonne@stable-antiques.co.uk; website - www.stable-antiques. co.uk. SER: Valuations.

This delft water bottle, c.1760, was an 'odd man out' in Bernard Watney's collection, and at £473 the price was also far cheaper than most of his porcelain of similar age.

From an article entitled 'Not So Potty After All – Early English Pottery' by John Sandon which appeared in the July/August 2000 issue of **Antique Collecting** magazine. For more details and to subscribe see page 147.

TOCKWITH, Nr. York

Tomlinson Antiques Ltd. & Period Furniture Ltd
Moorside. YO26 7QG. LAPADA. Est. 1971. Open, trade only, Mon-Fri. 8-4.30 or by appointment. Retail - Sat. 9-4.30 and Sun. 10-4. SIZE: Large. *STOCK: Furniture, £10-£20,000; clocks, porcelain, silver plate and decorative items, £10-£5,000.* LOC: A1 Wetherby take B1224 towards York. After 3 miles turn left on to Rudgate. At end of this road turn left, business 200m on left. PARK: Easy. TEL: 01423 358833; fax - 01423 358188; e-mail - sales@tomlinson. demon.co.uk; website - www.antique-furniture. co.uk. SER: Export; restorations; container packing, desk leathering. VAT: Stan/Spec.

WHITBY

Age of Jazz
85 Church St. YO22 4BH. (P.A. Smith). Est. 1983. Open 10.30-12.30 and 1-5 (Sat. and Sun. only Nov. to Mar.). SIZE: Medium. *STOCK: Clarice Cliff, £100-£750.* LOC: A174. PARK: Nearby. TEL: 01947 600512. SER: Valuations; buys at auction (Clarice Cliff).

The Bazaar
7 Skinner St. YO21 3AH. (F.A. Doyle). Est. 1970. Open 10.30-5.30. *STOCK: Jewellery, furniture, general antiques, 19th C.* TEL: 01947 602281.

'Bobbins' Wool, Crafts, Antiques
Wesley Hall, Church St. YO22 4DE. (D. and P. Hoyle). Open 10-5 every day. SIZE: Small. *STOCK: General antiques especially oil lamps, bric-a-brac, kitchenalia, 19th-20th C.* LOC: Between Market Place and steps to Abbey on cobbled East Side. PARK: Nearby (part of Church St. is pedestrianised). TEL: 01947 600585 (answerphone). SER: Repairs and spares (oil lamps). VAT: Stan.

Caedmon House
14 Station Sq. YO21 1DU. (E.M. Stanforth). Est. 1977. Open 10-5. SIZE: Medium. *STOCK: General, mainly small, antiques including jewellery, dolls, Disney and china, especially Dresden, to £1,200.* PARK: Easy. TEL: 01947 602120; home - 01947 603930. SER: Valuations; restorations (china); repairs (jewellery). VAT: Stan/Spec.

Coach House Antiques
75 Coach Rd., Sleights. YO22 5BT. (C.J. Rea). Resident. Est. 1973. Open by appointment. SIZE:

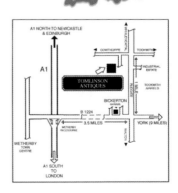

Small. *STOCK: Furniture, especially oak and country; metalware, paintings, pottery, textiles, unusual and decorative items.* LOC: On A169, 3 miles south west of Whitby. PARK: Easy, opposite. TEL: 01947 810313.

WHIXLEY

Garth Antiques
The Old School, Franks Lane. YO26 8AP. (I. Chapman). Est. 1978. Open Tues-Sat. 10-5. SIZE: Medium. *STOCK: Furniture, 18th-19th C, £50-£3,000; brass and copper, 19th C, £1-£500; oils and watercolours, £5-£3,000.* LOC: A59, turn towards Whixley at the Cattle/Whixley junction, then left opposite The Anchor into old village, next to Village Hall. PARK: Easy. TEL: 01423 331055; fax - 01423 331733. VAT: Stan/Spec.

YARM, Nr.Stockton-on-Tees

Ruby Snowden Antiques
6 Fairfax Court, High St. TS15 9QZ. (R.H. Snowden). Est. 1977. Open 9-5.30, Wed. 9-5, Sun. by appointment. SIZE: Medium. *STOCK: Furniture, 1700-1930's, £50-£200; porcelain and Staffordshire, £5-£200; jewellery, silver, glass, copper and brass.* PARK: Easy. TEL: 01642 801188; home - 01642 819918. SER: Valuations. VAT: Stan/Spec.

YORK

Barbican Bookshop
24 Fossgate. YO1 9TA. Est. 1961. Open 9.15-5.30. *STOCK: Antiquarian books.* TEL: 01904 653643; fax - 01904 653643; e-mail - barbican@cwcom.net. VAT: Stan.

Bishopsgate Antiques
23/24 Bishopsgate St. YO2 1JH. (R. Wetherill). Open 9.15-6, Sun. 12-5. *STOCK: General antiques.* TEL: 01904 623893; fax - 01904 626511.

Barbara Cattle   BADA
45 Stonegate. YO1 8AW. Open 9-5.30.
STOCK: Jewellery and silver, Georgian to date.
TEL: 01904 623862.

Cavendish Antiques & Collectors Centre
44 Stonegate. YO1 8AS. (Anthony Gilberthorpe). Est. 1996. Open seven days 9-6. SIZE: Large. *STOCK: Wide range of general antiques, £1-£7,000.* LOC: In pedestrianised thoroughfare

between minster and main shopping area. PARK: Nearby. TEL: 01904 621666/613888; fax - 01904 644400. VAT: Stan.

Coulter Galleries
YO24 1LX. Open by appointment only. *STOCK: Watercolours and oils, pre-1900; frames.* TEL: 01904 702101; fax - 01904 701908; e-mail - R.Coulter@tesco.net.

Ruth Ford Antiques
39 Fossgate. YO1 2TA. Est. 1976. Open 11.30-4.30. CL: Wed. SIZE: Small. *STOCK: 18th-19th C country furniture, pine, treen and collectables, £5-£1,000.* LOC: Near Merchant Adventurers Hall. PARK: Nearby. TEL: Home - 01904 632864.

The French House (Antiques) Ltd.
74 Micklegate. YO1 6LF. (S.B. and M.J. Hazell). Est. 1995. Open Thurs., Fri., Sat. and Sun., other days by appointment. SIZE: Large. *STOCK: Wooden beds, 18th-19th C, £900-£2,500; gilt mirrors, 19th C, £300-£2,000; lighting, 19th-20th C, £200-£1,000; all French.* LOC: Main entry to city from A64. PARK: Side streets. TEL: 01904 624465; fax - 01904 629965. SER: Restorations (cabinet making, upholstery, French polishing, painting). VAT: Stan/Spec.

Golden Memories of York
14 Newgate. YO1 7LA. (M.S. and D.J. Smith). NAG. Est. 1991. Open 9-5.30. SIZE: Small. *STOCK: Antique and secondhand jewellery and silver, £5-£3,000.* LOC: Adjacent York market, off Parliament St. PARK: Multi-storey. TEL: 01904 655883. VAT: Stan/Spec.

Minster Antiques
24 Goodramgate. YO1 7LG. (M. Tanner and K. Nevens). Est. 1982. Open daily. SIZE: Small. *STOCK: Brass and copper, silver, scientific instruments, 19th C, £5-£500.* LOC: 2 minutes from Minster, past St. William's College towards Monk Bar. PARK: Loading only. TEL: 01904 655481; e-mail -enquiries@minster-antiques-york.co.uk; website - www.minster-antiques-york.co.uk. SER: Valuations.

Minster Gate Bookshop
8 Minster Gates. YO1 2HL. (N. Wallace). Est. 1970. Open 9.30-5.30. SIZE: Large. *STOCK: Antiquarian and secondhand books; old maps and prints.* LOC: Opposite south door of minster. PARK: Nearby. TEL: 01904 621812. SER: Valuations; restorations; book finding.

Robert Morrison and Son   BADA
Trentholme House, 131 The Mount. YO24 1DU. (C. and P. Morrison). Est. 1890. Open 9-

5. SIZE: Large. *STOCK: English furniture, 1700-1900; porcelain and clocks.* LOC: Near racecourse, one mile from city centre on Leeds Rd. From A1, take A64 to outskirts of York, then take A1036 York west road. PARK: Easy. TEL: 01904 655394; email - info@york-antiques.com; website - www.york-antiques.com. VAT: Stan/Spec.

The Red House Antiques Centre

Duncombe Place. (Ginnel Antiques Centres - P. Stephenson). Open Mon.-Sat. 9.30-6, (June-Sept. 9.30-8), Sun. 10.30-5.30. LOC: 200 yards from Minster. TEL: 01904 637000; e-mail - enquiries @redhouseyork; website - www. redhouse york.co.uk. SER: Shipping; packing; arts and antiques lectures. Below are listed the specialist dealers at this centre.

A & S Antiques
English and oriental ceramics, Staffordshire figures, glassware and treen.

Appleton Antiques
19th and 20th C pottery - Moorcroft, Carlton, Linthorpe and crested china.

Fiona Aston
19th C porcelain, silver and objets d'art.

Baytree Antiques
19th C furniture and decorative items.

Margaret Bedi
18th-19th C furniture, oil paintings and watercolours.

Bootham Antiques
19th C silver, porcelain, glass and curios.

Brackmoor Antiques
Silver, porcelain and objets d'art.

P.J. Bramall
Victorian ceramics, glass and metalware, costume jewellery and curios.

Bygones

Corylus Antiques
19th -20th C pottery and porcelain.

Cottage Collection
Victorian pottery, metalware and treen.

A. & A. Cox
18th to early 19th C ceramics.

T. Cunningham
Decorative French furniture and furnishings.

Eaton-Smith Antiques
19th-20th C decorative arts.

Eve Antiques
English pottery and porcelain - Doulton, Maling and Worcester, and north-east glass.

Robert M. Himsworth
Fine York and provincial silver.

Hogarth Antiques
Silver, plate, porcelain and treen.

Susan Judge
20th C ceramics - Moorcroft, Doulton, Susie Cooper, Charlotte Rhead.

Keelman Antiques
19th -20th C pottery.

G. Kendall
19th C ceramics, metalware and curios.

Laura Antiques
Small silver, plate and jewellery.

Laurel Bank Antiques
Georgian, Victorian and Edwardian furniture, longcase wall and mantel clocks.

Libra Antiques
Georgian, Victorian and Edwardian furniture, decorative items and Cranberry glass.

Lodge Antiques
Silver, plate, ceramics and glass.

Catherine Lough
19th C French furniture and furnishings, decorative items and objets d'art.

Lycurgus Glass
19th -20th C decorative art glass and mirrors.

Stella Mar Antiques
19th C furniture and furnishings, porcelain, metalware, treen and objets d'art.

Olivia Meyler
Jewellery and Russian artefacts.

John Moor
Ancient art and antiques.

Sheila Morgan
Silver, ceramics and curios.

Susan Mosley
Textiles, personal effects and decorative items.

Mulberry Bush
Prints, watercolours, ceramics and clocks.

Needful Things
Silver, ceramics, north east glass - Davidsons.

Past and Present
Buttons, badges, costume accessories, lace and costume jewellery.

Past Reflections
Victorian and Edwardian ceramics, glass, silver and plate.

Period Pictures
Framed and unframed prints, engravings and watercolours, Victorian and Edwardian furniture.

Pywakit
Jewellery, ceramics, glass and ephemera.

P.W. Raine
Silver, pewter, metalware and ceramics.

Mary Shortle
Dolls, teddy bears, toys and juvenalia.

Silver Thimble Antiques
19th C silver, glass, porcelain and metalware.

Timothy Simon
18th-19th C furniture, mirrors and lamps.

Small Fish Antiques
19th C furniture, mirrors, glass, pottery, toys, advertising materials and ephemera.

Gordon Steel
Silver, jewellery, glass, treen and pipes.

Terry's Art Co
Oriental porcelain, jade and wood, snuff bottles and netsuke.

Brian Thacker
Glass, porcelain, jewellery and curios.

Val Thornhill
18th to early 19th pottery and porcelain.

Topaz Antiques
Victorian and Edwardian pottery and porcelain.

A silver box and cover by The Guild of Handicrafts which was lifted by the enamelled landscape and sold for £900.

From an Auction Report by Christopher Wight on 20th Century British Decorative Arts at Christie's South Kensington, London, 4th May 2000 which appeared in the July/August issue of **Antique Collecting** magazine. For more details and to subscribe see page 147.

C.E. Tweedale
Victorian and Edwardian pottery and porcelain.

C. Walker-Sherriff
Silver, plate, glass, jewellery and decorative items.

A. Wardale
Textiles and decorative items.

Paul Wheeler
Glass, pottery, porcelain and metalware.

Ann Wilkinson
Silver, porcelain, jewellery and ephemera.

Eileen Wilson
Arts & Crafts, Nouveau and Deco ceramics, jewellery and decorative items.

Wycliffe Antiques
19th C ceramics, pot lids, Baxter and Le Blond prints.

J. Smith
47 The Shambles. YO1 7LX. Est. 1962. Open 9.30-4.30. SIZE: Small. *STOCK: Numismatic items, £5-£1,000; British stamps, £1-£100.* TEL: 01904 654769; fax - 01904 677988. VAT: Stan/Spec.

Ken Spelman
70 Micklegate. YO1 6LF. (P. Miller and A. Fothergill). ABA. Est. 1948. SIZE: Large. *STOCK: Secondhand and antiquarian books especially fine arts and literature, 50p-£10,000.* PARK: Easy. TEL: 01904 624414; fax - 01904 626276; e-mail - rarebooks@kenspelman.com; website - www. kenspelman.com. SER: Valuations; buys at auction (books); catalogues issued. FAIRS: Bath, Oxford, York, Harrogate, Cambridge, Edinburgh and London PBFA and ABA. VAT: Spec.

St. John Antiques
26 Lord Mayor's Walk. YO3 7HA. (R. and N. Bell). Open 10-5. CL: Mon. *STOCK: Victorian stripped pine, curios, blue and white pottery.* PARK: At rear. TEL: 01904 644263.

Stonegate Antiques Centre
41 Stonegate. YO1 8AW. (Anthony Gilberthorpe). Est. 1996. Open seven days 9-6. SIZE: Large. *STOCK: Wide range of general antiques, from £1-£7,000.* LOC: In pedestrianised thoroughfare between minster and main shopping area. PARK: Nearby. TEL: 01904 613888/ 621666; fax - 01904 644400. VAT: Stan.

York Antiques Centre
2 Lendal. YO1 8AA. Open 10-5. SIZE: 20 dealers. *STOCK: Antiques and collectable items, 18th-20th C.* LOC: Opposite the museum gardens. PARK: Easy. TEL: 01904 641445/ 641582.

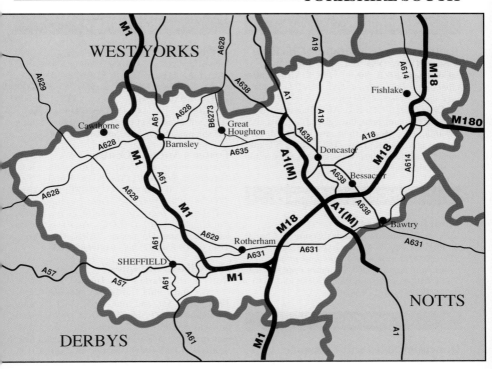

Dealers and Shops in South Yorkshire

Barnsley	2	Cawthorne	1	Great Houghton	1
Bawtry	2	Doncaster	1	Rotherham	5
Bessacarr	1	Fishlake	1	Sheffield	20

BARNSLEY

Charisma Antiques Trade Warehouse
The Old Chapel, 6b Market St., Hoyland. S74 9QR. (J.C.Simmons). Est. 1976. Open 10-5. SIZE: Large. *STOCK: Furniture, shipping goods, pictures.* LOC: 1.5 miles off M1, exit 36. PARK: Easy. TEL: 01226 747599; home - 01226 790482.

Christine Simmons Antiques
St. Paul's Former Methodist Chapel, Market St., Hoyland. S74 9QR. Est. 1976. Open 10-4. SIZE: Medium. *STOCK: Smalls and pictures.* LOC: 1.5 miles from exit 36, M1. PARK: Easy. TEL: 01226 747599/790482.

BAWTRY, Nr. Doncaster

Swan Antiques
2 Swan St. DN10 6JQ. Open 10-5 including Sun. SIZE: Large. *STOCK: Furniture, silver, ceramics, collectables, costume jewellery.* PARK: Easy. TEL: 01302 710301.

Treasure House Antiques Centre
4-10 Swan St. DN10 6JQ. Est. 1982. Open 10-5 including Sun. CL: Wed. SIZE: Large - various dealers. *STOCK: Silver, porcelain, furniture, carnival glass, postcards, toy trains and general antiques.* PARK: Easy. TEL: 01302 710621.

BESSACARR, Nr. Doncaster

Keith Stones Grandfather Clocks
5 Ellers Drive. DN4 7DL. Est. 1988. Open by appointment. SIZE: Small. *STOCK: Grandfather clocks especially painted dial with 30 hour and 8 day movements, Georgian to early 19th C, £1,250-£3,750.* LOC: Take A638 Bawtry road off racecourse roundabout, through traffic lights after 3/4 mile, take second right into Ellers Rd. then second left. PARK: Easy. TEL: 01302 535258; home - same; website - www.kstones.fsnet.co.uk. SER: Valuations.

CAWTHORNE, Nr. Barnsley

Madalyn S. Jones
Unit 14, Cawthorne Antiques Centre, 2 Church St. PBFA. Open 10-4, Sun. 10.30-4.30. CL: Wed. *STOCK: Old and rare books and prints, new books on antiques.* LOC: 5 minutes from junction 37/38, M1, near Cannon Hall. PARK: Easy. TEL: 01226 792237. SER: Valuations.

DONCASTER

Doncaster Sales and Exchange
20 Copley Rd. DN1 2PF. Open 9.30-5. CL: Thurs. *STOCK: General small antiques.* TEL: 01302 344857. VAT: Stan.

FISHLAKE

Fishlake Antiques
Pinfold Lane. DN7 5LA. Resident. Est. 1972. Open Sat. 1-5, and by appointment. SIZE: Medium. *STOCK: Rural furniture especially stripped pine; clocks including longcase and wall clocks, Victorian to mid-19th C, £30-£1,000; smalls, £3-£70.* LOC: Off A63. PARK: Own. TEL: 01302 841411.

GREAT HOUGHTON, Nr. Barnsley

Farmhouse Antiques
7 High St. S72 0AA. Open Mon., Tues.1.30-4.30, Thurs. and Sat. 10.30-12 and 1.30-4.30, other times by appointment. *STOCK: 19th-20th C furniture, ceramics, glass, textiles, linen, kitchenalia, Susie Cooper, Art Deco, soft furnishings.* TEL: 01226 754057; home - 01226 753263; mobile - 07887 722202.

ROTHERHAM

Roger Appleyard Ltd
Fitzwilliam Rd., Eastwood Trading Estate. S65 1SL. LAPADA. Open 8-5, Sat. 8-12. SIZE: Large. *STOCK: General antiques, £5-£10,000.* LOC: A630. PARK: Easy. TEL: 01709 367670/377770; fax - 01709 829395; e-mail - apple.antiques@dial.pipex.com. SER: Packing and shipping. VAT: Stan/Spec. *Trade Only.*

Foster's Antique Centre
Foster's Garden Centre, Doncaster Rd., Thrybergh. S65 4BE. (The Foster Family). Est. 1996. Open 10-4.30, Sun. 11-5. SIZE: 20 dealers. *STOCK: Wide range of general antiques and collectables including furniture, jewellery, Rockingham china.* LOC: A630 between Rotherham and Doncaster. PARK: Own large. TEL: 01709 850337; fax - 01709 851905.

Holly Farm Antiques
Holly Farm, Harley Rd., Harley. S62 7UD. (Trevor and Linda Hardwick). Resident. Est. 1988. Open Sat. and Sun. 10-5, other days by appointment. SIZE: Small. *STOCK: Rockingham porcelain, 1830-1842, from £80; porcelain, pottery, clocks and watches, lamps, glass, silver, furniture.* LOC: B6090 quarter mile off A6135 Sheffield to Barnsley, between junctions 35/36 M1. PARK: Own. TEL: 01226 744077; home - same. SER: Valuations; buys at auction.

John Mason Jewellers Ltd
36 High St. S60 1PP. Open 9-5.30. *STOCK: Silver, jewellery.* TEL: 01709 382311. SER: Valuations; repairs. VAT: Spec.

Philip Turnor Antiques
94a Broad St., Parkgate. Open 9-5, Sat. 10-4. *STOCK: Shipping furniture including oak, 1880-1940.* PARK: Easy. TEL: 01709 524640. SER: Export.

SHEFFIELD

Acorn Antiques
298-300 Abbeydale Rd. S7 1FL. (R.C. and B.C. Priest). Est. 1984. Open 10-5. SIZE: Medium. *STOCK: Furniture, 19th-20th C, £20-£500; bronzes, sculptural and unusual items.* LOC: A625 to Bakewell. PARK: Easy. TEL: 0114 255 5348; home - same.

Beech House
361 Abbeydale Rd. S7 1FS. (J.M. and A.J. Beech). Est. 1996. Open 10-5. CL: Thurs. SIZE: Small. *STOCK: Pine furniture, £250-£400; art*

and ceramics, £100-£5000. LOC: 1 mile from city centre. PARK: Easy. TEL: 0114 250 1004; fax - same; home - 07970 196126. SER: Buys at auction (pine, rustic and country furniture).

Cobwebs
208 Whitham Rd., Broomhill. S10 2SS. (Sue Sleath). Est. 1975. Open 10-5. CL: Tues. and Thurs. SIZE: Small. *STOCK: General antiques, 19th-20th C, £50-£100.* LOC: Main shopping area. PARK: Nearby. TEL: 0114 268 1923; fax - 0114 230 8166. SER: Valuations.

Court House Antique Centre
2-6 Town End Rd., Ecclesfield. S35 9YY. (J.P. & K.E. Owram). Open 10.30-5, Sun. 11.30-5. SIZE: Large - 35+ dealers. *STOCK: Town and country furniture, French bedroom furniture, antiquarian maps, decorative items, ceramics, glass, clocks, barometers, kitchenalia, books, silver, jewellery, lighting, mirrors, collectables, £5-£5,000.* LOC: 2 miles from M1, junction 35. Down hill, bear left into Nether Lane, through lights to church, turn left 250 yards on right. PARK: Easy. TEL: 0114 257 0641.

Dronfield Antiques
375-377 Abbeydale Rd. S7 1FS. (H.J. Greaves). Est. 1968. Open 10.30-5.30. CL: Thurs. and Sat. except by appointment. SIZE: Large + warehouses. *STOCK: Trade and shipping goods, Victoriana, glass, china.* LOC: A621, 1 mile south of city centre. PARK: Easy. TEL: 0114 2550172/2581821; home and fax - 0114 2556024. SER: Container packing facilities. VAT: Stan.

F S Antiques
Court House Antiques Centre, 2-6 Town End Rd., Ecclesfield. S35 9YY. Open 10.30-5, Sun. 11.30-4.30. SIZE: Small. *STOCK: Longcase, wall and mantel clocks, £150-£3,000.* LOC: 2 miles from M1, junction 35. PARK: Easy. TEL: 0114 25 70641; home - 01226 382805; mobile - 07718 531333; e-mail - antique@clocksforall. f9.co.uk; website - www.antiqueclocksforall. co.uk. SER: Restorations.

Fun Antiques
72 Abbeydale Rd. S7 1FD. (B. Harrap). Est. 1978. Open by appointment. SIZE: Medium. *STOCK: Unusual and collectable items including sporting, toys, advertising, Christmas, arcade and fairground, 20th C, £5-£1,000.* PARK: Easy. TEL: 0114 2553424. SER: Valuations; installations. FAIRS: Ardingly; Newark; Shepton Mallet; Wembley; Birmingham. VAT: Stan. *Trade Only.*

Julie Goddard Antiques
Court House Antiques Centre, Town End Rd., Ecclesfield. S35 9YY. Est. 1982. Open 10.30-5, Sun. 11.30-5. *STOCK: 19th C English mahogany, oak and walnut furniture, decorative items.* LOC: 5 mins from junction 35 M1, next to St. Mary's Church. PARK: Easy. TEL: 0114 257 0641; tel/fax - 0114 246 0194. VAT: Spec.

Peter James Antiques
336 Abbeydale Rd. S7 1FN. (P.J. Conboy). Est. 1980. Open 9.30-4.30. SIZE: Medium. *STOCK: Georgian, Victorian and Edwardian mahogany, walnut, oak and pine furniture.* PARK: Easy. TEL: 0114 2551554. SER: Restorations. VAT: Stan/Spec.

A.E. Jameson and Co
63 Wilkinson St. S10 2GJ. (P. Jameson). LAPADA. Est. 1883. Open 9-5.45. SIZE: Large. *STOCK: Furniture, pre-1820, £20-£15,000; glass, china, weapons.* LOC: A57. TEL: 0114 2723846; home - 0114 2726189. SER: Valuations; restorations (furniture); buys at auction. VAT: Stan/Spec.

Langtons Antiques & Collectables
443 London Rd./Courtyard, 100 Guernsey Rd., Heeley Bottom. S2 4HJ. (Langton Family). Open

10-5 including Sun. SIZE: Large. *STOCK: Furniture, architectural items, military, china, porcelain, jewellery, clocks, Art Deco, from 1850, £5-£3,000.* LOC: A61 to city centre. PARK: Easy. TEL: 0114 258 1791. FAIRS: Newark. VAT: Stan.

Nichols Antique Centre

The Nichols Building, Shalesmoor. S3 8UJ. (T. and M. Vickers). Est. 1994. Open 10-5, Sat. and Sun. 10.30-4.30. SIZE: Large. *STOCK: Ceramics, furniture, clocks and collectables, mainly 19th-20th C, £50-£1,000.* LOC: A61, half mile from city centre. PARK: Easy. TEL: 0114 281 2811; fax - 0114 281 2812. SER: Valuations; restorations; re-upholstery. VAT: Stan.

The Oriental Rug Shop

763 Abbeydale Rd. S7 2BG. (Kian A. Hezaveh). Open 10-5. *STOCK: Handmade rugs and carpets especially large carpets.* TEL: 0114 2552240; fax - 0114 2509088; website - www.rugs.btinternet.co.uk.

A pair of parrots, c.1925, one turned to show 'Made in Czechoslovakia' mark, 7in. high, £25.

By the end of the 19th century, a great diversity of cheap seaside souvenirs was available. Christopher Spencer trawls the Falmouth antique shops to find out what is still around today in his article entitled 'Oh, I do like to be beside the Seaside' which appeared in the February 2001 issue of **Antique Collecting** magazine. For more details and to subscribe see page 147.

Paraphernalia

66/68 Abbeydale Rd. S7 1FD. Est. 1972. *STOCK: General antiques, stripped pine, lighting, brass and iron beds.* TEL: 0114 2550203. VAT: Stan.

Renishaw Antiques

32 Main Rd., Renishaw. S21 3UT. (B. Findley). Open Mon.-Sat. 9-3. *STOCK: Furniture, architectural items, pine doors and leaded glass.* LOC: 1 mile off M1, junction 30. TEL: 01246 435521. SER: Door stripping.

N.P. and A. Salt Antiques

Abbeydale House, Barmouth Rd. S7 2DH. LAPADA. Open 9.30-4.30. CL: Sat. SIZE: Large. *STOCK: Victorian furniture, shipping goods, smalls and toys.* TEL: 0114 2582672. SER: Valuations; packing; shipping; courier. *Trade Only.*

Sheffield Antiques Emporium and the Chapel

15 Clyde Rd. and 99 Broadfield Rd., Heeley. Open 10-5, Sun. 11-5. SIZE: 70+ dealers. *STOCK: Furniture, collectables, linens, glass, militaria, china, books, Art Deco, £1-£5,000.* LOC: 1st right off Broadfield Rd., which is opposite Broadfield public house on Abbeydale Rd. PARK: Easy. TEL: 0114 258 4863/258 8288; fax - 0114 255 5609. SER: Valuations; restorations (furniture and pottery); upholstery.

Tilley's Vintage Magazine Shop

281 Shoreham St. (A.G.J. and A.A.J.C. Tilley). Est. 1978. Open Tues.-Sat. 9.30-4.30, other times by appointment. SIZE: Large. *STOCK: Magazines, comics, newspapers, books, postcards, programmes, posters, cigarette cards, prints, ephemera.* LOC: Opposite Sheffield United F.C. PARK: Easy. TEL: 0114 2752442; fax - same; e-mail - tilleys281@aol.com; website - www.tilleysmagazines.com. SER: Mail order; valuations.

Top Hat Antique Centre

529 Ecclesall Rd. (Richard Crabtree). Est. 1993. Open 10-4. CL: Thurs pm. SIZE: Large - 5 showrooms. *STOCK: 18th-19th C furniture and clocks, £200-£5,000, porcelain, £100-£5,500.* LOC: Main road from city centre. PARK: Easy. TEL: 0114 2666876. SER: Valuations; restorations (clocks and barometers, rush and cane work). FAIRS: Newark, Ardingly.

Paul Ward Antiques

Owl House, 8 Burnell Rd., Owlerton. S6 2AX. Resident. Est. 1976. Open by appointment. SIZE: Large. *STOCK: Matched sets of Victorian dining and kitchen chairs, country chairs, general antiques.* LOC: 2 miles north of city on A61. TEL: 0114 2335980. VAT: Stan/Spec.

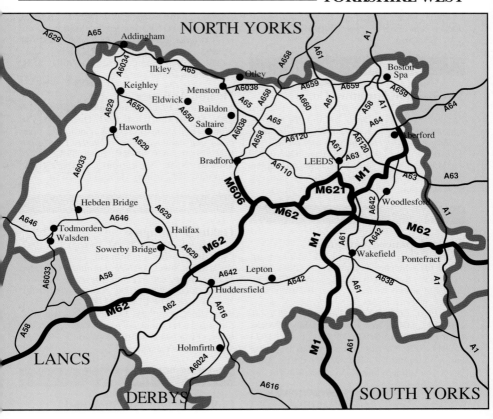

Dealers and Shops in West Yorkshire

ABERFORD

Aberford Antiques Ltd t/a Aberford Country Furniture

Hicklam House. LS25 3DP. (J.W.H. Long and C.A. Robinson). Est. 1973. Open 9-5.30, Sundays 10-5.30. CL: Mon. SIZE: Large. *STOCK: French oak furniture; pine and mahogany, £10-£4,000; Victoriana and collectables, £5-£1,000.* LOC: Large detached property at south end of village.

PARK: Easy. TEL: 0113 2813209; fax - 0113 2813121; e-mail - jwhlong@aol.com; website - www.aberfordpine.com.uk.. SER: Fitted pine and oak kitchens. VAT: Stan/Spec.

ADDINGHAM, Nr. Ilkley

Manor Barn

Burnside Mill, Main St. LS29 0PJ. (Whiteley Wright Ltd). Est. 1972. Open 9-5. SIZE: Ware-

house. *STOCK: Pine, 17th-19th C and reproduction; oak.* PARK: Easy. TEL: 01943 830176.
VAT: Stan/Spec.

BAILDON, Nr. Bradford

The Baildon Furniture Co.
Spring Mills, Otley Rd. BD17 6AD. (Richard
Parker). Est. 1972. Open 10.30-4.30, Sun. by
appointment. SIZE: Large. *STOCK: Furniture,
architectural fitments, pottery and metalware,
17th-20th C, £5-£5,000.* PARK: Easy. TEL: 01274
414345; fax - same. SER: Valuations; restorations
(cabinet work, repolishing, upholstery, pottery);
buys at auction. VAT: Stan/Spec.

BATLEY

Tansu Japanese Antiques
Redbrick Mill, 218 Bradford Rd., Batley Carr.
WF17 6JF. (Stephen P. Battye). Est. 1993. Open
9.30-5.30, Sun. 11-5. SIZE: Large. *STOCK:
Japanese granite lanterns, chests including shop
display, wheeled trunks, laligraphy boxes, mainly
1850-1900, £350-£20,000; kimonos, 1930-1960,
£10-£500.* LOC: Close to M1 and M62. PARK:
Own large. TEL: 01924 460044; fax - 01924
462844. SER: Valuations; restorations (Japanese
antique furniture). FAIRS: Ripley Castle; BBC
Homes & Antiques Sale. VAT: Spec/Margin.

BOSTON SPA, By. Wetherby

London House Oriental Rugs and Carpets
London House, High St. LS23 6AD. (M.A. and
Mrs I.T.H. Ries). Open 10-5.30 including Sun.
CL: Mon. SIZE: Large. *STOCK: Caucasian,
Turkish, Afghan and Persian rugs, runners and
carpets, £50-£10,000; kelims, tapestries and
textiles.* LOC: Off A1, south of Wetherby.
PARK: Easy. TEL: 01937 845123; home - same.
SER: Valuations; restorations (Oriental carpets
and rugs); buys at auction (Oriental carpets and
rugs). VAT: Stan.

BRADFORD

The Corner Shop
89 Oak Lane. BD9 4QU. (Miss Badland). Est.
1961. Open Tues. and Thurs. 2-5.30, Wed. 12.30-
3.30 and Sat. 11-5.30. *STOCK: Pottery, small
furniture, clocks and general items.*

Cottingley Antiques
286 Keighley Rd., Frizinghall. BD9. (Peter and

Barbara Nobbs). Est. 1981. Open 9-5. SIZE:
Medium. *STOCK: Victorian stripped and
restored pine, £100-£500.* LOC: Right hand side
of A650 from Keighley. PARK: Easy. TEL:
01274 545829; home - 01274 569091. SER:
Restorations (furniture).

Heaton Antiques
1 Hammond Place, Emm Lane, Heaton. BD9
4AN. (T. Steward). Est. 1991. Open 10-5. CL:
Mon. SIZE: Medium. *STOCK: Furniture, silver
plate and bric-a-brac, pre 1930, £10-£1,000.*
LOC: Near A650. PARK: Easy. TEL: 01274
480630. SER: Valuations. FAIRS: NEC;
Yorkshire Showground, Harrogate; Newark.

ELDWICK, Nr. Bingley

Oakleigh Antiques
82 Otley Rd., BD16 3EE. (M. Throup). Est. 1997.
Open 10-5 or by appointment. CL: Tues. and
Wed. SIZE: Small. *STOCK: Furniture, Georgian
to Edwardian, £200-£2,500; longcase, wall and
mantel clocks, £200-£4,000; paintings and prints,
19th to early 20th C, £50-£1,000.* Not Stocked:
Pine, silver, jewellery. LOC: A650 to Bingley;
Eldwick is 1.5 miles on road to Otley. PARK:
Easy. TEL: 01274 568167; home - 01274
532219. SER: Valuations.

HALIFAX

Collectors Old Toy Shop and Antiques
89 Northgate. HX1 1XF. (S. Haley). Open 10.30-
4.30. CL: Thurs. *STOCK: Collectors toys, clocks
and antiques.* TEL: 01422 360434/822148.

Halifax Antiques Centre
Queens Rd. HX1 4LR. Est. 1981. Open Tues.-
Sat. 10-5. SIZE: Large - 30 dealers. *STOCK: Art
Deco, jewellery, porcelain, linen, costume, pine,
oak, mahogany, French furniture, kitchenalia,
decorative collectables.* LOC: A58 to King
Cross, turn at Trafalgar Inn into Queens Rd.
corner, 3rd set of lights. PARK: Own. TEL:
01422 366657.

Muir Hewitt Art Deco Originals
Halifax Antiques Centre, Queens Rd. Mills. HX1
4LR. Open Tues.-Sat. 10-5. *STOCK: 20th C
ceramics including Clarice Cliff, Susie Cooper,
Charlotte Rhead, Shelley; furniture, metalware,
lighting and mirrors.* LOC: 1 mile west of town
centre off A58 (A646)Aachen Way/Burnley
Rochdale road. Turn right at Trafalgar Inn traffic
lights. Centre at 3rd of traffic lights, opposite
Lloyds TSB. PARK: Easy. TEL: 01422 347377;

fax - same; website - www.muir-hewitt.com/ hewitt. VAT: Spec.

Andy Thornton Architectural Antiques Ltd

Victoria Mills, Stainland Rd., Greetland. HX4 8AD. Open 8.30-5.30, Sat. 9-5, Sun. 10.30-4.30. SIZE: Large. *STOCK: Architectural antiques - doors, stained glass, fireplaces, panelling, garden furniture, light fittings, pews and decor items.* PARK: Easy. TEL: 01422 377314; fax - 01422 310372. VAT: Stan.

HAWORTH, Nr. Keighley

Bingley Antiques

Springfield Farm Estate, Flappit. BD21 5PT. (J.B. and J. Poole). Est. 1965. Open Tues.-Sat. 8.30-5. SIZE: Large. *STOCK: Furniture, 18th-19th C; shipping goods, porcelain, architectural antiques.* LOC: Near Haworth. PARK: Easy. TEL: 01535 646666; website - www.bingley-antiques.co.uk. SER: Valuations. VAT: Stan/Spec.

HEBDEN BRIDGE, Nr. Halifax

Cornucopia Antiques

9 West End. HX7 8JP. (C. Nassor). Open Thurs., Fri. and Sun. 1-5, Sat. 11-5. *STOCK: Furniture, Art Deco, lighting, mirrors, stoves and bric-a-brac.* LOC: Town centre behind Pennine Information Centre. PARK: Easy. TEL: 01422 844497.

HOLMFIRTH, Nr. Huddersfield

Chapel House Fireplaces

Netherfield House, St. Georges Rd., Scholes. HD7 1UH. Open strictly by appointment Tues. 9-7, Wed.-Sat. 9-5. SIZE: Large. *STOCK: Georgian, Victorian and Edwardian grates and mantels; French chimneypieces.* TEL: 01484 682275.

The Toll House Bookshop

32/34 Huddersfield Rd. HD9 2JS. (E.V. Beardsell). Est. 1978. Open 10-5. *STOCK: Books including antiquarian.* TEL: 01484 686541.

Upperbridge Antiques

9 Huddersfield Rd. HD7 1JR. (I. and B. Ridings). Open Wed., Thurs. and Sat. 1-5, Sun. 2-5. SIZE: Small. *STOCK: Pottery, metalware, lighting, linen, interesting items, Victorian to 1950's, £5-£200.* Not Stocked: Clocks and jewellery. LOC: A635. PARK: Nearby. TEL: 01484 687200.

HUDDERSFIELD

D.W. Dyson (Antique Weapons)

Wood Lea, Shepley. HD8 8ES. Est. 1974. Open by appointment only. *STOCK: Antique weapons including cased duelling pistols, armour, miniature arms, cigar and smoking related accessories, rare and unusual items.* LOC: Off A629. PARK: Easy. TEL: 01484 607331; home - same. SER: Valuations; buys at auction (antique weapons); special presentation items made to order in precious metals; restorations; interior design; finder (film props). FAIRS: Dorchester Hotel, London; Dortmund, Stuttgart and other major foreign. VAT: Spec.

Huddersfield Antiques

Est. 1971. Open by appointment only. SIZE: Medium. *STOCK: Victoriana, collectors' items, postcards; warehouse of trade and shipping goods.* TEL: 01484 662311. SER: Valuations; buys at auction.

Huddersfield Picture Framing Co

Cloth Hall Chambers, Cloth Hall St. HD1 2EG. (Miss Pamela Ward). Est. 1962. Open 9-5, Sat. 9-4. SIZE: Large. *STOCK: Watercolours, picture mouldings, swept frames, ovals and circles.* LOC: Between Market St. and New St. PARK: Meters or nearby. TEL: 01484 546075; home - 01484 687598. SER: Valuations; restorations (especially oil paintings). VAT: Stan.

Geoff Neary (incorporating Fillans Antiques Ltd)

2 Market Walk. HD1 2QA. NAG, FGA. Est. 1852. Open 9.30-5.15. SIZE: Small. *STOCK: English silver, 1700-1980; Sheffield plate, 1760-1840, £10-£500; jewellery, £50-£10,000.* Not Stocked: Other than above. PARK: Town centre multi-storey. TEL: 01484 531609. SER: Valuations; restorations; buys at auction (English silver and jewellery). VAT: Stan/Spec.

Objects of Vertu

26 Lidget St., Lindley. HD3 3JP. (Christopher J.L. Dawes). Est. 1995. Open 10-5. CL: Mon. and Wed. SIZE: Small. *STOCK: Silver, glass and porcelain, 19th-20th C, £20-£400.* PARK: Nearby. TEL: 01484 649515. SER: Valuations; buys at auction. FAIRS: Newark; Elliott Antiques & Collectors.

ILKLEY

Coopers of Ilkley

46-50 Leeds Rd. LS29 8EQ. LAPADA. Est. 1910. Open 9-1 and 2-5.30. SIZE: Large. *STOCK: English and Continental furniture, pre-*

1900, £100-£10,000; porcelain and metalware. LOC: A65. PARK: Own. TEL: 01943 608020. SER: Valuations; restorations (furniture); buys at auction. VAT: Stan/Spec.

The Grove Bookshop
10 The Grove. LS29 9EG. (Andrew and Janet Sharpe). PBFA. Open 9-5.30. SIZE: Medium. *STOCK: Antiquarian books and maps; topographical and sporting prints.* LOC: 200 yards from A65. PARK: Easy. TEL: 01943 609335. SER: Valuations; restorations (book-binding and framing); buys at auction (as stock).

Jack Shaw and Co
The Old Grammar School, Skipton Rd. LS29 9EJ. Est. 1945. Open Thurs., Fri. and Sat. 9.30-12.45 and 2-5.30. *STOCK: Silver especially cutlery and 18th C domestic.* TEL: 01943 609467. VAT: Spec.

KEIGHLEY

Barleycote Hall Antiques
2 Janet St., Crossroads. BD22 9ET. (R. Hoskins). Resident. Est. 1968. Open most days 11-5. *STOCK: Georgian and Victorian furniture, porcelain, metalwork, paintings, jewellery, Victorian and Edwardian clothing, clocks of all types.* LOC: A629, turn right towards Haworth, 600yds. on right. TEL: 01535 644776. VAT: Stan/Spec.

A rare plaque designed for Wood and Sons Ltd by Charlotte Rhead in about 1918.

Charlotte Rhead made a significant and influential contribution to the British ceramics industry. She was also one of the first acknowledged female designers of the 20th century. From an article entitled 'Tube-line Variations' by Andrew Casey which appeared in the March 2001 issue of **Antique Collecting** magazine. For more details and to subscribe see page 147.

Real Macoy
2 Janet St. BD22 9ET. (D. Seal). Open most days 11-5. *STOCK: Quilts, textiles, period clothing.* TEL: 01535 644776.

LEEDS

Aladdin's Cave
19 Queens Arcade. LS1 6LF. (A. and R. Spencer). Est. 1954. SIZE: Small. *STOCK: Jewellery, £15-£5,000; collectors' items.* LOC: Town centre. PARK: 100 yards. TEL: 0113 245703. SER: Valuations; repairs. VAT: Stan.

Bruton Gallery
Trafalgar House, 29 Park Place. LS1 2SP. (Helen Robinson). Est. 1969. Open 11-5, Sat. and Sun. by appointment. SIZE: Medium. *STOCK: French sculpture, 19th-20th C, from £1,000+; contemporary British art, to £10,000.* LOC: Off Wellington St., off central ring road. PARK: Limited. TEL: 0113 242 2321; fax - 0113 242 1447. SER: Valuations; buys at auction. FAIRS: Glasgow; Oxford; London. VAT: Stan/Spec.

Cottage Antiques
78 Otley Rd., Headingley. LS6 4BA. (David Atkinson). Est. 1989. SIZE: Small. *STOCK: Furniture and clocks, 19th C, £100-£300; pottery, 20th C, £20-£50.* LOC: A660. PARK: Easy. TEL: 01132 955125; home - 01132 948136. SER: Valuations; restorations (furniture repolishing). FAIRS: Newark, Harrogate.

Geary Antiques
114 Richardshaw Lane, Stanningley, Pudsey. LS28 6BN. (J.A. Geary). Est. 1933. Open 10-5.30, Sun. 12-4. SIZE: Large + warehouse. *STOCK: Furniture, Georgian, Victorian and Edwardian; copper and brass.* LOC: 500 yds. from West Leeds Ring Rd. PARK: Easy. TEL: 0113 2564122. SER: Restorations (furniture); interior design. VAT: Stan/Spec.

Headrow Antiques Centre
Level 3 Headrow Shopping Centre, The Headrow. (Pat Cooper and Sally Hurrell). Est. 1991. Open 10-5, Sun.11-4 (Nov.-Dec). SIZE: 25 dealers. *STOCK: Ceramics, jewellery and furniture, £5-£2,000.* LOC: City centre. PARK: NCP Albion St. TEL: 0113 2455344; home - 0113 2749494.

J. Howorth Antiques/Swiss Cottage Furniture
85 Westfield Crescent, Burley. LS3 1DJ. Est. 1986. Open 10-5.30, Sun. 1-5.30. CL: Tues. SIZE: Warehouse. *STOCK: Collectables, furniture, architectural items, £5-£3,000.* LOC: Town hall to Burley Rd., road opposite YTV.

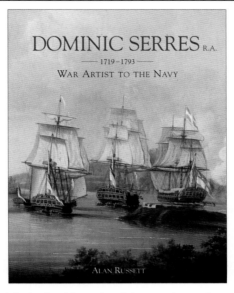

DOMINIC SERRES R.A.
—— 1719–1793 ——
WAR ARTIST TO THE NAVY

ALAN RUSSETT

This exceptional book is the first biography of the superior marine painter, Dominic Serres R.A. and is the result of extensive research. It is the story of an artist who, after being brought to England as a prisoner-of-war, became the most dominant marine painter of his era. Granted naval patronage, he played his part in a crucial period of development in British painting and of growing national awareness through colonial wars in the Americas and worldwide. Serres recorded national events and naval engagements, and chronicled the naval history of epic years in prints and paintings.

Dominic Serres R.A. – War Artist to the Navy contains the latest examination of the artist's life and work, and extensive picture research demonstrated with hundreds of lavish colour plates and exceptional black and white illustrations. The first in-depth study of artistic patronage by naval commanders is documented here and their actions are set in historical context. In addition to the wealth of information concerning Serres' work, the reader is provided with a comprehensive view of the artist as his life, family and close friendships are discussed.

Over 200 reproductions of Serres' work have been assembled – work that began as landscapes and evolved into predominantly large maritime oils and canvases. Although Serres remained a landscapist at heart, this beautiful book, saturated with incomparable illustrations, proves that he was truly one of the foremost marine painters.

Alan Russett read Modern History at Oxford and maintained an interest in art history during an international business career in the oil industry. He has since completed a university course in the history of art and has been researching, writing and reviewing a number of topics in 18th and 19th century marine painting and history. He is a Fellow of the Royal Society of Arts and a Council Member of the Friends of the National Maritime Museum, Greenwich.
ISBN 1 85149 360 3, 223pp., 72 col., 120 b.&w. illus. **£35.00/$69.50**

For a free copy of our catalogue, please contact
ANTIQUE COLLECTORS' CLUB
5 Church Street, Woodbridge, Suffolk, IP12 1DS, UK
Tel: (01394) 385501 Fax: (01394) 384434
Sales Office Direct Fax: (01394) 388994
Email: sales@antique-acc.com Website: www.antique-acc.com

or

Market Street Industrial Park, Wappingers' Falls, NY 12590, USA
Tel: (845) 297 0003 Fax: (845) 297 0068 ORDERS: (800) 252 5231
Email: info@antiquecc.com Website: www.antiquecc.com

PARK: Easy. TEL: 0113 2306268/2429994. SER: Prop. hire for film and TV. FAIRS: Newark. VAT: Stan/Spec.

Oakwood Gallery

613 Roundhay Rd., Oakwood. Open 9-6. *STOCK: Fine paintings and prints.* PARK: Easy. TEL: 0113 2401348. SER: Framing; restorations; conservation.

The Piano Shop

39 Holbeck Lane. LS11 9UL. (B. Seals). Open 9-5. *STOCK: Pianos, especially decorated cased grand.* TEL: 0113 2443685. SER: Restorations; French polishing; hire.

Swiss Cottage Furniture

85 Westfield Crescent. LS3 1DJ. (J. Howorth). Est. 1985. Open 10-5, Sun. 1-5. CL: Tues. SIZE: Large. *STOCK: Fireplaces, pine doors, 19th C, £75-£700; architectural salvage.* LOC: Behind Yorkshire TV Studios. PARK: Easy. TEL: 0113 242 9994. VAT: Stan/Spec.

Tomasso Brothers

Bardon Hall, Weetwood Lane. LS16 8HJ. (D., G. & R. Tomasso). Resident. Est. 1984. Open Mon.-Sat., Sun. by appointment. SIZE: Large. *STOCK: English and Continental furniture, sculpture and works of art, 16th-19th C, paintings and drawings, 15th-19th C; Roman, Egyptian and Greek ancient sculpture.* LOC: Half-mile from Leeds ring road, near Harrogate-Leeds road. PARK: Easy. TEL: 01132 755545; fax - 01132 755565; mobile - 07710 065677. VAT: Spec.

Windsor House Antiques (Leeds) Ltd.

18-20 Benson St. LS7 1BL. (D.K. Smith). LAPADA. Est. 1959. Open 9-5. CL: Sat. SIZE: Large. *STOCK: English furniture, 18th-19th C; paintings, objects.* PARK: Easy. TEL: 0113 2444666; fax - 0113 2426394; e-mail - sales@ windsorhouseantiques.co.uk; website - www. windsorhouseantiques.co.uk. SER: Shipping arranged. VAT: Stan/Spec.

Year Dot

16 Market St. Arcade. LS1 6DH. (A. Glithro). Open 9.30-5. *STOCK: Jewellery, watches, silver, pottery, porcelain, glass, clocks, prints, paintings, bric-a-brac.* TEL: 0113 2460860.

K.L.M. & Co. Antiques

The Antique Shop, Wakefield Rd. HD8 0EL. (K.L. & J. Millington). Est. 1980. Open 10.30-5, other times by appointment. SIZE: 8 showrooms and warehouse. *STOCK: Furniture including*

stripped pine, satin walnut, to 1940's; pianos, all £25-£1,500. LOC: A642 Wakefield road from Huddersfield, shop opposite village church. PARK: Easy and at rear. TEL: 01484 607763; home - 01484 607548. SER: Valuations. VAT: Stan.

Antiques

101 Bradford Rd. LS29. (W. and J. Hanlon). Est. 1974. Open 2.30-5. CL: Tues. and Wed. *STOCK: Handworked linen, textiles, pottery, porcelain, Art Nouveau, Art Deco, silver, plate, jewellery, small furniture, collectors items, barometers.* PARK: Forecourt. TEL: 01943 877634; home - 01943 463693.

Park Antiques

2 North View, Main St. LS29 6JU. Resident. Est. 1975. Open Thurs.-Sun. SIZE: Medium. *STOCK: Furniture, Georgian to Edwardian, £500-£5,000; decorative items, £100-£1,000, soft furnishings, £500-£2,000.* Not Stocked: Pine, silver. LOC: Opposite the park. PARK: Easy. TEL: 01943 872392. VAT: Stan/Spec.

Mayfair Antiques

26 Cross Green. LS21 1HD. (Ivor Hughes). Est. 1998. Open 10-6. CL: Wed. SIZE: Medium. *STOCK: French faience, garden antiques, metalware, 19th C; French decorative art, 1850-1930.* LOC: A658, on left leaving Otley towards Harrogate. PARK: Easy. TEL: 01943 463380; mobile - 07802 740012; e-mail - ivor@frantique. fsnet.co.uk; website - www.frantique.co.uk. SER: Valuations; restorations (clocks and furniture); translation. FAIRS: Harrogate.

Otley Antique Centre

6 Bondgate. LS21 3AB. (A. Monkman). Est. 1991. Open 10-5, Wed. 10-4. SIZE: Small. *STOCK: 20th C collectables; jewellery, paintings, 19th-20th C: all £50-£100.* LOC: Top of High St., opposite parish church on Leeds road. PARK: Next to church. TEL: 01943 850342.

Cottage Antiques

Heaton House, 24 Wakefield Rd., Ackworth. WF7 7AB. (Sheila Whittaker). Est. 1987. Open 12-4. CL: Thurs. *STOCK: 18th-19th C pine and country furniture; bedroom and kitchen furniture,* ceramics, linen and kitchenalia. PARK: Easy. TEL: 01977 599989/ 611146. SER: Restorations (furniture). FAIRS: Newark (Stand F32).

D. Turner Antiques
The Old Coach House, Bondgate. (Dennise Turner). Est. 1988. Open 11-5. CL: Thurs. SIZE: Medium. *STOCK: Furniture, £30-£300; pottery, £20-£100, both late 19th to early 20th C; collectables, £5-£25.* LOC: Just off A1 towards town. PARK: Easy. TEL: 01977 798818; home - 01226 751802. SER: Valuations; buys at auction (furniture). FAIRS: Newark, Harrogate and Ardingly.

SALTAIRE, Nr. Shipley

The Victoria Centre
3-4 Victoria Rd. BD18 3LA. (M. and M. Gray and Andrew Draper). Est. 1995. Open 10.30-5.30. CL: Mon. and Tues. SIZE: Large - 40+ dealers. *STOCK: Wide range of general antiques including fine furniture, paintings, silver, clocks, porcelain, pine and collectables, £5-£10,000.* PARK: Nearby. TEL: 01274 530611. SER: Valuations. VAT: Stan/Spec.

SOWERBY BRIDGE, Nr. Halifax

Memory Lane
69 Wakefield Rd. HX6 2UX. (L. Robinson). Open 10.30-5. SIZE: Warehouse. *STOCK: Pine, oak and teddies.* TEL: 01422 833223.

Talking Point Antiques
66 West St. HX6 3AP. (P. and L. Austwick). Open Thurs., Fri., Sat. 10.30-5.30, other days by appointment. *STOCK: Restored gramophones and phonographs, 78rpm records, gramophone accessories and related items; small furniture; pottery, porcelain and curios.* TEL: 01422 834126; e-mail - tpagrams@aol.com.

TODMORDEN

Robert Davidson Antiques
56 Burnley Rd. OL14 5EY. (J. Ratcliff). Est. 1982. Open 10-5, Sun. by appointment. CL: Mon. SIZE: Medium + warehouse. *STOCK: Country, antique and quality furniture, £1-£3,500; small architectural items and curiosities.* LOC: A646 Burnley road. PARK: Easy. TEL: 01706 816053. SER: Valuations.

Echoes
650a Halifax Rd., Eastwood. OL14 6DW. (P. Oldman). Est. 1980. CL: Mon. and Tues. SIZE: Medium. *STOCK: Costume, textiles, linen and lace, £5-£500; jewellery, £5-£150; all 19th-20th C.* LOC: A646. PARK: Easy. TEL: 01706 817505; home - same. SER: Valuations; restorations (costume); buys at auction (as stock).

Todmorden Antiques Centre
Sutcliffe House, Halifax Rd. OL14 5DG. (Mr and Mrs Hoogeveen). Open 10-5, Sat. 10-4, Sun. 12-4. SIZE: 20 dealers. *STOCK: General antiques, furniture and jewellery.* TEL: 01706 818040.

WAKEFIELD

Robin Taylor Fine Arts
36 Carter St. WF1 1XJ. Open 9.30-5.30. *STOCK: Oils and watercolours.* TEL: 01924 381809.

WALSDEN, Nr. Todmorden

Cottage Antiques (1984) Ltd
788 Rochdale Rd. OL14 7UA. (G. Slater). Resident. Est. 1978. Open Tues.-Sun. SIZE: Medium. *STOCK: Country and decorative painted furniture, kitchenalia, collectables; elm and cherrywood reproductions.* PARK: Easy. TEL: 0170 681 3612. SER: Restorations; pine stripping; import/export of European pine and collectables.

WOODLESFORD, Nr. Leeds

Trafalgar Antiques Centre
Trafalgar Works, Astley Lane, Bowers Row. LS26 8AN. Open 9-5.30, Sat. 10-5, Sun. 11-5.30. SIZE: Large. *STOCK: Mahogany, walnut and oak, 18th to early 20th C.* LOC: Off M62, junction 30 towards Garforth, into Swillington, 2 miles down Astley Lane. PARK: Own. TEL: 0113 287 5955; fax - 0113 287 5966. SER: Valuations; restorations. VAT: Stan/Spec

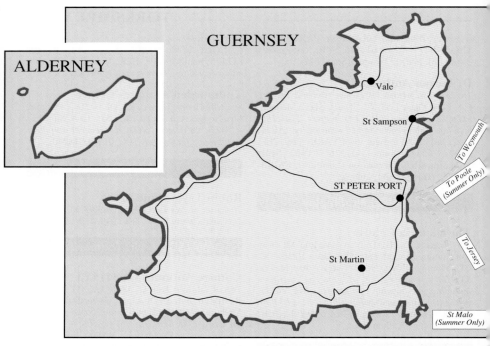

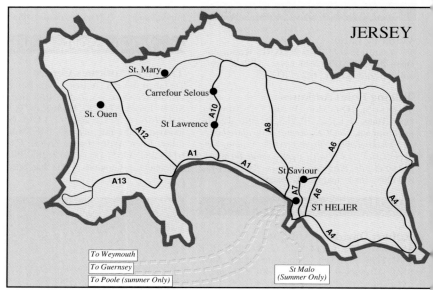

Dealers and Shops on the Channel Islands

			St Helier	12
ALDERNEY	2	St Sampson	2	St Lawrence	1
GUERNSEY		Vale	1	St. Mary	1
St Martin	1	JERSEY		St. Ouen	1
St Peter Port	6	Carrefour Selous	1	St Saviour	1

Alderney

Beverley J. Pyke - Fine British Watercolours
22 Victoria St. GY9 3TA. Open by appointment only. *STOCK: 20th C watercolours, £150-£2,000.* TEL: 01481 824092.

Victoria Antiques
St. Catherine's, Victoria St. GY9 3TA. (P.A. Nightingale). Open 10-12.30 or by appointment. *STOCK: Period and Victorian furniture, glass, silver, china, jewellery, small objets d'art.* TEL: 01481 823260. SER: Valuations.

Guernsey

ST. MARTIN

Mark Blower Antiques
The Rectory, Le Bourg Forest. Est. 1978. Open by appointment only. SIZE: Small. *STOCK: Furniture, 18th C, £1,000-£20,000; garden* ornament, pictures, 18th-19th C, £500-£5,000. PARK: Easy. TEL: 01481 239098. SER: Valuations; restorations (furniture and pictures); fine art packing and shipping; buys at auction.

ST. PETER PORT

Stephen Andrews Gallery
5 College Terrace, Grange. GY1 2PX. (J. Geddes and S. Wilkowski). Est. 1984. Open 9.30-5. SIZE: Medium. *STOCK: Furniture, pottery and porcelain, paintings, 19th-20th C.* LOC: Main road. PARK: Adjacent. TEL: 01481 710380. SER: Buys at auction. FAIRS: Local.

Channel Islands Galleries Ltd
Trinity Square Centre, Trinity Sq. GY1 1LX. (G.P. and Mrs C. Gavey). Est. 1967. Open 10-5. *STOCK: Antique maps, sea charts and prints of the Channel Islands; oil paintings, watercolours, Channel Islands' books, illustrated, historical, social, geographical and natural history.* Not Stocked: General antiques. TEL: 01481 723247; home - 01481 247337; fax - 01481 714669; e-mail - geoff.gavey@cigalleries.f9.co.uk; website - www.cigalleries.f9.co.uk.

The Collectors Centre
1 Sausmarez St. GY1 2PT. (Andrew Rundle). Est. 1984. Open 11-6. SIZE: Small. *STOCK: Prints and engravings, stamps, postcards, books, from 18th C, £5-£50.* PARK: Opposite. TEL: 01481 725209. SER: Valuations.

N. St John Paint and Sons Ltd
26-29 The Pollet. GY1 1HP. (Michael St John Paint). NAG. Est. 1955. SIZE: Large. *STOCK: Jewellery and silver, 18th-20th C, £50-£25,000.* LOC: Town centre. TEL: 01481 721096; fax - 01481 710241. SER: Valuations; restorations (silver and jewellery).

The Pine Collection
La Route de la Garenne, Pitronnerie Road Industrial Estate, GY1 2RL. (P. Head). Est. 1986. Open 9.30-5.30. *STOCK: Pine.* TEL: 01481 726891.

St. James's Gallery Ltd
18-20 Smith St. GY1 2JQ. (Mrs C.O. Whittam). Est. 1955. Open 10-1 and 2-5, Sat. 10-1. SIZE: Large. *STOCK: Furniture, 19th C, £300-£30,000; paintings, 19th-20th C, £100-£20,000; silver, 19th-20th C, £10-£5,000.* LOC: Town centre, just off High St. PARK: Nearby. TEL: 01481 720070; fax - 01481 721132; home - 01481 723999. SER: Valuations.

ST. SAMPSON

The Old Curiosity Shop
Commercial Rd. GY2 4QP. Est. 1978. CL: Mon. and Thurs. *STOCK: Old and antiquarian books, prints, postcards, coins, ephemera, paintings, small furniture, china, glass, silver, brass, £1-£5,000.* TEL: 01481 45324. FAIRS: Organiser.

Ray & Scott Ltd
The Bridge. GY2 4QN. (M. J. Search). NAG. Open 9-5.15, Sat. 9-5. SIZE: Small. *STOCK: Jewellery, 19th C, £500-£1,000+.* PARK: Easy. TEL: 01481 244610; fax - same. SER: Valuations; restorations (jewellery and engraving).

VALE

Geoffrey P. Gavey
Les Clospains, Rue de L'Ecole. GY3 5LL. Est. 1967. Open by appointment. *STOCK: Maps, sea charts and prints of the Channel Islands; oil and watercolour paintings; Channel Islands books, illustrated, historical, social, geographic and natural history.* Not Stocked: General antiques. TEL: 01481 247337; fax - 01481 714669; e-mail - geoff.gavey@cigalleries.f9.co.uk; website - www.cigalleries.f9.co.uk.

Jersey

CARREFOUR SELOUS, ST. LAWRENCE

David Hick Antiques
Alexandra House. Est. 1977. Open Wed., Fri. and Sat. 9.30-5. SIZE: Large and warehouse. *STOCK: Furniture and small items.* TEL: 01534 865965; fax - 01534 865448.

ST. HELIER

John Blench & Son
50 Don St. JE2 4TR. *STOCK: Fine books, bindings, local maps and prints.* TEL: 01534 725281; fax - 01534 758789; e-mail - segart@itl.net; website - www.selectiveeye.com.

John Cooper Antiques
16 The Market. JE2. *STOCK: General antiques.* TEL: 01534 723600.

Falle Fine Art Limited
The Napier Gallery, 86 Halkett Place. JE2 4WH (John Falle). LAPADA. Open Tues.-Fri. 11-5, Sat. 9.30-1, Mon. by appointment. SIZE: Medium. *STOCK: 20th C paintings, watercolours and bronzes.* LOC: Opposite Public Library. PARK: Easy. TEL: 01534 887877; fax - 01534 723459; e-mail - info@fallefineart.co.uk. SER: Valuations; restorations; exhibitions.

David Hick Antiques
45 Halkett Place. JE2 4WQ. Open 10-5, Thurs. 10-1. *STOCK: Furniture and smalls.* TEL: 01534 721162; fax - same.

Jeremiah's Antiques
14 1/2 Queen St. JE2. (K.J. O'Keeffe). Est. 1981. Open 10-5. CL: Mon. SIZE: Small. *STOCK: Fine wrist and pocket watches, clocks; silver, porcelain, bronzes, jewellery, small furniture.* LOC: Main shopping area. PARK: Nearby. TEL: 01534 23153; website - www.jeremiahs antiques.com. SER: Valuations; restorations (clocks and watches); buys at auction (clocks and watches). FAIRS: Miami, Munich, London.

Peter Le Vesconte's Collectables
62 Stopford Rd. JE2 4LZ. Est. 1979. Open 10-3. CL: Thurs. SIZE: Medium. *STOCK: Toys, 1920-1999, £5-£500; militaria, 1900-1945, £1-£500; small items, 1900-1970, £5-£300.* LOC: Road opposite Hotel de France. PARK: Easy. TEL: 01534 732481; fax - same. SER: Valuations; buys at auction (toys and militaria).

The New Hall specialist, Tim Olney, will have these two late 18th century teapots, each costing £225, on his stand at the Cumberland Hotel Ceramics Fair on 8th-10th January.

From a Fairs Preview which appeared in the December 1998/January 1999 issue of **Antique Collecting** magazine. For more details and to subscribe see page 147.

A. & R. Ritchie
7 Duhamel Place. JE2. Open 9.30-4.30. *STOCK: Militaria and jewellery.* TEL: 01534 873805.

Roberts Antiques
14 York St. JE2 3RQ. (Robert Michieli). Est. 1975. Open 9.30-4.45. SIZE: Medium. *STOCK: English silver, ceramics, clocks, glass, jewellery, 19th C, £50-£10,000.* LOC: Opposite town hall. PARK: Easy. TEL: 01534 509071; home - 01534 865005. SER: Valuations; buys at auction (as stock).

The Selective Eye Gallery
50 Don St. JE2 4TR. (J. and P. Blench). Est. 1958. Open 9-5. CL: Thurs. and Sat. pm. SIZE: Medium. *STOCK: Oil paintings, 19th-20th C; maps, prints and antiquarian books, 16th-20th C.* Not Stocked: General antiques. LOC: Town centre. PARK: Multi-storey 100yds. TEL: 01534 725281; fax - 01534 758789; e-mail - segart@itl.net; website - www.selectiveeye.com. SER: Valuations; restorations (pictures). FAIRS: Jersey.

Thesaurus (Jersey) Ltd
3 James St. JE2 4TT. (I. Creaton). Est. 1973. Open 9-4.30. SIZE: Small. *STOCK: Antiquarian and out of print books, £1-£2,000; maps and prints.* Not Stocked: General antiques. LOC: Town centre. PARK: 100yds. TEL: 01534 37045. SER: Buys at auction. VAT: Spec.

Joan Thomson Antiques
12 Burrard St. JE2. Est. 1967. Open 10-3. CL: Thurs. SIZE: Medium. *STOCK: Smalls, £10-£500, jewellery, linen, collectors' items, Oriental.* PARK: Nearby. TEL: 01534 737206; home - 01534 856908.

Thomson's
60 Kensington Place and 44 Don St. JE2 3PA. Est. 1967. Open 10-6. SIZE: Large. *STOCK: General antiques and collectors's items, mainly furniture.* LOC: 60 Kensington Place at the side of Grand Hotel; 44 Don St. opposite Bonhams. TEL: 01534 723673/618673; mobile - 07797 766806

ST. LAWRENCE

I.G.A. Old Masters Ltd
5 Kimberley Grove, Rue de Haut. (I.G. and Mrs C.B.V. Appleby). Est. 1953. Open by appointment. *STOCK: Old Master and 19th C paintings.* LOC: Near glass church. PARK: Easy. TEL: 01534 724226; home - same.

ST. MARY

Country House and Cottage Antiques
La Foret, Rue es Boeufs. JE3 3EQ. (Mrs Sarah Jo Howson). Resident. Est. 1985. Open Tues.-Sat. 10-5, Wed. 10-1 or by appointment. SIZE: Large. *STOCK: Furniture - Georgian, Victorian, Art Nouveau, Art Deco and decorative, £100-£6,000.* PARK: Easy. TEL: 01534 862547. SER: Valuations; restorations.

ST. OUEN

Stephen Cohu Antiques
La Ville de L'Eglise. JE3 2LR. Est. 1990. Open 10-5, Wed. 2-5, prior telephone call advisable. CL: Mon. SIZE: Medium + warehouse. *STOCK: Furniture and clocks, 18th-20th C, £50-£10,000; porcelain and pottery, 17th-20th C, £10-£2,000; glass, 18th-20th C, £5-£1,000.* LOC: Opposite parish church. PARK: Own. TEL: 01534 485177; fax - same; mobile - 07797 723895. SER: Valuations; restorations (furniture and china); buys at auction. FAIRS: NEC and Newark.

ST. SAVIOUR

Grange Gallery - Fine Arts Ltd
10 Victoria Rd., JE2 7QG. (G.J. Morris). Est. 1973. Open 9-5.30. SIZE: Medium. *STOCK: 19th-20th C oil paintings and watercolours, local items, £10-£10,000.* LOC: 1 mile east of St Helier. PARK: Forecourt. TEL: 01534 720077. SER: Valuations; restorations (paintings); framing.

The Bell Gallery
13 Adelaide Park. BT9 6FX. (J.N. Bell). Est. 1964. Open 10-6. SIZE: Medium. *STOCK: British and Irish art, 19th-20th C.* LOC: Off Malone Rd. TEL: 028 9066 2998. SER: Valuations; restorations (paintings); buys at auction. VAT: Stan/Spec.

Emerald Isle Books
539 Antrim Rd. BT15 3BU. Est. 1966. Open by appointment. *STOCK: Travel, Ireland, theology.* TEL: 028 9037 0798; fax - 028 9077 7288. SER: Catalogues available.

T.H. Kearney & Sons
Treasure House, 123 University St. BT7 1HP. Resident. *STOCK: Small antiques.* TEL: 028 9023 1055. SER: Restorations and upholstery. VAT: Stan.

Charlotte and John Lambe
41 Shore Rd. BT15 3PG. Open 10-5. CL: Sat. *STOCK: English and French furniture, 19th C; pictures and works of art.* TEL: 028 9037 0761.

Well loved. Dating from 1908, this Steiff blond mohair teddy will call for bids of £800-£1,200 when offered at Bonhams Knightsbridge on 17th December.

From an Auction Preview which appeared in the December 1998/January 1999 issue of **Antique Collecting** magazine. For more details and to subscribe see page 147.

Co. Antrim

The Country Antiques
219B Lisnevenagh Rd. BT41 2JT. (David Wolfenden). LAPADA. Open 10-6. SIZE: Large. *STOCK: Furniture, £200-£5,000; jewellery and porcelain, £100-£3,000; all 19th C.* LOC: Main Antrim-Ballymena line. PARK: Easy. TEL: 028 9442 9498. SER: Valuations; restorations. VAT: Stan/Spec.

Dunluce Antiques
33 Ballytober Rd. BT57 8UU. (Mrs C. Ross). Est. 1978. Open 2-6 or by appointment. CL: Fri. SIZE: Small. *STOCK: Furniture, £100-£5,000; porcelain and glass, £10-£2,000; silver, £10-£2,000; all Georgian to 1930's; paintings, mainly Irish, £100-£10,000.* LOC: 1.5 miles off Antrim coast rd. at Dunluce Castle. PARK: Easy. TEL: 028 2073 1140. SER: Restorations (porcelain).

Robert Christie Antiques
The Courtyard, 38 Scotch Quarter. BT38 7DP. IADA. Est. 1976. Open 11-5. SIZE: Medium. *STOCK: Furniture, 1750-1900, £200-£3,000; clocks, 1750-1900, £500-£2,000; decorative objects, 1800-1900, £50-£500.* PARK: Easy. TEL: 028 9336 1333/9334 1149; mobile - 07802 968846. SER: Valuations. FAIRS: Kings Hall, Belfast; all RDS fairs; Culloden Hotel, Holywood.

Parvis Sigaroudinia
Mountainview House, 40 Sandy Lane, Ballyskeagh. BT27 5TL. IADA. Est. 1974. Open by appointment at any time. *STOCK: Oriental and European carpets and tapestries (extra large sizes stocked); cushions, lamps, William Yeoward crystal, David Williams-Ellis bronze sculpture, decorative items.* LOC: Take Malone Road from Belfast, then Upper Malone Road towards Lisburn, cross Ballyskeagh bridge over M1, 1st left into Sandy Lane. PARK: Easy. TEL: 028 9262 1824; home - same; fax - 028 9262 3311; e-mail - parvissig@aol.com; website - www.parvis.co.uk. SER: Valuations; buys at auction; exhibitions held in Belfast. FAIRS: Culloden, Belfast; IADA in RDS Dublin. VAT: Stan.

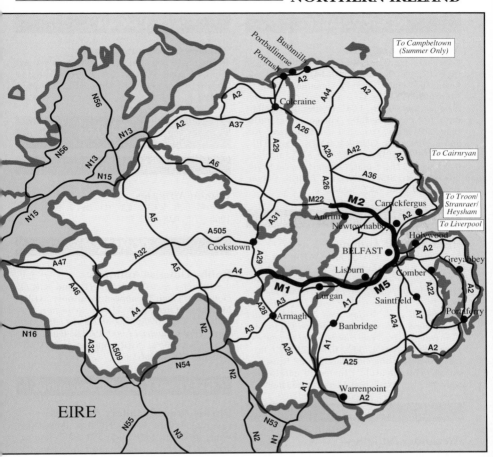

Bushmills
Portballintrae
Portrush
A2
Coleraine
A2
A44
A2
A2
A26
A37
A29
A26
A26
A42
A2
A6
A26
A36

To Campbeltown (Summer Only)

To Cairnryan

M22
M2
Carrickfergus
Antrim
Newtownabbey
A2
A2

To Troon/ Stranraer/ Heysham

To Liverpool

A5
A31
A505
Cookstown
A29
BELFAST
Holywood
A2
Greyabbey
A32
A5
A4
Lisburn
Comber
A47
A46
A4
M1
Lurgan
M5
Saintfield
A22
A2
Portaferry
N15
N16
A509
A28
A3
Armagh
A1
Banbridge
A24
A7
A32
N54
N2
A3
A28
A1
A25
A2
N55
N3
N2
N1
A1
Warrenpoint
A2

EIRE

N53

LONDONDERRY
ANTRIM
TYRONE
FERMANAGH
ARMAGH
DOWN

NORTHERN IRELAND

Belfast	4	Co Down	
		Banbridge	1
Co Antrim		Comber	1
Antrim	1	Greyabbey	2
Bushmills	1	Holywood	1
Carrickfergus	1	Portaferry	1
Lisburn	1	Saintfield	4
Newtownabbey	1	Warrenpoint	1
Portballintrae	1		
Portrush	1	Co Londonderry	
		Coleraine	2
Co Armagh			
Armagh	1	Co Tyrone	
Lurgan	1	Cookstown	2

MacHenry Antiques
Caragh Lodge, Glen Rd., Jordanstown. BT37 0RY. (R. and A. MacHenry). IADA. Est. 1964. Open Tues.-Sat. 2-7 or by appointment. SIZE: Medium. *STOCK: Georgian and Victorian furniture and objects.* LOC: 6 miles from Belfast on M2/M5 to Whiteabbey village, left at traffic lights at Woody's, then left into Old Manse Rd. and continue into Glen Rd. PARK: Easy. TEL: 028 9086 2036; fax - 028 9085 3281; mobile - 07831 135226; e-mail - rupert.machenry@ ntlworld.com. SER: Valuations. FAIRS: Dublin, Belfast and Irish. VAT: Stan/Spec.

Brian R. Bolt Antiques
88 Ballaghmore Rd. BT57 8RL. IADA. Open 11-5.30 and by appointment. CL: Wed. and Fri. *STOCK: Silver - small and unusual items, objects of vertu, snuff boxes, vesta cases, table, Scottish and Irish provincial; treen; English and Continental glass, antique and 20th C; art and studio glass and ceramics; Arts and Crafts, Art Nouveau and Art Deco jewellery and metalwork; vintage fountain pens.* TEL: 028 2073 1129; fax - same; e-mail - brianbolt@antiques88.freeserve. co.uk. SER: Search; illustrated catalogues available; worldwide postal service; valuations.

Alexander Antiques
108 Dunluce Rd. BT56 8NB. (Mrs M. and D. Alexander). Est. 1974. Open 10-6. CL: Sun. except by appointment. SIZE: Large. *STOCK: Furniture, silver, porcelain, fine art, 18th-20th C; oils and watercolours, 19th-20th C.* Not Stocked: Militaria, jewellery, coins. LOC: 1 mile from Portrush on A2 to Bushmills. PARK: Easy. TEL: 028 7082 2783. SER: Valuations; buys at auction. VAT: Stan/Spec.

Co. Armagh

The Hole-in-the-Wall
Market St. BT61 7BW. (I. Emerson). Est. 1953. *STOCK: General antiques.* LOC: City centre. VAT: Stan/Spec.

Charles Gardiner Antiques
48 High St. BT66 8AU. Est. 1968. Open 9-1 and 2-6. CL: Wed. *STOCK: Clocks, furniture and general antiques.* PARK: Own. TEL: 028 3832 3934.

Co. Down

Cameo Antiques
41 Bridge St. BT32 3LY. (D. and J. Bell). Est. 1966. TEL: 028 4062 3241.

Bobby Douglas Antiques
9 Killinchy St. BT23 5SD. (B. and N.R.G. Douglas). Open by appointment only. SIZE: Medium and trade barn. *STOCK: Irish furniture, 18th-19th C, £1,000-£25,000; unusual collectors' items, 19th C, under £1,000.* PARK: Easy. TEL: 028 9752 8351. SER: Valuations. VAT: Stan/Spec. *Trade only.*

Phyllis Arnold Gallery Antiques
Hoops Courtyard. BT22 2NE. Est. 1968. Open Wed., Fri. and Sat. 11-5. *STOCK: General antiques, jewellery, small furniture, Irish paintings and watercolours, portrait miniatures, maps and engravings of Ireland.* TEL: 028 4278 8199; home - 028 9185 3322; fax - same. SER: Restorations (maps, prints, watercolours, portrait miniatures); conservation framing. FAIRS: Culloden.

Marjorie McAuley - The Antique Shop
9 Main St. BT22 2NE. Est. 1968. *STOCK: General antiques.* TEL: Home - 028 4273 8333.

Herbert Gould and Co.
21-23 Church Rd. BT18 9BU. (Robert Brown). Est. 1897. Open 9.15-5.30. SIZE: Medium. *STOCK: Pine, 19th C, £75-£200; collectables, architectural antiques, 19th-20th C, £10-£100.* LOC: 20 yards from maypole in town centre. PARK: Opposite. TEL: 028 9042 7916. SER: Valuations; pine stripping; buys at auction (as stock). VAT: Stan.

PORTAFERRY

Time & Tide Antiques
36 Shore Rd. BT22 1JZ. (D. Dunlop). Open Wed., Fri., Sat. and Sun. 12-5.30 or by appointment. SIZE: Medium. *STOCK: Clocks, barometers, marine instruments, pictures, nautical memorabilia and small furniture, £50-£10,000.* LOC: A20 from Newtownards through Greyabbey. PARK: On Promenade. TEL: 028 4272 8935; home - same. SER: Valuations; restorations and repairs.

SAINTFIELD

Ashley Pine
88 Main St. BT24 7AB. (Mrs Truda K. Martin). Est. 1995. Open Mon. 1-5, Tues.-Fri. 10.30-5 and Sat. 10-5.30. SIZE: Small. *STOCK: General antiques and pine.* PARK: Easy. TEL: 028 9751 1855. SER: Restorations (furniture).

Attic Antiques
90 Main St. (Caesar and Reuben Doyle). Est. 1992. Open 10-5, Sat. 10-5.30. SIZE: Large. *STOCK: Victorian and Edwardian furniture, £50-£2,000; Victorian jewellery, £5-£1,000; bric-a-brac, to £100. (+ Irish, European and reclaimed pine, £30-£1,000 at Attic Pine).* PARK: Easy. TEL: 028 9751 1057. SER: Valuations.

Saintfield Antiques & Fine Books
68 Main St. BT24 7AB. (Joseph Leckey). Est. 1978. Open Thurs., Fri. and Sat. 11.30-5. SIZE: Small. *STOCK: Silver, 18th-20th C, £25-£750; porcelain, 18th-19th C, £50-£500; fine and antiquarian books, 19th-20th C, £10-£500.* PARK: Easy. TEL: Home - 028 9752 8428; fax - same; e-mail - home@antiquesireland.com. SER: Buys at auction (silver).

Town & Country Antiques
92 Main St. BT24 7AB. (Patrica Keller). Est. 1997. Open 10.30-5.30. CL: Mon. SIZE: Medium. *STOCK: 19th C furniture, £100-£1,000; 19th C small silver, £100-£300; tapestries; 18th-19th C botanical and sporting prints, £100-£200; racing and hunting prints, hunting crops, riding boots and other equestrian items; mirrors.* PARK: Easy. TEL: 028 9754 1659; fax - 028 9754 1950; mobile - 07710 840090. SER: Restorations (furniture, prints and tapestries). VAT: Stan.

WARRENPOINT

Antiques and Fine Art Gallery
3 Charlotte St. BT34 3LF. (B. Woods). Est. 1991.

Open 10.30-1 and 2.30-5.30. CL: Mon. and Wed. SIZE: Medium. *STOCK: Furniture, Georgian to Edwardian, £50-£5,000; paintings especially Irish, 20th C, £50-£10,000.* LOC: Turn off main road at Newry. PARK: Easy. TEL: 028417 52905. SER: Valuations. framing.

Co. Londonderry

COLERAINE

The Forge Antiques
24 Long Commons. BT52 1LH. (M.W. Walker). Est. 1977. Open 10-5.30. CL: Thurs. *STOCK: General antiques, silver, clocks, jewellery, porcelain, paintings.* TEL: 028 7035 1339. VAT: Stan.

Homes, Pubs and Clubs
1-5 Portrush Rd. BT52 1RL. (McNulty Wholesalers). Resident. Est. 1983. Open 9-6, Sun. 2.30-6. SIZE: Large. *STOCK: Pine and mahogany, small interesting items.* LOC: Main Portrush road, near traffic lights. PARK: At rear. TEL: 028 7035 5733. SER: Valuations; restorations. FAIRS: Newark. VAT: Stan.

Co. Tyrone

COOKSTOWN

Cookstown Antiques
16 Oldtown St. BT80 8EF. (G. Jebb). Est. 1976. Open Thurs. and Fri. 2-5.30, Sat. 10.30-5.30. SIZE: Small. *STOCK: Jewellery, silver, £10-£2,000; coins, £25-£200; pictures, ceramics and militaria, £5-£1,000; general antiques, all 19th-20th C.* Not Stocked: Large furniture. LOC: Going north, through both sets of traffic lights, on left at rear of estate agency. PARK: Easy. TEL: 028 8676 5279; fax - 028 8676 2946; home - 028 8676 2926. SER: Valuations; buys at auction.

The Saddle Room Antiques
4 Coagh St. BT80 8NG. (C.J. Leitch). Est. 1968. Open 10-5.30. CL: Mon. and Wed. *STOCK: China, silver, furniture, glass, jewellery.* TEL: 028 8676 4045.

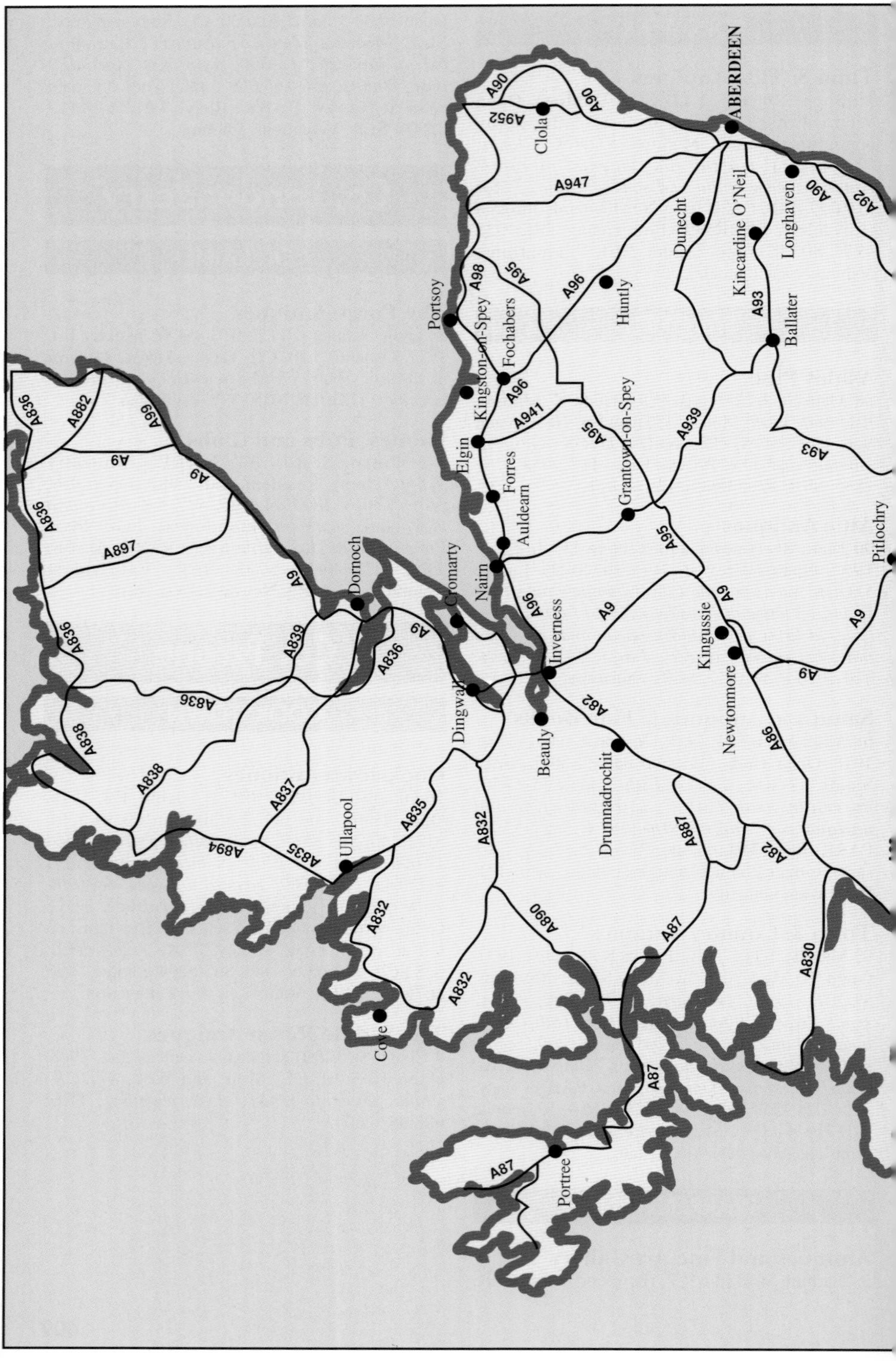
ABERDEEN
Clola
Dunecht
Kincardine O'Neil
Longhaven
Huntly
Ballater
Portsoy
Kingston-on-Spey
Fochabers
Elgin
Forres
Auldearn
Nairn
Grantown-on-Spey
Pitlochry
Dornoch
Cromarty
Inverness
Kingussie
Newtonmore
Dingwall
Beauly
Drumnadrochit
Ullapool
Cove
Portree
A90
A952
A947
A92
A98
A95
A96
A93
A941
A939
A9
A836
A882
A99
A897
A839
A838
A837
A835
A894
A832
A890
A82
A887
A87
A86
A830

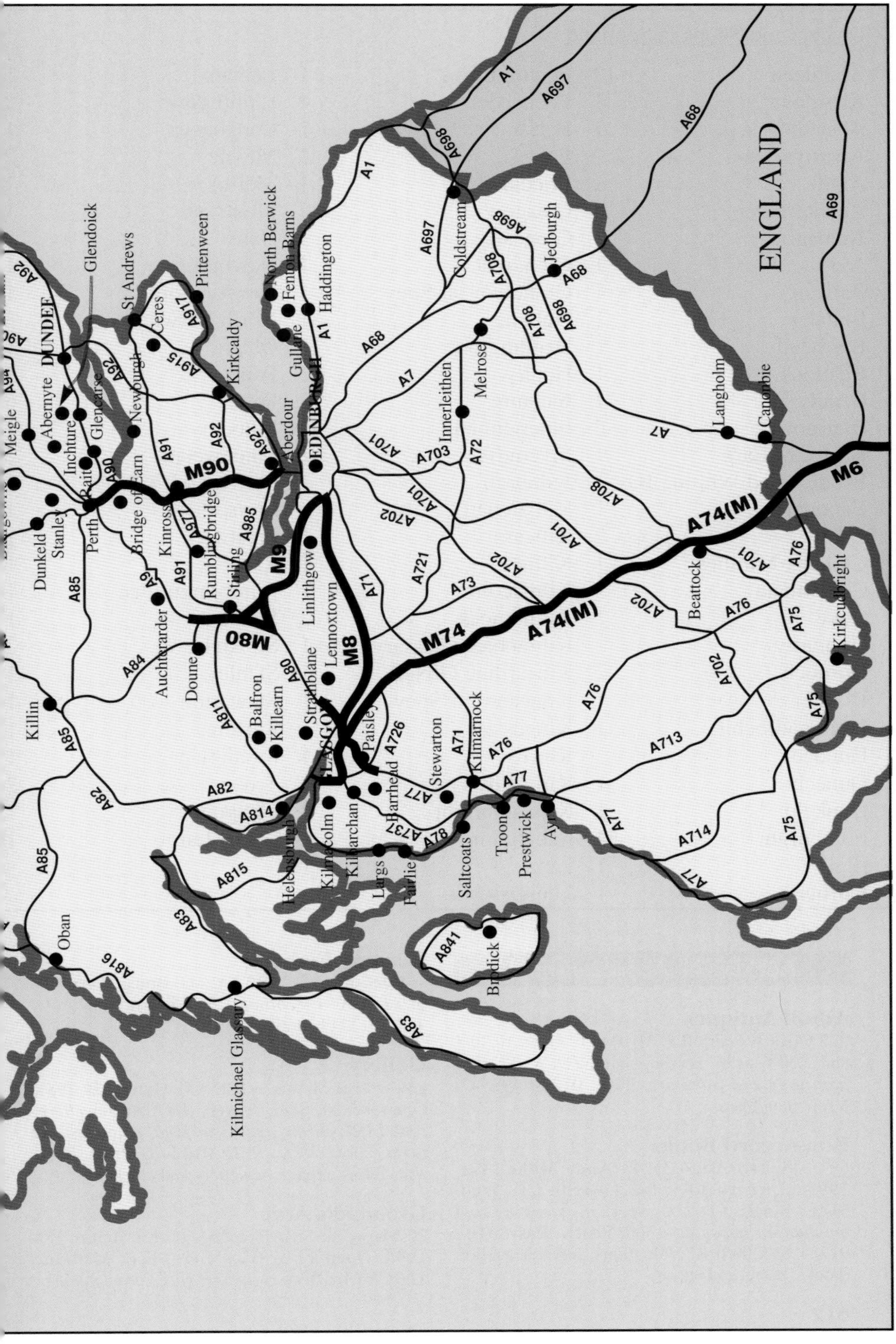
ENGLAND
DUNDEE
EDINBURGH
Glendoick
St Andrews
Pittenween
North Berwick
Fenton Barns
Haddington
Gullane
Ceres
Kirkcaldy
Newburgh
Abernyte
Inchture
Glencarse
Meigle
Dunkeld
Stanley
Perth
Bridge of Earn
Kinross
Rumblingbridge
Stirling
Aberdour
Linlithgow
Lennoxtown
Strathblane
Auchterarder
Doune
Balfron
Killearn
Killin
Oban
Kilmichael Glassary
Helensburgh
Kilmacolm
Kilbarchan
Paisley
Barrhead
Stewarton
Kilmarnock
Largs
Fairlie
Saltcoats
Troon
Prestwick
Ayr
Brodick
Coldstream
Jedburgh
Melrose
Innerleithen
Langholm
Canonbie
Beattock
Kirkcudbright
M90
M9
M80
M8
M74
A74(M)
M6
A1
A697
A698
A68
A69
A7
A708
A72
A701
A702
A703
A721
A73
A71
A76
A75
A77
A78
A713
A714
A726
A737
A841
A80
A811
A82
A83
A84
A85
A814
A815
A816
A9
A91
A92
A90
A94
A915
A917
A921
A977
A985

Dealers and Shops in Scotland

Aberdeen	12	Fenton Barns	1	Letham	1
Aberdour	1	Fochabers	4	Linlithgow	2
Aberfeldy	1	Forfar	1	Longhaven	1
Abernyte	2	Forres	1	Meigle	2
Alyth	1	Friockheim	1	Melrose	1
Auchterarder	5	Glasgow	22	Montrose	1
Auldearn	1	Glencarse	1	Nairn	1
Ayr	1	Glendoick	1	Newburgh	1
Balfron	1	Grantown-on-Spey	1	Newtonmore	1
Ballater	1	Gullane	1	North Berwick	3
Barrhead	1	Haddington	1	Oban	1
Beattock	1	Huntly	2	Paisley	2
Beauly	1	Inchture	2	Perth	6
Blairgowrie	2	Innerleithen	2	Pitlochry	1
Bridge of Earn	1	Inverness	1	Pittenweem	2
Brodick and Whiting Bay	1	Jedburgh	2	Portree	1
Canonbie	1	Kilbarchan	2	Portsoy	1
Ceres	2	Killearn	1	Prestwick	1
Clola by Mintlaw	1	Killin	1	Rait	1
Coldstream	3	Kilmacolm	1	Rumblingbridge	1
Cove	1	Kilmarnock	2	Saltcoats	1
Cromarty	1	Kilmichael Glassary	1	St. Andrews	2
Dornoch	2	Kincardine O'Neil	1	Stanley	1
Doune	1	Kingston-on-Spey	1	Stewarton	1
Drumnadrochit	1	Kingussie	1	Stirling	1
Dundee	3	Kinross	1	Strathblane	1
Dunecht	1	Kirkcaldy	2	Troon	2
Dunkeld	1	Kirkcudbright	2	Ullapool	1
Edinburgh	54	Langholm	1	Upper Largo	1
Elgin	1	Largs	1		
Fairlie	1	Lennoxtown	1		

ABERDEEN (Aberdeenshire)

Atholl Antiques
322 Great Western Rd. AB10 6PL. Open 10.30-1 and 2.30-6 or by appointment. *STOCK: Scottish paintings and furniture*. TEL: 01224 593547. VAT: Stan/Spec.

Bon-Accord Books
69-75 Spital. AB24 3HX. (Andy Milne). Est. 1995. Open 10.30-5, Sat.11-4.30. CL: Wed. SIZE: Small. *STOCK: Scottish, sporting and antiquarian books, £5-£800.* PARK: Easy. TEL: 01224 643209SER: Valuations; buys at auction (books, prints and maps).

Burning Embers
165-167 King St. AB2 3AE. (J. Bruce). Open 10-5. *STOCK: Fireplaces, bric-a-brac and pine.* TEL: 01224 624664.

Gallery
239 George St. AB25 1ED. (M. Gray). Est. 1981. Open 9-5.30. SIZE: Large. *STOCK: Jewellery, post 1850; curios and Victoriana, paintings and prints, post 1800.* TEL: 01224 632522. SER: Valuations; repairs (jewellery and clocks).

Grandad's Attic
20 Marischal St. AB11 5AJ. (Carol Smith). Est. 1995. Open 11-5. CL: Mon. SIZE: Medium. *STOCK: Art Deco ceramics, glass, gramophones,*

SCOTLAND
DISTRICTS

Caithness

Sutherland

Ross &
Cromarty

Skye

Moray

Nairn

Banff

Aberdeen

Inverness

Kincardine

Angus

Perth

Argyll

Fife

Kinross

Dunbarton

Stirling

West Lothian

East
Lothian

Renfrew

Midlothian

Berwick

Lanark

Peebles

Selkirk

Ayr

Roxburgh

Dumfries

Kirkcudbright

Wigtown

The Rendezvous Gallery
100 Forest Ave. AB15 4TL. Est. 1973. Open 10-1 and 2.30-6. CL: Fri. SIZE: Medium. *STOCK: Art Nouveau, Art Deco, glass, jewellery, bronzes, furniture, £100-£5,000; paintings, watercolours, Scottish School, £200-£6,000.* LOC: Just off Great Western Rd. to Braemar. PARK: Easy. TEL: 01224 323247; fax - 01224 326029; e-mail - info@rendezvous-gallery.co.uk. VAT: Stan/Spec.

Mr Reynolds
162/164 Skene St. AB10 1PE. Resident. *STOCK: General antiques.* SER: Restorations.

Thistle Antiques
28 Esslemont Ave. AB25 1SN. LAPADA. Est. 1967. TEL: 01224 634692. VAT: Spec.

Colin Wood (Antiques) Ltd
25 Rose St. AB10 1TX. Est. 1968. Open 9.30-5, Wed.and Thurs. 10-12.30 and 2.30-5. SIZE: Medium. *STOCK: Furniture, 17th-19th C; works of art, Scottish paintings, prints and silver; specialist in maps of Scotland, 16th-19th C.* PARK: Multi-storey in Chapel St. TEL: 01224 644786 (answerphone); fax - same. VAT: Stan/Spec.

ABERDOUR (Fife)

Antiques and Gifts
26 High St. KY3 0SW. Est. 1976. CL: Mon., Tues. am. and Wed. pm. SIZE: Small. *STOCK: China, pottery, glass and collectables.* LOC: A921. PARK: Nearby. TEL: 01383 860523. SER: Restorations (china).

ABERFELDY (Perthshire)

Sonia Cooper
19 Bridgend. PH15 2DF. Est. 1983. Open Thurs.-Sat. 11-4, Mon. in summer. SIZE: Medium. *STOCK: China, glass, wood and metal, from 18th C, £1-£100.* LOC: 10 miles from A9. PARK: Easy. TEL: 01887 820266. SER: Buys at auction.

ABERNYTE (Perthshire)

Becca Gauldie Antiques
Scottish Antiques & Arts Centre. PH14 9SJ. Est. 1993. Centre open 10-5 including Sun. For personal appointment, telephone mobile number. SIZE: Medium. *STOCK: British, mainly Scottish, curios including snuff boxes, sewing items, Mauchline ware (painted, tartan, fern, transfer and photographic), 1800-1930, from £30; country furnishings, Scottish pottery, glass and quilts, decorators items, 1750-1900, from £20.*

furniture and jewellery. LOC: Last street off top of Union St., going towards harbour. PARK: Pay and display. TEL: 01224 213699. SER: Valuations; buys at auction. FAIRS: Leeds Art Deco; Ingliston; Treetops Hotel, Ardoe House and Hoddo House, Aberdeen.

McCalls (Aberdeen)
90 King St. AB1 2JH. (B. McCall). Est. 1948. Open 10-5.30. *STOCK: Jewellery.* PARK: Nearby. TEL: 01224 641916.

McCalls Limited
11 Bridge St. AB11 6JL. Open 9.30-5.30, Thurs. 9.30-8. *STOCK: Jewellery.* TEL: 01224 405303.

The Odd Lot
24 Adelphi, Union St. AB11 5BL. (George Knight-Mudie). Est. 1995. Open 11-4, Thurs. 10-5, Fri. and Sat. 10-5.30. SIZE: Small. *STOCK: Furniture, 19th C, £50-£100; jewellery and china, 19th-20th C, £5-£100.* LOC: 2 mins. from Tourist Information Office. PARK: Easy. TEL: 01224 592551; fax - 01224 575813; home - 07771 926736. SER: Valuations; restorations (furniture and china); buys at auction.

LOC: 1.5 miles off A92 midway between Perth and Dundee. PARK: Easy. TEL: Mobile - 07770 741636; centre - 01828 686401. SER: Valuations; buys at auction. FAIRS: Little Chelsea; Earls Court; NEC; Old Swan, Harrogate; Bowes Museum; Hopetoun House (Edinburgh). VAT: Stan/Spec/Global/Export

Scottish Antique & Arts Centre
PH14 9SJ. (Templemans). Open 10-5 including Sun. SIZE: Large - 100 dealers. *STOCK: Furniture, £50-£5,000; accessories, £5-£2,000; collectibles, £5-£50; all 18th-19th C.* LOC: 1.5 miles from A90 Perth-Dundee link road. PARK: Own. TEL: 01828 686401; fax - 01828 686199. SER: Valuations; restorations. VAT: Stan/Spec/Global.

ALYTH (Perthshire)

Airlie Antiques
4 Mill St. PH11 8BJ. (Mrs Jeannette McGill). Est. 1982. Open Mon., Tues., Thurs. and Fri. afternoons and all day Sat. SIZE: Small. *STOCK: Textiles and lace, 19th C, £50-£150; general antiques, 19th-20th C, £25-£100; collectables, 20th C, £5-£50.* LOC: 3 miles north of A94. PARK: Easy. TEL: 01828 633101.

AUCHTERARDER (Perthshire)

Ian Burton Antique Clocks
at The Antique Galleries, 125 High St. PH3 1AA. Open 9-5, Sat. 10-5. *STOCK: Clocks.* TEL: 01334 471426; mobile - 07785 114800; e-mail - ian@ianburton.com; website - www.ianburton.com.

Paul Hayes Gallery
71 High St. PH3 1BN. PADA. Est. 1962. Open 10-1 and 2-5 or by appointment. CL: Wed. *STOCK: Fine paintings, especially Scottish landscapes, marine and Scottish post-impressionist, 18th-20th C.* TEL: 01764 662320/663442; fax - 01764 664179. VAT: Spec.

Nigel Stacy-Marks Ltd
92 High St. PH3 1BJ. Open 10-5. SIZE: Medium. *STOCK: Oils and watercolours, 19th-20th C, £250-£30,000; British etchings, late 19th C to mid 20th C, £100-£5,000.* LOC: Opposite library, next to Tourist Information Centre. PARK: Easy. TEL: 01764 663525; fax - same; e-mail - paintings @stacy-marks.co.uk; website - www.stacy-marks. co.uk. SER: Valuations; restorations; framing; regular exhibitions (catalogues on request). VAT: Stan/Spec.

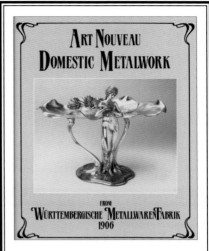

ART NOUVEAU DOMESTIC METALWORK FROM WÜRTTEMBERGISCHE METALLWARENFABRIK 1906

A splendid reprint of the 1906 catalogue of art nouveau and other decorative objects from a leading European producer whose work is now highly prized. Over 3,000 domestic pieces have hand drawn illustrations and are accompanied by descriptions in English. With details which include size, finish and cost, the descriptions will be a major source of information. There is an introduction by Graham Dry, a noted authority on 19th and 20th century decorative arts.

ISBN 1 85149 066 3
389pp., 13 col., 3,500 b.&w. illus.
£45.00/$79.50

Times Past Antiques
Broadfold Farm. PH3 1DR. (J.M. Brown). Est. 1970. Open 8-4.30, weekends and holidays 10-3. SIZE: Large. *STOCK: Stripped pine, 19th-20th C, from £50; shipping goods, £5-£500.* LOC: From town centre take Abbey Rd. to flyover A9 at T junction. Turn left, 1st farm on left. PARK: Easy. TEL: 01764 663166; fax - same. SER: Restorations (pine); courier; container-packing.

John Whitelaw and Sons Antiques
125 High St. PH3 1AA. LAPADA. Open 9-5, Sat. 10-1 and 2-5. *STOCK: General antiques; furniture, 17th-19th C.* PARK: Easy. TEL: 01764 662482; fax - 01764 663577. VAT: Stan/Spec.

AULDEARN, Nr. Nairn (Nairnshire)

Auldearn Antiques
Dalmore Manse, Lethen Rd. IV12 5HZ. Est. 1980. Open 10-6 including Sun. SIZE: Medium. *STOCK: Victorian linen and lace, kitchenalia, china, furniture, architectural items.* LOC: 1 mile from village. TEL: 01667 453087; home - same.

AYR (Ayrshire)

Antiques
39 New Rd. KA7 2PL. (T. Rafferty). Est. 1970. Open 10-5. *STOCK: General antiques.* TEL: 01292 265346.

BALFRON (Stirlingshire)

Amphora Galleries
16-18 Buchanan St. G63 0TT. (L. Ruglen). Resident. Est. 1961. Open 10-5.30 and by appointment. SIZE: Large. *STOCK: General antiques, furniture, decorative items.* LOC: A81. TEL: 01360 440329.

BALLATER (Aberdeenshire)

The McEwan Gallery
Bridge of Gairn. AB35 5UB. (D., P. and R. McEwan). LAPADA. Est. 1968. Open 10-5, Sun. 2-5, prior telephone call advisable during winter. SIZE: Medium. *STOCK: 18th-20th C British and European paintings, specialising in Scottish; rare and elusive polar, Scottish, golf, sporting and natural history books.* LOC: First house on the east side of A939 after its junction with A93 outside Ballater. PARK: Easy. TEL: 013397 55429; fax - 013397 55995. SER: Valuations; restorations (framing); buys at auction (paintings, watercolours, books); golf catalogues. VAT: Spec.

BARRHEAD, Nr. Glasgow (Renfrewshire)

C.P.R. Antiques and Services
96 Main St. G78 1SE. (C. Porterfield). Est. 1965. Open 10-1 and 1.30-5. CL: Tues. SIZE: Small. *STOCK: Brass, furniture and curios, 19th-20th C, to £3,000.* PARK: Easy. TEL: 0141 881 5379.

BEATTOCK (Dumfriesshire)

T.W. Beaty
Lochhouse Farm. DG10 9SG. Open for trade any time. SIZE: Large and warehouse. *STOCK: Furniture.* TEL: 01683 300451. VAT: Stan/Spec. *Trade only.*

BEAULY (Inverness-shire)

Iain Marr Antiques
3 Mid St. IV4 7DP. (I. and A. Marr). HADA. Est. 1975. Open 10.30-1 and 2-5.30. CL: Thurs. *STOCK: Silver, jewellery, clocks, porcelain, scientific instruments, arms, oils, watercolours, small furniture.* LOC: Off Square, on left going north (next to Coffee Shop). TEL: 01463 782372. VAT: Stan/Spec/Global.

BLAIRGOWRIE (Perthshire)

Blairgowrie Books
3 Meadow Place, Wellmeadow. PH10 6NQ. (Marlene Hughes). Est. 1982. Open 10.30-1 and 2-4.30, Sat. 10.30-5, Sun. by appointment. CL: Tues. SIZE: Medium. *STOCK: Books - mainly on Scottish fishing, shooting, hunting and climbing, £2.50-£150; children's and general.* LOC: Next to river Ericht, town centre. PARK: Easy. TEL: 01250 875855. SER: Valuations.

Roy Sim Antiques
The Granary Warehouse, Lower Mill St. PH10 6AQ. Est. 1977. Open 9-5.30, Sun. 12-5. SIZE: Large. *STOCK: Furniture, clocks, silver, EPNS, collectable, decorative and furnishing items.* TEL: 01250 873860.

BRIDGE OF EARN (Perthshire)

Imrie Antiques
Back St. PH2 9AE. (Mr and Mrs I. Imrie). LAPADA. Est. 1969. Open 10-1 and 2-5.30. SIZE: Large. *STOCK: Victorian and 18th C shipping goods.* PARK: Easy. TEL: 01738 812784. VAT: Stan.

BRODICK AND WHITING BAY (Isle of Arran)

Kames Antiques & Jewellery
Shore Rd. KA27 8AJ. (C.J. and J.M. Fieldhouse). Open 10-5. *STOCK: Furniture, porcelain, paintings, jewellery, collectables, objets d'art, silver and artists' materials.* TEL: 01770 302213.

CANONBIE, Nr. Carlisle (Dumfriesshire)

The Clock Showrooms
DG14 0SY. (John R. Mann). MBHI. Est. 1987. Open by appointment. SIZE: Large. *STOCK: Clocks - over 80 restored longcase, 17th-19th C, £2,500-£90,000; bracket, 17th-19th C, £3,500-£14,500; wall, 19th C, £500-£2,000.* LOC: Leave M6, junction 44, A7 north through Longtown, follow sign to village, premises next to Cross Keys Hotel. PARK: Easy. TEL: 013873 71337/71827; fax - 013873 71337; mobile - 07850 606147. SER: Valuations; restorations (clock movements, cases and dials); buys at auction (clocks). VAT: Stan.

CERES (Fife)

Ceres Antiques
1 High St. KY15. (Mrs E. Norrie). SIZE: Medium. *STOCK: General antiques, china.* PARK: Easy. TEL: 01334 828384.

Steeple Antiques
38 Main St. KY15 5NH. (Mrs Elizabeth Hart). Est. 1980. Open 2-5 including Sun., mornings by appointment. CL: Wed. pm. SIZE: Medium. *STOCK: Porcelain including some Wemyss, 1800-1950, £5-£500; cutlery, silver and plate, £5-£200+; Victorian linen, some furniture, £50-£400.* LOC: 3 miles from Cupar. PARK: Easy. TEL: Home - 01334 828553. SER: Valuations; buys at auction (silver, china and furniture).

CLOLA BY MINTLAW, Nr. Peterhead (Aberdeenshire)

Clola Antiques Centre
Shannas School House. AB42 5AE. (Joan and David Blackburn). Est. 1985. Open 10-5, Sun. 11-4.30 or by appointment. SIZE: Large - 10 dealers. *STOCK: Victorian and Edwardian furniture, antique and modern jewellery, collectables, china and militaria.* LOC: 3 miles south of Mintlaw and 25 miles north of Aberdeen on A952. PARK: Own. TEL: 01771 624584; fax - same. FAIRS: Aberdeen

COLDSTREAM (Berwickshire)

Coldstream Antiques
44 High St. TD12 4AS. (Mr and Mrs J. Trinder). Resident. Open daily. SIZE: Large. *STOCK: Furniture, 17th-20th C; general antiques, clocks, silver and shipping goods, 17th-19th C.* LOC: A697. TEL: 01890 882552. VAT: Stan/Spec.

Fraser Antiques
65 High St. TD12 4DL. Est. 1968. Open Tues.-Fri. 10-5, Sat. 9.30-12.30, other times by appointment. SIZE: Medium. *STOCK: Porcelain, glass, pictures, silver, small furniture, general antiques.* TEL: 01890 882450; fax - 01890 882451. SER: Valuations; restorations.

Hand in Hand
Hirsel Law Schoolhouse. (Mrs Ruth Hand). Est. 1969. Open by appointment. *STOCK: Paisley shawls, period costume, fine linens, quilts, curtains and interesting textiles.* TEL: 01890 883496; e-mail - ruth.hand@virgin.net; website - www.handinhand.uk.com.

COVE (Argyll & Bute)

Cove Curios
Shore Rd. G84 0LR. (R. and K.J. Young). Open daily May-Sept., other times by appointment. *STOCK: General antiques.* TEL: 01436 842222.

CROMARTY (Ross-shire)

Cromarty Antiques
24 Church St. IV7 8LY. (Jean and Jenny Henderson). Open summer - Thurs., Fri. and Sat. 10-5, Sun. 2-5, other days by appointment; winter - prior telephone call advisable. SIZE: Medium. *STOCK: Georgian, Victorian and Edwardian furniture, silver and porcelain.* LOC: On the Black Isle (just north of Inverness), follow signs for Cromarty from A9. PARK: Easy. TEL: 01381 600404; fax - 01381 610408; home - 01381 610264/269. SER: Buys at auction (as stock). VAT: Spec.

DORNOCH (Sutherland)

Castle Close Antiques
Castle Close. IV25 3SN. (Mrs J. Maclean). Est. 1982. Open 10-1 and 2-5. CL: Thurs. pm. SIZE: Medium. *STOCK: General antiques including furniture, stripped pine, porcelain, jewellery and silver, paintings.* PARK: Easy. TEL: 01862 810405; home - 01862 81057. VAT: Spec.

19th Century
BRITISH PORCELAIN

Fergus Gambon
Phillips

Figure 1.

Everywhere I go I hear the same complaint. The market just can't get enough good 19th century British porcelain. In London only Christie's South Kensington and Phillips in Bond Street have been able to offer regular sales, and the demand continues to exceed the supply. Prices for rarer and better quality lots have never been stronger, and overall the feeling is of great optimism.

The most important piece sold in London this year was the documentary Barr, Flight and Barr jug sold at Phillips for £62,100 in December 1998 (figure 2). Painted with a panel of shells and inscribed SS March 1807, the jug is one of just a handful of signed pieces painted by the artist Samuel Smith and is of great importance in attributing his work, having come down through the artist's family. The price is all the more remarkable considering the same jug had been sold by Phillips just nine years ago, in September 1989, for only £12,100. The trend is confirmed by the sale of a shell-painted coffee can, attributed to John Barker, for £2,415 at Phillips in May 1999. A similar can was sold in September 1996 for only £750. To prove that the magic ingredient isnot Worcester but shell decoration, two Coalport soup plates painted with shells, signed by Thomas Baxter and dated 1809 were sold in May for £6,210 each, whereas another signed and dated plate from the same series had only managed £3,450 in December 1997. On that occasion the shells were combined with other subjects.

The December sale at Phillips contained a good selection of Regency Worcester with other types of decoration. This also fared well with a pair of Barr, Flight and Barr triple spill vases reaching a hefty £20,700, while a garniture of three Flight, Barr and Barr vases sold for £7,820 in spite of damage. Away from the headline prices, a wide range of tea, dessert and dinnerwares sold for more modest prices, a topographical teacup and saucer making £633. Sotheby's special sale of Welsh and Regency Porcelain on 9th June 1998 contained a similar selection with prices in the hundreds rather than thousands. The 'set pattern' and later landscape-decorated pieces now look very cheap compared with their more glamorous relations and prices seem to have remained constant for some time.

Moving north from Worcestershire to Derbyshire, the small and short-lived factory at Pinxton is as popular as ever. A growing number of collectors compete for the few pieces that come up for sale and

Figure 2.

prices are rising rapidly. Teawares with standard patterns can fetch more than ten times as much as similar pieces from Staffordshire. Coffee cans of pattern 221, painted with oval landscape panels, were making £690 each in June 1998 and £1,265 in May 1999 at Phillips. The story is different with the porcelain made nearby at Derby. A good selection was offered at Sotheby's Regency sale with items making predictable rather than sensational prices. Notable was a dessert service painted with hunting scenes which made £27,600, but that was for 57 pieces. Phillips' sale of 4th June 1998 contained some good Derby pieces from the collection of the late Major Guy Dawnay, many of which were illustrated in John Twitchett's standard work on the subject. In spite of the provenance there were few surprises. The stable rather than excitable nature of the market was confirmed at the Bonhams sale on 2nd December 1998, where several of the more highly priced lots remained unsold and most others sold within estimate. It is still possible to buy finely decorated Derby tablewares for £200 or £300, a fact that I hope will start to tempt new collectors.

The two major offerings of Welsh porcelain were at Phillips and Sotheby's in June 1998. With 137 lots to choose from and few left unsold, the market showed it is strong enough to absorb a substantial number of items in one go. As a general rule, prices have yet to return to the levels seen in the late 1980s and early '90s. However, Sotheby's achieved £6,900 for a rare Nantgarw plate London-decorated in the Sèvres style that had sold in the same rooms in June 1990 for £2,470. A fine Swansea comport painted by Henry Morris with the arms of Clark of Hereford impaling Parkinson made a very impressive £10,580 and plates from the 'Lysaght' service made £1,897 and £1,840 each, a similar price to that achieved in the Sir Lesley Joseph sale back in 1992. Phillips' sale included a number of London-decorated Nantgarw plates from the 'Mackintosh' service (figure 3), making between £2,470 and £2,705 each, and a fine London-decorated Nantgarw cabinet plate painted with 'Pliny's Doves' made £5,410. A similar plate in the Lesley Joseph sale had achieved £7,700.

Very little Rockingham porcelain has been offered in the last year to tempt collectors of this very individual Yorkshire factory. A few of the items that have appeared were of great importance and achieved record prices. Most important was the pineapple comport from the service made for William IV and sold by Neales in Nottingham for £17,250, a record price for a single piece of Rockingham porcelain. By coincidence, a wine cooler from the same service appeared at Christie's King Street on the same day. Its provenance was impeccable as it was part of their sale of contents from Wentworth Woodhouse, home of 4th Earl Fitzwilliam and sponsor of the factory. It realised £14,950. Rockingham porcelain without a Royal connection is naturally far

Figure 3.

cheaper, but there is still a shortage resulting in buoyant prices.

In other factories, an historic provenance is just as important. A Coalport plate presented to Nelson in 1802 was sold at Phillips in May 1999 for £5,750 against a more cautious estimate of £2,500-£3,000 (figure 1). The estimate was based on a similar example sold in the same rooms on 6th December 1995 for only £2,185. I believe such price increases are the result of a greater number of private buyers present in the salerooms. Despite this, the market is extremely price sensitive. Most of the spectacular prices I have been quoting are for pieces fresh to the market. Give a piece a recent 'trade history' and it's a different story.

Away from the high prices, there is a wide range of highly decorative early and mid 19th

century porcelain still available at reasonable prices. Alcock, Coalport, Davenport, Daniel, Minton, New Hall, Ridgway and Spode are all plentiful and many fine teacups and saucers are available at prices below £200. A selection from the sale at Phillips in December 1998 is shown in figure 4. Prices have been constant for some years and nice cups and saucers represent very good value considering their age and quality of manufacture. Incredibly, full tea services in neo-rococo style by more minor Staffordshire factories, dating from the 1830s and 1840s, can fetch as little as £100.

This article appeared in the July/ August 1999 issue of **Antique Collecting** *magazine. For more details and to subscribe see page 147.*

Figure 4

Little Treasures

Shore Rd. IV25 3LS. (Allison Taylor). Est. 1993. Open 10-5, Sun. 12-4 (summer only). SIZE: Small. *STOCK: Jewellery, ceramics and glass, 19th-20th C, £5-£1,000.* LOC: Just off Cathedral Sq, road opposite Tourist Information. PARK: Easy. TEL: 01862 811175. SER: Valuations.

DOUNE (Stirlingshire)

Scottish Antique & Arts Centre

(Robert Templeman). Open 10-5 including Sun. SIZE: Large. *STOCK: General antiques.* LOC: A84 Stirling to Callander road, 1 mile north of Doune. PARK: Easy. TEL: 01786 841203; fax - 01786 842070. VAT: Stan./Spec.

DRUMNADROCHIT (Inverness-shire)

Joan Frere Antiques

Drumbuie House. IV3. (Mrs J. Frere). Open daily 9-8 May-October, other times by appointment. SIZE: Medium. *STOCK: Furniture especially English oak, pre-1800.* Not Stocked: Victoriana, reproductions. LOC: On Loch Ness just before Drumnadrochit village, on A82. PARK: Easy. TEL: 01456 450210; home - same.

DUNDEE (Angus)

Angus Antiques

4 St. Andrews St. DD1 2EX. Est. 1964. Open 10-4. CL: Sat. *STOCK: Militaria, badges, medals, swords, jewellery, silver, gold, collectors items, Art Nouveau, Art Deco, advertising and decorative items, tins, toys, teddy bears.* TEL: 01382 322128.

Neil Livingstone

3 Old Hawkhill. DD2 1LS. LAPADA. Open any time by appointment. SIZE: Large. *STOCK: Jewellery, Continental furniture and decorative items, 18th-20th C.* TEL: 01382 907788/221751; fax - 01382 566332; mobile - 07775 877715; e-mail - neil@westportgallery.sagehost.co.uk. SER: Shipping worldwide.

Westport Gallery

48 Westport. DD1 5ER. Est. 1976. Open 9-5. SIZE: Medium. *STOCK: Antique jewellery.* LOC: City centre end of Perth Road, turn into Tay St. and bear left, shop on the left. PARK: Easy. TEL: 01382 221751; fax - 01382 229707. SER: Valuations; jewellery repairs. VAT: Stan/Spec.

DUNECHT (Aberdeenshire)

The Magic Lantern

Nether Corskie. AB32 7EL. (Mr and Mrs P. Whyte). Est. 1978. SIZE: Medium. *STOCK: Georgian and Victorian furniture, £500-£1,000; silver and plate Victorian cutlery, £50-£100; china, porcelain, Scottish pottery, candlesticks, £25-£100.* LOC: A944, turn towards Kintore. PARK: Easy. TEL: 01330 860678; home - same. SER: Restorations (china).

DUNKELD (Perthshire)

Dunkeld Antiques

Tay Terrace. PH8 0AQ. (D. Dytch). LAPADA. Est. 1986. Open 10-5.30, Sun. 12-5.30. SIZE: Large. *STOCK: 18th-19th C items especially dining furniture, decorative boxes and clocks, Japanese ceramics, shooting and fishing memorabilia, out-of-print books.* LOC: Converted church, overlooking Tay river. PARK: Easy. TEL: 01350 728832; fax - 01350 727008. VAT: Spec.

EDINBURGH (Midlothian)

Antiques

48 Thistle St. EH2 1EN. (E. Humphrey). Est. 1946. Open 10-4, Sat. 10-12.30 or by appointment. *STOCK: Paintings, glass, china, curios, postcards.* TEL: 0131 226 3625.

Armchair Books

72 West Port. EH1 2LE. (David Gavan). Est. 1993. Open 12-5 and some Sun. SIZE: Small. *STOCK: Books, secondhand and Victorian, £2-£50.* LOC: West from Grassmarket. PARK: Nearby. TEL: 0131 229 5927. SER: Valuations; restorations (books).

Paddy Barrass

15 The Grassmarket. EH1 2HS. Est. 1974. Open 12-6, Sat. 10.30-5.30, Sun. in Aug. 2-7. SIZE: Small. *STOCK: Period clothing, textiles and household linen, 19th-20th C, £5-£500.* LOC: South side of High St., directly below castle. PARK: Easy. TEL: 0131 226 3087; website - www.vintagelinens.co.uk. SER: Valuations.

Bebes et Jouets

c/o Lochend Post Office. EH7 6HW. Est. 1988. Open by appointment only. SIZE: Small. *STOCK: Fine French and German dolls, vintage teddy bears, dolls' houses and miniature doll-related items, dolls' clothing and accessories.* LOC: 1/2 mile from Princes Street. PARK: Easy. TEL: 0131 332 5650; e-mail - bebesetjouets@u.genie.co.uk; website - www.you.genie.co.uk/bebesetjouets. SER: Photographs and videos of stock available.

Berland's of Edinburgh
143 Gilmore Place. EH3 9PW. (R. Melvin). Open
9-5. *STOCK: Restored antique light fittings.* TEL:
0131 228 6760.

Laurance Black Ltd   BADA
**60 Thistle St. EH2 1EN. Open 10.15-4.30, Sat.
10.15-1. SIZE: Small.** *STOCK: Scottish
furniture and decorative items, £50-£10,000;
glass, pottery, textiles, tartanware and treen,
18th-19th C.* **TEL: 0131 220 3387. VAT: Spec.**

Joseph Bonnar, Jewellers
72 Thistle St. EH2 1EN. Open 10.30-5 or by
appointment. SIZE: Medium. *STOCK: Antique
and period jewellery.* LOC: Parallel with Princes
St. TEL: 0131 226 2811; fax - 0131 225 9438.
VAT: Stan/Spec.

Bourne Fine Art Ltd
6 Dundas St. EH3 6HZ. (P. Bourne). Est. 1978.
Open 10-6, Sat. 11-2. SIZE: Medium. *STOCK:
British paintings, 1700-1950.* PARK: Easy. TEL:
0131 557 4050. SER: Valuations; restorations;
buys at auction; framing. VAT: Stan/Spec.

Broughton Books
2A Broughton Place. EH1 3RX. (P. Galinsky).
Est. 1964. Open 12-6, Sat. 10.30-5.30. CL: Mon.
SIZE: Medium. *STOCK: Books, secondhand and
antiquarian, £2.50-£250.* LOC: Off Broughton
St, close to Waverley station and top of Leith
Walk. TEL: 0131 557 8010; home - 0131 478
0614.

Calton Gallery   BADA
**10 Royal Terr. EH7 5AB. (A.G. Whitfield).
Est. 1979. Open 10-6, Sat. by appointment.
SIZE: Large.** *STOCK: Paintings, especially
Scottish marine and watercolours, £100-
£100,000; prints, £10-£1,000; sculpture, to
£20,000; all 19th to early 20th C.* **PARK: Easy.
TEL: 0131 556 1010; home - same; fax - 0131
558 1150. SER: Valuations; restorations (oils,
watercolours, prints); buys at auction
(paintings). VAT: Stan/Spec.**

The Carson Clark Gallery - Scotland's Map Heritage Centre
181-183 Canongate, The Royal Mile. EH8 8BN.
(A. Carson Clark). FRGS, FBCartS. Est. 1969.
Open 10.30-5.30. *STOCK: Maps, sea charts and
prints.* TEL: 0131 556 4710; fax - same; e-mail -
scotmap@aol.com. SER: Collections valued and
purchased.

The Collectors Shop
49 Cockburn St. EH1 1BS. (D. Cavanagh). Est.
1960. Open 11-5. *STOCK: Coins, medals,
militaria, cigarette and postcards, small
collectors' items, jewellery, silver and plate.* Not
Stocked: Postage stamps. TEL: 0131 226 3391.
SER: Buys at auction.

Craiglea Clocks
88 Comiston Rd. EH10 5QJ. (R.J. Rafter). Est.
1978. Open 10-5. CL: Mon. SIZE: Small.
STOCK: Antique clocks and barometers. LOC:
On Biggar road from Morningside. PARK:
Adjacent streets. TEL: 0131 452 8568. SER:
Restorations (clocks and barometers).

Da Capo Antiques
68 Henderson Row. EH3 5BJ. (Nick Carter). Est.
1975. Open Tues.-Sat. 10.30-5.30. SIZE: Small.
*STOCK: General antiques including brass
bedsteads and lighting, 18th to early 20th C,
£500-£1,000.* LOC: Off Dundas St. PARK: Easy.
TEL: 0131 557 1918; home - 0131 557 3621.
SER: Valuations; restorations (furniture including
upholstery). VAT: Spec.

Alan Day Antiques
25A Moray Place. EH3 6DA. LAPADA. Open by
appointment only. *STOCK: Furniture, paintings,
18th-19th C; general antiques.* TEL: 0131 225
2590.

A.F. Drysdale Ltd
35 and 20 North West Circus Place. EH3 6TW.
Est. 1974. Open 9.30-1 and 2-6. *STOCK: Quality
Continental reproduction lamps, decorative
furniture; antique prints.* TEL: 0131 225 4686.
VAT: Stan.

George Duff Antiques
254 Leith Walk. EH6 5EL. Open by appointment.
STOCK: Shipping goods, pre-1940. TEL: 0131
554 8164; home - 0131 337 1422. VAT: Stan.
Export Only.

Dunedin Antiques Ltd
4 North West Circus Place. EH3 6ST. (D. Ingram
and Theresa Ingram). Est. 1973. Open 10.30-1
and 2.30-5. SIZE: Large. *STOCK: Furniture,
period items, chimney pieces, architectural
fittings, 18th-19th C, £100-£15,000.* LOC: From
Princes St. down Frederick St. PARK: Easy.
TEL: 0131 220 1574; fax - same; home - 0131
556 8140; website - www.dunedinantiques.com.
SER: Valuations; buys at auction (furniture,
weapons). VAT: Stan/Spec.

EASY - Edinburgh & Glasgow Architectural Salvage Yards
Unit 6, Couper St., Off Coburg St., Leith. EH6
6HH. Est. 1985. Open 9-5. SIZE: Large. *STOCK:
Fireplaces, stained glass, roll-top baths.* TEL:
0131 554 7077.

An early, rudimentary manual glass press, c.1845, illustrated in Apsley Pellatt's Curiosities in Glassmaking, 1849. This model was based on Pellatt's 1831 patent covering 'a machine for pressing glass by the mode lately introduced from America'.

The invention of mechanically pressed glass in the late 1820s remains the most revolutionary development in glassmaking since ancient Rome. Rendering obsolete, or automating, production practices that had remained virtually unchanged since time immemorial, pressing enabled the working classes to own glassware for the first time. From an article entitled '19th Century Pressed Glass' by Andy McConnell which appeared in the November 2000 issue of **Antique Collecting** magazine. For more details and to subscribe see page 147.

Edinburgh Coin Shop
11 West Crosscauseway. EH8 9JW. (T.D. Brown). Open 10-5. *STOCK: Coins, medals, badges, militaria, postcards, cigarette cards, stamps, jewellery, clocks and watches, general antiques, bullion dealers.* TEL: 0131 668 2928/667 9095; fax - 0131 668 2926. VAT: Stan.

Donald Ellis incorporating Bruntsfield Clocks
7 Bruntsfield Place. EH10 4HN. (D.G. and C.M. Ellis). Est. 1970. Open 9.30-5.30. CL: Wed. pm. *STOCK: Clocks and general antiques.* LOC: Opposite Links Garage at Bruntsfield Links. PARK: Nearby. TEL: 0131 229 4720. SER: Clock repairs.

Georgian Antiques
10 Pattison St., Leith Links. EH6 7HF. LAPADA. Est. 1976. Open 8.30-5.30, Sat. 10-2. SIZE: 2 large warehouses. *STOCK: Furniture, Georgian, Victorian, inlaid, Edwardian; shipping goods, smalls, £10-£10,000.* LOC: Off Leith Links. PARK: Easy. TEL: 0131 553 7286 (24 hrs.); fax - 0131 553 6299; e-mail - georgianantiques@ btconnect.com; website - www.georgianantiques. net. SER: Valuations; restorations; buys at auction; packing; shipping; courier. VAT: Stan/Spec.

Gladrags
17 Henderson Row. EH3 5DH. (Kate Cameron). Est. 1977. Open Tues.-Sat. 10.30-6. *STOCK: Period clothes, linen, lace, beadwork, silk and paisley shawls, costume jewellery, silks and satins, cashmeres and accessories.* TEL: 0131 557 1916.

Goodwin's Antiques Ltd
15-16 Queensferry St. and 106A-108 Rose St. EH2 4QW. Est. 1952. Open 9-5.30, Sat. 9-5. SIZE: Medium. *STOCK: Antique and modern silver and jewellery.* LOC: Off Princes St., west end. TEL: 0131 225 4717; fax - 0131 220 1412; Rose St. - 0131 220 1230. VAT: Stan/Spec.

Harlequin Antiques
30 Bruntsfield Place. EH10 4HJ. (C. S. Harkness). Est. 1995. Open 10-5 and Sun. (Dec. only) 12-4. SIZE: Small. *STOCK: Clocks, silver, ceramics, small furniture, £25-£3,000.* LOC: 2 miles south of Princes St. (west end). PARK: Easy. TEL: 0131 228 9446. SER: Valuations; restorations (clocks); buys at auction (clocks).

Hawkins & Hawkins
9 Atholl Crescent. EH3 8HA. (Emma H. Hawkins). Resident. Est. 1989. Open by appointment only. SIZE: Medium. *STOCK: Taxidermy, 1890-1920, £100-£10,000; English furniture, 1800-1910, £500-£100,000.* LOC: Off Princes St. PARK: Easy. TEL: 0131 229 2828; fax - 0131 229 2128. FAIRS: Olympia (June). VAT: Spec/Stan.

Holyrood Architectural Salvage
Holyrood Business Park, 146 Duddingston Rd. West. EH16 4AP. (Ken Fowler). Est. 1993. Open 9-5. SIZE: Large. *STOCK: Georgian to reproduction fireplaces; rolltop and canopy baths; panelled doors.* LOC: 2 mins from Duddingston village - telephone for directions. PARK: Easy. TEL: 0131 661 9305; fax - 0131 656 9404. SER: Restorations (baths). VAT: Stan/Spec.

Gordon Inglis Antiques
8 Barclay Terrace. EH10 4HP. Est. 1990. Open 1-5, Tues., Thurs. and Sun. by appointment. SIZE:

Small. *STOCK: British art and studio pottery including Doulton, Minton and especially Scottish hand-painted pottery - Wemyss, Bough and MacMerry, £200-£1,000.* LOC: 5 minutes from castle and Princes St. PARK: Easy. TEL: 0131 221 1192; fax - same; mobile - 07966 505219; website - www.inglisantiques.com. SER: Valuations; worldwide free delivery. FAIRS: Hopetoun House, Pollock House, Prestonfield and local.

Allan K. L. Jackson
67 Causewayside. EH9 1QF. Est. 1974. Open 10-6. SIZE: Medium. *STOCK: General small antiques, from Victorian, £5-100.* PARK: Easy. TEL: 0131 668 4532; mobile - 07989 236443. SER: Valuations.

Kaimes Smithy Antiques
79 Howdenhall Rd. EH14 2LQ. (J. Lynch). Est. 1972. Open 1.30-5. CL: Mon. and Thurs. SIZE: Medium. *STOCK: Furniture, clocks, porcelain, glass, paintings, curios, 18th-20th C, £10-£3,000.* LOC: From City bypass take A701 (at Straiton junction) into city centre, located at 1st set of traffic lights. PARK: Easy. TEL: 0131 441 2076/664 0124. SER: Valuations; restorations.

London Road Antiques
15 Earlston Place, London Rd. EH7 5SU. (R. Forrest and T. Hardie). Open 10-5, Sun. 1-5. SIZE: Large + trade store. *STOCK: Georgian, Victorian and stripped pine furniture.* TEL: 0131 652 2790; e-mail - LRA@19thC.com; website - www.19thC.com.

J. Martinez Antiques
17 Brandon Terrace. EH3 5DZ. Est. 1975. Open 11-5. SIZE: Small. *STOCK: Clocks, jewellery and general antiques, mainly Victorian, £50-£1,000.* LOC: Off Dundas St. PARK: Easy. TEL: 0131 558 8720; fax - same. SER: Valuations; restorations (porcelain, clocks and watches); buys at auction. FAIRS: Midland Clock & Watch, NEC; Antique Clock & Watch, Haydock Park; Ingliston, Edinburgh; Freemasons Hall, Edinburgh.

John Mathieson and Co
48 Frederick St. EH2 1EX. Open 9-5.30, Sat. 9-4.30. *STOCK: Paintings, watercolours, prints.* TEL: 0131 225 6798. SER: Restorations (framing, gilding). VAT: Stan/Spec.

McNaughtan's Bookshop
3a and 4a Haddington Place. EH7 4AE. Est. 1957. Open 9.30-5.30. CL: Mon. *STOCK: Antiquarian books.* TEL: 0131 556 5897; fax - 0131 556 8220.

Montresor
35 St. Stephen St. EH3 5AH. (Pierre De Fresne and Gareth Jones). Est. 1989. Open 10.30-1 and 2-6. SIZE: Small. *STOCK: Costume and designer jewellery, 1850-1950, £50-£200; Art Deco and Art Nouveau lighting, china and glass, £50-£1,000.* LOC: North from Princes St. to Stockbridge. PARK: Easy. TEL: 0131 220 6877. SER: Valuations; restorations (paste jewellery).

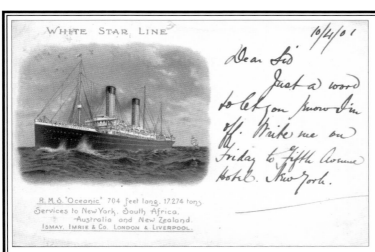

A White Star card by Charles Dixon from 1901.

From an article entitled 'Ocean Liner Postcards and Marine Art' by Robert Wall which appeared in the February 2001 issue of **Antique Collecting** magazine. For more details and to subscribe see page 147.

T. and J. W. Neilson Ltd
76 Coburg St., Leith. EH6 6HJ. (J. and A. Neilson). Est. 1932. Open 9.30-5, Sat. 9.30-4. SIZE: Large. *STOCK: Fireplaces, 18th-20th C, £100-£20,000; interiors, stoves, fenders, fire irons; marble (including French), wood and stone chimney pieces.* LOC: Continuation of Ferry Rd. PARK: Own. TEL: 0131 554 4704; fax - 0131 555 2071; website - www.chimneypiece.co.uk. SER: Installations (fireplaces). VAT: Stan.

Now and Then (Toy Centre)
7 and 9 West Crosscauseway. EH8 9JW. Usually open from 2.30 pm, prior telephone call advisable. *STOCK: Telephones, tin and diecast toys, clockwork and electric model trains, collectable mechanical ephemera, automobilia, juvenalia, clocks, gold and silver watches, small furniture, old advertisements, bric-a-brac.* LOC: City centre off A68. PARK: Nearby. TEL: 0131 668 2927; evenings - 0131 226 2867; mobile - 07976 360283; e-mail - nowandthenuk@aol.com. SER: Valuations; buys at auction.

Open Eye Gallery Ltd
75/79 Cumberland St. EH3 6RD. (T. and P. Wilson). Est. 1976. Open 10-6, Sat. 10-4. SIZE: Medium. *STOCK: Early 20th C etchings, contemporary paintings, ceramics and jewellery.* LOC: From Princes St. go east, left into Frederick St. right at bottom of hill. PARK: Easy. TEL: 0131 557 1020. SER: Valuations; restorations (paintings and ceramics); buys at auction. VAT: Mainly Spec.

H. Parry
Castle Antiques, 330 Lawnmarket. EH1 2PN. *STOCK: Silver, porcelain, English and Continental furniture, clocks.* TEL: 0131 225 7615.

R.L. Rose Oriental Carpets Ltd
8 Howe St. EH3 6TD. Open 10-6. *STOCK: Antique and fine old Oriental rugs and carpets.* TEL: 0131 225 8785. SER: Repair; cleaning.

Royal Mile Curios
363 High St. EH1 1PW. (L. Bosi and R. Eprile). Open 10.30-5. *STOCK: Jewellery and silver.* TEL: 0131 226 4050.

Royal Mile Gallery
272 Canongate, Royal Mile. EH8 8AA. (J. A. Smith). Est. 1970. Open 11.30-5. SIZE: Medium. *STOCK: Maps, engravings, etchings and lithographs.* LOC: Between castle and Holyrood Palace. PARK: New Street. TEL: 0131 558 1702; home - 0131 668 4007; e-mail james@royalmile gallery.co uk. SER: Valuations; restorations; framing; buys at auction.

James Scott
43 Dundas St. EH3 6JN. Est. 1964. Open 11-1 and 2-5.30. CL: Thurs. pm. *STOCK: Curiosities, unusual items, silver, jewellery, small furniture.* TEL: 0131 556 8260; home - 0131 332 0617. VAT: Stan.

The Scottish Gallery
16 Dundas St. EH3 6HZ. (Aitken Dott Ltd). Est. 1842. Open 10-6, Sat. 10-4. *STOCK: 20th C and contemporary Scottish paintings and contemporary crafts.* LOC: New Town. TEL: 0131 558 1200. VAT: Stan/Spec.

Second Edition
9 Howard St. EH3 5JP. (Mr and Mrs W.A. Smith). Est. 1978. Open 12-5.30, Sat. 9.30-5.30. SIZE: Medium. *STOCK: Antiquarian and secondhand books, £7-£500; maps and prints, £7-£75; all late 19th to early 20th C.* LOC: 200 yards south of Royal Botanical Gardens. PARK: Nearby. TEL: 0131 556 9403; home - 0131 552 1850. SER: Valuations; book-binding.

The Talish Gallery
168 Canongate. EH8 8DF. (John R. Martin). Est. 1970. Open 11-3. SIZE: Medium. *STOCK: Silver, plate, collectors' items, rugs, pictures, small furniture, £10-£10,000.* LOC: Bottom of Royal Mile, opposite clock. PARK: Easy. TEL: 0131 557 8435. SER: Valuations. VAT: Spec.

The Thrie Estaits
49 Dundas St. EH3 6RS. Est. 1970. Open Tues.-Sat. *STOCK: Pottery, porcelain, glass, paintings and prints, unusual and decorative items, some furniture.* TEL: 0131 556 7084.

Trinity Curios
4-6 Stanley Rd.,Trinity. (Alan Ferguson). Resident. Est. 1987. Open 10-5, Wed. and Sat. 12-6, Sun. 2-5. CL: Mon. SIZE: Medium. *STOCK: Furniture, ceramics and silver, 19th C, £50-£1,000.* LOC: From Ferry Rd. turn north on to Newhaven Rd., shop 300 yards on left. PARK: Easy. TEL: 0131 552 8481. SER: Restorations (furniture including upholstery; china). VAT: Stan.

Unicorn Antiques
65 Dundas St. EH3 6RS. (N. Duncan). Est. 1967. Usually open 11-6. SIZE: Medium. *STOCK: Architectural and domestic brassware, lights, mirrors, glass, china, cutlery and bric-a-brac. Not Stocked: Weapons, coins, jewellery.* LOC: From Princes St. turn into Hanover St. Dundas St. is a continuation of Hanover St. TEL: 0131 556 7176; home - 0131 332 9135.

John Whyte
116b Rose St. EH2 3JF. Est. 1928. Open 9.30-5.15, Sat. 9.30-5. STOCK: Jewellery, watches, clocks and silver. TEL: 0131 225 2140. VAT: Stan.

Whytock and Reid
Sunbury House, Belford Mews. EH4 3DN. (D.C. Reid). Est. 1807. Open 9-5.30, Sat. 10-2. SIZE: Large. STOCK: Furniture, English and Continental, 18th-19th C, £50-£20,000; Eastern rugs, carpets, £50-£10,000. LOC: 1/2 mile from West End, off Belford Rd. PARK: Own. TEL: 0131 226 4911; fax - 0131 226 4595; e-mail - @whytock-and-reid.demon.co.uk. SER: Restorations (furniture, rugs); buys at auction; interiors. VAT: Stan/Spec.

Wild Rose Antiques
15 Henderson Row. EH3 5DH. (K. and E. Cameron). Est. 1975. Open Tues.-Sat. 10.30-6. STOCK: General antiques - silver, jewellery, glass, pottery, porcelain, small furniture, objects, Paisley shawls, brassware. TEL: 0131 557 1916.

Anthony Woodd Gallery
4 Dundas St. EH3 6HZ. Est. 1981. Open 10-6, Sat. 11-4. STOCK: Scottish landscape, sporting and military pictures. TEL: 0131 558 9544/5; fax - 0131 558 9525; e-mail - sales@anthonywoodd.com; website - www.anthonywoodd.com. SER: Valuations; restorations; buys at auction; framing. VAT: Spec.

Young Antiques
185 Bruntsfield Place. EH10 4DG. (T.C. Young). Est. 1979. Open 10.30-1.30 and from 2.30. CL: Wed. pm. SIZE: Medium. STOCK: Victorian and Edwardian furniture, £50-£1,000; ceramics, £20-£2,000; Persian rugs, oils and watercolours, £50-£1,500. PARK: Easy. TEL: 0131 229 1361. SER: Valuations; buys at auction (Persian rugs, art pottery).

ELGIN (Morayshire)

West End Antiques
35 High St. IV30 1EE. (F. Stewart). HADA. Est. 1969. Open 9.30-12.30 and 1.45-4.30, Wed. 9.30-12.30. STOCK: Silver, clocks and watches, jewellery and bric-a-brac. TEL: 01343 547531; home - 01343 543216/812556.

FAIRLIE (Ayrshire)

Fairlie Antique Shop
86 Main Rd. KA29 0AD. (E.A. Alvarino). Est. 1976. Open Thurs.-Sat. 12-5. SIZE: Small.

STOCK: Ornaments, £10-£1,000; small furniture, clocks and silver, £50-£2,000; jewellery; all Victorian or Edwardian. LOC: A78. PARK: 25yds. TEL: 01475 568613. SER: Valuations.

FENTON BARNS, Nr. North Berwick (East Lothian)

Deco by Design
Unit 4, Turkey-Torium. EH39 5BW. (Bob Dobbie and Hazel Roberts). Est. 1990. Open Sat. 10.30-4.30, Sun. 11-4.30, other days by appointment. SIZE: Large. STOCK: Art Deco furniture and lighting, £40-£3,500; general antiques, 19th-20th C, £5-£500. LOC: 17 miles east of Edinburgh, off A1 - follow signs for Drem and Fenton Barns. PARK: Easy. TEL: 0402 059315; home - 0131 669 5771. SER: Valuations; buys at auction (Art Deco). FAIRS: Ingliston, Edinburgh. VAT: Stan.

FOCHABERS (Morayshire)

Antiques (Fochabers)
22 The Square. IV32. (J. and M.L. Holstead). Est. 1983. Open 10.15-5. SIZE: Medium. STOCK: General collectables, Oriental, clocks including longcase, from 18th C oak to 1930's. PARK: Easy. TEL: 01343 820838; home - 01343 820572. FAIRS: Tree Tops.

Country Collectables
22 The Square. IV32. (A. Holstead). Open 10-1 and 2-5. STOCK: Pine furniture and collectables. PARK: Easy. TEL: 01303 820838; home - 01340 831663. FAIRS: Treetops, Aberdeen.

Pringle Antiques
High St. IV32 7EP. (G. A. Christie). Est. 1983. Open 10.30-4.30 April-Sept. SIZE: Medium. STOCK: Furniture, Victorian, £20-£5,000; general antiques, pictures, brass, pottery, silver and jewellery. Not Stocked: Books and clothing. LOC: A96, premises are a converted church. PARK: Easy. TEL: 01343 821204; home - 01343 820599. VAT: Stan/Spec.

Marianne Simpson
61/63 High St. IV32 7DU. (M.R. Simpson). Est. 1990. Open Easter-Oct: Mon.-Sat. 10-1 and 2-4; Oct.-Easter: Tues., Thurs., Sat. 10-1 and 2-4, or by appointment. SIZE: Small. STOCK: Books and ephemera, 19th-20th C, £1-£100. LOC: A96. PARK: Easy. TEL: 01343 821192; home - same.

Minton majolica tureen, 1864, 11in. high.

From an article entitled 'A Christmas Gallimaufry' by Sally Kevill-Davies which appeared in the December 1998/January 1999 issue of **Antique Collecting** magazine. For more details and to subscribe see page 147.

FORFAR (Angus)

Gow Antiques
Pitscandly Farm. DD8 3NZ. (Jeremy Gow). BAFRA. Est. 1986. Open by appointment. SIZE: Medium. *STOCK: 17th-19th C furniture, £50-£10,000.* LOC: 3 miles off A90, take B9134 out of Forfar, through Lunenhead, first right after Myreside village sign, premises next left, in farmyard. PARK: Easy. TEL: 01307 465342; mobile - 07711 416786; e-mail - jeremy@ gowantiques.co.uk; website - www.gowantiques. co.uk.

FORRES (Morayshire)

Michael Low Antiques
45 High St. IV36 2PB. Est. 1967. TEL: 01309 673696. VAT: Stan.

FRIOCKHEIM, Nr. Arbroath (Angus)

M.J. and D. Barclay
29 Gardyne St. DD11 4SQ. Est. 1965. Open 2-5.30. CL: Thurs. *STOCK: General antiques including furniture, jewellery, silver, porcelain and clocks.* Not Stocked: Stamps, books, coins. PARK: Easy. TEL: 01241 828265. VAT: Stan.

GLASGOW (Lanarkshire)

All Our Yesterdays
6 Park Rd., Kelvinbridge. G4 9JG. (Susie Robinson). Est. 1989. Open 11.30-5.30. SIZE: Small. *STOCK: Kitchenalia, mainly 1850-1949, £5-£500; smalls, especially decorative arts, advertising related items, books, etchings and postcards, mechanical items, crystals and minerals, smokers sundries and oddities, to £500.* LOC: Near junction with Gt. Western Rd. and university. PARK: Easy. TEL: 0141 334 7788; answerphone/fax - 0141 339 8994; e-mail - antiques@allouryesterdays.fsnet.co.uk. SER: Valuations; buys at auction; search and hire.

E.A. Alvariño - Antiques
13 Radnor St., Kelvingrove. G3 7UA. Est. 1976. Open Mon.-Fri. 1-5. *STOCK: Furniture, 18th-19th C, £50-£5,000; silver and ornaments, pictures, jewellery, clocks and instruments.* LOC: Near Kelvingrove Art Gallery & Museum. PARK: Easy. TEL: 0141 334 1213; e-mail - sales@ alvarinoantiques.com. SER: Valuations; restorations; buys at auction.

The Antiques Warehouse
Unit 3b, Yorkhill Quay Estate. G3 8QE. (P. Mangan). Open 9-5, Sat. 10-5, Sun. 12-5. SIZE:

19 dealers. *STOCK: Antique pine, Oriental rugs and carpets, general antiques, furnishings, smalls and fine arts.* TEL: 0141 334 4924. SER: Import and export worldwide.

The Roger Billcliffe Fine Art
134 Blythswood St. G2 4EL. Est. 1876. Open 9.30-5.30, Sat. 10-1. SIZE: Large. *STOCK: British paintings, watercolours, drawings, sculpture, especially Scottish, from 1850; jewellery, metalwork, glass and woodwork.* TEL: 0141 332 4027; fax - 0141 332 6573. VAT: Spec.

Brown's Clocks
13 Radnor St., Kelvingrove. G3 7UA. (J. Wilson and J. Cairns). Est. 1933. Open 9.30-5, Sat. 10.30-12.30. *STOCK: Fine clocks and barometers.* TEL: 0141 334 6308. SER: Restorations.

Butler's Furniture Galleries
191 Scotland St. G5 8PL. (Laurence Butler). Open 10-5 or by appointment. CL: Sat. *STOCK: Georgian, Victorian and Edwardian furnishings.* TEL: 0141 429 8808/639 3396. SER: Valuations; restorations; repolishing.

The Den of Antiquity
Langside Lane, 539 Victoria Rd., Queenspark. G42 8BH. Est. 1960. Open 9.30-5.30, Sun. 12-5. *STOCK: General antiques, especially pine.* TEL: 0141 423 7122; evenings - 0141 644 5860; e-mail - AntiquityGlasgow@aol.com; website - www.denofantiquity.co.uk. VAT: Stan/Spec.

James Forrest and Co (Jewellers) Ltd
53 West Nile St. G1 2QB. Est. 1957. CL: Sat. pm. *STOCK: Silver, jewellery, clocks.* LOC: City centre. TEL: 0141 221 0494. VAT: Stan.

A.D. Hamilton and Co
7 St. Vincent Place. G1 2DW. (Jeffrey Lee Fineman). Est. 1890. Open 9-5.15. SIZE: Small. *STOCK: Jewellery and silver, 19th to early 20th C, £100-£3,000; British coins, medals and banknotes, £10-£1,000.* LOC: City centre, next to George Square. PARK: Meters. TEL: 0141 221 5423; fax - 0141 248 6019. SER: Valuations. VAT: Stan/Spec.

Kollectables
51 Parnie St., Trongate. G1 5LU. Est. 1984. Open Tues.-Sat. 10-5. *STOCK: Edwardian postcards, cigarette cards, football memorabilia.* LOC: Directly behind Tron Theatre. PARK: Meters. TEL: 0141 552 2208.

Mercat-Hughes Antiques
85 Queen St., 1 Royal Exchange Court. G2 4QY. (P. Hughes and C. Forrester). Open 10-5.30 or by appointment. CL: Sat. *STOCK: Small furniture, brass, ceramics, clocks, watches, E.P. and silver, jewellery and trade items.* TEL: 0141 357 6878; home - 0141 770 4572.

Muirhead Moffat and Co
182 West Regent St. G2 4RU. (D.J. Brewster and J.D. Hay). Est. 1896. Open 10-12.30 and 1.30-5. CL: Sat. and Sun. except by appointment. SIZE: Medium. *STOCK: Period furniture, barometers and jewellery; clocks, silver, weapons, porcelain, tapestries and pictures.* LOC: Off Blythswood Sq. PARK: Easy. TEL: 0141 226 4683/226 3406. SER: Valuations; restorations (furniture, clocks, barometers and jewellery); buys at auction. VAT: Stan/Spec.

Ewan Mundy Fine Art Ltd
Lower Ground Floor, 211 West George St. G2 2LW. Est. 1981. Open daily. SIZE: Medium. *STOCK: Fine Scottish, English and French oils and watercolours, 19th-20th C, from £250; Scottish and English etchings and lithographs, 19th-20th C, from £100; Scottish contemporary paintings, from £50.* LOC: City centre. PARK: Nearby. TEL: 0141 248 9755. SER: Valuations; restorations arranged; buys at auction (pictures). FAIRS: New York. VAT: Stan/Spec.

There was something to suit all tastes and pockets at Bearne's Autumn sale in Exeter in October. A job lot of walking sticks, including these five carved with dogs' heads, made £410.

From an Auction Report by Tim Ford on the Autumn Fine Art Sale at Bearne's, Exeter on 20th and 21st October, 1998. This feature appeared in the December 1998/January 1999 issue of **Antique Collecting** magazine. For more details and to subscribe see page 147.

SCOTLAND

Pastimes Vintage Toys
126 Maryhill Rd. G20 7QS. (Gordon and Anne Brown). Est. 1980. Open 10-5. SIZE: Medium. *STOCK: Vintage toys, die-cast, railways and dolls' houses, from 1910, £1-£300.* LOC: From the west off junction 17, M8; from the east junction 16, M8. PARK: Easy. TEL: 0141 331 1008. SER: Valuations. VAT: Stan.

The Renaissance Furniture Store
103 Niddrie Rd., Queens Park. G42 8PR. (Bruce Finnie). Open 10.30-5, Sat. and Sun. 12.30-5. CL: Mon. *STOCK: General antiques; Arts & Crafts and Art Nouveau furniture; fire inserts and surrounds.* PARK: Easy. TEL: 0141 423 0022. SER: Buys at auction.

R.L. Rose Oriental Carpets Ltd
Unit 3b, Yorkhill Quay. G3 8QE . Open 9-5, Sat. 10-5, Sun. 12-5. *STOCK: Oriental and decorative carpets.* TEL: 0141 339 7290; fax - 0141 334 1499. SER: Repair; cleaning.

Jeremy Sniders Antiques
158 Bath St. G2 4TB. Est. 1983. Open 9-5, Sat. 10-4. SIZE: Medium. *STOCK: British decorative arts including furniture, 1850-1960, £30-£1,000; Scandinavian decorative arts including furniture, 1900 to date, £30-£5,000; silver, mainly 19th-20th C, £30-£3,000.* LOC: Next door to Christies. PARK: Nearby - Sauchiehall St. Centre. TEL: 0141 332 0043; fax - 0141 332 5505. SER: Will source Scandinavian articles - E.G. Georg, Jensen, Royal Copenhagen, etc. VAT: Spec.

Strachan Antiques
40 Darnley St., Pollokshields. G41 2SE. (Alex and Lorna Strachan). Est. 1990. Open 10-5, Sun. 12-5. SIZE: Warehouse. *STOCK: Furniture, especially Arts & Crafts, Art Nouveau and Glasgow Style, also Victorian and Edwardian, £50-£5,000; some decorative items.* LOC: 2 mins from M8, junction 20 westbound, junction 21 eastbound. PARK: Own. TEL: 0141 429 4411. VAT: Stan/Spec.

Victoria Antiques Ltd
350 Pollokshaws Rd., G41 1QS. Est. 1963. Open daily, Sat. 10.30-4. SIZE: Large. *STOCK: General antiques, Victoriana, shipping goods.* TEL: 0141 423 7216; fax - 0141 423 6497. SER: Valuations; buys at auction. VAT: Stan/Spec.

The Victorian Village Antiques
93 West Regent St. G2 1PB. Open 10-5. SIZE: 3 floors. LOC: Near Hope St. PARK: At rear and meters. TEL: 0141 332 0808/9808. VAT: Stan/Spec. Below are listed the dealers at these premises.

Golden Oldies
Jewellery. SER: Repairs; commissions.

Cathy McLay "Saratoga Trunk"
Textiles, lace, jewellery. TEL: 0141 331 2707.

Stuart Myler
Silverware.

Putting-on-the-Ritz
Art Deco, china, jewellery, 1920's curios. TEL: 0141 332 9808.

Rosamond Rutherford
Victorian jewellery, Scottish agate, silver, Sheffield plate. TEL: 0141 332 9808.

West of Scotland Antique Centre Ltd
Langside Lane, 539 Victoria Rd., Queen's Park. G42 8BH. (Wosac Ltd). Est. 1969, Open 9.30-5.30, Sun. 12-5. SIZE: Large. *STOCK: Pine, Georgian to Edwardian, £50-£3,000.* PARK: Easy. TEL: 0141 423 7122; e-mail - Antiquity Glasgow@aol.com; website - www.denof antiquity.co.uk. VAT: Stan/Spec.

Tim Wright Antiques
147 Bath St. G2 4SQ. (T. and J. Wright). LAPADA. Est. 1971. Open 9.45-5, Sat. 10.30-2. SIZE: 6 showrooms. *STOCK: Furniture, European and Oriental ceramics and glass, decorative items, silver and plate, brass and copper, mirrors and prints, textiles, samplers, all £50-£6,000.* LOC: On opposite corner to Christie's. PARK: Multi-storey opposite and meters. TEL: 0141 221 0364; fax - same. VAT: Mainly Spec.

Michael Young Antiques at Glencarse
Main St. PH2 7LX. Est. 1887. Open 10-6 and by appointment *STOCK: 17th-19th C furniture, paintings and silver.* LOC: A90 3 miles east of Perth. TEL: 01738 860001; fax - same; e-mail - michael.d.young@lineone.net.

Glendoick Antiques
PH2 7NR. (Malcolm Wood). Est. 1992. Open 10.30-4.30 including Sun. SIZE: Large. *STOCK: Dining furniture, 17th-18th C, £1,000-£9,000; watercolours and oils, 18-19th C, £50-£2,000; general antiques, 18th-19th C, £50-£10,000.* LOC: A90. PARK: Easy. TEL: 01738 860870. VAT: Stan/Spec.

Strathspey Gallery
40 High St. PH26 3EH. (Franfam Ltd). LAPADA. HADA. Est. 1971. Open 10-1 and 2-5

```
Phone: INCHTURE (01828) 686412          On A90 Perth-Dundee Trunk road
Fax: INCHTURE (01828) 686748
```

LARGE STOCK
OF
PERIOD
FURNITURE
—
OIL PAINTINGS
and
WATERCOLOURS

C.S. MORETON
and
Inchmartine Fine Art
at
Inchmartine House
INCHTURE • PERTHSHIRE • PH14 9QQ
Prop. PAUL & MARY STEPHENS

ALSO
ORIENTAL
CARPETS and RUGS
—
METALWARE and
CERAMICS
—
TOOLS

(1-2 by appointment), Thurs. 10-1. SIZE: Medium. *STOCK: Furniture including early oak; collectors' ceramics and metalware; pictures including wildlife and sporting.* LOC: Town centre. PARK: Easy and behind shop. TEL: 01479 873290; fax - 01479 873383; home - 01479 873434; e-mail - strathspey.prestel.co.uk. SER: Valuations. VAT: Mainly Spec.

GULLANE (East Lothian)

Gullane Antiques
5 Rosebery Place. EH31 2AN. (E.A. Lindsey). Est. 1981. Open 10.30-1 and 2.30-5. CL: Wed. and Thurs. SIZE: Medium. *STOCK: China and glass, 1850-1930, £5-£100; prints and watercolours, early 20th C, £25-£100; metalwork, 1900's, £5-£50.* LOC: 6 miles north of Haddington, off A1. PARK: Easy. TEL: 01620 842994.

HADDINGTON (East Lothian)

Leslie and Leslie
EH41 3JJ. Open 9-1 and 2-5. CL: Sat. *STOCK: General antiques.* TEL: 01620 822241; fax - same. VAT: Stan.

HUNTLY (Aberdeenshire)

Bygones
1 Bogie St. AB54 8DX. (Sue and Bruce Watts). Open Wed. and Sat. 10-2, other days by appointment. SIZE: Medium. *STOCK: Clocks and pocket watches, £50-£3,000; furniture, barometers, Victoriana, curios and collectables, 19th-20th C, £10-£3,000.* LOC: Off Duke Street, towards railway station. TEL: 01466 794412. SER: Restorations (clocks).

Huntly Antiques
43 Duke St. AB54 8DT. (Mrs J. Barker). Open Mon. and Sat. 10-1 and 2-5, Thurs. 10-1, other

times by appointment. SIZE: Small. *STOCK: Jewellery, china, glass and furniture, 19th-20th C, £5-£250.* LOC: Off Aberdeen/Inverness road. PARK: Easy. TEL: 01466 793307.

INCHTURE (Perthshire)

Inchmartine Fine Art
Inchmartine House. PH14 9QQ. (P.M. Stephens). Est. 1998. Open 9-5.30. *STOCK: Mainly Scottish oils and watercolours, £150-£1,500.* LOC: Take A90 Perth/Dundee road, entrance on left at Lodge. PARK: Easy. TEL: 01828 686412; home - same; fax - 01828 686748; mobile - 07702 190128; e-mail - paul@toolbazaar.freeserve.co.uk. FAIRS: Buxton; Tatton Park; SECC (Glasgow); Chester. VAT: Spec.

C.S. Moreton (Antiques)
Inchmartine House. PH14 9QQ. (P.M. and Mrs M. Stephens). Est. 1922. Open 9-5.30. *STOCK: Furniture, £50-£10,000; carpets and rugs, £50-£3,000; ceramics, metalware; all 16th C to 1860; old cabinet makers' tools.* LOC: Take A90 Perth/Dundee road, entrance on left at Lodge. PARK: Easy. TEL: 01828 686412; home - same; fax - 01828 686748; mobile - 07702 190128; e-mail - paul@toolbazaar.freeserve.co.uk. SER: Valuations; cabinet making and repairs. FAIRS: Buxton; Tatton Park; SECC (Glasgow); Chester. VAT: Mainly Spec.

INNERLEITHEN (Peebleshire)

Keepsakes
96 High St. EH44 6HF. (Margaret Maxwell). CL: Tues., Wed. and lunchtimes. SIZE: Small. *STOCK: Ceramics and glass, £50-£200; dolls, teddies and toys, £100-£500; books, post and cigarette cards, £5-£25; jewellery, £5-£100; all 20th C.* LOC: A72. PARK: Easy. TEL: 01896 831369; home - 01896 830701. FAIRS: Ingliston; some Border.

Last Century Antiques

34 High St. EH44 6HF. (Gill and Keith Miller). Est. 1990. Open 11-5. SIZE: Small. *STOCK: General antiques including furniture, paintings and prints, £5-£100.* PARK: Easy. TEL: 01896 831759. SER: Valuations. FAIRS: Ingliston.

INVERNESS (Inverness-shire)

Gallery Persia

Upper Myrtlefield, Nairnside. IV2 5BX. (G. MacDonald). *STOCK: Persian, Turkoman, Afghanistan, Caucasus, Anatolian rugs and carpets, late 19th C to 1940, £500-£2,000+; quality contemporary pieces, £100+.* LOC: From A9 1st left after flyover, 1st left at roundabout, then 2.25 miles on B9006, then 1st right, 1st left. PARK: Easy. TEL: 01463 798500; home - 01463 792198; fax - same; e-mail - mac@gallery persia.co.uk; website - www.gallerypersia.co.uk. SER: Valuations; restorations (cleaning and repair). FAIRS: Treetops Hotel, Aberdeen (monthly); Inverness (July); Game, Scone Palace, Perth (July).

JEDBURGH (Roxburghshire)

Mainhill Gallery

Ancrum. TD8 6XA. (Diana Bruce). Est. 1981. Open by appointment. SIZE: Medium. *STOCK: Oil paintings, watercolours, etchings, some sculpture and ceramics, 19th C to contemporary, £35-£7,000.* LOC: Just off A68, 3 miles north of Jedburgh, centre of Ancrum. PARK: Easy. TEL: 01835 830518; fax - same; website - www. mainhill.bordernet.co.uk. SER: Exhibitions. VAT: Spec.

R. and M. Turner (Antiques Ltd)

34-36 High St. TD8 6AG. LAPADA. Est. 1965. Open 9.30-5.30, Sat. 10-5. SIZE: Large. *STOCK: Furniture, clocks, porcelain, paintings, silver, jewellery, 17th-20th C and fine reproductions.* LOC: On A68 to Edinburgh. PARK: Own. TEL: 01835 863445; fax - 01835 863349. SER: Valuations; packing; shipping. VAT: Stan/Spec.

KILBARCHAN (Renfrewshire)

Gardner's The Antique Shop

Wardend House, Kibbleston Rd. PA10 2PN. (G.D. and R.K.F. Gardner). LAPADA. Est. 1950. Open to Trade 7 days, retail 9-6, Sat. 10-5. SIZE: Large. *STOCK: General antiques.* LOC: 12 miles from Glasgow, at far end of Tandlehill Rd. 10 mins. from Glasgow Airport. TEL: 01505 702292.

McQuade Antiques

7 Shuttle St. PA10 2JN. (W. G. & W. J. McQuade). Est. 1975. Open 10-5.30, Sun. 2-5.30. CL: Sat. SIZE: Large. *STOCK: Furniture, porcelain, clocks, brass and silver, 19th-20th C, to £1,000.* LOC: Next to Weavers Cottage. PARK: Easy. TEL: 01505 704249. SER: Valuations. FAIRS: Newark. VAT: Spec.

KILLEARN, Nr. Glasgow (Stirlingshire)

Country Antiques

G63 9AJ. (Lady J. Edmonstone). Est. 1975. Open Mon.-Sat. *STOCK: Small antiques and decorative items.* Not Stocked: Reproduction. LOC: A81. In main street. PARK: Easy. TEL: Home - 01360 770215. SER: Interior decoration.

KILLIN (Perthshire)

Maureen H. Gauld

Craiglea, Main St. FK21 8UN. Est. 1975. Open March-Oct. 10-5, Nov.-Feb. Thurs., Fri., Sat. SIZE: Medium. *STOCK: General antiques, furniture, silver, paintings and etchings, £5-£3,500.* PARK: Easy. TEL: 01567 820475; home - 01567 820605.

LARGE STOCK OF FURNITURE, PORCELAIN ETC.

GARDNER'S

THE ANTIQUE SHOP

WARDEND HOUSE, KIBBLESTON ROAD KILBARCHAN PA10 2PN

20 MINUTES FROM GLASGOW CENTRE
10 MINUTES FROM GLASGOW AIRPORT

LAPADA
MEMBER

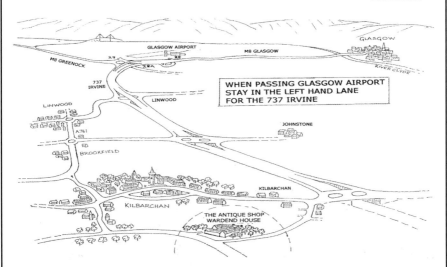

WHEN PASSING GLASGOW AIRPORT
STAY IN THE LEFT HAND LANE
FOR THE 737 IRVINE

TELEPHONE & FAX: KILBARCHAN 01505 702292
E-Mail: GARDANTIQUES@colloquium.co.uk
ESTABLISHED 1950

KILMACOLM (Renfrewshire)

Kilmacolm Antiques Ltd
Stewart Place. PA13 4AF. (H. Maclean). Est. 1973. Open 10-1 and 2.30-5.30. CL: Sun. except by appointment. SIZE: Medium. *STOCK: Furniture, 18th-19th C, £100-£8,000; objets d'art, 19th C; jewellery, £5-£5,000; paintings, £100-£5,000.* LOC: First shop on right when travelling from Bridge of Weir. PARK: Easy. TEL: 01505 873149. SER: Restorations (furniture, silver, jewellery, porcelain). FAIRS: Hopetown, Pollock House, Edinburgh, Inverness. VAT: Stan/Spec.

KILMARNOCK (Ayrshire)

MacInnes Antiques
5c David Orr St., Bonnington. KA1 2KQ. (Mrs M. MacInnes). Est. 1973. Open by appointment. *STOCK: General antiques.* TEL: 01563 526739.

QS Antiques and Cabinetmakers
Moorfield Industrial Estate. KA2 0DP. (J.R. Cunningham and D.A. Johnson). Est. 1980. Open 9-5.30, Sat. 9-5. SIZE: Large. *STOCK: Furniture including stripped pine, 18th-19th C; shipping goods, architectural and collectors' items.* PARK: Easy. TEL: 01563 571071. SER: Restorations (upholstery, stripping); custom-built kitchens and furniture. VAT: Stan.

KILMICHAEL GLASSARY
By Lochgilphead (Argyllshire)

Rhudle Mill
PA31 8QE. (D. Murray). Est. 1979. Open daily, weekends by appointment. SIZE: Medium. *STOCK: Furniture, 18th C to Art Deco, £30-£3,000; small items and bric-a-brac, £5-£500.* LOC: Signposted 3 miles south of Kilmartin on A816 Oban to Lochgilphead road. PARK: Easy. TEL: 01546 605284; home - same. SER: Restorations (furniture); French polishing; buys at auction.

KINCARDINE O'NEIL
Nr. Aboyne (Aberdeenshire)

Dunmore Antiques
27 North Deeside Rd. AB34 5AA. (Pauline Baird). Est. 1988. Open Thurs., Fri. and Sat. 10-5, other times by appointment. SIZE: Small. *STOCK: China, 1800-1960, £10-£1,000; glass, silver, 20th C, £10-£300.* PARK: Easy. TEL: 013398 84449; home - 013398 82640; fax - same. SER: Valuations. FAIRS: Treetops, Newark. VAT: Global.

KINGSTON-ON-SPEY (Morayshire)

Collectables
Lein Rd. IV32 7NW. (J. Penman and B. Taylor). Est. 1987. Open daily including most weekends, prior telephone call required. SIZE: Small. *STOCK: Militaria and jewellery, lap desks, china, collectables, small silver, £5-£1,000.* LOC: On B9105. PARK: Easy. TEL: 01343 870462. SER: Valuations. FAIRS: Inverness and Aberdeen.

KINGUSSIE (Inverness-shire)

Mostly Pine
High St. PH21 1HR. Est. 1980. Open 10-5.30 (also store in Spey Street - open Sat. 10-5.30 and by appointment). *STOCK: Furniture and collectibles.* LOC: A9. TEL: 01540 661838. SER: Restorations (pine). VAT: Stan/Spec.

KINROSS (Kinross)

Miles Antiques
Mill St. KY13 8DR. (K. and S. Miles). LAPADA. Est. 1979. Open Mon.-Fri. 12-5. SIZE: Large. *STOCK: Furniture including decorative, Georgian, Victorian and Edwardian, £100-£5,000; china and pottery, £50-£500.* LOC: Off M90, junction 6. Take right at High St. then second left. PARK: Easy. TEL: 01577 864858. SER: Restorations (upholstery, polishing, small repairs). VAT: Stan/Spec.

KIRKCALDY (Fife)

Book-Ends
Sailor's Walk, 449 High St. KY1 2SN. (M. Potter). Est. 1990. CL: Mon. SIZE: Small. *STOCK: Books, maps and prints, 19th-20th C, £1-£100.* PARK: Easy. TEL: 01592 205294. SER: Book search.

Second Notions Antiques
4B Normand Rd., Dysart. KY1 2XJ. (James Sinclair). Est. 1996. Open 12-5, Sat. 10-5. SIZE: Medium. *STOCK: General antiques especially furniture and longcase clocks, £2-£3000; shipping furniture.* LOC: A92. PARK: Easy. TEL: 01592 650505; home/fax - same. SER: Valuations; buys at auction. FAIRS: Swinderby.

KIRKCUDBRIGHT (Kirkcudbrightshire)

The Antique Shop
69 St Mary St. DG6 4DU. Open 10-5. SIZE: 3

dealers. *STOCK: General antiques, collectors' items, linen and lace, kichenalia, furniture and bric-a-brac, 18th-20th C, to £1,500.* TEL: 01557 332400.

Osborne Antiques
41 Castle St. and 63 High St. DG6 4JD. (David and Robert A. Mitchell). LAPADA. Est. 1949. Open 9-12.30 and 1.30-5, or by appointment. TEL: 01557 330441. VAT: Stan/Spec.

The Antique Shop
High St. DG13 0DH. (R. and V. Baird). Est. 1970. Open 10.30-5. CL: Wed. pm. SIZE: Small. *STOCK: China, glass, pictures, 18th-20th C; jewellery, rugs, 19th-20th C; trade warehouse - furniture, shipping goods and antiquarian books.* LOC: 20 miles north of Carlisle on A7. PARK: 100yds. TEL: 0138 73 80238.

Narducci Antiques
11 Waterside St. KA30 9LN. (G. Narducci). Open Tues., Thurs. and Sat., 2.30-5.30 or by appointment - trade anytime. SIZE: Warehouse. *STOCK: General antiques and shipping goods.* TEL: 01475 672612; 01294 461687; fax - 01294 470002; mobile - 07771 577777. SER: Packing and shipping; road haulage (Europe). *Mainly Trade and Export.*

Campsie Antiques
2 Service St. G65. (R. Allen). Open 10-5.30, Sun.12-4. SIZE: Small. *STOCK: Collectables.* LOC: A891. PARK: Easy. TEL: 01360 311100.

Idvies Antiques
Idvies House. DD8 2QJ. (Tim Slingsby). Est. 1988. Open by appointment or chance (7 days). *STOCK: Furniture, 18th-19th C, £250-£1,500; pictures, 19th C, £100-£400; smalls, 18th-19th C, £5-£100.* LOC: Approximately 5 miles south-east from Forfar on B9128. PARK: Easy. TEL: 01307 818402; fax - 01307 818933; home - same; e-mail - tim.slingsby@icscotland.net. SER: Valuations; restorations; cabinet-making.

Heritage Antiques
222 High St. EH49 7ES. (Ann J. R. Davidson). Est. 1980. Open 10-1 and 2-5. CL: Wed. *STOCK: Jewellery, china, glass, silver, small furniture and objects.* PARK: Nearby. TEL: 01506 847460. SER: Valuations; repairs (jewellery).

Mir Russki
Est. 1994. *STOCK: Russian silver, 18th C to 1917.* TEL: 01506 843973; website - www.russiansilver.co.uk. SER: Mail order. FAIRS: NEC and other major.

Grannie Used To Have One
Sanderling. AB42 0NX. (Mrs Jacqui Harvey). Est. 1991. Open Thurs. and Fri. 1-5, Sat. and Sun. 11-5, Mon and Tues by appointment. SIZE: Large. *STOCK: Pottery including Scottish, 18th-19th C, £5-£2,000; porcelain and glass, wooden items, curios and furniture, 20th C.* LOC: A90 6 miles south of Peterhead. PARK: Own. TEL: 01779 813223; fax/home - same; e-mail jacqui@grannieused to.co.uk; website - www. grannieusedto.co.uk SER: Buys at auction. FAIRS: Hilton Treetops, Aberdeen.

Airlie Antiques
Alyth Rd. PH12 8RP. (J. McGill and H. Sudron). Est. 1995. Open seven days. SIZE: Medium. *STOCK: Furniture, Victorian and Edwardian, £100-£5,000; china and glass, Victorian and Edwardian, £10-£1,000; metalware and collectables.* LOC: A94 from Perth or B954 from Dundee. PARK: Own large. TEL: 01828 640617. VAT: Stan/Spec

Herrald of Edinburgh
Kings of Kinloch. PH12 8QX. Est. 1882. Open 9.30-1 and 2-5, Sun. 2-5. SIZE: Large. *STOCK: Furniture, Persian rugs, Continental and Eastern china, brass, copper and crystal.* TEL: 01828 640273; fax - same; e-mail - herrald@sol.co.uk. SER: Restorations; custom build; brochure available. VAT: Stan/Spec.

Michael Vee Design - Birch House Antiques
High St. TD6 9PB. (Michael Vee and Enid Cranston). Est. 1990. Open 9.30-12.30 and 1.30-

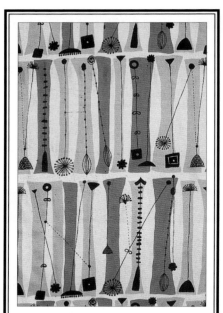

The Palisade pattern designed for British Celanese in 1953.

From an article entitled 'Lucienne Day – In the Spirit of the Age' by Andrew Casey which appeared in the May 2001 issue of **Antique Collecting** magazine. For more details and to subscribe see page 147.

5, Sat. 9.30-4, Sun. by appointment. SIZE: Medium. *STOCK: Mirrors and lighting, French, English, decorative and some garden furniture, 1850-1920, £20-£5,000.* LOC: 1.5 miles off A68. PARK: Easy. TEL: 01896 822116; home - 01896 822835. SER: Restorations; interior design.

MONTROSE (Angus)

Harper-James
25-27 Baltic St. DD10 8EX. (D.R. James). LAPADA. Resident. Est. 1991. Open 10-5, other times by appointment. SIZE: Large. *STOCK: Furniture, clocks, silver and jewellery, 1690-1910, £50-£6,000; ceramics and pottery, 1800-1945, £10-£650+; general antiques and curios, £2-£750.* LOC: From south turn right at Peel statue, then first left. PARK: Easy. TEL: 01674 671307; home - same; website - www. harperjamesantiques @compuserve.com. SER: Valuations; restorations (furniture, upholstery); French polishing; export. FAIRS: Major U.K. VAT: Stan/Spec.

NAIRN (Nairnshire)

Moray Antiques
78 High St. IV12 4AU. (Mrs. Melanie Muir). Est. 1997. Open 10.30-1 and 2-5, Wed. 10.30-1, Sat. 10.30-5. SIZE: Medium. *STOCK: Victorian silver and plate, £50-£500; Victorian glass, 1920's-1930's pottery, £50-£200; 19th C furniture, £250-£2,000.* LOC: Sign on A96, 15 miles from Inverness. PARK: Easy. TEL: 01667 455570; fax - same. SER: Valuations; buys at auction.

NEWBURGH (Fife)

Newburgh Antiques
222 High St. KY14 6DZ. (Dorothy Fraser). Est. 1991. Open 10.30-12 and 1.30-5. CL: Mon. SIZE: Small. *STOCK: Wemyss ware, 1882-1930, £100-£2,000; Scottish watercolours and oil paintings, 1800-1950's, £100-£1,500; furniture, 1750-1900, £200-£2,000.* LOC: A913. PARK: Easy. TEL: 01337 841026; home - 01337 840725. SER: Valuations.

NEWTONMORE (Inverness-shire)

The Antique Shop
Main St. PH20 1DD. (J. Harrison). Est. 1964. Open 9.30-5.30. SIZE: Medium. *STOCK: Furniture, £20-£1,000; glass, china, silver, plate, copper, brass, secondhand books, vintage fishing tackle.* LOC: On A86 opposite Mains Hotel. PARK: Easy. TEL: 01540 673272.

NORTH BERWICK (East Lothian)

Kirk Ports Gallery
49A Kirk Ports. EH39 4HL. (Alan Lindsey). Open 10-5. CL: Thurs. SIZE: Medium. *STOCK: Oil paintings, £100-£500; watercolours, £50-£300; etchings and prints, £30-£100; all 19th C to 1940.* LOC: Behind main street. PARK: Easy. TEL: 01620 894114. SER: Valuations.

Lindsey Antiques
49a Kirk Ports. EH39 4HL. (Stephen Lindsey). Est. 1993. Open 10-1 and 2-5. CL: Thurs. SIZE: Medium. *STOCK: Ceramics and glass, 1800-1935, £20-£500; furniture, 1750-1910, £150-£2,000.* LOC: Behind main street. PARK: Easy. TEL: 01620 894114. SER: Valuations. FAIRS: Ingliston.

Penny Farthing
23 Quality St. EH39 4HR. (S. Tait). Est. 1981. Open daily. SIZE: Medium. *STOCK: Secondhand books, collectables, 20th C, £5-£25.* PARK: Easy. TEL: 01620 894400; fax - same. SER: Valuations; buys at auction. FAIRS: Scot, Meadowbank, Edinburgh.

OBAN (Argyllshire)

Oban Antiques

35 Stevenson St. PA34 5NA. (P. and P. Baker). Est. 1970. Open 10-5, some seasonal variation. SIZE: Medium. *STOCK: Furniture and general antiques, mainly 19th to early 20th C; books, prints, jewellery, silver, ceramics and collectables, £5-£1,500.* LOC: Off George (main) St. PARK: Easy. TEL: 01631 566203; e-mail - obanantiques.rubylane.com; obantiques. rubylane.com; websites - www. chanonrypoint. com/ObanAntiques/; www.chanonry point. com/oabooks/.

PAISLEY (Renfrewshire)

Corrigan Antiques

Woodlands, High Calside. PA2 6BY. Open by appointment only. SIZE: Small. *STOCK: Furniture and accessories.* LOC: 5 minutes from Glasgow Airport. TEL: 0141 889 6653; fax - 0141 848 9700; mobile - 07802 631110.

Paisley Fine Books

17 Corsebar Crescent. PA2 9QA. (Mr and Mrs B. Merrifield). Est. 1985. Open by appointment. SIZE: Small. *STOCK: Books on architecture, art, antiques and collecting.* TEL: 0141 581 0095; fax - 0141 884 2661; e-mail - bernieafc@aol.com. SER: Free book search; catalogues issued.

PERTH (Perthshire)

Ainslie's Antique Warehouse

Unit 3, Gray St. PH2 0JH. (T.S. and A. Ainslie). Open 9-5, by appointment at weekends. SIZE: Large. *STOCK: General antiques.* TEL: 01738 636825.

A.S. Deuchar and Son

10-12 South St. PH2 8PG. (A.S. and A.W.N. Deuchar). Open 10-1 and 2-5. CL: Sat. SIZE: Large. *STOCK: Victorian shipping goods, furniture, 19th C paintings, china, brass, silver and plate.* LOC: Glasgow to Aberdeen Rd., near Queen's Bridge. PARK: Easy. TEL: 01738 626297; home - 01738 551452. VAT: Stan/Spec.

Hardie Antiques

25 St. John St. PH1 5SH. (T.G. Hardie). PADA. Est. 1980. Open 9.30-5, Sat. 10-4.30. SIZE: Medium. *STOCK: Jewellery and silver, 18th-20th C, £5-£5,000.* PARK: Nearby. TEL: 01738 633127; fax - same; home - 01738 551764; e-mail - info@timothyhardie.co.uk. SER: Valuations. VAT: Stan/Spec.

Henderson

5 North Methven St. PH1 5PN. (J.G. Henderson). Est. 1935. Open 9.30-5. CL: Wed. pm. SIZE: Small. *STOCK: Porcelain, glass, 1720-1950, £5-£500; silver, jewellery, medals, £1-£1,000.* Not Stocked: Furniture. LOC: A9. PARK: Easy. TEL: 01738 624836; home - 01738 621923. SER: Valuations. VAT: Stan.

Nigel Stacy-Marks Ltd

23 George St. PH1 5JY. (Nigel and Ginny Stacy-Marks). LAPADA. Open 9.30-5.30. SIZE: Medium. *STOCK: Oils and watercolours, 19th-20th C, £250-£30,000; British etchings, late 19th C to mid 20th C, £100-£5,000.* LOC: Town centre, just south of museum, behind Tay St. PARK: Nearby. TEL: 01738 626300; fax - 01738 620460; e-mail - paintings@stacy-marks.co.uk; website - www.stacy-marks.co.uk. SER: Valuations; restorations; framing; regular exhibitions (catalogues on request). VAT: Stan/Spec.

Yesterdays Today

267 High St. PH1 5QN. (Bill and Nora MacGregor). Open 9-5. SIZE: Small. *STOCK: General collectables especially china, £25-£1,000.* LOC: Follow signs for Tourist Information Centre. PARK: Nearby. TEL: 01738 443534. SER: Valuations; buys at auction.

A mahogany armchair of the Chippendale period (circa 1765) displaying a delicious collection of blooms freshly gathered in armfuls from the garden seem casually, though artistically, thrown over the red brown background, all canvaswork embroidery.

From an article entitled 'Needlework Furnishings – A Crucial Feature of Historic Interiors' by Lanto Synge which appeared in the May 2001 issue of **Antique Collecting** magazine. For more details and to subscribe see page 147.

PITLOCHRY (Perthshire)

Blair Antiques
14 Bonnethill Rd. PH16 5BS. (Duncan Huie). Est.
1976. Open 9-5. CL: Thurs. pm. *STOCK: Period
furniture, Scottish oil paintings, silver - some
provincial, curios, clocks, pottery and porcelain.*
LOC: Beside Scotlands Hotel, off A9 to Inverness.
TEL: 01796 472624; fax - 01796 474202. SER:
Valuations; buys at auction. VAT: Stan/Spec.

PITTENWEEM (Fife)

The Antiques Shop
27 High St. KY10 2RQ. (R. J. Clark). Est. 1985.
Open 10,30-5, Sun. 11-4. SIZE: Medium.
*STOCK: Scottish pottery including Wemyss,
furniture, 19th C, £100-£1,000; collectibles.*
PARK: Easy. TEL: 01333 312870; home - 01333
720331. SER: Valuations.

The Little Gallery
20 High St. KY10 2LA. (Dr. Ursula Ditchburn-
Bosch). Est. 1988. Open 10-5, Sun. 2-5. CL: Mon.
and Tues. SIZE: Small. *STOCK: China, 18th C to
1930's, £5-£100; small furniture, mainly Victorian,
£30-£300; rustica, £5-£150; contemporary
paintings, £40-£700.* LOC: From Market Sq.
towards church, on right. PARK: Easy. TEL: 01333
311227; home - same. SER: Valuations.

PORTREE (Isle of Skye)

Croft Comforts Antiques
2 Wentworth St. IV51 9EJ. (Ms Fiona Middleton).
Est. 1984. Open daily. CL: Tues. and Wed. Oct. to
April. SIZE: Small. *STOCK: China, porcelain,
curios and stoneware, 19th-20th C; furniture, 19th
C and Edwardian.* PARK: Nearby. TEL: 01478
613762; fax - same. SER: Buys at auction.

PORTSOY (Banff)

Other Times Antiques
13-15 Seafield St. AB45 2QT. (D. McLean and
T. Matheson). Est. 1986. Open 10-5 including
Sun. CL: Wed. *STOCK: General antiques, 1700-
1950.* TEL: 01261 842866. VAT: Stan/Spec.

PRESTWICK (Ayrshire)

Crossroads Antiques
7 The Cross. KA9 1AJ. (Timothy Okeeffe). Est.
1989. Open 9-5. SIZE: Medium. *STOCK: Furniture,
18th-20th C, £5-£1,000+; china and silver, 19th-
20th C, £5-£500+.* PARK: Nearby. TEL: 01292
474004. SER: Valuations; buys at auction.

RAIT (Perthshire)

Rait Village Antiques Centre
PH2 7RT. LOC: Midway between Perth and
Dundee, 1 mile north of A90. PARK: Easy.
Below are listed the dealers at this centre:

Fair Finds
(Lynda Templeman). *Large stock of antique and
early 20th C country house furnishings, pictures,
rugs, silver and clocks, £50-£10,000.* TEL: 01821
670379.

Gordon Loraine Antiques
(Liane and Gordon Loraine). *Georgian, Victorian
and Edwardian furniture, decorative items and
collectables.* TEL: 01821 670760.

Manor Collectables
(Iris Miller). *Georgian, Victorian and Edwardian
furniture, china, glass, Scottish silver, decorative
items.* TEL: 01307 464851; mobile - 07715 119390.

Claire Mills
Porcelain, lace, decorative items.

J. and L. Newton
*Upholstered furniture, antique pine, decorative
accessories, textiles and cushions.* TEL: 01821 670205

Rait Antiques
*Period and decorative furniture, woodworking
tools.* TEL: 01821 670318.

Whimsical Wemyss
(Lynda Templeman and Chris Comben).
Wemyssware, £50-£3,000. TEL: 01821 67039.

RUMBLINGBRIDGE (Kinross)

Bridge Bygones
KY13 0PT. (David and Angela de Boer). Est.
1986. Open Sat. and Sun. 12-5, other days by
appointment. SIZE: Large. *STOCK: Furniture,
19th-20th C, £200-£500; silver and china,
collectables, 20th C, £5-£100.* LOC: 100 yards
from A823/A977 junction. PARK: Easy. TEL:
01577 840280; home - 01577 840251. SER:
Valuations; restorations (furniture and upholstery).

SALTCOATS (Ayrshire)

Narducci Antiques
Factory Place. KA21 5LA. (G. Narducci). Est.
1972. Open 10-1 and 2.30-5.30 or by appointment
- trade anytime. *STOCK: Furniture, general
antiques and shipping goods.* TEL: 01294 461687
and 01475 672612; mobiles - 07831 100152 and
07771 577777. SER: Packing, export, shipping and
European haulage. *Mainly Trade and Export.*

ST. ANDREWS (Fife)

Old St. Andrews Gallery
9 Albany Place. KY16 9HH. (Mr and Mrs D.R.
Brown). Est. 1973. CL: 1-2 daily. SIZE: Medium.
*STOCK: Golf memorabilia, 19th C, £100-
£20,000; silver, jewellery especially Scottish,
19th-20th C, £100-£10,000; general antiques,
from 18th C, £50-£5,000.* LOC: Main street.
PARK: Easy. TEL: 01334 477840. SER: Valuations; restorations (jewellery, silver); buys at
auction (golf memorabilia). VAT: Stan.

St. Andrews Fine Art
84 Market St. KY16 9PA. Open 10-1 and 2-5.
*STOCK: Scottish oils, watercolours and drawings,
19th-20th C.* TEL: 01334 474080.

STANLEY (Perthshire)

Coach House Antiques Ltd
Charleston. PH1 4PN. (John Walker). Est. 1971.
Open by appointment. SIZE: Medium. *STOCK:
Period furniture, decorative items, 18th-19th C;
garden furniture.* LOC: 9 miles north of Perth off
A9. Take first slip road to Luncarty and Stanley,
continue 2 miles through village, sign at end of road
Charleston. PARK: Easy. TEL: 01738 828627;
home - same; mobile - 07710 122244. SER: Valu-
ations; restorations; buys at auction (furniture).
VAT: Spec.

STEWARTON (Ayrshire)

**Woolfsons of James Street Ltd t/a
Past & Present**
3 Lainshaw St. KA3 5BY. Est. 1983. Open 9.30-
5.30, Sun. 12-5.30. SIZE: Medium. *STOCK:
Furniture, £100-£500; porcelain, £25-£500; bric-
a-brac, £5-£50; all from 1800.* LOC: Stewarton
Cross. PARK: Easy. TEL: 01560 484113; fax -
same. SER: Valuations; restorations (French
polishing, upholstery, wood). VAT: Stan/Spec.

STIRLING (Stirlingshire)

Abbey Antiques
35 Friars St. FK8 1HA. (S. Campbell). Resident.
Est. 1980. Open 10-5. SIZE: Small. *STOCK:
Jewellery, £10-£5,000; silver, £5-£1,000;
furniture including pine, £20-£1,000; paintings,
£50-£2,500; bric-a-brac, £1-£100; coins and
medals, £1-£1,000; all 18th-20th C.* LOC: Off
Murray Place, part of main thoroughfare. PARK:
Nearby. TEL: 01786 447840. SER: Valuations.

STRATHBLANE (Stirlingshire)

Whatnots
16 Milngavie Rd. G63 9EH. (F. Bruce). Est. 1965.
*STOCK: Furniture, paintings, jewellery, silver and
plate, clocks, small items, shipping goods, horse
drawn and old vehicles.* LOC: 25 miles from
Stirling and 10 miles from Glasgow. PARK: Easy.
TEL: 01360 770310. VAT: Stan/Spec.

TROON (Ayrshire)

Old Troon Sporting Antiques
49 Ayr St. KA10 6EB. (R.S. Pringle). Est. 1984.
CL: Wed. pm. and Sat. pm. SIZE: Medium.
STOCK: Golf items, 19th C, to £500+. LOC: 5
minutes from A77. PARK: Easy. TEL: 01292
311822; home - 01292 313744; fax - 01292
313111. SER: Valuations; buys at auction (golf
items). VAT: Stan.

Tantalus Antiques
79 Templehill. KA10 6BQ. (Iain D. Sutherland).
Open 10-5, Sun. by appointment. SIZE: Medium.
*STOCK: Furniture, clocks and watches, pictures
and paintings, silverware, jewellery, ceramics.*
LOC: Town centre, main road to the harbour.
PARK: Easy. TEL: 01292 315999; fax - 01292
316611. SER: Valuations; restorations.

ULLAPOOL (Wester Ross)

Wishing Well Antiques
Shore St. IU26 2RL. (Simon and Eileen Calder).
Est. 1988. Open 10-6, including Sun. in summer.
SIZE: Medium. *STOCK: China, glass, silver,
pottery, furniture, country artefacts, curiosities;
books, prints and paintings.* LOC: Village centre,
50 miles from Inverness. PARK: Easy. TEL:
01854 613265; mobile - 07714 498569. SER:
Valuations; restorations; wood stripping.

UPPER LARGO (Fife)

Waverley Antiques
13 Main St. KY8 6EL. (D.V. and C.A. St. Clair).
Est. 1962. Open 10.30-5.30, Sun. by appointment.
SIZE: Medium. *STOCK: Pictures, furniture, china,
pottery, glass and works of art.* LOC: Coast road
from Leven to St. Andrews. PARK: Easy. TEL:
01333 360437; home - same. SER: Valuations.

ABERGAVENNY

Henry H. Close
36 Cross St. NP3 3AY. (Mr and Mrs H. Close).
Est. 1968. Open 9-5. *STOCK: 18th-19th C
furniture, porcelain, pottery, glass, brass, copper,
silver, prints.* TEL: 01873 853583.

ABERYSTWYTH

The Furniture Cave
33 Cambrian St. SY23 1NZ. (P. David). Est. 1975.
Open 9-5, Sat. 10-4. *STOCK: Pine, 1700-1930,
from £100; general antiques, Victorian and
Edwardian, £30-£3,000; small items, 19th C, £10-
£500.* LOC: First right off Terrace Rd., at railway
station end. PARK: Nearby. TEL: 01970 611234;
e-mail - info@the-furniture-cave.co.uk; website -
www.the-furniture-cave.co.uk. SER: Restorations.

Howards of Aberystwyth   BADA
**10 Alexandra Rd. SY23 1LE. LAPADA. Open
by appointment only.** *STOCK: Pottery including
Gaudy Welsh, early British, copper lustre,
Staffordshire animals and decorative figures.*
TEL: 01545 570576; mobile - 07831 850544.
FAIRS: Olympia; BADA.

BANGOR

David Windsor Gallery
173 High St. LL57 1NU. Est. 1970. Open 10-5.
CL: Wed. *STOCK: Oils and watercolours, 18th-
20th C; maps, engravings, lithographs.* TEL:
01248 364639. SER: Restorations; framing;
mounting. VAT: Stan/Spec.

BARMOUTH

Chapel Antiques Centre
High St. LL42 1DS. (Danny Jones). Est. 1985.
Open 10.30-5. CL: Wed. SIZE: Medium.
*STOCK: General antiques including furniture
and glass, 18th-20th C, £5-£2,000.* PARK:
Nearby. TEL: 01341 281377; fax - same.

Fronhouse Antiques
Jubilee Rd. LL42 1EE. (Tony and Barbara
Howard). Est. 1977. Open seven days 10-5. CL:
Wed. and Sun. Dec to Mar. SIZE: Small.
*STOCK: Nautical items, 19th C £5-£250; oil
lamps, bric-a-brac and small furniture, £5-£200.*
LOC: On corner of Church St. PARK: Easy.
TEL: 01341 280649; home/fax - same. SER:
Valuations; restorations (nautical items). FAIRS:
Swinderby, Newark.

BARRY

Flame 'n' Grate
99-100 High St. CF6 8DS. (A. Galsworthy).
Open 9-5.30. *STOCK: Antique and reproduction
fireplaces and surrounds.* TEL: 01446 744788.

BEAUMARIS (Anglesey)

Museum of Childhood Memories
1 Castle St. LL58 8AP. *STOCK: Children's toys
and memorabilia collectables.* TEL: 01248
712498.

BLAENAU FFESTINIOG

The Antique Shop
Bryn Marian. LL41 3HD. (Mrs R. Roberts). Est.
1971. *STOCK: Victoriana, furniture, brass and
copper, oil lamps, clocks and watches.* TEL:
01766 830629/830041.

BRECON

Hazel of Brecon
6 The Bulwark. LD3 7LB. (H. Hillman). Est.
1969. Open 10-5.30. CL: Wed. SIZE: Medium.
STOCK: Jewellery, 19th-20th C, £20-£10,000.
LOC: Main square, town centre. PARK: Easy.
TEL: 01874 625274 (24 hr. answering service).
SER: Valuations; repairs.

Maps, Prints and Books
7 The Struet. LD3 7LL. (Mr and Mrs D.G. Evans).
Est. 1961. Open 9-1 and 2-5. CL: Wed. SIZE:
Large. *STOCK: Books, maps, prints, 17th C, £5-
£500.* LOC: A438, opposite Kwik Save. PARK:
Opposite. TEL: 01874 622714. VAT: Stan.

Silvertime
6 The Bulwark. LD3 7LB. (L. Hillman). Open
10-5.30. CL: Wed. SIZE: Small. *STOCK: Silver
and gold watches; antique and collectors' clocks;
19th-20th C silver and plate.* LOC: Town centre,
on main square. PARK: Easy. TEL: 01874
625274 (24 hr. answering service). SER:
Valuations; repairs.

BRIDGEND

Hart Antiques
1A Dunraven Place. CF31 1JF. (Mrs Cheryl
Hart). Open 9-3. SIZE: Small. *STOCK: Textiles,
18th to early 20th C, £10-£1,000; small furniture,
lighting and decorative accessories, mainly 19th*

WALES

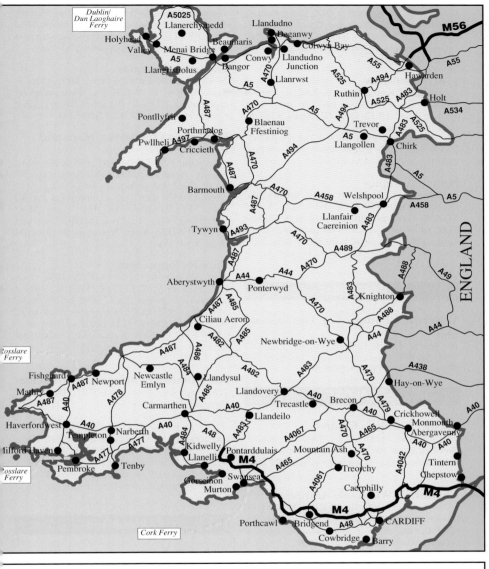

Dealers and Shops in Wales

C, French, £5-£1,000. LOC: Town centre, 100yds from Post Office and Cenotaph. PARK: Easy. TEL: Mobile - 07714 443429. SER: Interior design; valuations. FAIRS: Shepton Mallet; specialist textile.

J. & A. Antiques
1 Prince Rd., Kenfig Hill. CF33 6ED. (Jennifer Lawson). Est. 1990. Open 10-12.30 and 2-4.30, Wed. and Sat. 10-12.30. SIZE: Small. *STOCK: Furniture, china and clocks, 19th to early 20th C, £10-£600.* LOC: From A48 Pyle take B4281. PARK: Easy. TEL: 01656 746681; home - 01656 744709.

Nolton Antiques
66 Nolton St. CF31 3BP. (Gittings and Beynon). Est. 1997. Open 9.30-5. CL: Wed. SIZE: Large. *STOCK: General antiques including Clarice Cliff, majolica and Victorian furniture.* LOC: Turn off M4 at junction 35. PARK: Nearby. TEL: 01656 667774. SER: Valuations; buys at auction (named china).

CAERPHILLY

Yesterday's Future - G.J. Gittins and Son
10 Clive St. CF8 1GE. Open 9-4, Sat. 10-5. CL: Wed. *STOCK: General antiques, jewellery and shipping goods.* TEL: 029 2086 8835.

CARDIFF

Cardiff Antiques Centre
10/12 Royal Arcade. CF1 2AE. (C. and J. Rowles). Open 10-5.30. *STOCK: Antiques and collectables.* LOC: Town centre. TEL: 029 2039 8891.

Charlotte's Wholesale Antiques
26A Whitchurch Rd., Heath. CF14 3LW. (P.G. Cason). Open 10-4. SIZE: Large warehouse. *STOCK: Pine, shipping goods, general antiques, period furniture.* TEL: 029 2075 9809.

Jacobs Antique Centre
West Canal Wharf. CF10 5DB. Open Thurs.-Sat. 9.30-5. SIZE: Large - 50 dealers. *STOCK: General antiques and collectables.* LOC: 2 mins. from main railway and bus stations. PARK: 100yds. TEL: 029 2039 0939. SER: Valuations; restorations.

Kings Fireplaces, Antiques and Interiors
The Old Church, Adamsdown Sq., Adamsdown. CF2 1EZ. (B. Quinn). Est. 1984. SIZE: Medium.

STOCK: Period fireplaces including French marble; Victorian and Edwardian furniture. TEL: 029 2049 2439. SER: Restorations (furniture and fireplaces); fireplace installations. VAT: Stan.

Llanishen Antiques
26 Crwys Rd., Cathays. CF2 4NL. (Mrs J. Boalch). Open 10.30-4.30. CL: Wed. except by appointment. *STOCK: Furniture, silver, china, glass, bric-a-brac.* TEL: 029 2039 7244.

Pontcanna Old Books, Maps and Prints
1 Pontcanna St. CF11 9HQ. (W.A. Beynon). WBDA. Open 10-5. SIZE: Medium. *STOCK: Books, £1-£2,000; maps, 17th-19th C, £1-£1,000; prints, £1-£500.* LOC: Off Cathedral Rd. PARK: Easy. TEL: 02920 641047; fax - same. SER: Valuations; buys at auction (books, maps and prints). FAIRS: Royal National; Bonnington Hotel. VAT: Stan.

Roberts Emporium
58-60 Salisbury Rd. CF24 4AD. Est. 1980. Open 12-5, Mon. 11-5. SIZE: Large. *STOCK: General antiques, Victorian, £5-£1,000; collectables, 50's, 60's, '70's.* LOC: In road near Museum of Wales. PARK: Easy. TEL: 02920 235630; fax - 02920 641430. SER: Valuations; restorations (ceramics and furniture); buys at auction; prop. hire. FAIRS: Newark.

San Domenico Stringed Instruments
175 Kings Rd., Pontcanna. CF1 9DF. (H.W. Morgan). Open 10-4, Sat. 10-1. SIZE: Small. *STOCK: Fine violins, violas, cellos and bows, mainly 18th-19th C, £300-£20,000.* LOC: Off Cathedral Rd. or Cowbridge Rd. PARK: Easy. TEL: 029 2023 5881; fax - 029 2034 4510; home - 029 2077 7156; e-mail - HWM@san-domenico.co.uk; website - www.san-domenico.co.uk. SER: Valuations; restorations; buys at auction. VAT: Stan/Spec.

CARMARTHEN

Audrey Bull
2 Jacksons Lane. SA31 1QD. Open 10-5. *STOCK: Period and Welsh country furniture, general antiques especially jewellery and silver.* TEL: 01267 222655; home - 01834 813425. VAT: Spec.

Cwmgwili Mill
Bronwydd Arms. SA33 6HX. (M.J. Sandell). Est. 1950. Open 9-1 and 2-6, Sat. 9-1 and 2-6, Sun. by appointment. SIZE: Large. *STOCK: Furniture, oak, mahogany, pine, 18th-20th C.* PARK: Easy. TEL: 01267 231500; home - 01267 237215.

Merlins Antiques
Market Hall. SA31 1QY. (Mrs J.R. Perry). Open 10-4.30 including Sun. *STOCK: Small items - porcelain, pottery, glass, silver and plate, postcards.* TEL: 01267 233814.

The Mount Antiques Centre
1 and 2 The Mount, Castle Hill. SA31. (R. Lickley). Est. 1987. Open 10-5, Sun. 11-3. SIZE: Large. *STOCK: Fine furniture including country, 18th-19th C, £500-£1,000+; china and collectables, 19th-20th C, £50-£500; architectural salvage, musical instruments, 19th C, £50-£1,500.* LOC: A40 near county hall. PARK: Easy. TEL: 01267 220005. SER: Valuations; restorations (furniture and china). FAIRS: Towy - Cowbridge, Bristol and Cardiff.

Foxgloves
11 St. Mary St. NP6 5EU. (Leslie Brain). Open Tues.-Sat. 10ish-5. *STOCK: Period and antique furniture; pictures, china and objet d'art.* TEL: 01291 622386.

Glance Back Bookshop
17 Upper Church St. NP6 5EX. Open 10ish-5.30, including Bank Holidays, Easter-October. SIZE: 8 rooms. *STOCK: Books including antiquarian; stamps, coins, tokens, medals, postcards pre-1930, banknotes, military cap badges, antiquarian maps and prints.* LOC: Town centre. PARK: Easy. SER: Restorations (works of art on paper, canvas or board); framing and colouring.

Glance Gallery
17a Upper Church St. NP6 5EX. Open 10ish-5.30. SIZE: Large. *STOCK: Antiquarian prints and maps.* LOC: Town centre. PARK: Easy. SER: Valuations; restorations (canvas, board or paper); framing; hand-colouring.

Intaglio
(John Harrison). Est. 1995. By appointment only. SIZE: Small. *STOCK: Sculpture, marble, 19th to early 20th C, £500-£20,000.* PARK: Easy. TEL: 01291 621476 or 01873 810036; fax - 01291 621476; e-mail - intaglio@ukgateway.net; authorised seller on - Sothebys.com. SER: Valuations; restorations (cleaning and conservation; buys at auction (bronze and marble sculpture). FAIRS: NEC; Bailey.

Plough House Interiors
Upper Church St. NP6 5HU. (Mr and Mrs P. Jones). Est. 1972. Open 10-5, Sat. 10-4.30, Sun. by appointment. CL: Wed. SIZE: Large. *STOCK: Victorian and Edwardian furniture and shipping*

goods. LOC: 2 miles from Severn Bridge and M4. PARK: Easy. TEL: 01291 625200; home - same. SER: Valuations; restorations; buys at auction. VAT: Stan/Spec.

Seventh Heaven
Chirk Mill. LL14 5BU. Est. 1971. Open every day. SIZE: Large. *STOCK: Brass, iron and wooden beds including half-tester, four-poster and canopied, mainly 19th C.* LOC: B5070, below village, off A5 bypass. PARK: Easy. TEL: 01691 777622/773563; fax - 01691 777313; website - www.seventh-heaven.co.uk; e-mail - requests@ seventh-heaven.co.uk. VAT: Stan.

K.W. Finlay Antiques
The Forge, Neuaddlwyd. SA48 8DQ. Est. 1969. Usually open but prior telephone call advisable. SIZE: Medium. *STOCK: Furniture, 18th-20th C, £50-£3,000.* Not Stocked: Militaria, jewellery, smalls. LOC: A482. PARK: Easy. TEL: 01545 570536; home - same. VAT: Stan/Spec.

North Wales Antiques - Colwyn Bay
58 Abergele Rd. LL29 7PP. (F. Robinson). Est. 1958. Open 10-4. SIZE: Large warehouse. *STOCK: Shipping items, Victorian, early oak, mahogany and pine.* LOC: On A55. PARK: Easy. TEL: 01492 530521; evenings - 01352 720253. VAT: Stan.

Russell Worby
P O Box 43. LL29 8WS. Est. 1996. Open by appointment only. SIZE: Small. *STOCK: Welsh country furniture, 18th-19th C, £250-£15,000.* LOC: 3 miles from A55 expressway. PARK: Easy. TEL: 01492 512794; home/fax - same.

Paul Gibbs Antiques and Decorative Arts
25 Castle St. LL32 8AY. Open 10-5. *STOCK: Antiques and Decorative Arts, 1880-1940's; art pottery, especially major factories.* TEL: 01492 593429; fax - same.

Teapot World - Museum and Shop
25 Castle St. LL32 8AY. Open every day Easter to end Oct. *STOCK: Traditional and novelty*

Figure 1. Sarough Faraghan carpet, Central Persia, c.1900, 13ft. 7in. x 10ft. 5in., £16,025. (Sotheby's)

CARPETS

Jonathan Wadsworth

The new millennium has brought a number of interesting developments to the carpet market. The introduction of serious Internet auctions, the booming economies in the United States and, to a lesser degree, Europe, the revitalised interest in the art market as a whole and an increase in the global production of new goods have all influenced the market in the last year. Not to be lulled into a false sense of security, the volatility that has prevailed for the last decade still exists.

Essentially, the last year has seen a consolidation of the market. The emphasis has been on the acquisition of that which is considered the best. The question is, how does one classify that? Fashion has been a major determining factor, the technical quality of the object certainly taking second place; but there are indications that the scene is likely to change in this regard as the year progresses. The middle market has suffered and the lower end suffered considerably; with this in mind however, it is essential to look at the various areas within this vast marketplace in order to build a clear picture as to what has happened and as to what is likely to happen in the year ahead.

There is no doubt that the strongest area of the market has been in what is generally classified as the decorative market. This refers to carpets made during the latter years of the 19th century and the early years of the 20th century, essentially of large size (approximately over 12ft. by 9ft.) and, more particularly, carpets with dimensions of 18ft. long by 12ft. wide, up to 28ft. long by 16ft. wide. These larger-scale pieces are particularly sought after in the booming North American market. The optimum size of a New York apartment accommodates a carpet of 24ft. x 14ft. or thereabouts. However, not any old carpet of that size will do. The 'blond' look is in. Fine Tabriz carpets from North West Persia displaying overall designs, either small detailed patterns like the *herati* design, or bold patterns of large palmettes and scrolling vines command huge interest. The only provision is that the colours must be extremely subtle, ivory ground ideal, almost a monochromatic colour combination; in other words, safe colours with an appealing design – an overall repeat design preferred to those supporting a central medallion.

A carpet with an ivory coloured field and overall *herati* design achieved £34,500 against an estimate of £12,000-£18,000 at Sotheby's in October 1999. Not an object of great quality but the 'look' was perfectly in tune with current decorating styles. By comparison, in the same sale, a far superior quality carpet from Tabriz displaying an intricate *herati* design on a delicate terracotta ground and supporting a similarly decorated ivory central medallion, whilst achieving a good price of £27,600 (estimate £15,000-£20,000), should have achieved much more on the strength of artistic quality alone. Another all-over design carpet similar to the first example mentioned but not in such good condition, measuring 21ft. 3in. by 13ft. 4in., sold for £22,350 in April against an estimate of £15,000-£20,000.

The record so far this year goes to a Tabriz carpet dating to around 1900, 21ft. 7in. by 15ft., of coarse quality, but with that all-important look with bold ivory palmettes linked by scrolling vinery ending in leaves, all on a dove-grey background; it achieved a staggering £179,500, against an estimate of £10,000-15,000 in April. Few carpets of this colouration appear on the market, and the timing was perfect to appeal to the fashion-conscious buying market. So what will happen when the fashion changes? Remember, this was not a carpet of great quality.

Another important factor which may well have affected this price is the lifting of the trade embargo on Persian goods going to the States. The embargo had been in place since 1987 and has had a deleterious effect on the Persian carpet market during this time. Therefore there is now increased competition

Figure 2. Ushak carpet, West Anatolia, c.1890, 17ft. 9in. x 14ft. 3in., £17,175. (Sotheby's)

for Persian goods in a potentially hungry market. There is a real possibility of the fashion-conscious market shifting emphasis in a different direction, perhaps back towards the more traditional Persian carpets with their intense floral scrolls and rich deep colour palette. Time will tell, but the following two examples indicate that this could be so. In April Sotheby's offered a Sarough Faraghan carpet, circa 1900, 13ft. 7in. by 10ft. 5in. (figure 1) with a seemingly optimistic estimate of £12,000-£18,000; however, it sold for £16,025. Christie's sale in April included a Kashan Mochtasham carpet, 13ft. 4in. by 9ft. 9in., made with fine wool, a terracotta background colour supporting blue medallion and spandrels with the typical intense scrolling vines; this sold for £12,000 against an estimate of £7,000-£10,000.

The year has seen continuing popularity for other types of 19th century decorative carpet. From Persia, the Ziegler carpets with their timeless bold designs in pastel shades are still performing well and are becoming more scarce. The Heriz carpets from North West Persia are plentiful in supply, but the market is more unpredictable here, the accent is definitely on finer quality examples with softer colour combinations, the more ordinary types with bolder colours and coarser weave performing less well. Turkish Ushak carpets, which in recent years have become extremely popular, still remain strong. Figure 2 is a typical example of this popular type. Notice particularly the appealing colour palette and the bold design. This carpet, measuring 17ft. 9in. by 14ft. 3in. sold for £17,175 on an estimate of £12,000-£18,000. Such carpets again appeal to the fashion of the day. Will this market now falter with the lifting of the Persian embargo to the States? After all, there is little merit in the quality of such pieces, and they only started achieving such prices within the last decade whilst the ban has been in place. A definite case of 'watch this space'! Similarly, Indian carpets have proved popular in the last decade. Carpets were made in the jails in North India during the latter years of the 19th century, Agra and Amritsar being the most prolific centres of production. Figure 3 illustrates an Amritsar carpet, circa 1890, measuring 15ft. 3in. by 10ft 2in. A decorative tour de force, it sold for £15,450 against an estimate of £5,000-£7,000. The considerable

Figure 3. An Amritsar carpet, North India, c.1890, 15ft. 3in. x 10ft. 2in., £15,450. (Sotheby's)

Figure 4. A Kuba rug, North Caucasus, c.1880, 9ft. 2in. x 4ft. 1in., £13,150. (Sotheby's)

wear did not deter the competition. It is the look that counts.

The market has, without question, been focused on carpets as opposed to rugs, that is to say, pieces of smaller proportions. Unless the pieces are rare or of exceptional quality then there seems to be little interest, and certainly no increase in values. This applies to Persian town rugs, namely Kashan, Esfahan and Kerman, and tribal pieces from the South West of Persia, Ghashghai and Afshar. Where have the collectors gone?

The traditional collecting area of 19th century Caucasian rugs is also unpredictable. The emphasis here is on quality and condition, both critical factors in today's discerning market. The best of any type is holding up well with the rest finding little interest. Figure 4 illustrates a Kuba rug, circa 1880, 9ft. 2in. by 4ft. 1in., which displays a highly decorative design in wonderful jewel-like colours, presented in full pile, it sold in April for £13,150 (estimate £10,000-£15,000). Examples estimated in the £1,000-£5,000 price range are decidedly unpredictable, no real change here on recent years. Confidence has been knocked in this area as we are seeing a greater number of remarkably good reproductions and fakes made in Turkey creeping on to the market. This can have only a negative impact on the market, denting the confidence of potential new collectors or, at very worst, scaring them off entirely.

On the subject of reproductions,

the 19th century French Aubusson market has been under attack. In recent years these carpets have proved extremely popular for decoration, so much so that they are being reproduced in considerable quantities in China. The types most often manufactured now are in the late 19th century Napoleon III style in pastel colours. These reproductions have the advantage of being available in a range of sizes and presented in perfect condition, whereas period examples are often damaged – flat woven carpets are prone to splitting and tearing. For this reason, prices of period Napoleon III carpets, if not perfect, have fallen dramatically recently, sometimes by as much as two-thirds. I fear that this is a situation which is likely to become more prolific during the year ahead.

Jonathan Wadsworth is Head of the Rugs and Carpets Department at Sotheby's, London.

This article appeared in the July/August 2000 issue of **Antique Collecting** magazine. For more details and to subscribe see page 147.

teapots and tea-related items. Also permanent display of 1,000+ antique, rare and novelty teapots from 1730. TEL: 01492 596533; 01492 593429; fax - same; website - www.teapotworld. co.uk.

COWBRIDGE

Cowbridge Antique Centre
75 Eastgate. CF7 7AA. (T.C. Monaghan). Est. 1974. Open 10-5.30. SIZE: Medium. *STOCK: Furniture, 18th-19th C, £50-£1,000+; ceramics, 18th-20th C, £10-£750; collectables, 19th-20th C, £10-£500.* PARK: Easy. TEL: 01446 775841; home - same. SER: Valuations; restorations; upholstery.

Eastgate Antiques
6 High St. CF7 7AG. (Liz Herbert). Est. 1984. Open 10-1 and 2-5.30. CL: Mon. SIZE: Medium. *STOCK: Furniture, silver, jewellery, 18th C to Edwardian.* LOC: Off A48. PARK: Nearby. TEL: 01446 775111; home - 01446 773505. SER: Buys at auction (furniture). VAT: Stan/Spec.

Havard and Havard
59 Eastgate. CF71 7EL. (Philip and Christine Havard). LAPADA. Est. 1992. Open 10-1 and 2-5.30, Sat. 10-5.30. CL: Wed. and Mon. SIZE: Small. *STOCK: Oak, mahogany and walnut furniture especially provincial, £100-£10,000; metalware and samplers, £25-£1,000; all 18th-19th C.* LOC: Main street, 500 yards after lights on right. PARK: Easy. TEL: 01446 775021. SER: Valuations. VAT: Stan/Spec.

Renaissance Antiques
The Antiques Centre, Ebenezer Chapel, 48A Eastgate. CF7 7AB. (R.W. and J.A. Barnicott). Est. 1984. Open 10-5. SIZE: Small. *STOCK: Small furniture, Georgian, Victorian and Edwardian, £100-£3,000; brass, copper, plate, decorative ceramics, Staffordshire figures, objets d'art, 18th to 20th C, £5-£500.* Not Stocked: Coins, militaria, reproductions. LOC: Main street.

CRICCIETH

Capel Mawr Collectors Centre
21 High St. LL52 0BS. (Alan and Dee Turner). Resident. Est. 1991. Open in summer 10-5, Sun. 11-4. SIZE: Large. *STOCK: Books, from 18th C, £1-£500; postcards, 1894-1960, £1-£50; Sylvac, £5-£100.* LOC: A497. PARK: Nearby. TEL: 01766 523600; home - 01766 523435. SER: Valuations. VAT: Stan.

CRICKHOWELL

Gallop and Rivers Architectural Antiques
Ty'r Ash, Brecon Rd. NP8 1SF. (G. P. Gallop and R. A. Rivers). Open 9.30-5. *STOCK: Architectural items, pine and country furniture.* TEL: 01873 811084. VAT: Stan.

DEGANWY

Acorn Antiques
Castle Buildings. LL31 9EJ. (K.S. Bowers-Jones). Open 10-5. *STOCK: Ceramics, glass, furniture, pictures, brass and copper, 19th C.* TEL: 01492 584083.

FISHGUARD

Manor House Antiques
Main St. SA65 9HG. (R.E. Davies). Open in summer 10-5, prior 'phone call advisable in winter. *STOCK: General antiques especially porcelain and pottery.* TEL: 01348 873260.

GORSEINON, Nr. Swansea

Gold and Silver Shop
1 Cross St. SA1 1BA. (D. Paine). Open 9-2. *STOCK: Gold and silver, general antiques.* TEL: 01792 891874.

HAVERFORDWEST

Kent House Antiques
Kent House, Market St. SA61 1NF. (G. Fanstone and P. Thorpe). Est. 1987. Open 10-5. CL: Mon. SIZE: Medium. *STOCK: Victoriana, decorative items, hand-made rugs, £5-£500+.* LOC: Town centre. PARK: Easy. TEL: 01437 768175; home - same. SER: Valuations; restorations (furniture, some china).

Gerald Oliver Antiques
14 Albany Terrace, St. Thomas Green. SA61 1RH. Est. 1957. Open 9.30-4.30. *STOCK: Furniture, pre-1910, £20-£6,000; ceramics, treen, metalwork, silver, from £20; unusual, decorative and local interest items.* LOC: Via Freemans Way by-pass and up Merlins Hill. PARK: Easy. TEL: 01437 762794. SER: Valuations. VAT: Spec.

HAWARDEN

On the Air Ltd
The Vintage Technology Centre, The Highway.
CH5 3DN. (Steve Harris). Est. 1990. Open 10-5,
Sun. 11-4.30. CL: Mon. Christmas to Easter.
SIZE: Small. *STOCK: Vintage wireless, gramo-
phones and telephones, £50-£500.* LOC: Near St.
David's Park, Enloe, opposite Crown & Liver
public house. PARK: Rear of premises. TEL:
01244 530300; fax - same; website - www.
vintageradio.co.uk. SER: Valuations; restorations
(vintage wireless and gramophones). FAIRS:
National Vintage Communications, NEC and
Wembley.

HAY-ON-WYE

Richard Booth's Bookshop Ltd
44 Lion St. and Hay Castle. HR3 5AA. Est. 1974.
Open 7 days 9-5.30, later at weekends and during
summer. SIZE: Very large. *STOCK: Books,
magazines, photographs, records, postcards, leather
bindings.* LOC: Town centre. TEL: 01497 820322;
fax - 01497 821150; Hay Castle - 01497 820503; e-
mail - enquiries@richardbooth bookseller.com;
website (Hay-on-Wye Bookbuyers Ltd) - www.
booktown.org.

Hay Antique Market
6 Market St. HR3 5AF. Open 10-5, Sun. 11-5.
SIZE: 17 units. *STOCK: Antiques and collectables.* LOC: By the Butter Market. TEL: 01497
820175.

Hebbards of Hay
7 Market St. HR3 5AF. (P.E. Hebbard). Est.
1958. Open 10-5. SIZE: Small. *STOCK: Pottery
and porcelain.* LOC: A438, opposite the Post
Office. PARK: Own. TEL: 01497 820413.

Lion Fine Arts
19 Lion St. HR3 5AD. (Charles Spencer). Est.
1986. Open Mon., Thurs. and Sat. 10.30-5 (prior
'phone call advisable), other times by appointment. SIZE: Small. *STOCK: Pottery, porcelain
and glass, 18th to mid 19th C, £25-£250;
furniture, prints and objets d'art, £30-£900; some
second-hand and antiquarian books.* LOC: Turn
right from Oxford Rd. car park, then second
turning left. PARK: Limited. TEL: 01497
821726; home - same.

Rose's Books
14 Broad St. HR3 5DB. (Maria Goddard).
Resident. Est. 1992. Open 7 days. SIZE: Medium.
STOCK: Children's books, 1900-1960, £5-£25.
TEL: 01497 820013; fax - 01497 820031. SER:
Valuations. VAT: Stan.

Mark Westwood Antiquarian Books
High Town. HR3 5AE. ABA. PBFA. Est. 1976.
Open 10.30-5.30, including Sun. *STOCK:
Antiquarian and secondhand books on most
subjects, £2-£1,000.* TEL: 01497 820068. SER:
Valuations; buys at auction (antiquarian books).
VAT: Stan.

HOLT, Nr. Wrexham

Furn Davies Partnership
Rock Cottage, Bridge St. LL13 9JG. Open
Thurs., Fri. and Sat. 10-5, other times by
appointment. *STOCK: Furniture, 18th-19th C;
decorative items.* TEL: 01829 270210. SER:
Valuations; restorations.

HOLYHEAD (Anglesey)

Gwynfair Antiques
74 Market St. LL65 1UW. (Mrs. A.D. McCann).
Est. 1984. Open 10.30-4.30. CL: Tues. and Thurs.
SIZE: Small. *STOCK: China, ornaments, £5-
£250, furniture, £20-£1,000, all 1860-1950's.*
PARK: Loading outside shop, parking 100 yds.
TEL: 01407 763740; home - same. SER:
Valuations.

Country Antiques (Wales) BADA
Old Castle Mill. SA17 4UU. (R. and L. Bebb). LAPADA. Open Tues.-Sat. 10-5 or by appointment. SIZE: Large. STOCK: Welsh oak furniture and folk art; Welsh dressers, cupboards, clocks, pottery. LOC: Leave bypass (A484), into centre of village, turn by Boot and Shoe public house. PARK: Easy. TEL: 01554 890534; e-mail - info@countryantiqueswales.fsnet.co.uk; website - www.richardbebb.com. SER: Valuations; lectures. VAT: Stan/Spec.

Kidwelly Antiques
31 Bridge St. SA17 4UU. (R. and L. Bebb). Open 10-5. CL: Mon. SIZE: Large. STOCK: Georgian and Victorian furniture and accessories; collectables. LOC: Leave bypass (A484), into centre of village. PARK: Opposite shop. TEL: 01554 890328. VAT: Stan/Spec.

Offa's Dyke Antique Centre
4 High St. LD7 1AT. (Mrs. H. Hood and I. Watkins). Est. 1985. Open 10-1 and 2-5. SIZE: Medium - 16 dealers. STOCK: Pottery, bijouterie,18th-19th C furniture, £5-£1,000. LOC: Near town clock. PARK: Easy. TEL: 01547 528635; evenings - 01547 528940/560272.

Islwyn Watkins
4 High St. LD7 1AT. Est. 1978. Open 10-1 and 2-5. SIZE: Small. STOCK: Pottery including studio, 18th-20th C, £25-£1,000; country and domestic bygones, treen, 18th-20th C, £5-£200; small country furniture, 18th-19th C, £20-£600. Not Stocked: Jewellery, silver, militaria. LOC: By town clock. PARK: Easy. TEL: 01547 520145; home - 01547 528940. SER: Valuations.

Jim and Pat Ash
The Warehouse, 5 Station Rd. SA19 6NG. Est. 1977. Open 9.30-5. SIZE: Large. STOCK: Victorian and antique furniture, Welsh country, oak, mahogany, walnut. LOC: 50yds. off A40. PARK: Easy. TEL: 01558 823726/822130; fax - same. SER: Valuations. VAT: Stan/Margin/ Export.

Phillips Antiques
11 Market Sq. SA20 0AB. (Mr and Mrs P.A.

Wyvill-Bell). Open 9-5. SIZE: Small. *STOCK: Furniture, clocks and ceramics, 18th C.* LOC: A40. PARK: Nearby. TEL: 01550 421355; home - 01550 420945. SER: Valuations; restorations (furniture including French polishing, clocks).

LLANDUDNO

The Antique Shop
24 Vaughan St. LL30 1AH. (C.G. Lee). Est. 1938. Open 9-5.30. SIZE: Medium. *STOCK: Jewellery, silver, porcelain, glass, ivories, metalware, from 1700; period furniture, shipping goods.* LOC: Near promenade. PARK: Easy. TEL: 01492 875575.

LLANDUDNO JUNCTION

Collinge Antiques
Old Fyffes Warehouse, Conwy Rd. LL31 9LU. (Nicky Collinge). Est. 1978. Open seven days. SIZE: Large. *STOCK: General antiques including Welsh dressers, dining, drawing and bedroom furniture, clocks, porcelain and pottery, silver, copper and brass, paintings, prints, glass and collectables, mainly Victorian and Edwardian.* LOC: Just off A55, Deganwy exit

Valerie Ganz's watercolours of industrial scenes were a refreshing exception to the mass of rural landscapes at Margam. 'British Steel, Port Talbot', was sold to the National Museum of Wales for £2,200.

From an Auction Report by Christopher Wight entitled 'The Welsh Sale' held at Sotheby's, Margam Park, Glamorgan on 23rd March 2001. This featured in the June 2001 issue of **Antique Collecting** magazine. For more details and to subscribe see page 147.

(A546). PARK: Easy. TEL: 01492 580022; fax - same; e-mail - collinge.antiques@exl.co.uk. SER: Valuations; restorations including French polishing; buys at auction. VAT: Stan/Spec.

The Country Seat
35 Conwy Rd. LL31 9LU. (Steve and Helen Roberts). Open 10-4.30, Mon 10-1, Tues. 12-4, Sun. 12.30-4.30. SIZE: Small. *STOCK: Old and interesting items including paintings, pottery and porcelain, jewellery, furniture, linen, ephemera and bric-a-brac; decorative arts, 19th-20th C.* LOC: Just off A55. PARK: Easy. TEL: 01492 573256; e-mail - hkjroberts@hotmail.com; website - www.thecountryseat.co.uk.

LLANDYSUL, Nr. Newcastle Emlyn

Michael Lloyd Antiques
The Alma, Wind St. SA44 4BD. Est. 1987. Open by appointment. SIZE: Large. *STOCK: Country furniture, decorative items.* LOC: Village centre. TEL: 01559 363880. VAT: Stan/Spec. *Trade Only.*

LLANELLI

John Carpenter
SA14 7HA. Resident. Est. 1973. Open by appointment. *STOCK: Musical instruments, furniture, general antiques.* LOC: 5 minutes from Cross Hands. TEL: 01269 831094.

LLANERCHYMEDD (Anglesey)

Two Dragons Oriental Antiques
8 High St. LL71 8EA. Open by appointment. SIZE: Large warehouse. *STOCK: Chinese country furniture.* TEL: 01248 470204/470100.

LLANFAIR CAEREINION, Nr. Welshpool

Heritage Restorations
Maes y Glydfa. SY21 0HD. (Jo and Fran Gluck). Est. 1970. Open 9-5. SIZE: Large. *STOCK: Pine and country furniture, £50-£5,000; some oak and architectural items, all 18th-19th C.* LOC: A458 from Welshpool. Past village, after 2 miles take first left after river bridge and caravan park, then follow signs. PARK: Easy. TEL: 01938 810384; home - same; fax - 01938 810900; website - www.heritagerestorations.co.uk. SER: Restorations (furniture including pine stripping). VAT: Stan/Spec.

LLANGOLLEN

J. and R. Langford
12 Bridge St. LL20 8PF. (P. and M. Silverston). Est. 1960. CL: Thurs. pm. and 1-2 daily. SIZE: Medium. *STOCK: Furniture, £100-£7,000; pottery and porcelain, £50-£2,000; silver, general antiques, clocks, paintings, £20-£4,000; all 18th-20th C.* LOC: Turn right at Royal Hotel, shop on right. PARK: Easy. TEL: 01978 860182; home - 01978 860493. SER: Valuations.

Passers Buy (Marie Evans)
Oak St/Chapel St. LL20 8NR. (Mrs M. Evans). Est. 1970. Open 11-5 - always on Tues., Fri. and Sat, often on Mon., Wed. and Thurs. - prior 'phone call advisable, Sun. by appointment. SIZE: Medium. *STOCK: Furniture, Staffordshire figures, Gaudy Welsh, fairings and general antiques.* LOC: Just off A5. Junction of Chapel St. and Oak St. PARK: Easy. TEL: 01978 860861/757385. FAIRS: Anglesey (June and Oct.)

LLANGRISTIOLUS (Anglesey)

Michael Webb Fine Art
Cefn-Llwyn. LL62 5DN. LAPADA. Open by appointment only. *STOCK: Victorian and 20th C oil paintings and watercolours.* TEL: 01407 840336. SER: Valuations; restorations; framing. VAT: Spec.

LLANRWST

Carrington House
26 Ancaster Sq. LL26 0LD. (R. Newstead and John Roberts). Est. 1975. Open 10.30-1.30 and 2.30-5, Mon. 1.30-2.30; Mon. pm. and Sun. by appointment. SIZE: Medium. *STOCK: 19th C pine, £200-£1,000; oak and mahogany, 19th-20th C, £150-£2,000.* LOC: From A55 from Chester take A470. PARK: Easy. TEL: 01492 642500; fax - same; home - 01492 641279. SER: Valuations. VAT: Spec.

Prospect Books
18 Denbigh St. LL26 0LL. (M.R. and M.R. Dingle). Est. 1980. CL: Mon. SIZE: Small. *STOCK: Books.* LOC: A55. PARK: Easy. TEL: 01492 640111; fax - same; mobile - 07801 844430.

Snowdonia Antiques
LL26 0EP. (J. Collins). Est. 1961. Open 9-5.30, Sun. by appointment. SIZE: Medium. *STOCK: Period furniture especially longcase clocks.* LOC: Turn off A5 just before Betws-y-Coed on

WALES

to A496 for 4 miles. PARK: Easy. TEL: 01492
640789. SER: Restorations (furniture); repairs
(grandfather clocks).

MATHRY

Cartrefle Antiques
SA62 5AD. (M. Hughes and Y. Chesters). Open
in summer 10-5.30; in winter Wed.-Sat. 10.30-4.
STOCK: General antiques especially jewellery.
PARK: Easy. TEL: 01348 831591/837868.

MENAI BRIDGE (Anglesey)

Better Days
33 High St. LL59 5EF. (Mr and Mrs S. Rutter).
Est. 1988. Open 10.30-4.30, Wed. 11-1, Sat.
10.30-5. CL: Mon. SIZE: Small. *STOCK:
Decorative smalls, early 19th to mid 20th C, £5-
£200; furniture, late 19th to mid 20th C, £50-
£1,000; metal and miscellaneous, mid 19th C to
early 20th C, £10-£150.* PARK: Rear of premises.
TEL: 01248 716657; e-mail rosy@breathemail.net
SER: Pine stripping; buys at auction. FAIRS:
Mona Showground, Anglesey.

MILFORD HAVEN

Milford Haven Antiques
Robert St. SA73 2JQ. Est. 1968. Open 10-5.
STOCK: General antiques. TEL: 01646 692152.

MONMOUTH

Frost Antiques & Pine
8 Priory St. NP25 3BR. (Nicholas Frost).
Resident. Est. 1960. Open 9-5, Sun. and other
times by appointment. SIZE: Small. *STOCK:
Pine furniture and Staffordshire pottery, 19th C,
£100-£1,500.* PARK: Easy. TEL: 01600 716687;
website - www.frostantiques.com. SER: Valuations; restorations (furniture); buys at auction
(Victorian furniture and ceramics).

MOUNTAIN ASH

Trading Post
3-4 Oxford Buildings, Oxford St. CF45 3HE.
(Catherine Davies and Jeffrey Woodrow). Open
10-5. CL: Thurs. SIZE: Large. *STOCK:
Edwardian and Victorian pine, satinwood and
mahogany furniture; Continental items, china,
glass, pictures and textiles.* LOC: Take A4059 off
A470. PARK: Opposite. TEL: 01443 478855;
mobile - 07989 332514.

MURTON, Nr. Swansea

West Wales Antiques
18 Manselfield Rd. SA3 3AR. (W.H. Davies).
LAPADA. Est. 1956. Open 10-1 and 2-5. CL:
Mon. *STOCK: Porcelain, 18th C, £20-£800;
Welsh porcelain, 1800-1820; 18th-19th C
furniture, silver, pottery, glass, jewellery and
collectors' items.* LOC: M4-A4067-B4436,
entrance to Gower Peninsula. TEL: 01792
234318. VAT: Stan/Spec.

NARBETH

Malt House Antiques
Back Lane. SA67 7AR. (J. Williams and P.
Griffiths). Est. 1995. Open 10-5.30, Sun. 11-4.
SIZE: Large. *STOCK: Country furniture, 18th-
20th C, £5-£1,000.* LOC: Village centre. PARK:
Easy. TEL: 01834 860303.

NEWBRIDGE-ON-WYE
Nr. Llandrindod Wells

Allam Antiques
Old Village Hall. LD1 6HL. (Paul Allam). Est.
1985. Open 10-5, Sun. by appointment. SIZE:
Medium. *STOCK: Furniture, 1700-1930, £50-
£3,000; reproduction furniture, £50-£500.* LOC:
A470. PARK: Easy. TEL: 01597 860654; home -
01597 860455. SER: Valuations; restorations;
commission reproduction; paint stripping.

NEWCASTLE EMLYN

John Latter Antiques
3 Market Sq. SA38 9AQ. Est. 1959. Open 10-1
and 2-5, Sun. by appointment. SIZE: Small.
*STOCK: Decorative furniture, 18th-20th C,
£100-£200; fabrics, 19th-20th C, £100-£200;
objets de vertu, 18th-20th C, £50-£100.* LOC:
Town centre by clock tower. PARK: Easy. TEL:
01239 711117; home - 01239 711500; e-mail -
latter.nu; website - www.antiqueswales.co.uk.
SER: Valuations.

NEWPORT (Pembs.)

The Carningli Centre
East St. SA42 05Y. (Ann Gent and Graham
Coles). Est. 1994. Open 10-5.30, Sun. by appointment only. SIZE: Medium. *STOCK: Furniture,
17th-19th C, £50-£5,000; railwayana, nautical*

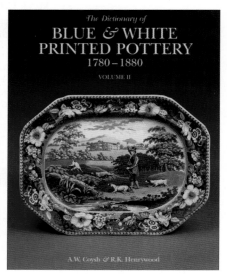

Designed as a comprehensively cross-referenced companion to the original *Dictionary*, this extensively illustrated volume includes 1,000 new or extended entries. These cover many previously unrecorded patterns, recent attributions, and newly discovered design sources. A feature is the Appendix illustrating unidentified patterns, which may be found by the diligent collector.

"No collector should be without both volumes, not only for reference, but because new designs by unknown potters keep coming to light"
Financial Times

"Vast amounts of information contained in either volume affordable by even the impecunious collector" **The Art Newspaper**

ISBN 1 85149 093 0
240pp., 28 col., 420 b.&w. illus.
£25.00/$49.50

This illustrated dictionary brings together as many facts as possible about blue and white printed pottery at the height of its popularity and production. It is a comprehensive guide to the firms, crafts-men, techniques, wares, patterns and titles as well as giving the background to the history of the ceramics industry and the personalities and problems involved in the production.

Bill Coysh has many books to his credit and was, until recently, President of the Friends of Blue Society. Dick Henrywood is a freelance author and lecturer on antiques and related subjects. He was a former member of the Friends of Blue and first Keeper of the Records.

ISBN 0 907462 06 5
424pp., 30 col., 706 b.&w. illus.
£35.00/$65.50

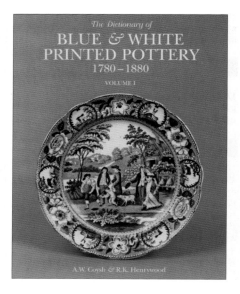

items, country collectables including oil lamps and tools, £1-£500; secondhand books, fine art gallery. PARK: Free in Long St. TEL: 01239 820724. SER: Valuations; restorations (furniture); polishing; turning; buys at auction (railwayana).

PEMBROKE

Pembroke Antiques Centre
Wesley Chapel, Main St. SA71 4DE. Open 10-5. SIZE: Large. *STOCK: Pine, oak, mahogany and shipping furniture; china, rugs, paintings, Art Deco enamel signs, kitchenalia, pottery, toys, curios and collectables..* TEL: 01646 687017.

PONTARDDULAIS, Nr. Swansea

The Emporium
112 St Teilo St. SA4 1SS. (Laura Jeremy). Est. 1992. Open 10.30-6. SIZE: Medium. *STOCK: Furniture, 1900-1950, £5-£500; Victorian metalware, collectables, bric-a-brac.* LOC: Off M4, junction 48. PARK: Easy. TEL: 01792 885185. SER: Restorations. FAIRS: Local.

PONTERWYD, Nr. Aberystwyth

Doggie Hubbard's Bookshop
Ffynnon Cadno. SY23 3AD. (Mrs Siiri Hubbard). ABA. Est. 1946. Open 10-5, Sun. by appointment. SIZE: Medium. *STOCK: Rare books on dogs, 18th-20th C, £50-£1,000; prints and pictures, £50-£1,500.* LOC: 1/2 mile from Ponterwyd westwards on A44. PARK: Easy. TEL: 01970 890224; home - same; e-mail - siiri@doggie hubbard.com. SER: Valuations; buys at auction (rare dog books).

PONTLLYFRII, Nr. Caernarfon

Sea View Antiques
LL54 5EF. (David A. Ramsell). Resident. Est. 1995. Open daily. SIZE: Small. *STOCK: General antiques and collectables, 18th-20th C, £5-£1,500.* LOC: Main Caernarfon to Pwllheli road. PARK: Easy. TEL: 01286 660436.

PORTHCAWL

Harlequin Antiques
Dock St. CF36 3BL. (Ann and John Ball). Est. 1974. Open 10-4. *STOCK: General antiques; textiles; early 19th to 20th C books.* TEL: 01656 785910.

Typical of the Welsh antiques offered at Margam Park, this 19th century painted sycamore harp sold for £2,400.

From an Auction Report by Christopher Wight entitled 'The Welsh Sale' held at Sotheby's, Margam Park, Glamorgan on 23rd March 2001. This featured in the June 2001 issue of **Antique Collecting** magazine. For more details and to subscribe see page 147.

Huw Williams Antiques

Madoc St. LL49 9LR. Est. 1993. Open 10-5, Mon. 12-5. CL: Wed. SIZE: Small. *STOCK: Weapons, 18th-19th C, £50-£3,000; country furniture, 18th-19th C, £100-£1,000; general antiques, 19th-20th C, to £300.* LOC: Opposite entrance to main car park. PARK: Opposite. TEL: 01766 514741; mobile - 07785 747561. FAIRS: Stockport Arms; International Arms, Motorcycle Museum, Birmingham; Gwyn Davies, Mona, Anglesey; Big Brum (Rag Market).

Rodney Adams Antiques

Hall Place, Old Town Hall and 62 High St. LL53 5DH. Resident. Est. 1965. CL: Sun. except by appointment. *STOCK: Longcase clocks, country oak and pine furniture.* TEL: 01758 613173; evenings - 01758 614337. VAT: Stan/Spec.

R. and S. M. Percival Antiques

Porth-y-Dwr, 65 Clwyd St. LL15 1HN. Est. 1979. Open daily, Sun. and Mon. by appointment. SIZE: Medium. *STOCK: Pine, mahogany and oak furniture and decorative smalls, 18th-19th C, £100-£1,000+.* PARK: Behind shop. TEL: 01824 704454; home - 01978 790370. SER: Valuations; buys at auction (furniture). FAIRS: Newark.

James Allan

22 Park St. SA1 3DJ. (S.J. Allan). Est. 1929. Open 9.30-4.30. SIZE: Small. *STOCK: Jewellery, 1850 to date, £50-£5,000.* LOC: Off Kingsway, round corner from Mothercare. PARK: Nearby. TEL: 01792 652176. SER: Valuations. VAT: Stan.

Bygone Antiques

12 St. Helens Rd. SA1 4AW. (C.A. Oliver). Open 9.30-5. *STOCK: China, furniture, linen and collectors' items.* TEL: 01792 468248.

Keith Chugg Antiques

Gwydr Lane, Uplands. Open 9-5.30, Sat. 9-1. *STOCK: Pianos and general antiques including furniture.* TEL: 01792 472477.

Clydach Antiques

83 High St., Clydach. SA6 5LJ. (R.T. Pulman). Open 10-5, Sat. 10-1. *STOCK: General antiques.* TEL: 01792 843209.

Dylan's Bookshop

Salubrious Passage. SA1 3RT. (J.M. Towns). Open 10-5. *STOCK: Antiquarian books on Welsh history and topography, Anglo/Welsh literature and general books.* TEL: 01792 655255; fax - same; website - www.dylans.com.

Anne and Colin Hulbert (Antiques)

17 Approach Rd., Manselton. SA5 8PD. Est. 1962. CL: Sun. pm. SIZE: Small. *STOCK: Shipping goods and general antiques.* PARK: Easy. TEL: 01792 653818; home - same. SER: Valuations; buys at auction (furniture). *Trade Only.*

Magpie Antiques

57 St. Helens Rd. SA1 4BH. (H. Hallesy). Est. 1984. Open 10-5. CL: Thurs. *STOCK: Ceramics including Swansea, Lllanelly and other Welsh potteries; oak and country furniture.* PARK: Opposite. TEL: 01792 648722. SER: Valuations; restorations (furniture).

Barn Court Antiques, Crafts & Tearoom

Barn Court. SA67 8SL. (D., A. and M. Evans). Est. 1989. Open 10-5. SIZE: Medium. *STOCK: Mahogany, walnut, rosewood and oak furniture, Georgian to late Victorian, £100-£3,000; oils and watercolours, £100-£2,000; china and glass, mainly Victorian, £10-£500.* LOC: Off A40 on A478 Narberth to Tenby road. PARK: Easy. TEL: 01834 861224; e-mail - info@barncourtantiques.com; website - www.barncourtantiques.com.

Audrey Bull

15 Upper Frog St. SA70 7DJ. Open 9.30-5. *STOCK: Period and Welsh country furniture, general antiques, especially jewellery and silver.* TEL: 01834 843114; workshop - 01834 871873; home - 01834 813425. VAT: Spec.

Potboard Antiques

Astridge Farm. SA70 8RE. (Nigel and Gill Batten). Est. 1987. Open by appointment only. *STOCK: 18th-19th C pine and country furniture.* LOC: Three miles from Tenby. TEL: 01834 842699; fax - 01834 842788; website - www.

potboard.co.uk. SER: Restorations (furniture, including stripping); buys at auction (pine). VAT: Spec.

TINTERN

Tintern Antiques
The Old Bakehouse. NP6 6SE. (Dawn Floyd). Open 9.30-5.30. *STOCK: Antique jewellery and general antiques.* TEL: 01291 689705.

TRECASTLE, Nr. Brecon

Trecastle Antiques Centre
The Old School. LD3 8YA. (A. Perry). Est. 1980. Open 10-5 including Sun. SIZE: Large. *STOCK: General antiques, £5-£1,500.* LOC: A40. PARK: Easy. TEL: 01874 638007. SER: Valuations; restorations. FAIRS: Newark, Shepton Mallet.

TREORCHY

All Old Exports Ltd.
Unit 35, Ynyswen Industrial Estate. CF42 6EP. (Steven Evans). Est. 1981. Open 9-5, Sat 10-5. SIZE: Warehouse. *STOCK: Victorian mahogany, Edwardian to 1920's oak, shipping goods.* LOC: Junction 34, M4, then A4119. PARK: Own. TEL: 01443 776410/431756; fax - 01443 776982; mobile - 07785 308567. SER: North American and Japanese market specialists; container packing and shipping. VAT: Stan/Spec.

TREVOR, Nr. Llangollen

Romantiques
Bryn Seion Chapel, Station Rd. LL20 7TP. (Miss S.E. Atkin). Est. 1994. Open 10-5 including Sun., or by appointment. SIZE: Large. *STOCK: Furniture, £50-£4,000; collectables, £1-£1,000; clocks and barometers, £50-£3,000.* LOC: Off A5 and A539 Llangollen roads. PARK: Easy. TEL: 01978 822879; mobile - 07778 279614; website - www.romantiques.co.uk. SER: Valuations; restorations (furniture, upholstery, clocks); courier. VAT: Stan/Spec.

TYWYN

Welsh Art
(Miles Wynn Cato). Open by appointment only (also in London). *STOCK: Welsh paintings, 1550-1950; Welsh portraits of all periods and*

historical Welsh material. TEL: 020 7259 0306 and 01654 711715.

VALLEY, Nr. Holyhead (Anglesey)

Ann Evans
Carna Shop, Station Rd. LL65 3HB. Open Thurs.-Sat. 10-4.30, other days by appointment. *STOCK: Oak dressers, Welsh pottery, cranberry glass, Staffordshire figures.* PARK: Easy. TEL: 01407 741733

WELSHPOOL

A. & H. Antiques
19 High St. SY21 7JP. Est. 1980. Open 10-5, Sat. 10-2. CL: Tues. SIZE: Small. *STOCK: Furniture, 18th-19th C; china.* LOC: Off A483. PARK: Easy. TEL: 01938 552421; home - same; e-mail - anh.antiques@amserve.net. SER: Valuations; buys at auction. FAIRS: Shepton Mallett. *Trade Only.*

F.E. Anderson and Son
5-6 High St. SY21 7JF. (D. and I. Anderson). LAPADA. Open daily. *STOCK: Furniture, 17th-19th C; mirrors, paintings and early metalware.* TEL: 01938 553340; home - 01938 590509; mobile - 07889 896832.

William Lyssel Dommersen (1850-1927), 'On the Lyssec, Meer Hoorn'; tampered signature and inscription verso, oil on canvas, 15½in. x 23½in. Worth about £1,000. A wholly authentic William, tampered and upgraded to be passed off as Pieter Christian Dommersen.

In his practical approach to spotting fakes and forgeries, Richard Kay identifies seven categories of which the collector should beware. From an article entitled 'Guilty Until Proven Innocent' by Richard Kay which appeared in the October 2000 issue of **Antique Collecting** magazine. For more details and to subscribe see page 147.

Index of Packers and Shippers:
Exporters of Antiques (Containers)

AR · GS International Transport Ltd.

SHIPPERS & PACKERS OF ANTIQUES, FINE ART & REMOVALS TO **ITALY**

Tel: 020 7833 3955 or 01444 414667
Fax: 020 7837 8672

**North London Freight Centre,
York Way, Kings Cross, London N1 OBB**

LONDON

Anglo Pacific International plc
Standard Rd., NW10 6DF. LAPADA. Tel: 020 8838 8008; fax - 020 8453 0225; e-mail - antiques@anglopacific.co.uk. *Specialist antique and fine art packers and shippers serving worldwide destinations by land, sea or air. Free estimates and advice. Courier sevices available.*

AR. GS International Transport Ltd
North London Freight Centre, York Way, Kings Cross, N1 0BB. Tel: 020 7833 3955; fax - 020 7837 8672. *Fine art and antiques removals by road transport, Europe, especially Italy, door-to-door service. Documentation.*

Art Logistics Ltd
2 Old Oak Common Lane. NW10 6DX. LAPADA. Tel: 020 8961 7627; fax - 020 8961 8764; e-mail - mail@antlogistics.co.uk. *Fine art packing, freight forwarding.*

**Atlantic Fine Art & Antiques
(Packing & Shipping) Ltd**
Unit 23 Riverside Business Park, Lyon Rd., Merton. SW19 2RL. Tel: 020 8544 9919; fax - 020 8542 3085; e-mail - oricordini@aol.com. *Fine art and antiques packers and shippers; international household removals.*

B B F Fine Art Services Ltd
Copenhagen House, Copenhagen Place, E14 7DE. Tel: 020 7515 7005; fax - 020 7515 6001; e-mail - mailbox@bbfwwide.demon.co.uk; website - www.bbfwwide.demon.co.uk. *Fine art packers, worldwide shippers by sea, air and road.*

Robert Boys Shipping

Unit D Tunnel Avenue Trading Estate, Tunnel Avenue, Greenwich SE10 0QH. LAPADA. Tel: 020 8858 3355; fax - 020 8858 3344; e-mail - boysship@ftech.co.uk. *Worldwide shipping. Air and sea cargo. Specialists in fine art and furniture to Japan with part load containers to Japan on a weekly basis. Japanese speaking staff.*

Constantine Ltd

Constantine House, 134 Queens Rd., SE15 2HR. LAPADA. Tel: 020 7732 8123; fax - 020 7732 2631. *Specialists in the international movement of antiques and fine art for over a hundred and fifty years - services incorporate all requirements from case making to documentation and insurance. Freight groupage specialists.*

Davies Turner Worldwide Movers Ltd.

London Headquarters : 49 Wates Way, Mitcham, CR4 4HR. Tel: 020 7622 4393; fax - 020 7720 3897; e-mail - antiques@daviesturner.co.uk. *Fine art and antiques packers and shippers. Courier and finder service. Full container L.C.L. and groupage service worldwide.*

Focus Packing Services Ltd

37-39 Peckham Rd., SE5 8UH. Tel: 020 7703 4715; fax - same; e-mail - A.clough@tinyonline. co.uk.

Gander and White Shipping Ltd.

Head Office, 21 Lillie Rd., SW6 1UE. LAPADA. Tel: 020 7381 0571; fax - 020 7381 5428. *Specialist packers and shippers of antiques and works of art.*

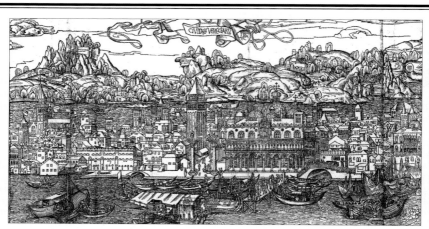

The City of Venice, 1483 (detail) from Bernhard Breydenbach's Peregrinatio in Terram Sanctam, Mainz. Woodcut by Erhard Reuwich.

From an article entitled 'Marine Painting: Part I' by James Taylor which appeared in the October 2000 issue of **Antique Collecting** magazine. For more details and to subscribe see page 147.

LONDON - NEW YORK - PARIS

UNITED KINGDOM
Gander & White Shipping Ltd.
21 Lillie Road, London SW6 1UE
Tel: 00 44 20 7381 0571
Fax: 00 44 20 7381 5428

Newpound, Wisborough Green, Billingshurst,
West Sussex RH14 0AY
Tel: 00 44 1403 70 00 44
Fax: 00 44 1403 70 08 14

FRANCE
Gander & White Shipping Ltd.
8, rue de Duras, 75008 Paris
Tél: 01 43 12 31 32
Fax: 01 43 12 31 33

USA
Gander & White Shipping Inc.
21-44, 44th Road, Long Island City
New York 11101
Tel: 00 1 718 784 8444
Fax: 00 1 718 784 9337

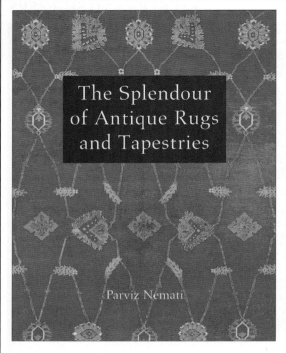

Hedleys Humpers Ltd

3 St Leonards Rd., North Acton NW10 6SX. LAPADA. Tel: 020 8965 8733 (10 lines); fax - 020 8965 0249. *Weekly door to door services to Europe, plus part load shipments by air and sea worldwide. Offices in London, Paris and New York.*

Interdean.Interconex

Central Way, Park Royal, NW10 7XW. Tel: 020 8961 4141; telex - 922119; fax - 020 8965 4484. *Antiques and fine art packed, shipped and airfreighted worldwide. Storage and international removals. Full container L.C.L. and groupage service worldwide.*

Interpack Worldwide plc

Hannah CloseGreat Central Way. NW10 0UX. Tel: 020 8965 5550; fax - 020 8453 0544. *Worldwide shipping, packing, insurance.*

Berengaria by Charles Turner from a series for Cunard.

From an article entitled 'Ocean Liner Postcards and Marine Art' by Robert Wall which appeared in the February 2001 issue of **Antique Collecting** magazine. For more details and to subscribe see page 147.

Kuwahara Ltd.

6 McNicol Drive, NW10 7AW. LAPADA. Tel: 020 8963 1100; fax - 020 8963 0100; e-mail - kuwahara@uk2.so-net.com. *Specialist packers and shippers of antiques and works of art. Regular groupage service to Japan.*

Lockson Services Ltd

29 Broomfield St., Limehouse, E14 6BX. LAPADA. Tel: 020 7515 8600 (6 lines); fax - 020 7515 4043; mobile (weekends) - 07831 621428; New York office - 201 392 9800; fax - 201 392 8830; e-mail - enquiries@lockson.co.uk; website -

This Marklin grey mountain Etat locomotive is included in Christie's South Kensington sale Trains Galore on 18th December. Estimate £4,000-£6,000.

From an Auction Preview which appeared in the December 2000/January 2001 issue of **Antique Collecting** magazine. For more details and to subscribe see page 147.

www.lockson.co.uk. *Specialist packers and shippers of fine art and antiques by air, sea and road to the USA, Japan, Far East, Canada and other worldwide destinations. A complete personalised service. At all Olympia, Newark and Ardingly fairs.*

Masterpack Ltd - Fine Art Packers & Shippers
Nationwide Building, Stanley Gardens, The Vale, W3 7SZ. Tel: 020 7262 8274; fax - 020 7262 5334. *Fine art packers and shippers. Personal service guaranteed.*

Momart Ltd
199-205 Richmond Rd., E8 3NJ. Tel: 020 8986 3624; fax - 020 8533 0122; e-mail - enquiries@ momart.co.uk. *Fine art handling including transportation, case making and packing: import/export services, exhibition installation and storage.*

Stephen Morris Shipping plc
North London Freight Depot, York Way, N1 0UZ. Tel: 020 7713 0080; fax - 020 7713 0151; e-mail - enquiries@stemo.co.uk; website - www. stemo.co.uk. *Specialist packers and shippers of antiques and fine art worldwide. Weekly European service.*

Nelson Shipping
Unit C3, Six Bridges Trading Estate, Marlborough Grove, SE1 5JT. Tel: 020 7394 7770; fax - 020 7394 7707. *Expert export and packing service.*

The Packing Shop
6-12 Ponton Rd., SW8 5BA. Tel: 020 7498 3255; fax - 020 7498 9017. *Fine art and antiques export packed. World-wide shipping, scheduled European vehicles, New York weekly consols. International exhibitions. High security bonded storage. New York office and warehouse.*

Pitt and Scott Ltd
60 Coronation Rd., NW10 7PX. Tel: 020 7278 5585; fax - 020 7278 5592; e-mail - enquiries@ pittandscott.co.uk. *Packers and shippers of antiques and fine art. Shipping, forwarding and airfreight agents. Comprehensive service provided for visiting antique dealers. Insurance arranged.*

Robinsons International
The Gateway, Staples Corner. NW2 7AJ. LAPADA. Tel: 020 8208 8484; fax - 020 8208 8488; website - www.robinsons-intl.com. *Specialist packers and shippers of antiques and fine art worldwide. Established over 100 years.*

T. Rogers and Co. Ltd
PO Box No. 8, 1A Broughton St., SW8 3QL. Tel: 020 7622 9151; fax - 020 7627 3318. *Specialists in storage, packing, removal, shipping and forwarding antiques and works of art. Insurance.*

Trans-Euro Fine Art Division
Drury Way, Brent Park, NW10 0JN. LAPADA.
Tel: 020 8784 0100; fax - 020 8459 3376.
*Specialist packing and worldwide shipping
services by air, sea and road. Single items, part
loads or full containers. Courier and buyer
services.*

BUCKINGHAMSHIRE

Clark's of Amersham
Higham Mead, Chesham. HP5 2AH. Tel: 01494
774186; fax - 01494 774196; website - www.
bluelorry.com. *Removals and storage, domestic
and commercial; export packing and shipping -
worldwide door to door.*

CHESHIRE

The Rocking Chair Antiques
Unit 3, St. Peters Way, Warrington, WA27 7BL.
Tel: 01925 652409; fax - same; mobile - 07774
492891. *Exporters and packers.*

DEVON

Barnstaple Removal
14/15 Meadow Way, Treebeech Rural Enterprise
Park, Gunn, Barnstaple. EX32 7NZ. Tel: 01271
831164; fax - 01271 831165; e-mail - barnstaple.
removals@sosi.net; website - www. barnstaple.
removals.co.uk. *Container packing and shipping
worldwide.*

Bishop's Blatchpack
Kestrel Way, Sowton Industrial Estate, Exeter, EX2
7PA. Tel: 01392 202040; fax - 01392 201251.
International fine art packers and shippers.

DORSET

Alan Franklin Transport
26 Blackmoor Rd., Ebblake Industrial Estate,
Verwood, BH31 6BB. LAPADA. Tel: 01202
826539; fax - 01202 827337. *Container packing
and shipping. Weekly door-to-door European
service. Paris office - 2 Rue Etienne Dolet, 93400
St. Ouen, Paris. Tel: 00 33140 115000; fax - 00
33140 114821. South of France office - Quartier
la tour de Sabran, 84440 Robion (Vaucluse). Tel:
00 33490 764900; fax - 00 33490 764902.
Belgian office - De Klerckstraat 41, B8300,
Knokke. Tel: 00 3250 623579; fax - same.*

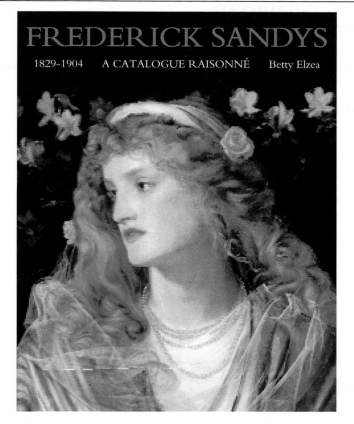

L.J. Roberton
Established 1948

ANTIQUE AND FINE ART SPECIALISTS IN PACKING AND SHIPPING

Door to Door Worldwide Service By Air, Sea & Road

Comprehensive Customs Documentation Service With Full Storage Facilities.

OVER 50 YEARS' EXPERIENCE OFFERING A PERSONAL SERVICE AT COMPETITIVE AND REALISTIC COSTS.

Mallard House, 402 Roding Lane South, Woodford Green, Essex IG8 8EY
Tel: (020) 8551-9188 Fax: (020) 8551-9199 Email: international@harrowgreen.com

ESSEX

Geo. Copsey and Co. Ltd
178 Crow Lane, Romford. RM7 0ES. Tel: 01708 740714 or 020 8592 1003. *Worldwide packers and shippers.*

Crown Worldwide Movers
Security House, Abbey Wharf Industrial Estate, Kingsbridge Rd., Barking, IG11 0BD. Tel: 020 8591 3388; fax - 020 8594 4571. *Packers and shippers - 12 offices throughout U.K.*

L.J. Roberton
Mallard House, 402 Roding Lane South, Woodford Green, IG8 8EY. LAPADA. Tel: 020 8551 9188; fax - 020 8551 9199.

GLOUCESTERSHIRE

The Removal Company - Loveday & Loveday
2 Wilkinson Rd., Cirencester, GL7 1YT. Tel: 01285 651505. *Shipping and packing.*

Part of a collection of 59 candle extinguishers which will come under Robin A. Fenner's hammer in Tavistock on 23rd October.

From an Auction Preview which appeared in the October 2000 issue of **Antique Collecting** magazine. For more details and to subscribe see page 147.

The Shipping Company
Exporting made easy
For a quotation, please:
Telephone: 01451 822451 Fax: 01451 810985
www.theshippingcompanyltd.com
Email: enquiries@theshippingcompanyltd.com

Bourton Industrial Park, Bourton-on-the-Water
Cheltenham, Gloucestershire GL54 2HQ

The Shipping Company Ltd.
Bourton Industrial Park, Bourton-on-the-Water.
GL54 2HQ 01451 822451; fax - 01451 810985;
website - www.theshippingcompanyltd.com.
*Export packers and shippers specialising in the
antique, fine art and interior design markets
worldwide. Single, consolidated and full
container shipments by air and sea. All risks
insurance offered.*

A.J. Williams (Shipping)
607 Sixth Ave., Central Business Park, Hengrove,
Bristol, BS14 9BZ. LAPADA. Tel: 01275
892166; fax - 01275 891333.

Robinsons International
16 Millbank St., Southampton, SO14 5QQ.
LAPADA. Tel: 023 8022 0069; fax - 023 8033
1274; e-mail - southampton@robinsons-intl.com;
website - www.robinsons-intl.com. *Specialist
packers and shippers of antiques and fine art
worldwide. Established over 100 years.*

Robinsons International
Telford Rd., Basingstoke, RG21 6YU. LAPADA.
Tel: 01256 465533; fax - 01256 324959; website
- www.robinsons-intl.com. *Specialist packers and
shippers of antiques and fine art worldwide.
Established over 100 years.*

Sutton Valence Antiques
North St., Sutton Valence, Maidstone, ME17
3AP. LAPADA. Tel: 01622 843333; fax - 01622
843499; e-mail - svantiques@aol.com; website -
www.svantiques.co.uk. *Antique and shipping
furniture. Container packing and shipping.
Facilities for 20ft and 40ft containers, all
documentation. Worldwide service.*

Robinsons International
32 Stanley Rd., Manchester, M45 8QX.
LAPADA. Tel: 0161 766 8414; fax - 0161 767
9057; website - www.robinsons-intl.com.
*Specialist packers and shippers of antiques and
fine art worldwide. Established over 100 years.*

John Mason International Ltd
35 Wilson Rd., Huyton Business Park, Liverpool,
L36 6AE. LAPADA. Tel: 0151 449 3938. *Specialist
packer, full and part container loads, groupage
service worldwide, courier and finder service.*

Air-Sea Packing Group Ltd
Air-Sea House, Third Cross Rd., Twickenham,
TW2 5EB. Tel: 020 8893 3303; fax - 020 8893
3068; e-mail - aspuk@airseapacking.com; website
- www.airseapacking.com. *Specialist packers and
shippers.*

McN International
Unit 10 Shield Drive, West Cross Centre,
Brentford. TW8 8EX. Tel: 020 8580 1001; fax -
020 8580 1002. *Fine interiors project manage-
ment, antique and fine art shippers, incorporating
Vitesse in conjunction with Federal Express.*

Nippon Express (UK) Ltd
Ocean Freight Division, Unit 7, Parkway Trading
Estate, Cranford Lane, Heston, Hounslow, TW5
9NE. Tel: Commercial (Export) - 020 8737 4240;
fax - 020 8737 4249; (Import) - 020 8737 4260;
fax - 020 8737 4269; Removal (Cargo) - 020 8737
4200; fax - 020 8737 4209. *Mainly Japanese
imports/exports, both commercial and removals.
Also import/export all other Far East countries.*

Oakey Removals Limited

Modern Fleet
Carriers of Antiques and Fine Art
Household Removals and Storage
Single Piece to Full Loads
Countrywide Service
Keen Competitive Pricing

Ring *John Oakey*

on *01636 706122*
or fax *01636 605182*

to discuss your requirements

Oakey Removals Limited, Unit 1
1 Sanigar Court, Whittle Close, off Brunel
Drive,
Newark on Trent, Nottingham NG24 2DT

Sovereign International Freight Ltd
Sovereign House, 8-10 St. Dunstans Rd., Feltham, TW13 4JU. Tel: 020 8751 3131; fax - 020 8751 4517; e-mail - info@sovereignlondon. co.uk. *Heathrow Airport based shippers and packers registered to BS 5750 quality. Holders of the Queen's Award for Export and National Training Award. Specialist in antiques and the fine art trades.*

Vulcan International Services Ltd
Units 13/14, Ascot Rd., Clockhouse Lane, Feltham, TW14 8QF. LAPADA. Tel: 01784 244152; 01784 248183. *Fine art packers and shippers worldwide.*

NOTTINGHAMSHIRE

Oakey Removals Ltd
Unit 1, 1 Sanigar Court, Whittle Close, off Brunel Drive, Newark on Trent, Nottingham. NG24 2DT. Tel: 01636 706122; fax - 01636 605182. *Carriers of antiques and fine arts. Household removals and storage. Single items or full loads, countrywide service.*

OXFORDSHIRE

Cotswold Carriers
Unit 2 The Walk, Hook Norton Rd., Chipping Norton, OX7 5TG. Tel: 01608 730500; fax - 01608 730600. *Removals, storage, shipping, door-to-door Continental deliveries.*

Robinsons International
Nuffield Way, Abingdon, OX14 1TN. LAPADA. Tel: 01235 552255; fax - 01235 553573; website - www.robinsons-intl.com. *Specialist packers and shippers of antiques and fine art worldwide. Established over 100 years.*

Hugh Thomas Shipping
Park House, Bladon, Woodstock. OX20 1RW. Tel: 01993 812817; fax - 01993 812912; e-mail - hughthomas@htshipping.com; website - www. htshipping.com. *Antique furniture exporter and shipper. Finder service. Single items or many shipped to all USA cities. Large free pick up area. Large dealer co-operative in USA. Full and half container rates also available.*

Samuel Scott, 'Custom House Quay', oil on canvas, 48in. x 24in. Almost certainly a composite image of various maritime locations close to the Thames. Scott painted several versions of this picture. (Private collection)

From an article entitled 'Marine Painting: Part I' by James Taylor which appeared in the October 2000 issue of **Antique Collecting** magazine. For more details and to subscribe see page 147.

SOMERSET

Louis Degregorio
Old Bacon Factory, Huntspill Rd., Highbridge, TA9 3DE. Tel: 01278 788590/788603. *Packing, transport, shipping goods.*

Robinsons International
Aldermoor Way, Longwell Green, Bristol. BS30 7DA. LAPADA. Tel: 0117 980 5858; fax - 0117 980 5830; website - www.robinsons-intl.com. *Specialist packers and shippers of antiques and fine art worldwide. Established over 100 years.*

STAFFORDSHIRE

Crown Relocations
Crown House, Unit 1 Ninian Way, Tame Valley Industrial Estate, Wilnecote, Tamworth, B77 5ES Tel: 01827 264100; fax - 01827 264101.

Kenpack
65 Newcastle Rd., Leek, ST13 5RT. Tel: 01538 399670; fax - 01538 398175. *Open Mon.-Fri. 8.30-5. Container packing and export documentation.*

SURREY

W. Ede & Co
The Edes Business Park, Restmor Way, Wallington, SM2 5AA. Tel: 020 8773 9933; fax - 020 8773 9011. *Worldwide packing and shipping, complete documentation and removals service, container packing.*

SUSSEX EAST

Global Services
West St., Lewes, BN7 2NJ. Tel: 01273 475903. *Packers and shippers of antiques, arms, armour and fine works of art.*

SUSSEX WEST

Gander and White Shipping Ltd
Newpound, Wisborough Green, Billingshurst, RH14 0AY. LAPADA. Tel: 01403 700044; fax - 01403 700814; e-mail - ukinfo@ganderandwhite.com. *Specialist packers and shippers of fine art and antiques.*

Martells International
Queen's Rd., East Grinstead. RH19 1BA. Tel: 01342 321303; fax - 01342 317522. *National and international removers, export packers and shippers.*

TYNE AND WEAR

Owen Humble (Packing and Shipping) Ltd
Clayton House, Walbottle Rd., Lemington, Newcastle-upon-Tyne, NE15 9RU. Tel: 0191 267 7220. *Worldwide service.*

WEST MIDLANDS

The British Shop - Shipping U.S.A.
Old Sandwell House, Sandwell St., Walsall, WS1 3DR. Tel: 01922 721088; fax - 01922 723123; (USA - 336 434 4645; fax - 336 434 7765) *Weekly container from Birmingham to High Point, North Carolina, USA. Pick-up and pack, no minimums.*

Clentons Removals Ltd.
94 Caldmore Road, Walsall. WS1 3PD 01922 624431; fax - 01922 613053; e-mail - clentons@yahoo.co.uk; website - www.clentonsremovals.com. *Collections arranged in UK and Europe for clients' goods. Storage available. Packing and wrapping of all goods for container shipments. All paperwork done for containers. Packing of containers and shipment of containers.*

ART BOOK SERVICES

Art Book Services are delighted to announce that their new 2001 mail-order catalogue is now available!

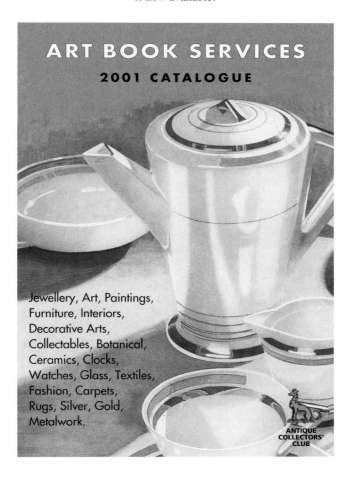

With over 250 book titles there is sure to be something of interest to all *Antique Collecting* subscribers, whatever their interest. Not only will you find select titles from the Antique Collectors' Club **Standard Works of Reference** but also the very best new titles from a wide range of art publishers from around the world.

To request your free catalogue please telephone
Art Book Services today on 01394 385504.

Robinsons International
22A Bartleet Rd., Washford, Redditch B98 0DG.
LAPADA. Tel: 01527 830860; fax - 01527
500777; website - www.robinsons-intl.com.
*Specialist packers and shippers of antiques and
fine art worldwide. Established over 100 years.*

WILTSHIRE

Martin Bros Ltd
The Old Sawmills, The Street, Kilmington, Nr.
Warminster. BA12 6RG. Tel: 01985 844144; fax
- 01985 844113. *Specialist carriers of fine art
and furniture throughout mainland UK.*

WORCESTERSHIRE

Simon Hall Freight
Willersey Industrial Estate, Willersey, Nr.
Broadway, WR12 7RR. Tel: 01386 858555; fax -
01386 858501. *Specialist packers and shippers for
fine art and antiques world wide. UK collections
and deliveries. Humidity controlled containerised
and conventional storage.*

YORKSHIRE EAST

Peter Smith t/a Boothferry Antiques
388 Wincolmlee, Hull, HU2 0QL. Tel: 01482
225220/666033. *Single items or container loads.
Couriers covering north of England. Full
documentation.*

SCOTLAND

Crown Relocations
Containerbase, Gartsherrie Rd., Coatbridge,
Lanarkshire. ML5 2DT. Tel: 01236 449666; fax -
01236 449888. *Packers and shippers.*

Bloomsbury Book Auctions

3 and 4 Hardwick St., EC1R 4RY. Tel: 020 7833 2636/7; fax - 020 7833 3954; e-mail - info@ bloomsbury-book-auct.com; website - www. bloomsbury-book-auct.com. *Twenty-four sales a year of books on all subjects and of all values, manuscripts, autograph letters, prints, maps, drawings, photographs, posters and ephemera. Valuations. Collection service.*

Bonhams & Brooks, Knightsbridge

Montpelier St., Knightsbridge, SW7 1HH. Tel: 020 7393 3900; fax - 020 7393 3905. *Regular auctions of vintage motor cars, automobilia, sporting items, watercolours, Old Masters, European and modern pictures, portrait miniatures, prints, carved frames, furniture, clocks and watches, Lalique, commercial scent bottles, Oriental and contemporary ceramics, objects of art, tribal art and antiquities, silver, jewellery, objects of vertu, books and manuscripts, antique and modern guns, musical instruments, Oriental carpets and rugs. Annual theme sales to coincide with Cowes Week, The Boat Show and The Westminster Dog Show, NY - pictures, sculptures and related works of art. Viewing Mon.-Fri. 9-4.30, Sun. 11-3.*

Bonhams Chelsea

65-69 Lots Rd., Chelsea, SW10 0RN. Tel: 020 7393 3900; fax - 020 7393 3906. *Regular sales of British, European and Russian pictures including watercolours, oils, prints and frames; clocks; ceramics including Art Nouveau & Art Deco; furniture, carpets & objects of art; light fittings and garden statuary; collectors items such as toys, dolls & teddies, textiles, cameras & scientific instruments, rock & pop, rare records & entertainment sales. Viewing Mon.-Fri. 9-4.30, Sun. 11-4.*

Christie's

8 King St., St.James's, SW1Y 6QT. Tel: 020 7839 9060; fax - 020 7839 1611. *Porcelain, pottery, objets d'art and miniatures, pictures including Old Masters, English, Victorian, Continental, Impressionist, Contemporary, prints, drawings, watercolours, Art Deco, Art Nouveau; Japanese and Chinese, Islamic and Persian works of art; glass, silver, jewellery, books, modern guns, furniture, carpets, tapestries, clocks and watches, garden statuary, photographs, Russian works of art, sculpture, wine, house sales (contents only).*

Christie's South Kensington Ltd

85 Old Brompton Rd., SW7 3LD. Tel: 020 7581 7611; fax - 020 7321 3311. *Sales of jewellery,*

This large 'stumpwork' picture with raised (padded) embroidery mounted on a satin ground and with additional directly embroidered motifs (all delightfully out of scale, as they were taken from various sources) shows a female figure, probably representing the delightful sense, smell, framed in a cartouche of embroidered laurel leaves.

From an article entitled 'Needlework Furnishings – a Crucial Feature of Historic Interiors by Lanto Synge which appeared in the May 2001 issue of **Antique Collecting** magazine. For more details and to subscribe see page 147.

silver, pictures, watercolours, drawings and prints; furniture and carpets, ceramics and works of art, printed books; costume, textiles and embroidery; toys and games, dolls, wines, Art Nouveau, Art Deco, cameras. Periodic sales of automata, mechanical music and vintage machines, motoring and aeronautical items including car mascots; Staffordshire portrait figures, miniatures.

Stanley Gibbons Auctions

399 Strand, WC2R 0LX. Tel: 020 7836 8444; fax - 020 7836 7342; e-mail - auctions@stanley gibbons.co.uk; website - www.stanleygibbons. com. 1901. *Regular auctions throughout the year.*

Glendining's and Co

101 New Bond St., W1S 1SR. Tel: 020 7493 2445. *Specialist auctioneers of coins and medals. Quarterly sales of coins; three sales annually of orders, decorations and medals.*

Harmers of London Stamp Auctioneers Ltd.

111 Power Rd., Chiswick, London W4 5PY. Tel: 020 8747 6100; fax - 020 8996 0649. *Auctions of Great Britain, British Commonwealth, foreign countries, airmail stamps, also postal history and literature, stamp boxes, postal scales and related ephemera, monthly. Fully illustrated catalogues. Valuations for sale, probate or insurance.*

Hornsey Auctions Ltd

54-56 High St., Hornsey. N8 7NX. Tel: 020 8340 5334; fax - same. *Sales weekly on Wed. at 6.30. Viewing Tues. 5-7.30 and Wed. from 10. Open Thurs., Fri. 9.30-5.30 and Sat. 10-4 to take in for next auction.*

Lloyds International Auction Galleries Ltd

118 Putney Bridge Rd., Putney, SW15 2NQ. Tel: 020 8788 7777; fax - 020 8874 5390; website - www.lloyds-auction.co.uk. *Fortnightly Saturday sales of antique and modern furniture, china, glassware, pictures and collectables. Website catalogue.*

Lots Road Galleries

71-73 Lots Rd., Chelsea, SW10 0RN. Tel: 020 7376 6800; fax - 020 7376 6899; website - www.lotsroad.com. *Auctions every Monday at 1 pm (modern and reproduction) and 6 pm (antique), approx. 600 lots of antique, traditional and decorative furniture, Oriental carpets, paintings, prints, ceramics, clocks, glass, silver, objets d'art and soft furnishings. On view Thurs. 5-7, Fri. 9-7, Sat. 10-4 and Sun. 11-5, all day Mon. Goods accepted Mon.-Fri. Payment by*

direct credit 9 days after the sale. Catalogue details and auction results by fax, phone or live auction line. Valuers, consultants and carriers. VAT registered.

Phillips

101 New Bond St., W1S 1SR. Tel: 020 7629 6602; fax - 020 7629 8876; website - www. phillips-auctions.com. *Regular sales of fine furniture, paintings, ceramics, jewellery, silver, clocks, watches, Oriental works of art, textiles, books, musical instruments, works of art, stamps, medals and decorative arts.*

Phillips Bayswater

10 Salem Rd., W2 4DL. Tel: 020 7313 2700. *Weekly, Mon., sales of furniture, works of art and carpets. Regular monthly sales of jewellery, ceramics and oriental works of art and glass, silver, pictures. Specialist sales of pianos, fishing, chess and bicycles. Viewing Fri. 9-5, Sat. 10-5, Sun. 11-5 and other viewing dependent upon sale day.*

Rippon Boswell and Co.

The Arcade, South Kensington Station. SW7 2NA. Tel: 020 7589 4242. *International specialist auctioneers of old and antique Oriental carpets. Periodical auctions in London. Also in Germany, Switzerland, USA and Far East.*

Rosebery Fine Art Ltd.

74-76 Knights Hill, West Norwood. SE27 0JD. Tel: 020 8761 2522; fax - 020 8761 2524. *Quarterly selected and monthly antique and collectors auctions on a Tues. and Wed. Fortnightly, Mon., general auctions. Specialist auctions of toys and collectors items, decorative arts, modern design, musical instruments, books and textiles held periodically.*

Sotheby's

34-35 New Bond St., W1A 2AA. Tel: 020 7293 5000. *Open for free valuations Mon.-Fri. 9-5. Daily sales of paintings, drawings, watercolours, prints, books and manuscripts, European sculpture and works of art, antiquities, silver, ceramics, glass, jewellery, Oriental works of art, furniture, musical instruments, clocks and watches, vintage cars, wine, postage stamps, coins, medals, toys and dolls and other collectors' items.*

Southgate Auction Rooms

55 High St., Southgate, N14 6LD. Tel: 020 8886 7888; website - www.southgateauctionrooms. com. *Weekly Mon. sales at 5 pm of jewellery, silver, china, porcelain, paintings, furniture. Viewing Sat. 9-12 noon and from 9 on day of sale.*

BEDFORDSHIRE

W. & H. Peacock
The Auction Centre, 26 Newnham St., Bedford, MK40 3JR. Tel: 01234 266366; website - www. peacockauctions.co.uk. *Antiques sale first Fri. monthly. Viewing Fri. prior 9am-8pm. General sales every Sat. at 9.30.*

Douglas Ross (Auctioneers)
The Old Town Hall, Woburn. MK17 9PZ. Tel: 01525 290502. *Sales every four weeks on Thurs.*

BERKSHIRE

Dreweatt Neate
Donnington Priory, Donnington, Nr. Newbury, RG14 2JE. Tel: 01635 553553; fax - 01635 553599; e-mail - fineart@dreweatt-neate.co.uk; website - www.auctions.dreweatt-neate.co.uk. *Sales on the premises mainly on a weekly basis. General furnishings - fortnightly on Tues. Antique furniture - six annually. Paintings, books, prints, silver and jewellery, ceramics - three of each annually. Buyers' premium 17.625% including VAT.*

Edwards & Elliott
32 High St., Ascot. SL5 7HG. Tel: 01344 625022. *Regular sales of antique furniture, porcelain and glass; silver, plate and jewellery; oil paintings, watercolours and prints; rugs and assorted collectables at the Silver Ring Grandstand, Ascot Racecourse.*

Martin and Pole Nicholas
The Auction House, Milton Rd., Wokingham. RG40 1DB. Tel: 0118 979 0460; fax - 0118 977 6166. *Sale of antiques and collectables held usually on 3rd Wed. every month at above address.*

Thimbleby & Shorland
31 Great Knollys St., Reading. RG1 7HU. Tel: 0118 950 8611. *Collective sales of antique and modern furniture and effects held monthly on Sat. at Reading Cattle Market. Also four specialist sales of horse-drawn vehicles, harness, horse brasses, driving sundries, whips and lamps, etc.*

BUCKINGHAMSHIRE

Amersham Auction Rooms
125 Station Rd., Amersham. HP7 0AH. Tel: 01494 729292. *Weekly general and monthly selected antique sales held on Thurs. at 10.30.*

CAMBRIDGESHIRE

Cheffins
The Cambridge Saleroom, 2 Clifton Rd., Cambridge. CB1 4BW. Tel: 01223 213343 (10 lines); website - www.cheffins.co.uk. *Regular fine art and general auction sales including pictures, furniture, works of art, silver and jewellery, ceramics and collectors' items.*

Grounds and Co.
2 Nene Quay, Wisbech. PE13 1AQ. Tel: 01945 585041/2. *Three specialist sales annually, each approximately 600 lots.*

Hyperion Auctions Ltd
Station Rd., St. Ives. PE27 5BH Tel: 01480 464140; fax - 01480 497552; e-mail - enquiries@ hyperionauctions.co.uk; website - www.hyperion auctions.co.uk. Est. 1995. *Regular sales of antiques and collectables.*

W. & H. Peacock
The Auction Centre, 75 New St., St Neots. PE19 1AJ. Tel: 01480 474550. *General sale every Thurs. at 11.*

Phillips
The Golden Rose, 17 Emmanuel Rd., Cambridge. CB1 1JW. Tel: 01223 366523. *Regular sales of good furniture, pictures, silver, ceramics and Victoriana. Enquiries to Clodagh Sapsford.*

Rowley Fine Art Auctioneers & Valuers
The Old Bishop's Palace, Little Downham, Ely. CB6 2TD. Tel: 01353 699177; fax - 01353 699088; website - www.rowleyfineart.com. *Regular sales of fine art and antiques at Tattersalls Sale Ring, Newmarket. Valuations.*

CHESHIRE

Andrew, Hilditch and Son Ltd.
Hanover House, 1A The Square, Sandbach. CW11 0AP. Tel: 01270 767246/762048. *Quarterly sales of fine pictures and period furnishings. General and Edwardian furniture sales held weekly.*

Cheyne's
38 Hale Rd., Altrincham. WA14 2EX. Tel: 0161 941 4879. *Bi-monthly sales held at St Peter's Assembly Rooms, Cecil Road, Hale. Viewing day prior 2-4.30 and 6-8 and sale morning 9-10.30.*

Halls Fine Art
Booth Mansion, 30 Watergate St., Chester. CH1

AUCTIONEERS

2LA. Tel: 01244 312300; fax - 01244 312112. *Quarterly antique sales (Fri.) and fortnightly Victoriana and collectors sales (Wed.).*

Frank R. Marshall and Co.
Marshall House, Church Hill, Knutsford. WA16 6DH. Tel: 01565 653284; fax - 01565 652341; e-mail - antiques@frankmarshall.co.uk. *Regular sales of antique furniture, objets d'art, silver, pewter, glass, porcelain, pictures, brass and copper. Fortnightly household collective sales including bric-a-brac. Specialised sales at The Knutsford Auction Salerooms.*

Phillips de Pury and Luxembourg
New House, 150 Christleton Rd., Chester. CH3 5TD. Tel: 01244 313936; fax - 01244 340028. *22 salerooms countrywide including Chester.*

Peter Wilson Fine Art Auctioneers
Victoria Gallery, Market St., Nantwich. CW5 5DG. Tel: 01270 623878; fax - 01270 610508; e-mail - auctions@peterwilson.co.uk; website - www.peterwilson.co.uk. *Five catalogued (illustrated in colour) two-day sales each year. Uncatalogued auctions every Thursday - shipping goods and household effects (500+ lots).*

Wright Manley Auctioneers
Beeston Castle Salerooms, Tarporley. CW6 9NZ Tel: 01829 262150; fax - 01829 262110. *Fortnightly Victoriana and household sales and quarterly catalogued fine art and furniture sales.*

CORNWALL

Jefferys
The Auction Rooms, 5 Fore St., Lostwithiel. PL22 0BP. Tel: 01208 872245; fax - 01208 873260; e-mail - jefferys.lostwithiel@btinternet.com. *Fortnightly sales of antique furniture, ceramics, glass, jewellery, silver and plate, pictures, prints and collectors items, on Wed. at 10 am.*

Lambrays
Polmorla Walk Galleries, The Platt, Wadebridge. PL27 7AE. Tel: 0120 881 3593. *Fortnightly sales of antiques and pine. Quarterly auctions of antiques and objets d'art. Illustrated catalogues.*

W. H. Lane & Son
Jubilee House, Queen St., Penzance. TR18 4DF. Tel: 01736 361447; fax - 01736 350097; e-mail - Graham.Bazley@excite.com. *Six picture sales annually (specialists in the Newlyn and St. Ives Schools). Valuations for insurance, probate and family division.*

David Lay FRICS
The Penzance Auction House, Alverton, Penzance. TR18 4RE. Tel: 01736 361414; fax - 01736 360035. *Regular sales of fine art, antiques, collectors' items, books and studio pottery. Three-weekly general household sales.*

Phillips Cornwall
Cornubia Hall, Par. PL24 2AQ. Tel: 01726 814047. *Monthly sales of antiques, Victorian and later furnishings, silver, jewellery, pictures and collectors' items.*

Martyn Rowe Auctioneers and Valuers
The Truro Auction Centre, City Wharf, Malpas Rd., Truro. TR1 1QH. Tel: 01872 260020; fax - 01872 261794. *Weekly on Thurs. at 10 am - Victorian, Edwardian and general sales. Viewing morning of sale and previous Wed 2-6 pm. Antique and picture sales - every 6-8 weeks. Collectors and sporting sales - every 6-8 weeks. Quarterly sales of vintage and classic motorcycles, cars and automobilia. House, commercial, industrial and receivership sales on site or at auction centre.*

CUMBRIA

Cumbria Auction Rooms
12 Lowther St., Carlisle. CA3 8DA. Tel: 01228 525259. *Twice weekly sales of Victorian and later furnishings and household effects. Quarterly catalogue sales of antiques and works of art.*

Mitchell's Auction Co.
The Furniture Hall, 47 Station Rd., Cockermouth. CA13 9PZ. Tel: 01900 827800; fax - 01900 828073. *Weekly (Thurs.) sales of antique, reproduction and modern furniture and effects, approximately 800 lots, starting at 9.30 am. Viewing Wed. 2-7 and throughout sale. Six fine art sales per annum, viewing prior Tues. 11-5 and Wed. 10-7 and prior to sale.*

Penrith Farmers' and Kidds plc
Skirsgill Saleroom, Skirsgill, Penrith. CA11 0DN. Tel: 01768 890781; fax - 01768 895058; e-mail - penrith.farmers@virgin.net. *Weekly sales of household furniture and effects on three Wed. each month, commencing 9.30am., view Tues. 3-6. Monthly sales of antiques and Victoriana on Wed., usually each month, except when quarterly sales of antiques and collectors' items are held at end of Mar., June, Sept. and Dec. - 10.30am. start. Viewing 2 days prior - Mon. 10-5, Tues. 10-7.*

James Thompson
64 Main St., Kirkby Lonsdale. LA6 2AJ. Tel: 015242 71555; fax - 015242 72939; e-mail-

sales@jthompson-auctioneers.co.uk; website - www.jthompson-auctioneers.co.uk. *Monthly two day sales of silver, ceramics, general antiques. Picture sales six times a year.*

Thomson, Roddick and Laurie Ltd.
19 Crosby St., Carlisle. CA1 1DQ. Tel: 01228 528939; fax - 01228 592128. *Bi-monthly catalogue sales of antiques and collectors' items and regular specialist sales particularly antiquarian books, silver and pictures at Carlisle and Wigton. Monthly general furniture sales at Wigton.*

DERBYSHIRE

Armstrong Auctions
Midland Rd., Swadlincote, DE11 0AH. Tel: 01283 217772. *Weekly general sales and periodic antique sales held in Swadlincote Auction Rooms.*

Noel Wheatcroft & Son
Matlock Auction Gallery, The Old Picture Palace, Dale Rd., Matlock. DE4 3LU. Tel: 01629 57460; fax - 01629 57956; website - www.wheatcroft-noel. co.uk. *Monthly sales of antiques and general items.*

DEVON

Bearne's
St Edmund's Court, Okehampton St., Exeter. EX4 1DU. Tel: 01392 207000. *Regular sales of antique furniture, works of art, silver, jewellery, collectors' items, books, clocks and watches, paintings, ceramics and glass, carpets and rugs.*

Bonhams & Brooks
Dowell St., Honiton. EX14 1LX. Tel: 01404 41872; fax - 01404 43137. *Regular monthly auctions of furniture, works of art, ceramics, silver and jewellery, collectors' items, wine, sporting and fishing memorabilia.*

Kingsbridge Auction Sales (R.D. Morgan)
113 Fore St., Kingsbridge. TQ7 1BG. Tel: 01364 643439; mobile - 07798 626230. *Regular sales of antique and general household furniture and effects.*

Lyme-Bay Auction Galleries
28 Harbour Rd., Seaton. EX12 2NA. Tel: 01297 22453. *General household and antique auctions held every four to six weeks.*

Phillips
38/39 Southernhay East, Exeter, EX1 1PE. Tel: 01392 455955; fax - 01392 455962. *Seasonal sales of antiques and fine art held at Powderham*

Castle, near Exeter, to include silver, plated articles, European ceramics and glass, objects and works of art, clocks, antique furniture and West Country pictures.

Potbury and Sons
The Auction Rooms, Temple St., Sidmouth, EX10 8LN. Tel: 01395 515555/517300; fax - 01395 512608. *Fortnightly sales; fine arts every two months.*

Rendells
Stone Park, Ashburton, TQ13 7RH. Tel: 01364 653017: fax - 01364 654251. *Sales every four weeks (Thurs. and Fri.) of antique and reproduction furniture, ceramics, silver, jewellery, pictures, clocks and barometers, copper and brass, miscellanea, toys and collectables. No buyers premium.*

Taylor's
Honiton Galleries, 205 High St., Honiton, EX14 1LQ. Tel: 01404 42404. *Sales of paintings and prints, antiques, silver, books and porcelain.*

Ward and Chowen
Tavistock Auction Rooms, Market Rd., Tavistock, PL19 0BW. Tel: 01822 612603; fax - 01822 617311.

Whitton and Laing
32 Okehampton St., Exeter, EX4 1DY. Tel: 01392 252621; fax - 01392 496607. *Monthly auctions of antiques, silver and jewellery. Book and stamp auctions two or three times a year. Picture sales bi-monthly. General auctions weekly.*

DORSET

Cottees
The Market, East St., Wareham, BH20 4NR. Tel: 01929 552826; fax - 01929 554916. *Furniture and effects every two weeks.*

Hy. Duke and Son
Fine Art Salerooms, Weymouth Avenue, Dorchester, DT1 1QS. Tel: 01305 265080; fax - 01305 260101. *Est. 1823. Regular six weekly sales including specialist sections of silver and jewellery, Oriental and English porcelain, English and Continental furniture, pictures, books and Oriental rugs. Complete valuation and advisory service, including insurance, probate and forward tax planning.*

Hy. Duke and Son
The Weymouth Salerooms, Nicholas St., Weymouth. Tel: 01305 761499; fax - 01305 260101. *Regular bi-weekly sales of Victoriana and later furniture and effects.*

AUCTIONEERS

House and Son
Lansdowne House, Christchurch Rd., Bournemouth, BH1 3JW. Tel: 01202 298044. *Fortnightly sales of selected furniture, pictures, books, silver, porcelain and glass. Catalogues £2.50 including postage.*

Wm. Morey and Sons
Salerooms, St. Michaels Lane, Bridport, DT6 3RB. Tel: 01308 422078; website - www. wmoreyandsons.co.uk. *Antique and general sales held every three to four weeks on Thurs.*

Phillips Auctioneers
3 Cheap St., Sherborne, DT9 3PT. Tel: 01935 815271.

Riddetts of Bournemouth
177 Holdenhurst Rd.,Bournemouth. BH8 8DQ. Tel: 01202 555686; fax - 01202 311004. *Fortnightly sales which include fine antiques, jewellery, silver, plate, pictures. Illustrated sale programme free. Catalogue subscription £45 p.a.*

DURHAM

Denis Edkins
Auckland Auction Rooms, 58 Kingsway, Bishop Auckland, DL14 7JF. Tel: 01388 603095. *General and antique sales from time to time.*

Thomas Watson and Son
Northumberland St., Darlington, DL3 7HJ. Tel: 01325 462559. *Regular sales of antiques and good quality house contents.*

ESSEX

Ambrose
Ambrose House, Old Station Rd., Loughton. IG10 4LZ. Tel: 020 8502 3951; website - www. ambrose auction.co.uk. *Antique sales fortnightly/ monthly.*

Cooper Hirst Auctions
The Granary Salerooms, Victoria Rd., Chelmsford, CM2 6LH. Tel: 01245 260535. *Regular sales of antiques every 8/9 weeks and weekly Tues. sales of Victoriana, bric-a-brac etc. Catalogue subscription service available.*

Reeman Dansie Howe & Son
Head Gate Auction Rooms, 12 Head Gate, Colchester, CO3 3BT. Tel: 01206 574271. *Sales held every Wed. Viewing Tues. 9-7 prior. Bi-monthly Fine Art sales.*

Simon H. Rowland
Chelmsford Auction Rooms, 42 Mildmay Rd., Chelmsford, CM2 0DZ. Tel: 01245 354251. *Regular sales by order of the Sheriff of Essex and private vendors.*

Saffron Walden Auctions
1 Market St., Saffron Walden, CB10 1JB. Tel: 01799 513281. *Sales of antique and fine furniture, antique effects and objets d'art held every two months.*

John Stacey & Sons (Leigh-on-Sea) Ltd
Leigh Auction Rooms, 86-90 Pall Mall, Leigh-on-Sea, SS9 1RG. Tel: 01702 477051. *Monthly sales of period and other furniture, works of art and collectors' items. Catalogue subscription £40.*

Stanfords
11 East Hill, Colchester, CO1 2QX. Tel: 01206 868070. *Weekly Tues. sales of antique and modern furniture, china, glass, silver and decorative items at 10 a.m. Bi-monthly specialists sales of antique furniture and collectables - please ring for further information.*

G.E. Sworder and Sons
14 Cambridge Rd., Stansted Mountfitchet. CM24 8BZ. Tel: 01279 817778; fax - 01279 817779; website - www.sworder.co.uk. *Monthly auctions of antique furniture, ceramics, silver, pictures, decorative items. Viewing Fri. 2-5, Sat. 10-4 and Mon. prior 9-5. Weekly Thurs. at 11 auction of Victorian, Edwardian and later furniture and collectables. Viewing morning of sale and Wed. 2-5.*

Trembath Welch (incorporating J.M. Welch & Son)
Old Town Hall, Great Dunmow, CM6 1AU. Tel: 01371 873014; fax - 01371 878239. *At the Salerooms, Chequers Lane - selected antique furniture and effects sales quarterly. Sales of collectables, household furniture and antiques every two weeks. Catalogue subscription service available.*

GLOUCESTERSHIRE

BK The Property Assets Consultancy
Albion Chambers, 111 Eastgate St., Gloucester, GL1 1PZ. Tel: 00 44 (0) 1452 521267; fax - 00 44 (0) 1452 300184; e-mail - artantiques@ bkonline. co.uk; website - www.bkonline.co.uk. *Free auction valuations; confidential valuation services. Auctions held regularly.*

Bristol Auction Rooms Ltd
St. John's Place, Apsley Rd., Clifton, Bristol, BS8 2ST. Tel: 0117 973 7201; fax - 0117 973 5671; website - www.bristolauctionrooms.co.uk.

Monthly auctions of antique furniture, clocks, rugs, textiles, paintings and prints, glass, pottery, porcelain, books and ephemera, silver, objects of vertu, toys and collectables. View Sat. prior 9.30-1; day prior from 9.30-7, and on day from 9 to sale at 10.30. Fortnightly auctions of Victorian and modern household furniture and effects. View day prior to sale from 12-6 and on day from 9 until sale at 10.30. Specialist auctions and house sales held throughout the year. Catalogue subscription service. Buyers' premium.

Corinium Galleries

25 Gloucester St., Cirencester, GL7 2DJ. Tel: 01285 659057. *Monday auctions of postcards and printed ephemera every six weeks.*

Fraser Glennie and Partners

The Coach House, Upper Siddington, Cirencester, GL7 6HL. Tel: 01285 659677; fax - 01285 642256. *Monthly sales of antiques, other furniture, collectors' items and musical instruments at the Bingham Hall, Cirencester.*

Mallams Fine Art Auctioneers and Valuers

26 Grosvenor St., Cheltenham, GL52 2SG. Tel: 01242 235712; fax - 01242 241943. Est. 1788. *Regular sales of furniture, ceramics, paintings, textiles, rugs and works of art, sporting, toy and collectors items.*

Moore, Allen & Innocent

The Salerooms, Norcote, Cirencester, GL7 5RH. Tel: 01285 646050. *Fortnightly sales of over 1,000 lots of antique and other furniture and effects. Quarterly sales of selected antiques. Bi-annual specialist picture and sporting sales. Fri. at 9.30. Viewing day prior 10.30-8. 10% buyers premium.*

Short Graham and Co

City Chambers, 4/6 Clarence St., Gloucester. GL1 1DX. Tel: 01452 521177. *Sales of Georgian, Victorian, Edwardian and later furniture, ceramics, glass, metalwork, silver, plate, jewellery, miscellanea, collectors' items, books, pictures and outside effects every four to six weeks.*

Wotton Auction Rooms Ltd

(formerly Sandoe Luce Panes) Tabernacle Rd., Wotton-under-Edge, GL12 7EB. Tel: 01453 844733; fax - 01453 845448; website - www. wottonauctionrooms.co.uk. *Monthly 2-day sales of antiques and collectables, 1,500+ lots. Calendar cards on request. Valuations.*

HAMPSHIRE

Jacobs and Hunt Fine Art Auctioneers

Lavant St., Petersfield, GU32 3EF. Tel: 01730 233933. *General antique sales every six to eight weeks on Fri.*

George Kidner Auctioneers

The Old School, The Square, Pennington, Lymington. SO41 8GN. Tel: 01590 670070; fax - 01590 675167. Emsworth Rd. - 01590 679487. *Monthly specialist sales - furniture, works of art, silver and jewellery, collectors' items, oils, prints and watercolours, European ceramics, Oriental works of art, books and marine items, collectable toys, model railways and railwayana. Viewing - Mon. 9.30-4.30, Tues. 9.30-7. Also saleroom at Emsworth Rd., Lymington - Victorian, Edwardian and later furniture and effects. Viewing - day previous 9.30-7.*

May and Son

18 Bridge St., Andover, SP10 1BH. Tel: 01264 323417; fax - 01264 338841; e-mail - mayandson @enterprise.net. *Monthly sales of antique furniture and effects at Penton Mewsey Village Hall (Lots from private sources only). No buyers' premium.*

D.M. Nesbit and Co.

7 Clarendon Rd., Southsea, Portsmouth, PO5 2ED. Tel: 023 9286 4321; fax - 023 9229 5522. *Monthly sales of antique furniture, silver, porcelain and pictures.*

Phillips Auctioneers

54 Southampton Rd., Ringwood, BH24 1JD. Tel: 01425 473333.

HEREFORDSHIRE

Brightwells

The Fine Art Saleroom, Ryelands Rd., Leominster, HR6 8NZ. Tel: 01568 611122; fax - 01568 610519. *Monthly 2-day sales of antiques and collectors' items (approx. 1,000 lots per sale). Two or three sales per month of antique and household effects.*

HERTFORDSHIRE

Brown and Merry - Tring Market Auctions

Brook St., Tring. HP23 5EF. Tel: 0144282 6446. *Fortnightly Sat. sales of antiques and collectables held at The Market Premises, Brook St., Tring. Fine art sales held on last Fri. of alternate months.*

AUCTIONEERS

Shanklin Auction Rooms
79 Regent St., Shanklin, PO37 7AP. Tel: 01983 863441. *Monthly auctions of antiques and fine arts.*

Ways
The Auction House, Garfield Rd., Ryde, PO33 2PT. Tel: 01983 562255; e-mail - ways@ waysauction rooms.fsbusiness.co.uk; website - www.waysauction rooms.fsbusiness.co.uk. *Five-weekly sales of antique and modern furniture, silver, copper and brass, oils, watercolours and prints, jewellery, china, clocks. No buyers premium.*

Bracketts
Fine Art Auctioneers, Auction Hall, Pantiles, Tunbridge Wells, TN2 5QL. Tel: 01892 544500; website - www.bfaa.co.uk. *Fortnightly Saturday sales of antique and later furniture and effects and specialist Tunbridge Ware sales.*

The Canterbury Auction Galleries
40 Station Rd. West, Canterbury, CT2 8AN. Tel: 01227 763337; fax - 01227 456770. *Bi-monthly auctions of fine art and antiques held on Tues. at 10.30, viewing Mon. prior 10-7. Auctions of Victorian and later furniture held on first Sat. monthly at 10, viewing Fri. prior 3-8. Valuations.*

Halifax Property Services
15 Cattle Market, Sandwich, CT13 9AW Tel: 01304 614369; fax - 01304 612023. *Antique and other furniture and effects on Wed., 16 sales per year. Held at The Drill Hall, The Quay, Sandwich.*

Hobbs Parker
Romney House, Ashford Market, Orbital Park, Ashford, TN24 0HB. Tel: 01233 502222; fax - 01233 502211. *Monthly sales of antiques and household furniture.*

Hogben Fine Art Auctioneers & Valuers
Unit C Highfield Industrial Estate, Off Warren Rd., Folkestone. CT19 6DD. Tel: 01303 240808/246810; fax - 01303 246256. *Fine art saleroom - monthly sales.*

Ibbett, Mosely
125 High St., Sevenoaks, TN13 1UT. Tel: 01732 456731; fax - 01732 740910. *Antiques and objets d'art.*

Lambert & Foster Auction Sale Rooms
102 High St., Tenterden, TN30 6HU. Tel: 01580 762083. *Four offices in Kent. Monthly general sales of antique and other furniture and effects.*

B.J. Norris
The Quest, West St., Harrietsham. ME17 1JD. Tel: 01622 859515; e-mail - norrisoz@globalnet. co.uk; website - www.antiquesbulletin.com/ bjnorris. *Regular sales at The Agricultural Hall, Maidstone at 10 am. Viewing from 8 am. on morning of sale.*

Phillips International Auctioneers & Valuers
49 London Rd., Sevenoaks, TN13 1AR. Tel: 01732 740310. *Monthly sales of antique furniture and objects of art.*

Acorn Philatelic Auctions
PO Box 152, Salford, Manchester. M17 1BP. Tel: 0161 877 8818. *Tues. sales, approximately every 5 weeks, held at Unit 6, Block C, Astra Business Centre, Guiness Rd., Trafford Park, Manchester. 10 per year all specialising in paper collectables - postage stamps and history, manuscripts, autographs, picture and cigarette cards, books, prints, drawings and watercolours. Sales commence at 2 pm., viewing Mon. previous 10.30-6.30, and sale morning 9-1.15.*

Capes Dunn & Co Fine Art Auctioneers & Valuers
The Auction Galleries, 38 Charles St., Manchester, M1 7DB. Tel: 0161 273 1911; fax - 0161 273 3474. Est. 1826. *Catalogues of weekly specialist sales available on request. Regional office in Lytham.*

Kingsway Auction Rooms Ltd
The Galleries, Kingsway, Ansdell, Lytham St. Annes, FY8 1AB. Tel: 01253 735442. *Sales of antique, reproduction and modern furnishings and appointments held fortnightly or every three weeks on Tues. Approximately 400-600 lots commencing 9.30. Viewing Fri. 2-4, Sat. 10-12, Mon. 9-4. Buyers' premium 12%.*

Warren & Wignall Ltd
The Mill, Earnshaw Bridge, Leyland. PR5 3PH. Tel: 01772 451430; fax - 01772 454516. *Sales of general antiques every three weeks. All sales Wed. at 10, viewing Tues. 9-7.*

LEICESTERSHIRE

Freckeltons
1 Leicester Rd., Loughborough, LE11 2AE. Tel: 01509 214564; fax - 01509 236114. *Monthly sales of general antiques.*

Gilding's Auctioneers and Valuers
Roman Way, Market Harborough, LE16 7PQ. Tel: 01858 410414; website - www.gildings. co.uk. *Regular antique and Victoriana sales and free, over-the-counter valuations.*

Heathcote Ball & Co
Castle Auction Rooms, 78 St. Nicholas Circle, Leicester, LE1 5NW. Tel: 0116 2536789; fax - 0116 2538517; e-mail - heathcote-ball@clara. co.uk. *Auctions every four to six weeks.*

LINCOLNSHIRE

DDM Auction Rooms Ltd
Old Courts Rd., Brigg. DN20 8JJ. Tel: 01652 650172; fax - 01652 650085. *Fine art and antique auctions every six weeks: Victorian and household auctions fortnightly on a Saturday. Valuations for insurance, probate and sale. Free valuation "clinic" every Thursday 9.30-12.*

Eleys Auctioneers
26 Wide Bargate, Boston, PE21 6RX. Tel: 01205 361687; fax - 01205 351091; e-mail - sales@j-eley.co.uk; website - www.j-eley.co.uk/eleys/. *Regular antique and collectors sales.*

Escritt and Barrell
Saleroom - Dysart Rd. Office - 24 St Peter's Hill, Grantham, NG31 6QF. Tel: 01476 566991. *Three-weekly general shipping and antique sales, quarterly antique sales.*

Thomas Mawer & Son Ltd
Dunstan House, Portland St., Lincoln, LN5 7NN. Tel: 01522 524984. *Sales on first Sat. every month at 10 am. Catalogue sales quarterly.*

Richardsons
Bourne Auction Rooms, Spalding Rd., Bourne, PE10 9LE. Tel: 01778 422686. *Antiques sales every month. Antique and modern sales every other Sat. Various specific sales periodically, eg silver, clocks, bygones, transport.*

Marilyn Swain
The Old Barracks, Sandon Rd., Grantham, NG31 9AS. Tel: 01476 568861; fax - 01476 576100. *Bi-monthly antique, fine art and collectable sales. Fortnightly sales of Victorian and later furniture, general effects and collectables. Valuations.*

MERSEYSIDE

J. Kent (Auctioneers) Ltd.
2/6 Valkyrie Rd., Wallasey, L45 4RQ. Tel: 0151 638 3107; fax - 0151 512 2343. *Antique, fine art and collectors' items on first Wed. of each month at 10. Viewing Tues. 9-6.*

Kingsley and Co. Auctioneers
3/4 The Quadrant, Hoylake. L47 2EE. Tel: 0151 632 5821; fax - 0151 632 5823. *Sales every Tues. at 10, of antiques, fine arts, general chattels. Viewing Sat. 9-12.30, Mon. 9-5 and Tues. 9-10.*

Outhwaite and Litherland
Kingsway Galleries, Fontenoy St., Liverpool, L3 2BE. Tel: 0151 236 6561; fax - 0151 236 1070; e-mail - auction@lots.uk.com; website - www. lots.uk.com. *Victorian, Edwardian and later furnishings - weekly Tues. Collectors cavalcade sale of general antiques and collectibles - monthly Tues. Fine art and antiques - quarterly Wed. Clocks, watches, scientific instruments - bi-annually Wed. Specialist sales of books, wines, stamps etc. periodically. Members of SOFAA. Branch offices at Southport and Hoylake, Wirral.*

NORFOLK

James Beck Auctions
The Cornhall, Cattle Market St., Fakenham, NR21 9AW. Tel: 01328 851557. *Weekly sales of antique furniture and collectables every Thurs. at 11.*

Clowes Nash Auctions
Norwich Livestock & Commercial Centre, Hall Rd., Norwich, NR4 6EQ. Tel: 01603 504488. *Antiques and general furniture weekly sales.*

Ewings
Market Place, Reepham, Norwich, NR10 4JJ. Tel: 01603 870473. *Periodic sales of antiques and modern furniture and effects.*

Thos. Wm. Gaze and Son
Diss Auction Rooms, Roydon Rd., Diss, IP22 4LN. Tel: 01379 650306; fax - 01379 644313; website - www.twgaze.com. *Weekly catalogue sales of antiques and cottage furniture on Fri. at 11am. Periodic specialist sales including fine antiques, rural bygones, architectural salvage and statuary, decorative arts, automobilia, toys and nostalgia, etc. Online catalogues.*

AUCTIONEERS

G.A. Key - Aylsham Salerooms

Auctioneers & Valuers, 8 Market Place, Aylsham, NR11 6EH. Tel: 01263 733195; website - www.aylshamsalerooms.co.uk. *Three weekly sales of period, antique and Victorian furniture, silver, porcelain etc. Bi-monthly picture sales - oils, watercolours and prints etc. Six book sales annually and regular collectors' sales. Weekly sales of modern and secondhand furniture.*

NORTHAMPTONSHIRE

Goldsmith Howard

15 Market Place, Oundle, PE8 4BA. Tel: 01832 272349. *Sales approximately bi-monthly.*

Southams

Corn Exchange, Thrapston, NN14 4JJ. Tel: 01832 734486. Est. 1900. *First Thurs. each month, viewing Wed. 9.30-8 sales of antiques and superior furniture, silver, plate, copper and brass, fine china, glass, Oriental rugs, oil paintings, watercolours and prints. 10% buyer's premium. Catalogues £2 including postage. Annual subscription £18.*

Wilfords Ltd.

76 Midland Rd., Wellingborough, NN8 1NB. Tel: 01933 222760/222762. *Weekly antique and general sales, Thurs. from 9.30 (1400 lots).*

NOTTINGHAMSHIRE

Arthur Johnson and Sons (Auctioneers)

The Nottingham Auction Centre, Meadow Lane, Nottingham. NG2 3GY. Tel: 0115 986 9128; fax - 0115 986 2139. *Approximately 1,000 lots weekly on Sat. at 10 am of antique and shipping furniture, silver, gold, porcelain, metalware and collectables.*

Mellors & Kirk Fine Art Auctioneers

Gregory St., Nottingham. NG7 2NL. Tel: 0115 979 0000; e-mail - mellkirk@dircon.co.uk. *Fine sales of selected antique furniture, clocks, pictures, ceramics, oriental works of art, printed books and ephemera, collectors toys and dolls, coins and medals and other categories of specialist interest. Weekly general sales of 500-800 lots Tues. 10.30, viewing Sat. 9-12 and Mon. 9-5.*

Neales

192-194 Mansfield Rd., Nottingham, NG1 3HU. Tel: 0115 962 4141; fax - 0115 985 6890; e-mail - fineart@neales.co.uk. *Bi-monthly specialist sales of paintings, drawings, prints and books; silver, jewellery, bijouterie and watches; European and Oriental ceramics and works of art, glass; furniture and decoration; clocks, barometers and mechanical music; metalwork, fabrics, needlework, carpets and rugs; collectors' toys and dolls; stamps, coins and medals, post and cigarette cards; autographs and collectors' items. Weekly collective sales (Mon.) of general antique and later furnishings, shipping goods and reproduction furnishings. Period and later ceramics, glass and decorative effects. Contents sales on the premises of town and country properties.*

Richard Watkinson and Partners

17 Northgate, Newark, NG24 1EX. Tel: 01636 677154. *Monthly sales of antique and Victorian furniture, oil paintings, silver etc. Weekly sales of early 20th C and general household furniture.*

OXFORDSHIRE

Holloways

49 Parsons St., Banbury, OX16 5PF. Tel: 01295 817777; fax - 01295 817701; e-mail - enquiries@hollowaysauctioneers.co.uk; website - www.hollowaysauctioneers.co.uk. *General or specialist sales on the premises every other week.*

Mallams

Fine Art Auctioneers, Bocardo House, 24A St. Michael's St., Oxford, OX1 2EB. Tel: 01865 241358. *Frequent sales of furniture, silver, paintings and works of art. House sales arranged on the premises.*

Mallams incorporating Messengers

Pevensey House, 27 Sheep St., Bicester, OX26 7JF. Tel: 01869 252901; fax - 01869 320283; e-mail - bicester@mallams.co.uk; website - www.mallams.co.uk/fineart. *Regular sales of antiques and later furniture, clocks, ceramics and glass, paintings, books and miscellany. Special annual garden sale.*

Phillips International Fine Art Auctioneers

39 Park End St., Oxford, OX1 1JD. Tel: 01865 723524; fax - 01865 791064; internet - www.phillips-auctions.com. *Fortnightly sales of Victoriana and general effects. Specialist sales of fine furniture, rugs, works of art, silver, jewellery, ceramics, collectors' items and paintings throughout the year.*

Simmons and Sons

32 Bell St., Henley-on-Thames. RG9 2BH. Tel: 01491 571111; fax - 01491 579833; website - www.simmonsandsons.com. *Eight antique and*

eight general sales per year held at *The Saleroom Watcombe Manor, Ingham Lane, Watlington, Oxon. Sales start 10.30, viewing Sat. previous 9.30-12.30, Mon. prior 2-7, Tues. prior 10-6 and morning of sale.*

SHROPSHIRE

Hall and Lloyd, Auctioneers
Cosford Auction Rooms, Long Lane, Cosford. TF11 8PJ. Tel: 01902 375555; fax - 01902 375566. *Est. 1882. Monthly sales of Victoriana, shipping and modern furniture and effects. Fine art and antique sales every 6 weeks.*

Halls Fine Art
Welsh Bridge Salerooms, Shrewsbury, SY3 8LA. Tel: 01743 231212; fax - 01743 271014. *Weekly household and Victoriana sales (Fri.). Monthly catalogued antique sales.*

Perry and Phillips
Auction Rooms, Old Mill Antique Centre, Mill St., Bridgnorth, WV15 5AG. Tel: 01746 762248. *Monthly (Tues.) antiques and collectables.*

Walker Barnett and Hill
Cosford Auction Rooms, Long Lane, Cosford. TF11 8PJ. Tel: 01902 375555; fax - 01902 375556. *Monthly sales of Victoriana, reproduction, shipping, modern furniture and effects on Tues. 10.30. Fine art and antiques sales every 6-8 weeks.*

SOMERSET

Aldridges of Bath
Newark House, 26-45 Cheltenham St., Bath, BA2 3EX. Tel: 01225 462830; fax - 01225 311319. *Fortnightly (Tues.) sales, broken down into specialist categories:- Antique furniture to include clocks and Oriental carpets; silver and porcelain, glass and metalware; paintings and prints; collector's sales; Victorian and general furniture. Viewing Sat. 9-12 and Mon. 9-6. Catalogues available upon annual subscription.*

Clevedon Salerooms
Herbert Rd., Clevedon, BS21 7ND. Tel: 01275 876699; fax - 01275 343765; e-mail - clevedon. salerooms@cableinet.co.uk; website - www. clevedon-salerooms.com. *Quarterly auctions of antique furniture, fine art and collectors' items. Fortnightly sales of Victorian, Edwardian and general furniture and effects. Occasional specialist sales and sales held on vendors' property. Valuations.*

Cooper & Tanner Chartered Surveyors
The Agricultural Centre, Standerwick, Frome, BA11

2QB. Tel: 01373 831010. *Weekly sales of antiques and general household chattels Wed. 10.30 am. Viewing morning of sale. Haulage service.*

Gardiner Houlgate
9 Leafield Way, Corsham, Bath, SN13 9SW. Tel: 01225 812912; fax - 01225 811777; e-mail - auctions@gardiner-houlgate.co.uk. *Regular sales of antique furniture and works of art. Frequent sales of Victorian and later furnishings. Fortnightly jewellery sales, quarterly musical instrument sales, specialist clocks and watches sales. Valuations.*

Greenslade Taylor Hunt Fine Art
Magdalene House, Church Square, Taunton, TA1 1SB. Tel: 01823 332525; fax - 01823 353120. *Monthly, last Thurs., sales of antique furniture, ceramics, glass, metalwork, paintings and prints. Specialist sales of silver and jewellery; collectors items, printed books, clocks and watches, sporting. Fortnightly, Wed., sales, of antique and shipping furniture, china, glass and effects.*

Lawrence Auctioneers
The Corfield Hall, Magdalene St., Taunton. TA1 1SG. Tel: 01823 330567; fax - 01823 330596. *Fine art auction on fourth Tues., general sales on first and third Tues. each month.*

Lawrence Fine Art Auctioneers Ltd.
South St., Crewkerne, TA18 8AB. Tel: 01460 73041; fax - 01460 74627. *Specialist auctioneers and valuers. Regular sales of antiques and fine art. General sales every Wed. except first Wed. of each month.*

The London Cigarette Card Co. Ltd
Sutton Rd., Somerton, TA11 6QP. Tel: 01458 273452; fax - 01458 273515; e-mail - cards@ londoncigcard.co.uk; website - www.london cigcard.co.uk. *Suppliers of thousands of different series of cigarette and trade cards and special albums. Publishers of catalogues, reference books and monthly magazine. Regular auctions in London and Somerset. S.A.E. for details. Showroom in West St. open Mon-Sat. or mail order.*

Phillips Auctioneers - Bath
1 Old King St., Bath, BA1 2JT. Tel: 01225 788988; fax - 01225 446675. *A branch of Phillips, Son & Neale Ltd. Regular sales of antique furniture and Victoriana as well as silver, pictures, books and fine wine, ceramics, glass and 20th C art and design.*

Tamlyn and Son
56 High St., Bridgwater, TA6 3BN. Tel: 01278 458241; fax - 01278 458242; saleroom - 01278 445251.

AUCTIONEERS

Wellington Salerooms
Mantle St., Wellington, TA21 8AR. Tel: 01823 664815. *Six-weekly sales of general antiques. Three-weekly sales of Victorian, Edwardian and shipping goods.*

STAFFORDSHIRE

Bagshaws Wintertons Fine Arts
The Estate Saleroom, High St., Uttoxeter, ST14 7HP. Tel: 01889 562811; fax - 01889 563795. *Monthly sales of Victorian and general household furniture and effects.*

John German
1 Lichfield St., Burton-on-Trent, DE14 3QZ. Tel: 01283 512244; fax - 01283 517896. *Occasional sales of major house contents; specialist fine art valuation department.*

Louis Taylor Fine Art Auctioneers
Britannia House, 10 Town Rd., Hanley, Stoke-on-Trent. ST1 2QG. Tel: 01782 214111. *Quarterly fine art sales including furniture, pictures, pottery, porcelain, silver and works of art. Specialist Royal Doulton and Beswick auctions. General Victoriana auctions held every two weeks.*

Wintertons
Lichfield Auction Centre, Fradley Park, Fradley, Lichfield, WS13 8NF. Tel: 01543 263256. *Bi-monthly sales of antiques and fine art and sales of Victorian and general furniture every 2-3 weeks.*

SUFFOLK

Abbotts Auction Rooms
Campsea Ashe, Nr. Woodbridge, IP13 0PS. Tel: 01728 746323; fax - 01728 748173. *Extensive calendar of fine art and antique auctions held on Wed. Sales calendar and catalogues available. Weekly sales of Victoriana & household furniture held on Mon. Viewing Sat. 9-11 am.*

Boardman - Fine Art Auctioneers
Station Road Corner, Haverhill. CB9 0EY. Tel: 01440 730414. *Large sales held quarterly specialising in selected fine furniture (particularly oak), clocks and paintings.*

Diamond Mills and Co. Fine Art Auctioneers
117 Hamilton Rd., Felixstowe, IP11 7BL. Tel: 01394 282281 (3 lines). Ipswich office - 01473 218600. *Periodic fine art sales. Monthly general sales. Auctions at The Orwell Hall, Orwell Rd., Felixstowe.*

Durrant's
The Auction Rooms, Gresham Rd., Beccles. NR34 9QN. Tel: 01502 713490; e-mail - durrants.auctionrooms@virgin.net.co.uk. *Antique and general furniture auctions every Fri.*

Dyson & Son
The Auction Room, Church St., Clare. CO10 8PD. Tel: 01787 277993; e-mail - info@dyson-auctioneers.co.uk; website - www.dyson-auctioneers.co.uk. *Sales of antiques and chattels every three weeks on Sat. at 11am., viewing Fri. 9am-9pm, Sat. from 9am.*

Lacy Scott and Knight Fine Art & Furniture
10 Risbygate St., Bury St. Edmunds, IP33 3AA. Tel: 01284 748600; fax - 01284 748620. *Quarterly sales of fine art including antique and decorative furniture, silver, pictures, ceramics etc. on behalf of executors and private vendors. Regular (every three weeks) sales of Victoriana and general household contents. Also quarterly sales of live steam models, scale models, diecast and tinplate toys.*

Neal Sons and Fletcher
26 Church St., Woodbridge, IP12 1DP. Tel: 01394 382263; fax - 01394 383030; e-mail - allatnsf@aol.com; website - www.nsf.co.uk. *Two special mixed antiques sales annually. Individual specialised sales and complete house contents sales as required. Household furniture sales on a Wed. of each month.*

Olivers
The Saleroom, Burkitts Lane, Sudbury, CO10 1HB. Tel: 01787 880305. *Fortnightly sales of Victorian and later furniture and household effects. Regular sales of antiques and works of art. Enquiries to James Fletcher FRICS.*

Phillips East Anglia
32 Boss Hall Rd., Ipswich, IP1 5DJ. Tel: 01473 740494. *Five two-day specialist sales annually at Bury St. Edmunds. Eight mixed sales in Ipswich.*

SURREY

Clarke Gammon Fine Art Auctioneers
The Guildford Auction Rooms, Bedford Rd., Guildford, GU1 4SJ. Tel: 01483 880915; fax - 01483 880918.

Croydon Auction Rooms (Rosan and Co.) (incorporating E.Reeves Auctions)
145/151 London Rd., Croydon. CR0 2RG. Tel: 020 8688 1123. *Fortnightly collective sales - 10 am Sat., viewing Fri. prior.*

Ewbank Auctioneers

Burnt Common Auction Rooms, London Rd., Send, Woking. GU23 7LN. Tel: 01483 223101; fax - 01483 222171. *Monthly general and fine art sales on a Thurs., viewing Wed. 10am-8pm and Tues. 2pm-5pm.*

Hamptons International

Baverstock House, 93 High St., Godalming, GU7 1AL. Tel: 01483 423567; fax - 01483 426392; e-mail - fineart@hamptons-int.com. *Regular (Wed. and Thurs.) fine art sales at 93 High Street, specialising in selected fine furniture, rugs, paintings and watercolours, porcelain, glass, jewellery, silver, objets d'art and books. Two sales each month of general and Victorian furniture, shipping goods and household effects, held on first and third Sat. House sales conducted on the premises when instructed. Valuations.*

Lawrences' - Auctioneers Limited

Norfolk House, 80 High St., Bletchingley, RH1 4PA. Tel: 01883 743323; fax - 01883 744578. *Six-weekly antique and reproduction furniture and effects.*

Parkins

18 Malden Rd., Cheam. SM3 8SD. Tel: 020 8644 6633/4. *Sales of general household furniture and effects 2nd and 4th Mon. at 10. Viewing Fri. 2-4 and Sat. 10-4. Special antique sale on 1st Mon. at 10. Small antiques and collectables one Fri. evening each month at 7 pm - please telephone for details.*

Richmond and Surrey Auctions

The Old Railway Parcels Depot, Kew Rd., Richmond. TW9 2NA. Tel: 020 8948 6677; fax - 020 8948 2021. *Est. 1992. Auctioneers, valuers and consultants. Sales every Thurs. 6pm.*

P.F. Windibank Fine Art Auctioneers & Valuers

Dorking Halls, Reigate Rd., Dorking, RH4 1SG. Tel: 01306 884556/876280; fax - 01306 884669; e-mail - sjw@windibank.co.uk; website - www.windibank.co.uk. *Antique auctions held every four to five weeks throughout the year.*

SUSSEX EAST

Burstow and Hewett

Abbey Auction Galleries and Granary Sale Rooms, Battle, TN33 0AT. Tel: 01424 772374. *Monthly sales of antique furniture, silver, jewellery, porcelain, brass, rugs etc. at the Abbey Auction Galleries. Also monthly evening sales of fine oil paintings, watercolours, prints, and engravings. At the Granary Sale Rooms - monthly sales of furniture, china, silver, brass, etc.*

Gorringe's Auction Galleries

Terminus Rd., Bexhill-on-Sea, TN39 3LR. Tel: 01424 212994; fax - 01424 224035; website - www.gorringes.co.uk. *Monthly sales of antique and modern furniture, metalware, European, Oriental, ceramics and glass, silver plate, plated goods, jewellery, bijouterie, objet d'art, pictures, libraries of books, etc.*

Gorringe's Auction Galleries

15 North St., Lewes. BN7 2PD. Tel: 01273 472503. *Sales approximately every six weeks of period furniture, Oriental carpets and rugs, oil paintings, watercolour drawings and prints, decorative china, glass, silver plate, jewellery etc.*

Edgar Horn's Fine Art Auctioneers

46/50 South St., Eastbourne, BN21 4XB. Tel: 01323 410419. *Fortnightly antique and later furniture and effects sales (Tues). Six specialist antique furniture, silver and jewellery, ceramics and glass, oil paintings and watercolours and works of art sales (Wed).*

Raymond P. Inman

The Auction Galleries, 35 and 40 Temple St., Brighton, BN1 3BH. Tel: 01273 774777; fax - 01273 735660. *Monthly sales of antiques, furniture, china, brass, pictures, silver, jewellery, collectables, etc.*

Scarborough Perry Fine Arts

Hove St., Hove. BN3 2GL. Tel: 01273 735266; fax - 01273 723813. *Monthly sales of fine art including antique furniture, pictures, silver, Oriental carpets and rugs and ornamental items. Specialised sales of primitive art, coins, books and jewellery.*

Wallis and Wallis

West Street Auction Galleries, Lewes. BN7 2NJ. Tel: 01273 480208. *Est. 1928. Nine annual sales of arms and armour, militaria, coins and medals. Specimen catalogue £4.50. Current catalogues £7. Die-cast and tin plate toys and models - catalogue £5.50. Commission bids (without charge) accepted. Valuations.*

SUSSEX WEST

John Bellman Ltd

New Pound, Wisborough Green, Billingshurst. RH14 0AZ. Tel: 01403 700858; fax - 01403 700059. *Two day sale once a month - Thurs. am -*

AUCTIONEERS

ceramics and Oriental, Thurs. pm - silver, jewellery, clocks; Fri. am - collectors' items, works of art, paintings, Fri. pm - furniture. Viewing Sat. 9-12, Mon. 9-4, Tues. 9-7, Wed. 9-1. Book sales quarterly.

Denham's
The Auction Galleries, Warnham, Nr. Horsham, RH12 3RZ. Tel: 01403 255699; fax - 01403 253837; e-mail - denhams@lineone.net. *Antique sales held monthly - good furniture of all periods, silver, jewellery, European and Oriental ceramics and collectors' items, paintings, drawings, prints and bronzes, metalware and Oriental carpets and rugs. Also monthly sales of general antiques, modern and shipping furniture. Periodic sales of books, stamps, coins and medals, arms and armour and specialist collections as advertised.*

R.H. Ellis and Sons
44/46 High St., Worthing. BN11 1LL. Tel: 01903 238999. *Monthly specialist auctions of antique, Victorian and Edwardian furniture and porcelain. Quarterly auctions of silver, watercolours, paintings, Oriental carpets and rugs.*

King & Chasemore
Midhurst Auction Rooms, West St., Midhurst, GU29 9NQ. Tel: 01730 812456; fax - 01730 814514. *General sales of antique and modern furniture and effects every six weeks.*

Sotheby's Sussex
Summers Place, Billingshurst, RH14 9AD. Tel: 01403 833500; fax - 01403 833699. *Regular sales of paintings, furniture, clocks, ceramics, glass, silver, jewellery, vertu, sporting guns, militaria, Oriental items and garden statuary.*

Stride and Son
Southdown House, St. John's St., Chichester, PO19 1XQ. Tel: 01243 780207; fax - 01243 786713. *Sales last Fri. monthly - antiques and general; periodic book and document sales.*

Worthing Auction Galleries
Fleet House, Teville Gate, Worthing, BN11 1UA. Tel: 01903 205565. *Monthly sales of antique, 20th C and reproduction furniture, ceramics, glass, silver, silver plate, jewellery, pictures and collectables. View Sat. prior 9-12, Fri. and Mon. prior 9-1 and 2-4. Sale Tues. and Wed. both days commencing at 10am.*

Anderson and Garland
Fine Art Salerooms, Marlborough House, Marlborough Crescent, Newcastle-upon-Tyne, NE1 4EE. Tel: 0191 232 6278; fax - 0191 261 8665; agarland@compuserve.com; website - www.auction-net.co.uk. *Regular sales of paintings, prints, antique furniture, silver and collectors' items.*

Anderson and Garland
Kepier Chare, Crawcrook, Ryton. NE40 4TS. Tel: 0191 413 8348. *Fortnightly sales of Victorian and later furnishings.*

Boldon Auction Galleries
24a Front St., East Boldon, NE36 0SJ. Tel: 0191 537 2630; website - www.boldonauctions.co.uk. *Quarterly antique auctions.*

Thomas N. Miller Auctioneers
Algernon Rd., Byker, Newcastle-upon-Tyne, NE6 2UN. Tel: 0191 265 8080; fax - 0191 265 5050; e-mail - millerlot1@aol.com. *Antique auctions every Wed. at 10 am.*

Bigwood Auctioneers Ltd
The Old School, Tiddington, Stratford-upon-Avon, CV37 7AW. Tel: 01789 269415. *Monthly Victoriana sales. Monthly sales of fine furniture and works of art. Quarterly sales of wines, sporting goods and other specialist sales. Catalogues and calendars on request. Valuations for all purposes.*

Henley-in-Arden Auction Sales Ltd
The Estate Office, Warwick Rd., Henley-in-Arden, B95 5BH. Tel: 01564 792154. *Sales of antique and modern furniture and effects, second and fourth Sat. each month.*

Locke & England
18 Guy St., Leamington Spa, CV32 4RT. Tel: 01926 889100; e-mail - valuers@leauction.co.uk; websites - www.leauction.co.uk; www.invaluable.com. *Antique sales fortnightly/monthly.*

Warwick and Warwick Ltd
Chalon House, Scar Bank, Millers Rd., Warwick. CV34 5DB. Tel: 01926 499031; fax - 01926 491906. *Philatelic auctioneers and private treaty specialists. Stamp auctions held monthly. Postcards, cigarette cards, autographs, ephemera, medals, militaria, coins, banknotes and other collectables sold by auction periodically.*

WEST MIDLANDS

Biddle & Webb

Ladywood Middleway, Birmingham, B16 0PP. Tel: 0121 455 8042. *Fine art sales first Fri. monthly; antique sales on second Fri. monthly; silver, jewellery, medals, coins and watches on fourth Fri. monthly; toys, dolls, model railways and juvenalia sales on Fri. alternate months, all sales at 11. Weekly Tues. sales of Victoriana and collectables at 10.30. Three decorative art and 20th C ceramic sales a year.*

Fellows and Sons

Augusta House, 19 Augusta St., Hockley, Birmingham, B18 6JA. Tel: 0121 212 2131; fax - 0121 212 1249. *Auctioneers and valuers of jewels, silver, fine art.*

Old Hill Antiques & Auction Rooms

220 Halesowen Rd., Old Hill, Cradley Heath. B64 6HN. Tel: 01384 411121. *Auctioneers and valuers.*

Phillips Midlands

The Old House, Station Rd., Knowle, Solihull, B93 0HT. Tel: 01564 776151; fax - 01564 778069. *Specialised weekly sales of fine furniture, paintings, works of art, clocks, carpets; silver and jewellery; ceramics and 19th-20th C decorative arts; collectors items, toys, dolls, lace and linen, printed ephemera. Subscription available. Free sales programmes on request.*

Weller and Dufty Ltd

141 Bromsgrove St., Birmingham, B5 6RQ. Tel: 0121 692 1414; fax - 0121 622 5605. *Ten sales annually, approximately every five weeks, of antique and modern firearms, edged weapons, militaria etc. Periodic sales of specialist items - military vehicles and associated military equipment. Six fine art and antiques sales per year Postal bids accepted. Illustrated catalogue available.*

WILTSHIRE

Hamptons Auctioneers & Valuers

20 High St., Marlborough, SN8 1AA. Tel: 01672 516161; fax - 01672 515882. *Antique and selected quality furniture and effects sales first Wed. bi-monthly. General household sales first Wed. bi-monthly and every third Wed. monthly.*

Laynes House Auctions

Laynes House, Oaksey. SN16 9SE. Tel: 01666 577603; e-mail - lyon@lyon-oliver.demon.co.uk. *Quarterly sales of decorative antiques.*

Swindon Auction Rooms

The Planks, Old Town, Swindon, SN3 1QP. Tel: 01793 615915. *Sales every two weeks.*

Woolley and Wallis

Salisbury Salerooms Ltd 51-61 Castle St., Salisbury, SP1 3SU. Tel: 01722 424500; fax - 01722 424508; e-mail - enquiries@woolleyand wallis.co.uk; website - www.woolleyandwallis. co.uk. *Specialist sales of antique furniture, ceramics, pictures, silver and jewellery, rugs and textiles, books and wine. Fortnightly general sales. Written valuations for probate and insurance.*

WORCESTERSHIRE

Griffiths and Charles

57 Foregate St., Worcester, WR1 1DZ. Tel: 01905 26464; e-mail - info@griffiths - charles.co.uk.

Philip Laney - FRICS - Fine Art

Malvern Auction Centre, Portland Rd., off Victoria Rd., Malvern. WR14 2TA. Tel: 01684 893933. *Monthly sales of antiques and collectors' items.*

Phipps and Pritchard

31 Worcester St., Kidderminster. DY10 1EQ. Tel: 01562 822244. *Regular six-weekly sales of antique furniture, watercolours and oil paintings, copper, brass, glass, china and porcelain, stamps and coins, silver. Private house sales also conducted.*

Philip Serrell - Auctioneers & Valuers

The Malvern Sale Room, Barnards Green Rd., Malvern. Tel: 01684 892314. *Bi-monthly catalogued antique and fine art auctions. Fortnightly general sales. Specialist on the premises sales. Free sales estimates.*

YORKSHIRE EAST

Gilbert Baitson

The Edwardian Auction Galleries, Wiltshire Rd., Hull. HU4 6PG. Tel: 01482 500500; after hours - 01482 645241; fax - 01482 500501; website - www.gilbert-baitson.co.uk. *Sales of antique and modern furnishings every Wed. at 10.30. Viewing day prior until 8 pm.*

Dee Atkinson & Harrison - Agricultural and Fine Arts

The Exchange Saleroom, Driffield, YO25 7LJ. Tel: 01377 253151; fax - 01377 241041; e-mail - exchange@dee-atkinson-harrison; website - www.dee-atkinson-harrison.co.uk. *Regular bi-monthly sales of antiques, Victorian, Edwardian and quality furnishings, paintings, silver, jewellery etc. Viewing two days prior. Fortnightly household sales. Biennial collectors' toys and sporting sales.*

AUCTIONEERS

H. Evans and Sons - Auctioneers & Valuers
1 Parliament St., Hull. HU1 2AR. Tel: 01482 323033; fax - 01482 211954. *Regular auctions of antiques and modern furniture and effects.*

Spencers Auctioneers and Estate Agents
The Imperial and Repository Salerooms, 18 Quay Rd., Bridlington, YO15 2AP. Tel: 01262 676724. *General auctions every Thurs. Regular sales of antiques and fine arts.*

YORKSHIRE NORTH

Bairstow Eves Fine Art
West End Rooms, The Paddock, Whitby, YO21 3AX. Tel: 01947 820033/820011. *Monthly antiques sales. 10% buyers premium including VAT.*

Boulton and Cooper Ltd
St. Michaels House, Market Place, Malton, YO17 0LR. Tel: 01653 696151. *Members of SOFAA. Alternating monthly antique sales at Malton and York. Fortnightly general sales at Pickering.*

Hutchinson-Scott
The Grange, Marton-le-Moor, Ripon, HG4 5AT. Tel: 01423 324264. *Periodic general sales plus two or three catalogue sales annually. Specialist in fine antiques and works of art.*

Morphets of Harrogate
6 Albert St., Harrogate, HG1 1JL. Tel: 01423 530030; fax - 01423 500717; website - www.morphets.co.uk. *Sales of antiques and works of art, interspersed with regular sales of general furniture and effects. Catalogue subscription scheme.*

Scarthingwell Auction Centre
Scarthingwell, Nr. Tadcaster. LS24 9PG. Tel: 01937 557955; fax - same. *Evening antique and general sales held twice-monthly on Mon. and Tues. evenings, approx 1,000 lots. Viewing on prior Sun. 12-5 and sale days Mon. from 2pm and Tues. from 4pm.*

Stephensons
10 Colliergate, York. YO1 8BP. Tel: 01904 625533. *Six sales annually of antique and Victorian furniture, silver and paintings.*

Summersgill Auctioneers
8 Front St., Acomb, York, YO24 3BZ. Tel: 01904 791131. *Auctions of antiques and household effects and collectors' items.*

Tennants
The Auction Centre, Leyburn, DL8 5SG. Tel: 01969 623780; fax - 01969 624281. (Office - 34 Montpellier Parade, Harrogate. Tel : 01423 531661; fax - 01423 530990). *Minimum of three 1000 lot non-catalogue sales each month of antiques and later house contents, mainly on Sat. at 9.30, viewing Fri. 9-7. Three fine art sales each year. Catalogue subscription service. Specialist sales of collectors' items, books, etc.*

YORKSHIRE SOUTH

A.E. Dowse and Son Sheffield
Cornwall Galleries, Scotland St., Sheffield, S3 7DE. Tel: 0114 2725858; fax - 0114 2490550. *Monthly Sat. sales of antiques. Bi-monthly fine art and antique sales. Quarterly sales of diecast, tin plate and collectors' toys. Monthly sales of modern furniture and shipping goods.*

YORKSHIRE WEST

De Rome
12 New John St., Westgate, Bradford. BD1 2QY. Tel: 01274 734116/9. *Regular sales.*

Andrew Hartley Fine Arts
Victoria Hall Salerooms, Little Lane, Ilkley, LS29 8EA. Tel: 01943 816363. *Fifty sales annually including six good antique and fine art and other specialist sales.*

Phillips Auctioneers
Hepper House, 17a East Parade, Leeds, LS1 2BH. Tel: 0113 2448011; fax - 0113 2429875. *Quarterly fine sales of pictures, silver and jewellery, ceramics and furniture. Monthly general sales. Sales calendars sent on request.*

John H. Raby & Son
Salem Auction Rooms, 21 St. Mary's Rd., Bradford, BD8 7QL. Tel: 01274 491121. *Sales of antique furniture and pictures every four to six weeks, shipping goods and collectables every week.*

CHANNEL ISLANDS

Bonhams & Brooks & Langlois Auctioneers
Westaway Chambers, Don St., St. Helier, Jersey, JE2 4TR. Tel: 01534 722441; fax - 01534 759354. *Regular antique and specialised auctions, general sales (Wed).*

SCOTLAND

Frasers (Auctioneers)
8a Harbour Rd., Inverness, Inverness-shire, IV1 1SY. Tel: 01463 232395; fax - 01463 233634. *Weekly sales on Wed. at 6 pm.*

Leslie and Leslie
Haddington, East Lothian, EH41 3JJ. Tel: 01620 822241; fax - same. *Antique auctions every three months.*

Loves Auction Rooms
52-54 Canal St., Perth, Perthshire, PH2 8LF. Tel: 01738 633337; fax - 01738 629830. *Regular sales of antique and decorative furniture, jewellery, silver and plate, ceramics, works of art, metalware, glass, pictures, clocks, mirrors, pianos, Eastern carpets and rugs, garden furniture, architectural items. Weekly Fri. sales of Victoriana and household effects at 10.30. Specialist sales of books and collectors' items. Valuations.*

Macdougalls Auctioneers & Valuers
Lower Breakish, Breakish, Isle of Skye. IV42 8QA. Tel: 01471 822777; fax - same. *Sales held every eight weeks of antiques and general furniture. Sales held Sat. at 2pm in Broadford Hall (10 mins. from the Skye bridge).*

McTear's
Clydeway Business Centre, 8 Elliot Place, Glasgow G3 8EP. Tel: 0141 221 4456; fax - 0141 204 5035;l e-mail - enquiries@mctears.co.uk; website - www.mctears.co.uk. *Weekly Fri. sales at 10.30 of antique, reproduction and shipping furniture, jewellery, silver, porcelain and paintings. Viewing prior Thurs. 10-4.*

John Milne
9 North Silver St., Aberdeen, Aberdeenshire, AB1 1RJ. Tel: 01224 639336. *Weekly general sales, regular catalogue sales of antiques, silver, paintings, books, jewellery and collectors' items.*

Paterson's
8 Orchard St., Paisley, Glasgow, PA1 1UZ. Tel: 0141 889 2435. *Fortnightly Tues. sales.*

Phillips Scotland
65 George St., Edinburgh, Midlothian, EH2 2JL. Tel: 0131 225 2266. *Regular specialist sales of oils and watercolours, furniture, clocks, rugs and works of art, silver and jewellery, Oriental and European ceramics and books. Decorative arts, post war, garden and dolls and textiles sales are also held. Monthly general sales. Annual Scottish Sale, held during the Edinburgh Festival, includes important Scottish furniture, paintings, silver, books and sporting memorabilia.*

L.S. Smellie and Sons Ltd.
The Furniture Market, Lower Auchingramont Rd., Hamilton, Lanarkshire, ML10 6BE. Tel: 01698 282007. *Fine antiques auctions - third*

Thurs. in Feb., May, Aug. and Nov. Weekly sales every Mon. at 9.30 am. (600 lots) household furniture, porcelain and jewellery.

Taylor's Auction Rooms
11 Panmure Row, Montrose, Angus, DD10 8HH. Tel: 01674 672775. *Antiques sales held every second Sat.*

Thomson, Roddick & Medcalf
20 Murray St., Annan, Dumfriesshire. DG12 6EG. Tel: 01387 279879. *Fortnightly sales of household furnishing and effects. Also sales of fishing tackle and sporting effects.*

Thomson, Roddick & Medcalf Ltd.
60 Whitesands, Dumfries, Dumfriesshire, DG1 2RS. Tel: 01387 279879. *Quarterly catalogued antique and collectors sales. Specialist sales of art pottery, silver, jewellery, sporting and fishing tackle. Fortnightly general sales.*

Thomson Roddick & Medcalf Ltd
44/3 Hardengreen Business Park, Eskbank, Edinburgh. EH22 3NX Tel: 0131 454 9090; fax - 0131 454 9191. *Weekly auctions of antiques and general furnishings, regular specialist sales, particularly Scottish provincial silver, quarterly catalogued fine art and antique sales; also quarterly sales in Dumfries and bi-monthly general sales in Annan.*

WALES

Dodds Property World
Victoria Auction Galleries, Mold, Flintshire, CH7 1EB. Tel: 01352 755705; fax - 01352 752542. *Weekly Wed. auctions of general furniture and shipping goods at 10.30am. Bi-monthly auctions of antique furniture, silver, porcelain and pictures etc. at 10.30am on Sat. Catalogues available.*

Peter Francis
Curiosity Salerooms, 19 King St., Carmarthen, South Wales SA31 1BH. Tel: 01267 233456/7; fax - 01267 233458; website - www.peterfrancis. co.uk. *Catalogued antiques and fine art sales every six weeks. Regular general sales.*

Newland Rennie Wilkins
87 Monnow St., Monmouth, Gwent, NP5 3EW. Tel: 01600 712916. *Periodic sales of antique furniture and effects, usually on Thurs.*

Harry Ray & Co
Lloyds Bank Chambers, Broad St., Welshpool. SY21 7RR. Tel: 01938 552555. *Monthly country sales.*

Fairs Calendar

In an attempt to make the Fairs listings for England more logical, we have rearranged the regional boundaries. At the beginning of each section there is a list of the counties included. Because this list is compiled in advance, alterations or cancellations to the Fairs listed can occur. We strongly advise anyone wishing to attend a Fair, especially if they have to travel any distance, to telephone the organiser to confirm the details given.

LONDON (including Greater London)

Adams Antiques Fairs - 020 7254 4054
Antiques & Collectors' Fair, The Royal Horticultural Hall, New Hall, Greycoat Street (behind the Old Hall), Victoria, SW1 - **July 15; September 2; October 14; November 4; December 16**
Antiques Fair, Chelsea Town Hall, King's Road, Chelsea, SW3 - **July 14; September 1; December 8**
The Brocante Fair, Olympia, Kensington, London W14 - **September 9**
Centre Exhibitions - 0121 767 2665
The LAPADA Fair, The Commonwealth Institute, Kensington High Street, W8 - **October 10-14**
Clarion Events Ltd - 020 7370 8188
The Winter Olympia Fine Art & Antiques Fair, The National Hall, Olympia Exhibition Centre, Hammersmith Road, W14 - **November 12-18**
DMG Fairs - 01636 702326
Antiques & Collectors Fair, Lee Valley Leisure Centre, Edmonton, London - **July 3; September 2; October 7; November 4; December 2**
Antiques & Collectors' Fair, Hall 3, Wembley Exhibition Centre, Empire Way, Wembley - **August 27; December 27**
DPL Fairs - 020 8205 1518
Toy & Train Fair, Edgware School, Green Lane (off Spur Road), Edgware, Middx - **October 3; December 5**
David Bannister - 01242 514287
Antique Map Fair, The Bonnington Hotel, Southampton Row, WC1 - **July 9; August 13; September 10; October 15; November 5; December 10**
Mr Dungate - 01895 834694
The Brunel Clock & Watch Fair, Brunel University, Kingston Lane, Uxbridge, Middx -

September 9; December 16
Gay Hutson - 020 8742 1611
The 20/21 British Art Fair, Royal College of Art, SW7 - **September 26-30**
Granny's Goodies - 020 8693 5432
The London International Antique & Artist Dolls, Toys, Miniatures & Teddy Bear Fair, Kensington Town Hall, Exhibition & Conference Centre, Hornton Street, W8 - **September 9; November 11**
Heritage Antiques Fairs - 020 7624 5173
Antiques Fair, Rembrandt Hotel, Thurloe Place (opposite the Victoria & Albert Museum), SW7 - **July 8; September 23; October 21; December 2**
Antiques Fair, The Lanesborough, 1 Lanesborough Place, SW1 - **September 9; October 7; November 11**
Antiques Fair, London Marriott Hotel, Grosvenor Square, W1 - **July 1; November 25; December 9**
Antiques Fair, Hotel Inter-Continental, 1 Hamilton Place, Hyde Park Corner, W1 - **September 16**
The Decorative Antiques & Textiles Fair, The Marquee, Battersea Park (through Chelsea Gate), SW11 - **September 25-30**
Mainwarings Antique Fairs - 01225 723094
Antiques Fair, Chelsea Town Hall, King's Road, SW3 - **July 15; September 2, 30; November 4, 18; December 9**
Marcel Fairs - 020 8950 1844
Antiques Fair, St Paul's Church Hall, The Ridgeway, NW7 - **July 7; August 4; September 1; October 6; November 3; December 1**
Penman Fairs - 01444 482514
Chelsea Antiques Fair, Chelsea Old Town Hall, King's Road, Chelsea, SW3 - **September 14-23**
Pig & Whistle Promotions - 020 8883 7061
Alexandra Palace Antique & Collectors' Fair,

The Great Hall, Alexandra Palace, Wood Green, N22 - **September 23** (100th Antiques Fair)**; November 18**
Simmons Gallery - 020 7831 2080
The London Coin Fair, The Cumberland Hotel, Carlisle Suite, Marble Arch, W1 - **September 8; November 3**
Talbot Promotions - 020 8969 7011
The International Antique Scientific & Medical Instrument Fair, The Radisson SAS Portman Hotel, Portman Square, W1 - **October 28**
West Promotions - 020 8641 3224
The London Paper Money Fair, The Bonnington Hotel, 92 Southampton Row, WC1 - **July 15; September 2; November 18**
F Wilkinson - 020 7278 9829
The London Arms Fair, The Royal National Hotel, Bedford Way, WC1 - **September 20-21**

SOUTH EAST AND EAST ANGLIA

Includes Bedfordshire, Cambridgeshire, Essex, Hertfordshire, Kent, Norfolk, Suffolk, Surrey, Sussex.

Allen Lewis Fairs - 01202 604306
The 2nd Loseley Park Antiques Fair, Guildford, Surrey - **October 19-21**

The 61st Southern Antiques Fair, Goodwood House, Chichester, West Sussex - **November 16-18**
Antiques & Collectors World - 01737 812989
Antiques & Collectors' Fair, Lingfield Park Racecourse, Lingfield, Surrey - **August 12; October 14; November 11**
Antiques & Collectors' Fair, Goodwood Racecourse, Goodwood, Near Chichester, West Sussex - **August 27; September 30; October 28; November 25**
Best of Fairs - 01787 280306
Antiques & Collectors' Fair, The Church Rooms, Lavenham, Suffolk - **July 21**
Big Surrey Fairs Ltd - 020 8390 1230
Antiques & Collectors' Fair, Tolworth Recreation Centre, A3 Kingston Bypass, Hook junction (A243), Fullers Way North, Surrey - **July 1; August 5; September 2; October 7; November 4; December 2**
Antique & Collectors' Fair, The Edge, Woolmer Hill (A3/A287 south of Hindhead), Haslemere, Surrey - **September 23; October 28; November 25; December 30**
Antiques & Collectors' Fair, The Public Hall, Stafford Road, Wallington, Surrey - **September 16; October 21; November 18**
Summer Fair, Civic Hall (near High Street/London Road station), Guildford, Surrey - **September 9**

In the style of Louis Wain this comical Austrian moving picture will cost £950 on Gasson Antiques' stand at the annual Kensington Antiques Fine Art Fair at Kensington Town Hall on 11th-13th August.

From a Fairs Preview which appeared in the July/August 2000 issue of **Antique Collecting** magazine. For more details and to subscribe see page 147.

Antiques & Collectors' Fair, Leisure Centre, Hurst Road (A3050), Walton on Thames. Surrey - **November 11**

Autumn Fair, Civic Hall (near High Street/London Road station), Guildford, Surrey - **December 9**

Camfair Antiques Fairs - 01945 870160/07860 517048

Antiques Fair, The Castle Hall, Hertford, Herts **July 28; August 25; September 29; October 27; November 17; December 15**

Cooper Antiques Fair - 01249 661111

The Annual Snape Antiques Fair, Snape Maltings, Suffolk - **July 12-15**

The Oak & Country Antiques Fair, Kentwall Hall, Long Melford, Suffolk - **September 28-30**

Cross Country Fairs Ltd - 0147483 4120

Antiques & Collectors' Fair, The Copthorne Effingham Park Hotel, West Park Road, Copthorne (near East Grinstead), West Sussex **July 1; August 5; September 2; October 7; November 4; December 2**

Cultural Exhibitons Ltd - 01483 422562

The 34th Surrey Antiques Fair, Guildford Civic, Guildford, Surrey - **October 4-7**

DMG Antiques Fairs - 01636 702326

Antiques & Collectors' Fair, Rowley Mile Racecourse, Newmarket, Suffolk - **November 25**

Antiques & Collectors' Fair, The South of England Showground, Ardingly, West Sussex - **July 17-18; September 11-12; October 30-31**

International Antiques & Collectors' Fair, Kent County Showground, Detling, Maidstone, Kent - **July 28-29; September 15-16; October 27-28**

DPL Fairs - 020 8205 1518

Toy & Train Fair, Elm Court Youth & Community Centre, Mutton Lane, Potters Bar, Herts (M25 J24) - **September 9; November 4**

Toy & Train Fair, John Bunyan Upper School, Mile Road (A5134), Bedford, Beds - **July 15; September 30; November 25**

Camera Fair, Francis Bacon School, Drakes Drive (1 mile London Colney roundabout A1081/A414), St Albans, Herts - **July 22**

Camera Fair, St Peter's Catholic School, Horseshoe Lane East, Merrow, Guildford, Surrey - **October 7**

G Deakin - 01273 845141

Ditchling Antiques Fair, Ditchling Village Hall, Lewes Road, West Sussex - **October 14; December 9**

Galloway Antiques Fairs - 01423 522122

Antiques Fair, Princess Helena College, Preston, Hitchin, Hertfordshire - **July 20-22**

Antiques Fair, Cranleigh School, Cranleigh, Surrey - **July 27-29**

Antiques Fair, Seaford College, Near Petworth, West Sussex - **October 19 -21**

Antiques Fair, Firle Place, Near Lewes, East Sussex - **November 9-11**

Gemsco - 01234 381701

The 52nd Luton Antiques Fair, Putteridge Bury House Herts (on the A505 Luton to Hitchin Road) - **October 20-21**

The 2nd Mid Beds Antiques Fair, The Silsoe Conference Centre, Silsoe, Beds (just off the A6, midway between Luton & Bedford) - **December 1-2**

Graham Turner Antiques Fairs - 01473 658224

Antiques Fair, The Village (Memorial) Hall, Long Melford, Suffolk - **July 4; August 1, 18-19; September 5; October 3; November 7, 17-18; December 5**

Little Easton Manor Two Day Fair, Little Easton Manor, Near Great Dunmow, Essex - **July 7-8; October 6-7**

Snape Special Four Day Annual Fair, The Village Hall, Snape, Suffolk - **July 12-15**

Antiques Fair, Furze Hill, Banqueting Centre, Margaretting, Near Chelmsford, Essex - **October 14; November 11; December 9**

Shuttleworth Mansion Two Day Fair, Shuttleworth Mansion, Old Warden Park, Biggleswade, Bedfordshire - **October 20-21**

Hallmark Antiques Fairs Ltd - 01702 710383

Antiques Fair, Courage Hall, Brentwood School, Middleton Hall Lane, Brentwood, Essex - **October 14**

Antiques Fair, Southend Tennis & Leisure Centre, Eastern Avenue, Southend on Sea, Essex - **September 2**

Antiques Fair, Cressing Temple Barns (between Witham & Braintree on the B1018), Essex - **September 9**

Antiques Fair, Southend Cliffs Pavilion, Station Road, Westcliff on Sea, Essex - **October 28**

Antiques Fair, Grignon Hall, Felsted School, Felsted, Essex - **November 3-4**

Harlequin Fairs - 01462 671688

Antiques Fair, Elstree Moat House Hotel (on

A1 adjacent to Borehamwood exit, 2 miles south of M25), Herts - **July 29; September 30; October 28; November 25**
Janba Fairs - 01945 870160/07860 517048
Antiques Fair, Knights Hill Hotel, South Wootton, King's Lynn, Norfolk - **September 23; October 28; December 16**
Antiques Fair, Burgess Hall, St Ivo Recreation Centre, St Ives, Cambridgeshire - **August 26-27; October 21; November 18**
Kyson Fairs - 01473 735528
Woodbridge Antiques Fair, Woodbridge Community Centre, Station Road, Woodbridge, Suffolk - **August 27; September 23; October 21; November 18; December 16**
Lomax Antiques Fairs - 01603 737631
Tenth East Anglian Antique Dealers' Fair, Langley Park School, Loddon, Norfolk - **October 26-28**
Magnum Antiques Fairs - 01491 681009
Antiques Fair, The Grange Centre, Bepton Road, Midhurst, West Sussex - **August 5; October 7; December 2**
R & S Fairs - 01702 345222/600331
Antiques Fair, Brentwood Centre, Doddinghurst Road, Brentwood, Essex - **August 26-27; November 10-11**
Antiques Fair, Colchester Leisure World, Cowdray Avenue, Colchester, Essex - **September 16; October 14; November 18; December 30**
Antiques Fair, Dolphin Leisure Centre, Pasture Hill Road, Haywards Heath, West Sussex - **September 30; December 9**
Antiques Fair, Hornchurch Sports Centre, Harrow Lodge Park, Hornchurch Road, Hornchurch, Essex - **September 23; November 25**
The Essex Doulton, Beswick & Wade Fair, The Manhattan Suite, City Limits, Collier Row Road, Collier Row, Romford, Essex - **November 4**
Ridgeway Fairs - 01702 710383
Antiques Fair, Marconi Sports & Social Club, Beehive Lane, Great Baddow, Chelmsford, Essex - **October 21**
Antiques Fair, Southend Bandstand, Clifftown Parade, Southend on Sea, Essex - **August 19**
Antiques Fair, Community Centre, Elm Road, Leigh on Sea, Essex - **July 29; December 9**
Antiques Fair, Marks Hall Estate, Coggeshall, Essex - **August 4-5**
Antiques Fair, Marconi Sports & Social Club,

Gardiners Lane South, Basildon, Essex - **August 12**
Antiques Fair, Mill Hall, Bellingham Lane, Rayleigh, Essex - **September 16**
Antiques Fair, Keys Hall, Eagle Way, Great Warley, Near Brentwood, Essex - **September 23**
Antiques Fair, Thurrock Civic Hall, Blackshott's Lane, Grays, Essex - **September 30**
Antiques Fair, The Hollywood Restaurant, Shipwright's Drive, Thundersley, Benfleet, Essex - **November 11**
Antiques Fair, The Paddocks, Long Road, Canvey Island, Essex - **November 25**
Antiques Fair, Sports & Leisure Centre, Main Road, Danbury, Essex - **December 2**
Robert Bailey Fairs - 01277 214699
The 2nd West Sussex Antiques Fair, Sotheby's South, Billingshurst, Sussex - **August 17-19**
The 18th Hertfordshire Antiques & Fine Art Fair, Hatfield House, The Goscoyne Cecil Estate, Hatfield Park, Hertfordshire - **November 16-18**
Shirley Mostyn Fairs - 01903 752961/755116
Antiques Fair, Hove Town Hall, Norton Road, Hove, Sussex - **July 24; August 21; September 18; October 16; December 4**
Antiques Fair, The Brighton Centre, Kings Road, Brighton, Sussex - **November 15**
Wakefield Ceramics Fairs - 01303 258635
Ceramics Fair, Hatfield House, Hatfield, Hertfordshire - **October 20-21**
Wonder Whistle Enterprises - 020 7249 4050
Antiques Fairs, The Exhibition Centre, Sandown Park Racecourse, Esher, Surrey - **October 2; November 27**

SOUTH WEST

Includes Avon, Berkshire, Buckinghamshire, Cornwall, Devon, Dorset, Gloucestershire, Hampshire, Isle of Wight, Oxfordshire, Somerset, Wiltshire.

Adams Antiques Fairs - 020 7254 4054
Antiques Fair, Newbury Racecourse - **August 29; October 24; December 5**
B C Antique Fairs - 020 8950 1844/01923 282446
Antique & Collectors' Fair, The Beaconsfield Masonic Centre, Windsor End, Old Beaconsfield, Bucks - **July 12; August 9; September 13; October 11; November 8; December 13**

FAIRS

Cooper Antiques Fair - 01249 661111
The North Cotswolds Antiques Fair, Stanway House, Near Winchcombe, Glos - **July 20-22**
The South Cotswold Antiques Fair, Westonbirt School, Tetbury, Glos - **August 17-19; December 15-16**

Crispins Fairs - 0118 983 3020
Antiques & Collectables Fair, St Crispin's Sports Centre, London Road (A329), Berks - **July 1; August 5; September 2; October 7; November 4; December 2**
Antiques & Collectors' Fair, Victoria Hall, Hartley Wintney, Hants (situated on the main A30 between Camberley & Basingstoke) - **July 17; August 21; September 9, 18; October 14, 16; November 11, 20; December 9, 18**

DMG Antiques Fairs - 01636 702326
Antiques & Collectors' Fair, The Royal Bath & West Showground, Shepton Mallet, Somerset - **July 7-8; September 21-23; November 17-18**

DPL Fairs - 020 8205 1518
Camera Fair, Trinity School, Love Lane, Newbury, Berks - **August 12; October 21**
Toy & Train Fair, Beaconsfield School, Wattleton Road, Beaconsfield, Bucks - **September 15; November 17**
Camera Fair, Beaconsfield School, Wattleton Road, Beaconsfield, Bucks - **September 16; December 9**

Devon County Antiques Fairs - 01363 82571
Matford Antiques & Collectables Fair, Exeter Livestock Centre, Matford Park Road, Marsh Barton, Exeter, Devon - **August 4; September 15; October 13; November 24**
Yeovil Antique & Collectors' Fair, Westland Sports & Social Club, Westbourne Close, Yeovil, Somerset - **August 5; October 14; November 25**
Salisbury Antiques & Collectables Fair, Salisbury Leisure Centre, The Butts, Hulse Road, Salisbury, Wilts - **September 29; December 8**
Westpoint Antiques & Collectables Fair, Westpoint Exhibition Centre, Devon County Showground, Clyst St Mary, Exeter, Devon - **September 1-2; November 3-4**

W.W. Windred (20th century, contemporary), 'Mr. Crowfield's Brown Red Cock "Goliath" and Two Hens'; oil on canvas, 6in. x 9in. Worth about £50. Modern paint on an old canvas in a primitive style. Highly deceptive.

From an article entitled 'Guilty Until Proven Innocent' by Richard Kay which appeared in the October 2000 issue of **Antique Collecting** magazine. For more details and to subscribe see page 147.

E W Services Antiques Fairs - 01933 225674
Antiques & Collectors' Fair, The Community Centre, Cornwalls Meadows Shopping Precinct, Buckingham, Bucks - **July 7; August 4; September 1; October 6; November 3; December 1**
The 5th Milton Keynes Antiques Fair, Middleton Hall, Central Milton Keynes Regional Shopping Centre, Milton Keynes, Bucks - **September 6-9**
Galloway Antiques Fairs - 01423 522122
Antiques & Collectors' Fair, Rookesbury Park, Wickham, Hampshire - **August 24-27**
Antiques Fair, Longleat House, Warminster, Wiltshire - **December 7-9**
Grandma's Attic Antiques Fairs - 01590 677687
Antiques & Collectors' Fair, Kingston Maurward House, Dorchester, Dorset - **July 14-15; September 15-16; November 10-11**
Antiques & Collectors' Fair, The Masonic Hall (bottom of High Street), Lymington, Hampshire - **August 4, 25; September 22; October 6, 20; November 3**
Antiques & Collectors' Fair, Winchester Guildhall, The Broadway, Winchester (off the M3), Hampshire - **August 5, November 4**
Antiques & Collectors' Fair, Lyndhurst Park Hotel, High Street, Lyndhurst, Hampshire - **August 26; September 30; December 2**
Antiques & Collectors' Fair, The Allendale Centre, Hanham Road, Wimborne, Dorset - **August 27; October 7; December 27**
Antiques & Collectors' Fair, Brockenhurst Village Hall, Highwood Road (off Sway Road), New Forest, Brockenhurst, Hants - **September 9; October 21; November 18**
Antiques & Collectors' Fair, The Potters Heron Hotel, Ampfield (Junction 12, M3), Hants - **September 23;**
Antiques & Collectors' Fair, Pavilion Ballroom (Westover Road), Bournemouth - **October 13-14; December 29-30**
Antiques & Collectors' Fair, Botleigh Grange Hotel, Botley, Hedge End, Near Southampton, Hampshire (Junction 7, M27) - **October 28**
Antiques & Collectors' Fair, The Littledown Centre, Castle Lane, north east of Bournemouth (A3060), Dorset - **November 25**
Harlequin Fairs - 01462 671688
Antiques Fair, Centre for Epilepsy, Chalfont Lane, Chalfont St Peter, Bucks - **July 1; August 5; September 2; October 7;**

November 4; December 2
Hyson Fairs Ltd - 01647 231459
Antiques & Collectors' Fair, The Pavilions, Sea Front, Exmouth, Devon - **July 8; August 12; September 9; October 14; November 1; December 9**
Antiques & Collectors' Fair, The Memorial Hall, Holsworthy, Devon - **July 15; August 19; September 16; October 21; November 25; December 16**
Charity Antiques & Collectors' Fair in aid of Leukaemia Research, The Jubilee Hall, Chagford, Devon - **July 28; November 10**
Specialist Textiles Fair, The Tote Pavilion, Newton Abbot Racecourse, Devon - **August 25**
Specialist Ephemera Fair, The Manicou Room, Newton Abbot Racecourse, Devon - **August 25**
Specialist 'Second Childhood' Fair, The Tote Pavilion, Newton Abbot Racecourse, Devon - **October 20**
Specialist Beanie Baby Fair, The Manicou Room, Newton Abbot Racecourse, Devon - **October 20**
Specialist Glass Fair, The Tote Pavilion, Newton Abbot Racecourse, Devon - **October 27**
Specialist Pottery Fair, The Manicou Room, Newton Abbot Racecourse, Devon - **October 27**
Specialist Deco & Modernist Fair, The Tote Pavilion, Newton Abbot Racecourse, Devon - **December 1**
Jay Fairs - 01235 815633
Hungerford Antiques Market, Town Hall, Hungerford, Berks (exit 14 M4) - **July 18; August 15; September 19; October 17; November 21; December 19**
Quality Antiques Fair, Fawley Court, Henley on Thames, Oxon - **July 2; November 25**
Antiques & Collectors' Fair & Drive-In, Crowmarsh Village Hall, Near Wallingford, Oxon - **August 27**
Antiques & Collectors' Fair, Drayton Village Hall, Near Abingdon, Oxon - **September 16; November 19**
Antiques & Collectors' Fair, The Village Hall, Dorchester on Thames, Oxon - **October 14; December 9**
Magnum Antiques Fairs - 01491 681009
Antiques Fair, River Park Leisure Centre, Gordon Road, Winchester, Hampshire - **August 27**
Melba Fairs - 01934 412923
Cotswolds' Premier Monthly Antiques Fair, Cheltenham Racecourse, Cheltenham,

FAIRS

Gloucestershire - **July 29; September 23; October 28; November 25; December 30**
Midas Fairs - 01494 674170
Antique Fair, The Bellhouse Hotel, Oxford Road (A40), Beaconsfield, Bucks (from Junction 2, M40, follow A40 sign to Gerrards Cross) - **July 8; August 12; September 9; October 14; November 11; December 9**
Two Day Fine Art & Antique Fair, The Bellhouse Hotel, Oxford Road (A40), Beaconsfield, Bucks (from Junction 2, M40, follow A40 sign to Gerrards Cross) - **August 26-27**
Penman Fairs - 01444 482514
Petersfield Antiques Fair, The Festival Hall, Heath Road, Petersfield, Hants - **September 7-9**
Bath Antiques & Fine Art Fair, The Pavilion, North Parade Road, Bath, Somerset - **November 1-4**
Renaissance Fairs - 01929 400343
Antique & Collectors' Fair, Corfe Castle Village Hall, Corfe Castle, Dorset - **July 1; August 5; September 2; October 7; November 4; December 2**
Silhouette Fairs - 01635 44338
Antiques & Collectors' Fair, The Abbey Hall, Abingdon, Oxon - **July 15; August 19; September 16; October 21; November 18; December 9**
Talisman Fairs - 01225 872522
Antiques & Collectables Market, Brunel Great Train Shed, Brunel's Historic Station, Temple Meads, Bristol, Avon - **July 8; August 12; September 9; October 14; November 11; December 19**
Antique & Collectors' Fair, St Margaret's Hall, Bradford on Avon, Wilts - **July 21; August 18; September 15; October 20; November 17; December 15**
Antiques & Collectors' Fair, Torquay Sea Front, Belgrave Hotel, Torquay, Devon - **July 22; August 26; September 23; October 28; November 25; December 16**
Jazz Art Deco Fair, Ashton Court Mansion, Bristol, Avon (west of Bristol city centre, from Junction 18 or 19, M5, with direct access from the A369 Portishead road) - **October 28**
Wakefield Ceramics Fairs - 01303 258635
Ceramics Fair, Burford School, Burford, Oxon - **July 7-8; October 6-7**
Ceramics Fair, The Michael Herbert Hall, Wilton, Wiltshire - **September 29-30**

WEST MIDLANDS

Includes Birmingham, Coventry, Herefordshire, Shropshire, Staffordshire, Warwickshire, Worcestershire.

Bowman Antiques Fairs - 07071 284 333
Giant 3 Day Quality Antiques Fair, The Bingley Hall, County Showground, Weston Road, Stafford, Staffs (A518, 5 mins J14, M6) - **August 17-19; September 28-30; December 7-9**
Centre Exhibitions - 0121 767 2760
Antiques for Everyone, Hall 5, The National Exhibition Centre, Birmingham, West Midlands - **August 2-5; November 22-25**
DMG Antiques Fairs - 01636 702326
Antiques & Collectors' Fair, The Three Counties Showground, Malvern, Worcs - **July 1; August 5; September 2; October 14; November 4; December 2**
Mr Dungate - 01895 834694
The Midland Clock & Watch Fair, National Motorcycle Museum (opposite NEC), Solihull, West Midlands - **August 19; November 18**
Geoffrey Whitaker - 01636 704060
Giant British Antiques & Collectors' Fair, The Royal Showground, NAC Stoneleigh Park, Coventry - **October 1**
Jay Ball Fairs & Events UK - 01246 251340
Antiques & Collectors' Fair, Uttoxeter Racecourse (Derby-Stoke A50) - **July 7-8; September 22-23; October 20-21; December 28-29**
Profile Promotions - 0121 449 4246
Antiques & Collectors' Fair, Straftord upon Avon Visitors Centre, Bridgefoot, Stratford upon Avon, Warks - **July 22; August 12; September 23; October 14; November 18; December 9**
Antiques & Collectors' Fair, The National Motorcycle Museum (opposite N E C, Junction 6, M42/A45), West Midlands - **July 8; August 5; September 9; October 7, 28; November 11; December 30**
Antiques & Collectors' Fair, The AT7 Centre, Bell Green Road, Coventry, West Midlands (off Junction 3, M6) **August 27**
Antiques & Collectors' Fair, The Royal Spa Centre, Newbold Terrace, Leamington Spa, Warks - **September 1; November 3**
Antiques & Collectors' Fair, King Edward VI Camp Hill School, Vicarage Road, Kings

Quality, Vetted Fairs

*Knowledgeable Exhibitors with
Integrity and a flair for Display.*

A warm welcome awaits you at:

2001:

June 1-3　　　　**PETERSFIELD Antiques Fair**
*Festival Hall, Heath Road, A3, Hampshire
43 stands, wide variety of traditional & decorative antiques.*

September 9 - 11　**PETERSFIELD Antiques Fair** *as June*

September 14 - 23 CHELSEA Antiques Fair
*Chelsea Old Town Hall, Kings Rd, SW3
Traditional, elegant, the Penman Flagship
Furniture pre Victorian - all with Style!*

October 25 - 28　**CHESTER** Antiques & Fine Art Show
*Grandstand, Chester Racecourse, Cheshire
Antiques mainly pre 1914, + art inclding some modern work
55 stands on 3 floors. The Best in the North West.*

2002:

January 17 - 20　**WEST LONDON** Antiques & Fine Art Fair
*Kensington Town Hall, W8.　60+ stands
Traditional & decorative Antiques.*

February 8 - 10　**PETERSFIELD Antiques Fair** *as June*

February 14 - 17　**CHESTER** Antiques & Fine Art Show

March 15 - 24　**CHELSEA Antiques Fair**

April 25 - 28　**CHELSEA ART Fair**, Chelsea Old Town Hall, Kings Rd,
SW3. 50 Galleries. Art in all media, mainly modern.

PLEASE PHONE TO CHECK BEFORE TRAVELLING A LONG DISTANCE

CAROLINE PENMAN, PENMAN FAIRS, TEL **01444 482514** / FAX **483412**
P.O. BOX 114, HAYWARDS HEATH, SUSSEX RH16 2YU
E-MAIL info@penman-fairs.co.uk

Times: 3 day fairs open
Fri/Sat 11-6, Sun 11-5
4-day fairs open Thurs/Fri 11-8,
Sat 11-6, Sun 11-5
At Chelsea: Weekdays 11-8,
Sats 11-7, Suns 11-5

PRINT OUT YOUR OWN
COMPLIMENTARY TICKET
ON THE WEB: **WWW.
penman-fairs.co.uk**

695

Heath, Birmingham, West Midlands - **September 16; October 21; November 11; December 2**
Shelley Group - 01455 202164
The Shelley Group Annual Collectors' Fair, The Royal Court Hotel, Keresley, Near Coventry - **October 28**
Wakefield Ceramics Fairs - 01303 258635
Ceramics Fair, The Bank House Hotel, Bransford, Worcs - **November 3-4**
Waverley Fairs - 0121 550 4123
Antiques & Collectors' Fair, New Market Hall, Bromsgrove, Worcs - **every Wednesday, and July 22; August 26; September 23; October 28; November 25**
Antiques & Collectors' Fair, The Community Centre, Kinver, Staffs - **August 5; September 2; October 7; November 4; December 2**
Book Fair, Powick Village Hall, Worcs - **July 8; August 12; September 9; October 14; November 11; December 9**
Book Fair, The Community Centre, Kinver, Staffs - **July 15; August 19; September 16; October 21; November 18; December 16**
Book Fair, Callow End Village Hall, Worcs - **October 30**

EAST MIDLANDS

Includes Derbyshire, Leicestershire, Lincolnshire, Northamptonshire, Nottinghamshire, Rutland, Sheffield.

DMG Antiques Fairs - 01636 702326
Antiques & Collectors' Fair, The Newark & Notts Showground, Newark, Notts - **August 6-7; October 8-9; December 3-4**
Jaguar Fairs Ltd - 01332 556139
Antiques Fair, Derby University, Kedleston Road, Derby - **July 21-22; November 3-4; December 15-16**
Peak Fairs - 01629 812449
Antiques Fair, The Town Hall, Bakewell, Derbyshire - **every Saturday, Sunday & Monday**
Robert Bailey Fairs - 01277 214699
The 9th Buxton Autumn Fine Art & Antiques Fair, Pavilion Gardens , Buxton. Derbyshire - **October 11-14**
Top Hat Exhibitions - 0115 9419141/925 8769
The National Art Deco Fair, Town Hall, Loughborough, Leics - **July 15; September 23; November 4**

Unicorn Fairs Ltd - 0161 773 7001
Antiques & Collectors' Fair, The Pavilion Gardens, Buxton, Derbyshire - **July 21-22; August 25-27; October 6-7; November 3-4; December 1-2, 29-30**

NORTH

Includes Cheshire, County Durham, Cumbria, Humberside, Lancashire, Manchester, Northumberland, Tyne and Wear, Yorkshire.

Albany Fairs - 0191 584 2934
Antiques Fair, The Village Hall, Pooley Bridge, Cumbria - **29-July 1; July 27-29; August 17-19; September 7-9, 21-23; October 12-14, 26-28; November 9-12; December 29-31**
Antiques Fair, The Scarth Hall, Staindrop, Co Durham - **September 16**
Antiques Fair, The Community Centre, Lanchester, Co Durham - **November 18**
Arthur Swallow Fairs - 01298 27493/73188
International Antiques & Collectors' Fair, RAF Swinderby (between Newark & Lincoln on the A46) - **August 3-5; October 5-7; November 30-December 2**
Cartmel Antiques Fairs - 01253 396209
Antiques Fair, The Village Hall, Cartmel, Cumbria - **July 5-8; August 16-19; September 13-16; 28-30; October 25-28; November 9-11**
Colin Caygill Events - 0191 261 9632
Antiques & Collectors' Fair, The Kendal Leisure Centre, Kendal, Cumbria - **September 23; November 11**
Antiques & Collectors' Fair, The County Hall, Durham City, Co Durham - **August 19; October 28; December 9**
Antiques & Collectors' Fair, The Wentworth Leisure Centre, Hexham, Northumberland - **July 10; August 21; September 11; October 9; November 6; December 11**
Antiques & Collectors' Fair, The Riverside Leisure Centre, Morpeth, Northumberland - **August 27; December 26**
Antiques & Collectors' Fair, The Newcastle Racecourse, Newcastle Upon Tyne, Tyne & Wear - **October 7**
Antiques & Collectors' Fair, Linden Hall Hotel, Longhorsley, Northumberland - **July 1; September 30**
Antiques & Collectors' Fair, The International Stadium, Gateshead, Tyne & Wear - **July 8;**

September 9; November 18
Antiques & Collectors' Fair, The Graham Sports Centre, Durham University, Co Durham - **July 15; September 16; November 25**
Antiques & Collectors' Fair, The Sands Centre, City of Carlisle, Cumbria - **July 22; September 2; November 4**
Antiques & Collectors' Fair, Skirsgill Hall, PFK Mart, Penrith, Cumbria - **July 29; October 14**
Antiques & Collectors' Fair, Kirkley Hall, Ponteland, Northumberland - **October 20-21**
Antiques & Collectors' Fair, Ponteland Leisure Centre, Ponteland, Northumberland - **December 2**
Cooper Antiques Fairs - 01249 661111
The Cheshire County Antiques Fair, Arley Hall, Near Knutsford, Cheshire - **October 5-7**
E W Services Antiques Fairs - 01933 225674
The Trafford Centre Antiques Fair, The Place, The Trafford Centre (Shopping Centre), Manchester (J9 & J10, M60) - **October 12-14**
Galloway Antiques Fairs - 01423 522122
The Duncombe Park Antiques Fair, Near Helmsley, North Yorks - **November 2-4**
Antiques Fair, Ripley Castle, Ripley, Near Harrogate, North Yorks - **July 13-15**
Antiques Fair, Naworth Castle, Brampton, Cumbria - **August 31-September 2**
Antiques Fair, The Old Swan Hotel, Harrogate, North Yorks - **September 21-23**
Antiques Fair, Stonyhurst College, Clitheroe, Lancs - **October 26-28**

Great Northern International Antiques & Collectors' Fairs - 01325 380077
Antiques & Collectors' Fair, Yorkshire Showground, Harrogate (on the A661 Harrogate/Wetherby Road), **July 20-22; September 7-9; November 2-4**
Jaguar Fairs Ltd - 01332 556139
Antiques Fair, Wetherby Racecourse - **July 7-8; September 22-23; November 24-25**
Louise Walker - 01823 323363
The Harrogate Antique Fair, The Harrogate International Centre (Hall A), Harrogate, North Yorks - **September 28-October 2**
N & B Fairs - 01565 722144
Antiques & Collectors' Fair, Plumley Village Hall, Near Knutsford, Cheshire - **July 29; August 26; September 30; October 28; November 25**
Penman Antiques Fairs - 01444 482514
Chester Antiques & Fine Art Show, The County Grandstand, Chester Racecourse, Chester, Cheshire - **October 25-28**
Robert Bailey Fairs Ltd - 01277 214699
Manchester International Antiques & Fine Art Fair, G-MEX, Manchester - **December 6-9**
The 32nd Cheshire Summer Antiques & 20th Century Fair, Tatton Park, Knutsford, Cheshire - **July 13-15**
The 32nd Cheshire Antiques Fair, Tatton Park, Knutsford, Cheshire - **September 6-9**
The 51st Northern Antiques Fair, Pavilions of Harrogate, Great Yorkshire Showground -

Egg cups, (left to right) Coalport, c.1870, £65; Minton, c.1830, £595; Davenport, c.1870, £98. On Amherst Antiques' stand at the Petersfield Antiques Fair on 8th-10th September.

From a Fairs Preview which appeared in the September 2000 issue of **Antique Collecting** magazine. For more details and to subscribe see page 147.

FAIRS

September 20-25
The Annual Wirral Antiques & Fine Art Fair, Hulme Hall in the Wirral, Cheshire - **October 26-28**
The 12th Cumbrian Antiques Fair, Holker Hall, Cark-in-Cartmel, Cumbria - **November 9-11**
Stancie Cutler Fairs - 01270 624288
Book Fairs with Ephemera, 'The Gables' (opposite Civic Hall), Beam Street, Nantwich, Cheshire - **October 20**
Antique Collectors' Fair, Nantwich Civic Hall, Cheshire (J16, M6) - **July 26; August 30; September 27; October 25; November 29; December 20, 27**
Beanies Fairs, 'The Gables' (opposite Civic Hall), Beam Street, Nantwich, Cheshire - **July 28; August 25; September 29; October 27; November 24; December 29**
Antique Collectors' Jamboree, Nantwich Civic Hall, Nantwich, Cheshire - **August 27**
Unicorn Fairs Ltd - 0161 773 7001
Antiques & Collectors' Fair, The Exhibition Halls, Park Hall, Charnock Richard, Lancs - **every Sunday**
Wakefield Ceramics Fairs - 01303 258635
Ceramics Fair, The Crown Hotel, Crown Place, Harrogate, West Yorkshire - **September 14-16**

Nottingham dealer, Cynthia Walmsley, has a varied selection of Sunderland jugs, including this example titled 'Northumberland 74' at the NEC, Birmingham. The view is of the Iron Bridge and the jug will cost £680.

From a Fairs Preview which appeared in the November 2000 issue of **Antique Collecting** magazine. For more details and to subscribe see page 147.

SCOTLAND

Albany Fairs - 0191 584 2943
Antiques Fair, The Town Hall, Moffat, Dumfriesshire - **July 20-22; August 24-27; September 28-30; October 19-21**
Antiques Fair, Town Hall, St Andrews, Fife - **July 17-18; August 9-11**
Antiques Fair, Victory Hall, St Andrews, Fife - **July 13-15; August 31-September 2**
Allen Lewis Fairs - 01202 604306
The 47th Antique Dealers' Fair of Scotland, Hopetoun House, South Queensferry - **October 12-14**
The 3rd Prestonfield House Antiques Fair, Prestonfield House, Edinburgh - **November 23-25**
Centre Exhibitions - 0121 767 2760
Antiques for Everyone, Scottish Exhibition & Conference Centre (SECC), Glasgow - **August 24-26**
Galloway Antiques Fairs - 01423 522122
Antiques Fair, Scone Palace, Perth - **November 16-18**

WALES

Allen Lewis Fairs - 01202 604306 - The Antique Dealers' Fair of Wales, The Orangery, Margam Park, Port Talbot, South Wales - **September 7-9**
The 45th Portmeirion Antiques Fair, Portmeirion, Gwynedd - **November 2-4**
Towy Antiques Fairs - 01267 236569
Antiques & Collectors' Fair, The United Counties Showground, Carmarthen - **July 21-22; September 15-16; December 15-16**
Antique & Collectors' Fair, Sophia Gardens, Cardiff - **September 8-9**
Antique & Collectors' Fair, Brangwyn Hall, Guildhall, Swansea - **December 1-2**

OVERSEAS

Haughton Fairs - 020 7734 5491
The International Fine Art & Antique Dealers Show, Seventh Regiment Armory, Park Avenue at 67th Street, New York City, New York 10021, USA - **October 19-25**
The International 20th Century Arts Fair, Seventh Regiment Armory, Park Avenue at 67th Street, New York City, New York 10021, USA - **November 24-28**

Services

This section has been included to enable us to list those businesses which do not sell antiques but are in associated trades, mainly restorations. The following categories are included.

Art, Books, Carpets & Rugs, Ceramics, Clocks & Barometers, Consultancy, Courier, Enamel, Engraving, Fireplaces, Framing, Furniture, Glass, Insurance & Finance, Ivory, Jewellery & Silver, Locks & Keys, Metalwork, Musical Instruments, Photography, Reproduction Stonework, Suppliers, Textiles, Tortoiseshell, Toys.

We would point out that the majority of dealers also restore and can give advice in this field.

Below are listed the trade associations mentioned within this section.

BAFRA	-	British Antique Furniture Restorers' Assn
FTAG	-	Fine Art Trade Guild
GADAR	-	Guild of Antique Dealers & Restorers
GMC	-	Guild of Master Craftsmen
MBHI	-	Member of British Horological Institute
UKIC	-	UK Institute for Conservation
CGCG	-	Ceramic & Glass Conservation Group
BTCM	-	British Traditional Cabinet Makers
BFMA	-	British Furniture Manufacturers' Assn
BCFA	-	British Contract Furniture Assn
ASFI	-	Assn of Suppliers to Furniture Industry
GAI	-	Guild of Architectural Ironmongers
MBWCG	-	Member British Watch & Clockmakers Guild

ART

The Antique Restoration Studio
See entry under Furniture.

Armor Paper Conservation Ltd
Glebe Cottage, 2 The Green, Garsington, Oxon. OX44 9DF. Tel: 01865 361741; fax - 01865 361815. TVADA. *Conservation and restoration of drawings, prints, watercolour paintings, documents and archive material.*

Paul Congdon-Clelford
The Conservation Studio, 59 Peverells Wood Ave., Chandler's Ford, Hants. SO53 2FX. Tel: 02380 268167; fax - same; e-mail - WinStudio@aol.com; website - www. conservationstudio.co.uk. IPC, ABPR, FATG, GADAR. *Conservators of oil paintings and works of art on paper; home consultations; collection and delivery in all areas. Conservators to museums and galleries.*

Kirkgate Fine Art & Conservation
18 Kirkgate, Thirsk, Yorks North. YO7 1PQ. (Richard Bennett). Tel: 01845 524085; home - same. UKIC, AABPR. Est. 1979. Open by appointment. *Oil paintings cleaned and lined on the premises; gilt/gesso frames restored and repaired; framing.*

Manor House Fine Arts
73 Pontcanna St. Cardiff, CF11 9HS. (S. K. Denley-Hill). Tel: 02920 227787; fax - 02920 641132; e-mail - valuers@manorhouse finearts. co.uk; website - www.manorhousefine arts.uk.

National Association of Valuers & Auctioneers. Est. 1976. Open 10-5.30. *Auctioneers, valuers, restorers, fine arts, antiques and chattels.*

Stephen Messer Picture Restoration
Tarifa, Millstream Moorings, Mill Lane, Clewer, Windsor, Berks. SL4 5JH. Tel: 01753 622335. Associate member ABPR. *Restorations - paintings, mainly oils including re-lining, frames including gilding.*

Claudio Moscatelli Oil Painting Restoration
46 Cambridge St., London SW1V 4QH. Tel: 020 7828 1304. *Oil paintings cleaned, relined, retouched and varnished.*

Plowden & Smith Ltd
190 St Ann's Hill, London SW18 2RT. Tel: 020 8874 4005; fax - 020 8874 7248; e-mail - Info @plowden-smith.co.uk; website - www. plowden-smith.co.uk. *Conservation and restoration of fine art and antiques. Specialist departments for furniture, ceramics, paintings, metal, stone, decorative arts, mounting/display.* VAT: Stan.

Colin A. Scott
1st Floor Studio, Anthony Hurst Antiques, 13 Church St., Woodbridge, Suffolk. IP12 1DS. Tel: 01394 388528. *Picture restoration and framing.*

Thicke Gallery
SA2 8BG. Tel: 01792 207515. (T.G. Thicke). Est. 1981. Open by appointment. *Advice on purchase/sale of paintings; valuations; restorations (oils, watercolours, samplers).*

BOOKS

Brignell Bookbinders
2 Cobbles Yard, Napier St., Cambridge, Cambs. CB1 1HP. Tel: 01223 321280; fax - same. Society of Bookbinders, GMC. Est. 1982. *Book restoration, conservation, table tops, leather photo cases, journal and thesis bindings, boxes and limited editions.* VAT: Stan.

The Manor Bindery Ltd.
Calshot Rd., Fawley, Southampton, Hampshire. SO4 1BB. Tel: 023 8089 4488; fax - 023 8089 9418. *Manufacturers of false books, either to use as a display or for cabinet makers to apply to doors and cupboards. Also decorative objects and accessories, various decorative replica book boxes. Leather library shelf edging.*

CARPETS AND RUGS

Barin Carpets Restoration
57a New Kings Rd., London SW6 4SE. Tel: 020 7731 0546. GMC. Conservation Register Museums and Galleries Commission. *Oriental carpets, rugs, European tapestries, Aubussons expertly cleaned, restored and lined. Expert advice, free estimates.*

The Restoration Studio
Unit 11 Kolbe House, 63 Jeddo Rd., London W12 9EE. Tel: 020 8740 4977. Member Rug Restorers Assn. *Restoration, cleaning, lining and mounting of tapestries, Aubusson carpets, kilims and all kinds of needlework.*

CERAMICS

The Antique Restoration Studio
See entry under Furniture.

G. Bagshaw Restorations
The Old Smithy, Capesthorne Hall Estate Yard, Siddington, Nr Macclesfield, Cheshire. SK11 9JX. Tel: 01625 860909; e-mail - gordon.bagshaw@ lineone.net. Est. 1971. Open 10-5.30. *General restoration - mainly ceramics and clocks.*

China Repairers
The Old Coach House, King's Mews, off King Street, London N2 8DY. (V.Baron). Tel: 020 8444 3030. Est. 1952. *Specialised restoration of all pottery and porcelain; restoration courses given.*

The China Repairers
1 Street Farm Workshops, Doughton, Tetbury, Glos. GL8 8TH. Tel: 01666 503551. TADA. *Specialised restoration of porcelain and pottery, mirror frame gilding.*

Porcelain Repairs
240 Stockport Rd., Cheadle Heath, Stockport, Cheshire. SK3 0LX. (I. Norman and A. Jones). Tel: 0161 428 9599; fax - 0161 286 6702. CGCG, UKIC. Est. 1970. *Highest standard restorations of European and Oriental ceramics, especially under glaze blue and white, museum repairs, carat gilding and modelling. Cracks and crazing removed without any overpainting or glazing.*

CLOCKS AND BAROMETERS

Apollo Southerns
Penygraig Industrial Estate, Tonypandy, Mid. Glam., South Wales. CS40 1JA. Tel: 01443 420420; mobile - 07800 373941. BJA; MBWCG;

Jewellery Industry Distributors Assn. *Watch and clock replacement and restoration materials; specialised tools for the horological trade.* VAT: Stan. *Trade Only.*

G. Bagshaw Restorations
See entry under Ceramics.

Clive and Lesley Cobb
3 Pembroke Crescent, Hove, East Sussex. BN3 5DH. Tel: 01273 772649. Listed by the Conservation Unit of the Museum and Galleries Commission. Est. 1972. *Quality, sympathetic restoration of lacquer clock cases and furniture, and painted clock dials.*

Edmund Czajkowski and Son
See entry under Furniture.

Martin H. Dunn
Glebe Farm, Clarke's Rd., North Killingholme, Lincs. DN40 3JQ. Tel: 01469 540901; fax - 01469 541512. Guild of Lincolnshire Craftsmen. *Clock movements and dials, brass work. Agent for several German clock movement makers.* VAT: Stan.

Richard Higgins (Conservation)
See entry under Furniture.

E. Hollander (David Pay)
1 Bennetts Castle, 89 The Street, Capel, Dorking, Surrey. RH5 5JX. Tel: 01306 713377; fax - 01306 712013. Open Mon.-Fri. 8-4.30, or by appointment. *Restoration of all forms of clocks, mechanisms, cases, dials and barometers.*

A.C. Layne
48 Cecil St., Carlisle, Cumbria. CA1 1NT. Tel: 01228 545019. Open 8-11.30 and 1-4. *Repairs to antique clocks and complicated watches.*

Robert B. Loomes
3 St Leonard's Street, Stamford, Lincs. PE9 1HD. Tel: 01780 481319. MBWCG. Open 9-3. CL: Sat. *British antique clock restoration - longcase, lantern and bracket.*

William C. Mansell
24 Connaught St., Marble Arch, London W2 2AF. Tel: 020 7723 4154; fax - 020 7724 2273; e-mail - williammansell@email.com; website - www. williammansell.co.uk. Est. 1864. *Repair/ restoration/ sales of all types of clocks, watches, barometers, etc., also antique jewellery and silverware.*

Meadows and Passmore Ltd
1 Ellen Street, Portslade, Brighton, East Sussex. BN41 1EU. Tel: 01273 421321; fax - 01273 421322. *Clock and barometer parts, tools and materials.*

Established in Portsea before 1880

E. HOLLANDER

1 BENNETT'S CASTLE
89 THE STREET
CAPEL
DORKING, SURREY RH5 5JX
Telephone: (01306) 713377

DAVID PAY

Maintains a family tradition
extending over five generations;
in the restoration of

CLOCKS
AND BAROMETERS

Menim Restorations
Bow St., Langport, Somerset. Tel: 01458 252157. GMC. Est. 1830. *Specialists in English and French clocks, full cabinet making and horological service; French polishing.*

Repton Clocks
Acton Cottage, 48 High St., Repton, Derbys. DE65 6GF. Tel: 01283 703657; fax - 01283 702367. MBWCMG; MBHI. Open by appointment 9-6. CL: Sat. *Antique and modern watch and clock restoration; musical box repairs; gear cutting; clocks made to order.*

Kevin Sheehan
15 Market Place, Tetbury, Glos. GL8 8DD. Tel: 01666 503099. Open 9-4.30, Sat. 10-12. *Specialist repairer of English and French 18th-19th C clocks. Written estimates given, all work guaranteed. Awarded Royal Warrant.*

Athena Antiques
59 Elvetham Rd., Fleet, Hants. (Richard Briant). Tel: 01252 615526; home - same; mobile - 07881 541748. Est. 1975. *Available seven days by appointment. Consultancy; valuations (jewellery, silver, clocks and furniture); restorations (clocks*

and furniture); buys at auction on commission; militaria. LOC: Near Fleet railway station.

John Fell-Clark
Wall Farm, Harkstead Rd., Holbrook, Ipswich, Suffolk. IP9 2RQ. LAPADA. Tel: 01473 327707. Est. 1971. By appointment. *Valuations; restorations; consultancy and interior design; buys at auction (17th-20th C furniture and textiles).* VAT: Spec.

Geoffrey Godden
3 The Square, Findon, West Sussex. BN14 0TE. Tel: 01903 873456. *Consultant and lecturer in ceramics.*

David Pettifer Ltd
73 Glebe Place, London SW3 5JB. Tel: 020 7352 3088; fax - 020 7352 4088. Est. 1963. Open by appointment. *Consultant and agent for 18th and early 19th C furniture and works of art.*

Quest
1 Garway Road, Bayswater, London W2 4PH. (John and Fay Lambert). Tel: 020 7221 1863; fax - same. Est. 1995. Any time by appointment. *Finder service - disposals as well as acquisitions -items from £1000.*

Gerald Sattin Ltd   BADA
P O Box 20627, London NW6 7GA. (G. and M. Sattin). Tel: 020 8451 3295; fax - same; e-mail - gsattin@compuserve.com. By appointment only. *Consultants and commission agents for the purchase of English and Continental porcelain, 1720-1900; English glass, 1700-1900; English silver, 1680-1920.* **VAT: Stan/Spec.**

COURIER

Antique Tours & Conrad Chauffeur Hire
11 Farleigh Rise, Monkton Farleigh, Nr. Bradford-on-Avon, Wilts. BA15 2QP. (John Veal). Tel: 01225 858527 (answerphone); fax - same; mobile - 07860 489831; e-mail - conradveal@hotmail.com. Est. 1988. *Private hire chauffeur service; car tours of antique shops in the West Country, or any other area, for up to four persons; service to and from air and sea ports; packing and shipping arranged. Genealogical research also undertaken.*

The English Room
London SW11 4PY. (Mrs Val Cridland). Tel: 020 7720 6655; mobile - 07770 275414; fax - 020 7978 2397. Est. 1985. By appointment only. *Search and courier (trade and private), London and country - shipment of goods purchased arranged.* VAT: Stan/Spec.

Janet Love Interiors
5A Furlong Road, London N7 8LS. Tel: 020 7619 9668; fax - 020 7619 9667; mobile - 07768 7815733. *Personal antique furniture shopping service and Olympia personal shopping service.*

Neil Robson Antiques Courier Service
10 Towrise, Sulgrave, Banbury, Oxon. OX17 2SB. Tel: 01295 760045; mobile - 07785 785447; e-mail - antiques.courier@virgin.net. TVADA. *Complete service for overseas buyers, throughout Britain and into Europe. Personalised itineraries covering all aspects of the trade - specialist dealers, fair, markets, auction, restorers and reproduction sources. Clients met at airport with spacious car or people carrier and accompanied throughout trip. Collection, packing, shipping and documentation of goods arranged.*

ENAMEL

Istvan Markovits - Enameller Consultant
11 Mallard Place, Strawberry Vale, Twickenham, Middx. TW1 4SW. Tel: 020 8891 1743; fax - 020 8891 1890. *Badgemakers. Worldwide restorers of enamel antique jewellery. Restorers of clock faces and ceramics.*

ENGRAVING

Eastbourne Engraving
12 North Street, Eastbourne, East Sussex. BN21 3HG. (D. Ricketts). Tel: 01323 723592. Est. 1882. Open Tues.-Fri. 9.15-4.45. *Engraving trophies, polishing, silver plating, repairs, hardwood plinths, etc.*

The Woods Engraving Co
174 London Road, Southend-on-Sea, Essex. SS1 1PH. Tel: 01702 338754. GMC. Est. 1970. *Engraving for silversmiths, polishers and platers, jewellery manufacturers; chapter rings, barometer dials, etc.* VAT: Stan.

FIREPLACES

Antiques and Restoration
Old Town Hall, 965 Stockport Rd, Levenshulme, Manchester, Lancs. (A. Warburton). Tel: 0161 256 4644; mobile - 07976 985982. Open 10-5, Sun. 11-4. *Antiques, fireplaces and restoration, also carpentry and re-claimed pine furniture.*

FRAMING

Natural Wood Framing
Eight Bells Gallery, 14 Church St., Tetbury, Glos. GL8. Tel: 01666 505070. FATG. *Bespoke framing specialising in antiques, textiles and restorations. Contemporary and sporting art stocked.*

FURNITURE

Absolutely Fabulous Interiors with Michael Jeffries
3 Upper Lambridge St., Larkhall, Bath, Somerset. BA1 6RY. Tel: 01225 310417; 01225 448103. *Antique upholstered furniture; decorative pieces.* VAT: Stan.

Timothy Akers - Antique Furniture Restorations
The Forge, 39 Chancery Lane, Beckenham, Kent. BR3 2NR. Tel: 020 8650 9179; website - www.akersofantiques.com. BAFRA. *Restorations of 17th-19th C English furniture, longcase and bracket clocks.*

Alan's Antique Restorations
PO Box 355. Woking, Surrey. GU22 9QE. (A.V. Wellstead). Tel: 01483 724666; fax - 01483 750366.

Anthony Allen Antique Restorers
Old Wharf Workshop, Redmoor Lane, New Mills, High Peak, Derbys. SK22 3JL. Tel: 01663 745274. BAFRA. *Boulle, marquetry, walnut, oak, veneering restorations and upholstery; clock movements and clockcases.*

The Antique Restoration Centre
14 Suffolk Rd., Cheltenham, Glos. GL50 2AQ. Tel: 01242 262549. Open Mon-Fri 9.30-5. *All types of restoration - all restorers BADA qualified.*

The Antique Restoration Studio
The Old Post Office, Newport Road, Stafford, Staffs. ST18 9JH. (P. Albright). el: 01785 780424; e-mail - ars@uk-hq.demon.co.uk. Open 9-5. *Repairs and restoration (furniture, rush and cane, French polishing, leatherwork and upholstery, ceramics, glassware, paintings, clocks and watches, rare books, documents and photographs). Five year guarantee on all work. Collection and delivery service.*

Antiques and Restoration
See entry under Fireplaces.

Michael Barrington
The Old Rectory, Warmwell, Dorchester, Dorset. DT2 8HQ. Tel: 01305 852104; fax - 854822. BAFRA. *Conservator and restorer of 17th-20th C furniture, clocks, barometers, gilding, upholstery, metalwork, music boxes and barrel pianos, automatons and rocking horses.*

Batheaston
20 Leafield Way, Corsham, Wilts. SN13 9SW. Tel: 01225 811295; fax - 01225 810501. BFMA. BCFA. *Oak reproduction furniture made from solid kiln dried timbers, antique hand finish. Extensive range of Windsor, ladderback and country Hepplewhite chairs; refectory, gateleg and other extendable tables, Welsh dressers, sideboards and other cabinet models. Trade Only.*

David Battle
Brightley Pound, Umberleigh, Devon. EX37 9AL. Tel: 01769 540483. BAFRA. *Cabinet making, restoration and conservation work; polishing, clock cases, veneer and marquetry work, woodturning. Specialists in 17th-19th C English and Continental furniture. Collections and deliveries.*

Keith Bawden - Restorer of Antiques
Mews Workshops, Montpellier Retreat, Cheltenham, Glos. GL50 2XG. Tel: 01242 230320. BAFRA. *All period furniture, plus restoration of items made from wood, metals, porcelain, pottery, fabrics, leather, ivory, papier-mâché, etc.*

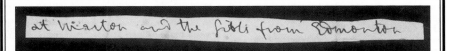

A line of Nelson's manuscript, the highlight in a bundle of correspondence originally given by the Admiral's doctor William Beatty to friend and fellow practitioner James Fellowes, which sold for £3,200.

From an Auction Report by Christopher Wight on Maritime and Naval Battles, Christie's South Kensington, 9th November 2000. This sale was featured in the February 2001 issue of **Antique Collecting** magazine. For more details and to subscribe see page 147.

Clive Beardall
104b High St., Maldon, Essex. CM9 5ET. Tel: 01621 857890. BAFRA.

Bell Passage Antiques
38 High Street, Wickwar, Glos. GL12 8NP. LAPADA. Tel: 01454 295251; fax - same. Est. 1966. *Restorers of antique and modern furniture, specialists in French and wax polishing, picture restoration, traditional and modern upholstery and caning. Work carried out on site.*

Belvedere Reproductions
11 Dove St., Ipswich, Suffolk. IP4 1NG. Tel: 01473 214573; fax - 01473 253229; mobile - 07860 782888. *Suppliers of traditionally constructed and hand polished oak and fruit-wood country furniture.* VAT: Stan.

Dan Bent
Newholt, Court Rd., Newton Ferrers, Plymouth, Devon. PL8 1DE. Tel: 01752 872831. BAFRA.

Berry & Crowther
9 Whitestones Workshop, Stocksmoor, Huddersfield, West Yorks. HD4 6XQ. Tel: 01484 609800; fax - same; e-mail - peternberry@ aol.com. *Fine antique restorers and conservators; restoration with traditional methods to highest standards on fine furniture and clocks. Insurance work approved.*

Rupert Bevan
40 Fulham High St., London SW6 3LQ. Tel: 020 7731 1919; fax - same. *Gilding, carving and painting.* VAT: Stan.

Peter Binnington
Barn Studio, Botany Farm, East Lulworth, Wareham, Dorset. BH20 5QH. Tel: 01929 400224; fax - 01929 400744. BAFRA. *Restoration of verre églomisé, giltwork, decorated surfaces, period furniture.*

Maxwell Black
Brookhouse Studios, Novington Lane, East Chiltington, Lewes, East Sussex. BN7 3AX. Tel: 01273 890175.

Martin Body - Giltwood Restoration
7 Addington Sq., London SE5 7JZ. Tel: 020 7703 4351. *Specialist conservation of fine gilded furniture and frames.*

Richard Bolton
The Old Dairy, Painswick House, Painswick, Glos. GL6 6TH. Tel: 01452 814881. BAFRA. *All aspects of furniture restoration undertaken; tuition given.* LOC: Rear of Painswick House.

David J. Booth - A.E. Booth & Son
9 High St., Ewell, Surrey. KT17 1SG. Tel: 020 8393 5245. BAFRA. *Restoration, polishing and upholstery of antique and reproduction furniture.*

A.E. Booth & Son
Crows Nest, Edgeley Rd., Barton, Torquay, Devon. TQ2 8ND. Tel: 01803 312091. *Restorations, polishing, upholstery. Barometers, longcase, mahogany and walnut.*

Stuart Bradbury - M & S Bradbury
The Barn, Hanham Lane, Paulton, Somerset. BS39 7PF. Tel: 01761 418910. BAFRA. *All aspects of antique furniture restoration.*

Lawrence Brass
154 Sutherland Avenue, Maida Vale, London W9. Tel: 0122 585 2222. UKIC. Approved by the Museums and Galleries Commission. *Conservation and restoration of fine antiques, metal work, gilding and upholstery.*

A. J. Brett & Co Ltd
168c Marlborough Rd., London N19 4NP. Tel: 020 7272 8462; fax - 020 7272 5102. *Restorers of antique furniture and upholstery; French polishing and gilding; free estimates.*

Bruton Classic Furniture Company Ltd.
Unit 1 Station Road Industrial Estate, Bruton, Somerset. BA10 0EH. Tel: 01749 813266; fax - same; mobile - 07973 342047. *Quality antique replica furniture - mahogany, teak and pine.*

Peter Campion Restorations
Myrtle Cottage, Gretton, Cheltenham, Glos. GL54 5EP. Tel: 01242 604403; fax - same; website - www.petercampion.co.uk. BAFRA. Est. 1959. *Furniture restoration, conservation, polishing, insurance work, furniture designed and made to order.*

Cane & Able Antiques - Cane & Rush Furniture Restoration
The Limes, 22 The Street, Beck Row, Bury St. Edmunds, Suffolk. IP28 8AD. Tel: 01638 515529; fax - 01638 583905; e-mail - caneandable@enetsale.com. *Specialists in antique and designer cane, furniture, upholstery and rush seating.*

John B. Carr - Charles Perry Restorations Ltd
Praewood Farm, Hemel Hempstead Rd., St. Albans, Herts. AL3 6AA. Tel: 01727 853487. BAFRA.

Carvers & Gilders
9 Charterhouse Works, Eltringham St., London SW18 1TD. Tel: 020 8870 7047; fax - 020 8874 0470; e-mail - acc@carversandgilders.com; website - www.carversandgilders.com. UKIC; Master Carver's Assn; Furniture History Society.

Restoration and conservation of fine decorative woodcarving and giltwood. Specialists in fine water gilding. Designers and makers of carved and giltwood furniture, mirror frames and other decorative pieces in both period and contemporary styles. VAT: Stan.

Peter G. Casebow
Pilgrims, Mill Lane, Worthing, West Sussex. BN13 3DE. Tel: 01903 264045. BAFRA. *Period furniture, turning, marquetry, metalwork, fretwork, polishing.*

Graham Childs - Alpha (Antique) Restorations
High St., Compton, Newbury, Berks. RG20 6NL. Tel: 01635 578245; mobile - 07860 575203. BAFRA. *Fine oak, walnut and mahogany. Traditional hand finishes. Veneering and inlaying. Clock cases.*

Clare Hall Company
The Barns, Clare Hall, Cavendish Rd., Clare, Nr. Sudbury, Suffolk. CO10 8PJ. Tel: 01787 278445; fax - 01787 278803; 01787 277510 (ansaphone). Est. 1970. *Replicas of 18th and 19th C floor standing and table globes. Full cabinet making especially four poster beds; restoration of all antiques and upholstery.* VAT: Stan/Spec.

Classic Reproductions
Swan Corner, Pewsey, Wilts. SN9 5HL. Tel: 01672 563333; fax - 01672 562391. *Suppliers of replica antiques from Java and manufacturers of custom designed pine furniture including tables, beds, chests, bookcases and desks.*

Benedict Clegg
Rear of 20 Camden Rd., Tunbridge Wells. Kent. TN1 2PT. Tel: 01892 548095. BAFRA.

Lucinda Compton
of Compton & Schuster Ltd
The Old Laundry, Newby Hall, Ripon, North Yorks. HG4 5AE. Tel: 01423 324290. BAFRA. *Furniture - painted, gilded, lacquer, papier mâché, tôle.*

Compton & Schuster Ltd
Studio A133 Riverside Business Centre, Haldane Place, London SW18 4UQ. Tel: 020 8874 0762; fax - 020 8870 8060. BAFRA. *Conservation and restoration - lacquer, gilding, painted furniture, paper-mâché, tôle, architectural gilding.*

William Cook
167 Battersea High St., London SW11 3JS. Tel: 020 7736 5329 or 01672 513017. BAFRA. *18th C and English period furniture.*

William Cook
High Trees House, Savernake Forest, Marlborough, Wilts. SN8 4NE. Tel: 01672 513017. BAFRA.

Robert H. Crawley
75 St. Mary's Rd., Ealing, London W5 5RH. Tel: 020 8566 5074. BAFRA.

Marie Louise Crawley
39 Woodvale, London SE23 3DS. Tel: 020 8516 0002; fax - same. BAFRA. *Painted furniture, papier-mâché, tôle ware, lacquer and gilding.*

J.W. Crisp Antiques
1-9 Tennyson Rd., Wimbledon, London SW19 8SH. (Michael Murren). Tel: 020 8543 1118; fax - same. Open by appointment. *Restoration of antique furniture and French polishing.*

Michael Czajkowski - Edmund Czajkowski and Son
96 Tor-o-Moor Rd., Woodhall Spa, Lincs. LN10 6SB. Tel: 01526 352895; fax - same; e-mail - sales@czajkowskiandson.co.uk. BAFRA. *Furniture, clocks (including church) and barometers restored. Veneering, marquetry, English lacquer and boulle work, carving and gilding.*

D.H.R. Limited
8/10 Lea Lane, Thame Rd., Long Crendon, Aylesbury, Bucks. HP18 9RN. Tel: 01844 202213; fax - 01844 202214. BAFRA. *Boulle, cabinetwork, carving, gilding, lacquer, leather, marble, marquetry, ormolu, upholstery.*

D Restoration
4 Gleneldon Mews, London, SW16 2AZ. Tel: 020 7274 2847. *French polishing, gilding, wood carving, restoration.*

Michael Dolling
Church Farm Barns, Glandford, Holt, Norfolk. NR25 7JR. Tel: 01263 741115. BAFRA.

Raymond Dudman - W. Thomas Ltd.
12 Warwick Place. London. W9 2PX. Tel: 020 7286 1945. BAFRA.

Brian Duffy and Katie Keat - Hope & Piaget
12 and 13 Burmarsh Workshops, Marsden St., London NW5 3JA. Tel: 020 7267 6040; fax - same; e-mail - mail@hope-piaget.co.uk; website - www.hope-piaget.co.uk. BAFRA. UKIC.

Michael Durkee
Castle House, 1 Bennetts Field Estate, Wincanton, Somerset. BA9 9DT. Tel: 01963 33884. BAFRA. *Restoration, conservation and finishing of all styles of period furniture. Boulle and inlay work.*

EFMA

4 Northgate Close, Rottingdean, Brighton, East Sussex. BN2 7DZ. (Anthony and Patrick Hoole). Tel: 01273 589744; fax - 01273 589745. Fed. of Sussex Industries, IDDA, Inst. of Export, Inst. of Linguists. *Hand-finished reproductions in walnut, elm, myrtle, yew, mahogany, satinwood. Custom-work and bespoke polishing - 18th C, Biedermeier, Victorian, mahogany dining tables. Country furniture - distressed oak and cherry refectory, gateleg and coffee tables, Windsor chairs. Tables reproduced from old timber.* VAT: Stan.

D.S. Embling - The Cabinet Repair Shop

Woodlands Farm, Blacknest, Alton, Hants. GU34 4QB. Tel: 01252 794260. C&G London Inst; GMC; League of Professional Craftsmen. Est. 1977. *Antique and modern furniture restoration and repair including marquetry and veneering, French polishing, modern finishes. Parts made, wood turning, collection and delivery; insurance claim repairs.*

Everitt and Rogers

Dawsnest Workshop, Grove Rd., Tiptree, Essex. CO5 0JE. Tel: 01621 816508; fax - 01621 814685. GADAR. Est. 1969. *Expert antique furniture restoration.*

Duncan Everitt - D.M.E. Restorations Ltd

11 Church St., Ampthill, Beds. MK45 2PL. Tel: 01525 405819; fax - 01525 756177; website - www.dmerestoration.co.uk. BAFRA.

John Farbrother Furniture Restoration

Ivy House, Main St., Shipton-by-Beningbrough, York, North Yorks. YO30 1AB. Tel: 01904 470187; website - www.jf-frenchpolishing.co.uk. GADAR. Est. 1987. *All repairs undertaken, refinishing process from complete strip to reviving existing finish. French polishing, oil, wax and lacquers. Pressurised fluid application woodworm treatment.*

Fauld Town and Country Furniture

Whitestone Park, Whitestone, Hereford, Herefs. HR1 3SE. Tel: 01432 851992; fax - 01432 851994; website - www.fauld.com. Est. 1972. Open 8-5, appointment advisable. *Windsor chairs, extensive range of farmhouse tables, dressers and racks and many other case pieces. Bespoke work a speciality to traditional styles and methods.* VAT: Stan.

Fenlan

17B Stilebrook Rd., Yardley Road Industrial Estate, Olney, Bucks. Tel: 01234 711799; fax - same. Est. 1982. *Furniture restoration. Restoration products and fittings supplied; cabinet making and non-caustic stripping.* VAT: Stan/Spec.

Andrew Foott

4 Claremont Rd., Cheadle Hulme, Cheshire. SK8 6EG. Tel: 0161 485 3559. *Sympathetic restoration and conservation of antique furniture and mercurial barometers; free advice and estimates; quality items occasionally for sale.*

Forge Studio Workshops

Stour St., Manningtree, Essex. CO11 1BE. Tel: 01206 396222. BAFRA. *Carving, general restoration, copying and bespoke cabinet making.*

Glen Fraser-Sinclair - G. and R. Fraser-Sinclair

Hays Bridge Farm, Brickhouse Lane, South Godstone, Surrey. RH9 8JW. Tel: 01342 844112. BAFRA. *18th C furniture.*

Alistair J. Frayling-Cork

2 Mill Lane, Wallingford, Oxon. OX10 0DH. Tel: 01491 826221. BAFRA. *Antique and period furniture, clock cases, ebonising, wood turning, stringed instruments and brass fittings repaired.*

Georgian Cabinets Manufacturers Ltd

Unit 4 Fountayne House, 2-8 Fountayne Rd., London N15 4QL. Tel: 020 8885 1293; fax - 020 8365 1114. Est. 1964. *Manufacturers, restorers and polishers. Large stock of inlaid furniture.* LOC: Near Seven Sisters underground, Tottenham. VAT: Stan.

Sebastian Giles Furniture

11 Junction Mews, London W2 1PN. Tel: 020 7258 3721. BAFRA.

Melven Glander

Tel: 01284 828429. *Restoration and repair service to furniture, woodwork, clocks and period fixtures and fittings; free estimates and advice. Collection and delivery. Upholstery arranged.*

Gow Antiques & Restoration

Pitscandly Farm, Forfar, by Lunanhead, Angus, Scotland. DD8 3NZ. (Jeremy Gow). Tel: 01307 465342; mobile - 07711 416786; e-mail - Jeremy@gowantiques. co.uk; website - www.gowantiques.co.uk. BAFRA. Accredited by GMC, Historic Scotland and the Museums and Galleries Commission. Appointment advisable. *17th-19th C English and Continental furniture. Specialist in marquetry, tortoiseshell and fine furniture.*

Greycroft Antiques

Greycroft, Station Rd., Errol, Perthshire, Scotland. PH2 7SN. (D. and Mrs J. Pickett). Tel: 01821 642221; home - same. Est. 1981. Open 10-5.30 or by appointment.

Jeffrey Hall - Malvern Studios

56 Cowleigh Rd., Malvern, Worcs. WR14 1QD. Tel: 01684 574913; fax - 01684 569475. BAFRA.

SERVICES

Jeremy Hall - Peter Hall & Son
Danes Rd., Staveley, Kendal, Cumbria. LA8 9PL.
Tel: 01539 821633; fax - 01539 821905.

John Hartley
Johnson's Barn, Waterworks Rd., Sheet, Petersfield,
Hants. GU32 2BY. Tel: 01730 233792; fax - 01730
233922. BAFRA. *Comprehensive restoration and
conservation service, including carving, gilding,
painted furniture, lacquer, marquetry, boulle and
architectural woodwork. Adviser to The National
Trust.*

Philip Hawkins
Glebe Workshop, Semley, Shaftesbury, Dorset.
SP7 9AP. Tel: 01747 830830; e-mail - hawkins
semley@hotmail.com. BAFRA. *16th to early
18th C oak furniture restoration.*

Roland Haycraft
The Lamb Arcade, Wallingford, Oxon. Tel:
01491 839622. *All aspects of antique restorations; one-off reproductions and copying
service. Fine furniture designed and made to
traditional standards.*

Michael Hedgecoe
21 Burrow Hill Green, Chobham, Surrey. GU24
8QS. LAPADA. Tel: 01276 858206; fax - 01276
857352. BAFRA. *General restorations, cabinet
work, polishing, upholstery, chair making.*

Alan Hessel
The Old Town Workshop, St. George's Close,
Moreton-in-Marsh, Glos. GL56 0LP. Tel: 01608
650026; fax - same. BAFRA. *Comprehensive
restoration service. English and Continental fine
period furniture.*

Richard Higgins (Conservation)
The Old School, Longnor, Nr. Shrewsbury, Shrops.
SY5 7PP. Tel: 01743 718162; fax - 01743 718022.
BAFRA. LBHI. Conservation Register Museums
and Galleries Commission. *Comprehensive
restoration of all fine furniture and clocks,
including movements and dials; specialist work to
boulle, marquetry, carving, turning, cabinet and
veneer work, lacquer, ormolu, metalwork, casting,
glazing, polishing, upholstery, cane and rush
seating. Stocks of old timber, veneers, tortoiseshell
etc. held to ensure sympathetic restoration.*

Stephen Hill - Brewery Antiques
11 Cirencester Workshops, Brewery Court,
Cirencester, Glos. GL7 1JH. Tel: 01285 658817;
fax - 01285 644060; mobile - 07976 722028.
BAFRA. *General furniture including oak,
walnut, mahogany, 17th-19th C gilding, carving,
upholstery, rush and cane seating. Furniture
made by commission only.*

Stuart Hobbs Antique Furniture Restoration
Meath Paddock, Meath Green Lane, Horley,
Surrey. RH6 8HZ. Tel: 01293 782349. GMC.
BAFRA. *Full restoration service for period
furniture.*

B.R. Honeyborne
The Whyle Cottage, Pudleston, Leominster,
Herefs. HR6 0RE. Tel: 01568 750250. Guild of
Herefordshire Craftsmen. *Antique furniture
restoration and restoration courses; postal
service of mouldings and bracket feet.*

Christian Macduff Hunt - Hunt and Lomas
Village Farm Workshops, Preston Village,
Cirencester, Glos. GL7 5PR. Tel: 01285 640111.
BAFRA. *17th-19th C oak, mahogany, walnut,
satinwood, carving.*

Donald Hunter
The Old School Room, Shipton Oliffe,
Cheltenham, Glos. GL54 4JB. Tel: 01242
820755. *Restoration of fine antiques, cabinet
making, water gilding, lacquer work, decorative
finishes.*

Rodney F. Kemble
16 Crag Vale Terrace, Glusburn, Nr. Keighley,
West Yorks. BD20 8QU. Tel: 01535 636954/
633702. BAFRA. *Cabinet restorations, clock
cases, traditional hand finishes and upholstery.*

Raymond Konyn Antique Restorations
The Old Wheelwright's, Brasted Forge, Brasted,
Kent. TN16 1JL. Tel: 01959 563863; fax - 01959
561262; website - www.antique-restorations.
org.uk. BAFRA. *Furniture, traditional upholstery,
longcase and bracket clock cases, polishing, brass
casting. Consultancy.*

Roderick Larwood
The Oaks, Station Rd., Larling, Norfolk. NR16
2QS. Tel: 01953 717937; fax - same. BAFRA.
*Brass inlay, 18th to early 19th C furniture;
French polishing.*

E.C. Legg and Son
3 College Farm Workshops, Tetbury Rd.,
Cirencester, Glos. GL7 6PY. Tel: 01285 650695. Est.
1902. Open 9-5. CL: Sat. *Restoration of furniture
and gilt frames; caning; re-leathering desk tops.*

Andrew Lelliott
6 Tetbury Hill, Avening, Tetbury, Glos. GL8
8LT. Tel: 01453 835783/832652. BAFRA.

UKIC. Conservation Register Museums & Galleries Commission. *Comprehensive restorations; specialized wooden mouldings.*

David C. E. Lewry
Wychelms, 66 Gorran Avenue, Rowner, Gosport, Hants. PO13 0NF. Tel: 01329 286901; fax - 01329 289964; mobile - 07785 766844. BAFRA. *17th to early 19th C furniture.*

John Lloyd
The Old Bakehouse, The Street, Bolney, West Sussex. RH17 5PG. Tel: 01444 881988; fax - same; e-mail - lloydjohn@aol.com. BAFRA. *Sympathetic restoration and conservation of English and Continental furniture; traditional hand finishing, veneering, marquetry and inlay work, carving and turning, gilding, upholstery, rush/cane work, leather lining and tooling, lock repairs and keys. Antique furniture copied or designed and made to order. Regular delivery/ collection service to London.*

Lomas Pigeon & Co. Ltd
37 Beehive Lane, Great Baddow, Chelmsford, Essex. CM2 9TQ. Tel: 01245 353708; fax - 01245 355211; website - www.lomas-pigeon. co.uk. BAFRA. *Restoration, French polishing, traditional and modern upholstery. Retailers of fine furniture and rocking horses.*

Timothy Long Restoration
St. John's Church, London Rd., Dunton Green, Sevenoaks, Kent. TN13 2 TE. Tel: 01732 743368; fax - 01732 742206. BAFRA. *Cabinet restoration, French polishing, upholstery.*

Bruce Luckhurst
The Little Surrenden Workshops, Ashford Rd., Bethersden, Kent. TN26 3BG. Tel: 01233 820589; fax - 01580 243068; e-mail - training@ woodwise.newnet.co.uk; website - www.bruce luckhurst.co.uk. BAFRA. *Conserv-ation and restoration training plus comprehensive restoration service.*

Simon Marsh
The Old Butchers Shop, High St., Bletchingly. Surrey. RH1 4PA. Tel: 01883 743350; fax - 01883 744844.

Richard J. Marson - R.M. Restoration
Unit 8 Hilltop Meadows, Old London Rd., Knockholt, Kent. TN14 7JW. Tel: 01959 533771. BAFRA. *Period furniture, traditional upholstery, French polishing.*

Mortlake Antiques
Nelson House Workshop, Kaber, Kirkby Stephen, Cumbria. CA17 4EF. (C.J. and Miss J.A. Bate). Tel: 017683 71666. Est. 1945. *Antique furniture restoration.*

Timothy Naylor
24 Bridge Rd., Chertsey, Surrey. KT16 8JN. Tel: 01932 567129; fax - 01932 564948. BAFRA. *Antique furniture restoration.*

M. R. Nelms
Unit 2 Trench Farm, Tilley Green, Wem, Shrops. SY4 5PJ. Tel: 01939 235463; fax - 01939 235416; e-mail - heritageantiques@btconnect.com; website - www.heritageantiques.co.uk. GADAR. *Furniture, including antique and fitted, full restoration service, antique boxes and clock cases a speciality.*

Nicholas J. Newman
22 Eastcroft Rd., West Ewell, Surrey. KT19 9TX. Tel: 020 8224 3347. *Comprehensive restorations including exterior woodwork and locks.*

Ben Norris & Co
Knowl Hill Farm, Knowl Hill, Kingsclere, Newbury, Berks. RG20 4NY. Tel: 01635 297950; fax - 01635 299851. BAFRA. *All aspects of furniture restoration including carving, gilding, copy chair making and architectural woodwork. Excellent storage facilities.* VAT: Stan.

Nigel Northeast Cabinet Makers
Furniture Workshops, Back Drove, West Winterslow, Salisbury, Wilts. SP5 1RY. Tel: 01980 862051; fax - 01980 863986. GADAR. Est. 1982. *Antique restoration and French polishing. New furniture made to order, chairs made to complete sets. Cane and rush seating; fire and flood damage service.* VAT: Stan.

Simon Paterson Fine Furniture Restoration
Whitelands, West Dean, Chichester. West Sussex. PO18 0RL. Tel: 01243 811900; e-mail - sp@hotglue.fsnet.co.uk. BAFRA.

Clive Payne
Unit 4 Mount Farm, Churchill, Chipping Norton, Oxon. OX7 6NP. LAPADA. Tel: 01608 658856; fax - same; mobile - 07801 088363. BAFRA.

Noel Pepperall
Dairy Lane Cottage, Walberton, Arundel, West Sussex. BN18 0PT. Tel: 01243 551282; e-mail - pepperall@amserve.net; website - www.pepperall. co.uk. BAFRA. *Antique furniture restoration.*

Eva-Louise Pepperall
Dairy Lane Cottage, Walberton, Arundel, West Sussex. BN18 0PT. Tel: 01243 551282; e-mail - pepperall@amserve.net; website - www. pepperall. co.uk. BAFRA. *Gilding and japanning.*

T. L. Phelps - Fine Furniture Restoration
8 Mornington Terrace, Harrogate, North Yorks. HG1 5DH. Tel: 01423 524604. BAFRA. UKIC. Est. 1984. *Specialist restoration and conservation services; all cabinet work, including dining tables, large items; all veneer work; architectural woodwork; traditional hand polishing, colouring and waxed finishes.*

Pinewood Furniture Studio Ltd
1 Eagle Trading Estate, Stourbridge Rd., Halesowen, West Midlands. B63 3UA. Tel: 0121 550 8228; fax - 0121 585 5611. *Manufacturers of pine furniture. Special orders undertaken.* VAT: Stan.

Plain Farm Workshop
The Old Dairy, Plain Farm, East Tisted, Alton, Hants. GU34 3RT. (Simon Worte). Tel: 01420 588362. *18th to early 19th C English furniture restoration.*

Plowden & Smith Ltd
See entry under Art.

Albert Plumb Furniture Co
Briarfield, Itchenor Green, Chichester, West Sussex. PO20 7DA. Tel: 01243 513700/1; fax - same. BAFRA. *Oak, walnut, mahogany and country furniture, upholstery and cabinet making.*

Nathan Polley Restorations
The Barn, Upton Grove, Tetbury Upton, Tetbury, Glos. GL8 8LR. Tel: 01666 504997. TADA. *Fine furniture restorers and cabinet makers. Inlay work, wood turning, French polishing, waxing. Specialist in period mahogany, walnut and early oak.*

Neil Postons Restorations
29 South St., Leominster, Herefordshire. HR6 8JQ. Tel: 01568 616677; fax - same; mobile - 07710 297602. UKIC. Registered with the Museums and Galleries Commission. Open 8.45-5.30, Sat. and other times by appointment. *Antique and fine furniture restorations including re-construction, veneering, carving, turning, French and wax polishing, re-upholstery, rush and cane seating.*

Ludovic Potts Restorations
Unit 1/1A, Haddenham Business Park, Station Rd., Haddenham, Ely, Cambs. CB6 3XD. Tel: 01353 741537; fax - 01353 741822; e-mail - mail@restorers.co.uk. BAFRA.

The Real Wood Furniture Company
16 Oxford St., Woodstock, Oxon. OX20 1TS. (Chris Baylis). Open 10.30-5.30, Sun. 11-5. Tel: 01993 813887; fax - 01993 812379; e-mail - rwood@mcmcil.com; webiste - www.realwood furniture.co.uk. *Large stock of superb hand crafted country furniture in traditional antique styles - solid oak, ash and cherry. Tables, dressers etc made to order. Large range of rush seated, Windsor and kitchen style chairs.*

Rectory Bungalow Workshop
Main Road, Elton, Nr. Bingham, Notts. NG13 9LP.(E.M. and Mrs M.G. Mackie). Tel: 01949 850878. Est. 1981. *Restorations - cane and rush seating, painted furniture.*

Nicholas S. Reeve
Barton Grange, Worlingworth, Woodbridge, Suffolk. IP13 7PE. Tel: 01728 628121; fax - 01728 628676; mobile - 07850 817216; e-mail - enquiries@nreeve.flexnet.co.uk; on-line catalogue - www.nreeve.flexnet.co.uk. Est. 1860. *Makers of 16th-18th C oak and cherry English country period furniture.* VAT: Stan.

Riches
Wixamtree, 69 Wood Lane, Cottonend, Beds. MK45 3AP. (R.J.Jennings). Tel: 01234 742121. *Re-upholstery, repairs and re-caning.*

S. R. Robertson
Athlehampton House, Athelhampton, Puddletown, Dorset. Tel: 01305 849499. BAFRA.

Raymond Robertson - Tolpuddle Antique Restorers
The Stables, Southover House, Tolpuddle, Dorchester, Dorset. DT2 7HF. Tel: 01305 848739. West Dean/BADA Award Winner. *Furniture, clock and barometer cases, marquetry, veneering and boulle work, lacquer, lacquer, japaning and gilding, insurance work undertaken.*

R.S. Rust (Replicas)
83 Main Rd., Kesgrave, Ipswich, Suffolk. IP5 1AF. Tel: 01473 623092. Est. 1977. Open Tues., Thurs., Fri. 9-5. *Replica hardwood furniture.*

David A. Sayer - Courtlands Restorations
Courtlands, Park Rd., Banstead, Surrey. SM7 3EF. Tel: 01737 352429; fax - 01737 373255; website - www.bafra.org.uk/members/dsayer. html. BAFRA. *Full restoration service including repairs, polishing, carving, turning, veneering, gilding. Metal parts - replacement or repair.*

Michael Schryver Antiques Ltd
The Granary, 10 North Street, Dorking, Surrey,

RH4 1DN. Tel: 01306 881110. Est. 1970. Open 8.30-5.30, Sat. 8-12. *Cabinet work, polishing, upholstery, metal work.* VAT: Stan/Spec.

Phillip Slater
93 Hewell Rd., Barnt Green, Worcs. B45 8NL. Tel: 0121 445 4942. BAFRA.

Alun Courtney Smith
45 Windmill Rd., Brentford, Middx. TW8 0QQ. Tel: 020 8568 5249; fax - same. BAFRA.

Eric Smith - Antique Furniture Restorations
The Church, Park Rd., Darwen, Lancs. BB3 2LD. Tel: 01254 776222. BAFRA. UKIC. MA. Conservation Register Museums & Galleries Commission. *Restoration of longcase clocks and furniture. Comprehensive conservation and restoration of fine furniture.*

Solomons Furniture
4 Tauber Close, Elstree, Herts. WD6 3PE. Tel: 020 8985 6674; fax - 020 8986 6206. British Traditional Cabinet Makers. *Manufacturers of traditional furniture especially in burr/burl elm and burr/burl walnut veneers.* VAT: Stan. *Trade Only.*

Alan Stacey - Boxwood Antique Restorers
Somerset. Tel: 01963 33988; fax - 01963 32555. BAFRA. Open by appointment. *Finest quality antique restoration and conservation. Wax polishing, French polishing, carving, metalwork, brass fittings, specialist cabinet making, tortoiseshell specialists (tea caddies, frames, brushes, etc.), ivory, shagreen, horn, mother of pearl, etc. Regular deliveries to London and surrounding areas.* VAT: Stan.

Julian Stanley Woodcarving - Furniture
Unit 5 Bourton Link, Bourton Industrial Park, Bourton-on-the-Water, Glos. GL54 2HQ. Tel: 01451 822577; fax - same; e-mail - julian@ julianstanley-woodcarvingfurniture.co.uk; website - www.julianstanley-woodcarving furniture.co.uk. *Carved furniture - the classical work of the 18th C is re-created alongside contemporary designs, figure work and architectural pieces. Showroom on site includes contemporary paintings and sculpture.* VAT: Stan/Spec.

Robert Tandy Restoration
Unit 5 Manor Workshops, Manor Park, West End, Nailsea, Bristol, Somerset. BS48 4DD. Tel: 01275 856378. BAFRA. *Furniture restoration especially 17th-19th C longcase clock cases; French polishing and traditional oil and wax finishing.* VAT : Stan.

Thakeham Furniture
Marehill Rd., Pulborough, West Sussex. RH20 2DY. (Timothy Chavasse). Tel: 01798 872006. *Cabinet work, veneer repairs, wax and French polishing, turning, marquetry, carving, etc.*

Rodrigo Titian
318 Kensal Rd., London W10 5BN. Tel: 020 8960 6247; fax - 020 8969 6126; e-mail - enquiries@ titianstudios.co.uk. BAFRA. *Carving, gilding, lacquer, painted furniture, French polishing.*

Clifford J. Tracy
Unit 3 Shaftesbury Industrial Centre, Icknield Way, Letchworth, Herts. SG6 1HE. Tel: 01462 684855; fax - 01462 684833. BAFRA. *General restorations including boulle, marquetry, leather lining, upholstery.*

Treen Antiques
Treen House, 72 Park Rd., Prestwich, Manchester, Lancs. M25 0FA. Tel: 0161 720 7244; fax - same; mobile - 07973 471185. GADAR, RFS, FHS, UKIC. Open by appointment. *Conservation and restoration of all antique furniture (including vernacular) and woodwork, with emphasis on preserving original finish. Research undertaken, housekeeping advice, environmental monitoring and all aspects of conservation. Furniture assessment and advice on purchase and sales. Courses in restoration work held on request. Listed in Bonham's Directory.*

Neil Trinder Furniture Restoration
Burrowle House, Broughton Road, Hillsborough, Sheffield, South Yorks. S6 2AS. Tel: 0114 2852428. BAFRA. *Boulle, gilding, marquetry, carving, upholstery, fine furniture.*

William Trist
135 St Leonard's St., Edinburgh, Scotland. EH8 9RB. Tel: 0131 667 7775; fax - 0131 667 4333. BAFRA.

Clive Underwood
46 High Street, Colsterworth, Lincs. NG33 5NF. Tel: 01476 860689. Open by appointment. *Restoration, caning, rushing.*

Tony Vernon
15 Follett Rd., Topsham, Devon. EX3 0JP. Tel: 01392 874635. BAFRA. *Furniture, cabinet making, upholstery, gilding, veneering, inlay and French polishing.*

Fabio Villani
Clover, Alves, Forres, Scotland. IV36 2RA. Tel: 01343 850007; mobile - 07990 694972; e-mail - fabio@fabiovillani.co.uk; website - www. fabiovillani.co.uk. BAFRA. *Consultation and tuition for conservation of gilded frames and sculptures, objets d'art, furniture and wooden fittings. Traditional finishes and patina imitation. Lectures.*

SERVICES

Barry J. Wateridge
Padouk, Portsmouth Rd., Bramshott Chase, Hindhead, Surrey. GU26 6DB. Tel: 01428 607235. *French polishing and antique furniture restorations.*

Weaver Neave and Daughter
17 Lifford St. Putney, London SW15 1NY. Tel: 020 8785 2464. *Re-caning and re-rushing of antique furniture in traditional manner with traditional materials.*

Gerald Weir Antiques
Unit 1, Riverside Industrial Park, Wherstead Rd., Ipswich, Suffolk. Tel: 01473 692300; fax - 01473 692333. Open by appointment. *Suppliers of reproduction oak furniture for European markets and decorative furniture for American markets. Trade Only.*

Laurence Whitfield
The Old School, Winstone, Cirencester, Glos. GL7 7JX. Tel: 01285 821342. BAFRA.

Bryan Wigington - Antique Furniture Restoration
The Courtyard, Pembertons, 4 Hightown, Hay-on-Wye, Hereford, HR3 5AE. Tel: 01497 820545 (24 hr.) BAFRA. Est. 1961. Open any time by appointment. *Furniture conservation and restoration.* LOC: Next to Post Office.

Jonathan Wilbye
Blue Bell Farm, North Stainmore, Kirkby Stephen, Cumbria, CA17 4DY. Tel: 01768 341715. *Full restoration service including all carving, inlay, turning and polishing. Longcase clock cases a speciality.*

Peter Williams Antique Furniture Restoration
Silkmill House, 4 Charlton Rd., Tetbury, Glos. GL8. Tel: 01666 502311. *Early oak, period mahogany, walnut and country furniture. Woodturning, French polishing and wax finish, gold tooled leather. Insurance claims. Antiques bought and sold. Established over 25 years.*

GLASS

The Antique Restoration Studio
See entry under Furniture.

Sargeant Restorations
21 The Green, Westerham, Kent. TN16 1AX. *Restoration and cleaning of chandeliers, lustres and candelabra.*

INSURANCE AND FINANCE

Antique & Fine Art Finance Ltd
The Malthouse, 50 Kington St. Michael, Chippenham, Wilts. SN14 6JE. Tel: 01249 750701; fax - 01249 750771; website - www. antiques-finance.co.uk. *Provision of finance facilities to the clients of antique and fine art dealers.*

The Art and Antiques Service
10 Eltisley Avenue, Newnham, Cambridge, Cambs. CB3 9JG. Tel: 01223 303051; fax - 01223 303071; mobile - 07850 932894; e-mail - artservice@clara.net. *Professional valuations and insurance for probate, family division. Buying specific items or total refurbishments including architectural - fireplaces, doors. Advice on building up or scaling down collections and placing items for sale.*

Lockson Insurance Consultants
29 Broomfield St, London E14 6BX. Tel: 020 7515 8600; fax - 020 7515 4866; e-mail - enquiries @lockson.co.uk; internet - www.lockson.co.uk. *Specialists in all types of fine art, exhibition and memorabilia insurance.*

Anthony Wakefield & Company Ltd
4 Guildford Rd., Westcott, Dorking, Surrey. RH4 3NR. Tel: 01306 740555; fax - 01306 740770; e-mail - wakefieldco@compuserve.com. Members IIB. *Fine art and household insurance brokers; special terms for collectors; exclusive antique and fine art dealers policy with Axa Insurance UK plc; exclusive Connoisseur household policy with dealers/fairs extension.*

Windsor Insurance Brokers Ltd - Fine Art & Antiques Division
160-166 Borough High St., London SE1 1JR. Tel: 020 7407 7144; fax - 020 7827 9312. Lloyds Insurance Brokers. *Specialist Lloyd's brokers in antique and fine art dealers, fine art galleries, contemporary art galleries, restorers and conservators, antique centres, auctioneers and valuers "Heirloom" designed for dealers' own collections and household and all risks insurance brokers. Official brokers to LAPADA, BAFRA, The Fine Art Trade Guild, IDDA.*

IVORY

Boxwood Antique Restorers
See entry under Furniture - Alan Stacey.

Coromandel
Wimbledon, London SW19. *See entry under London SW19 in dealer listing.*

E. and C. Royall Antiques
See entry under Metalwork.

JEWELLERY AND SILVER

Eastbourne Engraving
See entry under Engraving.

Goldcare
5 Bedford St., Middlesborough, Cleveland. TS1 2LL. Tel: 01642 231343; website - www. gold care repairs.co.uk. *Jewellery repair, engraving, re-stringing, stone cutting. Restoration of silver and cutlery; brass, copper, pinchbeck restoration.* VAT: Stan.

LOCKS AND KEYS

Bramah Security Centres Ltd.
31 Oldbury Place, London W1U 5PT. Tel: 020 7935 7147; fax - 020 7935 2779. Open Mon.-Fri. 8.30-5.30, Sat. 9-1. *Keys cut to old locks; old locks opened; repair of old locks; new locks made to an old design; original Bramah locks dated. Quotation provided. Overseas work undertaken.* LOC: Near Baker Street tube station. VAT: Stan.

METALWORK

Optimum Brasses
7 Castle St., Bampton, Devon. EX16 9NS. Tel: 01398 331515; fax - 01398 331164; e-mail - brass@obida.com; website - www.obida.com. *Over 5,000 replica brass handles etc. for antique furniture.*

Plowden & Smith Ltd
See entry under Art.

E. and C. Royall Antiques
10 Waterfall Way, Medbourne, Leics. LE16 8EE. Tel: 01858 565744. Open 9-5. *Restorations - bronzes, ivories, brass including inlay work, metalware, woodcarving, upholstery, French polishing.*

Shawlan Antiques Metal Restorers
Croydon/South London area. Tel: 020 8684 5082; fax - same. *High quality restoration of metalware, using traditional methods and materials. Over 25 years experience.*

MUSICAL INSTRUMENTS

J V Pianos & Cambridge Pianola
85 High St., Landbeach, Cambridge, Cambs. CB4

713

8DR. (Tom Poole). Tel: 01223 861348/861408; fax - 01223 441276; e-mail - ftpoole@talk21. com; website - www.cambridgepianolacompany. co.uk. Est. 1972. Open Mon.-Fri., prior 'phone call advisable, or by appointment. *Restoration and sales of period pianos, pianolas and player pianos; music rolls, repair materials, books and accessories.*

PHOTOGRAPHY

Gerry Clist Photography LMPA
London NW6. Tel: 020 7624 0716. *Specialising in sculptures, antiques and works of art photography - studio and location.*

REPRODUCTION STONEWORK

Hampshire Gardencraft
Rake Industries, Rake, Nr. Petersfield, Hants. GU31 5DR. Tel: 01730 895182; fax - 01730 893216; e-mail - Sales@hampshire-gardencraft. com; website - www.hampshire-gardencraft.com; *Manufacturers of antiqued garden ornaments, troughs and pots in reconstituted stone in an old Cotswold stone finish. Many designs, catalogue available.*

SUPPLIERS

C. and A.J. Barmby
140 Lavender Hill, Tonbridge, Kent. TA9 2NJ. (Chris and Angela Barmby). Tel: 01732 771590; fax - same; e-mail - Bookpilot@aol.com. Est. 1980. Open by appointment. *Suppliers of display stands in wire, acrylic and wood; reference books and catalogues; lamps and magnifers. Exhibitor at Alexandra Palace, Ardingly, Newark.* VAT: Stan.

Dauphin Display (Oxford) Ltd
PO Box 602, Oxford, Oxon. OX44 9LU. (John Harrison-Banfield). Tel: 01865 343542; fax - 01865 343307. Est. 1985. Open 9-5, Sat. by appointment. Please telephone for directions. *Design and manufacture of stands, mounts, cabinets and environmental cases. Mounting service. Acrylic display stands - other materials utilised include glass, wood, metal, stone, marble, brass and bronze. Free mail order catalogue available.*

The Display Stand Company Ltd
5 Rickett St., London SW6 1RU. (D. Mayes). Tel: 07000 785017; fax - same; e-mail - dmayes @ globalnet.co.uk. Est. 1993. Open by appointment only. *Specialist suppliers of display stands, bespoke stands for individual works of art.* VAT: Stan.

Just Bros. and Co.
Roeder House, Vale Rd., London N4 1QA. Tel: 020 8880 2505; fax - 020 8802 0062; e-mail - just@freenet.co.uk. Member British Jewellery and Giftware Federation Ltd. Open 9-5, Fri. 9-12.30. *One of the largest suppliers of quality jewellery and presentation cases in Europe. Catalogue on request.*

Marshall Brass
Keeling Hall Rd., Foulsham, Norfolk. NR20 5PR. Tel: 01362 684105; fax - 01362 684280; e-mail - admin@marshall-brass.com; website - www. marshall-brass.com. GMC. *Suppliers of quality period furniture fittings in brass and iron.*

Martin and Co. Ltd
119 Camden St., Birmingham, West Midlands. B1 3DJ. Tel: 0121 233 2111; fax - 0121 236 0488. ASFI, GAI. *Cabinet hardware supplied - handles, locks, hinges, castors etc. Trade Only.*

Alan Morris Wholesale
Stonecourt, Townsend, Nympsfield, Glos. GL10 3UF. Tel: 01453 861069. *Display stands - coated wire, plastic, acrylic and wood for plates, cups, saucers, bowls etc; wire and disc; jewellery boxes, polishing and cleaning cloths, peelable white labels and strung tickets. Mail order available.* VAT: Stan.

Relics
35 Bridge St., Witney, Oxon. OX8 6DA. (B. Wiles and C. Walker). Tel: 01993 704611; website - www.tryrelics.co.uk. Est. 1987. Open 9-5. *Suppliers of furniture restoration material, brass castors, handles, locks, waxes and polish, upholstery and caning requisites, Farrow & Ball and reproduction paints, stencils, etc. Mail order also. Online catalogue.* LOC: Main road.

J. Shiner and Sons Ltd.
8 Windmill St. , London W1T 2JE. Tel: 020 7636 0740; fax - 020 7580 0740. *Suppliers of brass handles, castors, locks, brass grills and leathers.*

Suffolk Brass
Thurston, Bury St. Edmunds, Suffolk. IP31 3SN. Tel: 01359 233383; fax - 01359 233384. *Period replica cabinet fittings in brass and iron. One-off castings in lost wax or sand. Catalogue £5. Trade Only.*

The Victorian Ring Box Company
Unit 1, Fleetside, Gatehouse of Fleet, Kirkcudbrightshire, Scotland. DG7 2JY. (The Franca Bruno Company). Tel: 01557 814466/814054; fax - same; e-mail - victorianringbox.co.@scotland.com. By appointment only. *Manufacturers and distributors of high quality antique style presentation boxes. Alsoo available with sterling silver tops and in tartan.*

The Textile Conservancy Company Ltd
Unit 3A Pickhill Business Centre, Smallhythe Road, Tenterden, Kent. TN30 7LZ. Tel: 01580 761600; fax - same; e-mail - alex@textile-conservation.co.uk; website - www.textile-conservation.co.uk. UKIC *Cleaning and repair of historic textiles, tapestries and rugs. Professional advice on correct storage and display.*

The Textile Restoration Studio
2 Talbot Rd., Bowdon, Altrincham, Cheshire. WA14 3JD. Tel: 0161 928 0020; fax - same; website - www.conservationconsortium.com. Conservation Register UK Institute for Conservation. *Cleaning and repair of all antique textiles including tapestries, samplers, canvas work, beadwork, lace, costume, ecclesiastical vestments and furnishings, dolls and fans. Mail order catalogue of specialist textile conservation materials (free with large stamped addressed envelope). Home cleaning kits for needlework and acid free tissue packs available to the trade for resale.*

Boxwood Antique Restorers
See entry under Furniture - Alan Stacey.

Robert Mullis Rocking Restoration Services Ltd
55 Berkeley Rd., Wroughton, Swindon, Wilts. SN4 9BN. Tel: 01793 813583; fax - 01793 813577. British Toymakers Guild. *Full or partial restorations of antique horses, some wooden toy restoration. Traditional methods and materials used. Collection and delivery. New rocking horses made in five sizes, commissions undertaken.*

Tobilane Designs
Newton Holme Farm, Whittington, Carnforth, Lancs. LA6 2NZ. (Paul and Elaine Commander). Tel: 015242 72662; home - same; e-mail - tobilane@commander.clara.net; website - www.commander.clara.net/tobilane.htm. Est. 1985. Open 10-5 including Sun. *Traditional toymakers and restorers of old toys including rocking horses and teddies. Identification and valuation service.* LOC: B6254 3 miles south of Kirkby Lonsdale, between Whittington and Arkholme. VAT: Stan.

ALPHABETICAL LIST OF TOWNS AND VILLAGES AND COUNTIES UNDER WHICH THEY ARE LISTED.

A

Abbots Langley, Herts.
Abbots Leigh, Somerset.
Aberdeen, Scotland.
Aberdour, Scotland.
Aberfeldy, Scotland.
Aberford, Yorks. West.
Abergavenny, Wales.
Abernyte, Scotland.
Aberystwyth, Wales.
Aberystwyth, Wales.
Abinger Hammer, Surrey.
Abridge, Essex.
Accrington, Lancs.
Acle, Norfolk.
Acrise, Kent.
Addingham, Yorks. West.
Adversane, Sussex West.
Alcester, Warks.
Aldeburgh, Suffolk.
Alderley Edge, Cheshire.
Aldermaston, Berks.
Alderney, C.I.
Alfreton, Derbys.
Alfriston, Sussex East.
Allington, Lincs.
Allonby, Cumbria.
Alnwick, Northumbs.
Alresford, Hants.
Alrewas, Staffs.
Alsager, Cheshire.
Alston, Cumbria.
Altrincham, Cheshire.
Alyth, Scotland.
Amersham, Bucks.
Ampthill, Beds.
Andover, Hants.
Andoversford, Glos.
Angarrack, Cornwall.
Angmering, Sussex West.
Antrim, Co. Antrim, N. Ireland.
Appledore, Kent.
Armagh, Co. Armagh, N. Ireland.
Arthingworth, Northants.
Arundel, Sussex West.
Ascot, Berks.
Ascott-under-Wychwood, Oxon.
Ash, Kent.
Ash Priors, Somerset.
Ash Vale, Surrey.
Ashbourne, Derbys.
Ashburton, Devon.
Ashford, Kent.
Ashtead, Surrey.
Ashurst, Kent.

Aslockton, Notts.
Astley Bridge, Lancs.
Aston Tirrold, Oxon.
Astwood Bank, Worcs.
Atcham, Shrops.
Attleborough, Norfolk.
Atworth, Wilts.
Auchterarder, Scotland.
Auldearn, Scotland.
Axbridge, Somerset.
Axminster, Devon.
Aylesby, Lincs.
Aylsham, Norfolk.
Ayr, Scotland.

B

Badgworth, Somerset.
Bagshot, Surrey.
Baildon, Yorks. West.
Bakewell, Derbys.
Balcombe, Sussex West.
Balderton, Notts.
Baldock, Herts.
Balfron, Scotland.
Ballater, Scotland.
Bampton, Devon.
Banbridge, Co. Down, N. Ireland.
Bangor, Wales.
Barham, Kent.
Barkham, Berks.
Barley Mow, Northants.
Barlow, Derbys.
Barmouth, Wales.
Barnard Castle, Durham.
Barnet, Herts.
Barnsley, Glos.
Barnsley, Yorks. South.
Barnstaple, Devon.
Barnt Green, Worcs.
Barrhead, Scotland.
Barrington, Somerset.
Barry, Wales.
Barton, Cambs.
Barton, Cheshire.
Basingstoke, Hants.
Baston, Lincs.
Bath, Somerset.
Batheaston, Somerset.
Batley, Yorks. West.
Battlesbridge, Essex.
Bawdeswell, Norfolk.
Bawtry, Yorks. South.
Baythorne End, Essex.
Beaconsfield, Bucks.
Beaminster, Dorset.

Beattock, Scotland.
Beauly, Scotland.
Beaumaris (Anglesey), Wales.
Beccles, Suffolk.
Beckenham, Kent.
Bedale, Yorks. North.
Bedford, Beds.
Bedhampton, Hants.
Bedingfield, Suffolk.
Beech, Hants.
Beer, Devon.
Beetham, Cumbria.
Belfast, N. Ireland.
Belper, Derbys.
Bembridge, Isle of Wight.
Bentley, Suffolk.
Bere Regis, Dorset.
Berkeley, Glos.
Berkhamsted, Herts.
Berwick-on-Tweed, Northumbs.
Bessacarr, Yorks. South.
Betchworth, Surrey.
Beverley, Yorks. East.
Bewdley, Worcs.
Bexhill-on-Sea, Sussex East.
Bibury, Glos.
Bideford, Devon.
Bidford-on-Avon, Warks.
Biggleswade, Beds.
Billingham, Durham.
Billingshurst, Sussex West.
Binfield, Berks.
Birchington, Kent.
Birdbrook, Essex.
Birkenhead, Merseyside.
Birmingham, West Mids.
Birstwith, Yorks. North.
Bishop's Castle, Shrops.
Bishop's Stortford, Herts.
Bishops Cleeve, Glos.
Blackburn, Lancs.
Blackmore, Essex.
Blackpool, Lancs.
Bladon, Oxon.
Blaenau Ffestiniog, Wales.
Blairgowrie, Scotland.
Blakedown, Worcs.
Blakeney, Glos.
Blandford Forum, Dorset.
Bletchingley, Surrey.
Blewbury, Oxon.
Bloxham, Oxon.
Blythburgh, Suffolk.
Bodmin, Cornwall.
Bognor Regis, Sussex West.
Bollington, Cheshire.

Bolton, Lancs.
Bolton Abbey, Yorks. North.
Bolton-by-Bowland, Lancs.
Borehamwood, Herts.
Boroughbridge, Yorks. North.
Boscastle, Cornwall.
Boston, Lincs.
Boston Spa, Yorks. West.
Botley, Hants.
Bottisham, Cambs.
Boughton, Kent.
Bourne, Lincs.
Bourne End, Bucks.
Bournemouth, Dorset.
Bowdon, Cheshire.
Bowness on Windermere,
   Cumbria.
Brackley, Northants.
Bradford, Yorks. West.
Bradford-on-Avon, Wilts.
Bradwell, Derbys.
Brailsford, Derbys.
Bramhall, Cheshire.
Bramley, Surrey.
Brampton, Cumbria.
Brancaster Staithe, Norfolk.
Brandsby, Yorks. North.
Branksome, Dorset.
Brasted, Kent.
Braunton, Devon.
Brecon, Wales.
Bredbury, Cheshire.
Brentwood, Essex.
Brereton, Staffs.
Brewood, Staffs.
Bridge of Earn, Scotland.
Bridgend, Wales.
Bridgnorth, Shrops.
Bridlington, Yorks. East.
Bridport, Dorset.
Brierfield, Lancs.
Brightlingsea, Essex.
Brighton, Sussex East.
Brinklow, Warks.
Brinkworth, Wilts.
Bristol, Glos.
Brixham, Devon.
Broadstairs, Kent.
Broadway, Worcs.
Brockenhurst, Hants.
Brodick and Whiting Bay,
   Scotland.
Brook, Hants.
Broseley, Shrops.
Broughton Astley, Leics.
Broxted, Essex.
Bruton, Somerset.
Buckhurst Hill, Essex.
Buckingham, Bucks.
Budleigh Salterton, Devon.
Bungay, Suffolk.

Burford, Oxon.
Burgess Hill, Sussex West.
Burghfield Common, Berks.
Burlton, Shrops.
Burneston, Yorks. North.
Burnham Market, Norfolk.
Burnham-on-Sea, Somerset.
Burnley, Lancs.
Burscough, Lancs.
Burton Salmon, Yorks. North.
Burton-on-Trent, Staffs.
Burwash, Sussex East.
Burwell, Cambs.
Bury, Lancs.
Bury St. Edmunds, Suffolk.
Bushey, Herts.
Bushmills, Co. Antrim,
   N. Ireland.
Buxton, Derbys.

C
Cadnam, Hants.
Caerphilly, Wales.
Caistor, Lincs.
Callington, Cornwall.
Calne, Wilts.
Camborne, Cornwall.
Cambridge, Cambs.
Cambridge, Glos.
Canonbie, Scotland.
Canterbury, Kent.
Cardiff, Wales.
Carhampton, Somerset.
Carlisle, Cumbria.
Carmarthen, Wales.
Carrefour Selous, Jersey, C.I.
Carrickfergus, Co. Antrim,
   N. Ireland.
Carshalton, Surrey.
Cartmel, Cumbria.
Castle Ashby, Northants.
Castle Cary, Somerset.
Castle Combe, Wilts.
Castle Donington, Leics.
Castletown, Isle of Man.
Cavendish, Suffolk.
Caversham, Berks.
Cawood, Yorks. North.
Cawthorne, Yorks South.
Ceres, Scotland.
Cerne Abbas, Dorset.
Chacewater, Cornwall.
Chagford, Devon.
Chale, Isle of Wight.
Chalfont St. Giles, Bucks.
Chalford, Glos.
Chalgrove, Oxon.
Chalvington, Sussex East.
Chard, Somerset.
Charlton Marshall, Dorset.
Chatburn, Lancs.

Cheadle Hulme, Cheshire.
Cheam, Surrey.
Chelmsford, Essex.
Cheltenham, Glos.
Chepstow, Wales.
Cherhill, Wilts.
Cherington, Glos.
Chertsey, Surrey.
Chesham, Bucks.
Chester, Cheshire.
Chesterfield, Derbys.
Chichester, Sussex West.
Chilcompton, Somerset.
Chilton, Oxon.
Chippenham, Wilts.
Chipping Campden, Glos.
Chipping Norton, Oxon.
Chipping Ongar, Essex.
Chipping Sodbury, Glos.
Chirk, Wales.
Chislehurst, Kent.
Chittering, Cambs.
Chobham, Surrey.
Chorley, Lancs.
Chorleywood, Herts.
Christchurch, Dorset.
Christian Malford, Wilts.
Church Stretton, Shrops.
Churt, Surrey.
Ciliau Aeron, Wales.
Cirencester, Glos.
Clare, Suffolk.
Cleethorpes, Lincs.
Cleobury Mortimer, Shrops.
Clevedon, Somerset.
Clitheroe, Lancs.
Clola by Mintlaw, Scotland.
Clutton, Somerset.
Coalville, Leics.
Cobham, Surrey.
Cockermouth, Cumbria.
Cocking, Sussex West.
Codford, Wilts.
Codsall, Staffs.
Coggeshall, Essex.
Colchester, Essex.
Coldstream, Scotland.
Coleraine, Co. Londonderry,
   N. Ireland.
Coleshill, Warks.
Colne, Lancs.
Coltishall, Norfolk.
Colwyn Bay, Wales.
Comber, Co Down,
   N. Ireland.
Comberton, Cambs.
Congleton, Cheshire.
Consett, Durham.
Conwy, Wales.
Cooden, Sussex East.
Cookham Rise, Berks.

Cookstown, Co. Tyrone,
   N. Ireland.
Corbridge, Northumbs.
Corby Hill, Cumbria.
Corringham, Essex.
Corsham, Wilts.
Cottered, Herts.
Coulsdon, Surrey.
Cove, Scotland.
Coventry, West Mids.
Cowbridge, Wales.
Cowes, Isle of Wight.
Cowfold, Sussex West.
Coxley, Somerset.
Cranborne, Dorset.
Cranbrook, Kent.
Craven Arms, Shrops.
Crawley, Hants.
Crayford, Kent.
Crediton, Devon.
Cremyll, Cornwall.
Crewe, Cheshire.
Crewkerne, Somerset.
Criccieth, Wales.
Crickhowell, Wales.
Cricklade, Wilts.
Cromarty, Scotland.
Cromer, Norfolk.
Crosby Ravensworth, Cumbria.
Cross Hills, Yorks. North.
Cross in Hand, Sussex East.
Croydon, Surrey.
Crudwell, Wilts.
Cuckfield, Sussex West.
Cullompton, Devon.

D

Danbury, Essex.
Darlington, Durham.
Darlton, Notts.
Dartmouth, Devon.
Darwen, Lancs.
Datchet, Berks.
Davenham, Cheshire.
Deal, Kent.
Debden, Essex.
Debenham, Suffolk.
Deddington, Oxon.
Deganwy, Wales.
Depden, Suffolk.
Derby, Derbys.
Devizes, Wilts.
Disley, Cheshire.
Diss, Norfolk.
Ditchling, Sussex East.
Ditton, Kent.
Dobwalls, Cornwall.
Doncaster, Yorks. South.
Donington, Lincs.
Dorchester, Dorset.
Dorchester-on-Thames, Oxon.

Dorking, Surrey.
Dornoch, Scotland.
Dorridge, West Mids.
Douglas, Isle of Man.
Doune, Scotland.
Doveridge, Derbys.
Downham Market, Norfolk.
Driffield, Yorks. East.
Drinkstone, Suffolk.
Droitwich, Worcs.
Dronfield, Derbys.
Drumnadrochit, Scotland.
Duffield, Derbys.
Dulverton, Somerset.
Dundee, Scotland.
Dunecht, Scotland.
Dunham-on-Trent, Notts.
Dunkeld, Scotland.
Dunsfold, Surrey.
Dunster, Somerset.
Durham, Durham.
Duxford, Cambs.

E

Eaglescliffe, Durham.
Earl Shilton, Leics.
Earsham, Norfolk.
Easingwold, Yorks. North.
East Budleigh, Devon.
East Dereham, Norfolk.
East Grinstead, Sussex West.
East Hagbourne, Oxon.
East Molesey, Surrey.
East Peckham, Kent.
East Pennard, Somerset.
Eastbourne, Sussex East.
Ebrington, Glos.
Eccleshall, Staffs.
Eccleston, Lancs.
Edenbridge, Kent.
Edgware, Middx.
Edinburgh, Scotland.
Eldwick, Yorks. West.
Elgin, Scotland.
Elsworth, Cambs.
Ely, Cambs.
Empingham, Rutland.
Emsworth, Hants.
Enfield, Middx.
Epsom, Surrey.
Ermington, Devon.
Eversley, Hants.
Evesham, Worcs.
Ewell, Surrey.
Exeter, Devon.
Exmouth, Devon.
Eye, Suffolk.

F

Fairford, Glos.
Fairlie, Scotland.

Fakenham, Norfolk.
Faldingworth, Lincs.
Falmouth, Cornwall.
Fareham, Hants.
Faringdon, Oxon.
Farnborough, Hants.
Farnham, Surrey.
Farningham, Kent.
Faversham, Kent.
Felixstowe, Suffolk.
Feniscowles, Lancs.
Fenton Barns, Scotland.
Fernhurst, Sussex West.
Filey, Yorks. North.
Finchingfield, Essex.
Finedon, Northants.
Finningham, Suffolk.
Fishguard, Wales.
Fishlake, Yorks. South.
Flamborough, Yorks. East.
Flaxton, Yorks. North.
Fleet, Hants.
Flimwell, Sussex East.
Flore, Northants.
Fochabers, Scotland.
Folkestone, Kent.
Fontmell Magna, Dorset.
Fordham, Cambs.
Fordingbridge, Hants.
Forest Row, Sussex East.
Forfar, Scotland.
Forres, Scotland.
Four Elms, Kent.
Four Oaks, West Mids.
Fowlmere, Cambs.
Framlingham, Suffolk.
Freshford, Somerset.
Freshwater, Isle of Wight.
Frinton-on-Sea, Essex.
Friockheim, Scotland.
Frome, Somerset.
Froxfield, Wilts.
Fyfield, Essex.

G

Gainsborough, Lincs.
Gants Hill, Essex.
Gargrave, Yorks. North.
Gateshead, Tyne and Wear.
Gilberdyke, Yorks. East.
Gillingham, Dorset.
Glasgow, Scotland.
Glencarse, Scotland.
Glendoick, Scotland.
Glossop, Derbys.
Gloucester, Glos.
Godalming, Surrey.
Gomshall, Surrey.
Gorseinon, Wales.
Gosforth, Cumbria.
Gosforth, Tyne and Wear.

Gosport, Hants.
Goudhurst, Kent.
Grampound, Cornwall.
Grantham, Lincs.
Grantown-on-Spey, Scotland.
Grasmere, Cumbria.
Gravesend, Kent.
Grays, Essex.
Great Baddow, Essex.
Great Barrow, Cheshire.
Great Bookham, Surrey.
Great Chesterford, Essex.
Great Dunmow, Essex.
Great Glen, Leics.
Great Harwood, Lancs.
Great Houghton, Yorks. South.
Great Malvern, Worcs.
Great Missenden, Bucks.
Great Salkeld, Cumbria.
Great Shefford, Berks.
Great Shelford, Cambs.
Great Torrington, Devon.
Great Waltham, Essex.
Green Hammerton, Yorks.
   North.
Greyabbey, Co. Down,
   N. Ireland.
Greystoke, Cumbria.
Grimsby, Lincs.
Gt. Yarmouth, Norfolk.
Guildford, Surrey.
Gullane, Scotland.

H
Hacheston, Suffolk.
Haddenham, Bucks.
Haddington, Scotland.
Hadleigh, Suffolk.
Hadlow Down, Sussex East.
Hainault, Essex.
Hale, Cheshire.
Halesowen, West Mids.
Halesworth, Suffolk.
Halfway, Berks.
Halifax, Yorks. West.
Halstead, Essex.
Hampton, Middx.
Harefield, Middx.
Harpenden, Herts.
Harpole, Northants.
Harrogate, Yorks. North.
Harston, Cambs.
Hartlepool, Durham.
Hartley Wintney, Hants.
Harwich, Essex.
Haselbech, Northants.
Haslemere, Surrey.
Haslingden, Lancs.
Haslington, Cheshire.
Hastings, Sussex East.
Hatherleigh, Devon.

Hatton, Warks.
Haverfordwest, Wales.
Hawarden, Wales.
Hawes, Yorks. North.
Haworth, Yorks. West.
Hay-on-Wye, Wales.
Hayfield, Derbys.
Hayle, Cornwall.
Hayling Island, Hants.
Haywards Heath, Sussex West.
Heacham, Norfolk.
Headcorn, Kent.
Headington, Oxon.
Heathfield, Sussex East.
Hebden Bridge, Yorks. West.
Helmsley, Yorks. North.
Helsby, Cheshire.
Hemel Hempstead, Herts.
Hemswell Cliff, Lincs.
Henfield, Sussex West.
Henley-in-Arden, Warks.
Henley-on-Thames, Oxon.
Hereford, Herefs.
Hertford, Herts.
Heswall, Merseyside.
Hexham, Northumbs.
High Wycombe, Bucks.
Highbridge, Somerset.
Hinckley, Leics.
Hindhead, Surrey.
Hingham, Norfolk.
Hitchin, Herts.
Hitchin, Herts.
Hoby, Leics.
Hodnet, Shrops.
Holbeach, Lincs.
Holkham, Norfolk.
Holmfirth, Yorks. West.
Holt, Norfolk.
Holt, Wales.
Holyhead (Anglesey), Wales.
Holywood, Co. Down,
   N. Ireland.
Honiton, Devon.
Hook, Hants.
Horley, Surrey.
Horncastle, Lincs.
Horndean, Hants.
Horsebridge, Sussex East.
Horsell, Surrey.
Horsham, Sussex West.
Horton, Berks.
Houghton, Sussex West.
Hoylake, Merseyside.
Huddersfield, Yorks. West.
Hull, Yorks. East.
Hungerford, Berks.
Hunstanton, Norfolk.
Huntercombe, Oxon.
Huntingdon, Cambs.
Huntly, Scotland.

Hursley, Hants.
Hurst, Berks.
Hurst Green, Sussex East.
Hurstpierpoint, Sussex West.
Hythe, Kent.

I
Ibstock, Leics.
Ilchester, Somerset.
Ilfracombe, Devon.
Ilkley, Yorks. West.
Ilminster, Somerset.
Inchture, Scotland.
Ingatestone, Essex.
Innerleithen, Scotland.
Inverness, Scotland.
Ipswich, Suffolk.
Ironbridge, Shrops.
Isleworth, Middx.
Islip, Northants.
Iver, Bucks.
Ixworth, Suffolk.

J
Jedburgh, Scotland.
Jesmond, Tyne and Wear.

K
Keighley, Yorks. West.
Kelling, Norfolk.
Kelvedon, Essex.
Kendal, Cumbria.
Keswick, Cumbria.
Kettering, Northants.
Kew, Surrey.
Kew Green, Surrey.
Kidderminster, Worcs.
Kidwelly, Wales.
Kilbarchan, Scotland.
Killamarsh, Derbys.
Killearn, Scotland.
Killin, Scotland.
Kilmacolm, Scotland.
Kilmarnock, Scotland.
Kilmichael Glassary, Scotland.
Kincardine O'Neil, Scotland.
King's Lynn, Norfolk.
Kingsbridge, Devon.
Kingsclere, Hants.
Kingskerswell, Devon.
Kingsley, Staffs.
Kingsthorpe, Northants.
Kingston-on-Spey, Scotland.
Kingston-upon-Thames, Surrey.
Kingswear, Devon.
Kingswinford, West Mids.
Kingussie, Scotland.
Kinross, Scotland.
Kirk Deighton, Yorks. North.
Kirkby Lonsdale, Cumbria.
Kirkby Stephen, Cumbria.

Kirkcaldy, Scotland.
Kirkcudbright, Scotland.
Kirton, Lincs.
Kirton in Lindsey, Lincs.
Knaresborough, Yorks. North.
Knebworth, Herts.
Knighton, Wales.
Knipton, Leics.
Knutsford, Cheshire.

L

Lake, Isle of Wight.
Laleham, Surrey.
Lamberhurst, Kent.
Lancaster, Lancs.
Landbeach, Cambs.
Langford, Notts.
Langford, Somerset.
Langholm, Scotland.
Langley Burrell, Wilts.
Largs, Scotland.
Launceston, Cornwall.
Lavenham, Suffolk.
Leamington Spa, Warks.
Leatherhead, Surrey.
Leavenheath, Suffolk.
Lechlade, Glos.
Leckhampstead, Berks.
Ledbury, Herefs.
Leeds, Yorks. West.
Leedstown, Cornwall.
Leek, Staffs.
Leicester, Leics.
Leigh, Lancs.
Leigh, Staffs.
Leigh-on-Sea, Essex.
Leighton Buzzard, Beds.
Leiston, Suffolk.
Lennoxtown, Scotland.
Leominster, Herefs.
Lepton, Yorks. West.
Letham, Scotland.
Lewes, Sussex East.
Leyburn, Yorks. North.
Lichfield, Staffs.
Limpsfield, Surrey.
Lincoln, Lincs.
Lindfield, Sussex West.
Lingfield, Surrey.
Linlithgow, Scotland.
Lisburn, Co. Antrim, N. Ireland.
Liss, Hants.
Little Chalfont, Bucks.
Little Haywood, Staffs.
Little Horsted, Sussex East.
Little Malvern, Worcs.
Littlebourne, Kent.
Littlehampton, Sussex West.
Littleton, Cheshire.
Littleton, Somerset.
Litton Cheney, Dorset.

Liverpool, Merseyside.
Llandeilo, Wales.
Llandovery, Wales.
Llandudno, Wales.
Llandudno Junction, Wales.
Llandysul, Wales.
Llanelli, Wales.
Llanerchymedd (Anglesey),
  Wales.
Llanfair Caereinion, Wales.
Llangollen, Wales.
Llangristiolus (Anglesey),
  Wales.
Llanrwst, Wales.
Long Clawson, Leics.
Long Eaton, Derbys.
Long Hanborough, Oxon.
Long Marston, Warks.
Long Marton, Cumbria.
Long Melford, Suffolk.
Long Sutton, Lincs.
Longhaven, Scotland.
Looe, Cornwall.
Lostwithiel, Cornwall.
Loughborough, Leics.
Louth, Lincs.
Low Newton, Cumbria.
Lower Stondon, Beds.
Lubenham, Leics.
Ludlow, Shrops.
Lurgan, Co. Armagh,
  N. Ireland.
Luton, Beds.
Lydford, Devon.
Lye, West Mids.
Lymington, Hants.
Lymm, Cheshire.
Lyndhurst, Hants.
Lyneham, Wilts.
Lynton, Devon.
Lytchett Minster, Dorset.
Lythe, Yorks. North.

M

Macclesfield, Cheshire.
Maidencombe, Devon.
Maidenhead, Berks.
Maidstone, Kent.
Maldon, Essex.
Malmesbury, Wilts.
Malton, Yorks. North.
Malvern Link, Worcs.
Manchester, Lancs.
Manfield, Yorks. North.
Manningford Bruce, Wilts.
Manningtree, Essex.
Mansfield, Notts.
Manton, Rutland.
Marazion, Cornwall.
Margate, Kent.
Market Bosworth, Leics.

Market Deeping, Lincs.
Market Drayton, Shrops.
Market Harborough, Leics.
Market Weighton, Yorks. East.
Markington, Yorks. North.
Marlborough, Wilts.
Marlesford, Suffolk.
Marlow, Bucks.
Marple Bridge, Cheshire.
Martlesham, Suffolk.
Martock, Somerset.
Masham, Yorks. North.
Matching Green, Essex.
Mathry, Wales.
Matlock, Derbys.
Meigle, Scotland.
Melbury Osmond, Dorset.
Melksham, Wilts.
Melrose, Scotland.
Melton Mowbray, Leics.
Menai Bridge, Wales.
Mendlesham Green, Suffolk.
Menston, Yorks. West.
Mere, Wilts.
Merstham, Surrey.
Merton, Devon.
Middle Aston, Oxon.
Middleham, Yorks. North.
Middleton Village, Lancs.
Middleton-in-Teesdale, Durham.
Midhurst, Sussex West.
Midsomer Norton, Somerset.
Mildenhall, Suffolk.
Milford, Surrey.
Milford Haven, Wales.
Milton Keynes, Bucks.
Milton Lilbourne, Wilts.
Milverton, Somerset.
Minchinhampton, Glos.
Mobberley, Cheshire.
Modbury, Devon.
Monkton, Devon.
Monmouth, Wales.
Montrose, Scotland.
Morchard Bishop, Devon.
Morden, Surrey.
Morecambe, Lancs.
Morestead, Hants.
Moreton-in-Marsh, Glos.
Mountain Ash, Wales.
Much Wenlock, Shrops.
Murton, Wales.

N

Nairn, Scotland
Nantwich, Cheshire.
Narberth, Wales.
Narborough, Leics.
Nayland, Suffolk.
Needham, Norfolk.
Needham Market, Suffolk.

Nelson, Lancs.
Nether Stowey, Somerset.
Nettlebed, Oxon.
New Bolingbroke, Lincs.
Newark, Notts.
Newbridge-on-Wye, Wales.
Newburgh, Scotland.
Newby Bridge, Cumbria.
Newcastle Emlyn, Wales.
Newcastle-under-Lyme, Staffs.
Newcastle-upon-Tyne, Tyne and
  Wear.
Newent, Glos.
Newhaven, Sussex East.
Newington, Kent.
Newmarket, Suffolk.
Newmills, Derbys.
Newnham, Kent.
Newport, Essex.
Newport, Isle of Wight.
Newport, Shrops.
Newport, Wales.
Newton Abbot, Devon.
Newton St. Cyres, Devon.
Newton Tony, Wilts.
Newtonmore, Scotland.
Newtownabbey, Co. Antrim,
  N. Ireland.
North Aston, Oxon.
North Berwick, Scotland.
North Cave, Yorks. East.
North Petherton, Somerset.
North Shields, Tyne and
  Wear.
North Walsham, Norfolk.
North Wraxall, Wilts.
Northallerton, Yorks. North.
Northampton, Northants.
Northchapel, Sussex West.
Northfleet, Kent.
Northleach, Glos.
Northwich, Cheshire.
Norton, Durham.
Norton, Glos.
Norton, Yorks. North.
Norwich, Norfolk.
Nottingham, Notts.
Nutley, Sussex East.

O

Oakham, Rutland.
Oaksey, Wilts.
Oban, Scotland.
Odiham, Hants.
Okehampton, Devon.
Oldbury, West Mids.
Oldham, Lancs.
Ollerton, Notts.
Olney, Bucks.
Orford, Suffolk.
Ormskirk, Lancs.

Orpington, Kent.
Osgathorpe, Leics.
Oswestry, Shrops.
Otford, Kent.
Otley, Yorks. West.
Outwell, Cambs.
Oxford, Oxon.
Oxhey, Herts.
Oxted, Surrey.

P

Paignton, Devon.
Painswick, Glos.
Paisley, Scotland.
Pangbourne, Berks.
Parkstone, Dorset.
Pateley Bridge, Yorks.
  North.
Patrington, Yorks. East.
Peasenhall, Suffolk.
Pembroke, Wales.
Penkridge, Staffs.
Penn, Bucks.
Penrith, Cumbria.
Penryn, Cornwall.
Penshurst, Kent.
Penzance, Cornwall.
Pershore, Worcs.
Perth, Scotland.
Peterborough, Cambs.
Petersfield, Hants.
Petts Wood, Kent.
Petworth, Sussex West.
Pevensey, Sussex East.
Pevensey Bay, Sussex East.
Pickering, Yorks. North.
Pitlochry, Scotland.
Pittenweem, Scotland.
Plumley, Cheshire.
Plymouth, Devon.
Polegate, Sussex East.
Pontarddulais, Wales.
Pontefract, Yorks. West.
Ponterwyd, Wales.
Pontllyfrii, Wales.
Poole, Dorset.
Portaferry, Co. Down,
  N. Ireland.
Portballintrae, Co. Antrim,
  N. Ireland.
Porthcawl, Wales.
Porthmadog, Wales.
Portree, Scotland.
Portrush, Co. Antrim,
  N. Ireland.
Portslade, Sussex West.
Portsmouth, Hants.
Portsoy, Scotland.
Potter Heigham, Norfolk.
Potterspury, Northants.
Poulton-le-Fylde, Lancs.

Poynton, Cheshire.
Preston, Lancs.
Prestwick, Scotland.
Princes Risborough, Bucks.
Puckeridge, Herts.
Puddletown, Dorset.
Pulborough, Sussex West.
Pwllheli, Wales.

Q

Queen Camel, Somerset.
Queniborough, Leics.
Quorn, Leics.

R

Rainford, Merseyside.
Rait, Scotland.
Ramsbury, Wilts.
Ramsey, Cambs.
Ramsgate, Kent.
Raveningham, Norfolk.
Ravenstonedale, Cumbria.
Rayleigh, Essex.
Reading, Berks.
Redbourn, Herts.
Redditch, Worcs.
Redhill, Surrey.
Redruth, Cornwall.
Reepham, Norfolk.
Reigate, Surrey.
Retford, Notts.
Richmond, Surrey.
Rickmansworth, Herts.
Ringway, Cheshire.
Ringwood, Hants.
Ripley, Derbys.
Ripley, Surrey.
Ripon, Yorks. North.
Risby, Suffolk.
Robin Hood's Bay, Yorks.
  North.
Rochdale, Lancs.
Rochester, Kent.
Rode, Somerset.
Rodley, Glos.
Rolvenden, Kent.
Romiley, Cheshire.
Romsey, Hants.
Ross-on-Wye, Herefs.
Rotherham, Yorks. South.
Rottingdean, Sussex East.
Rowlands Castle, Hants.
Roxwell, Essex.
Rugeley, Staffs.
Rumblingbridge, Scotland.
Rumford, Cornwall.
Runfold, Surrey.
Rushden, Northants.
Ruthin, Wales.
Ryde, Isle of Wight.
Rye, Sussex East.

TOWNS AND VILLAGES

S

Sabden, Lancs.
Saffron Walden, Essex.
Saintfield, Co. Down, N. Ireland.
Sale, Cheshire.
Salisbury, Wilts.
Saltaire, Yorks. West.
Saltcoats, Scotland.
Samlesbury, Lancs.
Sanderstead, Surrey.
Sandgate, Kent.
Sandhurst, Berks.
Sandhurst, Kent.
Sandwich, Kent.
Sawbridgeworth, Herts.
Scarborough, Yorks. North.
Scratby, Norfolk.
Screveton, Notts.
Scunthorpe, Lincs.
Seaford, Sussex East.
Seaton, Devon.
Seaview, Isle of Wight.
Sedbergh, Cumbria.
Seething, Norfolk.
Semley, Wilts.
Settle, Yorks. North.
Sevenoaks, Kent.
Shaftesbury, Dorset.
Shaldon, Devon.
Shanklin, Isle of Wight.
Shardlow, Derbys.
Sharrington, Norfolk.
Sheffield, Yorks. South.
Shefford, Beds.
Shenfield, Essex.
Shenton, Leics.
Shepperton, Surrey.
Shepton Mallet, Somerset.
Sherborne, Dorset.
Shere, Surrey.
Sheringham, Norfolk.
Shifnal, Shrops.
Shipston-on-Stour, Warks.
Shirley, Surrey.
Shoreham-by-Sea, Sussex West.
Shrewsbury, Shrops.
Sible Hedingham, Essex.
Sidcup, Kent.
Sidmouth, Devon.
Sileby, Leics.
Skipton, Yorks. North.
Slad, Glos.
Sleaford, Lincs.
Sleights, Yorks. North.
Snainton, Yorks. North.
Snape, Suffolk.
Snargate, Kent.
Solihull, West Mids.
Somersham, Cambs.
Somerton, Somerset.
Sonning-on-Thames, Berks.

South Brent, Devon.
South Harting, Sussex West.
South Molton, Devon.
South Petherton, Somerset.
South Shields, Tyne and Wear.
South Walsham, Norfolk.
Southampton, Hants.
Southborough, Kent.
Southend-on-Sea, Essex.
Southport, Merseyside.
Southwell, Notts.
Southwold, Suffolk.
Sowerby Bridge, Yorks. West.
Spalding, Lincs.
Spennithorne, Yorks. North.
St. Albans, Herts.
St. Andrews, Scotland.
St. Annes-on-Sea, Lancs.
St. Austell, Cornwall.
St. Gerrans, Cornwall.
St. Helen Auckland, Durham.
St. Helier , Jersey, C.I.
St. Ives, Cambs.
St. Ives, Cornwall.
St. Lawrence , Jersey, C.I.
St. Leonards-on-Sea, Sussex
    East.
St. Martin, Guernsey, C.I.
St. Mary, Jersey, C.I.
St. Neots, Cambs.
St. Ouen, Jersey, C.I.
St. Peter Port , Guernsey, C.I.
St. Sampson, Guernsey, C.I.
St. Saviour, Jersey, C.I.
Stafford, Staffs.
Staines, Surrey.
Stalham, Norfolk.
Stamford, Lincs.
Standlake, Oxon.
Stanley, Scotland.
Stansted, Essex.
Stanton upon Hine Heath,
    Shrops.
Staunton Harold, Leics.
Staveley, Cumbria.
Stewarton, Scotland.
Steyning, Sussex West.
Stickney, Lincs.
Stiffkey, Norfolk.
Stillington, Yorks. North.
Stirling, Scotland.
Stock, Essex.
Stockbridge, Hants.
Stockbury, Kent.
Stockland, Devon.
Stockport, Cheshire.
Stoke Ferry, Norfolk.
Stoke-on-Trent, Staffs.
Storrington, Sussex West.
Stourbridge, West Mids.
Stow-on-the-Wold, Glos.

Stowmarket, Suffolk.
Stradbroke, Suffolk.
Stratford-upon-Avon, Warks.
Strathblane, Scotland.
Stretton, Cheshire.
Stretton-on-Fosse, Warks.
Stretton-under-Fosse, Warks.
Stroud, Glos.
Sturminster Newton, Dorset.
Suckley, Worcs.
Sudbury, Suffolk.
Sunderland, Tyne and Wear.
Sundridge, Kent.
Sunningdale, Berks.
Surbiton, Surrey.
Sutton, Surrey.
Sutton Bridge, Lincs.
Sutton Coldfield, West Mids.
Sutton Valence, Kent.
Sutton-in-Ashfield, Notts.
Sutton-on-Sea, Lincs.
Swaffham, Norfolk.
Swafield, Norfolk.
Swanage, Dorset.
Swansea, Wales.
Swindon, Wilts.
Swinford, Leics.
Swinstead, Lincs.

T

Tacolneston, Norfolk.
Taddington, Glos.
Tadley, Hants.
Tarleton, Lancs.
Tarporley, Cheshire.
Tarvin, Cheshire.
Tarvin Sands, Cheshire.
Tattenhall, Cheshire.
Tattershall, Lincs.
Taunton, Somerset.
Tavistock, Devon.
Taynton, Oxon.
Teignmouth, Devon.
Telford, Shrops.
Templeton, Wales.
Tenby, Wales.
Tenterden, Kent.
Tetbury, Glos.
Tetsworth, Oxon.
Tewkesbury, Glos.
Teynham, Kent.
Thame, Oxon.
Thames Ditton, Surrey.
Thetford, Norfolk.
Thirsk, Yorks. North.
Thornbury, Glos.
Thornton le Dale, Yorks. North.
Thornwood Common, Essex.
Tillington, Sussex West.
Tilston, Cheshire.
Tintern, Wales.

Titchfield, Hants.
Tockwith, Yorks. North.
Toddington, Beds.
Todenham, Glos.
Todmorden, Yorks. West.
Tonbridge, Kent.
Topsham, Devon.
Torquay, Devon.
Totnes, Devon.
Tottenhill, Norfolk.
Towcester, Northants.
Trawden, Lancs.
Trecastle, Wales.
Tregony, Cornwall.
Treorchy, Wales.
Trevor, Wales.
Tring, Herts.
Troon, Scotland.
Truro, Cornwall.
Tunbridge Wells, Kent.
Tutbury, Staffs.
Tuxford, Notts.
Twickenham, Middx.
Twyford, Berks.
Twyford, Hants.
Twyford, Norfolk.
Tynemouth, Tyne and Wear.
Tywyn, Wales.

U

Uckfield, Sussex East.
Ullapool, Scotland.
Ulverston, Cumbria.
Upper Largo, Scotland.
Uppingham, Rutland.
Upton-upon-Severn, Worcs.
Uttoxeter, Staffs.
Uxbridge, Middx.

V

Vale, Guernsey, C.I.
Valley, Wales.
Ventnor, Isle of Wight.

W

Waddington, Lincs.
Wadebridge, Cornwall.
Wadhurst, Sussex East.
Wainfleet, Lincs.
Wakefield, Yorks. West.
Wallasey, Merseyside.
Wallingford, Oxon.
Walsall, West Mids.
Walsden, Yorks. West.
Walton-on-Thames, Surrey.
Walton-on-the-Hill and
    Tadworth, Surrey.
Wansford, Cambs.
Wantage, Oxon.
Warboys, Cambs.
Wareham, Dorset.

Warfield, Berks.
Wargrave, Berks.
Warlingham, Surrey.
Warminster, Wilts.
Warrenpoint, Co. Down,
    N. Ireland.
Warrington, Cheshire.
Warsash, Hants.
Warwick, Warks.
Washington, Sussex West.
Washington, Tyne and Wear.
Watchet, Somerset.
Watlington, Oxon.
Watton, Norfolk.
Waverton, Cheshire.
Wedmore, Somerset.
Wednesbury, West Mids.
Weedon, Northants.
Weeford, Staffs.
Welling, Kent.
Wellingborough, Northants.
Wellington, Somerset.
Wells, Somerset.
Wells-next-the-Sea, Norfolk.
Welshpool, Wales.
Wendover, Bucks.
West Auckland, Durham.
West Bridgford, Notts.
West Buckland, Somerset.
West Byfleet, Surrey.
West Haddon, Northants.
West Kirby, Merseyside.
West Malling, Kent.
West Yatton, Wilts.
Westbury, Wilts.
Westcliff-on-Sea, Essex.
Westerham, Kent.
Weston, Herts.
Weston-on-the-Green, Oxon.
Weston-Super-Mare, Somerset.
Weybridge, Surrey.
Weymouth, Dorset.
Whaley Bridge, Derbys.
Whalley, Lancs.
Wheathampstead, Herts.
Whimple, Devon.
Whitby, Yorks. North.
Whitchurch, Bucks.
Whitchurch, Shrops.
White Colne, Essex.
White Roding, Essex.
Whitefield, Lancs.
Whitehaven, Cumbria.
Whitley Bay, Tyne and Wear.
Whitstable, Kent.
Whitwick, Leics.
Whixley, Yorks. North.
Wickham Bishops, Essex.
Wickham Market, Suffolk.
Wickwar, Glos.
Wigan, Lancs.

Williton, Somerset.
Wilmslow, Cheshire.
Wilstead (Wilshamstead), Beds.
Wilstone, Herts.
Wilton, Wilts.
Wimborne Minster, Dorset.
Wincanton, Somerset.
Winchcombe, Glos.
Winchester, Hants.
Windermere, Cumbria.
Windsor and Eton, Berks.
Wing, Rutland.
Wingham, Kent.
Winslow, Bucks.
Wisbech, Cambs.
Witney, Oxon.
Wittersham, Kent.
Wiveliscombe, Somerset.
Woburn, Beds.
Woking, Surrey.
Wokingham, Berks.
Wolseley Bridge, Staffs.
Wolverhampton, West Mids.
Wooburn, Bucks.
Woodbridge, Suffolk.
Woodbury, Devon.
Woodford Green, Essex.
Woodhall Spa, Lincs.
Woodhouse Eaves, Leics.
Woodlesford, Yorks. West.
Woodseaves, Staffs.
Woodstock, Oxon.
Woodville, Derbys.
Wooler, Northumbs.
Woolhampton, Berks.
Woolpit, Suffolk.
Woore, Shrops.
Wootton Bassett, Wilts.
Worcester, Worcs.
Workington, Cumbria.
Worsley, Lancs.
Wortham, Suffolk.
Worthing, Sussex West.
Wraysbury, Berks.
Wrentham, Suffolk.
Writtle, Essex.
Wrotham, Kent.
Wroxham, Norfolk.
Wychbold, Worcs.
Wymeswold, Leics.
Wymondham, Norfolk.

Y

Yarm, Yorks. North.
Yarnton, Oxon.
Yazor, Herefs.
Yealmpton, Devon.
Yeovil, Somerset.
York, Yorks. North.
Yoxall, Staffs.
Yoxford, Suffolk.

Specialist Dealers' Index

Most antique dealers in Britain sell a wide range of goods from furniture, through porcelain and pottery, to pictures, prints and clocks. Much of the interest in visting antiques shops comes from this diversity. However, there are a number of dealers who specialise and the following is a list of these dealers. Most of them will stock a representative selection of the items found under their classification.

The name of the business, together with the area of London or the town and county under which the detailed entry can be found are given in the listing. Again we would like to repeat the advice given in the introduction that, if readers are looking for a particular item, they are advised to telephone first, before making a long journey.

CLASSIFICATIONS

Antiques Centres and Markets
Antiquarian Books
Antiquities
Architectural Items
Arms & Armour
Art Deco & Art Nouveau
Barometers - see also Clock Dealers
Beds
Brass (see Metalwork)
Bronzes
Carpets & Rugs
Cars & Carriages
Chinese Art - see Oriental
Church Furniture & Furnishings
Clocks & Watches
Coins & Medals
Dolls & Toys
Etchings & Engravings
Fire Related Items
Frames
Furniture-
   Continental (mainly French)
   Country
   Georgian
   Oak
   Pine
   Victorian
Garden Furniture, Ornaments &
   Statuary
Glass - see also Glass Domes &
   Paperweights
Glass Domes
Icons - see Russian Art
Islamic Art
Japanese Art - see Oriental
Jewellery - see Silver & Jewellery
Lighting

Maps & Prints
Metalware/work
Miniatures
Mirrors
Musical Boxes, Instruments &
   Literature
Nautical Instruments - see Scientific
Needlework - see Tapestries
Netsuke - see Oriental
Oil Paintings
Oriental Items
Paperweights
Photographs & Equipment
Porcelain & Pottery
Prints - see Maps
Rugs - see Carpets
Russian/Soviet Art
Scientific Instruments
Sculpture
Shipping Goods & Period Furniture
   for the Trade
Silver and Jewellery
Sporting Items & Associated
   Memorabilia
Sporting Paintings & Prints
Stamps
Tapestries, Textiles & Needlework
Taxidermy
Tools - including Needlework &
   Sewing
Toys - see Dolls
Trade Dealers - see Shipping Goods
Treen
Vintage Cars - see Carriages & Cars
Watercolours
Wholesale Dealers - see Shipping Goods
Wine Related Items

Hungry Ghost

Chinese Antique Furniture • Decorative Accessories • Original Gifts

122 Fulham Road, London SW3 6HU Tel & Fax: 020 7370 6673

1 Brewery Yard, Sheep Street, Stow-on-the-Wold, Gloucestershire GL 54 1AA
Tel: 01451 870101 Fax: 01451 870012

Antiques Centres & Markets
Georgian Village Antiques Market, London E17.
Angel Arcade, London N1.
Camden Passage Antiques Market and Pierrepont Arcade Antiques Centre, London N1.
The Fleamarket, London N1.
London Militaria Market, London N1.
The Mall Antiques Arcade, London N1.
Palmers Green Antiques Centre, London N13.
Southgate Antiques & Collectables, London N14.
Hampstead Antique and Craft Market, London NW3.
Alfies Antique Market, London NW8.
Bermondsey Antiques Market, London SE1.
Greenwich Antiques Market, London SE10.
Sydenham Antiques Centre, London SE26.
Cobwebs, London SE9.
Northcote Road Antiques Market, London SW11.
Antiquarius, London SW3.
Bourbon-Hanby Antiques Centre, London SW3.
Magpies, London SW6.
Bond Street Antiques Centre, London W1.
Grays Antique Market, London W1.
Admiral Vernon Antiques Market, London W11.
Arbras Gallery, London W11.

The Corner Portobello Antiques Supermarket, London W11.
Crown Arcade, London W11.
Dolphin Arcade, London W11.
Kleanthous Antiques, London W11.
The Red Lion Antiques Arcade, London W11.
Roger's Antiques Gallery, London W11.
The Silver Fox Gallery (Portobello), London W11.
Still Too Few, London W11.
World Famous Portobello Market, London W11.
The Old Cinema Antique Department Store, London W4.
Kensington Church Street Antiques Centre, London W8.
Apple Market Stalls, London WC2.
Covent Garden Flea Market, London WC2.
The London Silver Vaults, London WC2.
Ampthill Antiques Emporium, Ampthill, Beds.
The Woburn Abbey Antiques Centre, Woburn, Beds.
Barkham Antique Centre, Barkham, Berks.
Great Grooms of Hungerford, Hungerford, Berks.
Hungerford Arcade, Hungerford, Berks.
Stables Antique Centre, Reading, Berks.
Moss End Antique Centre, Warfield, Berks.
Workingham Antiques Centre, Wokingham, Berks.

Buck House Antique Centre, Beaconsfield, Bucks.
Buckingham Antiques Centre, Buckingham, Bucks.
Marlow Antique Centre, Marlow, Bucks.
Well Cottage Antiques Centre, Princes Risborough, Bucks.
Antiques at.. Wendover Antiques Centre, Wendover, Bucks.
Winslow Antiques Centre, Winslow, Bucks.
Gwydir Street Antiques Centre, Cambridge, Cambs.
The Hive, Cambridge, Cambs.
Waterside Antiques Centre, Ely, Cambs.
Fitzwilliam Antiques Centre, Peterborough, Cambs.
Guildhall Fair - Chester, Chester, Cheshire.
Davenham Antiques Centre, Davenham, Cheshire.
Knutsford Antiques Centre, Knutsford, Cheshire.
Northwich Antiques Centre, Northwich, Cheshire.
E. R. Antiques Centre, Stockport, Cheshire.
Tarporley Antique Centre, Tarporley, Cheshire.
Wilmslow Antiques, Wilmslow, Cheshire.
Bodmin Antiques Centre, Bodmin, Cornwall.
Waterfront Antiques Market, Falmouth, Cornwall.

Chapel Street Antiques Arcade, Penzance, Cornwall.

The Cumbrian Antiques Centre, Brampton, Cumbria.

Carlisle Antiques and Craft Centre, Carlisle, Cumbria.

Cockermouth Antiques Market, Cockermouth, Cumbria.

Alfreton Antiques Centre, Alfreton, Derbys.

Chappells & The Antiques Centre, Bakewell, Derbys.

Bradwell Antiques Centre, Bradwell, Derbys.

Matlock Antiques and Collectables Centre, Matlock, Derbys.

Memory Lane Antiques Centre, Ripley, Derbys.

The Shambles, Ashburton, Devon.

North Devon Antiques Centre, Barnstaple, Devon.

The Antique Centre on the Quay, Exeter, Devon.

McBains Antiques, Exeter, Devon.

Phantique, Exeter, Devon.

The Quay Gallery Antiques Emporium, Exeter, Devon.

Honiton Antique Centre, Honiton, Devon.

St Leonards Antiques & Craft Centre, Newton Abbot, Devon.

Barbican Antiques Centre, Plymouth, Devon.

New Street Antique Centre, Plymouth, Devon.

Parade Antiques Market, Plymouth, Devon.

Sidmouth Antiques and Collectors Centre, Sidmouth, Devon.

The Antique & Interior Centre, South Molton, Devon.

Hardy's Collectables, Bournemouth, Dorset.

Bridport Antiques Centre, Bridport, Dorset.

Colliton Antique Centre, Dorchester, Dorset.

Mr. Punch's Antique Market, Shaftesbury, Dorset.

Sherborne World of Antiques, Sherborne, Dorset.

Battlesbridge Antique Centre, Battlesbridge, Essex.

Church Hall Farm Antique & Craft Centre, Broxted, Essex.

Trinity Antiques Centre, Colchester, Essex.

Finchingfield Antiques Centre, Finchingfield, Essex.

Baddow Antique Centre, Great Baddow, Essex.

Gallerie Antiques, Hainault, Essex.

Townsford Mill Antiques Centre, Halstead, Essex.

Harwich Antiques Centre, Harwich, Essex.

Kelvedon Antiques, Kelvedon, Essex.

Maldon Antiques and Collectors Market, Maldon, Essex.

Saffron Walden Antiques Centre, Saffron Walden, Essex.

Berkeley Antiques Market, Berkeley, Glos.

St. Nicholas Markets, Bristol, Glos.

Charlton Kings Antiques Centre, Cheltenham, Glos.

Cheltenham Antique Market, Cheltenham, Glos.

Cheltenham Antiques Centre, Cheltenham, Glos.

Struwwelpeter Antiques at the Schoolhouse, Cheltenham, Glos.

Cirencester Arcade, Cirencester, Glos.

Gloucester Antique Centre, Gloucester, Glos.

Jubilee Hall Antiques Centre, Lechlade, Glos.

Lechlade Arcade, Lechlade, Glos.

The Old Ironmongers Antiques Centre, Lechlade, Glos.

Antique Centre, Moreton-in-Marsh, Glos.

Windsor House Antiques Centre, Moreton-in-Marsh, Glos.

Durham House Antiques Centre, Stow-on-the-Wold, Glos.

Fox Cottage Antiques, Stow-on-the-Wold, Glos.

The Antique and Interior Centre, Tetbury, Glos.

The Antiques Emporium, Tetbury, Glos.

Tewkesbury Antiques & Collectables Centre, Tewkesbury, Glos.

Dolphin Quay Antique Centre, Emsworth, Hants.

The Antiques Centre, Hartley Wintney, Hants.

Cedar Antiques Centre Ltd, Hartley Wintney, Hants.

Lymington Antiques Centre, Lymington, Hants.

Lyndhurst Antiques Centre, Lyndhurst, Hants.

The Folly Antiques Centre, Petersfield, Hants.

Samuels Spencers Antiques and Decorative Arts Emporium, Winchester, Hants.

Hereford Antique Centre, Hereford, Herefs.

Leominster Antiques Market, Leominster, Herefs.

Ross-on-Wye Antiques Centre, Ross-on-Wye, Herefs.

Bushey Antique Centre, Bushey, Herts.

Hertford Antiques, Hertford, Herts.

The Herts and Essex Antiques Centre, Sawbridgeworth, Herts.

By George! Antiques Centre, St. Albans, Herts.

Royal Victoria Arcade, Ryde, Isle of Wight.

Beckenham Antiques & Collectors' Market, Beckenham, Kent.

Southdown House Antiques, Brasted, Kent.

The Village Antique Centre, Brasted, Kent.

Burgate Antique Centre, Canterbury, Kent.

Rastro Antiques, Canterbury, Kent.

Cranbrook Antique Centre, Cranbrook, Kent.

Pinions Collectors Centre, Ditton, Kent.

Malthouse Arcade, Hythe, Kent.

Beehive, Petts Wood, Kent.

The Antiques Centre, Sevenoaks, Kent.

Sidcup Antique and Craft Centre, Sidcup, Kent.

Barden House Antiques, Tonbridge, Kent.

Corn Exchange Antiques Centre, Tunbridge Wells, Kent.

Tunbridge Wells Antiques, Tunbridge Wells, Kent.

Castle Antiques Centre, Westerham, Kent.

Bolton Antique Centre, Bolton, Lancs.

Ironchurch Antiques Centre, Bolton, Lancs.

King's Mill Antique Centre, Burnley, Lancs.

Antiques and Crafts Centre, Chorley, Lancs.

Heskin Hall Antiques, ChorleyLancs.

Belgrave Antique Centre, Darwen, Lancs.

Holden Wood Antiques Centre, HaslingdenLancs.

The Assembly Rooms Market, Lancaster, Lancs.

G.B. Antiques Ltd, Lancaster, Lancs.

Lancaster Leisure Park Antiques Centre, Lancaster, Lancs.

Antiques Village, Manchester, Lancs.

The Ginnell Gallery Antique Centre, Manchester, Lancs.

The Antique Centre, Preston, Lancs.

Preston Antique Centre, Preston, Lancs.

Walter Aspinall Antiques, Sabden, Lancs.

Pendle Antiques Centre Ltd, Sabden, Lancs.

Oxford Street Antique Centre, Leicester, Leics.

Whitemoors Antiques and Fine Art, Shenton, Leics.

Portobello Row Antique & Collectors' Centre, Boston, Lincs.

Brownlow Antiques Centre, Faldingworth, Lincs.

Notions Antiques Centre, Grantham, Lincs.

Abbeygate Gallery & Antiques Centre, Grimsby, Lincs.

Astra House Antiques Centre, Hemswell Cliff, Lincs.

Hemswell Antiques Centres, Hemswell Cliff, Lincs.

Great Expectations, Horncastle, Lincs.

The Chapel Emporium Antique Centre, Long Sutton, Lincs.

Old Maltings Antique Centre, Louth, Lincs.

St. Martins Antiques Centre, Stamford, Lincs.

Phelps Antiques, Twickenham, Middx.

Coltishall Antiques Centre, Coltishall, Norfolk.

The Antiques & Collectors Centre (Diss), Diss, Norfolk.

Colbrook Antiques, Fakenham Norfolk.

Fakenham Antique Centre, Fakenham, Norfolk.

Le Strange Old Barns Antiques, Arts & Craft Centre, Hunstanton, Norfolk.

The Old Granary Antiques and Collectors Centre, King's Lynn, Norfolk.

Cloisters Antique & Collectors Fair, Norwich, Norfolk.

St. Michael at Plea Antiques and Book Centre, Norwich, Norfolk.

Tombland Antiques Centre, Norwich, Norfolk.

Wells Antique Centre, Wells-next-the-Sea, Norfolk.

SPECIALIST DEALERS

Brackley Antique Cellar, Brackley, Northants.

E.K. Antiques, Finedon, Northants.

Finedon Antiques (Centre), Finedon, Northants.

The Village Antique Market, Weedon, Northants.

Antiques and Bric-a-Brac Market, Wellingborough, Northants.

Castle Gate Antiques Centre, Newark, Notts.

Newark Antiques Centre, Newark, Notts.

Newark Antiques Warehouse, Newark, Notts.

Tudor Rose Antiques Centre, Newark, Notts.

Top Hat Antiques Centre, Nottingham, Notts.

Old George Inn Antique Galleries, Burford, Oxon.

Country Markets Antiques and Collectables, Chilton, Oxon.

Chipping Norton Antique Centre, Chipping Norton, Oxon.

The Quiet Woman Antiques Centre, Chipping Norton, Oxon.

Deddington Antiques Centre, Deddington, Oxon.

Friday Street Antique Centre (The Ferret), Henley-on-Thames, Oxon.

Antiques on High Ltd, Oxford, Oxon.

TheSwan at Tetsworth, Tetsworth, Oxon.

The Lamb Arcade, Wallingford, Oxon.

The Arbery Centre, Wantage, Oxon.

Span Antiques, Woodstock, Oxon.

Old Mill Antique Centre, Bridgnorth, Shrops.

Stretton Antiques Market, Church Stretton, Shrops.

Antique Centre, Cleobury Mortimer, Shrops.

Amanda's Secondhand Hypermarket, Newport, Shrops.

Princess Antique Centre, Shrewsbury, Shrops.

Shrewsbury Antique Centre, Shrewsbury, Shrops.

Shrewsbury Antique Market, Shrewsbury, Shrops.

Assembly Antiques Centre, Bath, Somerset.

Bartlett Street Antiques Centre, Bath, Somerset.

Bath Saturday Antiques Market, Bath, Somerset.

Fountain Antiques Market, Bath, Somerset.

Paragon Antiques and Collectors Market, Bath, Somerset.

Crewkerne Antique Centre, Crewkerne, Somerset.

County Antiques, Ilminster, Somerset.

Somerton Antiques Centre, Somerton, Somerset.

Taunton Antiques Market - Silver Street, Taunton, Somerset.

Green Dragon Antiques Centre, Wincanton, Somerset.

Rugeley Antique Centre, Brereton, Staffs.

The Leek Antiques Centre (Barclay House), Leek, Staffs.

Antique Forum, Newcastle-under-Lyme, Staffs.

Windmill Antiques, Stafford, Staffs.

Old Chapel Antique & Collectables Centre, Tutbury, Staffs.

Tutbury Mill Antiques Centre, Tutbury, Staffs.

Blackbrook Antiques Village, Weeford, Staffs.

Clare Antique Warehouse, Clare, Suffolk.

Long Melford Antiques Centre, Long Melford, Suffolk.

The Old Town Hall Antique Centre, Needham Market, Suffolk.

The Risby Barn, Risby, Suffolk.

Snape Antiques and Collectors Centre, Snape, Suffolk.

The Emporium Antiques and Collectors Centre, Southwold, Suffolk.

Memories, Bramley, Surrey.

Mimbridge Antiques Centre, Chobham, Surrey.

Dorking House Antiques, Dorking, Surrey.

Pilgrims Antique Centre, Dorking, Surrey.

Victoria and Edward Antiques Centre, Dorking, Surrey.

The Antiques Centre at Hampton Court, East Molesey, Surrey.

The Nostradamus Centre, East Molesey, Surrey.

Nostradamus II, East Molesey, Surrey.

Bourne Mill Antiques, Farnham, Surrey.

Farnham Antique Centre, Farnham, Surrey.

Maltings Monthly Market, Farnham, Surrey.

Haslemere Antique Market, Haslemere, Surrey.

Wood's Wharf Antiques Bazaar, Haslemere, Surrey.

Kingston Antique Market, Kingston-upon-Thames, Surrey.

Wagstaffs, Oxted, Surrey.

Town & Country Decorative, Richmond, Surrey.

Shere Antiques Centre, Shere, Surrey.

Brighton Flea Market, Brighton, Sussex East.

Chateaubriand Antiques Centre, Burwash, Sussex East.

Eastbourne Antiques Market, Eastbourne, Sussex East.

Enterprise Collectors Market, Eastbourne, Sussex East.

The Old Town Antiques Centre, Eastbourne, Sussex East.

Pharoahs Antiques Centre, Eastbourne, Sussex East.

George Street Antiques Centre, Hastings, Sussex East.

Horsebridge Antiques Centre, Horsebridge, Sussex East.

Church-Hill Antiques Centre, Lewes, Sussex East.

Cliffe Antiques Centre, Lewes, Sussex East.

The Emporium Antique Centre, Lewes, Sussex East.

Lewes Antique Centre, Lewes, Sussex East.

The Courtyard Antiques Market, Seaford, Sussex East.

Seaford's "Barn Collectors' Market" and Studio Bookshop, Seaford, Sussex East.

The Hastings Antique Centre, St. Leonards-on-Sea, Sussex East.

Old House Antique Centre, Adversane, Sussex West.

Nineveh House, Arundel, Sussex West.

Great Grooms Antique Centre, Billingshurst, Sussex West.

Almshouses Arcade, Chichester, Sussex West.

Chichester Antiques Centre, Chichester, Sussex West.

Spongs Antiques Centre, LindfieldSussex West.

Petworth Antique Market, Petworth, Sussex West.

Anna Harrison Antiques Centre, Gosforth, Tyne and Wear.

Trecastle Antiques Centre, Trecastle, Wales.

Malthouse Antiques Centre, Alcester, Warks.

Bidford Antiques Centre, Bidford-on-Avon, Warks.

The Stables Antique Centre, Hatton, Warks.

Henley Antiques Centre, Henley-in-Arden, Warks.

Barn Antiques Centre, Long Marston, Warks.

Stratford Antique Centre, Stratford-upon-Avon, Warks.

The Stratford Antiques and Interiors Centre Ltd, Stratford-upon-Avon, Warks.

The Old Cornmarket Antiques Centre, Warwick, Warks.

Vintage Antiques Centre, Warwick, Warks.

The Warwick Antique Centre, Warwick, Warks.

The Birmingham Antique Centre, Birmingham, West Mids.

Warley Antique Centre, Birmingham, West Mids.

Coventry Antique Centre, Coventry, West Mids.

Regency Antique Trading Centre, Stourbridge, West Mids.

Wolverhampton Antiques and Collectors Market, Wolverhampton, West Mids.

The Marlborough Parade Antique Centre, Marlborough, Wilts.

King Street Curios, Melksham, Wilts.

Antique and Collectors Market, Salisbury, Wilts.

The Avonbridge Antiques and Collectors Market, Salisbury, Wilts.

Dairy House Antiques, Semley, Wilts.

Warminster Antiques Centre, Warminster, Wilts.

Tubbjoys Antique Market, Wootton Bassett, Wilts.

Antiques and Curios, Worcester, Worcs.

Worcester Antiques Centre, Worcester, Worcs.

St Crispin Antique Centre, BeverleyYorks. East.

Grannie's Treasures, Hull, Yorks. East.

Hull Antique Centre, Hull, Yorks. East.

The Ginnel, Harrogate, Yorks. North.

Montpellier Mews Antique Market, Harrogate, Yorks. North.

Malton Antique Market, Malton, Yorks. North.

SPECIALIST DEALERS

Castle Antiques Centre, Middleham, Yorks. North.
Cavendish Antiques & Collectors Centre, YorkYorks. North.
The Red House Antiques Centre, York, Yorks. North.
Stonegate Antiques Centre, York, Yorks. North.
York Antiques Centre, York, Yorks. North.
Treasure House Antiques Centre, Bawtry, Yorks. South.
Foster's Antique Centre, Rotherham, Yorks. South.
Court House Antique Centre, Sheffield, Yorks. South.
Nichols Antique Centre, Sheffield, Yorks. South.
Sheffield Antiques Emporium and the Chapel, Sheffield, Yorks. South.
Halifax Antiques Centre, Halifax, Yorks. West.
Headrow Antiques Centre, Leeds, Yorks. West.
Otley Antique Centre, Otley, Yorks. West.
The Victoria Centre, Saltaire, Yorks. West.
Todmorden Antiques Centre, Todmorden, Yorks. West.
Trafalgar Antiques Centre, Woodlesford, Yorks. West.
Jacobs Antique Centre, Cardiff, Wales.
Scottish Antique & Arts Centre, Abernyte, Scotland.
Clola Antiques Centre, Clola by Mintlaw, Scotland.
The Antiques Warehouse, Glasgow, Scotland.
The Victorian Village Antiques, Glasgow, Scotland.
Rait Village Antiques Centre, Rait, Scotland.
Hay Antique Market, Hay-on-Wye, Wales.
Offa's Dyke Antique Centre, Knighton, Wales.
Pembroke Antiques Centre, Pembroke, Wales.

Antiquarian Books

Ash Rare Books, London EC3.
Judith Lassalle, London N1.
M.E. Korn, London N10.
Zeno Booksellers, London N13.
Nicholas Goodyer, London N5.
Fisher and Sperr, London N6.
Military History Bookshop, London NW1.
P.G. de Lotz, London NW3.
Keith Fawkes, London NW3.
Barrie Marks Ltd, London NW5.
H. Baron, London NW6.
Marcet Books, London SE10.
Rogers Turner Books, London SE10.
Classic Bindings, London SW1.
Thomas Heneage Art Books, London SW1.
Sims, Reed Ltd, London SW1.
Hünersdorff Rare Books, London SW10.
John Thornton, London SW10.
Paul Foster's Bookshop, London SW14.
Hanshan Tang Books, London SW15.
Earlsfield Bookshop, London SW18.
Robin Greer, London SW6.

The Gloucester Road Bookshop, London SW7.
Paul Orssich, London SW8.
Altea Maps & Books, London W1.
G. Heywood Hill Ltd, London W1.
Holland & Holland, London W1.
Maggs Bros Ltd, London W1.
Marlborough Rare Books Ltd, London W1.
The O'Shea Gallery, London W1.
Paralos Ltd, London W1.
Pickering and Chatto, London W1.
Jonathan Potter Ltd, London W1.
Bernard Quaritch Ltd (Booksellers), London W1.
Robert G. Sawers, London W1.
Bernard J. Shapero Rare Books, London W1.
Henry Sotheran Ltd, London W1.
Crawley and Asquith Ltd, London W11.
Demetzy Books, London W11.
D. Parikian, London W14.
Hosains Books and Antiques, London W2.
Adrian Harrington, London W8.
Russell Rare Books, London W8.
Atlantis Bookshop, London WC1.
Book Art & Architecture & Volume Gallery, London WC1.
Cinema Bookshop, London WC1.
Fine Books Oriental, London WC1.
Michael Finney Antique Prints and Books, London WC1.
Robert Frew Ltd, London WC1.
Marchmont Bookshop, London WC1.
The Museum Bookshop, London WC1.
Skoob Books Ltd, London WC1.
Bell, Book and Radmall, London WC2.
Blackwell's, London WC2.
David Drummond at Pleasures of Past Times, London WC2.
W. and G. Foyle Ltd, London WC2.
P. J. Hilton (Books), London WC2.
Henry Pordes Books Ltd, London WC2.
Reg and Philip Remington, London WC2.
Bertram Rota Ltd, London WC2.
Stage Door Prints, London WC2.
Storey's Ltd, London WC2.
Watkins Books Ltd, London WC2.
Zwemmer, London WC2.
Books for Collectors Ltd., Toddington, Beds.
Eton Antique Bookshop, Windsor and Eton, Berks.
Penn Barn, Penn, Bucks.
G. David, Cambridge, Cambs.
Deighton Bell and Co, Cambridge, Cambs.
Galloway and Porter Ltd, Cambridge, Cambs.
Sarah Key, Cambridge, Cambs.
Old Soke Books, Peterborough, Cambs.
Stothert Old Books, Chester, Cheshire.
Iain Campbell, Great Barrow, Cheshire.
Lion Gallery and Bookshop, Knutsford, Cheshire.
Mereside Books, Macclesfield, Cheshire.
New Street Bookshop, Penzance, Cornwall.
Bonython Bookshop, Truro, Cornwall.
Maurice Dodd Books, Carlisle, Cumbria.
Norman Kerr - Gatehouse Bookshop, Cartmel, Cumbria.
Peter Bain Smith (Bookseller), Cartmel, Cumbria.

Archie Miles Bookshop, Gosforth, Cumbria.
Lakes Crafts & Antiques Gallery, Grasmere, Cumbria.
G.K. Hadfield, Great Salkeld, Cumbria.
The Book House, Ravenstonedale, Cumbria.
R. F. G. Hollett and Son, Sedbergh, Cumbria.
Michael Moon - Antiquarian Booksellers, Whitehaven, Cumbria.
Alan Hill Books, Chesterfield, Derbys.
Derventio Books, Derby, Derbys.
Chantry Bookshop and Gallery, Dartmouth, Devon.
Exeter Rare Books, Exeter, Devon.
High Street Books, Honiton, Devon.
Honiton Old Bookshop, Honiton, Devon.
Geoffrey M. Woodhead, Honiton, Devon.
P.M. Pollak, South Brent, Devon.
R M Young Bookseller, South Molton, Devon.
Tavistock Books, Tavistock, Devon.
The Schuster Gallery, Torquay, Devon.
Collards Books, Totnes, Devon.
Pedlars Pack Books, Totnes, Devon.
Ancient and Modern Bookshop (including Garret's Antiques), Blandford Forum, Dorset.
Bridport Old Books, Bridport, Dorset.
Words Etcetera, Dorchester, Dorset.
Christopher Williams Antiquarian Bookseller, Parkstone, Dorset.
Antique Map and Bookshop, Puddletown, Dorset.
Chapter House Books, Sherborne, Dorset.
Keeble Antiques, Sherborne, Dorset.
Reference Works, Swanage, Dorset.
Books Afloat, Weymouth, Dorset.
Books & Bygones, Weymouth, Dorset.
Minster Books, Wimborne Minster, Dorset.
J. Shotton Antiquarian Books, Prints and Coins, Durham, Durham.
Castle Bookshop, Colchester, Essex.
Cotham Hill Bookshop, Bristol, Glos.
Pastimes, Bristol, Glos.
David Bannister FRGS, Cheltenham, Glos.
Michael Rayner, Cheltenham, Glos.
Ian Hodgkins and Co. Ltd, Slad, Glos.
Tetbury Old Books & Coach House Antiques, Tetbury, Glos.
Laurence Oxley, Alresford, Hants.
Kingsclere Old Bookshop, Kingsclere, Hants.
Hughes and Smeeth Ltd, Lymington, Hants.
The Petersfield Bookshop, Petersfield, Hants.
Academy Books, Portsmouth, Hants.
H.M. Gilbert and Son, Southampton, Hants.
Peter M. Daly, Winchester, Hants.
SPCK Bookshops, Winchester, Hants.
Bournville Books, Hereford, Herefs.
Ross Old Book and Print Shop, Ross-on-Wye, Herefs.
Gillmark Gallery, Hertford, Herts.
Eric T. Moore, Hitchin, Herts.
Clive A. Burden Ltd, Rickmansworth, Herts.
Charles Dickens Bookshop, Cowes, Isle of Wight.

Ventnor Rare Books, Ventnor, Isle of Wight.
The Canterbury Bookshop, Canterbury, Kent.
Chaucer Bookshop, Canterbury, Kent.
J. Clarke-Hall Ltd, Deal, Kent.
Periwinkle Press, Newnham, Kent.
Baggins Book Bazaar - The Largest Secondhand Bookshop in England, Rochester, Kent.
Baskerville Books, Tunbridge Wells, Kent.
Hall's Bookshop, Tunbridge Wells, Kent.
Taylor-Smith Books, Westerham, Kent.
Forest Books of Cheshire, Manchester, Lancs.
Gibb's Bookshop Ltd, Manchester, Lancs.
Eric J. Morten, Manchester, Lancs.
Halewood and Sons, Preston, Lancs.
Preston Book Co, Preston, Lancs.
The Book Shop, Castle Donington, Leics.
Anthony W. Laywood, Knipton, Leics.
Clarendon Books, Leicester, Leics.
Fairburn Books, Hemswell Cliff, Lincs.
P.J. Cassidy (Books), Holbeach, Lincs.
Golden Goose Books, Lincoln, Lincs.
Harlequin Gallery, Lincoln, Lincs.
Staniland (Booksellers), Stamford, Lincs.
C.K. Broadhurst and Co Ltd, Southport, Merseyside.
Ian Sheridan's Bookshop, Hampton, Middx.
Anthony C. Hall, Twickenham, Middx.
John Ives Bookseller, Twickenham, Middx.
Rita Shenton, Twickenham, Middx.
David Ferrow, Gt. Yarmouth, Norfolk.
Simon Gough Books, Holt, Norfolk.
Baron Art, Kelling, Norfolk.
J & D Clarke Book and Print Dealers, Norwich, Norfolk.
Peter Crowe, Antiquarian Book Seller, Norwich, Norfolk.
The Tombland Bookshop, Norwich, Norfolk.
R.L. Cook, Sheringham, Norfolk.
Turret House, Wymondham, Norfolk.
The Old Hall Bookshop, Brackley, Northants.
Occultique, Northampton, Northants.
Park Gallery & Bookshop, Wellingborough, Northants.
Emerald Isle Books, Belfast, N. Ireland.
Barter Books, Alnwick, Northumbs.
Priest Popple Books, Hexham, Northumbs.
The Book Shelf, Mansfield, Notts.
Castle Antiques, Nottingham, Notts.
E.M. Lawson and Co, East Hagbourne, Oxon.
Richard J. Kingston, Henley-on-Thames, Oxon.
Richard Way Bookseller, Henley-on-Thames, Oxon.
Blackwell's Rare Books, Oxford, Oxon.
Jericho Books, Oxford, Oxon.
Thorntons of Oxford Ltd, Oxford, Oxon.
Waterfield's, Oxford, Oxon.
Toby English, Wallingford, Oxon.
Tooley Adams & Co, Wallingford, Oxon.

Goldmark Books, Uppingham, Rutland.
M. and M. Baldwin, Cleobury Mortimer, Shrops.
Candle Lane Books, Shrewsbury, Shrops.
George Bayntun, Bath, Somerset.
Camden Books, Bath, Somerset.
George Gregory, Bath, Somerset.
Patterson Liddle, Bath, Somerset.
Rothwell and Dunworth, Dulverton, Somerset.
Janet Clarke, Freshford, Somerset.
Steven Ferdinando, Queen Camel,, Somerset.
Sterling Books, Weston-Super-Mare, Somerset.
Mike Abrahams Books, Lichfield, Staffs.
Images - Peter Stockham, Lichfield, Staffs.
The Staffs Bookshop, Lichfield, Staffs.
Besleys Books, Beccles, Suffolk.
Trinders' Fine Tools, Clare, Suffolk.
Abington Books, Finningham, Suffolk.
Claude Cox at College Gateway Bookshop, Ipswich, Suffolk.
R.G. Archer (Books), Lavenham,, Suffolk.
R.E. and G.B. Way, Newmarket, Suffolk.
Vandeleur Antiquarian Books, Epsom, Surrey.
J.W. McKenzie, Ewell, Surrey.
Thomas Thorp Bookseller, Guildford, Surrey.
Charles W. Traylen, Guildford, Surrey.
Lloyds of Kew, Kew, Surrey.
A. Burton-Garbett, Morden, Surrey.
Secondhand Bookshop, Oxted, Surrey.
Wagstaffs, Oxted, Surrey.
Reigate Galleries, Reigate, Surrey.
Raymond Slack FRSA & Shirley Warren, Sanderstead, Surrey.
Colin Page Antiquarian Books, Brighton, Sussex East.
Camilla's Bookshop, Eastbourne, Sussex East.
Roderick Dew, Eastbourne, Sussex East.
A. & T. Gibbard, Eastbourne, Sussex East.
Howes Bookshop, Hastings, Sussex East.
Bow Windows Book Shop, Lewes, Sussex East.
A. & Y. Cumming, Lewes, Sussex East.
Fifteenth Century Bookshop, Lewes, Sussex East.
The Book Jungle, St. Leonards-on-Sea, Sussex East.
R.D. Steedman, Newcastle-upon-Tyne, Tyne and Wear.
Oliver's Bookshop, Whitley Bay, Tyne and Wear.
The Stratford Bookshop, Stratford-upon-Avon, Warks.
Robert Vaughan, Stratford-upon-Avon, Warks.
Duncan M. Allsop, Warwick, Warks.
David Temperley Fine and Antiquarian Books, Birmingham, West Mids.
Clive Farahar and Sophie Dupré - Rare Books, Autographs and Manuscripts, Calne, Wilts.
Hilmarton Manor Press, Calne, Wilts.
The Military Parade Bookshop, Marlborough, Wilts.

Heraldry Today, Ramsbury, Wilts.
The Barn Book Supply, Salisbury, Wilts.
Victoria Bookshop, Swindon, Wilts.
Bookworms of Evesham, Evesham, Worcs.
Malvern Bookshop, Great Malvern, Worcs.
Antique Map and Print Gallery, Worcester, Worcs.
The Grove Country Bookshop with Coopers of Ilkley, Bolton Abbey, Yorks. North.
Potterton Books, Thirsk, Yorks. North.
Barbican Bookshop, York, Yorks. North.
Minster Gate Bookshop, York, Yorks. North.
Ken Spelman, York, Yorks. North.
The Toll House Bookshop, Holmfirth, Yorks. West.
The Grove Bookshop, Ilkley, Yorks. West.
Channel Islands Galleries Ltd, St. Peter Port, Guernsey, C.I.
Geoffrey P. Gavey, Vale, Guernsey, C.I.
John Blench & Son, St. Helier, Jersey, C.I.
The Selective Eye Gallery, St. Helier, Jersey, C.I.
Thesaurus (Jersey) Ltd, St. Helier, Jersey, C.I.
Saintfield Antiques & Fine Books, Saintfield, Co. Down, N. Ireland.
Bon-Accord Books, Aberdeen, Scotland.
The McEwan Gallery, Ballater, Scotland.
Blairgowrie Books, Blairgowrie, Scotland.
Armchair Books, Edinburgh, Scotland.
Broughton Books, Edinburgh, Scotland.
McNaughtan's Bookshop, Edinburgh, Scotland.
Second Edition, Edinburgh, Scotland.
Marianne Simpson, Fochabers, Scotland.
Paisley Fine Books, Paisley, Scotland.
Maps, Prints and Books, Brecon, Wales.
Pontcanna Old Books, Maps and Prints, Cardiff, Wales.
Glance Back Bookshop, Chepstow, Wales.
Richard Booth's Bookshop Ltd, Hay-on-Wye, Wales.
Mark Westwood Antiquarian Books, Hay-on-Wye, Wales.
Doggie Hubbard's Bookshop, Ponterwyd,, Wales.
Dylan's Bookshop, Swansea, Wales.

Antiquities

C.J. Martin (Coins) Ltd, London N14.
Robin Symes Ltd, London SW1.
Aaron Gallery, London W1.
Charles Ede Ltd, London W1.
Hadji Baba Ancient Art, London W1.
Mansour Gallery, London W1.
Seaby Antiquities, London W1.
Rupert Wace Ancient Art Ltd, London W1.
J. and B. Antiques, London W11.
Town Hall Antiques, Woburn, Beds.
The Ancient Art Shop, Windsor and Eton, Berks.
Past Treasures, Wendover, Bucks.
Valued History, Cambridge, Cambs.
Potter's Antiques and Coins, Bristol, Glos.

SPECIALIST DEALERS

Architectural Items
LASSCo, London EC2.
Westland & Company, London EC2.
Relic Antiques at Camden Passage, London N1.
Townsends, London NW8.
The Junk Shop, London SE10.
Lamont Antiques Ltd, London SE10.
Camberwell Architectural Salvage & Antiques, London SE5.
Crowther of Syon Lodge Ltd, London SW1.
Thornhill Galleries Ltd. in association with A. & R. Dockerill Ltd, London SW15.
Charles Edwards, London SW6.
Fairfax Antiques and Fireplaces, London SW6.
Thornhill Galleries Ltd, London SW6.
Architectural Antiques, London W6.
Architectural Antiques, Bedford, Beds.
T. Smith, Chalfont St. Giles, Bucks.
Solopark Plc, Cambridge, Cambs.
Nostalgia Architectural Antiques, Stockport, Cheshire.
Cheshire Brick and Slate Co, Tarvin Sands, Cheshire.
The Great Northern Architectural Antique Company Ltd, Tattenhall, Cheshire.
W.R.S. Architectural Antiques, Low Newton, Cumbria.
Havenplan's Architectural Emporium, Killamarsh, Derbys.
Ashburton Marbles, Ashburton, Devon.
Rex Antiques, Chagford, Devon.
Fagins Antiques, Exeter, Devon.
Dorset Reclamation, Bere Regis, Dorset.
Talisman, Gillingham, Dorset.
Antique Fireplace Centre, Hartlepool, Durham.
Churchgate Antiques, Sible Hedingham, Essex.
Robert Mills Architectural Antiques Ltd, Bristol, Glos.
Original Architectural, Cirencester, Glos.
Cox's Architectural Reclamation Yard, Moreton-in-Marsh, Glos.
Ronson's Architectural Effects, Norton, Glos.
Architectural Heritage, Taddington, Glos.
Burgess Farm Antiques, Morestead, Hants.
The Pine Cellars, Winchester, Hants.
Baileys Home & Garden, Ross-on-Wye, Herefs.
Pattison's Architectural Antiques incorporating The Architectural Salvage Store, Chorleywood, Herts.
Curios of Chale, Chale, Isle of Wight.
The Architectural Emporium, Tunbridge Wells, Kent.
Bygone Times International Plc, Eccleston, Lancs.
Old Smithy, Feniscowles, Lancs.
Antique Fireplace Warehouse, Manchester, Lancs.
In-Situ Manchester, Manchester, Lancs.
In-Situ Manchester South Architectural Antiques, Manchester, Lancs.
Old Hall Farm, Long Clawson, Leics.
Lindsey Court Architectural Antiques, Horncastle, Lincs.
Antique Fireplaces, Liverpool, Merseyside.

Peco, Hampton, Middx.
Crowther of Syon Lodge Ltd, Isleworth, Middx.
Mongers, Hingham, Norfolk.
Stiffkey Antiques, Stiffkey, Norfolk.
Rococo Antiques and Interiors, Weedon, Northants.
Woodside Reclamation (Architectural Antiques), Berwick-upon-Tweed, Northumbs.
Hallidays (Fine Antiques) Ltd, Dorchester-on-Thames, Oxon.
Aston Pine Antiques, Faringdon, Oxon.
Oxford Architectural Antiques, Faringdon, Oxon.
The Country Seat, Huntercombe, Oxon.
Willow Antiques and the Nettlebed Antique Merchants, Nettlebed, Oxon.
North Shropshire Reclamation, Burlton, Shrops.
David Bridgwater, Bath, Somerset.
Source, Bath, Somerset.
Walcot Reclamation, Bath, Somerset.
Chris's Crackers, Carhampton, Somerset.
Wells Reclamation Company, Coxley, Somerset.
Frome Reclamation, Frome, Somerset.
Castle Reclamation, Martock, Somerset.
Harrison House Antiques, North Petherton, Somerset.
J.C. Giddings, Wiveliscombe, Somerset.
Anvil Antiques Ltd, Leek, Staffs.
E.T. Webster, Blythburgh, Suffolk.
Antique Buildings Ltd, Dunsfold, Surrey.
Drummonds Architectural Antiques, Hindhead, Surrey.
The Packhouse, Runfold, Surrey.
Antique Church Furnishings, Walton-on-Thames, Surrey.
Brighton Architectural Salvage, Brighton, Sussex East.
Turnburrys, Jesmond, Tyne and Wear.
Shiners, Snobs Knobs, Newcastle-upon-Tyne, Tyne and Wear.
The Victorian Ironmonger, Brinklow, Warks.
Retro Antiques, Lye, West Mids.
Harriet Fairfax Fireplaces and General Antiques, Langley Burrell, Wilts.
Ray Coggins Antiques, Westbury, Wilts.
Holloways, Suckley, Worcs.
Kevin Marshall's Antiques Warehouse, Hull, Yorks. East.
Old Flames, Easingwold, Yorks. North.
The White House Antiques & Architectural Reclamation, Easingwold, Yorks. North.
Robert Aagaard & Co, Knaresborough, Yorks. North.
Daleside Antiques, Markington, Yorks. North.
Renishaw Antiques, Sheffield, Yorks. South.
The Baildon Furniture Co., Baildon, Yorks. West.
Andy Thornton Architectural Antiques Ltd, Halifax, Yorks. West.
Swiss Cottage Furniture, Leeds, Yorks. West.
Dunedin Antiques Ltd, Edinburgh, Scotland.
EASY - Edinburgh & Glasgow Architectural Salvage Yards, Edinburgh, Scotland.

Holyrood Architectural Salvage, Edinburgh, Scotland.
Gallop and Rivers Architectural Antiques, Crickhowell, Wales.

Arms & Armour
London Militaria Market, London N1.
Finchley Fine Art Galleries, London N12.
Laurence Corner, London NW1.
Peter Dale Ltd, London SW1.
Pieter Oosthuizen t/a de Verzamelaar, London SW3.
Blunderbuss Antiques, London W1.
Holland & Holland, London W1.
Michael German Antiques Ltd, London W8.
Robert Hales Antiques, London W8.
Trafalgar Square Collectors Centre, London WC2.
Anthony D. Goodlad, Chesterfield, Derbys.
Rex Antiques, Chagford, Devon.
Boscombe Militaria, Bournemouth, Dorset.
Sterling Coins and Medals, Bournemouth, Dorset.
Chris Grimes Militaria, Bristol, Glos.
Pastimes, Bristol, Glos.
Q & C Militaria, Cheltenham, Glos.
Military Curios, HQ84, Gloucester, Glos.
Hampton Gallery, Tetbury, Glos.
J F F Fire Brigade & Military Collectables, Bedhampton, Hants.
Romsey Medals, Romsey, Hants.
H.S. Greenfield and Son, Gunmakers (Est. 1805), Canterbury, Kent.
Bus Stop Curios, Manchester, Lancs.
Garth Vincent Antique Arms and Armour, Allington, Lincs.
The Old Brigade, Kingsthorpe, Northants.
Michael D. Long, Nottingham, Notts.
English Heritage, Bridgnorth, Shrops.
One Bell, Lavenham, Suffolk.
West Street Antiques, Dorking, Surrey.
Casque and Gauntlet Militaria, Farnham, Surrey.
Mark and David Hawkins The Lanes Armoury, Brighton, Sussex East.
St. Pancras Antiques, Chichester, Sussex West.
Steve Johnson Medals & Militaria, Newcastle-upon-Tyne, Tyne and Wear.
Arbour Antiques Ltd, Stratford-upon-Avon, Warks.
Edred A.F. Gwilliam, Cricklade, Wilts.
Magpie Jewellers and Antiques and Magpie Arms & Armour, Evesham, Worcs.
Cairncross and Sons, Filey, Yorks. North.
Hanover Antiques & Collectables, Scarborough, Yorks. North.
Adamson Armoury, Skipton, Yorks. North.
D.W. Dyson (Antique Weapons), Huddersfield, Yorks. West.
A. & R. Ritchie, St. Helier, Jersey, C.I.
Angus Antiques, Dundee, Scotland.
Huw Williams Antiques, Porthmadog, Wales.

Art Deco & Art Nouveau

After Noah, London N1.
The Antique Trader, London N1.
Art Nouveau Originals c. 1900, London N1.
Style Gallery, London N1.
Tadema Gallery, London N1.
Titus Omega, London N1.
Art Furniture, London NW1.
Beverley, London NW8.
Bizarre, London NW8.
The Studio, London NW8.
Behind the Boxes - Art Deco, London SE26.
Ciancimino Ltd, London SW1.
Gallery '25, London SW1.
Keshishian, London SW1.
Artchaos, London SW11.
Twentieth Century, London SW12.
The Arts & Crafts Furniture Co Ltd, London SW14.
After Noah, London SW3.
Butler and Wilson, London SW3.
David Gill, London SW3.
Gordon Watson Ltd, London SW3.
Victor Arwas Gallery - Editions Graphiques Gallery Ltd, London W1.
Liberty, London W1.
Mayfair Gallery, London W1.
B. and T. Antiques, London W11.
The Facade, London W11.
Themes and Variations, London W11.
Peter Farlow, London W8.
Haslam and Whiteway, London W8.
John Jesse, London W8.
New Century, London W8.
Pruskin Gallery, London W8.
20th Century, Cambridge, Cambs.
Bizarre Decorative Arts North West, Altrincham, Cheshire.
Aldersey Hall Ltd, Chester, Cheshire.
Maggie Mays, Buxton, Derbys.
Lionel Geneen Ltd, Bournemouth, Dorset.
Omega, Newport, Essex.
f@me - Fine Art Multimedia Europe, Lechlade, Glos.
Ruskin Decorative Arts, Stow-on-the-Wold, Glos.
Bona Arts Decorative Ltd, Fleet, Hants.
Alexanders, Titchfield, Hants.
Delf Stream Gallery, Sandwich, Kent.
A.S. Antique Galleries, Manchester, Lancs.
Circa 1900, Liverpool, Merseyside.
Osiris Antiques, Southport, Merseyside.
Arbiter, Wallasey, Merseyside.
Aspidistra Antiques, Finedon, Northants.
Willow Antiques and the Nettlebed Antique Merchants, Nettlebed, Oxon.
Decorative Antiques, Bishop's Castle, Shrops.
Expressions, Shrewsbury, Shrops.
A J Antiques, Bath, Somerset.
Puritan Values at the Dome, Southwold, Suffolk.
Decodream, Coulsdon, Surrey.
The Olde Bakehouse Antiques, Dorking, Surrey.
Bits and Pieces Antiques, Farnham, Surrey.
The Gooday Gallery, Richmond, Surrey.

Succession, Richmond, Surrey.
Cockrell Antiques, Surbiton, Surrey.
Art Deco Etc., Brighton, Sussex East.
Jezebel, Brighton, Sussex East.
Oasis Antiques, Brighton, Sussex East.
Wardrobe, Brighton, Sussex East.
Peter Hancock Antiques, Chichester, Sussex West.
Cradlewell Antiques, Jesmond, Tyne and Wear.
Tango Art Deco & Antiques, Warwick, Warks.
Muir Hewitt Art Deco Originals, Halifax, Yorks. West.
Grandad's Attic, Aberdeen, Scotland.
The Rendezvous Gallery, Aberdeen, Scotland.
Montresor, Edinburgh, Scotland.
Deco by Design, Fenton Barns, Scotland.
The Renaissance Furniture Store, Glasgow, Scotland.
Jeremy Sniders Antiques, Glasgow, Scotland.
Strachan Antiques, Glasgow, Scotland.
Rhudle Mill, Kilmichael Glassary, Scotland.
Paul Gibbs Antiques and Decorative Arts, Conwy, Wales.

Barometers - see also Clock Dealers

C.R. Frost and Son Ltd, London EC1.
Patric Capon, London N1.
Strike One, London N5.
R.E. Rose FBHI, London SE9.
John Carlton-Smith, London SW1.
Trevor Philip and Sons Ltd, London SW1.
The Clock Clinic Ltd, London SW15.
Aubrey Brocklehurst, London SW7.
Ronald Phillips Ltd, London W1.
Stair and Company Ltd, London W1.
Old Father Time Clock Centre, London W11.
Raffety & Walwyn, London W8.
The Clock Workshop, Caversham, Berks.
Alan Walker, Halfway, Berks.
The Old Malthouse, Hungerford, Berks.
M.V. Tooley, CMBHI, Chesham, Bucks.
John Beazor and Sons Ltd, Cambridge, Cambs.
Antique Barometers, Ramsey, Cambs.
T. W. Pawson - Clocks, Somersham, Cambs.
Derek and Tina Rayment Antiques, Barton, Cheshire.
Andrew Foott Antiques, Cheadle Hulme, Cheshire.
Mike Read Antique Sciences, St. Ives, Cornwall.
Musgrave Bickford Antiques, Crediton, Devon.
Honiton Clock Clinic, Honiton, Devon.
Barometer World Ltd, Merton, Devon.
Alan Jones Antiques, Okehampton, Devon.
Leigh C. Extence, Shaldon, Devon.
Good Hope Antiques, Beaminster, Dorset.
M.C. Taylor, Bournemouth, Dorset.
Timecraft Clocks, Sherborne, Dorset.

Tom Tribe and Son, Sturminster Newton, Dorset.
Mark Marchant (Antiques), Coggeshall, Essex.
Littlebury Antiques - Littlebury Restorations Ltd, Saffron Walden, Essex.
It's About Time, Westcliff-on-Sea, Essex.
Montpellier Clocks, Cheltenham, Glos.
Saxton House Gallery, Chipping Campden, Glos.
Bryden House Clocks & Antiques, Stow-on-the-Wold, Glos.
Antony Preston Antiques Ltd, Stow-on-the-Wold, Glos.
Styles of Stow, Stow-on-the-Wold, Glos.
Vanbrugh House Antiques, Stow-on-the-Wold, Glos.
Evans and Evans, Alresford, Hants.
Bryan Clisby Antique Clocks, Hartley Wintney, Hants.
The Clock Workshop, Winchester, Hants.
G.E. Marsh Antique Clocks Ltd, Winchester, Hants.
Barometer Shop, Leominster, Herefs.
Robert Horton Antiques, Hertford, Herts.
John Chawner, Birchington, Kent.
Michael Sim, Chislehurst, Kent.
Neill RobinsonBlaxill, Sevenoaks, Kent.
Marks Antiques, Westerham, Kent.
Tankerton Antiques, Whitstable, Kent.
Drop Dial Antiques, Bolton, Lancs.
Harrop Fold Clocks (F. Robinson), Bolton-by-Bowland, Lancs.
Ingleside Antiques, Colne, Lancs.
N. Bryan-Peach Antiques, Wymeswold, Leics.
Robin Fowler (Period Clocks), Aylesby, Lincs.
David J. Hansord & Son, Lincoln, Lincs.
Timepiece Repairs, Lincoln, Lincs.
Rita Shenton, Twickenham, Middx.
Keith Lawson Antique Clocks, Scratby, Norfolk.
Peter Wiggins, Chipping Norton, Oxon.
Rosemary and Time, Thame, Oxon.
R.G. Cave and Sons Ltd, Ludlow, Shrops.
Adrian Donnelly Antique Clocks, Shrewsbury, Shrops.
Dodington Antiques, Whitchurch, Shrops.
Kembery Antique Clocks (inc. K & D Antique Clocks), Bath, Somerset.
Bernard G. House, Wells, Somerset.
Edward A. Nowell, Wells, Somerset.
Grosvenor Clocks, Leek, Staffs.
James A. Jordan, Lichfield, Staffs.
Patrick Marney, Long Melford, Suffolk.
Suthburgh Antiques, Long Melford, Suffolk.
Trident Antiques, Long Melford, Suffolk.
Horological Workshops, Guildford, Surrey.
Surrey Clock Centre, Haslemere, Surrey.
B. M. and E. Newlove, Surbiton, Surrey.
Baskerville Antiques, Petworth, Sussex West.

SPECIALIST DEALERS

The Grandfather Clock Shop, Shipston-on-Stour, Warks.
'Time in Hand', Shipston-on-Stour, Warks.
Summersons, Warwick, Warks.
R. Collyer, Birmingham, West Mids.
Osborne Antiques, Sutton Coldfield, West Mids.
P.A. Oxley Antique Clocks and Barometers, Cherhill, Wilts.
Inglenook Antiques, Ramsbury, Wilts.
Hansen Chard Antiques, Pershore, Worcs.
Time and Motion, Beverley, Yorks. East.
Lewis E. Hickson FBHI, Gilberdyke, Yorks. East.
Craiglea Clocks, Edinburgh, Scotland.
Muirhead Moffat and Co, Glasgow, Scotland.

Beds
La Maison, London E1.
Tobias and The Angel, London SW13.
And So To Bed Limited, London SW6.
Simon Horn Furniture Ltd, London SW6.
Sleeping Beauty Antique Beds, London SW6.
The French House (Antiques) Ltd, London SW8.
Hirst Antiques, London W11.
The Pine Merchants, Great Missenden, Bucks.
The Country Bedroom, Keswick, Cumbria.
Staveley Antiques, Staveley, Cumbria.
The Antiques Warehouse, Buxton, Derbys.
The Grove Antiques Centre, Honiton, Devon.
Pugh's Farm Antiques, Monkton, Devon.
Annterior Antiques, Plymouth, Devon.
Antique Bed Shop, Halstead, Essex.
Deja Vu Antiques, Leigh-on-Sea, Essex.
Antique Four-Poster Beds, Bristol, Glos.
Simon Poyntz Antique Beds, Bristol, Glos.
Antique Bed Company, Emsworth, Hants.
Harriet Ann Sleigh Beds, Rolvenden, Kent.
House Things Antiques, Hinckley, Leics.
A Barn Full of Brass Beds, Louth, Lincs.
Graham Pickett Antiques, Stamford, Lincs.
Antiques & Gifts, Downham Market, Norfolk.
Rococo Antiques and Interiors, Weedon, Northants.
Manor Farm Antiques, Standlake, Oxon.
Swans, Oakham, Rutland.
Bedsteads, Bath, Somerset.
Antiques Warehouse, Framlingham, Suffolk.
Goodbreys, Framlingham, Suffolk.
Sleeping Beauty Antique Beds, Brighton, Sussex East.
The Victorian Brass Bedstead Company, Cocking, Sussex West.
Antiques and All Pine, Swindon, Wilts.
S.W. Antiques, Pershore, Worcs.
Penny Farthing Antiques, North Cave, Yorks. East.
The French House (Antiques) Ltd., York, Yorks. North.
Seventh Heaven, Chirk, Wales.

Brass - see Metalware

Bronzes
Furniture Vault, London N1.
Kevin Page Oriental Art, London N1.
Style Gallery, London N1.
Finchley Fine Art Galleries, London N12.
Deuxieme, London NW8.
No. 28 Antiques, London NW8.
Tara Antiques, London NW8.
Robert Bowman, London SW1.
Victor Franses Gallery, London SW1.
M. and D. Lewis, London SW1.
Peter Nahum at The Leicester Galleries, London SW1.
Christine Bridge, London SW13.
Anthony James and Son Ltd, London SW3.
Victor Arwas Gallery - Editions Graphiques Gallery Ltd, London W1.
Barry Davies Oriental Art, London W1.
Eskenazi Ltd, London W1.
The Sladmore Gallery of Sculpture, London W1.
Elizabeth Bradwin, London W11.
Cohen & Cohen (Oriental Porcelain), London W11.
Gavin Douglas, London W11.
M. and D. Lewis, London W11.
David Brower Antiques, London W8.
H. and W. Deutsch Antiques, London W8.
John Jesse, London W8.
Pruskin Gallery, London W8.
Mary Wise & Grosvenor Antiques, London W8.
West End Galleries, Buxton, Derbys.
The John Davies Gallery, Stow-on-the-Wold, Glos.
Michael Sim, Chislehurst, Kent.
Apollo Antique Galleries, Westerham, Kent.
London House Antiques, Westerham, Kent.
Edward Cross - Fine Paintings, Weybridge, Surrey.

Carpets & Rugs
Alexander Juran and Co, London N4.
Kennedy Carpets, London N4.
Joseph Lavian, London N4.
David J. Wilkins, London NW1.
Sabera Trading Co, London NW2.
Soviet Carpet & Art Galleries, London NW2.
Orientalist, London NW5.
Robert Franses and Sons, London NW8.
Belgrave Carpet Gallery Ltd, London SW1.
Victor Franses Gallery, London SW1.
S. Franses Ltd, London SW1.
Keshishian, London SW1.
Iftikhar Bokhari, London SW10.
Gideon Hatch Rugs, London SW11.
Shaikh and Son (Oriental Rugs) Ltd, London SW19.
Gallery Yacou, London SW3.
Orientalist, London SW3.
Perez, London SW3.
Robert Stephenson, London SW3.
Perez Antique Carpets Gallery, London SW6.
Anglo Persian Carpet Co, London SW7.
Atlantic Bay Carpets Gallery, London SW7.

Heskia, London SW8.
DavidAaron Ancient Arts & Rare Carpets, London W1.
Sibyl Colefax & John Fowler, London W1.
John Eskenazi Ltd, London W1.
Essie Carpets, London W1.
C. John (Rare Rugs) Ltd, London W1.
Mayfair Carpet Gallery Ltd, London W1.
Rabi Gallery Ltd, London W1.
Vigo Carpet Gallery, London W1.
Zadah Fine Oriental Carpets, London W1.
David Black Oriental Carpets, London W11.
Fairman Carpets Ltd, London W11.
Graham and Green, London W11.
Rezai Persian Carpets, London W11.
Coats Oriental Carpets, London W8.
Oriental Rug Gallery Ltd, Windsor and Eton, Berks.
Clive Rogers Oriental Rugs, Wraysbury, Berks.
Peter Norman Antiques and Restorations, Burwell, Cambs.
J.L. Arditti, Christchurch, Dorset.
Christchurch Carpets, Christchurch, Dorset.
Hamptons, Christchurch, Dorset.
Eric Pride Oriental Rugs, Cheltenham, Glos.
Anthony Hazledine, Fairford, Glos.
Samarkand Galleries, Stow-on-the-Wold, Glos.
The Odiham Gallery, Odiham, Hants.
Oriental Rug Gallery Ltd, St. Albans, Herts.
Kashan Carpets Ltd., Brasted, Kent.
Desmond and Amanda North, East Peckham, Kent.
Samovar Antiques, Hythe, Kent.
The Rug Gallery, Leicester, Leics.
Country and Eastern, Norwich, Norfolk.
M.D. Cannell Antiques, Raveningham, Norfolk.
Richard Purdon Antique Carpets, Burford, Oxon.
Thames Oriental Rug Co, Henley-on-Thames, Oxon.
Christopher Legge Oriental Carpets, Oxford, Oxon.
Oriental Rug Gallery Ltd, Oxford, Oxon.
Tattersall's, Uppingham, Rutland.
Haliden Oriental Rug Shop, Bath, Somerset.
Michael and Amanda Lewis Oriental Carpets and Rugs, Wellington, Somerset.
The Persian Carpet Studio, Long Melford, Suffolk.
Karel Weijand Fine Oriental Carpets, Farnham, Surrey.
Oriental Rug Gallery, Guildford, Surrey.
Lindfield Galleries - David Adam, Lindfield, Sussex West.
Persian Carpet Gallery of Petworth, Petworth, Sussex West.
A.W. Hone and Son Oriental Carpets, Birmingham, West Mids.
D & J Lines Antiques, Wychbold, Worcs.
London House Oriental Rugs and Carpets, Harrogate, Yorks. North.
Omar (Harrogate) Ltd, Knaresborough, Yorks. North.

The Gordon Reece Gallery,
Knaresborough, Yorks. North.
The Oriental Rug Shop, Sheffield,
Yorks. South.
London House Oriental Rugs and
Carpets, Boston Spa, Yorks. West.
Parvis Sigaroudinia, Lisburn, Co.
Antrim, N. Ireland.
R.L. Rose Oriental Carpets Ltd,
Edinburgh, Scotland.
Whytock and Reid, Edinburgh,
Scotland.
Young Antiques, Edinburgh, Scotland.
R.L. Rose Oriental Carpets Ltd,
Glasgow, Scotland.
C.S. Moreton (Antiques), Inchture,
Scotland.
Gallery Persia, Inverness, Scotland.
Herrald of Edinburgh, Meigle, Scotland.
Nigel Stacy-Marks Ltd, Perth, Scotland.

Cars & Carriages
Finesse Fine Art, Weymouth, Dorset.
Fieldings Antiques, Haslingden, Lancs.
The Complete Automobilist, Baston,
Lincs.
Whatnots, Strathblane, Scotland.
C.A.R.S. (Classic Automobilia &
Regalia Specialists), Brighton, Sussex
East.

Chinese Art - see Oriental

Church Furniture & Furnishings
Whiteway and Waldron London SW6.
Havenplan's Architectural Emporium,
Killamarsh, Derbys.
Robert Mills Architectural Antiques Ltd,
Bristol, Glos.
Antique Church Furnishings, Walton-on-
Thames, Surrey.

Clocks & Watches
Victoria Antiques, London E18.
City Clocks, London EC1.
C.R. Frost and Son Ltd, London EC1.
Patric Capon, London N1.
Sugar Antiques, London N1.
Strike One, London N5.
Penny Farthing Antiques, London SE1.
North London Clock Shop Ltd, London
SE25.
R.E. Rose FBHI, London SE9.
Camerer Cuss and Co, London SW1.
John Carlton-Smith, London SW1.
Charles Frodsham & Co Ltd, London
SW1.
Harrods Ltd, London SW1.
Somlo Antiques, London SW1.
The Clock Clinic Ltd, London SW15.
W. F. Turk Antique Clocks, London
SW20.
Norman Adams Ltd, London SW3.
Big Ben Antique Clocks, London SW6.
Gutlin Clocks and Antiques, London
SW6.
Aubrey Brocklehurst, London SW7.
A. & H. Page (Est.1840), London SW7.
Carrington and Co.Ltd, London W1.
Mallett and Son (Antiques) Ltd, London
W1.
Mallett at Bourdon House Ltd, London
W1.
Pendulum of Mayfair Ltd, London W1.
Ronald Phillips Ltd, London W1.

Michael Rose - Source of the Unusual,
London W1.
The Royal Arcade Watch Shop, London
W1.
Central Gallery (Portobello), London
W11.
Gavin Douglas, London W11.
Kleanthous Antiques, London W11.
Mayflower Antiques, London W11.
Old Father Time Clock Centre, London
W11.
The Silver Fox Gallery (Portobello),
London W11.
David Brower Antiques, London W8.
Raffety & Walwyn, London W8.
Roderick Antique Clocks, London W8.
Thomas Kettle Ltd, London WC2.
The London Silver Vaults, London
WC2.
House of Clocks, Ampthill, Beds.
Melnick House of Ascot, Ascot, Berks.
The Clock Workshop, Caversham,
Berks.
The Old Malthouse, Hungerford, Berks.
Times Past Antiques, Windsor and Eton,
Berks.
Wyrardisbury Antiques, Wraysbury,
Berks.
M.V. Tooley, CMBHI, Chesham, Bucks.
Robin Unsworth Antiques, Olney, Bucks.
Peter Norman Antiques and
Restorations, Burwell, Cambs.
John Beazor and Sons Ltd, Cambridge,
Cambs.
Mere Antiques, Fowlmere, Cambs.
Antique Clocks, Harston, Cambs.

T. W. Pawson - Clocks, Somersham,
Cambs.
Antiques & Curios (Steve Carpenter),
Wisbech, Cambs.
Adams Antiques, Chester, Cheshire.
Veevers, Chester, Cheshire.
J. Luffman, Haslington, Cheshire.
Chapel Antiques, Nantwich, Cheshire.
Clock Corner, Nantwich, Cheshire.
Coppelia Antiques, Plumley, Cheshire.
Paul Jennings Antiques, Angarrack,
Cornwall.
Little Jem's, Penzance, Cornwall.
Saint Nicholas Galleries Ltd. (Antiques
and Jewellery), Carlisle, Cumbria.
Acanthus Antiques/Country Seat
Antiques, Corby Hill, Cumbria.
G.K. Hadfield, Great Salkeld, Cumbria.
David Hill, Kirkby Stephen, Cumbria.
Lewis Antiques, Bakewell, Derbys.
Thornbridge Antiques, Bakewell,
Derbys.
Derbyshire Clocks, Glossop, Derbys.
Goodacre Engraving Ltd, Long Eaton,
Derbys.
Nimbus Antiques, Whaley Bridge,
Derbys.
Seaward and Around the Clock,
Brixham, Devon.
Musgrave Bickford Antiques, Crediton,
Devon.
Gold and Silver Exchange, Exeter,
Devon.
John Nathan Antiques, Exeter, Devon.
Honiton Clock Clinic, Honiton, Devon.
Leigh C. Extence, Shaldon, Devon.

SPECIALIST DEALERS

Good Hope Antiques, Beaminster, Dorset.
M.C. Taylor, Bournemouth, Dorset.
Derek J. Burgess - Horologist, Parkstone, Dorset.
Keeble Antiques, Sherborne, Dorset.
Timecraft Clocks, Sherborne, Dorset.
Tom Tribe and Son, Sturminster Newton, Dorset.
Eden House Antiques, West Auckland, Durham.
Mark Marchant (Antiques), Coggeshall, Essex.
Antique Clock Repair Shoppe, Gants Hill, Essex.
Memories, Great Dunmow, Essex.
It's About Time, Westcliff-on-Sea, Essex.
Antique Corner with A & C Antique Clocks, Bristol, Glos.
Montpellier Clocks, Cheltenham, Glos.
Saxton House Gallery, Chipping Campden, Glos.
School House Antiques, Chipping Campden, Glos.
Arthur S. Lewis, Gloucester, Glos.
Jeffrey Formby Antiques, Moreton-in-Marsh, Glos.
Jillings Antiques - Distinctive Antique Clocks, Newent, Glos.
Keith Harding's World of Mechanical Music, Northleach, Glos.
Colin Brand Antiques, Stow-on-the-Wold, Glos.
Bryden House Clocks & Antiques, Stow-on-the-Wold, Glos.
Styles of Stow, Stow-on-the-Wold, Glos.
Vanbrugh House Antiques, Stow-on-the-Wold, Glos.
Evans and Evans, Alresford, Hants.
Clockwise, Emsworth, Hants.
Bryan Clisby Antique Clocks, Hartley Wintney, Hants.
A.W. Porter and Son, Hartley Wintney, Hants.
Barry Papworth, Lymington, Hants.
Gaylords, Titchfield, Hants.
Twyford Antiques, Twyford, Hants.
The Clock Workshop, Winchester, Hants.
G.E. Marsh Antique Clocks Ltd, Winchester, Hants.
Robin Lloyd Antiques, Ross-on-Wye, Herefs.
Howards, Baldock, Herts.
David Penney, Bishop's Stortford, Herts.
Robert Horton Antiques, Hertford, Herts.
The Clock Shop - Philip Setterfield of St. Albans, St. Albans, Herts.
Country Clocks, Tring, Herts.
Weston Antiques, Weston, Herts.
John Corrin Antiques, Douglas, Isle of Man.
Ye Olde Village Clock Shop, Freshwater, Isle of Wight.
John Chawner, Birchington, Kent.
Clockshop, Boughton, Kent.
Old Manor House Antiques, Brasted, Kent.
Michael Sim, Chislehurst, Kent.
Gem Antiques, Maidstone, Kent.
Michael Fitch Antiques, Sandgate, Kent.
Nancy Wilson, Sandwich, Kent.
Neill Robinson Blaxill, Sevenoaks, Kent.
Gem Antiques, Sevenoaks, Kent.

Derek Roberts Fine Antique Clocks & Barometers, Tonbridge, Kent.
B.V.M. Somerset, Tonbridge, Kent.
Aaron Antiques, Tunbridge Wells, Kent.
Pantiles Spa Antiques, Tunbridge Wells, Kent.
The Vintage Watch Co., Tunbridge Wells, Kent.
The Old Clock Shop, West Malling, Kent.
Marks Antiques, Westerham, Kent.
Regal Antiques, Westerham, Kent.
Tankerton Antiques, Whitstable, Kent.
Drop Dial Antiques, Bolton, Lancs.
Harrop Fold Clocks (F. Robinson), Bolton-by-Bowland, Lancs.
Ingleside Antiques, Colne, Lancs.
Fieldings Antiques, Haslingden, Lancs.
P.W. Norgrove - Antique Clocks, Haslingden, Lancs.
Brittons - Watches, Nelson, Lancs.
Charles Howell Jeweller, Oldham, Lancs.
H.C. Simpson and Sons Jewellers (Oldham)Ltd, Oldham, Lancs.
Hackler's Jewellers, Preston, Lancs.
Edmund Davies & Son Antiques, Whalley, Lancs.
Northern Clocks, Worsley, Lancs.
Lowe of Loughborough, Loughborough, Leics.
Old Timers, Swinford, Leics.
Charles Antiques, Whitwick, Leics.
N. Bryan-Peach Antiques, Wymeswold, Leics.
Robin Fowler (Period Clocks), Aylesby, Lincs.
Trade Antiques, Donington, Lincs.
Grantham Clocks, Grantham, Lincs.
Wilkinson's, Grantham, Lincs.
Second Time Around, Hemswell Cliff, Lincs.
Staines Antiques, Horncastle, Lincs.
David J. Hansord & Son, Lincoln, Lincs.
Timepiece Repairs, Lincoln, Lincs.
Wilkinson's, Sleaford, Lincs.
Penman Clockcare, Spalding, Lincs.
Kevin Whay's Clocks & Antiques, Hoylake, Merseyside.
Theta Gallery, Liverpool, Merseyside.
Weldons Jewellery and Antiques, Southport, Merseyside.
Rita Shenton, Twickenham, Middx.
Village Clocks, Coltishall, Norfolk.
R.C. Woodhouse (Antiquarian Horologist), Hunstanton, Norfolk.
Tim Clayton Jewellery & Antiques, King's Lynn, Norfolk.
Jennifer and Raymond Norman Antiques, Needham, Norfolk.
Keith Lawson Antique Clocks, Scratby, Norfolk.
Parriss, Sheringham, Norfolk.
Norton Antiques, Twyford, Norfolk.
M.C. Chapman, Finedon, Northants.
Michael Jones Jeweller, Northampton, Northants.
Gordon Caris, Hexham, Northumbs.
David and Carole Potter Antiques, Nottingham, Notts.
Horseshoe Antiques and Gallery, Burford, Oxon.
Hubert's Antiques, Burford, Oxon.
Jonathan Howard, Chipping Norton, Oxon.

Craig Barfoot, East Hagbourne, Oxon.
Rosemary and Time, Thame, Oxon.
Witney Antiques, Witney, Oxon.
C. Reynolds Antiques, Oakham, Rutland.
Rutland Antique Clock Gallery, Oakham, Rutland.
Mytton Antiques, Atcham, Shrops.
R.G. Cave and Sons Ltd, Ludlow, Shrops.
Mitre House Antiques, Ludlow, Shrops.
Corner Farm Antiques, Shifnal, Shrops.
Adrian Donnelly Antique Clocks, Shrewsbury, Shrops.
Dodington Antiques, Whitchurch, Shrops.
John Hawley (MBHI) Antique Clocks, Badgworth, Somerset.
Kembery Antique Clocks (inc. K & D Antique Clocks), Bath, Somerset.
Quiet Street Antiques, Bath, Somerset.
J.C. White, Milverton, Somerset.
Bernard G. House, Wells, Somerset.
Edward A. Nowell, Wells, Somerset.
Grosvenor Clocks, Leek, Staffs.
James A. Jordan, Lichfield, Staffs.
Richard Midwinter Antiques, Newcastle-under-Lyme, Staffs.
R.A. James - The Clock Shop, Tutbury, Staffs.
Clock House, Leavenheath, Suffolk.
Antique Clocks by Simon Charles, Long Melford, Suffolk.
Suthburgh Antiques, Long Melford, Suffolk.
Village Clocks, Long Melford, Suffolk.
Antique Clocks by Simon Charles, Sudbury, Suffolk.
Edward Manson (Clocks), Woodbridge, Suffolk.
Simon Marsh, Bletchingley, Surrey.
Antique Clocks by Patrick Thomas, Dorking, Surrey.
The Coach House Antiques, Gomshall, Surrey.
Roger A. Davis Antiquarian Horologist, Great Bookham, Surrey.
Horological Workshops, Guildford, Surrey.
Surrey Clock Centre, Haslemere, Surrey.
Hill Rise Antiques, Richmond, Surrey.
B. M. and E. Newlove, Surbiton, Surrey.
S. Warrender and Co, Sutton, Surrey.
The Clock Shop Weybridge, Weybridge, Surrey.
Yellow Lantern Antiques Ltd, Brighton, Sussex East.
W. Bruford, Eastbourne, Sussex East.
John Cowderoy Antiques, Eastbourne, Sussex East.
Coach House Antiques, Hastings, Sussex East.
The Old Mint House, Pevensey, Sussex East.
Arundel Clocks, Arundel, Sussex West.
The Clock Shop, Hurstpierpoint, Sussex West.
Julian Antiques, Hurstpierpoint, Sussex West.
Churchill Clocks, Midhurst, Sussex West.
Baskerville Antiques, Petworth, Sussex West.
J. Powell (Hove) Ltd, Portslade, Sussex West.

734

Thakeham Furniture, Pulborough, Sussex West.

Peter Smith Antiques, Sunderland, Tyne and Wear.

The Grandfather Clock Shop, Shipston-on-Stour, Warks.

'Time in Hand', Shipston-on-Stour, Warks.

Summersons, Warwick, Warks.

R. Collyer, Birmingham, West Mids.

F. Meeks & Co, Birmingham, West Mids.

M. Allen Watch and Clockmaker, Four Oaks, West Mids.

Osborne Antiques, Sutton Coldfield, West Mids.

Afantiques, Wolverhampton, West Mids.

Avon Antiques, Bradford-on-Avon, Wilts.

Moxhams Antiques, Bradford-on-Avon, Wilts.

Trevor Waddington Antique Clocks, Bradford-on-Avon, Wilts.

P.A. Oxley Antique Clocks and Barometers, Cherhill, Wilts.

Inglenook Antiques, Ramsbury, Wilts.

Salisbury Antiques Warehouse, Salisbury, Wilts.

Chris Wadge Clocks, Salisbury, Wilts.

Allan Smith Antique Clocks, Swindon, Wilts.

Broadway Clocks, Broadway, Worcs.

Hansen Chard Antiques, Pershore, Worcs.

The Barber's Clock, Worcester, Worcs.

Time and Motion, Beverley, Yorks. East.

Lewis E. Hickson FBHI, Gilberdyke, Yorks. East.

John Pearson Antique Clock Restoration, Birstwith, Yorks. North.

Milestone Antiques, Easingwold, Yorks. North.

Haworth Antiques, Harrogate, Yorks. North.

Chris Wilde Antiques, Harrogate, Yorks. North.

Middleham Antiques, Middleham, Yorks. North.

Brian Loomes, Pateley Bridge, Yorks. North.

Tomlinson Antiques Ltd. & Period Furniture Ltd, Tockwith, Yorks. North.

Keith Stones Grandfather Clocks, Bessacarr, Yorks. South.

Fishlake Antiques, Fishlake, Yorks. South.

F S Antiques, Sheffield, Yorks. South.

Top Hat Antique Centre, Sheffield, Yorks. South.

Jeremiah's Antiques, St Helier, Jersey, C.I.

Stephen Cohu Antiques, St Ouen, Jersey, C.I.

Robert Christie Antiques, Carrickfergus, Co. Antrim, N. Ireland.

Time & Tide Antiques, Portaferry, Co. Down, N. Ireland.

Ian Burton Antique Clocks, Auchterarder, Scotland.

The Clock Showrooms, Canonbie, Scotland.

Craiglea Clocks, Edinburgh, Scotland.

Donald Ellis incorporating Bruntsfield Clocks, Edinburgh, Scotland.

Harlequin Antiques, Edinburgh, Scotland.

John Whyte, Edinburgh, Scotland.

West End Antiques, Elgin, Scotland.

Brown's Clocks, Glasgow, Scotland.

James Forrest and Co (Jewellers) Ltd, Glasgow, Scotland.

Muirhead Moffat and Co, Glasgow, Scotland.

Bygones, Huntly, Scotland.

Silvertime, Brecon, Wales.

Snowdonia Antiques, Llanrwst, Wales.

Rodney Adams Antiques, Pwllheli, Wales.

Coins & Medals

George Rankin Coin Co. Ltd, London E2.

C.J. Martin (Coins) Ltd, London N14.

Christopher Eimer, London NW11.

Vale Stamps and Antiques, London SE3.

The Armoury of St. James's Military Antiquarians, London SW1.

Knightsbridge Coins, London SW1.

Beaver Coin Room, London SW5.

Michael Coins, London W8.

Simmons Gallery, London WC1.

Spink and Son Ltd, London WC1.

A.H. Baldwin and Sons Ltd, London WC2.

M. Bord (Gold Coin Exchange), London WC2.

Philip Cohen Numismatics, London WC2.

Trafalgar Square Collectors Centre, London WC2.

Valued History, Cambridge, Cambs.

B.R.M. Coins, Knutsford, Cheshire.

Souvenir Antiques, Carlisle, Cumbria.

Penrith Coin and Stamp Centre, Penrith, Cumbria.

Sterling Coins and Medals, Bournemouth, Dorset.

Dorset Coin Company, Parkstone, Dorset.

The Treasure Chest, Weymouth, Dorset.

Robin Finnegan (Jeweller), Darlington, Durham.

J. Shotton Antiquarian Books, Prints and Coins, Durham, Durham.

Potter's Antiques and Coins, Bristol, Glos.

Military Curios, HQ84, Gloucester, Glos.

Romsey Medals, Romsey, Hants.

The Coin and Jewellery Shop, Accrington, Lancs.

Chard Coins, Blackpool, Lancs.

Gold and Silver Exchange, Gt. Yarmouth, Norfolk.

Clive Dennett Coins, Norwich, Norfolk.

Collectors' Gallery, Shrewsbury, Shrops.

Bath Stamp and Coin Shop, Bath, Somerset.

Neate Militaria & Antiques, Sudbury, Suffolk.

St. Pancras Antiques, Chichester, Sussex West.

Intercoin, Newcastle-upon-Tyne, Tyne and Wear.

Format of Birmingham Ltd, Birmingham, West Mids.

Castle Galleries, Salisbury, Wilts.

Whitmore, Great Malvern, Worcs.

B.B.M. Jewellery and Antiques, Kidderminster, Worcs.

C.J. and A.J. Dixon Ltd, Bridlington, Yorks. East.

Cookstown Antiques, Cookstown, Co. Tyrone, N. Ireland.

The Collectors Shop, Edinburgh, Scotland.

Edinburgh Coin Shop, Edinburgh, Scotland.

A.D. Hamilton and Co, Glasgow, Scotland.

Abbey Antiques, Stirling, Scotland.

Glance Back Bookshop, Chepstow, Wales.

Dolls & Toys

Donay Games & Pastimes, London N1.

Judith Lassalle, London N1.

Yesterday Child, London N1.

Dolly Land, London N21.

Bearly Trading of London, London SE20.

Engine 'n' Tender, London SE25.

Mimi Fifi, London W11.

Victoriana Dolls, London W11.

London Antique Gallery, London W8.

Tim Armitage, Nantwich, Cheshire.

Rosina's, Falmouth, Cornwall.

Abbey House, Derby, Derbys.

Honiton Antique Toys, Honiton, Devon.

The Vintage Toy and Train Shop, Sidmouth, Devon.

Boscombe Models and Collectors Shop, Bournemouth, Dorset.

Tilly's Antiques, Leigh-on-Sea, Essex.

The Doll's House, Northleach, Glos.

Park House Antiques, Stow-on-the-Wold, Glos.

Peter Pan's of Gosport, Gosport, Hants.

Athena Antiques Centre, Warsash, Hants.

The Attic, Baldock, Herts.

London House Antiques, Westerham, Kent.

Irving Antique Toys, Manchester, Lancs.

C. and K.E. Dring, Lincoln, Lincs.

Granny's Attic, Nottingham, Notts.

Images - Peter Stockham, Lichfield, Staffs.

Trench Puzzles, Stowmarket, Suffolk.

Childhood Memories, Farnham, Surrey.

C.A.R.S. (Classic Automobilia & Regalia Specialists), Brighton, Sussex East.

Paul Goble, Brighton, Sussex East.

Sue Pearson, Brighton, Sussex East.

Coach House Antiques, Hastings, Sussex East.

Recollect Dolls Hospital, Burgess Hill, Sussex West.

Antiquated, Petworth, Sussex West.

Cross's Curios, Birmingham, West Mids.

Dolly Mixtures, Birmingham, West Mids.

Robert Taylor, Four Oaks, West Mids.

Broadway Bears & Dolls, Broadway, Worcs.

Grannie's Parlour, Hull, Yorks. East.

Classic Rocking Horses, Thirsk, Yorks. North.

Fun Antiques, Sheffield, Yorks. South.

Collectors Old Toy Shop and Antiques, Halifax, Yorks. West.

Memory Lane, Sowerby Bridge, Yorks. West.

Angus Antiques, Dundee, Scotland.
Bebes et Jouets, Edinburgh, Scotland.
Now and Then (Toy Centre), Edinburgh,
Scotland.
Pastimes Vintage Toys, Glasgow,
Scotland.
Museum of Childhood Memories,
Beaumaris (Anglesey), Wales.

Etchings & Engravings

Moreton Street Gallery, London SW1.
Old Maps and Prints, London SW1.
The Map House, London SW3.
Old Church Galleries, London SW3.
King's Court Galleries, London SW6.
Julie Collino, London SW7.
The Wyllie Gallery, London SW7.
Agnew's, London W1.
Victor Arwas Gallery - Editions
Graphiques Gallery Ltd, London W1.
Royal Exchange Art Gallery at Cork St.,
London W1.
William Weston Gallery, London W1.
Justin F. Skrebowski Prints, London W11.
Foye Gallery, Luton, Beds.
The Lantern Shop Gallery, Sidmouth,
Devon.
Antique Map and Bookshop,
Puddletown, Dorset.
Oldfield Gallery, Portsmouth, Hants.
The Shanklin Gallery, Shanklin, Isle of
Wight.
Peter Goodall, Ventnor, Isle of Wight.
G. and D.I. Marrin and Sons, Folkestone,
Kent.
London House Antiques, Westerham,
Kent.
Hammond Smith (Fine Art), Leicester,
Leics.
Leicestershire Sporting Gallery and
Brown Jack Bookshop, Lubenham,
Leics.
Graftons of Market Harborough, Market
Harborough, Leics.
P.J. Cassidy (Books), Holbeach, Lincs.
TRADA, Chipping Norton, Oxon.
The Barry Keene Gallery, Henley-on-
Thames, Oxon.
Elizabeth Harvey-Lee, North Aston,
Oxon.
George Gregory, Bath, Somerset.
England's Gallery, Leek, Staffs.
King's Court Galleries, Dorking, Surrey.
Hampton Court Palace Antiques, East
Molesey, Surrey.
Limpsfield Watercolours, Limpsfield,
Surrey.
Reigate Galleries, Reigate, Surrey.
Palmer Galleries, Richmond, Surrey.
Boathouse Gallery, Walton-on-Thames,
Surrey.
The Witch Ball, Brighton, Sussex East.
Faringdon Gallery, Arundel, Sussex
West.
Osborne Fine Art Gallery, Jesmond,,
Tyne and Wear.
Ronald Carr, Salisbury, Wilts.
Heirloom & Howard Limited, West
Yatton, Wilts.
The Drawing Room - Interiors &
Antiques, Pershore, Worcs.
Open Eye Gallery Ltd, Edinburgh,
Scotland.
Royal Mile Gallery, Edinburgh,
Scotland.

Ewan Mundy Fine Art Ltd, Glasgow,
Scotland.
Mainhill Gallery, Jedburgh, Scotland.
Nigel Stacy-Marks Ltd, Perth, Scotland.
David Windsor Gallery, Bangor, Wales.

Fire Related Items

Westland & Company, London EC2.
House of Steel Antiques, London N1.
Chesney's Antique Fireplace
Warehouse, London N19.
Amazing Grates - Fireplaces Ltd,
London N2.
The Antique Shop (Valantique), London
N2.
Acquisitions (Fireplaces) Ltd, London
NW5.
Townsends, London NW8.
Oddiquities, London SE23.
Under Milkwood, London SE24.
Ward Antiques, London SE7.
The Fireplace, London SE9.
Nigel A. Bartlett, London SW1.
Crowther of Syon Lodge Ltd, London
SW1.
Nicholas Gifford-Mead, London SW1.
H.W. Poulter and Son, London SW10.
Thornhill Galleries Ltd. in association
with A. & R. Dockerill Ltd, London
SW15.
Mr Wandle's Workshop Ltd, London
SW18.
O.F. Wilson Ltd, London SW3.
Fairfax Antiques and Fireplaces, London
SW6.
Hollingshead and Co, London SW6.
Old World Trading Co, London SW6.
Thornhill Galleries Ltd, London SW6.
The Chiswick Fireplace Co., London
W4.
Architectural Antiques, London W6.
Architectural Antiques, Bedford, Beds.
Below Stairs of Hungerford, Hungerford,
Berks.
The Fire Place (Hungerford) Ltd,
Hungerford, Berks.
Grosvenor House Interiors,
Beaconsfield, Bucks.
Pillory House, Nantwich, Cheshire.
Nostalgia Architectural Antiques,
Stockport, Cheshire.
Antique Fireplaces, Tarvin, Cheshire.
Hearth & Home, Penrith, Cumbria.
Staveley Antiques, Staveley, Cumbria.
Finishing Touches, Derby, Derbys.
Wooden Box Antiques, Woodville,
Derbys.
Ashburton Marbles, Ashburton, Devon.
Antique Fireplace Centre, Plymouth,
Devon.
Antique Fireplace Centre, Hartlepool,
Durham.
Flame and Grate, Bristol, Glos.
Period Fireplaces, Bristol, Glos.
Original Architectural, Cirencester, Glos.
Cox's Architectural Reclamation Yard,
Moreton-in-Marsh, Glos.
Baileys Home & Garden, Ross-on-Wye,
Herefs.
Victorian Fireplace, Canterbury, Kent.
Ward Antiques, Sidcup, Kent.
Old Smithy, Feniscowles, Lancs.
Antique Fireplace Warehouse,
Manchester, Lancs.
Colin Blakey Fireplaces, Nelson, Lancs.

House Things Antiques, Hinckley, Leics.
Britain's Heritage, Leicester, Leics.
Antique Fireplaces, Liverpool,
Merseyside.
Peco, Hampton, Middx.
Crowther of Syon Lodge Ltd, Isleworth,
Middx.
Marble Hill Gallery, Twickenham,
Middx.
Rococo Antiques and Interiors, Weedon,
Northants.
Blacksmiths Forge, Balderton, Notts.
Hallidays (Fine Antiques) Ltd,
Dorchester-on-Thames, Oxon.
Aston Pine Antiques, Faringdon, Oxon.
Oxford Architectural Antiques,
Faringdon, Oxon.
Walcot Reclamation, Bath, Somerset.
Rickett & Co. Antiques, Shepperton,
Surrey.
Brighton Architectural Salvage,
Brighton, Sussex East.
Turnburrys, Jesmond, Tyne and Wear.
Shiners, Snobs Knobs, Newcastle-upon-
Tyne, Tyne and Wear.
Grate Expectations (Fireplaces),
Washington, Tyne and Wear.
The Victorian Ironmonger, Brinklow,
Warks.
Tudor House Antiques, Halesowen,
West Mids.
Old Flames, Easingwold, Yorks. North.
Robert Aagaard & Co, Knaresborough,
Yorks. North.
Chapel House Fireplaces, Holmfirth,
Yorks. West.
Swiss Cottage Furniture, Leeds, Yorks.
West.
Burning Embers, Aberdeen, Scotland.
EASY - Edinburgh & Glasgow
Architectural Salvage Yards,
Edinburgh, Scotland.
Holyrood Architectural Salvage,
Edinburgh, Scotland.
T. and J. W. Neilson Ltd, Edinburgh,
Scotland.
The Renaissance Furniture Store,
Glasgow, Scotland.
Flame 'n' Grate, Barry, Wales.
Kings Fireplaces, Antiques and Interiors,
Cardiff, Wales.

Frames

Paul Mason Gallery, London SW1.
Nigel Milne Ltd, London SW1.
Arnold Wiggins and Sons Ltd, London
SW1.
Paul Mitchell Ltd, London W1.
Rollo Whately Ltd, London W1.
Daggett Gallery, London W11.
Lacy Gallery, London W11.
Justin F. Skrebowski Prints, London
W11.
The Fairhurst Gallery, Norwich,
Norfolk.
Looking Glass of Bath, Bath, Somerset.
W. Greenwood (Fine Art), Burneston,
Yorks. North.
Coulter Galleries, York, Yorks. North.

Furniture - Continental (mainly French)

Charlton House Antiques, London N1.
Gordon Gridley, London N1.

Michel André Morin, London N1.
Relic Antiques at Camden Passage, London N1.
C. Tapsell, London N1.
Dean's Antique Emporium, London N12.
Relic Antiques Trade Warehouse, London NW1.
Deuxieme, London NW8.
The Galleries, London SE1.
Melbourne Antiques & Interiors, London SE22.
Robert E. Hirschhorn, London SE5.
Didier Aaron (London)Ltd, London SW1.
ADEC, London SW1.
Konrad O. Bernheimer Ltd, London SW1.
Blanchard Ltd, London SW1.
Ross Hamilton Ltd, London SW1.
Harris Lindsay, London SW1.
Hermitage Antiques plc, London SW1.
Carlton Hobbs, London SW1.
Christopher Howe, London SW1.
Jeremy Ltd, London SW1.
M. and D. Lewis, London SW1.
McClenaghan, London SW1.
Mark Ransom Ltd, London SW1.
Rogier et Rogier, London SW1.
Un Francais á Londres, London SW1.
Thomas Kerr Antiques Ltd, London SW10.
McVeigh & Charpentier, London SW10.
Orientation, London SW10.
The Woodpigeon, London SW11.
Simon Coleman Antiques, London SW13.
Jorgen Antiques, London SW15.
Adams Room Antiques, London SW19.
No. 12, London SW3.
Prides of London, London SW3.
O.F. Wilson Ltd, London SW3.
275 Antiques, London SW6.
I. and J.L. Brown Ltd, London SW6.
Rupert Cavendish Antiques, London SW6.
Nicole Fabre, London SW6.
Birdie Fortescue Antiques, London SW6.
Judy Greenwood, London SW6.
Christopher Jones Antiques, London SW6.
Lewin, London SW6.
Megan Mathers Antiques, London SW6.
Sylvia Napier Ltd, London SW6.
M. Pauw Antiques, London SW6.
The French House (Antiques) Ltd, London SW8.
Adrian Alan Ltd, London W1.
H. Blairman and Sons Ltd., London W1.
Howard Antiques, London W1.
Mallett at Bourdon House Ltd, London W1.
Partridge Fine Arts plc, London W1.
Pelham Galleries Ltd, London W1.
Jacob Stodel, London W1.
Toynbee-Clarke Interiors Ltd, London W1.
M. Turpin Ltd, London W1.
P.R. Barham, London W11.
Barham Antiques, London W11.
Canonbury, London W11.
Curá Antiques, London W11.
M. and D. Lewis, London W11.
Robin Martin Antiques, London W11.

David Alexander Antiques & Kate Thurlow, London W14.
Marshall Gallery, London W14.
Daniel Mankowitz, London W2.
David Brower Antiques, London W8.
Reindeer Antiques Ltd, London W8.
Sinai Antiques Ltd, London W8.
Pamela Teignmouth and Son, London W8.
Ulla Stafford Antiques, Binfield, Berks.
John A. Pearson Antiques, Horton, Berks.
Youll's Antiques, Hungerford, Berks.
La Maison, Bourne End, Bucks.
Jack Harness Antiques, Marlow, Bucks.
Archer's Antique and Country Furniture, Olney, Bucks.
Lafleure Antiques & Decoration, Wooburn, Bucks.
Phoenix Antiques, Fordham, Cambs.
Ivor and Patricia Lewis Antique and Fine Art Dealers, Peterborough, Cambs.
David H. Dickinson, Bramhall, Cheshire.
Adams Antiques, Chester, Cheshire.
Harris & Holt, Chester, Cheshire.
Antique Furniture Warehouse, Stockport, Cheshire.
Manchester Antique Company, Stockport, Cheshire.
Old Town Hall Antiques, Falmouth, Cornwall.
West End Galleries, Buxton, Derbys.
Merchant House Antiques, Honiton, Devon.
Pilgrim Antiques, Honiton, Devon.
Pugh's Farm Antiques, Monkton, Devon.
Colystock Antiques, Stockland, Devon.
Lionel Geneen Ltd, Bournemouth, Dorset.
Talisman, Gillingham, Dorset.
Georgina Ryder, Sherborne, Dorset.
Deja Vu Antiques, Leigh-on-Sea, Essex.
Old Barn Antiques, Thornwood Common, Essex.
Gloucester House Antiques Ltd, Fairford, Glos.
Gary Wright Antiques, Moreton-in-Marsh, Glos.
Craig Carrington Antiques, Painswick, Glos.
Ashton Gower Antiques, Stow-on-the-Wold, Glos.
Oonagh Black, Stow-on-the-Wold, Glos.
Annarella Clark Antiques, Stow-on-the-Wold, Glos.
Antony Preston Antiques Ltd, Stow-on-the-Wold, Glos.
The Decorator Source, Tetbury, Glos.
Gales Antiques, Tetbury, Glos.
Sieff, Tetbury, Glos.
Geoffrey Stead, Todenham, Glos.
Cotswold Antiques. com, Winchcombe, Glos.
Artemesia, Alresford, Hants.
Cedar Antiques Limited, Hartley Wintney, Hants.
David Lazarus Antiques, Hartley Wintney, Hants.
Phoenix Green Antiques, Hartley Wintney, Hants.
Csaky's Antiques, Hook, Hants.
Wick Antiques, Lymington, Hants.
Millers of Chelsea Antiques Ltd, Ringwood, Hants.

I. and J.L. Brown Ltd, Hereford, Herefs.
Great Brampton House Antiques Ltd, Hereford, Herefs.
Royal Standard Antiques, Cowes, Isle of Wight.
Lennox Cato, Edenbridge, Kent.
Samovar Antiques, Hythe, Kent.
Henry Baines, Southborough, Kent.
Flower House Antiques, Tenterden, Kent.
Claremont Antiques, Tunbridge Wells, Kent.
Up Country, Tunbridge Wells, Kent.
J. Green and Son, Queniborough,, Leics.
Graham Pickett Antiques, Stamford, Lincs.
J. and R. Ratcliffe, Waddington, Lincs.
Birkdale Antiques, Southport, Merseyside.
Ron Green, Towcester, Northants.
Helios & Co (Antiques), Weedon, Northants.
Jonathan Fyson Antiques, Burford, Oxon.
Gateway Antiques, Burford, Oxon.
Antique English Windsor Chairs - Michael Harding-Hill, Chipping Norton, Oxon.
Summers Davis Antiques Ltd, Wallingford, Oxon.
Witney Antiques, Witney, Oxon.
Swans, Oakham, Rutland.
Malthouse Antiques, Bridgnorth, Shrops.
Garrard Antiques, Ludlow, Shrops.
Jadis Ltd, Bath, Somerset.
Pennard House Antiques, East Pennard, Somerset.
Gilbert & Dale, Ilchester, Somerset.
Edward Marnier Antiques, Shepton Mallet, Somerset.
Dix-Sept, Framlingham, Suffolk.
Heath-Bullocks, Godalming, Surrey.
Marryat, Richmond, Surrey.
Ripley Antiques, Ripley, Surrey.
Dermot and Jill Palmer Antiques, Brighton, Sussex East.
Graham Lower, Flimwell, Sussex East.
John Botting Antiques & Others, Heathfield, Sussex East.
Graham Price Antiques Ltd, Polegate, Sussex East.
Julian Antiques, Hurstpierpoint, Sussex West.
The French Room, Petworth, Sussex West.
Ruddy Antiques, Petworth, Sussex West.
Sayer Antiques - The French Room, Petworth, Sussex West.
T.G. Wilkinson Antiques Ltd, Petworth, Sussex West.
Little Theatre Antiques Centre, Jesmond, Tyne and Wear.
Apollo Antiques Ltd, Warwick, Warks.
L.P. Antiques (Mids) Ltd, Walsall, West Mids.
Avon Antiques, Bradford-on-Avon, Wilts.
Moxhams Antiques, Bradford-on-Avon, Wilts.
St Mary's Chapel Antiques, Devizes, Wilts.
Brocante Antiques Centre, Marlborough, Wilts.
Obelisk Antiques, Warminster, Wilts.
Coopers of Ilkley, Ilkley, Yorks. West.

Charlotte and John Lambe, Belfast, N. Ireland.

Whytock and Reid, Edinburgh, Scotland.

Jeremy Sniders Antiques, Glasgow, Scotland.

Michael Vee Design - Birch House Antiques, Melrose, Scotland.

Furniture - Country

Michael Lewis Antiques, London N1.

Rookery Farm Antiques, London N1.

At the Sign of the Chest of Drawers, London N6.

Relic Antiques Trade Warehouse, London NW1.

This and That (Furniture), London NW1.

M. and D. Seligmann, London NW3.

Robert E. Hirschhorn, London SE5.

Rogier et Rogier, London SW1.

The Furniture Cave, London SW10.

Robert Young Antiques, London SW11.

Simon Coleman Antiques, London SW13.

I. and J.L. Brown Ltd, London SW6.

Alistair Sampson Antiques Ltd, London W1.

Alan Hodgson, Great Shefford, Berks.

The Hampden Trading Company, Great Missenden, Bucks.

Jack Harness Antiques, Marlow, Bucks.

Simon and Penny Rumble Antiques, Chittering, Cambs.

A.P. and M.A. Haylett, Outwell, Cambs.

Boustead-Bland Antiques, Chester, Cheshire.

Farmhouse Antiques, Chester, Cheshire.

Adams Antiques, Nantwich, Cheshire.

Blackwater Pine Antiques, Truro, Cornwall.

Simon Starkie Antiques, Cartmel, Cumbria.

Acanthus Antiques/Country Seat Antiques, Corby Hill, Cumbria.

David Hill, Kirkby Stephen, Cumbria.

Utopia Antiques Ltd, Low Newton, Cumbria.

Sandgate Antiques, Penrith, Cumbria.

Winton Hall Antiques, Ravenstonedale, Cumbria.

Peter Bunting Antiques, Bakewell, Derbys.

Byethorpe Furniture, Barlow, Derbys.

Godolphin Antiques, Chagford, Devon.

Rex Antiques, Chagford, Devon.

Cobweb Antiques, Cullompton, Devon.

Miller Antiques, Cullompton, Devon.

The Grove Antiques Centre, Honiton, Devon.

Wickham Antiques, Honiton, Devon.

Pugh's Farm Antiques, Monkton, Devon.

Timepiece, Teignmouth, Devon.

Fine Pine Antiques, Totnes, Devon.

English Rose Antiques, Coggeshall, Essex.

Dean Antiques, Colchester, Essex.

Julia Bennet (Antiques), Great Dunmow, Essex.

The Stores, Great Waltham, Essex.

Lennard Antiques, Sible Hedingham, Essex.

Denzil Verey, Barnsley, Glos.

J. and R. Bateman Antiques, Chalford, Glos.

John P. Townsend, Cheltenham, Glos.

Gloucester House Antiques Ltd, Fairford, Glos.

Jon Fox Antiques, Moreton-in-Marsh, Glos.

Oonagh Black, Stow-on-the-Wold, Glos.

Annarella Clark Antiques, Stow-on-the-Wold, Glos.

Keith Hockin Antiques, Stow-on-the-Wold, Glos.

Huntington Antiques Ltd, Stow-on-the-Wold, Glos.

The Chest of Drawers, Tetbury, Glos.

Gales Antiques, Tetbury, Glos.

Peter Norden Antiques, Tetbury, Glos.

Westwood House Antiques, Tetbury, Glos.

Cedar Antiques Limited, Hartley Wintney, Hants.

Phoenix Green Antiques, Hartley Wintney, Hants.

Burgess Farm Antiques, Morestead, Hants.

Millers of Chelsea Antiques Ltd, Ringwood, Hants.

The Pine Cellars, Winchester, Hants.

I. and J.L. Brown Ltd, Hereford, Herefs.

Robin Lloyd Antiques, Ross-on-Wye, Herefs.

Singleton Antiques, Ross-on-Wye, Herefs.

M. and J. Russell, Yazor, Herefs.

Tim Wharton Antiques, Redbourn, Herts.

Dinah Stoodley & Celia Jennings, Brasted, Kent.

Michael Pearson Antiques, Canterbury, Kent.

Douglas Bryan, Cranbrook, Kent.

Swan Antiques, Cranbrook, Kent.

Mill House Antiques, Goudhurst, Kent.

Henry Baines, Southborough, Kent.

Claremont Antiques, Tunbridge Wells, Kent.

Phoenix Antiques, Tunbridge Wells, Kent.

Up Country, Tunbridge Wells, Kent.

Edmund Davies & Son Antiques, Whalley, Lancs.

Quorn Pine and Decoratives, Quorn, Leics.

Hunters Antiques & Interior Design, Stamford, Lincs.

Graham Pickett Antiques, Stamford, Lincs.

Sinclair's, Stamford, Lincs.

Holt Antique Centre, Holt, Norfolk.

Paul Hopwell Antiques, West Haddon, Northants.

Mark Seabrook Antiques, West Haddon, Northants.

Horseshoe Antiques and Gallery, Burford, Oxon.

Swan Gallery, Burford, Oxon.

Antique English Windsor Chairs - Michael Harding-Hill, Chipping Norton, Oxon.

Key Antiques, Chipping Norton, Oxon.

Dorchester Antiques, Dorchester-on-Thames, Oxon.

Wychwood Antiques, Taynton, Oxon.

Julie Strachey, Weston-on-the-Green, Oxon.

Witney Antiques, Witney, Oxon.

Antiques of Woodstock, Woodstock, Oxon.

Chris Baylis Country Chairs, Woodstock, Oxon.

Ark Antiques, Bishop's Castle, Shrops.

John Clegg, Ludlow, Shrops.

Garrard Antiques, Ludlow, Shrops.

G. & D. Ginger Antiques, Ludlow, Shrops.

Marcus Moore Antiques, Stanton upon Hine Heath, Shrops.

Dodington Antiques, Whitchurch, Shrops.

Lansdown Antiques, Bath, Somerset.

Piccadilly Antiques, Batheaston, Somerset.

Chez Chalon, Chard, Somerset.

Hennessy, Crewkerne, Somerset.

Acorn Antiques, Dulverton, Somerset.

Anthony Sampson Antiques, Dulverton, Somerset.

Gilbert & Dale, Ilchester, Somerset.

J.C. White, Milverton, Somerset.

Johnson's, Leek, Staffs.

Dix-Sept, Framlingham, Suffolk.

The Green Shed, Framlingham, Suffolk.

Noel Mercer Antiques, Long Melford, Suffolk.

Antiques Warehouse (incorporating The Woodbridge Trading Co.), Marlesford, Suffolk.

Peasenhall Art and Antiques Gallery, Peasenhall, Suffolk.

Suffolk House Antiques, Yoxford, Suffolk.

Stoneycroft Farm, Betchworth, Surrey.

Cobham Galleries, Cobham, Surrey.

Christopher's Antiques, Farnham, Surrey.

Elm House Antiques, Merstham, Surrey.

Mollie Evans, Richmond, Surrey.

Anthony Welling Antiques, Ripley, Surrey.

Hadlow Down Antiques, Hadlow Down, Sussex East.

John Bird and Annette Puttnam Antiques, Lewes, Sussex East.

Pastorale Antiques, Lewes, Sussex East.

Graham Price Antiques Ltd, Polegate, Sussex East.

Park View Antiques, Wadhurst, Sussex East.

Antiquities, Arundel, Sussex West.

Michael Wakelin and Helen Linfield, Billingshurst, Sussex West.

Alexander Antiques, Henfield, Sussex West.

Angel Antiques, Petworth, Sussex West.

J.C. Tutt Antiques, Petworth, Sussex West.

King's Cottage Antiques, Leamington Spa, Warks.

L.P. Antiques (Mids) Ltd, Walsall, West Mids.

Combe Cottage Antiques, Castle Combe, Wilts.

Annmarie Turner Antiques, Marlborough, Wilts.

D & J Lines Antiques, Wychbold, Worcs.

The Antique Pine & Country Furniture Shop, Driffield, Yorks. East.

Bill Bentley, Harrogate, Yorks. North.

Elaine Phillips Antiques Ltd, Harrogate, Yorks. North.

York Cottage Antiques, Helmsley, Yorks. North.

Middleham Antiques, Middleham, Yorks. North.
Northern Antiques Company, Norton, Yorks. North.
Pateley Bridge Antiques, Pateley Bridge, Yorks. North.
John Gilbert Antiques, Robin Hood's Bay, Yorks. North.
Roy Precious Antiques & Fine Art, Settle, Yorks. North.
E. Thistlethwaite, Settle, Yorks. North.
Coach House Antiques, Whitby, Yorks. North.
Ruth Ford Antiques, York, Yorks. North.
Fishlake Antiques, Fishlake, Yorks. South.
Robert Davidson Antiques, Todmorden, Yorks. West.
Audrey Bull, Carmarthen, Wales.
The Mount Antiques Centre, Carmarthen, Wales.
Russell Worby, Colwyn Bay, Wales.
Havard and Havard, Cowbridge, Wales.
Gallop and Rivers Architectural Antiques, Crickhowell, Wales.
Country Antiques (Wales), Kidwelly, Wales.
Islwyn Watkins, Knighton, Wales.
Jim and Pat Ash, Llandeilo, Wales.
Collinge Antiques, Llandudno Junction, Wales.
Michael Lloyd Antiques, Llandysul, Wales.
Heritage Restorations, Llanfair Caereinion, Wales.
Audrey Bull, Tenby, Wales.

Furniture - Georgian

Andrew Lowe, London EC1.
Peter Chapman Antiques and Restoration, London N1.
Furniture Vault, London N1.
Gordon Gridley, London N1.
Jonathan James, London N1.
Regent Antiques, London N1.
Restall Brown and Clennell Ltd, London N1.
C. Tapsell, London N1.
Vane House Antiques, London N1.
Finchley Fine Art Galleries, London N12.
Martin Henham (Antiques), London N2.
Betty Gould and Julian Gonnermann Antiques, London N6.
G. and F. Gillingham Ltd, London NW2.
Patricia Beckman Antiques, London NW3.
David Wainwright, London NW3.
George Balot Antiques, London NW8.
Camden Art Gallery, London NW8.
Patricia Harvey Antiques and Decoration, London NW8.
Wellington Gallery, London NW8.
Young & Son, London NW8.
The Galleries, London SE1.
Tower Bridge Antiques, London SE1.
The Junk Shop, London SE10.
Relcy Antiques, London SE10.
Robert E. Hirschhorn, London SE5.
Antique Warehouse, London SE8.
Anno Domini Antiques, London SW1.
Hilary Batstone Antiques inc. Rosie Uniacke Interiors, London SW1.
John Bly, London SW1.
General Trading Co Ltd, London SW1.

Ross Hamilton Ltd, London SW1.
Harrods Ltd, London SW1.
Hotspur Ltd, London SW1.
Christopher Howe, London SW1.
Humphrey-Carrasco, London SW1.
Jeremy Ltd, London SW1.
Anthony Outred, London SW1.
Westenholz Antiques Ltd, London SW1.
The Furniture Cave, London SW10.
Stephen Long, London SW10.
Mallord Street Antiques, London SW10.
Pairs Antiques Ltd, London SW11.
The Dining Room Shop, London SW13.
Jorgen Antiques, London SW15.
H.C. Baxter and Sons, London SW16.
Adams Room Antiques, London SW19.
Norman Adams Ltd, London SW3.
Apter Fredericks Ltd, London SW3.
Richard Courtney Ltd, London SW3.
Robert Dickson and Lesley Rendall Antiques, London SW3.
Michael Foster, London SW3.
Godson and Coles, London SW3.
Anthony James and Son Ltd, London SW3.
Peter Jones at PJ2, London SW3.
John Keil Ltd, London SW3.
Michael Lipitch Ltd, London SW3.
Peter Lipitch Ltd, London SW3.
Prides of London, London SW3.
Charles Saunders Antiques, London SW3.
Clifford Wright Antiques Ltd, London SW3.
313 Antiques, London SW6.
Alasdair Brown, London SW6.
John Clay, London SW6.
Fergus Cochrane and Leigh Warren Antiques, London SW6.
George Floyd Ltd, London SW6.
HRW Antiques (London) Ltd, London SW6.
P.L. & M. James, London SW6.
Christopher Jones Antiques, London SW6.
L. and E. Kreckovic, London SW6.
Michael Luther Antiques, London SW6.
Michael Marriott Ltd, London SW6.
David Martin-Taylor Antiques, London SW6.
Megan Mathers Antiques, London SW6.
Ossowski, London SW6.
M. Pauw Antiques, London SW6.
Rogers & Co, London SW6.
Stephen Sprake, London SW6.
Ferenc Toth, London SW6.
H. Blairman and Sons Ltd., London W1.
Antoine Cheneviere Fine Arts, London W1.
Sibyl Colefax & John Fowler, London W1.
Fortnum and Mason plc, London W1.
Halcyon Days, London W1.
Patrick Jefferson Ltd, London W1.
Leuchars and Jefferson, London W1.
Mallett and Son (Antiques) Ltd, London W1.
Partridge Fine Arts plc, London W1.
Pendulum of Mayfair Ltd, London W1.
Ronald Phillips Ltd, London W1.
Scarisbrick and Bate Ltd, London W1.
Stair and Company Ltd, London W1.
Toynbee-Clarke Interiors Ltd, London W1.
M. Turpin Ltd, London W1.

B. and T. Antiques, London W11.
Butchoff Antiques, London W11.
The Coach House, London W11.
Michael Davidson, London W11.
Judy Fox, London W11.
Robin Martin Antiques, London W11.
Terence Morse and Son Ltd, London W11.
David Wainwright, London W11.
Trude Weaver, London W11.
Marshall Gallery, London W14.
J. Roger (Antiques) Ltd, London W14.
Daniel Mankowitz, London W2.
Aberdeen House Antiques, London W5.
Terrace Antiques, London W5.
Eddy Bardawil, London W8.
C. Fredericks and Son, London W8.
Lewis and Lloyd, London W8.
C.H. Major (Antiques) Ltd, London W8.
Reindeer Antiques Ltd, London W8.
Brian Rolleston Antiques Ltd, London W8.
Patrick Sandberg Antiques, London W8.
Pamela Teignmouth and Son, London W8.
Fluss and Charlesworth Ltd, London W9.
Jeremy Seale Antiques/Interiors, London WC1.
Victoria Antiques, Alderney, C.I.
Robert Harman Antiques, Ampthill, Beds.
Paris Antiques, Ampthill, Beds.
Pilgrim Antiques, Ampthill, Beds.
S. and S. Timms Antiques Ltd, Shefford, Beds.
Town Hall Antiques, Woburn, Beds.
Ulla Stafford Antiques, Binfield, Berks.
John A. Pearson Antiques, Horton, Berks.
Bow House Antiques & Interiors, Hungerford, Berks.
Roger King Antiques, Hungerford, Berks.
The Old Malthouse, Hungerford, Berks.
Turpins Antiques, Hungerford, Berks.
Widmerpool House Antiques, Maidenhead, Berks.
Rupert Landen Antiques, Reading, Berks.
Cavendish Fine Arts, Sonning-on-Thames, Berks.
John Connell - Wargrave Antiques, Wargrave, Berks.
Eton Antiques Partnership, Windsor and Eton, Berks.
Eton Gallery, Windsor and Eton, Berks.
Peter J. Martin, Windsor and Eton, Berks.
Times Past Antiques, Windsor and Eton, Berks.
The Cupboard Antiques, Amersham, Bucks.
June Elsworth - Beaconsfield Ltd, Beaconsfield, Bucks.
Grosvenor House Interiors, Beaconsfield, Bucks.
Period Furniture Showrooms, Beaconsfield, Bucks.
The Spinning Wheel, Beaconsfield, Bucks.
The Hampden Trading Company, Great Missenden, Bucks.
John Overland Antiques, Olney, Bucks.
Country Furniture Shop, Penn, Bucks.

SPECIALIST DEALERS

Bowood Antiques, Wendover, Bucks.

Wendover Antiques, Wendover, Bucks.

Peter Norman Antiques and Restorations, Burwell, Cambs.

Jess Applin Antiques, Cambridge, Cambs.

John Beazor and Sons Ltd, Cambridge, Cambs.

Mere Antiques, Fowlmere, Cambs.

Sara Frances Antiques, Alderley Edge, Cheshire.

Church Street Antiques, Altrincham, Cheshire.

David H. Dickinson, Bramhall, Cheshire.

Andrew Foott Antiques, Cheadle Hulme, Cheshire.

Adams Antiques, Chester, Cheshire.

Boustead-Bland Antiques, Chester, Cheshire.

Harris & Holt, Chester, Cheshire.

Melody's Antique Galleries, Chester, Cheshire.

Moor Hall Antiques, Chester, Cheshire.

Glynn Interiors, Knutsford, Cheshire.

John Titchner and Sons, Littleton, Cheshire.

David Bedale, Mobberley, Cheshire.

Chapel Antiques, Nantwich, Cheshire.

Coppelia Antiques, Plumley, Cheshire.

Cobwebs of Antiquities Ltd, Sale, Cheshire.

Manchester Antique Company, Stockport, Cheshire.

Page Antiques, Stockport, Cheshire.

Antique Chairs and Museum, Launceston, Cornwall.

Todd's, Launceston, Cornwall.

John Bragg Antiques, Lostwithiel, Cornwall.

Antiques & Fine Art, Penzance, Cornwall.

Pydar Antiques and Pine, Truro, Cornwall.

Victoria Antiques, Wadebridge, Cornwall.

Anthemion - The Antique Shop, Cartmel, Cumbria.

Jennywell Hall Antiques, Crosby Ravensworth, Cumbria.

Haughey Antiques, Kirkby Stephen, Cumbria.

Townhead Antiques, Newby Bridge, Cumbria.

Winton Hall Antiques, Ravenstonedale, Cumbria.

Ashbourne Antiques Ltd, Ashbourne, Derbys.

Pamela Elsom - Antiques, Ashbourne, Derbys.

Martin and Dorothy Harper Antiques, Bakewell, Derbys.

Lewis Antiques, Bakewell, Derbys.

Thornbridge Antiques, Bakewell, Derbys.

Water Lane Antiques, Bakewell, Derbys.

Hackney House Antiques, Barlow, Derbys.

The Antiques Warehouse, Buxton, Derbys.

N. and C.A. Haslam, Chesterfield, Derbys.

Ian Morris, Chesterfield, Derbys.

Brian Matsell, Derby, Derbys.

Wayside Antiques, Duffield, Derbys.

Shardlow Antiques Warehouse, Shardlow, Derbys.

Nimbus Antiques, Whaley Bridge, Derbys.

Wooden Box Antiques, Woodville, Derbys.

J. Collins and Son, Bideford, Devon.

John Prestige Antiques, Brixham, Devon.

Alison Gosling Antiques, Budleigh Salterton, Devon.

David J. Thorn, Budleigh Salterton, Devon.

Rex Antiques, Chagford, Devon.

Cullompton Old Tannery Antiques, Cullompton, Devon.

Mills Antiques, Cullompton, Devon.

McBains Antiques, Exeter, Devon.

Roderick Butler, Honiton, Devon.

The Grove Antiques Centre, Honiton, Devon.

Lombard Antiques, Honiton, Devon.

Maya Antiques, Honiton, Devon.

Merchant House Antiques, Honiton, Devon.

Pilgrim Antiques, Honiton, Devon.

Upstairs, Downstairs, Honiton, Devon.

Wickham Antiques, Honiton, Devon.

Bonstow and Crawshay Antiques, Kingskerswell, Devon.

W. J. Woodhams, Shaldon, Devon.

Philip Andrade, South Brent, Devon.

Extence Antiques, Teignmouth, Devon.

Past and Present, Totnes, Devon.

Anthony James Antiques, Whimple, Devon.

Colin Rhodes Antiques, Yealmpton, Devon.

Good Hope Antiques, Beaminster, Dorset.

Antiques for All, Blandford Forum, Dorset.

Lionel Geneen Ltd, Bournemouth, Dorset.

Sainsburys of Bournemouth Ltd, Bournemouth, Dorset.

David Mack Antiques, Branksome, Dorset.

Benchmark Antiques, Bridport, Dorset.

Zona Dawson Antiques, Charlton Marshall, Dorset.

Hamptons, Christchurch, Dorset.

Tower Antiques, Cranborne, Dorset.

Michael Legg Antiques, Dorchester, Dorset.

Legg of Dorchester, Dorchester, Dorset.

Laburnum Antiques, Poole, Dorset.

Shaston Antiques, Shaftesbury, Dorset.

Dodge and Son, Sherborne, Dorset.

Heygate Browne Antiques, Sherborne, Dorset.

Piers Pisani Antiques, Sherborne, Dorset.

Joan and David White Antiques, Barnard Castle, Durham.

Margaret Bedi Antiques & Fine Art, Billingham, Durham.

Alan Ramsey Antiques, Darlington, Durham.

Eden House Antiques, West Auckland, Durham.

Revival, Abridge, Essex.

Swan Antiques, Baythorne End, Essex.

Hutchison Antiques, Chelmsford, Essex.

Julia Bennet (Antiques), Great Dunmow, Essex.

Colton Antiques, Kelvedon, Essex.

Clive Beardall Antiques, Maldon, Essex.

West Essex Antiques (Stone Hall), Matching Green, Essex.

F.G. Bruschweiler (Antiques) Ltd, Rayleigh, Essex.

The Interior Design Shop, Saffron Walden, Essex.

Hedingham Antiques & Interiors, Sible Hedingham, Essex.

W.A. Pinn and Sons, Sible Hedingham, Essex.

Harris Antiques (Stansted), Stansted, Essex.

Linden House Antiques, Stansted, Essex.

Old Barn Antiques, Thornwood Common, Essex.

White Roding Antiques, White Roding, Essex.

Peter and Penny Proudfoot, Berkeley, Glos.

The Antiques Warehouse Ltd, Bristol, Glos.

H.W. Keil (Cheltenham) Ltd, Cheltenham, Glos.

Latchford Antiques, Cheltenham, Glos.

Manor House Antiques, Cheltenham, Glos.

Triton Gallery, Cheltenham, Glos.

Paul Nash Antiques, Cherington, Glos.

The Kettle House, Chipping Campden, Glos.

Swan Antiques, Chipping Campden, Glos.

Forum Antiques, Cirencester, Glos.

Hares, Cirencester, Glos.

Rankine Taylor Antiques, Cirencester, Glos.

Patrick Waldron Antiques, Cirencester, Glos.

Bernard Weaver Antiques, Cirencester, Glos.

Blenheim Antiques, Fairford, Glos.

Mark Carter Antiques, Fairford, Glos.

A.J. Ponsford Antiques with Decora, Gloucester, Glos.

Berry Antiques, Moreton-in-Marsh, Glos.

Dale House Antiques, Moreton-in-Marsh, Glos.

Lemington House Antiques, Moreton-in-Marsh, Glos.

Seaford House Antiques, Moreton-in-Marsh, Glos.

Simply Antiques, Moreton-in-Marsh, Glos.

Gary Wright Antiques, Moreton-in-Marsh, Glos.

Robson Antiques, Northleach, Glos.

Craig Carrington Antiques, Painswick, Glos.

Ashton Gower Antiques, Stow-on-the-Wold, Glos.

Duncan J. Baggott, Stow-on-the-Wold, Glos.

Baggott Church Street Ltd, Stow-on-the-Wold, Glos.

Colin Brand Antiques, Stow-on-the-Wold, Glos.

Bryden House Clocks & Antiques, Stow-on-the-Wold, Glos.

Christopher Clarke Antiques Ltd, Stow-on-the-Wold, Glos.

Fosse Way Antiques, Stow-on-the-Wold, Glos.

Huntington Antiques Ltd, Stow-on-the-Wold, Glos.

T.M. King-Smith & Simon W. Nutter, Stow-on-the-Wold, Glos.

SPECIALIST DEALERS

La Chaise Antique, Stow-on-the-Wold, Glos.
Roger Lamb Antiques & Works of Art, Stow-on-the-Wold, Glos.
Antony Preston Antiques Ltd, Stow-on-the-Wold, Glos.
Priests Antiques, Stow-on-the-Wold, Glos.
Queens Parade Antiques Ltd, Stow-on-the-Wold, Glos.
Michael Rowland Antiques, Stow-on-the-Wold, Glos.
Stow Antiques, Stow-on-the-Wold, Glos.
Styles of Stow, Stow-on-the-Wold, Glos.
Tudor House, Stow-on-the-Wold, Glos.
Vanbrugh House Antiques, Stow-on-the-Wold, Glos.
Wyndhams, Stow-on-the-Wold, Glos.
Ball and Claw Antiques, Tetbury, Glos.
Breakspeare Antiques, Tetbury, Glos.
The Chest of Drawers, Tetbury, Glos.
Gales Antiques, Tetbury, Glos.
Jacqueline Hall Antiques, Tetbury, Glos.
Bobbie Middleton, Tetbury, Glos.
Peter Norden Antiques, Tetbury, Glos.
Porch House Antiques, Tetbury, Glos.
Berkeley Antiques, Tewkesbury, Glos.
Gainsborough House Antiques, Tewkesbury, Glos.
Cotswold Antiques. com, Winchcombe, Glos.
Prichard Antiques, Winchcombe, Glos.
Mark Blower Antiques, St. Martin, Guernsey, C.I.
St. James's Gallery Ltd, St. Peter Port, Guernsey, C.I.
The Furniture Trading Co, Botley, Hants.
Nicholas Abbott, Hartley Wintney, Hants.
Andwells Antiques Limited, Hartley Wintney, Hants.
Antique House, Hartley Wintney, Hants.
Deva Antiques, Hartley Wintney, Hants.
David Lazarus Antiques, Hartley Wintney, Hants.
Phoenix Green Antiques, Hartley Wintney, Hants.
Csaky's Antiques, Hook, Hants.
Lita Kaye of Lyndhurst, Lyndhurst, Hants.
Millers of Chelsea Antiques Ltd, Ringwood, Hants.
Gasson Antiques and Interiors, Tadley, Hants.
Gaylords, Titchfield, Hants.
Burns and Graham, Winchester, Hants.
Winchester Antiques, Winchester, Hants.
Great Brampton House Antiques Ltd, Hereford, Herefs.
John Nash Antiques and Interiors, Ledbury, Herefs.
Serendipity, Ledbury, Herefs.
Jeffery Hammond Antiques, Leominster, Herefs.
Anthony Butt Antiques, Baldock, Herts.
Ralph and Bruce Moss, Baldock, Herts.
The Windhill Antiquary, Bishop's Stortford, Herts.
Tapestry Antiques, Hertford, Herts.
Michael Gander, Hitchin, Herts.
Hanbury Antiques, Hitchin, Herts.
Phillips of Hitchin (Antiques) Ltd, Hitchin, Herts.

Tom Salusbury Antiques, Hitchin, Herts.
J.N. Antiques, Redbourn, Herts.
Tim Wharton Antiques, Redbourn, Herts.
Charnwood Antiques, Sawbridgeworth, Herts.
John Bly, Tring, Herts.
New England House Antiques, Tring, Herts.
Weston Antiques, Weston, Herts.
Collins Antiques (F.G. and C. Collins Ltd.), Wheathampstead, Herts.
Michael Armson (Antiques) Ltd, Wilstone, Herts.
John Corrin Antiques, Douglas, Isle of Man.
Country House and Cottage Antiques, St Mary, Jersey, C.I.
Stephen Cohu Antiques, St Ouen, Jersey, C.I.
Stablegate Antiques, Barham, Kent.
David Barrington, Brasted, Kent.
Peter Dyke, Brasted, Kent.
Keymer Son & Co. Ltd, Brasted, Kent.
Roy Massingham Antiques, Brasted, Kent.
Tilings Antiques, Brasted, Kent.
Conquest House Antiques, Canterbury, Kent.
Chislehurst Antiques, Chislehurst, Kent.
Michael Sim, Chislehurst, Kent.
Vestry Antiques, Cranbrook, Kent.
Lennox Cato, Edenbridge, Kent.
Alan Lord Antiques, Folkestone, Kent.
Mill House Antiques, Goudhurst, Kent.
Newington Antiques, Newington, Kent.
J.D. and R.M. Walters, Rolvenden, Kent.
Christopher Buck Antiques, Sandgate, Kent.
Finch Antiques, Sandgate, Kent.
Michael Fitch Antiques, Sandgate, Kent.
Freeman and Lloyd Antiques, Sandgate, Kent.
James Porter Antiques, Sandwich, Kent.
Nancy Wilson, Sandwich, Kent.
Gem Antiques, Sevenoaks, Kent.
Steppes Hill Farm Antiques, Stockbury, Kent.
Sutton Valence Antiques, Sutton Valence, Kent.
Flower House Antiques, Tenterden, Kent.
Garden House Antiques, Tenterden, Kent.
The Pantiles Antiques, Tunbridge Wells, Kent.
Pantiles Spa Antiques, Tunbridge Wells, Kent.
Phoenix Antiques, Tunbridge Wells, Kent.
John Thompson, Tunbridge Wells, Kent.
Up Country, Tunbridge Wells, Kent.
Apollo Antique Galleries, Westerham, Kent.
London House Antiques, Westerham, Kent.
Marks Antiques, Westerham, Kent.
Taylor-Smith Antiques, Westerham, Kent.
Westerham Antiques Warehouse, Westerham, Kent.
Westerham House Antiques, Westerham, Kent.
Laurens Antiques, Whitstable, Kent.
Tankerton Antiques, Whitstable, Kent.

Silvesters, Wingham, Kent.
Brun Lea Antiques (J. Waite Ltd), Burnley, Lancs.
K.C. Antiques, Darwen, Lancs.
P.J. Brown Antiques, Haslingden, Lancs.
Luigino Vescovi, Morecambe, Lancs.
Brooks Antiques, Nelson, Lancs.
Alan Grice Antiques, Ormskirk, Lancs.
S.C. Falk, Rochdale, Lancs.
Old Bakehouse Antiques and Gallery, Broughton Astley, Leics.
Sitting Pretty, Great Glen, Leics.
Withers of Leicester, Hoby, Leics.
Corry's, Leicester, Leics.
Lowe of Loughborough, Loughborough, Leics.
Walter Moores and Son, Market Harborough, Leics.
J. Stamp and Sons, Market Harborough, Leics.
Ken Smith Antiques Ltd, Narborough, Leics.
David E. Burrows, Osgathorpe, Leics.
J. Green and Son, Queniborough,, Leics.
Paddock Antiques, Woodhouse Eaves, Leics.
G. Baker Antiques, Horncastle, Lincs.
Alan Read - Period Furniture, Horncastle, Lincs.
Laurence Shaw Antiques, Horncastle, Lincs.
Staines Antiques, Horncastle, Lincs.
David J. Hansord & Son, Lincoln, Lincs.
Dawson of Stamford Ltd, Stamford, Lincs.
Hunters Antiques & Interior Design, Stamford, Lincs.
Graham Pickett Antiques, Stamford, Lincs.
St. George's Antiques, Stamford, Lincs.
Robin Shield Antiques, Swinstead, Lincs.
J. and R. Ratcliffe, Waddington, Lincs.
Underwoodhall Antiques, Woodhall Spa, Lincs.
V.O.C. Antiques, Woodhall Spa, Lincs.
Stefani Antiques, Liverpool, Merseyside.
Colin Stock, Rainford, Merseyside.
Tony and Anne Sutcliffe Antiques, Southport, Merseyside.
Helen Horswill Antiques and Decorative Arts, West Kirby, Merseyside.
Tobias Jellinek Antiques, Twickenham, Middx.
Ivy House Antiques, Acle, Norfolk.
A.E. Bush and Partners, Attleborough, Norfolk.
M. and A. Cringle, Burnham Market, Norfolk.
Anne Hamilton Antiques, Burnham Market, Norfolk.
Market House, Burnham Market, Norfolk.
Roger Bradbury Antiques, Coltishall, Norfolk.
A.E. Seago, Cromer, Norfolk.
Peter Robinson, Heacham, Norfolk.
Arthur Brett and Sons Ltd, Norwich, Norfolk.
Nicholas Fowle Antiques, Norwich, Norfolk.
John Howkins Antiques, Norwich, Norfolk.
Echo Antiques, Reepham, Norfolk.

SPECIALIST DEALERS

Country House Antiques, Seething, Norfolk.
Leo Pratt and Son, South Walsham, Norfolk.
Stalham Antique Gallery, Stalham, Norfolk.
Norton Antiques, Twyford, Norfolk.
T.C.S. Brooke, Wroxham, Norfolk.
M.E. and J.E. Standley, Wymondham, Norfolk.
Courtyard Antiques, Brackley, Northants.
Simon Banks Antiques, Finedon, Northants.
M.C. Chapman, Finedon, Northants.
Robert Cheney Antiques, Finedon, Northants.
Huntershield Antiques and Granary Antiques, Flore, Northants.
Christopher Jones Antiques, Flore, Northants.
F. and C.H. Cave, Northampton, Northants.
Reindeer Antiques Ltd, Potterspury, Northants.
Barber Antiques, West Haddon, Northants.
Boadens Antiques, Hexham, Northumbs.
Hedley's of Hexham, Hexham, Northumbs.
James Miller Antiques, Wooler, Northumbs.
A.J. O'Sullivan Antiques, Darlton, Notts.
Antiques across the World, Nottingham, Notts.
Pegasus Antiques, Nottingham, Notts.
David and Carole Potter Antiques, Nottingham, Notts.
Ranby Hall, Retford, Notts.
Strouds (of Southwell Antiques), Southwell, Notts.
Burford Antique Centre, Burford, Oxon.
Gateway Antiques, Burford, Oxon.
Hubert's Antiques, Burford, Oxon.
Anthony Nielsen Antiques, Burford, Oxon.
David Pickup, Burford, Oxon.
Swan Gallery, Burford, Oxon.
Walkers, Burford, Oxon.
Rupert Hitchcox Antiques, Chalgrove, Oxon.
Georgian House Antiques, Chipping Norton, Oxon.
Hallidays (Fine Antiques) Ltd, Dorchester-on-Thames, Oxon.
The Faringdon Antique Centre, Faringdon, Oxon.
Richard J. Kingston, Henley-on-Thames, Oxon.
The Country Seat, Huntercombe, Oxon.
de Albuquerque Antiques, Wallingford, Oxon.
Chris and Lin O'Donnell Antiques, Wallingford, Oxon.
Mike Ottrey Antiques, Wallingford, Oxon.
Summers Davis Antiques Ltd, Wallingford, Oxon.
Cross Antiques, Watlington, Oxon.
Stephen Orton Antiques, Watlington, Oxon.
Colin Greenway Antiques, Witney, Oxon.

W.R. Harvey & Co (Antiques) Ltd, Witney, Oxon.
Joan Wilkins Antiques, Witney, Oxon.
Witney Antiques, Witney, Oxon.
Antiques of Woodstock, Woodstock, Oxon.
The Chair Set - Antiques, Woodstock, Oxon.
Robin Sanders and Sons, Woodstock, Oxon.
Churchgate Antiques, Empingham, Rutland.
Swans, Oakham, Rutland.
T.J. Roberts, Uppingham, Rutland.
Woodman's House Antiques, Uppingham, Rutland.
Robert Bingley Antiques, Wing, Rutland.
Mytton Antiques, Atcham, Shrops.
Longmynd Antiques, Church Stretton, Shrops.
R.G. Cave and Sons Ltd, Ludlow, Shrops.
Claymore Antiques, Ludlow, Shrops.
M. & R. Taylor Antiques Sarah Taylor Interiors, Ludlow, Shrops.
Teme Valley Antiques, Ludlow, Shrops.
Valentyne Dawes Gallery, Ludlow, Shrops.
Raynalds Mansion, Much Wenlock, Shrops.
Corner Farm Antiques, Shifnal, Shrops.
F.C. Manser and Son Ltd, Shrewsbury, Shrops.
Marcus Moore Antiques, Stanton upon Hine Heath, Shrops.
Brian James Antiques, Telford, Shrops.
Dodington Antiques, Whitchurch, Shrops.
A J Antiques, Bath, Somerset.
Alderson, Bath, Somerset.
Lawrence Brass, Bath, Somerset.
Geoffrey Breeze, Bath, Somerset.
Mary Cruz, Bath, Somerset.
Jadis Ltd, Bath, Somerset.
Montague Antiques, Bath, Somerset.
Quiet Street Antiques, Bath, Somerset.
Piccadilly Antiques, Batheaston, Somerset.
M.G.R. Exports, Bruton, Somerset.
Chris's Crackers, Carhampton, Somerset.
Guy Dennler Antiques, Dulverton, Somerset.
Anthony Sampson Antiques, Dulverton, Somerset.
Freshfords, Freshford, Somerset.
C.W.E. Dyte, Highbridge, Somerset.
Edward Marnier Antiques, Shepton Mallet, Somerset.
Edward A. Nowell, Wells, Somerset.
J.C. Giddings, Wiveliscombe, Somerset.
John Hamblin, Yeovil, Somerset.
Richard Midwinter Antiques, Newcastle-under-Lyme, Staffs.
The Potteries Antique Centre Ltd, Stoke-on-Trent, Staffs.
H.W. Heron and Son Ltd, Yoxall, Staffs.
Thompson's Gallery, Aldeburgh, Suffolk.
Saltgate Antiques, Beccles, Suffolk.
P. Dawson Furniture Restorers, Bentley, Suffolk.
Peppers Period Pieces, Bury St. Edmunds, Suffolk.

Cavendish Rose Antiques, Cavendish, Suffolk.
Robin Butler, Clare, Suffolk.
F.D. Salter Antiques, Clare, Suffolk.
Debenham Antiques, Debenham, Suffolk.
Denzil Grant Antiques, Drinkstone, Suffolk.
English and Continental Antiques, Eye, Suffolk.
The Green Shed, Framlingham, Suffolk.
Randolph, Hadleigh, Suffolk.
Hubbard Antiques, Ipswich, Suffolk.
J. and J. Baker, Lavenham,, Suffolk.
Warrens Antiques Warehouse, Leiston, Suffolk.
Karen Bryan Antiques, Long Melford, Suffolk.
Sandy Cooke Antiques, Long Melford, Suffolk.
Alexander Lyall Antiques, Long Melford, Suffolk.
Seabrook Antiques, Long Melford, Suffolk.
Suthburgh Antiques, Long Melford, Suffolk.
Martlesham Antiques, Martlesham, Suffolk.
Frank Collins Antiques, Mendlesham Green, Suffolk.
Mary Palmer Antiques, Stradbroke, Suffolk.
Napier House Antiques, Sudbury, Suffolk.
David Gibbins Antiques, Woodbridge, Suffolk.
Hamilton Antiques, Woodbridge, Suffolk.
Anthony Hurst Antiques, Woodbridge, Suffolk.
Sarah Meysey-Thompson Antiques, Woodbridge, Suffolk.
J.C. Heather, Woolpit, Suffolk.
Suffolk House Antiques, Yoxford, Suffolk.
John Anthony Antiques, Bletchingley, Surrey.
Simon Marsh, Bletchingley, Surrey.
G. D. Blay Antiques, Dorking, Surrey.
Dolphin Square Antiques, Dorking, Surrey.
Dorking Desk Shop, Dorking, Surrey.
Gallery Eleven, Dorking, Surrey.
Hampshires of Dorking, Dorking, Surrey.
Harman's Antiques, Dorking, Surrey.
Holmwood Antiques, Dorking, Surrey.
The House of Bulow Antiques, Dorking, Surrey.
Malthouse Antiques, Dorking, Surrey.
Mayfair Antiques, Dorking, Surrey.
Norfolk House Galleries, Dorking, Surrey.
Elaine Saunderson Antiques, Dorking, Surrey.
Thorpe and Foster Ltd, Dorking, Surrey.
The Vinery, Dorking, Surrey.
West Street Antiques, Dorking, Surrey.
A. E. Booth & Son, Ewell, Surrey.
Christopher's Antiques, Farnham, Surrey.
Heath-Bullocks, Godalming, Surrey.
The Coach House Antiques, Gomshall, Surrey.
M. J. Bowdery, Hindhead, Surrey.

Glencorse Antiques, Kingston-upon-Thames, Surrey.

Elm House Antiques, Merstham, Surrey.

Michael Andrews Antiques, Milford, Surrey.

F.G. Lawrence and Sons, Redhill, Surrey.

The Gallery, Reigate, Surrey.

M. & M. White Antique & Reproduction Centre, Reigate, Surrey.

Antique Mart, Richmond, Surrey.

Hill Rise Antiques, Richmond, Surrey.

Marryat, Richmond, Surrey.

J. Hartley Antiques Ltd, Ripley, Surrey.

Ripley Antiques, Ripley, Surrey.

Sage Antiques and Interiors, Ripley, Surrey.

Cockrell Antiques, Surbiton, Surrey.

B. M. and E. Newlove, Surbiton, Surrey.

Clifford and Roger Dade, Thames Ditton, Surrey.

Ian Caldwell, Walton-on-the-Hill and Tadworth, Surrey.

Church House Antiques, Weybridge, Surrey.

Weybridge Antiques, Weybridge, Surrey.

Alexandria Antiques, Brighton, Sussex East.

Alan Fitchett Antiques, Brighton, Sussex East.

Dudley Hume, Brighton, Sussex East.

Patrick Moorhead Antiques, Brighton, Sussex East.

Michael Norman Antiques Ltd, Brighton, Sussex East.

Ben Ponting Antiques, Brighton, Sussex East.

Yellow Lantern Antiques Ltd, Brighton, Sussex East.

Dycheling Antiques, Ditchling, Sussex East.

Hadlow Down Antiques, Hadlow Down, Sussex East.

Cliffe Gallery Antiques, Lewes, Sussex East.

The Old Mint House, Pevensey, Sussex East.

Bragge and Sons, Rye, Sussex East.

East Street Antiques, Rye, Sussex East.

Herbert Gordon Gasson, Rye, Sussex East.

Rye Antiques, Rye, Sussex East.

The Old House, Seaford, Sussex East.

Aarquebus Antiques, St. Leonards-on-Sea, Sussex East.

Ringles Cross Antiques, Uckfield, Sussex East.

Bygones, Angmering, Sussex West.

Michael Wakelin and Helen Linfield, Billingshurst, Sussex West.

Frensham House Antiques, Chichester, Sussex West.

Gems Antiques, Chichester, Sussex West.

David Foord-Brown Antiques, Cuckfield, Sussex West.

Richard Usher Antiques, Cuckfield, Sussex West.

Ashcombe Coach House, Henfield, Sussex West.

Stable Antiques, Lindfield, Sussex West.

Callingham Antiques, Northchapel, Sussex West.

Antiquated, Petworth, Sussex West.

Baskerville Antiques, Petworth, Sussex West.

Ronald G. Chambers Fine Antiques, Petworth, Sussex West.

J. Du Cros Antiques, Petworth, Sussex West.

Elliott's, Petworth, Sussex West.

Richard Gardner Antiques, Petworth, Sussex West.

Granville Antiques, Petworth, Sussex West.

William Hockley Antiques, Petworth, Sussex West.

Red Lion Antiques, Petworth, Sussex West.

H. G. Saunders, Petworth, Sussex West.

T.G. Wilkinson Antiques Ltd, Petworth, Sussex West.

J. Powell (Hove) Ltd, Portslade, Sussex West.

Georgia Antiques, Pulborough, Sussex West.

Thakeham Furniture, Pulborough, Sussex West.

Loewenthal Antiques, Tillington, Sussex West.

Wilsons Antiques, Worthing, Sussex West.

Ian Sharp Antiques, Tynemouth, Tyne and Wear.

Yesterdays, Leamington Spa, Warks.

The Grandfather Clock Shop, Shipston-on-Stour, Warks.

Apollo Antiques Ltd, Warwick, Warks.

William J. Casey Antiques, Warwick, Warks.

English Antiques, Warwick, Warks.

Patrick and Gillian Morley Antiques, Warwick, Warks.

James Reeve, Warwick, Warks.

Don Spencer Antiques, Warwick, Warks.

Peter Clark Antiques, Birmingham, West Mids.

Thomas Coulborn and Sons, Sutton Coldfield, West Mids.

Avon Antiques, Bradford-on-Avon, Wilts.

Mac Humble Antiques, Bradford-on-Avon, Wilts.

Moxhams Antiques, Bradford-on-Avon, Wilts.

Town and Country Antiques, Bradford-on-Avon, Wilts.

Harley Antiques, Christian Malford, Wilts.

Matthew Eden, Corsham, Wilts.

Blanchard, Froxfield, Wilts.

Andrew Britten Antiques, Malmesbury, Wilts.

Brocante Antiques Centre, Marlborough, Wilts.

Cook of Marlborough Fine Art Ltd, Marlborough, Wilts.

Katharine House Gallery, Marlborough, Wilts.

Robert Kime Antiques, Marlborough, Wilts.

Alan Jaffray, Melksham, Wilts.

Ray Best Antiques, Newton Tony, Wilts.

Boston Antiques, Salisbury, Wilts.

Robert Bradley Antiques, Salisbury, Wilts.

Edward Hurst Antiques, Salisbury, Wilts.

Pennyfarthing Antiques, Salisbury, Wilts.

Salisbury Antiques Warehouse, Salisbury, Wilts.

Bishopstrow Antiques, Warminster, Wilts.

Cassidy's Antiques, Warminster, Wilts.

Obelisk Antiques, Warminster, Wilts.

Bay Tree Antiques, Wilton, Wilts.

A.J. Romain and Sons, Wilton, Wilts.

Barnt Green Antiques, Barnt Green, Worcs.

John Hubbard Antique Restorations, Blakedown, Worcs.

Fenwick and Fenwick Antiques, Broadway, Worcs.

H.W. Keil Ltd, Broadway, Worcs.

Robert Belcher Antiques, Droitwich, Worcs.

Miscellany Antiques, Great Malvern, Worcs.

The Drawing Room - Interiors & Antiques, Pershore, Worcs.

Lower House Fine Antiques, Redditch, Worcs.

Bygones by the Cathedral, Worcester, Worcs.

Bygones of Worcester, Worcester, Worcs.

M. Lees and Sons, Worcester, Worcs.

Priory Antiques, Bridlington, Yorks. East.

Houghton Hall Antiques, Market Weighton, Yorks. East.

Bennett's Antiques & Collectables, Bedale, Yorks. North.

Anthony Graham Antiques, Boroughbridge, Yorks. North.

St. James House Antiques, Boroughbridge, Yorks. North.

R.S. Wilson and Sons, Boroughbridge, Yorks. North.

Milestone Antiques, Easingwold, Yorks. North.

Elm Tree Antiques, Flaxton, Yorks. North.

Bernard Dickinson, Gargrave, Yorks. North.

R.N. Myers and Son, Gargrave, Yorks. North.

Nigel Adamson, Harrogate, Yorks. North.

Armstrong, Harrogate, Yorks. North.

Bryan Bowden, Harrogate, Yorks. North.

Derbyshire Antiques Ltd, Harrogate, Yorks. North.

Garth Antiques, Harrogate, Yorks. North.

Haworth Antiques, Harrogate, Yorks. North.

David Love, Harrogate, Yorks. North.

Charles Lumb and Sons Ltd, Harrogate, Yorks. North.

Walker Galleries Ltd, Harrogate, Yorks. North.

Weatherell's of Harrogate Antiques and Fine Arts, Harrogate, Yorks. North.

Chris Wilde Antiques, Harrogate, Yorks. North.

Sturman's Antiques, Hawes, Yorks. North.

John Thompson Antiques, Knaresborough, Yorks. North.

SPECIALIST DEALERS

Joan and David White, Manfield, Yorks. North.
Daleside Antiques, Markington, Yorks. North.
Aura Antiques, Masham, Yorks. North.
Milton Holgate, Ripon, Yorks. North.
Sigma Antiques and Fine Art, Ripon, Yorks. North.
Anderson Slater Antiques, Settle, Yorks. North.
Corn Mill Antiques, Skipton, Yorks. North.
Antony, David & Ann Shackleton, Snainton, Yorks. North.
N.J. and C.S. Dodsworth, Spennithorne, Yorks. North.
Tomlinson Antiques Ltd. & Period Furniture Ltd, Tockwith, Yorks. North.
Garth Antiques, Whixley, Yorks. North.
Ruby Snowden Antiques, Yarm, Yorks. North.
Robert Morrison and Son, York, Yorks. North.
Peter James Antiques, Sheffield, Yorks. South.
A.E. Jameson and Co, Sheffield, Yorks. South.
Top Hat Antique Centre, Sheffield, Yorks. South.
The Baildon Furniture Co., Baildon, Yorks. West.
Bingley Antiques, Haworth, Yorks. West.
Coopers of Ilkley, Ilkley, Yorks. West.
Barleycote Hall Antiques, Keighley, Yorks. West.
Geary Antiques, Leeds, Yorks. West.
Windsor House Antiques (Leeds) Ltd., Leeds, Yorks. West.
Park Antiques, Menston, Yorks. West.
Dunluce Antiques, Bushmills, Co. Antrim, N. Ireland.
Robert Christie Antiques, Carrickfergus, Co. Antrim, N. Ireland.
MacHenry Antiques, Newtownabbey, Co. Antrim, N. Ireland.
Time & Tide Antiques, Portaferry, Co. Down, N. Ireland.
Antiques and Fine Art Gallery, Warrenpoint, Co. Down, N. Ireland.
Colin Wood (Antiques) Ltd, Aberdeen, Scotland.
T.W. Beaty, Beattock, Scotland.
Coldstream Antiques, Coldstream, Scotland.
The Magic Lantern, Dunecht, Scotland.
Laurance Black Ltd, Edinburgh, Scotland.
Dunedin Antiques Ltd, Edinburgh, Scotland.
Georgian Antiques, Edinburgh, Scotland.
London Road Antiques, Edinburgh, Scotland.
Whytock and Reid, Edinburgh, Scotland.
Gow Antiques, Forfar, Scotland.
E.A. Alvariño - Antiques, Glasgow, Scotland.
Butler's Furniture Galleries, Glasgow, Scotland.
Muirhead Moffat and Co, Glasgow, Scotland.
Michael YoungAntiques at Glencarse, Glencarse, Scotland.

Glendoick Antiques, Glendoick, Scotland.
C.S. Moreton (Antiques), Inchture, Scotland.
Kilmacolm Antiques Ltd, Kilmacolm, Scotland.
QS Antiques and Cabinetmakers, Kilmarnock, Scotland.
Rhudle Mill, Kilmichael Glassary, Scotland.
Miles Antiques, Kinross, Scotland.
Michael Vee Design - Birch House Antiques, Melrose, Scotland.
Harper-James, Montrose, Scotland.
Newburgh Antiques, Newburgh, Scotland.
Crossroads Antiques, Prestwick, Scotland.
Coach House Antiques Ltd, Stanley, Scotland.
Cwmgwili Mill, Carmarthen, Wales.
K.W. Finlay Antiques, Ciliau Aeron, Wales.
Cowbridge Antique Centre, Cowbridge, Wales.
Havard and Havard, Cowbridge, Wales.
Renaissance Antiques, Cowbridge, Wales.
Gerald Oliver Antiques, Haverfordwest, Wales.
Furn Davies Partnership, Holt, Wales.
Kidwelly Antiques, Kidwelly, Wales.
J. and R. Langford, Llangollen, Wales.
Snowdonia Antiques, Llanrwst, Wales.
Rodney Adams Antiques, Pwllheli, Wales.
Barn Court Antiques, Crafts & Tearoom, Templeton, Wales.
F.E. Anderson and Son, Welshpool, Wales.

Furniture - Oak
Robert E. Hirschhorn, London SE5.
Christopher Howe, London SW1.
The Furniture Cave, London SW10.
Robert Young Antiques, London SW11.
Apter Fredericks Ltd, London SW3.
Alistair Sampson Antiques Ltd, London W1.
Beedham Antiques Ltd, Hungerford, Berks.
Simon and Penny Rumble Antiques, Chittering, Cambs.
Melody's Antique Galleries, Chester, Cheshire.
Adams Antiques, Nantwich, Cheshire.
Pillory House, Nantwich, Cheshire.
Simon Starkie Antiques, Cartmel, Cumbria.
Acanthus Antiques/Country Seat Antiques, Corby Hill, Cumbria.
Jennywell Hall Antiques, Crosby Ravensworth, Cumbria.
Kendal Studios Antiques, Kendal, Cumbria.
Sandgate Antiques, Penrith, Cumbria.
Winton Hall Antiques, Ravenstonedale, Cumbria.
J H S Antiques, Ashbourne, Derbys.
Peter Bunting Antiques, Bakewell, Derbys.
Richard Glass, Whaley Bridge, Derbys.
Robert Byles, Bampton, Devon.
Rex Antiques, Chagford, Devon.

Cullompton Old Tannery Antiques, Cullompton, Devon.
Wickham Antiques, Honiton, Devon.
Alan Jones Antiques, Okehampton, Devon.
Colystock Antiques, Stockland, Devon.
Colin Rhodes Antiques, Yealmpton, Devon.
Grant's Antiques, Barnard Castle, Durham.
C. and J. Mortimer and Son, Great Chesterford, Essex.
Julia Bennet (Antiques), Great Dunmow, Essex.
Freemans Antiques, Roxwell, Essex.
Lennard Antiques, Sible Hedingham, Essex.
Peter and Penny Proudfoot, Berkeley, Glos.
J. and R. Bateman Antiques, Chalford, Glos.
Swan Antiques, Chipping Campden, Glos.
William H. Stokes, Cirencester, Glos.
Mark Carter Antiques, Fairford, Glos.
Gloucester House Antiques Ltd, Fairford, Glos.
A.J. Ponsford Antiques with Decora, Gloucester, Glos.
Lemington House Antiques, Moreton-in-Marsh, Glos.
Duncan J. Baggott, Stow-on-the-Wold, Glos.
J. and J. Caspall Antiques, Stow-on-the-Wold, Glos.
Keith Hockin Antiques, Stow-on-the-Wold, Glos.
T.M. King-Smith & Simon W. Nutter, Stow-on-the-Wold, Glos.
Priests Antiques, Stow-on-the-Wold, Glos.
Michael Rowland Antiques, Stow-on-the-Wold, Glos.
Arthur Seager Antiques, Stow-on-the-Wold, Glos.
Day Antiques, Tetbury, Glos.
Peter Norden Antiques, Tetbury, Glos.
Westwood House Antiques, Tetbury, Glos.
Underwood Oak, Alresford, Hants.
Quatrefoil, Fordingbridge, Hants.
Cedar Antiques Limited, Hartley Wintney, Hants.
Winchester Antiques, Winchester, Hants.
P. and S.N. Eddy, Leominster, Herefs.
Robin Lloyd Antiques, Ross-on-Wye, Herefs.
Singleton Antiques, Ross-on-Wye, Herefs.
M. and J. Russell, Yazor, Herefs.
Dobson's Antiques, Abbots Langley, Herts.
Tim Wharton Antiques, Redbourn, Herts.
Collins Antiques (F.G. and C. Collins Ltd.), Wheathampstead, Herts.
R. Kirby Antiques, Acrise, Kent.
Dinah Stoodley & Celia Jennings, Brasted, Kent.
Michael Pearson Antiques, Canterbury, Kent.
Douglas Bryan, Cranbrook, Kent.
Vestry Antiques, Cranbrook, Kent.
Old English Oak, Sandgate, Kent.
Henry Baines, Southborough, Kent.

Edmund Davies & Son Antiques, Whalley, Lancs.
Boulevard Antique and Shipping Centre, Leicester, Leics.
Lowe of Loughborough, Loughborough, Leics.
Sinclair's, Stamford, Lincs.
J. and R. Ratcliffe, Waddington, Lincs.
Tobias Jellinek Antiques, Twickenham, Middx.
Pearse Lukies, Aylsham, Norfolk.
Arthur Brett and Sons Ltd, Norwich, Norfolk.
Courtyard Antiques, Brackley, Northants.
Paul Hopwell Antiques, West Haddon, Northants.
Horseshoe Antiques and Gallery, Burford, Oxon.
Anthony Nielsen Antiques, Burford, Oxon.
Swan Gallery, Burford, Oxon.
Antique English Windsor Chairs - Michael Harding-Hill, Chipping Norton, Oxon.
Key Antiques, Chipping Norton, Oxon.
Witney Antiques, Witney, Oxon.
Antiques of Woodstock, Woodstock, Oxon.
G. & D. Ginger Antiques, Ludlow, Shrops.
Marcus Moore Antiques, Stanton upon Hine Heath, Shrops.
Dodington Antiques, Whitchurch, Shrops.
Stuart Interiors (Antiques) Ltd, Barrington, Somerset.
Lawrence Brass, Bath, Somerset.
Frank Dux Antiques, Bath, Somerset.
Anthony Sampson Antiques, Dulverton, Somerset.
John Nicholls, Leigh, Staffs.
Richard Midwinter Antiques, Newcastle-under-Lyme, Staffs.
P. Dawson Furniture Restorers, Bentley, Suffolk.
Peppers Period Pieces, Bury St. Edmunds, Suffolk.
Quercus, Debenham, Suffolk.
Denzil Grant Antiques, Drinkstone, Suffolk.
J. and J. Baker, Lavenham,, Suffolk.
Noel Mercer Antiques, Long Melford, Suffolk.
Seabrook Antiques, Long Melford, Suffolk.
Suthburgh Antiques, Long Melford, Suffolk.
Trident Antiques, Long Melford, Suffolk.
Frank Collins Antiques, Mendlesham Green, Suffolk.
Hamilton Antiques, Woodbridge, Suffolk.
Anthony Hurst Antiques, Woodbridge, Suffolk.
Suffolk House Antiques, Yoxford, Suffolk.
Stoneycroft Farm, Betchworth, Surrey.
Malthouse Antiques, Dorking, Surrey.
Sage Antiques and Interiors, Ripley, Surrey.
Anthony Welling Antiques, Ripley, Surrey.
B. M. and E. Newlove, Surbiton, Surrey.

E. and B. White, Brighton, Sussex East.
Graham Lower, Flimwell, Sussex East.
Herbert Gordon Gasson, Rye, Sussex East.
Rye Antiques, Rye, Sussex East.
Monarch Antiques, St. Leonards-on-Sea, Sussex East.
Park View Antiques, Wadhurst, Sussex East.
King's Cottage Antiques, Leamington Spa, Warks.
The Grandfather Clock Shop, Shipston-on-Stour, Warks.
James Reeve, Warwick, Warks.
Mac Humble Antiques, Bradford-on-Avon, Wilts.
A.J. Romain and Sons, Wilton, Wilts.
H.W. Keil Ltd, Broadway, Worcs.
Old Hall Antiques, Burton Salmon, Yorks. North.
R.N. Myers and Son, Gargrave, Yorks. North.
Bill Bentley, Harrogate, Yorks. North.
Derbyshire Antiques Ltd, Harrogate, Yorks. North.
Elaine Phillips Antiques Ltd, Harrogate, Yorks. North.
York Cottage Antiques, Helmsley, Yorks. North.
Middleham Antiques, Middleham, Yorks. North.
Pateley Bridge Antiques, Pateley Bridge, Yorks. North.
John Gilbert Antiques, Robin Hood's Bay, Yorks. North.
Roy Precious Antiques & Fine Art, Settle, Yorks. North.
Coach House Antiques, Whitby, Yorks. North.
Joan Frere Antiques, Drumnadrochit, Scotland.
Strathspey Gallery, Grantown-on-Spey, Scotland.
Cwmgwili Mill, Carmarthen, Wales.
Country Antiques (Wales), Kidwelly, Wales.

Furniture - Pine
Chest of Drawers, London N1.
Michael Lewis Antiques, London N1.
Rookery Farm Antiques, London N1.
Old School (Gardens & Interiors), London N19.
At the Sign of the Chest of Drawers, London N6.
This and That (Furniture), London NW1.
Abbott Antiques and Country Pine, London SE26.
The Furniture Cave, London SW10.
The Pine Mine (Crewe-Read Antiques), London SW6.
Remember When, London W3.
The Pine Parlour, Ampthill, Beds.
Alan Hodgson, Great Shefford, Berks.
Dee's Antique Pine, Windsor and Eton, Berks.
Bourne End Antiques Centre, Bourne End, Bucks.
T. Smith, Chalfont St. Giles, Bucks.
The Pine Merchants, Great Missenden, Bucks.
Jack Harness Antiques, Marlow, Bucks.
Archer's Antique and Country Furniture, Olney, Bucks.
Pine Antiques, Olney, Bucks.

Cambridge Pine, Bottisham, Cambs.
Abbey Antiques, Ramsey, Cambs.
Melody's Antique Galleries, Chester, Cheshire.
Steven Blackhurst, Crewe, Cheshire.
Town House Antiques, Marple Bridge, Cheshire.
Chapel Antiques, Nantwich, Cheshire.
Sue Ledger Antiques, Stockport, Cheshire.
Pine and Period Furniture, Grampound, Cornwall.
Blackwater Pine Antiques, Truro, Cornwall.
Pydar Antiques and Pine, Truro, Cornwall.
Ben Eggleston Antiques, Long Marton, Cumbria.
Utopia Antiques Ltd, Low Newton, Cumbria.
Early World Antiques, Alfreton, Derbys.
Friargate Pine Company Ltd, Derby, Derbys.
Pine Antiques Workshop, Doveridge, Derbys.
Michael Allcroft Antiques, Hayfield, Derbys.
Wooden Box Antiques, Woodville, Derbys.
W.G. Potter and Son, Axminster, Devon.
Robert Byles, Bampton, Devon.
Cobweb Antiques, Cullompton, Devon.
Cullompton Old Tannery Antiques, Cullompton, Devon.
C Short Antiques, Great Torrington, Devon.
Annterior Antiques, Plymouth, Devon.
Colystock Antiques, Stockland, Devon.
King Street Curios, Tavistock, Devon.
Timepiece, Teignmouth, Devon.
Fine Pine Antiques, Totnes, Devon.
Chorley-Burdett Antiques, Bournemouth, Dorset.
English Rose Antiques, Coggeshall, Essex.
Partners in Pine, Coggeshall, Essex.
Dean Antiques, Colchester, Essex.
Revival, Colchester, Essex.
Phoenix Trading, Frinton-on-Sea, Essex.
Hay Green Antiques, Fyfield, Essex.
The Stores, Great Waltham, Essex.
Churchgate Antiques, Sible Hedingham, Essex.
Fox and Pheasant Antique Pine, White Colne, Essex.
Denzil Verey, Barnsley, Glos.
Oldwoods, Bristol, Glos.
Relics - Pine Furniture, Bristol, Glos.
John P. Townsend, Cheltenham, Glos.
The Kettle House, Chipping Campden, Glos.
Ronson's Architectural Effects, Norton, Glos.
Kelly Antiques, Rodley, Glos.
Berkeley Antiques, Tewkesbury, Glos.
Thornbury Antiques, Thornbury, Glos.
Campden Country Pine Antiques, Winchcombe, Glos.
The Furniture Trading Co, Botley, Hants.
Squirrels, Brockenhurst, Hants.
C.W. Buckingham, Cadnam, Hants.
Folly Farm Antiques, Crawley, Hants.
Hursley Antiques, Hursley, Hants.
The Pine Emporium, Hursley, Hants.

SPECIALIST DEALERS

Burgess Farm Antiques, Morestead, Hants.
Smith & Sons, Ringwood, Hants.
The Pine Cellars, Winchester, Hants.
Dobson's Antiques, Abbots Langley, Herts.
Country Life Antiques, Bushey, Herts.
The Pine Emporium, Hemel Hempstead, Herts.
Galerias Segui, Cowes, Isle of Wight.
Rex Gully Antiques, Seaview, Isle of Wight.
Richard Moate Antiques and Back 2 Wood Pine Stripping, Appledore, Kent.
Antique and Design, Canterbury, Kent.
Vestry Antiques, Cranbrook, Kent.
Farningham Pine, Farningham, Kent.
Penny Lampard, Headcorn, Kent.
Harriet Ann Sleigh Beds, Rolvenden, Kent.
Old English Pine, Sandgate, Kent.
Claremont Antiques, Tunbridge Wells, Kent.
Ann and Peter Christian, Blackpool, Lancs.
Enloc Antiques, Colne, Lancs.
R.H. Latham Antiques, Tarleton, Lancs.
House Things Antiques, Hinckley, Leics.
Old Hall Farm, Long Clawson, Leics.
Country Pine Antiques, Market Bosworth, Leics.
David E. Burrows, Osgathorpe, Leics.
Quorn Pine and Decoratives, Quorn, Leics.
R. A. James Antiques, Sileby, Leics.
Bell Antiques, Grimsby, Lincs.
Kate, Hemswell Cliff, Lincs.
Andrew Thomas, Stamford, Lincs.
Antiques & Gifts, Downham Market, Norfolk.
Earsham Hall Pine, Earsham, Norfolk.
Heathfield Antiques & Country Pine, Holt, Norfolk.
Holt Antique Centre, Holt, Norfolk.
Echo Antiques, Reepham, Norfolk.
Laila Gray Antiques, Kingsthorpe, Northants.
The Country Pine Shop, West Haddon, Northants.
Bailiffgate Antique Pine, Alnwick, Northumbs.
Jack Spratt Antiques, Newark, Notts.
Harlequin Antiques, Nottingham, Notts.
Aston Pine Antiques, Faringdon, Oxon.
The Faringdon Antique Centre, Faringdon, Oxon.
Ark Antiques, Bishop's Castle, Shrops.
Garrard Antiques, Ludlow, Shrops.
Arty Faherty, Market Drayton, Shrops.
Lansdown Antiques, Bath, Somerset.
Antiques and Country Pine, Crewkerne, Somerset.
Hennessy, Crewkerne, Somerset.
Westville House Antiques, Littleton, Somerset.
Burton Antiques, Burton-on-Trent, Staffs.
Justin Pinewood Ltd, Burton-on-Trent, Staffs.
Country Cottage Interiors, Kingsley, Staffs.
Antiques Within Ltd, Leek, Staffs.
Anvil Antiques Ltd, Leek, Staffs.
Gemini Trading, Leek, Staffs.

Roger Haynes - Antiques Finder, Leek, Staffs.
Coblands Farm Antiques, Depden, Suffolk.
Abbott & Fisk, Framlingham, Suffolk.
The Green Shed, Framlingham, Suffolk.
Joyce Hardy Pine and Country Furniture, Hacheston, Suffolk.
Orwell Pine Co Ltd, Ipswich, Suffolk.
Mildenhall Antiques, Mildenhall, Suffolk.
House of Christian, Ash Vale, Surrey.
Cherub Antiques, Carshalton, Surrey.
M. & M. White Antique & Reproduction Centre, Reigate, Surrey.
The Packhouse, Runfold, Surrey.
Antique Church Furnishings, Walton-on-Thames, Surrey.
Hadlow Down Antiques, Hadlow Down, Sussex East.
John Bird and Annette Puttnam Antiques, Lewes, Sussex East.
Cliffe Gallery Antiques, Lewes, Sussex East.
Bob Hoare - Pine Antiques, Lewes, Sussex East.
Pastorale Antiques, Lewes, Sussex East.
Graham Price Antiques Ltd, Polegate, Sussex East.
Ann Lingard - Rope Walk Antiques, Rye, Sussex East.
Park View Antiques, Wadhurst, Sussex East.
Antiquities, Arundel, Sussex West.
Squire's Pantry Pine and Antiques, Cowfold, Sussex West.
Stable Antiques, Lindfield, Sussex West.
Red Lion Antiques, Petworth, Sussex West.
Stewart Antiques, Petworth, Sussex West.
Northumbria Pine, Whitley Bay, Tyne and Wear.
Christopher Peters Antiques, Brinklow, Warks.
Pine and Things, Shipston-on-Stour, Warks.
Tudor House Antiques, Halesowen, West Mids.
North Wilts Exporters, Brinkworth, Wilts.
Philip A. Ruttleigh Antiques incorporating Crudwell Furniture, Crudwell, Wilts.
Pillars Antiques, Lyneham, Wilts.
Sambourne House Antiques Ltd, Swindon, Wilts.
Gerard Guy Antiques, Bewdley, Worcs.
St. James Antiques, Little Malvern, Worcs.
The Antique Pine & Country Furniture Shop, Driffield, Yorks. East.
Imperial Antiques, Hull, Yorks. East.
Pieter Plantenga, Market Weighton, Yorks. East.
L.L. Ward and Son, Brandsby, Yorks. North.
Old Hall Antiques, Burton Salmon, Yorks. North.
Heathcote Antiques, Cross Hills, Yorks. North.
Fox's Old Pine & Country Furniture, Easingwold, Yorks. North.
Milestone Antiques, Easingwold, Yorks. North.

The Main Pine Co, Green Hammerton, Yorks. North.
Michael Green Pine & Country Antiques, Harrogate, Yorks. North.
Havelocks, Harrogate, Yorks. North.
Westway Pine, Helmsley, Yorks. North.
Daleside Antiques, Markington, Yorks. North.
Northern Antiques Company, Norton, Yorks. North.
Eskdale Antiques, Sleights, Yorks. North.
Millgate Pine & Antiques, Thirsk, Yorks. North.
Ruth Ford Antiques, York, Yorks. North.
St. John Antiques, York, Yorks. North.
Fishlake Antiques, Fishlake, Yorks. South.
Beech House, Sheffield, Yorks. South.
Peter James Antiques, Sheffield, Yorks. South.
Aberford Antiques Ltd t/a Aberford Country Furniture, Aberford, Yorks. West.
Manor Barn, Addingham, Yorks. West.
Cottingley Antiques, Bradford, Yorks. West.
K.L.M. & Co. Antiques, Lepton, Yorks. West.
Cottage Antiques, Pontefract, Yorks. West.
Memory Lane, Sowerby Bridge, Yorks. West.
Cottage Antiques (1984) Ltd, Walsden, Yorks. West.
The Pine Collection, St. Peter Port, Guernsey, C.I.
Herbert Gould and Co., Holywood, Co. Down, N. Ireland.
Ashley Pine, Saintfield, Co. Down, N. Ireland.
Attic Antiques, Saintfield, Co. Down, N. Ireland.
Homes, Pubs and Clubs, Coleraine, Co. Londonderry, N. Ireland.
Times Past Antiques, Auchterarder, Scotland.
London Road Antiques, Edinburgh, Scotland.
Country Collectables, Fochabers, Scotland.
West of Scotland Antique Centre Ltd, Glasgow, Scotland.
QS Antiques and Cabinetmakers, Kilmarnock, Scotland.
Mostly Pine, Kingussie, Scotland.
Abbey Antiques, Stirling, Scotland.
The Furniture Cave, Aberystwyth, Wales.
Cwmgwili Mill, Carmarthen, Wales.
Jim and Pat Ash, Llandeilo, Wales.
Heritage Restorations, Llanfair Caereinion, Wales.
Carrington House, Llanrwst, Wales.
Frost Antiques & Pine, Monmouth, Wales.
Trading Post, Mountain Ash, Wales.
R. and S. M. Percival Antiques, Ruthin, Wales.
Potboard Antiques, Tenby, Wales.

Furniture - Victorian
Old Cottage Antiques, London E11.
Andrew Lowe, London EC1.

746

Peter Chapman Antiques and Restoration, London N1.
Furniture Vault, London N1.
Jonathan James, London N1.
Chris Newland Antiques, London N1.
Regent Antiques, London N1.
Restall Brown and Clennell Ltd, London N1.
Marcus Ross Antiques, London N1.
C. Tapsell, London N1.
Dean's Antique Emporium, London N12.
Finchley Fine Art Galleries, London N12.
Betty Gould and Julian Gonnermann Antiques, London N6.
Dome Antiques (Exports) Ltd, London N7.
Solomon, London N8.
G. and F. Gillingham Ltd, London NW2.
Patricia Beckman Antiques, London NW3.
David Wainwright, London NW3.
George Balot Antiques, London NW8.
Camden Art Gallery, London NW8.
Church Street Antiques, London NW8.
Just Desks, London NW8.
Wellington Gallery, London NW8.
Young & Son, London NW8.
The Galleries, London SE1.
Tower Bridge Antiques, London SE1.
The Junk Shop, London SE10.
Relcy Antiques, London SE10.
The Waterloo Trading Co., London SE10.
Robert Whitfield Antiques, London SE10.
Peter Allen Antiques Ltd. World Wide Antique Exporters, London SE15.
Abbott Antiques and Country Pine, London SE26.
Oola Boola Antiques London, London SE26.
Ward Antiques, London SE7.
Antique Warehouse, London SE8.
Hilary Batstone Antiques inc. Rosie Uniacke Interiors, London SW1.
John Bly, London SW1.
General Trading Co Ltd, London SW1.
Ross Hamilton Ltd, London SW1.
Harrods Ltd, London SW1.
Christopher Howe, London SW1.
Humphrey-Carrasco, London SW1.
M. and D. Lewis, London SW1.
Westenholz Antiques Ltd, London SW1.
Christopher Edwards, London SW11.
Garland Antiques, London SW11.
Overmantels, London SW11.
Pairs Antiques Ltd, London SW11.
A. and J. Fowle, London SW16.
Just a Second, London SW18.
Chelsea Bric-a-Brac Shop Ltd, London SW20.
Prides of London, London SW3.
275 Antiques, London SW6.
Alasdair Brown, London SW6.
John Clay, London SW6.
Fergus Cochrane and Leigh Warren Antiques, London SW6.
HRW Antiques (London) Ltd, London SW6.
L. and E. Kreckovic, London SW6.
Michael Luther Antiques, London SW6.
David Martin-Taylor Antiques, London SW6.

Megan Mathers Antiques, London SW6.
Rogers & Co, London SW6.
Stephen Sprake, London SW6.
Adrian Alan Ltd, London W1.
Fortnum and Mason plc, London W1.
P.R. Barham, London W11.
Barham Antiques, London W11.
Butchoff Antiques, London W11.
Judy Fox, London W11.
Graham and Green, London W11.
M. and D. Lewis, London W11.
Terence Morse and Son Ltd, London W11.
Myriad Antiques, London W11.
David Wainwright, London W11.
Trude Weaver, London W11.
Marshall Gallery, London W14.
Craven Gallery, London W2.
Aberdeen House Antiques, London W5.
Terrace Antiques, London W5.
Haslam and Whiteway, London W8.
Lewis and Lloyd, London W8.
Pamela Teignmouth and Son, London W8.
Jeremy Seale Antiques/Interiors, London WC1.
Robert Harman Antiques, Ampthill, Beds.
Paris Antiques, Ampthill, Beds.
Pilgrim Antiques, Ampthill, Beds.
S. and S. Timms Antiques Ltd, Shefford, Beds.
Manor Antiques, Wilstead (Wilshamstead), Beds.
Town Hall Antiques, Woburn, Beds.
Melnick House of Ascot, Ascot, Berks.
Bow House Antiques & Interiors, Hungerford, Berks.
Roger King Antiques, Hungerford, Berks.
Hill Farm Antiques, Leckhampstead, Berks.
Widmerpool House Antiques, Maidenhead, Berks.
Rupert Landen Antiques, Reading, Berks.
John Connell - Wargrave Antiques, Wargrave, Berks.
Eton Antiques Partnership, Windsor and Eton, Berks.
Peter J. Martin, Windsor and Eton, Berks.
Studio 101, Windsor and Eton, Berks.
Times Past Antiques, Windsor and Eton, Berks.
The Cupboard Antiques, Amersham, Bucks.
June Elsworth - Beaconsfield Ltd, Beaconsfield, Bucks.
Period Furniture Showrooms, Beaconsfield, Bucks.
The Spinning Wheel, Beaconsfield, Bucks.
John Overland Antiques, Olney, Bucks.
Robin Unsworth Antiques, Olney, Bucks.
Country Furniture Shop, Penn, Bucks.
Bowood Antiques, Wendover, Bucks.
Jess Applin Antiques, Cambridge, Cambs.
Comberton Antiques, Comberton, Cambs.
Mere Antiques, Fowlmere, Cambs.
Ivor and Patricia Lewis Antique and Fine Art Dealers, Peterborough, Cambs.

Antiques & Curios (Steve Carpenter), Wisbech, Cambs.
Sara Frances Antiques, Alderley Edge, Cheshire.
Church Street Antiques, Altrincham, Cheshire.
Andrew Foott Antiques, Cheadle Hulme, Cheshire.
Boustead-Bland Antiques, Chester, Cheshire.
Moor Hall Antiques, Chester, Cheshire.
The Old Warehouse Antiques, Chester, Cheshire.
W. Buckley Antiques Exports, Congleton, Cheshire.
Affordable Antiques, Hale, Cheshire.
Glynn Interiors, Knutsford, Cheshire.
John Titchner and Sons, Littleton, Cheshire.
Chapel Antiques, Nantwich, Cheshire.
Cobwebs of Antiquities Ltd, Sale, Cheshire.
Limited Editions, Stockport, Cheshire.
Page Antiques, Stockport, Cheshire.
The Old Sofa Warehouse, Wilmslow, Cheshire.
Country Living Antiques, Callington, Cornwall.
Old Town Hall Antiques, Falmouth, Cornwall.
Antique Chairs and Museum, Launceston, Cornwall.
John Bragg Antiques, Lostwithiel, Cornwall.
Antiques & Fine Art, Penzance, Cornwall.
Pydar Antiques and Pine, Truro, Cornwall.
Victoria Antiques, Wadebridge, Cornwall.
Anthemion - The Antique Shop, Cartmel, Cumbria.
Haughey Antiques, Kirkby Stephen, Cumbria.
Thornbridge Antiques, Bakewell, Derbys.
Water Lane Antiques, Bakewell, Derbys.
Hackney House Antiques, Barlow, Derbys.
The Antiques Warehouse, Buxton, Derbys.
Maggie Mays, Buxton, Derbys.
N. and C.A. Haslam, Chesterfield, Derbys.
Ian Morris, Chesterfield, Derbys.
Wayside Antiques, Duffield, Derbys.
Taylor Robinson Antiques, Ripley, Derbys.
Nimbus Antiques, Whaley Bridge, Derbys.
Wooden Box Antiques, Woodville, Derbys.
TheDavies Gallery, Bideford, Devon.
John Prestige Antiques, Brixham, Devon.
Alison Gosling Antiques, Budleigh Salterton, Devon.
Mills Antiques, Cullompton, Devon.
McBains Antiques, Exeter, Devon.
Lombard Antiques, Honiton, Devon.
Merchant House Antiques, Honiton, Devon.
Upstairs, Downstairs, Honiton, Devon.
Bonstow and Crawshay Antiques, Kingskerswell, Devon.

SPECIALIST DEALERS

Farthings, Lynton, Devon.
Pugh's Farm Antiques, Monkton, Devon.
W. J. Woodhams, Shaldon, Devon.
Past and Present, Totnes, Devon.
Anthony James Antiques, Whimple, Devon.
Woodbury Antiques, Woodbury, Devon.
Colin Rhodes Antiques, Yealmpton, Devon.
Antiques for All, Blandford Forum, Dorset.
Chorley-Burdett Antiques, Bournemouth, Dorset.
Victorian Chairman, Bournemouth, Dorset.
David Mack Antiques, Branksome, Dorset.
Benchmark Antiques, Bridport, Dorset.
Zona Dawson Antiques, Charlton Marshall, Dorset.
Hamptons, Christchurch, Dorset.
Tower Antiques, Cranborne, Dorset.
Michael Legg Antiques, Dorchester, Dorset.
Hardy Country, Melbury Osmond, Dorset.
Laburnum Antiques, Poole, Dorset.
Shaston Antiques, Shaftesbury, Dorset.
Heygate Browne Antiques, Sherborne, Dorset.
Piers Pisani Antiques, Sherborne, Dorset.
Joan and David White Antiques, Barnard Castle, Durham.
Margaret Bedi Antiques & Fine Art, Billingham, Durham.
Alan Ramsey Antiques, Darlington, Durham.
Paraphernalia, Norton, Durham.
Eden House Antiques, West Auckland, Durham.
Revival, Abridge, Essex.
Swan Antiques, Baythorne End, Essex.
Hutchison Antiques, Chelmsford, Essex.
Argentum Antiques, Coggeshall, Essex.
Hay Green Antiques, Fyfield, Essex.
Memories, Great Dunmow, Essex.
Colton Antiques, Kelvedon, Essex.
Deja Vu Antiques, Leigh-on-Sea, Essex.
Tilly's Antiques, Leigh-on-Sea, Essex.
Clive Beardall Antiques, Maldon, Essex.
West Essex Antiques (Stone Hall), Matching Green, Essex.
F.G. Bruschweiler (Antiques) Ltd, Rayleigh, Essex.
Bush Antiques, Saffron Walden, Essex.
The Interior Design Shop, Saffron Walden, Essex.
Hedingham Antiques & Interiors, Sible Hedingham, Essex.
Harris Antiques (Stansted), Stansted, Essex.
Linden House Antiques, Stansted, Essex.
Old Barn Antiques, Thornwood Common, Essex.
Simpsons Antiques & Fine Interiors, Thornwood Common, Essex.
It's About Time, Westcliff-on-Sea, Essex.
White Roding Antiques, White Roding, Essex.
Peter and Penny Proudfoot, Berkeley, Glos.

The Antiques Warehouse Ltd, Bristol, Glos.
Bristol Guild of Applied Art Ltd, Bristol, Glos.
Oldwoods, Bristol, Glos.
Latchford Antiques, Cheltenham, Glos.
Manor House Antiques, Cheltenham, Glos.
Cottage Farm Antiques, Chipping Campden, Glos.
The Kettle House, Chipping Campden, Glos.
Swan Antiques, Chipping Campden, Glos.
Patrick Waldron Antiques, Cirencester, Glos.
Bernard Weaver Antiques, Cirencester, Glos.
Blenheim Antiques, Fairford, Glos.
Mark Carter Antiques, Fairford, Glos.
Berry Antiques, Moreton-in-Marsh, Glos.
Dale House Antiques, Moreton-in-Marsh, Glos.
Lemington House Antiques, Moreton-in-Marsh, Glos.
Seaford House Antiques, Moreton-in-Marsh, Glos.
Simply Antiques, Moreton-in-Marsh, Glos.
Gary Wright Antiques, Moreton-in-Marsh, Glos.
Robson Antiques, Northleach, Glos.
Ashton Gower Antiques, Stow-on-the-Wold, Glos.
Christopher Clarke Antiques Ltd, Stow-on-the-Wold, Glos.
T.M. King-Smith & Simon W. Nutter, Stow-on-the-Wold, Glos.
La Chaise Antique, Stow-on-the-Wold, Glos.
Queens Parade Antiques Ltd, Stow-on-the-Wold, Glos.
Styles of Stow, Stow-on-the-Wold, Glos.
Tudor House, Stow-on-the-Wold, Glos.
Wyndhams, Stow-on-the-Wold, Glos.
Ball and Claw Antiques, Tetbury, Glos.
Balmuir House Antiques, Tetbury, Glos.
The Chest of Drawers, Tetbury, Glos.
Bobbie Middleton, Tetbury, Glos.
Porch House Antiques, Tetbury, Glos.
Berkeley Antiques, Tewkesbury, Glos.
Cotswold Antiques. com, Winchcombe, Glos.
The Furniture Trading Co, Botley, Hants.
Eversley Antiques Centre, Eversley, Hants.
Antique House, Hartley Wintney, Hants.
Deva Antiques, Hartley Wintney, Hants.
Plestor Barn Antiques, Liss, Hants.
Wick Antiques, Lymington, Hants.
The Gallery, Portsmouth, Hants.
Gasson Antiques and Interiors, Tadley, Hants.
Gaylords, Titchfield, Hants.
Winchester Antiques, Winchester, Hants.
Warings of Hereford, Hereford, Herefs.
John Nash Antiques and Interiors, Ledbury, Herefs.
Serendipity, Ledbury, Herefs.
Jeffery Hammond Antiques, Leominster, Herefs.
Anthony Butt Antiques, Baldock, Herts.
Tapestry Antiques, Hertford, Herts.

Hanbury Antiques, Hitchin, Herts.
Phillips of Hitchin (Antiques) Ltd, Hitchin, Herts.
Tom Salusbury Antiques, Hitchin, Herts.
J.N. Antiques, Redbourn, Herts.
Charnwood Antiques, Sawbridgeworth, Herts.
New England House Antiques, Tring, Herts.
Collins Antiques (F.G. and C. Collins Ltd.), Wheathampstead, Herts.
The Old Bakery Antiques, Wheathampstead, Herts.
Michael Armson (Antiques) Ltd, Wilstone, Herts.
John Corrin Antiques, Douglas, Isle of Man.
Royal Standard Antiques, Cowes, Isle of Wight.
Hayter's, Ryde, Isle of Wight.
Stablegate Antiques, Barham, Kent.
Courtyard Antiques, Brasted, Kent.
Peter Dyke, Brasted, Kent.
Keymer Son & Co. Ltd, Brasted, Kent.
Roy Massingham Antiques, Brasted, Kent.
Graham Stead Antiques, Brasted, Kent.
Conquest House Antiques, Canterbury, Kent.
Chislehurst Antiques, Chislehurst, Kent.
Alan Lord Antiques, Folkestone, Kent.
Mill House Antiques, Goudhurst, Kent.
Samovar Antiques, Hythe, Kent.
Newnham Court Antiques, Maidstone, Kent.
Newington Antiques, Newington, Kent.
Northfleet Hill Antiques, Northfleet, Kent.
J.D. and R.M. Walters, Rolvenden, Kent.
Finch Antiques, Sandgate, Kent.
Michael Fitch Antiques, Sandgate, Kent.
Forge Antiques and Restorations, Sandhurst, Kent.
Gem Antiques, Sevenoaks, Kent.
Steppes Hill Farm Antiques, Stockbury, Kent.
Kentdale Antiques, Tunbridge Wells, Kent.
The Pantiles Antiques, Tunbridge Wells, Kent.
Pantiles Spa Antiques, Tunbridge Wells, Kent.
Phoenix Antiques, Tunbridge Wells, Kent.
Up Country, Tunbridge Wells, Kent.
Apollo Antique Galleries, Westerham, Kent.
Marks Antiques, Westerham, Kent.
Taylor-Smith Antiques, Westerham, Kent.
Westerham Antiques Warehouse, Westerham, Kent.
Westerham House Antiques, Westerham, Kent.
Laurens Antiques, Whitstable, Kent.
Tankerton Antiques, Whitstable, Kent.
Silvesters, Wingham, Kent.
Charles International Antiques, Wrotham, Kent.
Brun Lea Antiques (J. Waite Ltd), Burnley, Lancs.
Folly Antiques, Clitheroe, Lancs.
Cottage Antiques, Darwen, Lancs.
K.C. Antiques, Darwen, Lancs.
P.J. Brown Antiques, Haslingden, Lancs.

SPECIALIST DEALERS

R.J. O'Brien and Son Antiques Ltd, Manchester, Lancs.
Premiere Antiques, Manchester, Lancs.
Prestwich Antiques Ltd, Manchester, Lancs.
Luigino Vescovi, Morecambe, Lancs.
Brooks Antiques, Nelson, Lancs.
European Fine Arts and Antiques, Preston, Lancs.
The Glory Hole, Earl Shilton, Leics.
Sitting Pretty, Great Glen, Leics.
House Things Antiques, Hinckley, Leics.
Withers of Leicester, Hoby, Leics.
Corry's, Leicester, Leics.
J. Stamp and Sons, Market Harborough, Leics.
Ken Smith Antiques Ltd, Narborough, Leics.
J. Green and Son, Queniborough,, Leics.
Charles Antiques, Whitwick, Leics.
Grantham Furniture Emporium, Grantham, Lincs.
G. Baker Antiques, Horncastle, Lincs.
Seaview Antiques, Horncastle, Lincs.
Laurence Shaw Antiques, Horncastle, Lincs.
Staines Antiques, Horncastle, Lincs.
C. and K.E. Dring, Lincoln, Lincs.
Graham Pickett Antiques, Stamford, Lincs.
Sinclair's, Stamford, Lincs.
St. George's Antiques, Stamford, Lincs.
The Antique Shop, Sutton Bridge, Lincs.
Robin Shield Antiques, Swinstead, Lincs.
Underwoodhall Antiques, Woodhall Spa, Lincs.
V.O.C. Antiques, Woodhall Spa, Lincs.
Stefani Antiques, Liverpool, Merseyside.
Colin Stock, Rainford, Merseyside.
Tony and Anne Sutcliffe Antiques, Southport, Merseyside.
Gallerie Veronique, Enfield, Middx.
Hunter's of Hampton, Hampton, Middx.
Ivy House Antiques, Acle, Norfolk.
A.E. Bush and Partners, Attleborough, Norfolk.
M. and A. Cringle, Burnham Market, Norfolk.
A.E. Seago, Cromer, Norfolk.
Antiques & Gifts, Downham Market, Norfolk.
Peter Robinson, Heacham, Norfolk.
Norfolk Galleries, King's Lynn, Norfolk.
Eric Bates and Sons, North Walsham, Norfolk.
Nicholas Fowle Antiques, Norwich, Norfolk.
John Howkins Antiques, Norwich, Norfolk.
Echo Antiques, Reepham, Norfolk.
Country House Antiques, Seething, Norfolk.
Leo Pratt and Son, South Walsham, Norfolk.
Stalham Antique Gallery, Stalham, Norfolk.
Jubilee Antiques, Tottenhill, Norfolk.
M.E. and J.E. Standley, Wymondham, Norfolk.
Brackley Antiques, Brackley, Northants.
Courtyard Antiques, Brackley, Northants.
Simon Banks Antiques, Finedon, Northants.

Huntershield Antiques and Granary Antiques, Flore, Northants.
Christopher Jones Antiques, Flore, Northants.
F. and C.H. Cave, Northampton, Northants.
Bryan Perkins Antiques, Wellingborough, Northants.
Barber Antiques, West Haddon, Northants.
Charlotte and John Lambe, Belfast, N. Ireland.
Boadens Antiques, Hexham, Northumbs.
Hedley's of Hexham, Hexham, Northumbs.
James Miller Antiques, Wooler, Northumbs.
Blacksmiths Forge, Balderton, Notts.
A.J. O'Sullivan Antiques, Darlton, Notts.
Fair Deal Antiques, Mansfield, Notts.
Antiques across the World, Nottingham, Notts.
Harlequin Antiques, Nottingham, Notts.
Pegasus Antiques, Nottingham, Notts.
David and Carole Potter Antiques, Nottingham, Notts.
Ranby Hall, Retford, Notts.
Strouds (of Southwell Antiques), Southwell, Notts.
Burford Antique Centre, Burford, Oxon.
Gateway Antiques, Burford, Oxon.
Hubert's Antiques, Burford, Oxon.
Anthony Nielsen Antiques, Burford, Oxon.
David Pickup, Burford, Oxon.
Walkers, Burford, Oxon.
Rupert Hitchcox Antiques, Chalgrove, Oxon.
Georgian House Antiques, Chipping Norton, Oxon.
Hallidays (Fine Antiques) Ltd, Dorchester-on-Thames, Oxon.
The Faringdon Antique Centre, Faringdon, Oxon.
Richard J. Kingston, Henley-on-Thames, Oxon.
The Country Seat, Huntercombe, Oxon.
de Albuquerque Antiques, Wallingford, Oxon.
Chris and Lin O'Donnell Antiques, Wallingford, Oxon.
Cross Antiques, Watlington, Oxon.
Stephen Orton Antiques, Watlington, Oxon.
Colin Greenway Antiques, Witney, Oxon.
W.R. Harvey & Co (Antiques) Ltd, Witney, Oxon.
Joan Wilkins Antiques, Witney, Oxon.
Bees Antiques, Woodstock, Oxon.
Robin Sanders and Sons, Woodstock, Oxon.
Swans, Oakham, Rutland.
T.J. Roberts, Uppingham, Rutland.
Woodman's House Antiques, Uppingham, Rutland.
Robert Bingley Antiques, Wing, Rutland.
Mytton Antiques, Atcham, Shrops.
Malthouse Antiques, Bridgnorth, Shrops.
Longmynd Antiques, Church Stretton, Shrops.
Portcullis Furniture, Craven Arms, Shrops.

Hodnet Antiques, Hodnet, Shrops.
Claymore Antiques, Ludlow, Shrops.
M. & R. Taylor Antiques Sarah Taylor Interiors, Ludlow, Shrops.
Valentyne Dawes Gallery, Ludlow, Shrops.
Corner Farm Antiques, Shifnal, Shrops.
F.C. Manser and Son Ltd, Shrewsbury, Shrops.
Brian James Antiques, Telford, Shrops.
A J Antiques, Bath, Somerset.
Antiques of Bath, Bath, Somerset.
The Antiques Warehouse, Bath, Somerset.
Lawrence Brass, Bath, Somerset.
Geoffrey Breeze, Bath, Somerset.
Mary Cruz, Bath, Somerset.
Montague Antiques, Bath, Somerset.
Piccadilly Antiques, Batheaston, Somerset.
M.G.R. Exports, Bruton, Somerset.
Chris's Crackers, Carhampton, Somerset.
Guy Dennler Antiques, Dulverton, Somerset.
C.W.E. Dyte, Highbridge, Somerset.
Edward Marnier Antiques, Shepton Mallet, Somerset.
Selwoods, Taunton, Somerset.
John Hamblin, Yeovil, Somerset.
Gilligans Antiques, Leek, Staffs.
Richard Midwinter Antiques, Newcastle-under-Lyme, Staffs.
The Potteries Antique Centre Ltd, Stoke-on-Trent, Staffs.
White House Antiques, Uttoxeter, Staffs.
H.W. Heron and Son Ltd, Yoxall, Staffs.
Thompson's Gallery, Aldeburgh, Suffolk.
Saltgate Antiques, Beccles, Suffolk.
P. Dawson Furniture Restorers, Bentley, Suffolk.
Peppers Period Pieces, Bury St. Edmunds, Suffolk.
Cavendish Rose Antiques, Cavendish, Suffolk.
Robin Butler, Clare, Suffolk.
Debenham Antiques, Debenham, Suffolk.
English and Continental Antiques, Eye, Suffolk.
Halesworth Antiques Market, Halesworth, Suffolk.
A. Abbott Antiques, Ipswich, Suffolk.
The Edwardian Shop, Ipswich, Suffolk.
Hubbard Antiques, Ipswich, Suffolk.
Warrens Antiques Warehouse, Leiston, Suffolk.
Karen Bryan Antiques, Long Melford, Suffolk.
Alexander Lyall Antiques, Long Melford, Suffolk.
Mary Palmer Antiques, Stradbroke, Suffolk.
Gainsborough Antiques, Sudbury, Suffolk.
Napier House Antiques, Sudbury, Suffolk.
Ashe Antiques Warehouse, Wickham Market, Suffolk.
Hamilton Antiques, Woodbridge, Suffolk.
Anthony Hurst Antiques, Woodbridge, Suffolk.
Lambert's Barn, Woodbridge, Suffolk.

749

J.C. Heather, Woolpit, Suffolk.
Wrentham Antiques, Wrentham, Suffolk.
House of Christian, Ash Vale, Surrey.
Country Antiques, Bagshot, Surrey.
Dolphin Square Antiques, Dorking, Surrey.
Dorking Desk Shop, Dorking, Surrey.
Gallery Eleven, Dorking, Surrey.
Harman's Antiques, Dorking, Surrey.
Holmwood Antiques, Dorking, Surrey.
The House of Bulow Antiques, Dorking, Surrey.
Malthouse Antiques, Dorking, Surrey.
Mayfair Antiques, Dorking, Surrey.
Norfolk House Galleries, Dorking, Surrey.
The Vinery, Dorking, Surrey.
West Street Antiques, Dorking, Surrey.
A. E. Booth & Son, Ewell, Surrey.
The Antiques Warehouse, Farnham, Surrey.
Christopher's Antiques, Farnham, Surrey.
The Coach House Antiques, Gomshall, Surrey.
M. J. Bowdery, Hindhead, Surrey.
Glencorse Antiques, Kingston-upon-Thames, Surrey.
Elm House Antiques, Merstham, Surrey.
Michael Andrews Antiques, Milford, Surrey.
F.G. Lawrence and Sons, Redhill, Surrey.
The Gallery, Reigate, Surrey.
Antique Mart, Richmond, Surrey.
Hill Rise Antiques, Richmond, Surrey.
Marryat, Richmond, Surrey.
Sage Antiques and Interiors, Ripley, Surrey.
Cockrell Antiques, Surbiton, Surrey.
B. M. and E. Newlove, Surbiton, Surrey.
Brocante, Weybridge, Surrey.
Church House Antiques, Weybridge, Surrey.
Weybridge Antiques, Weybridge, Surrey.
Alexandria Antiques, Brighton, Sussex East.
Ashton's Antiques, Brighton, Sussex East.
Alan Fitchett Antiques, Brighton, Sussex East.
Dudley Hume, Brighton, Sussex East.
Patrick Moorhead Antiques, Brighton, Sussex East.
Ben Ponting Antiques, Brighton, Sussex East.
Colonial Times, Cross in Hand, Sussex East.
Dycheling Antiques, Ditchling, Sussex East.
Timothy Partridge Antiques, Eastbourne, Sussex East.
Hadlow Down Antiques, Hadlow Down, Sussex East.
Coach House Antiques, Hastings, Sussex East.
John Botting Antiques & Others, Heathfield, Sussex East.
Cliffe Gallery Antiques, Lewes, Sussex East.
The Old Mint House, Pevensey, Sussex East.

Graham Price Antiques Ltd, Polegate, Sussex East.
East Street Antiques, Rye, Sussex East.
Rye Antiques, Rye, Sussex East.
The Old House, Seaford, Sussex East.
Aarquebus Antiques, St. Leonards-on-Sea, Sussex East.
Nicholas Cole Antiques, St Leonards-on-Sea, Sussex East.
Bygones, Angmering, Sussex West.
W.D. Priddy Antiques, Chichester, Sussex West.
Richard Usher Antiques, Cuckfield, Sussex West.
Stable Antiques, Lindfield, Sussex West.
Callingham Antiques, Northchapel, Sussex West.
Antiquated, Petworth, Sussex West.
Baskerville Antiques, Petworth, Sussex West.
J. Du Cros Antiques, Petworth, Sussex West.
Elliott's, Petworth, Sussex West.
Richard Gardner Antiques, Petworth, Sussex West.
Red Lion Antiques, Petworth, Sussex West.
Ruddy Antiques, Petworth, Sussex West.
J. Powell (Hove) Ltd, Portslade, Sussex West.
Georgia Antiques, Pulborough, Sussex West.
Wilsons Antiques, Worthing, Sussex West.
Little Theatre Antiques Centre, Jesmond, Tyne and Wear.
Ian Sharp Antiques, Tynemouth, Tyne and Wear.
Cwmgwili Mill, Carmarthen, Wales.
Yesterdays, Leamington Spa, Warks.
Apollo Antiques Ltd, Warwick, Warks.
William J. Casey Antiques, Warwick, Warks.
English Antiques, Warwick, Warks.
John Goodwin and Sons, Warwick, Warks.
Patrick and Gillian Morley Antiques, Warwick, Warks.
James Reeve, Warwick, Warks.
Don Spencer Antiques, Warwick, Warks.
Peter Clark Antiques, Birmingham, West Mids.
Retro Antiques, Lye, West Mids.
Brett Wilkins Antiques, Wednesbury, West Mids.
Martin Taylor Antiques, Wolverhampton, West Mids.
Audley House Antiques, Bradford-on-Avon, Wilts.
Mac Humble Antiques, Bradford-on-Avon, Wilts.
Cross Hayes Antiques, Chippenham, Wilts.
Blanchard, Froxfield, Wilts.
Andrew Britten Antiques, Malmesbury, Wilts.
Brocante Antiques Centre, Marlborough, Wilts.
Cook of Marlborough Fine Art Ltd, Marlborough, Wilts.
Katharine House Gallery, Marlborough, Wilts.
Alan Jaffray, Melksham, Wilts.
Boston Antiques, Salisbury, Wilts.

Pennyfarthing Antiques, Salisbury, Wilts.
Salisbury Antiques Warehouse, Salisbury, Wilts.
Bishopstrow Antiques, Warminster, Wilts.
Cassidy's Antiques, Warminster, Wilts.
Isabella Antiques, Warminster, Wilts.
Obelisk Antiques, Warminster, Wilts.
K. and A. Welch, Warminster, Wilts.
Hingstons of Wilton, Wilton, Wilts.
Barnt Green Antiques, Barnt Green, Worcs.
John Hubbard Antique Restorations, Blakedown, Worcs.
Robert Belcher Antiques, Droitwich, Worcs.
Carlton Antiques, Great Malvern, Worcs.
Miscellany Antiques, Great Malvern, Worcs.
Gemini Antiques & Gallery, Kidderminster, Worcs.
S.W. Antiques, Pershore, Worcs.
Lower House Fine Antiques, Redditch, Worcs.
M. Lees and Sons, Worcester, Worcs.
Priory Antiques, Bridlington, Yorks. East.
Houghton Hall Antiques, Market Weighton, Yorks. East.
Penny Farthing Antiques, North Cave, Yorks. East.
Bennett's Antiques & Collectables, Bedale, Yorks. North.
Anthony Graham Antiques, Boroughbridge, Yorks. North.
St. James House Antiques, Boroughbridge, Yorks. North.
R.S. Wilson and Sons, Boroughbridge, Yorks. North.
Milestone Antiques, Easingwold, Yorks. North.
Elm Tree Antiques, Flaxton, Yorks. North.
Garth Antiques, Harrogate, Yorks. North.
Haworth Antiques, Harrogate, Yorks. North.
David Love, Harrogate, Yorks. North.
Chris Wilde Antiques, Harrogate, Yorks. North.
Sturman's Antiques, Hawes, Yorks. North.
John Thompson Antiques, Knaresborough, Yorks. North.
Joan and David White, Manfield, Yorks. North.
Milton Holgate, Ripon, Yorks. North.
Sigma Antiques and Fine Art, Ripon, Yorks. North.
John Gilbert Antiques, Robin Hood's Bay, Yorks. North.
Anderson Slater Antiques, Settle, Yorks. North.
Corn Mill Antiques, Skipton, Yorks. North.
Antony, David & Ann Shackleton, Snainton, Yorks. North.
Robert Morrison and Son, York, Yorks. North.
Acorn Antiques, Sheffield, Yorks. South.
Peter James Antiques, Sheffield, Yorks. South.

N.P. and A. Salt Antiques, Sheffield, Yorks. South.
Top Hat Antique Centre, Sheffield, Yorks. South.
Paul Ward Antiques, Sheffield, Yorks. South.
Aberford Antiques Ltd t/a Aberford Country Furniture, Aberford, Yorks. West.
The Baildon Furniture Co., Baildon, Yorks. West.
Bingley Antiques, Haworth, Yorks. West.
Barleycote Hall Antiques, Keighley, Yorks. West.
Geary Antiques, Leeds, Yorks. West.
Windsor House Antiques (Leeds) Ltd., Leeds, Yorks. West.
Park Antiques, Menston, Yorks. West.
Victoria Antiques, Alderney, C.I.
St. James's Gallery Ltd, St. Peter Port, Guernsey, C.I.
Country House and Cottage Antiques, St Mary, Jersey, C.I.
Stephen Cohu Antiques, St Ouen, Jersey, C.I.
The Country Antiques, Antrim, Co. Antrim, N. Ireland.
Dunluce Antiques, Bushmills, Co. Antrim, N. Ireland.
Robert Christie Antiques, Carrickfergus, Co. Antrim, N. Ireland.
MacHenry Antiques, Newtownabbey, Co. Antrim, N. Ireland.
Time & Tide Antiques, Portaferry, Co. Down, N. Ireland.
Attic Antiques, Saintfield, Co. Down, N. Ireland.
Antiques and Fine Art Gallery, Warrenpoint, Co. Down, N. Ireland.
Colin Wood (Antiques) Ltd, Aberdeen, Scotland.
T.W. Beaty, Beattock, Scotland.
Coldstream Antiques, Coldstream, Scotland.
The Magic Lantern, Dunecht, Scotland.
Dunkeld Antiques, Dunkeld, Scotland.
Laurance Black Ltd, Edinburgh, Scotland.
Alan Day Antiques, Edinburgh, Scotland.
Dunedin Antiques Ltd, Edinburgh, Scotland.
Georgian Antiques, Edinburgh, Scotland.
London Road Antiques, Edinburgh, Scotland.
Whytock and Reid, Edinburgh, Scotland.
Young Antiques, Edinburgh, Scotland.
Pringle Antiques, Fochabers, Scotland.
Gow Antiques, Forfar, Scotland.
E.A. Alvariño - Antiques, Glasgow, Scotland.
Butler's Furniture Galleries, Glasgow, Scotland.
Strachan Antiques, Glasgow, Scotland.
Michael YoungAntiques at Glencarse, Glencarse, Scotland.
Kilmacolm Antiques Ltd, Kilmacolm, Scotland.
QS Antiques and Cabinetmakers, Kilmarnock, Scotland.
Rhudle Mill, Kilmichael Glassary, Scotland.
Miles Antiques, Kinross, Scotland.
Airlie Antiques, Meigle, Scotland.

Michael Vee Design - Birch House Antiques, Melrose, Scotland.
Newburgh Antiques, Newburgh, Scotland.
A.S. Deuchar and Son, Perth, Scotland.
The Antiques Shop, Pittenweem, Scotland.
Crossroads Antiques, Prestwick, Scotland.
The Mount Antiques Centre, Carmarthen, Wales.
Plough House Interiors, Chepstow, Wales.
K.W. Finlay Antiques, Ciliau Aeron, Wales.
North Wales Antiques - Colwyn Bay, Colwyn Bay, Wales.
Cowbridge Antique Centre, Cowbridge, Wales.
Havard and Havard, Cowbridge, Wales.
Renaissance Antiques, Cowbridge, Wales.
Furn Davies Partnership, Holt, Wales.
Kidwelly Antiques, Kidwelly, Wales.
Collinge Antiques, Llandudno Junction, Wales.
J. and R. Langford, Llangollen, Wales.
Carrington House, Llanrwst, Wales.
Trading Post, Mountain Ash, Wales.
R. and S. M. Percival Antiques, Ruthin, Wales.
Barn Court Antiques, Crafts & Tearoom, Templeton, Wales.
All Old Exports Ltd., Treorchy, Wales.

Garden Furniture, Statuary and Ornaments

LASSCo, London EC2.
Westland & Company, London EC2.
Gordon Gridley, London N1.
House of Steel Antiques, London N1.
Old School (Gardens & Interiors), London N19.
Relic Antiques Trade Warehouse, London NW1.
David Wainwright, London NW3.
Crowther of Syon Lodge Ltd, London SW1.
Charles Edwards, London SW6.
Sylvia Napier Ltd, London SW6.
M. Pauw Antiques, London SW6.
Mallett at Bourdon House Ltd, London W1.
Myriad Antiques, London W11.
J. D. Marshall, London W4.
Below Stairs of Hungerford, Hungerford, Berks.
Garden Art, Hungerford, Berks.
The Antique Garden, Chester, Cheshire.
Cheshire Brick and Slate Co, Tarvin Sands, Cheshire.
The Great Northern Architectural Antique Company Ltd, Tattenhall, Cheshire.
Haughey Antiques, Kirkby Stephen, Cumbria.
Dorset Reclamation, Bere Regis, Dorset.
Talisman, Gillingham, Dorset.
I. Westrope, Birdbrook, Essex.
Julia Bennet (Antiques), Great Dunmow, Essex.
Jon Fox Antiques, Moreton-in-Marsh, Glos.
Robson Antiques, Northleach, Glos.

Ronson's Architectural Effects, Norton, Glos.
Duncan J. Baggott, Stow-on-the-Wold, Glos.
Architectural Heritage, Taddington, Glos.
Jardinique, Beech, Hants.
Jimmy Warren Antiques, Littlebourne, Kent.
The Architectural Emporium, Tunbridge Wells, Kent.
Folly Antiques, Clitheroe, Lancs.
Lindsey Court Architectural Antiques, Horncastle, Lincs.
Crowther of Syon Lodge Ltd, Isleworth, Middx.
Mongers, Hingham, Norfolk.
The Potting Shed, Holkham, Norfolk.
Reindeer Antiques Ltd, Potterspury, Northants.
The Country Seat, Huntercombe, Oxon.
John Garner, Uppingham, Rutland.
David Bridgwater, Bath, Somerset.
Source, Bath, Somerset.
Walcot Reclamation, Bath, Somerset.
Dix-Sept, Framlingham, Suffolk.
Drummonds Architectural Antiques, Hindhead, Surrey.
Sweerts de Landas, Ripley, Surrey.
The Packhouse, Runfold, Surrey.
Brighton Architectural Salvage, Brighton, Sussex East.
Dermot and Jill Palmer Antiques, Brighton, Sussex East.
John Bird and Annette Puttnam Antiques, Lewes, Sussex East.
Antiquated, Petworth, Sussex West.
Riverbank, Petworth, Sussex West.
Matthew Eden, Corsham, Wilts.
Holloways, Suckley, Worcs.
The White House Antiques & Architectural Reclamation, Easingwold, Yorks. North.
Coach House Antiques Ltd, Stanley, Scotland.

Glass - see also Glass Domes & Paperweights

R. Arantes - Lalique Glass, London N1.
Carol Ketley Antiques, London N1.
Wilkinson plc, London SE6.
Pullman Gallery, London SW1.
Christine Bridge, London SW13.
The Dining Room Shop, London SW13.
R.A. Barnes Antiques, London SW15.
Mark J. West - Cobb Antiques Ltd, London SW19.
W.G.T.Burne (Antique Glass) Ltd, London SW20.
Thomas Goode and Co (London) Ltd, London W1.
Ronald Phillips Ltd, London W1.
Wilkinson plc, London W1.
Mercury Antiques, London W11.
E.S. Phillips and Sons, London W11.
Tomkinson Stained Glass, London W11.
Craven Gallery, London W2.
Denton Antiques, London W8.
Jeanette Hayhurst Fine Glass, London W8.
Peter Shepherd Antiques, Hurst, Berks.
Cavendish Fine Arts, Sonning-on-Thames, Berks.

SPECIALIST DEALERS

Berkshire Antiques Co Ltd, Windsor and Eton, Berks.
Gabor Cossa Antiques, Cambridge, Cambs.
Antiques, Marazion, Cornwall.
Just Glass, Alston, Cumbria.
Elizabeth and Son, Ulverston, Cumbria.
Martin and Dorothy Harper Antiques, Bakewell, Derbys.
Potter's Antiques and Coins, Bristol, Glos.
Latchford Antiques, Cheltenham, Glos.
Rankine Taylor Antiques, Cirencester, Glos.
Grimes House Antiques & Fine Art, Moreton-in-Marsh, Glos.
Denys Sargeant, Westerham, Kent.
Jack Moore Antiques and Stained Glass, Trawden, Lancs.
Keystone Antiques, Coalville, Leics.
Liz Allport-Lomax, Norwich, Norfolk.
Dorothy's Antiques, Sheringham, Norfolk.
Laurie Leigh Antiques, Oxford, Oxon.
Joan Wilkins Antiques, Witney, Oxon.
Bees Antiques, Woodstock, Oxon.
Frank Dux Antiques, Bath, Somerset.
Somervale Antiques, Midsomer Norton, Somerset.
Mary Palmer Antiques, Stradbroke, Suffolk.
Marryat, Richmond, Surrey.
David R. Fileman, Steyning, Sussex West.
Asylum House Antiques, Bradford-on-Avon, Wilts.
Delomosne and Son Ltd, North Wraxall, Wilts.
Dragon Antiques, Harrogate, Yorks. North.
York Cottage Antiques, Helmsley, Yorks. North.
Dunluce Antiques, Bushmills, Co. Antrim, N. Ireland.
Brian R. Bolt Antiques, Portballintrae, Co. Antrim, N. Ireland.

Glass Domes
Get Stuffed, London N1.
John Burton Natural Craft Taxidermy, Ebrington,Glos.
Heads 'n' Tails, Wiveliscombe, Somerset.

Icons - see Russian Art

Islamic Art
Atlantic Bay Carpets Gallery, London SW7.
DavidAaron Ancient Arts & Rare Carpets, London W1.
Aaron Gallery, London W1.
Emanouel Corporation (UK) Ltd, London W1.
Hadji Baba Ancient Art, London W1.
Mansour Gallery, London W1.
Bashir Mohamed Ltd, London W1.
Axia Art Consultants Ltd, London W11.
Hosains Books and Antiques, London W2.
Sinai Antiques Ltd, London W8.
Clive Rogers Oriental Rugs, Wraysbury, Berks.

Japanese Art - see Oriental

Jewellery - see Silver

Lighting
Carlton Davidson Antiques, London N1.
Sara Lemkow, London N1.
Turn On Lighting, London N1.
The Antique Shop (Valantique), London N2.
David Malik and Son Ltd, London NW10.
No. 28 Antiques, London NW8.
B.C. Metalcrafts Ltd, London NW9.
Oddiquities, London SE23.
Wilkinson plc, London SE6.
Blanchard Ltd, London SW1.
Hermitage Antiques plc, London SW1.
Carlton Hobbs, London SW1.
Christopher Howe, London SW1.
Jeremy Ltd, London SW1.
Lion, Witch and Lampshade, London SW1.
McClenaghan, London SW1.
Rogier et Rogier, London SW1.
Carlton Davidson Antiques, London SW10.
H.W. Poulter and Son, London SW10.
Joy McDonald Antiques, London SW13.
W.G.T.Burne (Antique Glass) Ltd, London SW20.
275 Antiques, London SW6.
The Antique Lamp Shop, London SW6.
Christopher Bangs, London SW6.
Fergus Cochrane and Leigh Warren Antiques, London SW6.
Charles Edwards, London SW6.
Hector Finch Lighting, London SW6.
Judy Greenwood, London SW6.
Hollingshead and Co, London SW6.
Michael Luther Antiques, London SW6.
Sylvia Napier Ltd, London SW6.
Old World Trading Co, London SW6.
M. Pauw Antiques, London SW6.
Stephen Sprake, London SW6.
The French House (Antiques) Ltd, London SW8.
W. Sitch and Co. Ltd., London W1.
Stair and Company Ltd, London W1.
M. Turpin Ltd, London W1.
Wilkinson plc, London W1.
Jones Antique Lighting, London W11.
Marshall Gallery, London W14.
J. D. Marshall, London W4.
Mrs. M.E. Crick Chandeliers, London W8.
Denton Antiques, London W8.
George and Peter Cohn, London WC1.
Manor Antiques, Wilstead (Wilshamstead), Beds.
Below Stairs of Hungerford, Hungerford, Berks.
Temple Lighting (Jeanne Temple Antiques), Milton Keynes, Bucks.
Starlight, Wansford, Cambs.
Cobwebs of Antiquities Ltd, Sale, Cheshire.
Peter Johnson, Penzance, Cornwall.
Staveley Antiques, Staveley, Cumbria.
The Lantern Shop Gallery, Sidmouth, Devon.
Allegra's Lighthouse Antiques, Bournemouth, Dorset.
H.W. Keil (Cheltenham) Ltd, Cheltenham, Glos.
Triton Gallery, Cheltenham, Glos.

J. and J. Caspall Antiques, Stow-on-the-Wold, Glos.
Antony Preston Antiques Ltd, Stow-on-the-Wold, Glos.
Queens Parade Antiques Ltd, Stow-on-the-Wold, Glos.
Government House, Winchcombe, Glos.
Fritz Fryer Antique Lighting, Ross-on-Wye, Herefs.
Magic Lanterns, St. Albans, Herts.
Chislehurst Antiques, Chislehurst, Kent.
The Architectural Emporium, Tunbridge Wells, Kent.
Denys Sargeant, Westerham, Kent.
Prestwich Antiques Ltd, Manchester, Lancs.
The Stiffkey Lamp Shop, Stiffkey, Norfolk.
Barclay Antiques, Headington, Oxon.
Haygate Gallery, Telford, Shrops.
Ian McCarthy, Clutton, Somerset.
Post House Antiques, Bletchingley, Surrey.
Rickett & Co. Antiques, Shepperton, Surrey.
Libra Antiques, Hurst Green, Sussex East.
David R. Fileman, Steyning, Sussex West.
The Incandescent Lighting Company, Leamington Spa, Warks.
Delomosne and Son Ltd, North Wraxall, Wilts.
Inglenook Antiques, Ramsbury, Wilts.
Lower House Fine Antiques, Redditch, Worcs.
Old Flames, Easingwold, Yorks. North.
'Bobbins' Wool, Crafts, Antiques, Whitby, Yorks. North.
Berland's of Edinburgh, Edinburgh, Scotland.
Michael Vee Design - Birch House Antiques, Melrose, Scotland.

Maps & Prints
Ash Rare Books, London EC3.
Judith Lassalle, London N1.
York Gallery Ltd, London N1.
The Totteridge Gallery, London N20.
Centaur Gallery, London N8.
John Denham Gallery, London NW6.
Gallery Kaleidoscope, London NW6.
The Warwick Leadlay Gallery, London SE10.
Julian Hartnoll, London SW1.
Paul Mason Gallery, London SW1.
Old Maps and Prints, London SW1.
The Parker Gallery, London SW1.
Michael Parkin Fine Art Ltd, London SW1.
Henry Sotheran Ltd, London SW1.
Gallery Lingard, London SW3.
Stephanie Hoppen Ltd, London SW3.
The Map House, London SW3.
Old Church Galleries, London SW3.
20th Century Gallery, London SW6.
King's Court Galleries, London SW6.
Michael Marriott Ltd, London SW6.
Trowbridge Gallery, London SW6.
York Gallery Ltd, London SW6.
Paul Orssich, London SW8.
Altea Maps & Books, London W1.
Lumley Cazalet Ltd, London W1.
Andrew Edmunds, London W1.

H. Fritz-Denneville Fine Arts Ltd, London W1.
Map World, London W1.
The O'Shea Gallery, London W1.
Jonathan Potter Ltd, London W1.
Bernard J. Shapero Rare Books, London W1.
Stephen Somerville (W.A.) Ltd, London W1.
Henry Sotheran Ltd, London W1.
Crawley and Asquith Ltd, London W11.
Justin F. Skrebowski Prints, London W11.
Connaught Galleries, London W2.
The Lucy B. Campbell Gallery, London W8.
Adrian Harrington, London W8.
Austin/Desmond Fine Art, London WC1.
Michael Finney Antique Prints and Books, London WC1.
Robert Frew Ltd, London WC1.
Grosvenor Prints, London WC2.
Lee Jackson, London WC2.
Stage Door Prints, London WC2.
Storey's Ltd, London WC2.
The Witch Ball, London WC2.
Melnick House of Ascot, Ascot, Berks.
Graham Gallery, Burghfield Common, Berks.
The Studio Gallery, Datchet, Berks.
Omniphil Prints, Chesham, Bucks.
Penn Barn, Penn, Bucks.
Benet Gallery, Cambridge, Cambs.
The Lawson Gallery, Cambridge, Cambs.
Sebastian Pearson Paintings Prints and Works of Art, Cambridge, Cambs.
Norman Blackburn, Elsworth, Cambs.
Old Soke Books, Peterborough, Cambs.
J. Alan Hulme, Chester, Cheshire.
Moor Hall Antiques, Chester, Cheshire.
Iain Campbell, Great Barrow, Cheshire.
Lion Gallery and Bookshop, Knutsford, Cheshire.
John Maggs, Falmouth, Cornwall.
Souvenir Antiques, Carlisle, Cumbria.
Archie Miles Bookshop, Gosforth, Cumbria.
Kendal Studios Antiques, Kendal, Cumbria.
R. F. G. Hollett and Son, Sedbergh, Cumbria.
Alan Hill Books, Chesterfield, Derbys.
Medina Gallery, Barnstaple, Devon.
Medina Gallery, Bideford, Devon.
Chantry Bookshop and Gallery, Dartmouth, Devon.
The Lantern Shop Gallery, Sidmouth, Devon.
Birbeck Gallery, Torquay, Devon.
The Schuster Gallery, Torquay, Devon.
The Artist Gallery, Bournemouth, Dorset.
Bridport Old Books, Bridport, Dorset.
Words Etcetera, Dorchester, Dorset.
F. Whillock, Litton Cheney, Dorset.
Antique Map and Bookshop, Puddletown, Dorset.
Keeble Antiques, Sherborne, Dorset.
The Swan Gallery, Sherborne, Dorset.
The Treasure Chest, Weymouth, Dorset.
J. Shotton Antiquarian Books, Prints and Coins, Durham, Durham.
Castle Bookshop, Colchester, Essex.

Simon Hilton, Great Dunmow, Essex.
Newport Gallery, Newport, Essex.
Cleeve Picture Framing, Bishops Cleeve, Glos.
Alexander Gallery, Bristol, Glos.
Cotham Hill Bookshop, Bristol, Glos.
David Bannister FRGS, Cheltenham, Glos.
Kenulf Fine Arts, Stow-on-the-Wold, Glos.
Talbot Court Galleries, Stow-on-the-Wold, Glos.
Vanbrugh House Antiques, Stow-on-the-Wold, Glos.
Tetbury Gallery, Tetbury, Glos.
Laurence Oxley, Alresford, Hants.
Kingsclere Old Bookshop, Kingsclere, Hants.
Hughes and Smeeth Ltd, Lymington, Hants.
The Petersfield Bookshop, Petersfield, Hants.
Oldfield Gallery, Portsmouth, Hants.
Bell Fine Art, Winchester, Hants.
Ross Old Book and Print Shop, Ross-on-Wye, Herefs.
Gillmark Gallery, Hertford, Herts.
Eric T. Moore, Hitchin, Herts.
Clive A. Burden Ltd, Rickmansworth, Herts.
James of St Albans, St. Albans, Herts.
Galerias Segui, Cowes, Isle of Wight.
The Shanklin Gallery, Shanklin, Isle of Wight.
Ventnor Rare Books, Ventnor, Isle of Wight.
The Canterbury Bookshop, Canterbury, Kent.
Chaucer Bookshop, Canterbury, Kent.
Cranbrook Gallery, Cranbrook, Kent.
G. and D.I. Marrin and Sons, Folkestone, Kent.
The China Locker, Lamberhurst, Kent.
Periwinkle Press, Newnham, Kent.
Langley Galleries, Rochester, Kent.
London House Antiques, Westerham, Kent.
Halewood and Sons, Preston, Lancs.
Leicestershire Sporting Gallery and Brown Jack Bookshop, Lubenham, Leics.
P.J. Cassidy (Books), Holbeach, Lincs.
Golden Goose Books, Lincoln, Lincs.
Harlequin Gallery, Lincoln, Lincs.
The Boydell Galleries, Liverpool, Merseyside.
David Ferrow, Gt. Yarmouth, Norfolk.
Baron Art, Holt, Norfolk.
Baron Art, Kelling, Norfolk.
J & D Clarke Book and Print Dealers, Norwich, Norfolk.
Crome Gallery and Frame Shop, Norwich, Norfolk.
Peter Crowe, Antiquarian Book Seller, Norwich, Norfolk.
Right Angle, Brackley, Northants.
Savage Fine Art, Haselbech, Northants.
Park Gallery & Bookshop, Wellingborough, Northants.
Jane Neville Gallery, Aslockton, Notts.
TRADA, Chipping Norton, Oxon.
The Barry Keene Gallery, Henley-on-Thames, Oxon.
Elizabeth Harvey-Lee, North Aston, Oxon.

Magna Gallery, Oxford, Oxon.
Sanders of Oxford Ltd, Oxford, Oxon.
Toby English, Wallingford, Oxon.
Tooley Adams & Co, Wallingford, Oxon.
Churchgate Antiques, Empingham, Rutland.
The Old House Gallery, Oakham, Rutland.
Marc Oxley Fine Art, Uppingham, Rutland.
The Mount, Woore, Shrops.
Andrew Dando, Bath, Somerset.
Patterson Liddle, Bath, Somerset.
Sarah Russell Antiquarian Prints, Bath, Somerset.
Trimbridge Galleries, Bath, Somerset.
Michael Lewis Gallery - Antiquarian Maps & Prints, Bruton, Somerset.
Julian Armytage, Crewkerne, Somerset.
House of Antiquity, Nether Stowey, Somerset.
Besleys Books, Beccles, Suffolk.
King's Court Galleries, Dorking, Surrey.
Vandeleur Antiquarian Books, Epsom, Surrey.
Reigate Galleries, Reigate, Surrey.
Palmer Galleries, Richmond, Surrey.
Leoframes, Brighton, Sussex East.
The Witch Ball, Brighton, Sussex East.
A. & T. Gibbard, Eastbourne, Sussex East.
Murray Brown, Pevensey Bay, Sussex East.
Baynton-Williams, Arundel, Sussex West.
The Antique Print Shop, East Grinstead, Sussex West.
Julia Holmes Antique Maps and Prints, South Harting, Sussex West.
Osborne Fine Art Gallery, Jesmond,, Tyne and Wear.
Robert Vaughan, Stratford-upon-Avon, Warks.
Carleton Gallery, Birmingham, West Mids.
Bracebridge Fine Art, Astwood Bank, Worcs.
Antique Map and Print Gallery, Worcester, Worcs.
The Grove Country Bookshop with Coopers of Ilkley, Bolton Abbey, Yorks. North.
McTague of Harrogate, Harrogate, Yorks. North.
Minster Gate Bookshop, York, Yorks. North.
The Grove Bookshop, Ilkley, Yorks. West.
Oakwood Gallery, Leeds, Yorks. West.
Channel Islands Galleries Ltd, St. Peter Port, Guernsey, C.I.
Geoffrey P. Gavey, Vale, Guernsey, C.I.
John Blench & Son, St. Helier, Jersey, C.I.
The Selective Eye Gallery, St. Helier, Jersey, C.I.
Thesaurus (Jersey) Ltd, St. Helier, Jersey, C.I.
Phyllis Arnold Gallery Antiques, Greyabbey, Co. Down, N. Ireland.
Colin Wood (Antiques) Ltd, Aberdeen, Scotland.

SPECIALIST DEALERS

The McEwan Gallery, Ballater, Scotland.
Calton Gallery, Edinburgh, Scotland.
The Carson Clark Gallery - Scotland's
Map Heritage Centre, Edinburgh,
Scotland.
Royal Mile Gallery, Edinburgh,
Scotland.
David Windsor Gallery, Bangor, Wales.
Maps, Prints and Books, Brecon, Wales.
Pontcanna Old Books, Maps and Prints,
Cardiff, Wales.
Glance Back Bookshop, Chepstow,
Wales.
Glance Gallery, Chepstow, Wales.

Metalware/work

House of Steel Antiques, London N1.
Sara Lemkow, London N1.
Robert Young Antiques, London SW11.
Christopher Bangs, London SW6.
Jack Casimir Ltd, London W11.
Johnny Von Pflugh Antiques, London
W11.
Manor Antiques, Wilstead
(Wilshamstead), Beds.
Christopher Sykes Antiques, Woburn,
Beds.
Below Stairs of Hungerford, Hungerford,
Berks.
The Fire Place (Hungerford) Ltd,
Hungerford, Berks.
Turpins Antiques, Hungerford, Berks.
Berkshire Metal Finishers Ltd,
Sandhurst, Berks.
Peter J. Martin, Windsor and Eton,
Berks.
Sundial Antiques, Amersham, Bucks.
Phoenix Antiques, Fordham, Cambs.
A.P. and M.A. Haylett, Outwell,
Cambs.
The Antique Shop, Chester, Cheshire.
James Buchanan Antiques, Penzance,
Cornwall.
Simon Starkie Antiques, Cartmel,
Cumbria.
Pamela Elsom - Antiques, Ashbourne,
Derbys.
J H S Antiques, Ashbourne, Derbys.
Martin and Dorothy Harper Antiques,
Bakewell, Derbys.
Water Lane Antiques, Bakewell,
Derbys.
Roderick Butler, Honiton, Devon.
Morchard Bishop Antiques, Morchard
Bishop, Devon.
Alan Jones Antiques, Okehampton,
Devon.
J.B. Antiques, Wimborne Minster,
Dorset.
William H. Stokes, Cirencester, Glos.
J. and J. Caspall Antiques, Stow-on-the-
Wold, Glos.
Christopher Clarke Antiques Ltd, Stow-
on-the-Wold, Glos.
Country Life Antiques, Stow-on-the-
Wold, Glos.
Keith Hockin Antiques, Stow-on-the-
Wold, Glos.
Huntington Antiques Ltd, Stow-on-the-
Wold, Glos.
Tudor House, Stow-on-the-Wold, Glos.
Prichard Antiques, Winchcombe, Glos.
Cedar Antiques Limited, Hartley
Wintney, Hants.
P. and S.N. Eddy, Leominster, Herefs.

Michael Gander, Hitchin, Herts.
James Porter Antiques, Sandwich, Kent.
V.O.C. Antiques, Woodhall Spa, Lincs.
Peter Robinson, Heacham, Norfolk.
Arthur Brett and Sons Ltd, Norwich,
Norfolk.
M.D. Cannell Antiques, Raveningham,
Norfolk.
Huntershield Antiques and Granary
Antiques, Flore, Northants.
Rococo Antiques and Interiors, Weedon,
Northants.
Mark Seabrook Antiques, West Haddon,
Northants.
Jonathan Fyson Antiques, Burford,
Oxon.
Horseshoe Antiques and Gallery,
Burford, Oxon.
Anthony Nielsen Antiques, Burford,
Oxon.
Mike Ottrey Antiques, Wallingford,
Oxon.
Joan Wilkins Antiques, Witney, Oxon.
Witney Antiques, Witney, Oxon.
Brian and Caroline Craik Ltd, Bath,
Somerset.
Source, Bath, Somerset.
Ian McCarthy, Clutton, Somerset.
Bernard G. House, Wells, Somerset.
Peppers Period Pieces, Bury St.
Edmunds, Suffolk.
Anthony Welling Antiques, Ripley,
Surrey.
Rickett & Co. Antiques, Shepperton,
Surrey.
Heritage Antiques, Brighton, Sussex
East.
Rye Antiques, Rye, Sussex East.
Park View Antiques, Wadhurst, Sussex
East.
Michael Wakelin and Helen Linfield,
Billingshurst, Sussex West.
J. Du Cros Antiques, Petworth, Sussex
West.
Retro Antiques, Lye, West Mids.
Avon Antiques, Bradford-on-Avon,
Wilts.
Town and Country Antiques, Bradford-
on-Avon, Wilts.
Combe Cottage Antiques, Castle Combe,
Wilts.
Harriet Fairfax Fireplaces and General
Antiques, Langley Burrell, Wilts.
Rupert Gentle Antiques, Milton
Lilbourne, Wilts.
H.W. Keil Ltd, Broadway, Worcs.
D & J Lines Antiques, Wychbold,
Worcs.
Bill Bentley, Harrogate, Yorks. North.
Garth Antiques, Harrogate, Yorks.
North.
Charles Lumb and Sons Ltd, Harrogate,
Yorks. North.
Elaine Phillips Antiques Ltd, Harrogate,
Yorks. North.
York Cottage Antiques, Helmsley,
Yorks. North.
Aura Antiques, Masham, Yorks. North.
E. Thistlethwaite, Settle, Yorks. North.
Garth Antiques, Whixley, Yorks. North.
Minster Antiques, York, Yorks. North.
Geary Antiques, Leeds, Yorks. West.
Unicorn Antiques, Edinburgh, Scotland.
Tim Wright Antiques, Glasgow,
Scotland.

Miniatures

D.S. Lavender (Antiques) Ltd, London
W1.
S.J. Phillips Ltd, London W1.
H. and W. Deutsch Antiques, London
W8.
Wendover Antiques, Wendover, Bucks.
Simon Brett, Moreton-in-Marsh, Glos.
Michael Sim, Chislehurst, Kent.
Regal Antiques, Westerham, Kent.
Gough Bros. Art Shop and Gallery,
Bognor Regis, Sussex West.
Arden Gallery, Henley-in-Arden, Warks.

Mirrors

Andrew Lowe, London EC1.
George Balot Antiques, London NW8.
Anno Domini Antiques, London SW1.
Chelsea Antique Mirrors, London SW1.
Ossowski, London SW1.
Overmantels, London SW11.
Joy McDonald Antiques, London SW13.
Norman Adams Ltd, London SW3.
Anthony James and Son Ltd, London
SW3.
Peter Lipitch Ltd, London SW3.
Clifford Wright Antiques Ltd, London
SW3.
275 Antiques, London SW6.
Judy Greenwood, London SW6.
House of Mirrors, London SW6.
Christopher Jones Antiques, London
SW6.
Through the Looking Glass Ltd, London
SW6.
Ferenc Toth, London SW6.
Stair and Company Ltd, London W1.
M. Turpin Ltd, London W1.
Valerie Howard, London W8.
Through the Looking Glass Ltd, London
W8.
R. Wilding, Wisbech, Cambs.
Richmond Antiques, Bowdon, Cheshire.
Keeble Antiques, Sherborne, Dorset.
Simpsons - Mirrors & Carvings,
Brentwood, Essex.
Triton Gallery, Cheltenham, Glos.
Ashton Gower Antiques, Stow-on-the-
Wold, Glos.
Stow Antiques, Stow-on-the-Wold,
Glos.
Balmuir House Antiques, Tetbury, Glos.
Jacqueline Hall Antiques, Tetbury, Glos.
Burns and Graham, Winchester, Hants.
The Windhill Antiquary, Bishop's
Stortford, Herts.
Claymore Antiques, Ludlow, Shrops.
Looking Glass of Bath, Bath, Somerset.
Molland Antique Mirrors, Leek, Staffs.
Maria Cass Interiors, Nayland, Suffolk.
The Gallery, Reigate, Surrey.
Dermot and Jill Palmer Antiques,
Brighton, Sussex East.
Shirley Ann's Antiques - International
Interiors, Brighton, Sussex East.
Julian Antiques, Hurstpierpoint, Sussex
West.
Asylum House Antiques, Bradford-on-
Avon, Wilts.
Gemini Antiques & Gallery,
Kidderminster, Worcs.
The Drawing Room - Interiors &
Antiques, Pershore, Worcs.
W. Greenwood (Fine Art), Burneston,
Yorks. North.

The French House (Antiques) Ltd.,
York, Yorks. North.
Michael Vee Design - Birch House
Antiques, Melrose, Scotland.

Musical Boxes, Instruments & Literature

Boxes and Musical Instruments, London E8.
Vincent Freeman, London N1.
Tony Bingham, London NW3.
Otto Haas (A. and M. Rosenthal), London NW3.
Talking Machine, London NW4.
H. Baron, London NW6.
Robert Morley and Co Ltd, London SE13.
J & A Beare Ltd, London W1.
Peter Biddulph, London W1.
Pelham Galleries Ltd, London W1.
Mayflower Antiques, London W11.
Travis and Emery, London WC2.
Times Past Antiques, Windsor and Eton, Berks.
J.V. Pianos and Cambridge Pianola Company, Landbeach, Cambs.
Mill Farm Antiques, Disley, Cheshire.
Miss Elany, Long Eaton, Derbys.
M.C. Taylor, Bournemouth, Dorset.
Mark Marchant (Antiques), Coggeshall, Essex.
Mayflower Antiques, Harwich, Essex.
Arthur S. Lewis, Gloucester, Glos.
Keith Harding's World of Mechanical Music, Northleach, Glos.
Vanbrugh House Antiques, Stow-on-the-Wold, Glos.
Evans and Evans, Alresford, Hants.
Thwaites and Co, Oxhey, Herts.
Old Smithy, Feniscowles, Lancs.
Norfolk Polyphon Centre, Bawdeswell, Norfolk.
The Violin Shop, Hexham, Northumbs.
R.R. Limb Antiques, Newark, Notts.
Laurie Leigh Antiques, Oxford, Oxon.
Howard Hope Phonographs and Gramophones, East Molesey, Surrey.
Graham Webb, Brighton, Sussex East.
John Cowderoy Antiques, Eastbourne, Sussex East.
Pianos Galore, Little Horsted, Sussex East.
The Barber's Clock, Worcester, Worcs.
Thirkill Antiques, Leyburn, Yorks. North.
The Piano Shop, Leeds, Yorks. West.
K.L.M. & Co. Antiques, Lepton, Yorks. West.
Talking Point Antiques, Sowerby Bridge, Yorks. West.
San Domenico Stringed Instruments, Cardiff, Wales.
John Carpenter, Llanelli, Wales.
Keith Chugg Antiques, Swansea, Wales.

Nautical Instruments - see Scientific

Needlework - see Tapestries

Netsuke - see Oriental

Oil Paintings

Peter Chapman Antiques and Restoration, London N1.

Swan Fine Art, London N1.
Finchley Fine Art Galleries, London N12.
Martin Henham (Antiques), London N2.
Lauri Stewart - Fine Art, London N2.
The Totteridge Gallery, London N20.
Sandra Lummis Fine Art, London N8.
Barkes and Barkes, London NW1.
Leask Ward, London NW3.
Duncan R. Miller Fine Arts, London NW3.
Newhart (Pictures) Ltd, London NW3.
John Denham Gallery, London NW6.
Gallery Kaleidoscope, London NW6.
Camden Art Gallery, London NW6.
Nicholas Drummond/Wrawby Moor Art Gallery Ltd, London NW8.
Patricia Harvey Antiques and Decoration, London NW8.
The Greenwich Gallery, London SE10.
Relcy Antiques, London SE10.
Campbell Wilson, London SE11.
Didier Aaron (London)Ltd, London SW1.
Ackermann & Johnson, London SW1.
Verner Åmell Ltd, London SW1.
Antiquus, London SW1.
Artemis Fine Arts Limited, London SW1.
Chris Beetles Ltd, London SW1.
Konrad O. Bernheimer Ltd, London SW1.
John Bly, London SW1.
Brisigotti Antiques Ltd, London SW1.
Miles Wynn Cato, London SW1.
Chaucer Fine Arts Ltd, London SW1.
Cox and Company, London SW1.
Simon C. Dickinson Ltd, London SW1.
Douwes Fine Art Ltd, London SW1.
Eaton Gallery, London SW1.
Frost and Reed Ltd (Est. 1808), London SW1.
Martyn Gregory Gallery, London SW1.
Ross Hamilton Ltd, London SW1.
Harrods Ltd, London SW1.
Julian Hartnoll, London SW1.
Hazlitt, Gooden and Fox Ltd, London SW1.
Hermitage Antiques plc, London SW1.
Carlton Hobbs, London SW1.
Derek Johns Ltd, London SW1.
MacConnal-Mason Gallery, London SW1.
The Mall Galleries, London SW1.
Paul Mason Gallery, London SW1.
Mathaf Gallery Ltd, London SW1.
Matthiesen Fine Art Ltd., London SW1.
Messums, London SW1.
Moreton Street Gallery, London SW1.
Guy Morrison, London SW1.
Peter Nahum at The Leicester Galleries, London SW1.
Paisnel Gallery, London SW1.
The Parker Gallery, London SW1.
Michael Parkin Fine Art Ltd, London SW1.
Portland Gallery, London SW1.
Steven Rich & Michael Rich, London SW1.
Julian Simon Fine Art Ltd, London SW1.
Bill Thomson - Albany Gallery, London SW1.
Trafalgar Galleries, London SW1.
Tryon Gallery (incorporating Malcolm Innes), London SW1.

Rafael Valls Ltd, London SW1.
Rafael Valls Ltd, London SW1.
Johnny Van Haeften Ltd, London SW1.
Waterman Fine Art Ltd, London SW1.
Whitford Fine Art, London SW1.
Wildenstein and Co Ltd, London SW1.
Jonathan Clark & Co, London SW10.
Collins and Hastie Ltd, London SW10.
Lane Fine Art Ltd, London SW10.
Langton Street Gallery, London SW10.
Offer Waterman and Co. Fine Art, London SW10.
Park Walk Gallery, London SW10.
Pairs Antiques Ltd, London SW11.
Regent House Gallery, London SW11.
Alton Gallery, London SW13.
New Grafton Gallery, London SW13.
John Spink, London SW13.
Ted Few, London SW17.
The David Curzon Gallery, London SW19.
The Andipa Gallery, London SW3.
Campbell's of Walton Street, London SW3.
Gallery Lingard, London SW3.
Stephanie Hoppen Ltd, London SW3.
20th Century Gallery, London SW6.
Rupert Cavendish Antiques, London SW6.
Charles Edwards, London SW6.
Julie Collino, London SW7.
The Taylor Gallery Ltd, London SW7.
The Wyllie Gallery, London SW7.
Agnew's, London W1.
Victor Arwas Gallery - Editions Graphiques Gallery Ltd, London W1.
Browse and Darby Ltd, London W1.
Burlington Paintings Ltd, London W1.
Andrew Clayton-Payne Ltd, London W1.
P. and D. Colnaghi & Co Ltd, London W1.
Connaught Brown plc, London W1.
Dover Street Gallery, London W1.
Elwes and Hanham Ltd, London W1.
The Fine Art Society plc, London W1.
H. Fritz-Denneville Fine Arts Ltd, London W1.
Deborah Gage (Works of Art) Ltd, London W1.
The Graham Gallery, London W1.
Richard Green, London W1.
Hahn and Son Fine Art Dealers, London W1.
Patrick Jefferson Ltd, London W1.
The Lefevre Gallery, London W1.
Maas Gallery, London W1.
Mallet and Son (Antiques) Ltd, London W1.
Mallett Gallery, London W1.
Marlborough Fine Art (London) Ltd, London W1.
Messums (Contemporary), London W1.
John Mitchell and Son, London W1.
Omell Galleries, London W1.
Partridge Fine Arts plc, London W1.
W.H. Patterson Fine Arts Ltd, London W1.
Pyms Gallery, London W1.
Royal Exchange Art Gallery at Cork St., London W1.
Stephen Somerville (W.A.) Ltd, London W1.
Spink Leger Pictures, London W1.
Stoppenbach & Delestre Ltd, London W1.

SPECIALIST DEALERS

William Thuillier, London W1.
Walpole Gallery, London W1.
Waterhouse and Dodd, London W1.
The Weiss Gallery, London W1.
Wilkins and Wilkins, London W1.
Williams and Son, London W1.
Butchoff Antiques, London W11.
Caelt Gallery, London W11.
The Coach House, London W11.
Crawley and Asquith Ltd, London W11.
Curá Antiques, London W11.
Charles Daggett Gallery, London W11.
Fleur de Lys Gallery, London W11.
Gavin Graham Gallery, London W11.
Lacy Gallery, London W11.
Milne and Moller, London W11.
Richard Philp, London W11.
Piano Nobile Fine Paintings, London
    W11.
Justin F. Skrebowski Prints, London
    W11.
Stern Art Dealers, London W11.
Johnny Von Pflugh Antiques, London
    W11.
Marshall Gallery, London W14.
Manya Igel Fine Arts Ltd, London W2.
Aberdeen House Antiques, London W5.
Ealing Gallery, London W5.
Baumkotter Gallery, London W8.
George Dare, London W8.
Pawsey and Payne, London W8.
Austin/Desmond Fine Art, London
    WC1.
Baroq & David Ball Antiques, Leighton
    Buzzard, Beds.
Foye Gallery, Luton, Beds.
Woburn Fine Arts, Woburn, Beds.
Omell Galleries, Ascot, Berks.
Graham Gallery, Burghfield Common,
    Berks.
The Studio Gallery, Datchet, Berks.
John A. Pearson Antiques, Horton,
    Berks.
The Coworth Gallery, Sunningdale,
    Berks.
H.S. Wellby Ltd, Haddenham, Bucks.
Penn Barn, Penn, Bucks.
Cambridge Fine Art Ltd, Cambridge,
    Cambs.
Sebastian Pearson Paintings Prints and
    Works of Art, Cambridge, Cambs.
Storm Fine Arts Ltd, Great Shelford,
    Cambs.
Baron Fine Art, Chester, Cheshire.
Harris & Holt, Chester, Cheshire.
Harper Fine Paintings, Poynton,
    Cheshire.
Dunluce Antiques, Bushmills, Co.
    Antrim, N. Ireland.
Antiques and Fine Art Gallery,
    Warrenpoint, Co. Down, N. Ireland.
Copperhouse Gallery - W. Dyer & Sons,
    Hayle, Cornwall.
Tony Sanders Penzance Gallery and
    Antiques, Penzance, Cornwall.
Peter Haworth, Beetham, Cumbria.
The Gallery, Penrith, Cumbria.
R. F. G. Hollett and Son, Sedbergh,
    Cumbria.
Kenneth Upchurch, Ashbourne, Derbys.
Charles H. Ward, Derby, Derbys.
J. Collins and Son, Bideford, Devon.
TheDavies Gallery, Bideford, Devon.
Medina Gallery, Bideford, Devon.
Godolphin Antiques, Chagford, Devon.
Mill Gallery, Ermington, Devon.

Honiton Fine Art, Honiton, Devon.
Skeaping Gallery, Lydford, Devon.
Farthings, Lynton, Devon.
Gordon Hepworth Fine Art, Newton St.
    Cyres, Devon.
Michael Wood Fine Art, Plymouth,
    Devon.
Birbeck Gallery, Torquay, Devon.
Hampshire Gallery, Bournemouth,
    Dorset.
The Swan Gallery, Sherborne, Dorset.
Margaret Bedi Antiques & Fine Art,
    Billingham, Durham.
T.B. and R. Jordan (Fine Paintings),
    Eaglescliffe, Durham.
Brandler Galleries, Brentwood, Essex.
Neil Graham Gallery, Brentwood, Essex.
S. Bond and Son, Colchester, Essex.
Simon Hilton, Great Dunmow, Essex.
Newport Gallery, Newport, Essex.
Galerie Lev, Woodford Green, Essex.
Peter and Penny Proudfoot, Berkeley,
    Glos.
Cleeve Picture Framing, Bishops Cleeve,
    Glos.
The Priory Gallery, Bishops Cleeve,
    Glos.
Alexander Gallery, Bristol, Glos.
H.W. Keil (Cheltenham) Ltd,
    Cheltenham, Glos.
Manor House Antiques, Cheltenham,
    Glos.
Manor House Gallery, Cheltenham,
    Glos.
Triton Gallery, Cheltenham, Glos.
Peter Ward Fine Paintings, Cheltenham,
    Glos.
School House Antiques, Chipping
    Campden, Glos.
The Titian Gallery, Chipping Campden,
    Glos.
Astley House - Fine Art, Moreton-in-
    Marsh, Glos.
Astley House - Fine Art, Moreton-in-
    Marsh, Glos.
Berry Antiques, Moreton-in-Marsh,
    Glos.
Grimes House Antiques & Fine Art,
    Moreton-in-Marsh, Glos.
Nina Zborowska, Painswick, Glos.
Baggott Church Street Ltd, Stow-on-the-
    Wold, Glos.
Cotswold Galleries, Stow-on-the-Wold,
    Glos.
The John Davies Gallery, Stow-on-the-
    Wold, Glos.
The Fosse Gallery, Stow-on-the-Wold,
    Glos.
Fosse Way Antiques, Stow-on-the-Wold,
    Glos.
Kenulf Fine Arts, Stow-on-the-Wold,
    Glos.
Roger Lamb Antiques & Works of Art,
    Stow-on-the-Wold, Glos.
Styles of Stow, Stow-on-the-Wold, Glos.
Balmuir House Antiques, Tetbury, Glos.
Tetbury Gallery, Tetbury, Glos.
Antique House, Hartley Wintney, Hants.
Corfields Ltd, Lymington, Hants.
Robert Perera Fine Art, Lymington,
    Hants.
The Petersfield Bookshop, Petersfield,
    Hants.
Bell Fine Art, Winchester, Hants.
Lacewing Fine Art Gallery, Winchester,
    Hants.

Webb Fine Arts, Winchester, Hants.
The Shanklin Gallery, Shanklin, Isle of
    Wight.
Cooper Fine Arts Ltd, Brasted, Kent.
Peter Dyke, Brasted, Kent.
Michael Sim, Chislehurst, Kent.
Francis Iles, Rochester, Kent.
Langley Galleries, Rochester, Kent.
Sundridge Gallery, Sundridge, Kent.
Nicholas Bowlby, Tunbridge Wells,
    Kent.
Pantiles Spa Antiques, Tunbridge Wells,
    Kent.
Redleaf Gallery, Tunbridge Wells, Kent.
Apollo Antique Galleries, Westerham,
    Kent.
London House Antiques, Westerham,
    Kent.
Fulda Gallery Ltd, Manchester, Lancs.
St. James Antiques, Manchester, Lancs.
European Fine Arts and Antiques,
    Preston, Lancs.
Henry Donn Gallery, Whitefield, Lancs.
Corry's, Leicester, Leics.
Leicestershire Sporting Gallery and
    Brown Jack Bookshop, Lubenham,
    Leics.
P. Stanworth (Fine Arts), Market
    Bosworth, Leics.
Graftons of Market Harborough, Market
    Harborough, Leics.
Robin Shield Antiques, Swinstead,
    Lincs.
Ailsa Gallery, Twickenham, Middx.
Baron Art, Holt, Norfolk.
Baron Art, Kelling, Norfolk.
The Bank House Gallery, Norwich,
    Norfolk.
Crome Gallery and Frame Shop,
    Norwich, Norfolk.
The Fairhurst Gallery, Norwich,
    Norfolk.
Mandell's Gallery, Norwich, Norfolk.
The Westcliffe Gallery, Sheringham,
    Norfolk.
Staithe Lodge Gallery, Swafield,
    Norfolk.
Norton Antiques, Twyford, Norfolk.
Coughton Galleries Ltd, Arthingworth,
    Northants.
Right Angle, Brackley, Northants.
Castle Ashby Gallery, Castle Ashby,
    Northants.
Savage Fine Art, Haselbech, Northants.
Dragon Antiques, Kettering, Northants.
Clark Galleries, Towcester, Northants.
Ron Green, Towcester, Northants.
Bryan Perkins Antiques,
    Wellingborough, Northants.
The Bell Gallery, Belfast, N. Ireland.
Boadens Antiques, Hexham, Northumbs.
Jane Neville Gallery, Aslockton, Notts.
Anthony Mitchell Fine Paintings,
    Nottingham, Notts.
H.C. Dickins, Bloxham, Oxon.
Horseshoe Antiques and Gallery,
    Burford, Oxon.
Hubert's Antiques, Burford, Oxon.
The Stone Gallery, Burford, Oxon.
Swan Gallery, Burford, Oxon.
Georgian House Antiques, Chipping
    Norton, Oxon.
Hallidays (Fine Antiques) Ltd,
    Dorchester-on-Thames, Oxon.
The Barry Keene Gallery, Henley-on-
    Thames, Oxon.

Churchgate Antiques, Empingham, Rutland.
Fine Art of Oakham, Oakham, Rutland.
The Old House Gallery, Oakham, Rutland.
John Garner, Uppingham, Rutland.
Marc Oxley Fine Art, Uppingham, Rutland.
John Boulton Fine Art, Broseley, Shrops.
Teme Valley Antiques, Ludlow, Shrops.
Valentyne Dawes Gallery, Ludlow, Shrops.
Wenlock Fine Art, Much Wenlock, Shrops.
The Mount, Woore, Shrops.
Adam Gallery, Bath, Somerset.
Mary Cruz, Bath, Somerset.
AnthonyHepworth Fine Art Dealers, Bath, Somerset.
Trimbridge Galleries, Bath, Somerset.
Freshfords, Freshford, Somerset.
The Court Gallery, Nether Stowey, Somerset.
Nick Cotton Fine Art, Watchet, Somerset.
Sadler Street Gallery,, Wells, Somerset.
Everett Fine Art, West Buckland, Somerset.
England's Gallery, Leek, Staffs.
Thompson's Gallery, Aldeburgh, Suffolk.
J. and J. Baker, Lavenham,, Suffolk.
Trident Antiques, Long Melford, Suffolk.
Peasenhall Art and Antiques Gallery, Peasenhall, Suffolk.
The Falcon Gallery, Wortham, Suffolk.
Suffolk House Antiques, Yoxford, Suffolk.
Cider House Galleries Ltd, Bletchingley, Surrey.
Cobham Galleries, Cobham, Surrey.
The Whitgift Galleries, Croydon, Surrey.
Antique Clocks by Patrick Thomas, Dorking, Surrey.
Hampton Court Palace Antiques, East Molesey, Surrey.
Glencorse Antiques, Kingston-upon-Thames, Surrey.
Bourne Gallery Ltd, Reigate, Surrey.
The Gallery, Reigate, Surrey.
Roland Goslett Gallery, Richmond, Surrey.
Marryat, Richmond, Surrey.
Piano Nobile Fine Paintings, Richmond, Surrey.
Cedar House Gallery, Ripley, Surrey.
Sage Antiques and Interiors, Ripley, Surrey.
B. M. and E. Newlove, Surbiton, Surrey.
Boathouse Gallery, Walton-on-Thames, Surrey.
Edward Cross - Fine Paintings, Weybridge, Surrey.
Willow Gallery, Weybridge, Surrey.
John Day of Eastbourne Fine Art, Eastbourne, Sussex East.
Stewart Gallery, Eastbourne, Sussex East.
Murray Brown, Pevensey Bay, Sussex East.
E. Stacy-Marks Limited, Polegate, Sussex East.
Lannards Gallery, Billingshurst, Sussex West.

Gough Bros. Art Shop and Gallery, Bognor Regis, Sussex West.
Chichester Gallery, Chichester, Sussex West.
The Canon Gallery, Petworth, Sussex West.
T.G. Wilkinson Antiques Ltd, Petworth, Sussex West.
Georgia Antiques, Pulborough, Sussex West.
Wilsons Antiques, Worthing, Sussex West.
Anna Harrison Fine Antiques, Gosforth, Tyne and Wear.
MacDonald Fine Art, Gosforth, Tyne and Wear.
Osborne Fine Art Gallery, Jesmond,, Tyne and Wear.
The Dean Gallery Ltd, Newcastle-upon-Tyne, Tyne and Wear.
Arden Gallery, Henley-in-Arden, Warks.
Colmore Galleries Ltd, Henley-in-Arden, Warks.
Fine-Lines (Fine Art), Shipston-on-Stour, Warks.
Astley House - Fine Art, Stretton-on-Fosse, Warks.
Oldswinford Gallery, Stourbridge, West Mids.
Driffold Gallery, Sutton Coldfield, West Mids.
Salisbury Antiques Warehouse, Salisbury, Wilts.
Bracebridge Fine Art, Astwood Bank, Worcs.
John Hubbard Antique Restorations, Blakedown, Worcs.
Richard Hagen, Broadway, Worcs.
Haynes Fine Art of Broadway - Picton House Galleries, Broadway, Worcs.
John Noott Galleries, Broadway, Worcs.
The Highway Gallery, Upton-upon-Severn, Worcs.
James H. Starkey Galleries, Beverley, Yorks. East.
Anthony Graham Antiques, Boroughbridge, Yorks. North.
W. Greenwood (Fine Art), Burneston, Yorks. North.
Garth Antiques, Harrogate, Yorks. North.
Sutcliffe Galleries, Harrogate, Yorks. North.
Walker Galleries Ltd, Harrogate, Yorks. North.
E. Stacy-Marks Limited, Helmsley, Yorks. North.
Thirkill Antiques, Leyburn, Yorks. North.
Talents Fine Arts Ltd, Malton, Yorks. North.
Roy Precious Antiques & Fine Art, Settle, Yorks. North.
Rose Fine Art and Antiques, Stillington, Yorks. North.
Kirkgate Fine Art & Conservation, Thirsk, Yorks. North.
Garth Antiques, Whixley, Yorks. North.
Coulter Galleries, York, Yorks. North.
Oakwood Gallery, Leeds, Yorks. West.
Robin Taylor Fine Arts, Wakefield, Yorks. West.
Mark Blower Antiques, St. Martin, Guernsey, C.I.
Channel Islands Galleries Ltd, St. Peter Port, Guernsey, C.I.

St. James's Gallery Ltd, St. Peter Port, Guernsey, C.I.
Geoffrey P. Gavey, Vale, Guernsey, C.I.
Falle Fine Art Limited, St Helier, Jersey, C.I.
The Selective Eye Gallery, St. Helier, Jersey, C.I.
I.G.A. Old Masters Ltd, St. Lawrence, Jersey, C.I.
Grange Gallery - Fine Arts Ltd, St. Saviour, Jersey, C.I.
Atholl Antiques, Aberdeen, Scotland.
The Rendezvous Gallery, Aberdeen, Scotland.
Colin Wood (Antiques) Ltd, Aberdeen, Scotland.
Paul Hayes Gallery, Auchterarder, Scotland.
Nigel Stacy-Marks Ltd, Auchterarder, Scotland.
The McEwan Gallery, Ballater, Scotland.
Bourne Fine Art Ltd, Edinburgh, Scotland.
Calton Gallery, Edinburgh, Scotland.
John Mathieson and Co, Edinburgh, Scotland.
Open Eye Gallery Ltd, Edinburgh, Scotland.
The Scottish Gallery, Edinburgh, Scotland.
Anthony Woodd Gallery, Edinburgh, Scotland.
Young Antiques, Edinburgh, Scotland.
The Roger Billcliffe Fine Art, Glasgow, Scotland.
Ewan Mundy Fine Art Ltd, Glasgow, Scotland.
Michael YoungAntiques at Glencarse, Glencarse, Scotland.
Glendoick Antiques, Glendoick, Scotland.
Inchmartine Fine Art, Inchture, Scotland.
Mainhill Gallery, Jedburgh, Scotland.
Kilmacolm Antiques Ltd, Kilmacolm, Scotland.
Newburgh Antiques, Newburgh, Scotland.
Kirk Ports Gallery, North Berwick, Scotland.
Nigel Stacy-Marks Ltd, Perth, Scotland.
St. Andrews Fine Art, St. Andrews, Scotland.
Abbey Antiques, Stirling, Scotland.
David Windsor Gallery, Bangor, Wales.
Michael Webb Fine Art, Llangristiolus (Anglesey), Wales.
Barn Court Antiques, Crafts & Tearoom, Templeton, Wales.
Welsh Art, Tywyn, Wales.

Oriental
Nanwani and Co, London EC3.
Japanese Gallery, London N1.
Laurence Mitchell Antiques Ltd, London N1.
Kevin Page Oriental Art, London N1.
Marcus Ross Antiques, London N1.
Yingguoren Ltd., London N1.
Leask Ward, London NW3.
Malcolm Rushton - Early Oriental Art, London NW3.
B.C. Metalcrafts Ltd, London NW9.
Konrad O. Bernheimer Ltd, London SW1.
Ciancimino Ltd, London SW1.

SPECIALIST DEALERS

Shirley Day Ltd, London SW1.
Jeremy Mason (Sainsbury & Mason), London SW1.
Orientation, London SW10.
Sebastiano Barbagallo, London SW6.
Ki Design, London SW6.
Sylvia Napier Ltd, London SW6.
Daphne Rankin and Ian Conn, London SW6.
Redroom, London SW6.
Brandt Oriental Art, London W1.
Paul Champkins, London W1.
Barry Davies Oriental Art, London W1.
Eskenazi Ltd, London W1.
John Eskenazi Ltd, London W1.
Robert Hall, London W1.
Gerard Hawthorn Ltd, London W1.
Roger Keverne, London W1.
Sydney L. Moss Ltd, London W1.
Nicholas S. Pitcher Oriental Art, London W1.
Robert G. Sawers, London W1.
A & J Speelman Ltd, London W1.
Toynbee-Clarke Interiors Ltd, London W1.
Jan van Beers Oriental Art, London W1.
Linda Wrigglesworth Ltd, London W1.
Cohen & Cohen (Oriental Porcelain), London W11.
M.C.N. Antiques, London W11.
Oriental Furniture and Arts, London W4.
AntikWest AB, London W8.
Gregg Baker Asian Art, London W8.
Berwald Oriental Art, London W8.
David Brower Antiques, London W8.
Coats Oriental Carpets, London W8.
Cohen & Cohen, London W8.
H. and W. Deutsch Antiques, London W8.
J.A.N. Fine Art, London W8.
Japanese Gallery, London W8.
Peter Kemp, London W8.
S. Marchant & Son, London W8.
Robert McPherson, London W8.
Santos, London W8.
Jorge Welsh Oriental Porcelain & Works of Art, London W8.
Yang Guifei, London W8.
Clive Rogers Oriental Rugs, Wraysbury, Berks.
Glade Antiques, Marlow, Bucks.
Gabor Cossa Antiques, Cambridge, Cambs.
Highland Antiques, Stockport, Cheshire.
Peter Johnson, Penzance, Cornwall.
Brian Matsell, Derby, Derbys.
David L.H. Southwick Rare Art, Kingswear, Devon.
Mere Antiques, Topsham, Devon.
Lionel Geneen Ltd, Bournemouth, Dorset.
Hungry Ghost, Stow-on-the-Wold, Glos.
Oriental Gallery, Stow-on-the-Wold, Glos.
Artique, Tetbury, Glos.
Catherine Hunt, Tetbury, Glos.
Oriental Rug Gallery Ltd, St. Albans, Herts.
Michael Sim, Chislehurst, Kent.
Mandarin Gallery - Oriental Art, Otford, Kent.
Flower House Antiques, Tenterden, Kent.
The Rug Gallery, Leicester, Leics.
M.D. Cannell Antiques, Raveningham, Norfolk.

The Country Seat, Huntercombe, Oxon.
Peter Wain, Market Drayton, Shrops.
Haliden Oriental Rug Shop, Bath, Somerset.
Robin Kennedy, Richmond, Surrey.
Patrick Moorhead Antiques, Brighton, Sussex East.
Brian Page Antiques, Brighton, Sussex East.
Gensing Antiques, St. Leonards-on-Sea, Sussex East.
Ringles Cross Antiques, Uckfield, Sussex East.
Heirloom & Howard Limited, West Yatton, Wilts.
Tansu Japanese Antiques, Batley, Yorks. West.
Paul M. Peters Antiques, Harrogate, Yorks. North.
Two Dragons Oriental Antiques, Llanerchymedd (Anglesey), Wales.

Paperweights

Garrick D. Coleman, London W11.
Garrick D. Coleman, London W8.
Sweetbriar Gallery, Helsby, Cheshire.
Portique, Bournemouth, Dorset.
Todd and Austin Antiques of Winchester, Winchester, Hants.
The Stone Gallery, Burford, Oxon.
David R. Fileman, Steyning, Sussex West.

Photographs & Equipment

Jubilee Photographica, London N1.
Vintage Cameras Ltd, London SE26.
Jessop Classic Photographica, London WC1.
Medina Gallery, Barnstaple, Devon.
Medina Gallery, Bideford, Devon.
Peter Pan's Bazaar, Gosport, Hants.

Porcelain & Pottery

Diana Huntley, London N1.
Carol Ketley Antiques, London N1.
Laurence Mitchell Antiques Ltd, London N1.
Staffordshire Pride, London N1.
The Collector, London N11.
Finchley Fine Art Galleries, London N12.
Martin Henham (Antiques), London N2.
Sabera Trading Co, London NW2.
Klaber and Klaber, London NW3.
Albert Amor Ltd, London SW1.
Ross Hamilton Ltd, London SW1.
M. and D. Lewis, London SW1.
Stephen Long, London SW10.
Robert Young Antiques, London SW11.
The Dining Room Shop, London SW13.
R.A. Barnes Antiques, London SW15.
Jacqueline Oosthuizen, London SW3.
Pieter Oosthuizen t/a de Verzamelaar, London SW3.
Rogers de Rin, London SW3.
Thomas Goode and Co (London) Ltd, London W1.
Harcourt Antiques, London W1.
Brian Haughton Antiques, London W1.
Alistair Sampson Antiques Ltd, London W1.
Judy Fox, London W11.
M. and D. Lewis, London W11.
Mercury Antiques, London W11.
Schredds of Portobello, London W11.
Harold's Place, London W5.

Garry Atkins, London W8.
David Brower Antiques, London W8.
Davies Antiques, London W8.
Richard Dennis, London W8.
H. and W. Deutsch Antiques, London W8.
Hope and Glory, London W8.
Jonathan Horne, London W8.
Valerie Howard, London W8.
Roderick Jellicoe, London W8.
Peter Kemp, London W8.
Libra Antiques, London W8.
London Antique Gallery, London W8.
E. and H. Manners, London W8.
Simon Spero, London W8.
Stockspring Antiques, London W8.
Mary Wise & Grosvenor Antiques, London W8.
Anchor Antiques Ltd, London WC2.
Baroq & David Ball Antiques, Leighton Buzzard, Beds.
Ulla Stafford Antiques, Binfield, Berks.
Cavendish Fine Arts, Sonning-on-Thames, Berks.
Berkshire Antiques Co Ltd, Windsor and Eton, Berks.
Gabor Cossa Antiques, Cambridge, Cambs.
Abbey Antiques, Ramsey, Cambs.
Aldersey Hall Ltd, Chester, Cheshire.
The Antique Shop, Chester, Cheshire.
Cameo Antiques, Chester, Cheshire.
K D Antiques, Chester, Cheshire.
Made of Honour, Chester, Cheshire.
Watergate Antiques, Chester, Cheshire.
Littles Collectables, Congleton, Cheshire.
Imperial Antiques, Stockport, Cheshire.
Antiques, Marazion, Cornwall.
Clock Tower Antiques, Tregony, Cornwall.
Alan Bennett, Truro, Cornwall.
Saint Nicholas Galleries Ltd. (Antiques and Jewellery), Carlisle, Cumbria.
Souvenir Antiques, Carlisle, Cumbria.
Dower House Antiques, Kendal, Cumbria.
Kendal Studios Antiques, Kendal, Cumbria.
Jane Pollock Antiques, Penrith, Cumbria.
Kenneth Upchurch, Ashbourne, Derbys.
Bampton Gallery, Bampton, Devon.
Selected Antiques & Collectables, Barnstaple, Devon.
David J. Thorn, Budleigh Salterton, Devon.
Mere Antiques, Topsham, Devon.
Birbeck Gallery, Torquay, Devon.
Box of Porcelain, Dorchester, Dorset.
Geometrica, Sherborne, Dorset.
Heygate Browne Antiques, Sherborne, Dorset.
Reference Works, Swanage, Dorset.
Grant's Antiques, Barnard Castle, Durham.
E J Markham & Son Ltd, Colchester, Essex.
Bush House, Corringham, Essex.
Bush Antiques, Saffron Walden, Essex.
Harris Antiques (Stansted), Stansted, Essex.
Barling Fine Porcelain Ltd, Wickham Bishops, Essex.
Julian Tatham-Losh, Andoversford, Glos.

Stuart House Antiques, Chipping Campden, Glos.
Swan Antiques, Chipping Campden, Glos.
Sodbury Antiques, Chipping Sodbury, Glos.
Berry Antiques, Moreton-in-Marsh, Glos.
Chandlers Antiques, Moreton-in-Marsh, Glos.
Seaford House Antiques, Moreton-in-Marsh, Glos.
Colin Brand Antiques, Stow-on-the-Wold, Glos.
Church Street Antiques Centre, Stow-on-the-Wold, Glos.
Wyndhams, Stow-on-the-Wold, Glos.
Artemesia, Alresford, Hants.
Graylings Antiques, Andover, Hants.
Goss and Crested China Centre and Goss Museum, Horndean, Hants.
Platt's of Lymington, Lymington, Hants.
Lita Kaye of Lyndhurst, Lyndhurst, Hants.
Lane Antiques, Stockbridge, Hants.
Dinah Stoodley & Celia Jennings, Brasted, Kent.
W.W. Warner (Antiques), Brasted, Kent.
Serendipity, Deal, Kent.
Alan Wood, Gravesend, Kent.
Kent Cottage, Rolvenden, Kent.
Delf Stream Gallery, Sandwich, Kent.
Steppes Hill Farm Antiques, Stockbury, Kent.
Pantiles Spa Antiques, Tunbridge Wells, Kent.
The Emporium Antiques, Collectibles & Craft Centre, Welling, Kent.
Old Corner House Antiques, Wittersham, Kent.
Cottage Antiques, Darwen, Lancs.
Village Antiques, Manchester, Lancs.
Priory Collectables, Preston, Lancs.
Staines Antiques, Horncastle, Lincs.
Underwoodhall Antiques, Woodhall Spa, Lincs.
Ivy House Antiques, Acle, Norfolk.
Roger Bradbury Antiques, Coltishall, Norfolk.
Peter Robinson, Heacham, Norfolk.
Richard Scott Antiques, Holt, Norfolk.
Liz Allport-Lomax, Norwich, Norfolk.
Malcolm Turner, Norwich, Norfolk.
Dorothy's Antiques, Sheringham, Norfolk.
Leo Pratt and Son, South Walsham, Norfolk.
T.C.S. Brooke, Wroxham, Norfolk.
Peter Jackson Antiques, Brackley, Northants.
R. and M. Nicholas, Towcester, Northants.
Hedley's of Hexham, Hexham, Northumbs.
David and Carole Potter Antiques, Nottingham, Notts.
Swan Gallery, Burford, Oxon.
Bees Antiques, Woodstock, Oxon.
Robin Sanders and Sons, Woodstock, Oxon.
The Old House Gallery, Oakham, Rutland.
T.J. Roberts, Uppingham, Rutland.
Micawber Antiques, Bridgnorth, Shrops.
Tudor House Antiques, Ironbridge, Shrops.

Teme Valley Antiques, Ludlow, Shrops.
David and Sally March Antiques, Abbots Leigh, Somerset.
Andrew Dando, Bath, Somerset.
Quiet Street Antiques, Bath, Somerset.
T J Atkins, Taunton, Somerset.
Eveline Winter, Rugeley, Staffs.
The Potteries Antique Centre Ltd, Stoke-on-Trent, Staffs.
Top of the Hill (Ceramic Search), Stoke-on-Trent, Staffs.
White House Antiques, Uttoxeter, Staffs.
John Read, Martlesham, Suffolk.
Derby Cottage Antiques, Newmarket, Suffolk.
David Gibbins Antiques, Woodbridge, Suffolk.
Red House Antiques, Yoxford, Suffolk.
Churt Curiosity Shop, Churt, Surrey.
Decodream, Coulsdon, Surrey.
Dolphin Square Antiques, Dorking, Surrey.
The Olde Bakehouse Antiques, Dorking, Surrey.
Church Street Antiques, Godalming, Surrey.
Marryat, Richmond, Surrey.
Helena's Collectables, Shere, Surrey.
Susan Becker, Walton-on-Thames, Surrey.
Brocante, Weybridge, Surrey.
Patrick Moorhead Antiques, Brighton, Sussex East.
Yellow Lantern Antiques Ltd, Brighton, Sussex East.
Stewart Gallery, Eastbourne, Sussex East.
Southdown Antiques, Lewes, Sussex East.
Herbert Gordon Gasson, Rye, Sussex East.
Gems Antiques, Chichester, Sussex West.
Magic of Quimper, Littlehampton, Sussex West.
Richard Gardner Antiques, Petworth, Sussex West.
William Hockley Antiques, Petworth, Sussex West.
Ian Sharp Antiques, Tynemouth, Tyne and Wear.
Coleshill Antiques and Interiors Ltd, Coleshill, Warks.
Burman Antiques, Stratford-upon-Avon, Warks.
Castle Antiques, Warwick, Warks.
H. and R.L. Parry Ltd, Sutton Coldfield, West Mids.
Moxhams Antiques, Bradford-on-Avon, Wilts.
Antiques - Rene Nicholls, Malmesbury, Wilts.
Heirloom & Howard Limited, West Yatton, Wilts.
Bygones by the Cathedral, Worcester, Worcs.
Bygones of Worcester, Worcester, Worcs.
M. Lees and Sons, Worcester, Worcs.
Worcester Antiques Centre, Worcester, Worcs.
The Crested China Co, Driffield, Yorks. East.
Nigel Adamson, Harrogate, Yorks. North.

Bryan Bowden, Harrogate, Yorks. North.
David Love, Harrogate, Yorks. North.
York Cottage Antiques, Helmsley, Yorks. North.
Country Collector, Pickering, Yorks. North.
Nanbooks, Settle, Yorks. North.
Anderson Slater Antiques, Settle, Yorks. North.
Age of Jazz, Whitby, Yorks. North.
Ruby Snowden Antiques, Yarm, Yorks. North.
Holly Farm Antiques, Rotherham, Yorks. South.
Top Hat Antique Centre, Sheffield, Yorks. South.
Muir Hewitt Art Deco Originals, Halifax, Yorks. West.
St. James's Gallery Ltd, St. Peter Port, Guernsey, C.I.
Stephen Cohu Antiques, St Ouen, Jersey, C.I.
The Country Antiques, Antrim, Co. Antrim, N. Ireland.
Dunluce Antiques, Bushmills, Co. Antrim, N. Ireland.
Steeple Antiques, Ceres, Scotland.
Laurance Black Ltd, Edinburgh, Scotland.
Gordon Inglis Antiques, Edinburgh, Scotland.
Young Antiques, Edinburgh, Scotland.
Tim Wright Antiques, Glasgow, Scotland.
Strathspey Gallery, Grantown-on-Spey, Scotland.
Miles Antiques, Kinross, Scotland.
Grannie Used To Have One, Longhaven, Scotland.
Herrald of Edinburgh, Meigle, Scotland.
Harper-James, Montrose, Scotland.
Newburgh Antiques, Newburgh, Scotland.
The Antiques Shop, Pittenweem, Scotland.
Howards of Aberystwyth, Aberystwyth, Wales.
Nolton Antiques, Bridgend, Wales.
Paul Gibbs Antiques and Decorative Arts, Conwy, Wales.
Manor House Antiques, Fishguard, Wales.
Hebbards of Hay, Hay-on-Wye, Wales.
Islwyn Watkins, Knighton, Wales.
J. and R. Langford, Llangollen, Wales.
Passers Buy (Marie Evans), Llangollen, Wales.
Frost Antiques & Pine, Monmouth, Wales.
West Wales Antiques, Murton, Wales.
Magpie Antiques, Swansea, Wales.

Prints - see Maps

Rugs - see Carpets

Russian/Soviet Art
Barkes and Barkes, London NW1.
Soviet Carpet & Art Galleries, London NW2.
Hermitage Antiques plc, London SW1.
Jeremy Ltd, London SW1.
Mark Ransom Ltd, London SW1.
The Andipa Gallery, London SW3.
Richardson and Kailas Icons, London SW6.

SPECIALIST DEALERS

Antoine Cheneviere Fine Arts, London W1.
Wartski Ltd, London W1.
Temple Gallery, London W11.
The Mark Gallery, London W2.
Mir Russki, Linlithgow, Scotland.

Scientific Instruments
Finchley Fine Art Galleries, London N12.
Victor Burness Antiques and Scientific Instruments, London SE1.
Peter Laurie Antiques, London SE10.
Relcy Antiques, London SE10.
Thomas Mercer (Chronometers) Ltd, London SW1.
Trevor Philip and Sons Ltd, London SW1.
Langford's Marine Antiques, London SW10.
Captain O.M. Watts, London W1.
Peter Delehar, London W11.
Mayflower Antiques, London W11.
Johnny Von Pflugh Antiques, London W11.
Gillian Gould at Ocean Leisure, London WC2.
Arthur Middleton, London WC2.
Christopher Sykes Antiques, Woburn, Beds.
Principia Fine Art, Hungerford, Berks.
Mike Read Antique Sciences, St. Ives, Cornwall.
Branksome Antiques, Branksome, Dorset.
Nautical Antique Centre, Weymouth, Dorset.
Mayflower Antiques, Harwich, Essex.
The Chart House, Shenfield, Essex.
Chris Grimes Militaria, Bristol, Glos.
Country Life Antiques, Stow-on-the-Wold, Glos.
Barometer Shop, Leominster, Herefs.
Michael Sim, Chislehurst, Kent.
Bernard G. House, Wells, Somerset.
Patrick Marney, Long Melford, Suffolk.
Roy Arnold, Needham Market, Suffolk.
Odin Antiques, Brighton, Sussex East.
Minster Antiques, York, Yorks. North.
Time & Tide Antiques, Portaferry, Co. Down, N. Ireland.

Sculpture
Centaur Gallery, London N8.
Duncan R. Miller Fine Arts, London NW3.
No. 28 Antiques, London NW8.
Tara Antiques, London NW8.
Robert E. Hirschhorn, London SE5.
Robert Bowman, London SW1.
Chaucer Fine Arts Ltd, London SW1.
Shirley Day Ltd, London SW1.
Christopher Gibbs Ltd, London SW1.
Nicholas Gifford-Mead, London SW1.
Hazlitt, Gooden and Fox Ltd, London SW1.
Whitford Fine Art, London SW1.
Jonathan Clark & Co, London SW10.
Ted Few, London SW17.
Joanna Booth, London SW3.
Agnew's, London W1.
Adrian Alan Ltd, London W1.
Victor Arwas Gallery - Editions Graphiques Gallery Ltd, London W1.
Browse and Darby Ltd, London W1.
Lumley Cazalet Ltd, London W1.

Eskenazi Ltd, London W1.
The Fine Art Society plc, London W1.
The Graham Gallery, London W1.
Patrick Jefferson Ltd, London W1.
Messums (Contemporary), London W1.
The Sladmore Gallery of Sculpture, London W1.
Stoppenbach & Delestre Ltd, London W1.
Curá Antiques, London W11.
Hirst Antiques, London W11.
Milne and Moller, London W11.
Richard Philp, London W11.
Piano Nobile Fine Paintings, London W11.
Wolseley Fine Arts Ltd, London W11.
Simon Hilton, Great Dunmow, Essex.
Quatrefoil, Fordingbridge, Hants.
Lacewing Fine Art Gallery, Winchester, Hants.
Cooper Fine Arts Ltd, Brasted, Kent.
Francis Iles, Rochester, Kent.
Nicholas Bowlby, Tunbridge Wells, Kent.
London House Antiques, Westerham, Kent.
Pearse Lukies, Aylsham, Norfolk.
Arthur Brett and Sons Ltd, Norwich, Norfolk.
The Barry Keene Gallery, Henley-on-Thames, Oxon.
Anthony Hepworth Fine Art Dealers, Bath, Somerset.
Everett Fine Art, West Buckland, Somerset.
Piano Nobile Fine Paintings, Richmond, Surrey.
Apollo Antiques Ltd, Warwick, Warks.
Patrick and Gillian Morley Antiques, Warwick, Warks.
Bruton Gallery, Leeds, Yorks. West.
Calton Gallery, Edinburgh, Scotland.
The Roger Billcliffe Fine Art, Glasgow, Scotland.
Mainhill Gallery, Jedburgh, Scotland.
Intaglio, Chepstow, Wales.

Shipping Goods & Period Furniture for the Trade
Regent Antiques, London N1.
Keith Skeel Antiques, London N1.
Madeline Crispin Antiques, London NW1.
Antique Trade Warehouse, London SE1.
Penny Farthing Antiques, London SE1.
Tower Bridge Antiques, London SE1.
The Waterloo Trading Co., London SE10.
Oola Boola Antiques London, London SE26.
Tavistock Antiques, St. Neots, Cambs.
R. Wilding, Wisbech, Cambs.
W. Buckley Antiques Exports, Congleton, Cheshire.
Paul Jennings Antiques, Angarrack, Cornwall.
Ben Eggleston Antiques, Long Marton, Cumbria.
Michael Allcroft Antiques, Newmills, Derbys.
Shardlow Antiques Warehouse, Shardlow, Derbys.
John Prestige Antiques, Brixham, Devon.
Fagins Antiques, Exeter, Devon.

Adrian Hornsey Ltd, Exeter, Devon.
McBains Antiques, Exeter, Devon.
Sandy's Antiques, Bournemouth, Dorset.
Alan Ramsey Antiques, Darlington, Durham.
G.T. Ratcliff Ltd, Kelvedon, Essex.
Bristol Trade Antiques, Bristol, Glos.
Alan Lord Antiques, Folkestone, Kent.
Sutton Valence Antiques, Sutton Valence, Kent.
Charles International Antiques, Wrotham, Kent.
West Lancs. Antique Exports, Burscough, Lancs.
P.J. Brown Antiques, Haslingden, Lancs.
R.J. O'Brien and Son Antiques Ltd, Manchester, Lancs.
G.G. Exports, Middleton Village, Lancs.
Tyson's Antiques, Morecambe, Lancs.
John Robinson Antiques, Wigan, Lancs.
Boulevard Antique and Shipping Centre, Leicester, Leics.
Antique & Secondhand Traders, Bourne, Lincs.
Trade Antiques, Donington, Lincs.
Grantham Furniture Emporium, Grantham, Lincs.
Michael Brewer, Lincoln, Lincs.
C. and K.E. Dring, Lincoln, Lincs.
Bridge Antiques, Sutton Bridge, Lincs.
Old Barn Antiques Warehouse, Sutton Bridge, Lincs.
Kensington Tower Antiques Ltd, Liverpool, Merseyside.
The Original British American Antiques, Liverpool, Merseyside.
Swainbanks Ltd, Liverpool, Merseyside.
Theta Gallery, Liverpool, Merseyside.
Molloy's Furnishers Ltd, Southport, Merseyside.
Tony and Anne Sutcliffe Antiques, Southport, Merseyside.
Sheila Hart and John Giles, Aylsham, Norfolk.
Pearse Lukies, Aylsham, Norfolk.
John Roe Antiques, Islip, Northants.
Bryan Perkins Antiques, Wellingborough, Northants.
T. Baker, Langford, Notts.
Fair Deal Antiques, Mansfield, Notts.
Mitre House Antiques, Ludlow, Shrops.
M.G.R. Exports, Bruton, Somerset.
T.M. Dyte Antiques, Highbridge, Somerset.
Harrison House Antiques, North Petherton, Somerset.
J.C. Giddings, Wiveliscombe, Somerset.
Burton Antiques, Burton-on-Trent, Staffs.
Cordelia and Perdy's Antique Junk Shop, Lichfield, Staffs.
Goodbreys, Framlingham, Suffolk.
A. Abbott Antiques, Ipswich, Suffolk.
The Edwardian Shop, Ipswich, Suffolk.
Laurence Tauber Antiques, Surbiton, Surrey.
Bexhill Antique Exporters, Bexhill-on-Sea, Sussex East.
The Old Mint House, Pevensey, Sussex East.
John H. Yorke Antiques, St. Leonards-on-Sea, Sussex East.
J. Powell (Hove) Ltd, Portslade, Sussex West.
Peter Smith Antiques, Sunderland, Tyne and Wear.

Brett Wilkins Antiques, Wednesbury, West Mids.

Martin Taylor Antiques, Wolverhampton, West Mids.

North Wilts Exporters, Brinkworth, Wilts.

Cross Hayes Antiques, Chippenham, Wilts.

Harley Antiques, Christian Malford, Wilts.

Pillars Antiques, Lyneham, Wilts.

K. and A. Welch, Warminster, Wilts.

Joan and David White, Manfield, Yorks. North.

Tomlinson Antiques Ltd. & Period Furniture Ltd, Tockwith, Yorks. North.

Roger Appleyard Ltd, Rotherham, Yorks. South.

Philip Turnor Antiques, Rotherham, Yorks. South.

Dronfield Antiques, Sheffield, Yorks. South.

N.P. and A. Salt Antiques, Sheffield, Yorks. South.

Times Past Antiques, Auchterarder, Scotland.

Imrie Antiques, Bridge of Earn, Scotland.

Neil Livingstone, Dundee, Scotland.

George Duff Antiques, Edinburgh, Scotland.

Georgian Antiques, Edinburgh, Scotland.

Narducci Antiques, Largs, Scotland.

A.S. Deuchar and Son, Perth, Scotland.

Narducci Antiques, Saltcoats, Scotland.

Charlotte's Wholesale Antiques, Cardiff, Wales.

Michael Lloyd Antiques, Llandysul, Wales.

Anne and Colin Hulbert (Antiques), Swansea, Wales.

All Old Exports Ltd., Treorchy, Wales.

Silver & Jewellery

George Rankin Coin Co. Ltd, London E2.

Finecraft Workshop Ltd, London EC1.

Jonathan Harris (Jewellery) Ltd, London EC1.

Hirsh Ltd, London EC1.

Joseph and Pearce Ltd, London EC1.

A.R. Ullmann Ltd, London EC1.

D. Horton, London EC2.

Nanwani and Co, London EC3.

Searle and Co Ltd, London EC3.

Eclectica, London N1.

Rosemary Hart, London N1.

John Laurie (Antiques) Ltd, London N1.

Sugar Antiques, London N1.

Tisdall & Defries Antiques, London N1.

Silver Belle, London NW8.

Creek Antiques, London SE10.

Vale Stamps and Antiques, London SE3.

A.D.C. Heritage Ltd, London SW1.

J.H. Bourdon-Smith Ltd, London SW1.

Cornucopia, London SW1.

Kenneth Davis (Works of Art) Ltd, London SW1.

Alastair Dickenson Fine Silver Ltd, London SW1.

N. and I. Franklin, London SW1.

Harvey and Gore, London SW1.

Kojis Antique Jewellery Ltd, London SW1.

Longmire Ltd (Three Royal Warrants), London SW1.

Nigel Milne Ltd, London SW1.

thesilverfund.com, London SW1.

Mary Cooke Antiques Ltd, London SW14.

James Hardy and Co, London SW3.

McKenna and Co, London SW3.

Christine Schell, London SW3.

Gordon Watson Ltd, London SW3.

M.P. Levene Ltd, London SW7.

A. & H. Page (Est. 1840), London SW7.

Armour-Winston Ltd, London W1.

Victor Arwas Gallery - Editions Graphiques Gallery Ltd, London W1.

Asprey & Garrard Ltd, London W1.

Paul Bennett, London W1.

Bentley & Skinner Ltd, London W1.

Bond Street Silver Galleries, London W1.

John Bull (Antiques) Ltd JB Silverware, London W1.

Carrington and Co. Ltd, London W1.

Sandra Cronan Ltd, London W1.

A. B. Davis Ltd, London W1.

Demas, London W1.

Simon Griffin Antiques Ltd, London W1.

Hancocks and Co, London W1.

Hennell of Bond Street Ltd. Founded 1736 (incorporating Frazer and Haws (1868) and E. Lloyd Lawrence (1830)), London W1.

Holmes Ltd, London W1.

Johnson Walker & Tolhurst Ltd, London W1.

D.S. Lavender (Antiques) Ltd, London W1.

Marks Antiques, London W1.

Moira, London W1.

Richard Ogden Ltd, London W1.

S.J. Phillips Ltd, London W1.

David Richards and Sons, London W1.

Michael Rose - Source of the Unusual, London W1.

Tessiers Ltd, London W1.

Wartski Ltd, London W1.

Central Gallery (Portobello), London W11.

The Coach House, London W11.

J. Freeman, London W11.

Kleanthous Antiques, London W11.

Portobello Antique Store, London W11.

Schredds of Portobello, London W11.

The Silver Fox Gallery (Portobello), London W11.

Colin Smith and Gerald Robinson Antiques, London W11.

Craven Gallery, London W2.

M. McAleer, London W2.

H. and W. Deutsch Antiques, London W8.

Green's Antique Galleries, London W8.

John Jesse, London W8.

Howard Jones - The Silver Shop, London W8.

Lev (Antiques) Ltd, London W8.

Fay Lucas Gallery, London W8.

Nortonbury Antiques, London WC1.

Thomas Kettle Ltd, London WC2.

The London Silver Vaults, London WC2.

Pearl Cross Ltd, London WC2.

The Silver Mouse Trap, London WC2.

Styles Silver, Hungerford, Berks.

Berkshire Antiques Co Ltd, Windsor and Eton, Berks.

Turks Head Antiques, Windsor and Eton, Berks.

Buckies, Cambridge, Cambs.

Pembroke Antiques, Cambridge, Cambs.

D.J. Massey and Son, Alderley Edge, Cheshire.

Cameo Antiques, Chester, Cheshire.

Kayes of Chester, Chester, Cheshire.

Lowe and Sons, Chester, Cheshire.

Veevers, Chester, Cheshire.

Watergate Antiques, Chester, Cheshire.

D.J. Massey and Son, Macclesfield, Cheshire.

Highland Antiques, Stockport, Cheshire.

Imperial Antiques, Stockport, Cheshire.

Little Jem's, Penzance, Cornwall.

Alan Bennett, Truro, Cornwall.

Saint Nicholas Galleries Ltd. (Antiques and Jewellery), Carlisle, Cumbria.

Jane Pollock Antiques, Penrith, Cumbria.

Elizabeth and Son, Ulverston, Cumbria.

Mark Parkhouse Antiques and Jewellery, Barnstaple, Devon.

Timothy Coward Fine Silver, Braunton, Devon.

David J. Thorn, Budleigh Salterton, Devon.

Gold and Silver Exchange, Exeter, Devon.

Mortimers, Exeter, Devon.

John Nathan Antiques, Exeter, Devon.

Boase Antiques, Exmouth, Devon.

Otter Antiques, Honiton, Devon.

Extence Antiques, Teignmouth, Devon.

G.B. Mussenden and Son Antiques, Jewellery and Silver, Bournemouth, Dorset.

Geo. A. Payne and Son Ltd, Bournemouth, Dorset.

R.E. Porter, Bournemouth, Dorset.

Portique, Bournemouth, Dorset.

Batten's Jewellers, Bridport, Dorset.

Greystoke Antiques, Sherborne, Dorset.

Henry Willis (Antique Silver), Sherborne, Dorset.

Georgian Gems Antique Jewellers, Swanage, Dorset.

Heirlooms Antique Jewellers and Silversmiths, Wareham, Dorset.

Robin Finnegan (Jeweller), Darlington, Durham.

Argentum Antiques, Coggeshall, Essex.

Elizabeth Cannon Antiques, Colchester, Essex.

Grahams of Colchester, Colchester, Essex.

E J Markham & Son Ltd, Colchester, Essex.

J. Streamer Antiques, Leigh-on-Sea, Essex.

Harris Antiques (Stansted), Stansted, Essex.

Whichcraft Jewellery, Writtle, Essex.

Peter and Penny Proudfoot, Berkeley, Glos.

Grey-Harris and Co, Bristol, Glos.

Kemps, Bristol, Glos.

Greens of Cheltenham Ltd, Cheltenham, Glos.

Martin and Co. Ltd, Cheltenham, Glos.

Scott-Cooper Ltd, Cheltenham, Glos.

Swan Antiques, Chipping Campden, Glos.

SPECIALIST DEALERS

Sodbury Antiques, Chipping Sodbury,, Glos.
Walter Bull and Son (Cirencester) Ltd, Cirencester, Glos.
Rankine Taylor Antiques, Cirencester, Glos.
Squirrel Collectors Centre, Basingstoke, Hants.
A.W. Porter and Son, Hartley Wintney, Hants.
Barry Papworth, Lymington, Hants.
Meg Campbell, Southampton, Hants.
Robin Howard Antiques, Titchfield, Hants.
Warings of Hereford, Hereford, Herefs.
Abbey Antiques - Fine Jewellery & Silver, Hemel Hempstead, Herts.
Forget-me-Knot Antiques, St. Albans, Herts.
Christopher Wharton Goldsmiths, St. Albans, Herts.
J. and H. Bell Antiques, Castletown, Isle of Man.
R. J. Baker, Canterbury, Kent.
Owlets, Hythe, Kent.
Kaizen International Ltd, Rochester, Kent.
Steppes Hill Farm Antiques, Stockbury, Kent.
Chapel Place Antiques, Tunbridge Wells, Kent.
Glassdrumman Antiques, Tunbridge Wells, Kent.
Kent & Sussex Gold Refiners, Tunbridge Wells, Kent.
Pantiles Spa Antiques, Tunbridge Wells, Kent.
The Coin and Jewellery Shop, Accrington, Lancs.
Ancient and Modern, Blackburn, Lancs.
Mitchell's Antiques, Blackburn, Lancs.
Chard Coins, Blackpool, Lancs.
The Cutlery Ghost, Eccleston, Lancs.
Leigh Jewellery, Leigh, Lancs.
Cathedral Jewellers, Manchester, Lancs.
St. James Antiques, Manchester, Lancs.
Brittons - Watches, Nelson, Lancs.
Charles Howell Jeweller, Oldham, Lancs.
H.C. Simpson and Sons Jewellers (Oldham)Ltd, Oldham, Lancs.
Priory Collectables, Preston, Lancs.
Keystone Antiques, Coalville, Leics.
Corry's, Leicester, Leics.
Letty's, Leicester, Leics.
Stanley Hunt Jewellers, Gainsborough, Lincs.
Wilkinson's, Grantham, Lincs.
Rowletts of Lincoln, Lincoln, Lincs.
James Usher and Son Ltd, Lincoln, Lincs.
Wilkinson's, Sleaford, Lincs.
Dawson of Stamford Ltd, Stamford, Lincs.
C. Rosenberg, Heswall, Merseyside.
Kevin Whay's Clocks & Antiques, Hoylake, Merseyside.
Boodle and Dunthorne Ltd, Liverpool, Merseyside.
Edward's Jewellers, Liverpool, Merseyside.
Stefani Antiques, Liverpool, Merseyside.
Weldons Jewellery and Antiques, Southport, Merseyside.
Bond Street Antiques, Cromer, Norfolk.

Barry's Antiques, Gt. Yarmouth, Norfolk.
Folkes Antiques and Jewellers, Gt. Yarmouth, Norfolk.
Wheatleys, Gt. Yarmouth, Norfolk.
Tim Clayton Jewellery & Antiques, King's Lynn, Norfolk.
Albrow and Sons Family Jewellers, Norwich, Norfolk.
Clive Dennett Coins, Norwich, Norfolk.
Leona Levine Silver Specialist, Norwich, Norfolk.
Maddermarket Antiques, Norwich, Norfolk.
Oswald Sebley, Norwich, Norfolk.
Tombland Jewellers & Silversmiths, Norwich, Norfolk.
Parriss, Sheringham, Norfolk.
Michael Jones Jeweller, Northampton, Northants.
Boadens Antiques, Hexham, Northumbs.
Barclay Antiques, Headington, Oxon.
Reginald Davis Ltd, Oxford, Oxon.
Payne and Son (Goldsmiths) Ltd, Oxford, Oxon.
MGJ Jewellers Ltd., Wallingford, Oxon.
Churchgate Antiques, Empingham, Rutland.
English Heritage, Bridgnorth, Shrops.
Teme Valley Antiques, Ludlow, Shrops.
Hutton Antiques, Shrewsbury, Shrops.
The Little Gem, Shrewsbury, Shrops.
Abbey Galleries, Bath, Somerset.
D. and B. Dickinson, Bath, Somerset.
E.P. Mallory and Son Ltd, Bath, Somerset.
Castle Antiques, Burnham-on-Sea, Somerset.
Beach Antiques, Clevedon, Somerset.
M.G. Welch Jeweller, Taunton, Somerset.
Winston Mac (Silversmith), Bury St. Edmunds, Suffolk.
A. Abbott Antiques, Ipswich, Suffolk.
Temptations, Ashtead, Surrey.
T. M. Collins, Dorking, Surrey.
Hebeco, Dorking, Surrey.
Pauline Watson, Dorking, Surrey.
Cry for the Moon, Guildford, Surrey.
Glydon and Guess Ltd, Kingston-upon-Thames, Surrey.
Horton, Richmond, Surrey.
Lionel Jacobs, Richmond, Surrey.
S. Warrender and Co, Sutton, Surrey.
Church House Antiques, Weybridge, Surrey.
Not Just Silver, Weybridge, Surrey.
Harry Diamond and Son, Brighton, Sussex East.
James Doyle Antiques, Brighton, Sussex East.
Paul Goble, Brighton, Sussex East.
Douglas Hall Ltd, Brighton, Sussex East.
Hallmark Jewellers, Brighton, Sussex East.
The House of Antiques, Brighton, Sussex East.
Harry Mason, Brighton, Sussex East.
S.L. Simmons, Brighton, Sussex East.
W. Bruford, Eastbourne, Sussex East.
Trade Wind, Rottingdean, Sussex East.
Rye Antiques, Rye, Sussex East.
Aarquebus Antiques, St. Leonards-on-Sea, Sussex East.
Peter Hancock Antiques, Chichester, Sussex West.

Rathbone Law, Chichester, Sussex West.
Sovereign Antiques, Gateshead, Tyne and Wear.
Davidson's The Jewellers Ltd, Newcastle-upon-Tyne, Tyne and Wear.
Intercoin, Newcastle-upon-Tyne, Tyne and Wear.
Owen's Jewellers, Newcastle-upon-Tyne, Tyne and Wear.
Coleshill Antiques and Interiors Ltd, Coleshill, Warks.
Howards Jewellers, Stratford-upon-Avon, Warks.
Russell Lane Antiques, Warwick, Warks.
Peter Clark Antiques, Birmingham, West Mids.
Maurice Fellows, Birmingham, West Mids.
Rex Johnson and Sons, Birmingham, West Mids.
Piccadilly Jewellers, Birmingham, West Mids.
H. and R.L. Parry Ltd, Sutton Coldfield, West Mids.
Hardwick Antiques, Walsall, West Mids.
Cross Keys Jewellers, Devizes, Wilts.
Howards of Broadway, Broadway, Worcs.
Magpie Jewellers and Antiques and Magpie Arms & Armour, Evesham, Worcs.
B.B.M. Jewellery and Antiques, Kidderminster, Worcs.
Lower House Fine Antiques, Redditch, Worcs.
Bygones by the Cathedral, Worcester, Worcs.
Karen Guest Antiques, Beverley, Yorks. East.
Karen Guest Antiques, Driffield, Yorks. East.
Lesley Berry Antiques, Flamborough, Yorks. East.
Ogden of Harrogate Ltd, Harrogate, Yorks. North.
Mary Milnthorpe and Daughters Antique Shop, Settle, Yorks. North.
Barbara Cattle, York, Yorks. North.
Golden Memories of York, York, Yorks. North.
John Mason Jewellers Ltd, Rotherham, Yorks. South.
Geoff Neary (incorporating Fillans Antiques Ltd), Huddersfield, Yorks. West.
Jack Shaw and Co, Ilkley, Yorks. West.
Aladdin's Cave, Leeds, Yorks. West.
N. St John Paint and Sons Ltd, St Peter Port, Guernsey, C.I.
A. & R. Ritchie, St. Helier, Jersey, C.I.
Roberts Antiques, St Helier, Jersey, C.I.
The Country Antiques, Antrim, Co. Antrim, N. Ireland.
Dunluce Antiques, Bushmills, Co. Antrim, N. Ireland.
Brian R. Bolt Antiques, Portballintrae, Co. Antrim, N. Ireland.
Cookstown Antiques, Cookstown, Co. Tyrone, N. Ireland.
McCalls (Aberdeen), Aberdeen, Scotland.
McCalls Limited, Aberdeen, Scotland.
Joseph Bonnar, Jewellers, Edinburgh, Scotland.

Goodwin's Antiques Ltd, Edinburgh, Scotland.
Montresor, Edinburgh, Scotland.
Royal Mile Curios, Edinburgh, Scotland.
John Whyte, Edinburgh, Scotland.
West End Antiques, Elgin, Scotland.
James Forrest and Co (Jewellers) Ltd, Glasgow, Scotland.
A.D. Hamilton and Co, Glasgow, Scotland.
Jeremy Sniders Antiques, Glasgow, Scotland.
Tim Wright Antiques, Glasgow, Scotland.
Michael YoungAntiques at Glencarse, Glencarse, Scotland.
Kilmacolm Antiques Ltd, Kilmacolm, Scotland.
Mir Russki, Linlithgow, Scotland.
Harper-James, Montrose, Scotland.
Moray Antiques, Nairn, Scotland.
Hardie Antiques, Perth, Scotland.
Old St. Andrews Gallery, St. Andrews, Scotland.
Abbey Antiques, Stirling, Scotland.
Hazel of Brecon, Brecon, Wales.
Silvertime, Brecon, Wales.
Audrey Bull, Carmarthen, Wales.
Gold and Silver Shop, Gorseinon, Wales.
Cartrefle Antiques, Mathry, Wales.
James Allan, Swansea, Wales.
Audrey Bull, Tenby, Wales.

Sporting Items & Memorabilia

Holland & Holland, London W1.
Sean Arnold Sporting Antiques, London W2.
Below Stairs of Hungerford, Hungerford, Berks.
Sir William Bentley Billiards (Antique Billiard Table Specialist Company), Hungerford, Berks.
Warboys Antiques, Warboys, Cambs.
Beer Collectables, Beer, Devon.
Yesterday Tackle and Books, Bournemouth, Dorset.
John Burton Natural Craft Taxidermy Ebrington, Glos.
Simon Brett, Moreton-in-Marsh, Glos.
Hamilton Billiards & Games Co., Knebworth, Herts.
Garden House Antiques, Tenterden, Kent.
The Spinning Wheel Antiques, Southport, Merseyside.
Manfred Schotten Antiques, Burford, Oxon.
Billiard Room Antiques, Chilcompton, Somerset.
Academy Billiard Company, West Byfleet, Surrey.
Burman Antiques, Stratford-upon-Avon, Warks.
Grant Books, Droitwich, Worcs.
Fun Antiques, Sheffield, Yorks. South.
Dunkeld Antiques, Dunkeld, Scotland.
Old St. Andrews Gallery, St. Andrews, Scotland.
Old Troon Sporting Antiques, Troon, Scotland.

Sporting Paintings & Prints

Swan Fine Art, London N1.
Relcy Antiques, London SE10.
Ackermann & Johnson, London SW1.

Frost and Reed Ltd (Est. 1808), London SW1.
Paul Mason Gallery, London SW1.
Tryon Gallery (incorporating Malcolm Innes), London SW1.
Old Church Galleries, London SW3.
Richard Green, London W1.
Holland & Holland, London W1.
The O'Shea Gallery, London W1.
Frank T. Sabin Ltd, London W1.
Connaught Galleries, London W2.
Iona Antiques, London W8.
Grosvenor Prints, London WC2.
Coltsfoot Gallery, Leominster, Herefs.
G. and D.I. Marrin and Sons, Folkestone, Kent.
Leicestershire Sporting Gallery and Brown Jack Bookshop, Lubenham, Leics.
Paul Hopwell Antiques, West Haddon, Northants.
Jane Neville Gallery, Aslockton, Notts.
Sally Mitchell's Gallery, Tuxford, Notts.
H.C. Dickins, Bloxham, Oxon.
Julian Armytage, Crewkerne, Somerset.
Vandeleur Antiquarian Books, Epsom, Surrey.
Julia Holmes Antique Maps and Prints, South Harting, Sussex West.
Burman Antiques, Stratford-upon-Avon, Warks.
Paul Hayes Gallery, Auchterarder, Scotland.
Anthony Woodd Gallery, Edinburgh, Scotland.
Strathspey Gallery, Grantown-on-Spey, Scotland.

Stamps

Argyll Etkin Gallery, London W1.
Michael Coins, London W8.
Stanley Gibbons, London WC2.
Avalon Post Card and Stamp Shop, Chester, Cheshire.
Penrith Coin and Stamp Centre, Penrith, Cumbria.
Jeremy's (Oxford Stamp Centre), Oxford, Oxon.
A.J. Saywell Ltd. (The Oxford Stamp Shop), Oxford, Oxon.
Collectors' Gallery, Shrewsbury, Shrops.
Bath Stamp and Coin Shop, Bath, Somerset.
J. Smith, York, Yorks. North.
Edinburgh Coin Shop, Edinburgh, Scotland.
Glance Back Bookshop, Chepstow, Wales.

Tapestries, Textiles & Needlework

Linda Gumb, London N1.
The Textile Company, London N1.
Alexander Juran and Co, London N4.
Joseph Lavian, London N4.
Robert Franses and Sons, London NW8.
Gallery of Antique Costume and Textiles, London NW8.
S. Franses Ltd, London SW1.
Joss Graham, London SW1.
Keshishian, London SW1.
Peta Smyth - Antique Textiles, London SW1.
Iftikhar Bokhari, London SW10.

The Kilim Warehouse Ltd, London SW12.
The Dining Room Shop, London SW13.
Tobias and The Angel, London SW13.
Joanna Booth, London SW3.
Classic Fabrics with Robin Haydock, London SW3.
Orientalist, London SW3.
Robert Stephenson, London SW3.
Antiques and Things, London SW4.
Perez Antique Carpets Gallery, London SW6.
Atlantic Bay Carpets Gallery, London SW7.
Heskia, London SW8.
John Eskenazi Ltd, London W1.
C. John (Rare Rugs) Ltd, London W1.
Pelham Galleries Ltd, London W1.
Linda Wrigglesworth Ltd, London W1.
Zadah Fine Oriental Carpets, London W1.
Sheila Cook, London W11.
Daniel Mankowitz, London W2.
Coats Oriental Carpets, London W8.
Jonathan Horne, London W8.
Storm Fine Arts Ltd, Great Shelford, Cambs.
Martin and Dorothy Harper Antiques, Bakewell, Derbys.
The House that Moved, Exeter, Devon.
The Honiton Lace Shop, Honiton, Devon.
Georgina Ryder, Sherborne, Dorset.
Maureen Morris, Saffron Walden, Essex.
Catherine Shinn Decorative Textiles, Cheltenham, Glos.
Anthony Hazledine, Fairford, Glos.
Huntington Antiques Ltd, Stow-on-the-Wold, Glos.
Meg Andrews, Harpenden, Herts.
The Lace Basket, Tenterden, Kent.
Farmhouse Antiques, Bolton-by-Bowland, Lancs.
Jocelyn Chatterton, Louth, Lincs.
Country and Eastern, Norwich, Norfolk.
Witney Antiques, Witney, Oxon.
Clutter, Uppingham, Rutland.
Antique Linens and Lace, Bath, Somerset.
Antique Textiles & Lighting, Bath, Somerset.
Ann King, Bath, Somerset.
Susannah, Bath, Somerset.
Richard Midwinter Antiques, Newcastle-under-Lyme, Staffs.
Sarah Meysey-Thompson Antiques, Woodbridge, Suffolk.
Patrick and Gillian Morley Antiques, Warwick, Warks.
Avon Antiques, Bradford-on-Avon, Wilts.
Penny Farthing Antiques, North Cave, Yorks. East.
London House Oriental Rugs and Carpets, Boston Spa, Yorks. West.
Real Macoy, Keighley, Yorks. West.
Echoes, Todmorden, Yorks. West.
Hand in Hand, Coldstream, Scotland.
Gladrags, Edinburgh, Scotland.
Hart Antiques, Bridgend, Wales.

Taxidermy

Get Stuffed, London N1.
Below Stairs of Hungerford, Hungerford, Berks.
Yesterday Tackle and Books, Bournemouth, Dorset.

SPECIALIST DEALERS

John Burton Natural Craft Taxidermy, Ebrington, Glos.
Heads 'n' Tails, Wiveliscombe, Somerset.
The Enchanted Aviary, Bury St. Edmunds, Suffolk.
Hawkins & Hawkins, Edinburgh, Scotland.

Tools - including Needlework & Sewing

Thomas and Pamela Hudson, Cirencester, Glos.
Norton Antiques, Twyford, Norfolk.
Ark Antiques, Bishop's Castle, Shrops.
Peppers Period Pieces, Bury St. Edmunds, Suffolk.
Trinders' Fine Tools, Clare, Suffolk.
Roy Arnold, Needham Market, Suffolk.
The Tool Shop, Needham Market, Suffolk.

Toys - see Dolls

Trade Dealers - see Shipping Goods

Treen

Eldridge London, London EC1.
Halcyon Days, London EC3.
Robert Young Antiques, London SW11.
Halcyon Days, London W1.
Phoenix Antiques, Fordham, Cambs.
A.P. and M.A. Haylett, Outwell, Cambs.
Baggott Church Street Ltd, Stow-on-the-Wold, Glos.
Huntington Antiques Ltd, Stow-on-the-Wold, Glos.
Peter Norden Antiques, Tetbury ,, Glos.
Prichard Antiques, Winchcombe, Glos.
Millers of Chelsea Antiques Ltd, Ringwood, Hants.
Mark Seabrook Antiques, West Haddon, Northants.
Brian and Caroline Craik Ltd, Bath, Somerset.
Peppers Period Pieces, Bury St. Edmunds, Suffolk.
J. Du Cros Antiques, Petworth, Sussex West.
Moxhams Antiques, Bradford-on-Avon, Wilts.
Combe Cottage Antiques, Castle Combe, Wilts.
Annmarie Turner Antiques, Marlborough, Wilts.
Fenwick and Fenwick Antiques, Broadway, Worcs.
Bill Bentley, Harrogate, Yorks. North.
Michael Green Pine & Country Antiques, Harrogate, Yorks. North.
Brian R. Bolt Antiques, Portballintrae, Co. Antrim, N. Ireland.
Islwyn Watkins, Knighton, Wales.

Vintage Cars - see Cars & Carriages

Watercolours

Finchley Fine Art Galleries, London N12.
Lauri Stewart - Fine Art, London N2.
The Totteridge Gallery, London N20.
Centaur Gallery, London N8.
Sandra Lummis Fine Art, London N8.

Barkes and Barkes, London NW1.
Angela Hone Watercolours, London NW1.
Newhart (Pictures) Ltd, London NW3.
Gallery Kaleidoscope, London NW6.
The Greenwich Gallery, London SE10.
Ackermann & Johnson, London SW1.
Chris Beetles Ltd, London SW1.
Miles Wynn Cato, London SW1.
Douwes Fine Art Ltd, London SW1.
Frost and Reed Ltd (Est. 1808), London SW1.
Martyn Gregory Gallery, London SW1.
Messums, London SW1.
Moreton Street Gallery, London SW1.
Old Maps and Prints, London SW1.
Paisnel Gallery, London SW1.
Michael Parkin Fine Art Ltd, London SW1.
Bill Thomson - Albany Gallery, London SW1.
Waterman Fine Art Ltd, London SW1.
Langton Street Gallery, London SW10.
Park Walk Gallery, London SW10.
Regent House Gallery, London SW11.
Alton Gallery, London SW13.
John Spink, London SW13.
The David Curzon Gallery, London SW19.
Campbell's of Walton Street, London SW3.
Gallery Lingard, London SW3.
Stephanie Hoppen Ltd, London SW3.
20th Century Gallery, London SW6.
Julie Collino, London SW7.
Agnew's, London W1.
Victor Arwas Gallery - Editions Graphiques Gallery Ltd, London W1.
Andrew Clayton-Payne Ltd, London W1.
Connaught Brown plc, London W1.
Dover Street Gallery, London W1.
The Fine Art Society plc, London W1.
Maas Gallery, London W1.
Mallett and Son (Antiques) Ltd, London W1.
Mallett Gallery, London W1.
John Mitchell and Son, London W1.
Piccadilly Gallery, London W1.
Royal Exchange Art Gallery at Cork St., London W1.
Stephen Somerville (W.A.) Ltd, London W1.
Spink Leger Pictures, London W1.
Waterhouse and Dodd, London W1.
Crawley and Asquith Ltd, London W11.
Charles Daggett Gallery, London W11.
Milne and Moller, London W11.
Justin F. Skrebowski Prints, London W11.
Ealing Gallery, London W5.
George Dare, London W8.
Pawsey and Payne, London W8.
Simon Spero, London W8.
Beryl Kendall, The English Watercolour Gallery, London W9.
Abbott and Holder, London WC1.
Sebastian D'Orsai Ltd, London WC1.
Michael Finney Antique Prints and Books, London WC1.
Baroq & David Ball Antiques, Leighton Buzzard, Beds.
Foye Gallery, Luton, Beds.
Graham Gallery, Burghfield Common, Berks.
J. Manley, Windsor and Eton, Berks.

Grosvenor House Interiors, Beaconsfield, Bucks.
Windmill Fine Art, High Wycombe, Bucks.
Penn Barn, Penn, Bucks.
Cambridge Fine Art Ltd, Cambridge, Cambs.
Sebastian Pearson Paintings Prints and Works of Art, Cambridge, Cambs.
Storm Fine Arts Ltd, Great Shelford, Cambs.
Baron Fine Art, Chester, Cheshire.
Harper Fine Paintings, Poynton, Cheshire.
Copperhouse Gallery - W. Dyer & Sons, Hayle, Cornwall.
Tony Sanders Penzance Gallery and Antiques, Penzance, Cornwall.
St. Breock Gallery, Wadebridge, Cornwall.
Peter Haworth, Beetham, Cumbria.
The Gallery, Penrith, Cumbria.
Kenneth Upchurch, Ashbourne, Derbys.
Charles H. Ward, Derby, Derbys.
J. Collins and Son, Bideford, Devon.
The Davies Gallery, Bideford, Devon.
Medina Gallery, Bideford, Devon.
Godolphin Antiques, Chagford, Devon.
Chantry Bookshop and Gallery, Dartmouth, Devon.
Mill Gallery, Ermington, Devon.
Honiton Fine Art, Honiton, Devon.
Skeaping Gallery, Lydford, Devon.
Michael Wood Fine Art, Plymouth, Devon.
Hampshire Gallery, Bournemouth, Dorset.
The Swan Gallery, Sherborne, Dorset.
Margaret Bedi Antiques & Fine Art, Billingham, Durham.
T.B. and R. Jordan (Fine Paintings), Eaglescliffe, Durham.
Brandler Galleries, Brentwood, Essex.
Neil Graham Gallery, Brentwood, Essex.
S. Bond and Son, Colchester, Essex.
Richard Iles Gallery, Colchester, Essex.
Simon Hilton, Great Dunmow, Essex.
Newport Gallery, Newport, Essex.
Barling Fine Porcelain Ltd, Wickham Bishops, Essex.
Galerie Lev, Woodford Green, Essex.
Cleeve Picture Framing, Bishops Cleeve, Glos.
The Priory Gallery, Bishops Cleeve, Glos.
Alexander Gallery, Bristol, Glos.
The Loquens Gallery, Cheltenham, Glos.
Manor House Gallery, Cheltenham, Glos.
School House Antiques, Chipping Campden, Glos.
The Titian Gallery, Chipping Campden, Glos.
Astley House - Fine Art, Moreton-in-Marsh, Glos.
Nina Zborowska, Painswick, Glos.
The Fosse Gallery, Stow-on-the-Wold, Glos.
Kenulf Fine Arts, Stow-on-the-Wold, Glos.
Roger Lamb Antiques & Works of Art, Stow-on-the-Wold, Glos.
Styles of Stow, Stow-on-the-Wold, Glos.
Tetbury Gallery, Tetbury, Glos.
Laurence Oxley, Alresford, Hants.
Antique House, Hartley Wintney, Hants.

J. Morton Lee, Hayling Island, Hants.
Corfields Ltd, Lymington, Hants.
The Petersfield Bookshop, Petersfield, Hants.
Bell Fine Art, Winchester, Hants.
Lacewing Fine Art Gallery, Winchester, Hants.
Coltsfoot Gallery, Leominster, Herefs.
Galerias Segui, Cowes, Isle of Wight.
The Shanklin Gallery, Shanklin, Isle of Wight.
Cooper Fine Arts Ltd, Brasted, Kent.
Cranbrook Gallery, Cranbrook, Kent.
Periwinkle Press, Newnham, Kent.
Francis Iles, Rochester, Kent.
Langley Galleries, Rochester, Kent.
Judith Peppitt, Snargate, Kent.
Sundridge Gallery, Sundridge, Kent.
Nicholas Bowlby, Tunbridge Wells, Kent.
Redleaf Gallery, Tunbridge Wells, Kent.
Apollo Antique Galleries, Westerham, Kent.
Old Corner House Antiques, Wittersham, Kent.
Fulda Gallery Ltd, Manchester, Lancs.
Hammond Smith (Fine Art), Leicester, Leics.
P. Stanworth (Fine Arts), Market Bosworth, Leics.
Graftons of Market Harborough, Market Harborough, Leics.
The Boydell Galleries, Liverpool, Merseyside.
Crome Gallery and Frame Shop, Norwich, Norfolk.
The Fairhurst Gallery, Norwich, Norfolk.
Mandell's Gallery, Norwich, Norfolk.
The Westcliffe Gallery, Sheringham, Norfolk.
Staithe Lodge Gallery, Swafield, Norfolk.
Norton Antiques, Twyford, Norfolk.
Coughton Galleries Ltd, Arthingworth, Northants.
Right Angle, Brackley, Northants.
Savage Fine Art, Haselbech, Northants.
Dragon Antiques, Kettering, Northants.
Anthony Mitchell Fine Paintings, Nottingham, Notts.
John Harrison Fine Art, Aston Tirrold, Oxon.
H.C. Dickins, Bloxham, Oxon.
The Burford Gallery, Burford, Oxon.
Horseshoe Antiques and Gallery, Burford, Oxon.
The Stone Gallery, Burford, Oxon.
Wren Gallery, Burford, Oxon.
The Barry Keene Gallery, Henley-on-Thames, Oxon.
Fine Art of Oakham, Oakham, Rutland.
The Old House Gallery, Oakham, Rutland.
Marc Oxley Fine Art, Uppingham, Rutland.
John Boulton Fine Art, Broseley, Shrops.
Teme Valley Antiques, Ludlow, Shrops.
The Mount, Woore, Shrops.
Adam Gallery, Bath, Somerset.
Trimbridge Galleries, Bath, Somerset.
The Court Gallery, Nether Stowey, Somerset.
Sadler Street Gallery,, Wells, Somerset.
England's Gallery, Leek, Staffs.

Thompson's Gallery, Aldeburgh, Suffolk.
J. and J. Baker, Lavenham,, Suffolk.
Peasenhall Art and Antiques Gallery, Peasenhall, Suffolk.
The Falcon Gallery, Wortham, Suffolk.
Cobham Galleries, Cobham, Surrey.
Hampton Court Palace Antiques, East Molesey, Surrey.
Glencorse Antiques, Kingston-upon-Thames, Surrey.
Limpsfield Watercolours, Limpsfield, Surrey.
Bourne Gallery Ltd, Reigate, Surrey.
The Gallery, Reigate, Surrey.
Roland Goslett Gallery, Richmond, Surrey.
Marryat, Richmond, Surrey.
Palmer Galleries, Richmond, Surrey.
Cedar House Gallery, Ripley, Surrey.
Sage Antiques and Interiors, Ripley, Surrey.
Margaret Melville Watercolours, Staines, Surrey.
Boathouse Gallery, Walton-on-Thames, Surrey.
John Day of Eastbourne Fine Art, Eastbourne, Sussex East.
Faringdon Gallery, Arundel, Sussex West.
Lannards Gallery, Billingshurst, Sussex West.
Gough Bros. Art Shop and Gallery, Bognor Regis, Sussex West.
Chichester Gallery, Chichester, Sussex West.
The Antique Print Shop, East Grinstead, Sussex West.
The Canon Gallery, Petworth, Sussex West.
Wilsons Antiques, Worthing, Sussex West.
Anna Harrison Fine Antiques, Gosforth, Tyne and Wear.
MacDonald Fine Art, Gosforth, Tyne and Wear.
Osborne Fine Art Gallery, Jesmond,, Tyne and Wear.
The Dean Gallery Ltd, Newcastle-upon-Tyne, Tyne and Wear.
Arden Gallery, Henley-in-Arden, Warks.
Colmore Galleries Ltd, Henley-in-Arden, Warks.
Fine-Lines (Fine Art), Shipston-on-Stour, Warks.
The Loquens Gallery, Stratford-upon-Avon, Warks.
The Windmill Gallery, Birmingham, West Mids.
Oldswinford Gallery, Stourbridge, West Mids.
Driffold Gallery, Sutton Coldfield, West Mids.
Audley House Antiques, Bradford-on-Avon, Wilts.
John Hubbard Antique Restorations, Blakedown, Worcs.
Richard Hagen, Broadway, Worcs.
Haynes Fine Art of Broadway - Picton House Galleries, Broadway, Worcs.
John Noott Galleries, Broadway, Worcs.
The Highway Gallery, Upton-upon-Severn, Worcs.
James H. Starkey Galleries, Beverley, Yorks. East.
Anthony Graham Antiques,

Boroughbridge, Yorks. North.
W. Greenwood (Fine Art), Burneston, Yorks. North.
Garth Antiques, Harrogate, Yorks. North.
McTague of Harrogate, Harrogate, Yorks. North.
Walker Galleries Ltd, Harrogate, Yorks. North.
E. Stacy-Marks Limited, Helmsley, Yorks. North.
Talents Fine Arts Ltd, Malton, Yorks. North.
Rose Fine Art and Antiques, Stillington, Yorks. North.
Kirkgate Fine Art & Conservation, Thirsk, Yorks. North.
Garth Antiques, Whixley, Yorks. North.
Coulter Galleries, York, Yorks. North.
Robin Taylor Fine Arts, Wakefield, Yorks. West.
Beverley J. Pyke - Fine British Watercolours, Alderney, C.I.
Channel Islands Galleries Ltd, St. Peter Port, Guernsey, C.I.
Geoffrey P. Gavey, Vale, Guernsey, C.I.
Falle Fine Art Limited, St Helier, Jersey, C.I.
The Bell Gallery, Belfast, N. Ireland.
Phyllis Arnold Gallery Antiques, Greyabbey, Co. Down, N. Ireland.
The Rendezvous Gallery, Aberdeen, Scotland.
Nigel Stacy-Marks Ltd, Auchterarder, Scotland.
The McEwan Gallery, Ballater, Scotland.
Calton Gallery, Edinburgh, Scotland.
John Mathieson and Co, Edinburgh, Scotland.
Anthony Woodd Gallery, Edinburgh, Scotland.
Young Antiques, Edinburgh, Scotland.
The Roger Billcliffe Fine Art, Glasgow, Scotland.
Ewan Mundy Fine Art Ltd, Glasgow, Scotland.
Glendoick Antiques, Glendoick, Scotland.
Inchmartine Fine Art, Inchture, Scotland.
Mainhill Gallery, Jedburgh, Scotland.
Newburgh Antiques, Newburgh, Scotland.
Kirk Ports Gallery, North Berwick, Scotland.
Nigel Stacy-Marks Ltd, Perth, Scotland.
St. Andrews Fine Art, St. Andrews, Scotland.
David Windsor Gallery, Bangor, Wales.
Michael Webb Fine Art, Llangristiolus (Anglesey), Wales.
Barn Court Antiques, Crafts & Tearoom, Templeton, Wales.

Wholesale Dealers - see Shipping Goods

Wine Related Items

Christopher Sykes Antiques, Woburn, Beds.
Neil Willcox & Mark Nightingale, Penryn, Cornwall.
Robin Butler, Clare, Suffolk.
Bacchus Gallery, Petworth, Sussex West.

Dealers' Index

In order to facilitate reference both the names of individuals and their business name are indexed separately. Thus A E Jones and C Smith of High Street Antiques will be indexed under:

Jones, A E, Town, County.
Smith, C, Town, County.
High Street Antiques, Town, County.

A

& Barrington, Castle Gate Antiques Centre, Newark, Notts.
(55) For Decorative Living, London SW6.
20th Century Gallery, London SW6.
20th Century, Cambridge, Cambs.
21st Century Keepsakes, Grays Antique Market, London W1.
225 Jewellery Exchange, Antiquarius, London SW3.
275 Antiques, London SW6.
291 Antiques, London SW6.
313 Antiques, London SW6.
A & S Antiques, Red House Antiques Centre, York, Yorks. North
A Barn Full of Brass Beds, Louth, Lincs.
A J Antiques, Bath, Somerset.
A. & H. Antiques, Welshpool, Wales.
A. M. W. Silverware, London Silver Vaults, London WC2.
A.D.C. Heritage Ltd, London SW1.
A.S. Antique Galleries, Manchester, Lancs.
A1A Antiques, Ulverston, Cumbria.
Aagaard & Co, Robert, Knaresborough, Yorks. North.
Aaron (London)Ltd, Didier, London SW1.
Aaron Ancient Arts & Rare Carpets, David, London W1.
Aaron Antiques, Tunbridge Wells, Kent.
Aaron Gallery, London W1.
Aarquebus Antiques, St. Leonards-on-Sea, Sussex East.
Abbas Antiques, Sherborne, Dorset.
Abbey Antiques - Fine Jewellery & Silver, Hemel Hempstead, Herts.
Abbey Antiques, Ramsey, Cambs.
Abbey Antiques, Stirling, Scotland.
Abbey Galleries, Bath, Somerset.
Abbey House, Derby, Derbys.
Abbeygate Gallery & Antiques Centre, Grimsby, Lincs.
Abbot, Deborah, The Swan at Tetsworth, Oxon.
Abbot, Jason, The Swan at Tetsworth, Oxon.
Abbott & Fisk, Framlingham, Suffolk.
Abbott and Holder, London WC1.

Abbott Antiques and Country Pine, London SE26.
Abbott Antiques, A., Ipswich, Suffolk.
Abbott, C.N., Hartley Wintney, Hants.
Abbott, Dominic, Antiquarius, London SW3.
Abbott, Jaki, Antiquarius, London SW3.
Abbott, K., Bexhill-on-Sea, Sussex East.
Abbott, Nicholas, Hartley Wintney, Hants.
Abbott, Paul, Framlingham, Suffolk.
Abbott, S. and R., Needham Market, Suffolk.
Abe, Emmy, Bond Street Antiques Centre, London W1.
Aberdeen House Antiques, London W5.
Aberford Antiques Ltd t/a Aberford Country Furniture, Aberford, Yorks. West.
Abinger Bazaar, Abinger Hammer, Surrey.
Abington Books, Finningham, Suffolk.
Aboudara, M., Antiquarius, London SW3.
Abraham, Gillian, Lubenham, Leics.
Abrahams Books, Mike, Lichfield, Staffs.
Abstract, Kensington Church Street Antiques Centre, London W8.
Academy Billiard Company, West Byfleet, Surrey.
Academy Books, Portsmouth, Hants.
Acanthus Antiques & Collectables, Nottingham, Notts.
Acanthus Antiques/Country Seat Antiques, Corby Hill, Cumbria.
Acanthus Design, The Swan at Tetsworth, Oxon.
Accurate Trading Co Ltd, Alfies, London NW8.
Accurate Trading Co, Bond Street Antiques Centre, London W1.
Ackermann & Johnson, London SW1.
Ackroyd, J.L., Guildford, Surrey.
Acorn Antiques, Deganwy, Wales.
Acorn Antiques, Dulverton, Somerset.
Acorn Antiques, Durham House Antiques Centre, Stow-on-the-Wold, Glos.
Acorn Antiques, London SE21.
Acorn Antiques, Sheffield, Yorks. South.

Acorn Antiques, Worthing, Sussex West.
Acquisitions (Fireplaces) Ltd, London NW5.
AD Antiques, Woodseaves, Staffs.
Adam Antiques, Burnham-on-Sea, Somerset.
Adam Gallery, Bath, Somerset.
Adam, D. and A., Edenbridge, Kent.
Adam, Philip, Harrogate, Yorks. North.
Adams Antiques, Chester, Cheshire.
Adams Antiques, Nantwich, Cheshire.
Adams Antiques, Rodney, Pwllheli, Wales.
Adams Arts & Antiques Ltd, Farningham, Kent.
Adams Furniture Centre, Huntingdon, Cambs.
Adams Ltd, Norman, London SW3.
Adams Room Antiques, London SW19.
Adams Wireless & Bygones Shop, Tony, Ipswich, Suffolk.
Adams, B. and T., Chester, Cheshire.
Adams, Beth, Alfies, London NW8.
Adams, J., Farningham, Kent.
Adams, Maggie, Bath, Somerset.
Adamson Armoury, Skipton, Yorks. North.
Adamson, J.K., Skipton, Yorks. North.
Adamson, N.J.G., Harrogate, Yorks. North.
Adamson, Nigel, Harrogate, Yorks. North.
Adcock, Julie, Melton Mowbray, Leics.
Addison, Mrs Barbara, Colchester, Essex.
Addison, B. and T., Downham Market, Norfolk.
ADEC, London SW1.
Admiral Vernon Antiques Market, London W11.
Afantiques, Wolverhampton, West Mids.
Affordable Antiques, Hale, Cheshire.
After Noah, London N1.
After Noah, London SW3.
Age of Elegance, Whitchurch, Shrops.
Age of Jazz, Whitby, Yorks. North.
Ager, Adrian, Ashburton, Devon.
Agnew's, London W1.
Agnew, A., London W8.
Ahmed, A.H., Brighton, Sussex East.
Aigin, C., Henley-on-Thames, Oxon.

DEALERS' INDEX

Appley Hoare Antiques, London SW1.
Appleyard Ltd, Roger, Rotherham, Yorks. South.
Applin Antiques, Jess, Cambridge, Cambs.
Apter Fredericks Ltd, London SW3.
Arantes - Lalique Glass, R., London N1.
Arbery Centre, The, Wantage, Oxon.
Arbery, B., Saffron Walden, Essex.
Arbiter, Wallasey, Merseyside.
Arbour Antiques Ltd, Stratford-upon-Avon, Warks.
Arbras Gallery, London W11.
Arca, Grays Antique Market, London W1.
Arcade Antiques, Bournemouth, Dorset.
Arcadia Antiques, Bristol, Glos.
Arcadia, Oswestry, Shrops.
Arcane Antiques Centre, Sawbridgeworth, Herts.
Archer (Books), R.G., Lavenham, Suffolk.
Archer's Antique and Country Furniture, Olney, Bucks.
Architectural Antiques, Bedford, Beds.
Architectural Antiques, London W6.
Architectural Emporium, The, Tunbridge Wells, Kent.
Architectural Heritage, Taddington, Glos.
Architus Antiques, Kirkby Lonsdale, Cumbria.
Arden Gallery, Henley-in-Arden, Warks.
Arditti, J.L., Christchurch, Dorset.
Arena, S., Antiquarius, London SW3.
Arenski, Jay, London W11.
Argenteus Ltd, London Silver Vaults, London WC2.
Argentum Antiques, Coggeshall, Essex.
Argyll Etkin Gallery, London W1.
Argyll Etkin Ltd, London W1.
Ariel, Weybridge, Surrey.
Arieta, Valerie, London W8.
Aristocratz, Bristol, Glos.
Aritake. S., Antiquarius, London SW3.
Ark Antiques, Bishop's Castle, Shrops.
Arkea Antiques, Bath, Somerset.
Armchair Books, Edinburgh, Scotland.
Armett, C.H., Burton-on-Trent, Staffs.
Armitage, T.J., Nantwich, Cheshire.
Armitage, Tim, Nantwich, Cheshire.
Armour-Winston Ltd, London W1.
Armoury of St. James's Military Antiquarians, The, London SW1.
Arms & Armour Tokugawa, Antiquarius, London SW3.
Armson (Antiques) Ltd, Michael, Wilstone, Herts.
Armstrong, Harrogate, Yorks. North.
Armstrong, M.A., Harrogate, Yorks. North.
Armytage, Julian, Crewkerne, Somerset.
Arnold Gallery Antiques, Phyllis, Greyabbey, Co. Down, N. Ireland.
Arnold Sporting Antiques, Sean, London W2.
Arnold, Roy, Needham Market, Suffolk.
Aron, D., The Mall Antiques Arcade, Lower Mall, London N1.
Art & Antiques and Bridge Miniatures, Windsor and Eton, Berks.

Art and Antiques, Cheltenham, Glos.
Art Deco Etc., Brighton, Sussex East.
Art Furniture, London NW1.
Art Nouveau Originals c. 1900, London N1.
Artchaos, London SW11.
Artemesia, Alresford, Hants.
Artemis Fine Arts Limited, London SW1.
Arthy, Joe and Sandra, Grasmere, Cumbria.
Artique, Tetbury, Glos.
Artist Gallery, The, Bournemouth, Dorset.
Arts & Crafts Furniture Co Ltd, The, London SW14.
Arty Faherty, Market Drayton, Shrops.
Arundel Clocks, Arundel, Sussex West.
Arwas Gallery - Editions Graphiques Gallery Ltd, Victor, London W1.
Arwas, V., London W1.
Asbury Antiques, Peter, Birmingham, West Mids.
Ash Brothers Antiques, McBains Antiques, Exeter, Devon.
Ash Rare Books, London EC3.
Ash, Jim and Pat, Llandeilo, Wales.
Ashbourne Antiques Ltd, Ashbourne, Derbys.
Ashburton Marbles, Ashburton, Devon.
Ashby-Arnold, Sara, Norton, Yorks. North.
Ashcombe Coach House, Henfield, Sussex West.
Ashe Antiques Warehouse, Wickham Market, Suffolk.
Ashley Gallery, Long Melford, Suffolk.
Ashley Pine, Saintfield, Co. Down, N. Ireland.
Ashley, Keith J., Lyndhurst, Hants.
Ashton Gower Antiques, Stow-on-the-Wold, Glos.
Ashton's Antiques, Brighton, Sussex East.
Ashton, B., Stow-on-the-Wold, Glos.
Ashton, John, Bristol, Glos.
Ashton, K., Gants Hill, Essex.
Ashton, M. and C., Birmingham, West Mids.
Ashton, Mark and Nikki, Bath, Somerset.
Ashton, R., Brighton, Sussex East.
Asian Gallery Ltd, The, Grays Antique Market, London W1.
Aslangul, Veronica, Enfield, Middx.
Aslanian, Michael, Ross-on-Wye, Herefs.
Aspidistra Antiques, Finedon, Northants.
Aspinall Antiques, Walter, Sabden, Lancs.
Asprey & Garrard Ltd, London W1.
Assad, Elias, Grays Antique Market, London W1.
Assembly Antiques Centre, Bath, Somerset.
Assembly Rooms Market, The, Lancaster, Lancs.
Astbury, N.M., Weedon, Northants.
Astley House - Fine Art, Moreton-in-Marsh, Glos.

Astley House - Fine Art, Stretton-on-Fosse, Warks.
Aston Antiques, Durham House Antiques Centre, Stow-on-the-Wold, Glos.
Aston Pine Antiques, Faringdon, Oxon.
Aston, C.D. and Mrs I., Fordingbridge, Hants.
Aston, Fiona, The Ginnel, Harrogate, Yorks North.
Aston, Fiona, Red House Antiques Centre, York, Yorks. North
Aston, S., Alnwick, Northumbs.
Astra House Antiques Centre, Hemswell Cliff, Lincs.
Asylum House Antiques, Bradford-on-Avon, Wilts.
At the Movies, Antiquarius, London SW3.
At the Sign of the Chest of Drawers, London N6.
Athena Antiques Centre, Warsash, Hants.
Athey, G.M., Alnwick, Northumbs.
Atholl Antiques, Aberdeen, Scotland.
Atkin, Miss D.J., Nantwich, Cheshire.
Atkin, Miss S.E., Trevor, Wales.
Atkins, Garry and Julie, London W8.
Atkins, Garry, London W8.
Atkins, T J, Taunton, Somerset.
Atkinson, David, Leeds, Yorks. West.
Atkinson, Mrs M., Cheltenham, Glos.
Atlantic Antique Centres Ltd, London W1.
Atlantic Antiques Centres Ltd, London N1.
Atlantic Antiques Centres Ltd, London SW3.
Atlantic Bay Carpets Gallery, London SW7.
Atlantis Bookshop, London WC1.
Attfield, David, Holt, Norfolk.
Attic Antiques, Saintfield, Co. Down, N. Ireland.
Attic, The, Baldock, Herts.
Attic, The, Newton Abbot, Devon.
Atticus Books, Grays, Essex.
Audley Art Ltd, The Mall Antiques Arcade, London N1.
Audley House Antiques, Bradford-on-Avon, Wilts.
Auldearn Antiques, Auldearn, Scotland.
Aura Antiques, Masham, Yorks. North.
Aust, Brian, London SE20.
Austen, S.T. and R.J., Leigh-on-Sea, Essex.
Austin, Barbara, Chappells & The Antiques Centre, Bakewell, Derbys.
Austin, G., Winchester, Hants.
Austin, J., London WC1.
Austin, S., Swindon, Wilts.
Austin-Fell, A.J. and C.R., Holt, Norfolk.
Austin-Kaye, A.M., Chester, Cheshire.
Austin/Desmond Fine Art, London WC1.
Austwick, P. and L., Sowerby Bridge, Yorks. West.
Autodrome, Almshouses Arcade, Chichester, Sussex West

Bloom, A., London Silver Vaults, London WC2.

Bloomfield, Mr and Mrs, Rye, Sussex East.

Bloomstein Ltd, A. and B., Bond Street Silver Galleries, London W1.

Blower Antiques, Mark, St. Martin, Guernsey, C.I.

Blunderbuss Antiques, London W1.

Bly Valley Antiques, Wrentham, Suffolk.

Bly, J. and V., London SW1.

Bly, John, London SW1.

Bly, John, Tring, Herts.

Blyburgate Antiques, Beccles, Suffolk.

Boaden, Richard, Sandra and Chris, Hexham, Northumbs.

Boadens Antiques, Hexham, Northumbs.

Boalch, Mrs J., Cardiff, Wales.

Boam, Clare, Horncastle, Lincs.

Boase Antiques, Exmouth, Devon.

Boathouse Gallery, Walton-on-Thames, Surrey.

Bobbins Wool, Crafts, Antiques, Whitby, Yorks. North.

Bodhouse Antiques, Birkenhead, Merseyside.

Bodmin Antiques Centre, Bodmin, Cornwall.

Bokhari, Iftikhar, London SW10.

Bolla, Alexandra, Antiquarius, London SW3.

Bolt Antiques, Brian R., Portballintrae, Co. Antrim, N. Ireland.

Bolton Antique Centre, Bolton, Lancs.

Bomzer, Ken, Brighton, Sussex East.

Bon-Accord Books, Aberdeen, Scotland.

Bona Arts Decorative Ltd, Fleet, Hants.

Bond & Sons, S., The Swan at Tetsworth, Oxon.

Bond and Son, S., Colchester, Essex.

Bond Street Antiques Centre, London W1.

Bond Street Antiques, Cromer, Norfolk.

Bond Street Silver Galleries, London W1.

Bond, Mrs H., London W11.

Bond, Peter, The Swan at Tetsworth, Oxon.

Bond, R., Colchester, Essex.

Bonehill, Lynne and Richard, Truro, Cornwall.

Bonn, K. and E., Rochdale, Lancs.

Bonnar, Jewellers, Joseph, Edinburgh, Scotland.

Bonstow and Crawshay Antiques, Kingskerswell, Devon.

Bonstow, James, Kingskerswell, Devon.

Bontoft, P.W., Cirencester, Glos.

Bonython Bookshop, Truro, Cornwall.

Boodle and Dunthorne Ltd, Liverpool, Merseyside.

Book Art & Architecture & Volume Gallery, London WC1.

Book House, The, Ravenstonedale, Cumbria.

Book Jungle, The, St. Leonards-on-Sea, Sussex East.

Book Shelf, The, Mansfield, Notts.

Book Shop, The, Castle Donington, Leics.

Book-Ends, Kirkcaldy, Scotland.

Books & Bygones, Weymouth, Dorset.

Books Afloat, Weymouth, Dorset.

Books for Collectors Ltd., Toddington, Beds.

Bookworms of Evesham, Evesham, Worcs.

Booth & Son, A. E., Ewell, Surrey.

Booth's Bookshop Ltd, Richard, Hay-on-Wye, Wales.

Booth, C.M., Rolvenden, Kent.

Booth, David J. and Mrs Ann, Ewell, Surrey.

Booth, Joanna, London SW3.

Booth, Mr and Mrs C.M., Farnham, Surrey.

Booth, T.J., Rye, Sussex East.

Bootham Antiques, Red House Antiques Centre, York, Yorks. North

Bord (Gold Coin Exchange), M., London WC2.

Boscombe Militaria, Bournemouth, Dorset.

Boscombe Models and Collectors Shop, Bournemouth, Dorset.

Bosi, L., Edinburgh, Scotland.

Boskovic, Boris, Grays Antique Market, London W1.

Bosley, S., London N1.

Boston Antiques, Salisbury, Wilts.

Boston, Julia, London SW6.

Boston, Nicolaus, Kensington Church Street Antiques Centre, London W8.

Bosworth Antiques, Market Bosworth, Leics.

Botting Antiques & Others, John, Heathfield, Sussex East.

Boulevard Antique and Shipping Centre, Leicester, Leics.

Boulton Fine Art, John, Broseley, Shrops.

Bourbon-Hanby Antiques Centre, London SW3.

Bourdon-Smith Ltd, J.H., London SW1.

Bourne End Antiques Centre, Bourne End, Bucks.

Bourne Fine Art Ltd, Edinburgh, Scotland.

Bourne Gallery Ltd, Reigate, Surrey.

Bourne Mill Antiques, Farnham, Surrey.

Bourne, Fred, Hastings Antique Centre, St. Leonards-on-Sea, E. Sussex

Bourne, P., Edinburgh, Scotland.

Bourne, Pascal, Hastings Antique Centre, St. Leonards-on-Sea, E. Sussex

Bournville Books, Hereford, Herefs.

Boustead-Bland Antiques, Chester, Cheshire.

Bouyamourn, Z., Bristol, Glos.

Bow Cottage Antiques, Stratford-upon-Avon, Warks.

Bow House Antiques & Interiors, Hungerford, Berks.

Bow House, Hungerford, Berks.

Bow Windows Book Shop, Lewes, Sussex East.

Bowden Antiques, Elizabeth, The Ginnel, Harrogate, Yorks North

Bowden, Bryan, Harrogate, Yorks. North.

Bowden, David, The Mall Antiques Arcade, London N1.

Bowden, J.A., Scunthorpe, Lincs.

Bowdery, M. J., Hindhead, Surrey.

Bowdler, M.A., Shrewsbury, Shrops.

Bowen, Mrs S., Wilstead (Wilshamstead), Beds.

Bowers Chess Suppliers, Francis, Peterborough, Cambs.

Bowers-Jones, K.S., Deganwy, Wales.

Bowkett, Knaresborough, Yorks. North.

Bowlby, Nicholas, Tunbridge Wells, Kent.

Bowler, Mrs R., Woodville, Derbys.

Bowles, Evelyn, Bishop's Castle, Shrops.

Bowman, H., London W5.

Bowman, Robert, London SW1.

Bowmoore Gallery, Marlborough, Wilts.

Bowood Antiques, Wendover, Bucks.

Box of Porcelain, Dorchester, Dorset.

Boxes and Musical Instruments, London E8.

Boyce, Mark, London SW1.

Boyd-Platt, Mrs Kay, Lymington, Hants.

Boyd-Smith, P.R. and J.M., Southampton, Hants.

Boydell Galleries, The, Liverpool, Merseyside.

Boyer Antiques, Rex, Chappells & The Antiques Centre, Bakewell, Derbys.

Boylan, M. and A., Market Bosworth, Leics.

Boyle, R., Southampton, Hants.

Bracebridge Fine Art, Astwood Bank, Worcs.

Brackley Antique Cellar, Brackley, Northants.

Brackley Antiques, Brackley, Northants.

Brackmoor Antiques, The Ginnel, Harrogate, Yorks North

Brackmoor Antiques, Red House Antiques Centre, York, Yorks. North

Bradbury and Son, Edward, Cheltenham, Glos.

Bradbury Antiques, Roger, Coltishall, Norfolk.

Bradbury, Dennis and Caroline, Cowes, Isle of Wight.

Bradbury, O., Cheltenham, Glos.

Bradford, L., Screveton, Notts.

Bradley Antiques, Robert, Salisbury, Wilts.

Bradley's Past & Present, Petworth, Sussex West.

Bradley, M. and A., Petworth, Sussex West.

Bradley, P. and V., Bletchingley, Surrey.

Bradnum, Michael, Horley, Surrey.

Bradshaw, E.V., Stansted, Essex.

Bradshaw, Nicola D., Ilfracombe, Devon.

Bradwell Antiques Centre, Bradwell, Derbys.

Bradwin, Elizabeth, London W11.

Braemar Antiques, London SW11.

Bragg Antiques, John, Lostwithiel, Cornwall.

Bragge and Sons, Rye, Sussex East.

Bragge Antiques, Lesley, Petworth, Sussex West.

DEALERS' INDEX

Clark, Penelope and Michael, Topsham, Devon.
Clark, R. J., Pittenweem, Scotland.
Clark, Roger, Stow-on-the-Wold, Glos.
Clarke Antiques Ltd, Christopher, Stow-on-the-Wold, Glos.
Clarke Book and Print Dealers, J & D, Norwich, Norfolk.
Clarke, I.D., D.S. and S.F., Stow-on-the-Wold, Glos.
Clarke, Janet, Freshford, Somerset.
Clarke, R.A., Oakham, Rutland.
Clarke-Hall Ltd, J., Deal, Kent.
Classic Bindings, London SW1.
Classic Fabrics with Robin Haydock, London SW3.
Classic Rocking Horses, Thirsk, Yorks. North.
Claude & Martine, Antiquarius, London SW3.
Clay, John, London SW6.
Clay, Peter and Linda, Peterborough, Cambs.
Claymore Antiques, Ludlow, Shrops.
Clayton Jewellery & Antiques, Tim, King's Lynn, Norfolk.
Clayton, Teresa, Grays Antique Market, London W1.
Clayton-Payne Ltd, Andrew, London W1.
Cleeve Antiques, Bristol, Glos.
Cleeve Picture Framing, Bishops Cleeve, Glos.
Clegg, John, Ludlow, Shrops.
Clegg, William, Huntercombe, Oxon.
Clements Antiques, Carlisle, Cumbria.
Clements, K. R., London W1.
Clements, V. and R., Plumley, Cheshire.
Clermont Antiques, Watton, Norfolk.
Cleverly, Mrs M.A., Malton, Yorks. North.
Clewer, P. and J., Nottingham, Notts.
Clewer, Polly, London W5.
Cliffe Antiques Centre, Lewes, Sussex East.
Cliffe Antiques, Old Cornmarket Antiques Centre, Warwick, Warks.
Cliffe Gallery Antiques, Lewes, Sussex East.
Clifford and Son Ltd, T.J., Bath, Somerset.
Clifford, K., Lyneham, Wilts.
Clift, Margaret, Stratford-upon-Avon, Warks.
Clisby Antique Clocks, Bryan, Hartley Wintney, Hants.
Clock Clinic Ltd, The, London SW15.
Clock Corner, Nantwich, Cheshire.
Clock House, Leavenheath, Suffolk.
Clock Shop - Philip Setterfield of St. Albans, The, St. Albans, Herts.
Clock Shop Weybridge, The, Weybridge, Surrey.
Clock Shop, The, Hurstpierpoint, Sussex West.
Clock Shop, The, Winchcombe, Glos.
Clock Showrooms, The, Canonbie, Scotland.
Clock Tower Antiques, Tregony, Cornwall.
Clock Work Shop, The, Witney, Oxon.

Clock Workshop, The, Caversham, Berks.
Clock Workshop, The, Winchester, Hants.
Clocks in the Peak, Chappells & The Antiques Centre, Bakewell, Derbys.
Clockshop, Boughton, Kent.
Clockwise, Emsworth, Hants.
Cloisters Antique & Collectors Fair, Norwich, Norfolk.
Clola Antiques Centre, Clola by Mintlaw, Scotland.
Close Jewellery Restoration, R., Bond Street Silver Galleries, London W1.
Close, Henry H., Abergavenny, Wales.
Close, Mr and Mrs H., Abergavenny, Wales.
Clubb, A., Twickenham, Middx.
Clutter, Uppingham, Rutland.
Cluzan, M., Framlingham, Suffolk.
Clydach Antiques, Swansea, Wales.
Clyde Antiques, Patrington, Yorks. East.
Coach House Antiques Ltd, Stanley, Scotland.
Coach House Antiques, Canterbury, Kent.
Coach House Antiques, Hastings, Sussex East.
Coach House Antiques, The, Gomshall, Surrey.
Coach House Antiques, Whitby, Yorks. North.
Coach House, The, London W11.
Coakley-Webb, P., London N1.
Coats Oriental Carpets, London W8.
Coats, A., London W8.
Cobham Galleries, Cobham, Surrey.
Coblands Farm Antiques, Depden, Suffolk.
Cobra and Bellamy, London SW1.
Cobweb Antiques, Cullompton, Devon.
Cobwebs Antiques & Collectables, Church Stretton, Shrops.
Cobwebs of Antiquities Ltd, Sale, Cheshire.
Cobwebs, London SE9.
Cobwebs, Sheffield, Yorks. South.
Cobwebs, Southampton, Hants.
Cochrane and Leigh Warren Antiques, Fergus, London SW6.
Cockaday, Dean, Diss, Norfolk.
Cockburn, F.J., Northwich, Cheshire.
Cockermouth Antiques Market, Cockermouth, Cumbria.
Cockermouth Antiques, Cockermouth, Cumbria.
Cockman, N., Ross-on-Wye, Herefs.
Cockram, Mrs A., Lincoln, Lincs.
Cockram, T.A.M., Cowes, Isle of Wight.
Cockrell Antiques, Surbiton, Surrey.
Cockrell, Sheila and Peter, Surbiton, Surrey.
Cockton, Mrs L., London SE26.
Cocoa, Cheltenham, Glos.
Coda Antiques, Tony, Boston, Lincs.
Codling, J.M.E., Holt, Norfolk.
Coffey, Norman and Margaret, Louth, Lincs.
Coggins Antiques, Ray, Westbury, Wilts.

Cohen & Cohen (Oriental Porcelain), London W11.
Cohen & Cohen, London W8.
Cohen Numismatics, Philip, London WC2.
Cohen, A., Antiquarius, London SW3.
Cohen, Eli, Antiquarius, London SW3.
Cohen, Jeffrey S., Reigate, Surrey.
Cohen, M. and E., London W11.
Cohen, Mrs., The Mall Antiques Arcade, London N1.
Cohn, George and Peter, London WC1.
Cohu Antiques, Stephen, St Ouen, Jersey, C.I.
Coin and Jewellery Shop, The, Accrington, Lancs.
Coke, P., Sharrington, Norfolk.
Colbrook Antiques, Fakenham, Norfolk.
Coldstream Antiques, Coldstream, Scotland.
Cole Antiques, Nicholas, St Leonards-on-Sea, Sussex East.
Cole, J., London N1.
Cole, V., Newmarket, Suffolk.
Colefax & John Fowler, Sibyl, London W1.
Coleman Antiques, Robin, Piccadilly Antiques, Batheaston, Somerset.
Coleman Antiques, Simon, London SW13.
Coleman, G.D. and G.E., London W8.
Coleman, Garrick D., London W11.
Coleman, Garrick D., London W8.
Coles, D.A., Clevedon, Somerset.
Coles, Graham, Newport, Wales.
Coles, Lorna, Tetbury, Glos.
Coleshill Antiques and Interiors Ltd, Coleshill, Warks.
Coll, Mrs P., Long Melford, Suffolk.
Collard, B., Totnes, Devon.
Collards Books, Totnes, Devon.
Collectables, Kingston-on-Spey, Scotland.
Collector's Corner, Truro, Cornwall.
Collector, The, Barnard Castle, Durham.
Collector, The, Clevedon, Somerset.
Collector, The, London N11.
Collectors Cabin, Holt, Norfolk.
Collectors Centre - Antique City, London E17.
Collectors Centre, The, St Peter Port, Guernsey, C.I.
Collectors Choice, Modbury, Devon.
Collectors Corner, Almshouses Arcade, Chichester, Sussex West.
Collectors Corner, Carshalton, Surrey.
Collectors Corner, Northallerton, Yorks. North.
Collectors Old Toy Shop and Antiques, Halifax, Yorks. West.
Collectors Shop, The, Edinburgh, Scotland.
Collectors World, Alfies, London NW8.
Collectors World, Cromer, Norfolk.
Collectors World, Nottingham, Notts.
Collectors' Corner, Faversham, Kent.
Collectors' Gallery, Shrewsbury, Shrops.
Collectors' Paradise, Leigh-on-Sea, Essex.
Collectors' Place, Shrewsbury, Shrops.

778

DEALERS' INDEX

Cottage Style Antiques, Rochester, Kent.
Cotterill, P., Much Wenlock, Shrops.
Cottingley Antiques, Bradford, Yorks. West.
Cotton (Antiques), Joan, West Bridgford, Notts.
Cotton Fine Art, Nick, Watchet, Somerset.
Couchman, Steve, Canterbury, Kent.
Coughton Galleries Ltd, Arthingworth, Northants.
Coulborn and Sons, Thomas, Sutton Coldfield, West Mids.
Coulborn, P., Sutton Coldfield, West Mids.
Coulter Galleries, York, Yorks. North.
Country and Eastern, Norwich, Norfolk.
Country Antiques (Wales), Kidwelly, Wales.
Country Antiques, Bagshot, Surrey.
Country Antiques, Killearn, Scotland.
Country Antiques, Long Melford, Suffolk.
Country Antiques, The, Antrim, Co. Antrim, N. Ireland.
Country Bedroom, The, Keswick, Cumbria.
Country Clocks, Tring, Herts.
Country Collectables, Fochabers, Scotland.
Country Collector, Pickering, Yorks. North.
Country Cottage Interiors, Kingsley, Staffs.
Country Furniture Shop, Penn, Bucks.
Country House and Cottage Antiques, St Mary, Jersey, C.I.
Country House Antiques, Seething, Norfolk.
Country Life Antiques, Bushey, Herts.
Country Life Antiques, Stow-on-the-Wold, Glos.
Country Living Antiques, Callington, Cornwall.
Country Markets Antiques and Collectables, Chilton, Oxon.
Country Pine Antiques, Market Bosworth, Leics.
Country Pine Shop, The, West Haddon, Northants.
Country Seat, The, Huntercombe, Oxon.
Country Seat, The, Llandudno Junction, Wales.
County Antiques, Ashford, Kent.
County Antiques, Ilminster, Somerset.
Court Gallery, The, Nether Stowey, Somerset.
Court House Antique Centre, Sheffield, Yorks. South.
Courtney Ltd, Richard, London SW3.
Courts Miscellany, Leominster, Herefs.
Courtyard Antiques Market, The, Seaford, Sussex East.
Courtyard Antiques, Brackley, Northants.
Courtyard Antiques, Brasted, Kent.
Courtyard Antiques, Coxley, Somerset.
Courtyard Antiques, Olney, Bucks.
Courtyard Antiques, Williton, Somerset.
Courtyard Collectables, St. Ives, Cornwall.

Cousins and Son, E.W., Ixworth, Suffolk.
Cove Curios, Cove, Scotland.
Cove, Anthony, Windsor and Eton, Berks.
Cove, T. and Mrs K., Swindon, Wilts.
Covent Garden Flea Market, London WC2.
Coventry Antique Centre, Coventry, West Mids.
Coward Fine Silver, Timothy, Braunton, Devon.
Cowbridge Antique Centre, Cowbridge, Wales.
Cowderoy Antiques, John, Eastbourne, Sussex East.
Cowderoy, D.J. and R.A., Eastbourne, Sussex East.
Coworth Gallery, The, Sunningdale, Berks.
Cowpland, J.A., Tunbridge Wells, Kent.
Cox and Company, London SW1.
Cox at College Gateway Bookshop, Claude, Ipswich, Suffolk.
Cox's Architectural Reclamation Yard, Moreton-in-Marsh, Glos.
Cox, A & A, Red House Antiques Centre, York, Yorks. North
Cox, John, Antiquarius, London SW3.
Cox, John, Craven Arms, Shrops.
Cox, Mr and Mrs R., London SW1.
Cox, Nigel, Wimborne Minster, Dorset.
Coy, S.D. and J., Chipping Campden, Glos.
Crabbe Antiques, Peter, Cambridge, Cambs.
Crabtree, A., Sleaford, Lincs.
Crabtree, Richard, Sheffield, Yorks. South.
Crackston, I., Honiton, Devon.
Cradlewell Antiques, Jesmond, Tyne and Wear.
Craiglea Clocks, Edinburgh, Scotland.
Craik Ltd, Brian and Caroline, Bath, Somerset.
Craik, Angie, Haywards Heath, Sussex West.
Cranbrook Antique Centre, Cranbrook, Kent.
Cranbrook Gallery, Cranbrook, Kent.
Cranford Galleries, Knutsford, Cheshire.
Cranglegate Antiques, Swaffham, Norfolk.
Cranston, Enid, Melrose, Scotland.
Craven Gallery, London W2.
Crawford, Alastair, London SW1.
Crawford, M., London N1.
Crawford, M., London SW3.
Crawforth, Andrew, Jubilee Hall Antiques Centre, Lechlade, Glos.
Crawley and Asquith Ltd, London W11.
Crawley, Mrs M., Chislehurst, Kent.
Crawley, R.A. and I.D., Watlington, Oxon.
Crawshaw, H. and E., Lichfield, Staffs.
Crawshay, Simon, Kingskerswell, Devon.
Creasey, A.A. and S.J., Ipswich, Suffolk.
Creaton, I., St. Helier, Jersey, C.I.
Cree, G.W., Market Deeping, Lincs.
Creek Antiques, London SE10.

Creeke, Miss J.M., Sidmouth, Devon.
Creese-Parsons, S.H., Bath, Somerset.
Cremer-Price, T., Plymouth, Devon.
Cremyll Antiques, Cremyll, Cornwall.
Crest Collectables, Eastbourne, Sussex East.
Crested China Co, The, Driffield, Yorks. East.
Crewe-Read, D., London SW6.
Crewkerne Antique Centre, Crewkerne, Somerset.
Crick Chandeliers, Mrs. M.E., London W8.
Criddle, G.H. and J., Cambridge, Cambs.
Cringle, M. and A., Burnham Market, Norfolk.
Crispin Antiques, Madeline, London NW1.
Cristobal, Alfies, London NW8.
Crocket, Sue, Brockenhurst, Hants.
Crockwell Antiques, Durham House Antiques Centre, Stow-on-the-Wold, Glos.
Crocus, Royal Victoria Arcade, Ryde, I. of Wight
Croft Comforts Antiques, Portree, Scotland.
Crofts, Peter A., Wisbech, Cambs.
Cromarty Antiques, Cromarty, Scotland.
Crome Gallery and Frame Shop, Norwich, Norfolk.
Cromwell House Antique Centre, Battlesbridge Antique Centre, Essex
Cronan Ltd, Sandra, London W1.
Crook, Sandra, Bredbury, Cheshire.
Crook, W.V. and A., Kidderminster, Worcs.
Crooked Window, The, Dunster, Somerset.
Cross - Fine Paintings, Edward, Weybridge, Surrey.
Cross Antiques, Watlington, Oxon.
Cross Hayes Antiques, Chippenham, Wilts.
Cross Keys Jewellers, Devizes, Wilts.
Cross's Curios, Birmingham, West Mids.
Cross, B. J., Kendal, Cumbria.
Cross, F., Ryde, Isle of Wight.
Cross, John and Valerie, Birmingham, West Mids.
Cross, M. and R., Swaffham, Norfolk.
Crossley, Peter & Mary, Haslingden, Lancs.
Crossroads Antiques, Prestwick, Scotland.
Crouchman, C.C., Shenfield, Essex.
Crowe, Antiquarian Book Seller, Peter, Norwich, Norfolk.
Crown Arcade, London W11.
Crows Nest, The, Weymouth, Dorset.
Crowson, Colin and Julie, Wainfleet, Lincs.
Crowston, M., Earl Shilton, Leics.
Crowther of Syon Lodge Ltd, Isleworth, Middx.
Crowther of Syon Lodge Ltd, London SW1.
Crowther, D.J., Hartlepool, Durham.
Crowther, Mrs V., London SW4.
Crozier, G.R., Bishop's Stortford, Herts.

Cruck House Antiques, Much Wenlock, Shrops.
Cruz, Mary, Bath, Somerset.
Cry for the Moon, Guildford, Surrey.
Csaky's Antiques, Hook, Hants.
Cudlipp, Jane, Bungay, Suffolk.
Cullen, A. and R.S., Hemel Hempstead, Herts.
Cullen, James, Ripley, Derbys.
Cullompton Antiques Ltd, Cullompton, Devon.
Cullompton Old Tannery Antiques, Cullompton, Devon.
Cullup, S. and K., The Swan at Tetsworth, Oxon.
Cumbley, G.R., King's Lynn, Norfolk.
Cumbrian Antiques Centre, The, Brampton, Cumbria.
Cumming, A. & Y., Lewes, Sussex East.
Cunnell, Barbara, London SW11.
Cunningham, J.R., Kilmarnock, Scotland.
Cunningham, Mrs Patricia, Leamington Spa, Warks.
Cunningham, T., Red House Antiques Centre, York, Yorks. North
Cupboard Antiques, The, Amersham, Bucks.
Curá Antiques, London W11.
Curios of Chale, Chale, Isle of Wight.
Curiosity Shop, The, South Shields, Tyne and Wear.
Curry, Peter, Finchingfield, Essex.
Curtis, P., London SW3.
Curzon Gallery, The David, London SW19.
Cusack, T., Barnstaple, Devon.
Cutlery Ghost, The, Eccleston, Lancs.
Cutting, Mrs T., Bury St. Edmunds, Suffolk.
Cwmgwili Mill, Carmarthen, Wales.
Cyjer Jewellery Ltd, Grays Antique Market, London W1.
Cyrlin, Mr., Bond Street Antiques Centre, London W1.

D

D & J Lines Antiques, Wychbold, Worcs.
D'Ardenne, D.L and P.J., Branksome, Dorset.
D'Eyncourt, Chertsey, Surrey.
D'Orsai Ltd, Sebastian, London WC1.
D'Oyly, N.H., Saffron Walden, Essex.
D. & R. Antiques, The Swan at Tetsworth, Oxon.
D.M. Restorations, Weston-Super-Mare, Somerset.
Da Capo Antiques, Edinburgh, Scotland.
Dachinger, Peran, Alfies, London NW8.
Dadajan, A Hakim, Grays Antique Market, London W1.
Dade, Clifford and Roger, Thames Ditton, Surrey.
Dagger, R. K., Farningham, Kent.
Daggett Gallery, Charles, London W11.
Daggett Gallery, London W11.
Daggett, Caroline, London W11.
Daggett, Charles and Caroline, London W11.

Dahling Antiques, Oscar, Croydon, Surrey.
Dahling, Oscar, Croydon, Surrey.
Dairy House Antiques, Semley, Wilts.
Daisycrest Ltd, Grays Antique Market, London W1.
Dale House Antiques, Moreton-in-Marsh, Glos.
Dale Ltd, Peter, London SW1.
Dale, G.M. and S.M., Wilmslow, Cheshire.
Dale, John, London W11.
Dale, Sharon, Grays Antique Market, London W1.
Daleside Antiques, Markington, Yorks. North.
Daly, M. and S., Wadebridge, Cornwall.
Daly, Peter M., Winchester, Hants.
Dam Mill Antiques, Codsall, Staffs.
Dams, Tim, Shifnal, Shrops.
Danbury Antiques, Danbury, Essex.
Dance, T.A.B., Martock, Somerset.
Dando, A.P. and J.M., Bath, Somerset.
Dando, Andrew, Bath, Somerset.
Daniel, Anjula, Brighton, Sussex East.
Daniel, Francoise, Jubilee Hall Antiques Centre, Lechlade, Glos.
Daniel, Francoise, Span Antiques, Woodstock, Oxon.
Daniell, J., Upton-upon-Severn, Worcs.
Daniels, M.P., Bond Street Antiques Centre, London W1.
Daniels, Mrs Gina, Brighton, Sussex East.
Daniels, P., London Silver Vaults, London WC2.
Dann Antiques Ltd, Melksham, Wilts.
Dann, M., Hatherleigh, Devon.
Danz, Gill, Alfies, London NW8.
Daphne's Antiques, Penzance, Cornwall.
Dare, George, London W8.
Darer, Alan, Grays Antique Market, London W1.
Daszewski, A.A.W., East Grinstead, Sussex West.
Davenham Antiques Centre, Davenham, Cheshire.
Davey, Alison, Woodseaves, Staffs.
Davey, Ann, Alfies, London NW8.
Davey, Mrs P., Blandford Forum, Dorset.
David, G., Cambridge, Cambs.
David, P., Aberystwyth, Wales.
Davidson Antiques, Carlton, London N1.
Davidson Antiques, Robert, Todmorden, Yorks. West.
Davidson's The Jewellers Ltd, Newcastle-upon-Tyne, Tyne and Wear.
Davidson, Ann J. R., Linlithgow, Scotland.
Davidson, Michael, London W11.
Davie, Janet, Pershore, Worcs.
Davies & Son Antiques, Edmund, Whalley, Lancs.
Davies Antiques, London W8.
Davies Gallery, The John, Stow-on-the-Wold, Glos.
Davies Gallery, The, Bideford, Devon.
Davies Oriental Art, Barry, London W1.

Davies, Catherine, Mountain Ash, Wales.
Davies, E. and P., Whalley, Lancs.
Davies, Elinor, Penzance, Cornwall.
Davies, G., Cockermouth, Cumbria.
Davies, H., Coxley, Somerset.
Davies, H.Q.V., London W8.
Davies, Jerome and Teresa, Bideford, Devon.
Davies, L., Botley, Hants.
Davies, Mr and Mrs, Chertsey, Surrey.
Davies, P.A., Tunbridge Wells, Kent.
Davies, R. and D., Wendover, Bucks.
Davies, R.E., Fishguard, Wales.
Davies, W.H., Murton, Wales.
Davies,John, Piccadilly Antiques, Batheaston, Somerset.
Davis (Works of Art) Ltd, Kenneth, London SW1.
Davis Antiquarian Horologist, Roger A., Great Bookham, Surrey.
Davis Ltd, A. B., London W1.
Davis Ltd, Reginald, Oxford, Oxon.
Davis, Amanda, Brighton, Sussex East.
Davis, Andrew, Kew Green, Surrey.
Davis, Jesse, Antiquarius, London SW3.
Davis, Mrs J., Bletchingley, Surrey.
Dawes, Christopher J.L., Huddersfield, Yorks. West.
Dawkins, Mrs Lynn, Cranbrook, Kent.
Dawson Antiques, Zona, Charlton Marshall, Dorset.
Dawson Furniture Restorers, P., Bentley, Suffolk.
Dawson of Stamford Ltd, Stamford, Lincs.
Dawson, Brian, Leighton Buzzard, Beds.
Dawson, J., Stamford, Lincs.
Day Antiques, Alan, Edinburgh, Scotland.
Day Antiques, Tetbury, Glos.
Day Ltd, Richard, London W1.
Day Ltd, Shirley, London SW1.
Day of Eastbourne Fine Art, John, Eastbourne, Sussex East.
Day, Gillian, Rowlands Castle, Hants.
Day, M., London W1.
Day, Vic, Ascot, Berks.
Days of Grace, Budleigh Salterton, Devon.
De Cacqueray, A., London SW1.
De Fresne, Pierre, Edinburgh, Scotland.
De Martini, Massimo, London W1.
De Vine Antiques, Chappells & The Antiques Centre, Bakewell, Derbys.
de Albuquerque Antiques, Wallingford, Oxon.
de Beaumont, Dominic, London NW8.
de Boer, David and Angela, Rumblingbridge, Scotland.
de Havilland, Adele, Bond Street Antiques Centre, London W1.
de Kort, E.J., Bembridge, Isle of Wight.
de Lotz, P.G., London NW3.
de Rin, V., London SW3.
de Rouffignac, Colin, Wigan, Lancs.
Deacon Antiques, Susan, Grays Antique Market, London W1.
Dean Antiques, Colchester, Essex.
Dean Gallery Ltd, The, Newcastle-upon-Tyne, Tyne and Wear.

DEALERS' INDEX

Gallery, Aberdeen, Scotland.
Gallery, The, Penrith, Cumbria.
Gallery, The, Portsmouth, Hants.
Gallery, The, Reigate, Surrey.
Galliard Antiques, Rickmansworth, Herts.
Gallop and Rivers Architectural Antiques, Crickhowell, Wales.
Gallop, G. P., Crickhowell, Wales.
Galloway and Porter Ltd, Cambridge, Cambs.
Galsworthy, A., Barry, Wales.
Gander, Michael, Hitchin, Herts.
Gange, C.C., Marlborough, Wilts.
Ganymede Antiques, Chappells & The Antiques Centre, Bakewell, Derbys.
Garden Art, Hungerford, Berks.
Garden House Antiques, Tenterden, Kent.
Gardiner and Gardiner, Alfies, London NW8.
Gardiner Antiques, Charles, Lurgan, Co. Armagh, N. Ireland.
Gardiner Antiques, John, Somerton, Somerset.
Gardiner, Helen, Alfies, London NW8.
Gardner Antiques, Michael, Bond Street Silver Galleries, London W1.
Gardner Antiques, Richard, Petworth, Sussex West.
Gardner's The Antique Shop, Kilbarchan, Scotland.
Gardner, G.D. and R.K.F., Kilbarchan, Scotland.
Gardner, J., Bishops Cleeve, Glos.
Gardner, Richard and Janice, Petworth, Sussex West.
Garforth Gallery, Market Weighton, Yorks. East.
Gargrave Gallery, Gargrave, Yorks. North.
Garland Antiques, London SW11.
Garner, G., Monkton, Devon.
Garner, John, Uppingham, Rutland.
Garner, N., Hainault, Essex.
Garrard Antiques, Ludlow, Shrops.
Garrard, Caroline, Ludlow, Shrops.
Garratt Antiques, Birmingham, West Mids.
Garratt, S.D., Hertford, Herts.
Garraway, W., Alfies, London NW8.
Garry, Sonia, Marlow, Bucks.
Garth Antiques, Harrogate, Yorks. North.
Garth Antiques, Whixley, Yorks. North.
Gasson Antiques and Interiors, Tadley, Hants.
Gasson, Herbert Gordon, Rye, Sussex East.
Gatehouse Antiques, Macclesfield, Cheshire.
Gateway Antiques, Burford, Oxon.
Gatland, T. and Mrs D., Ashburton, Devon.
Gauld, Maureen H., Killin, Scotland.
Gauldie Antiques, Becca, Abernyte, Scotland.
Gaunt, Peter, Grays Antique Market, London W1.
Gavan, David, Edinburgh, Scotland.

Gavey, G.P. and Mrs C., St. Peter Port, Guernsey, C.I.
Gavey, Geoffrey P., Vale, Guernsey, C.I.
Gavin, J.M., Penryn, Cornwall.
Gay, M. and B.M., Romsey, Hants.
Gaylords, Titchfield, Hants.
Geach, Julian, London SW1.
Gealer, Mrs R., Falmouth, Cornwall.
Geary Antiques, Leeds, Yorks. West.
Geary, J.A., Leeds, Yorks. West.
Geddes, J., St Peter Port, Guernsey, C.I.
Gee, Colin, Tetbury, Glos.
Geering, A.F., Southwold, Suffolk.
Gem Antiques, Maidstone, Kent.
Gem Antiques, Sevenoaks, Kent.
Gemini Antiques & Gallery, Kidderminster, Worcs.
Gemini Trading, Leek, Staffs.
Gems Antiques, Chichester, Sussex West.
Geneen Ltd, Lionel, Bournemouth, Dorset.
General Trading Co Ltd, London SW1.
Genie, Alfies, London NW8.
Gensing Antiques, St. Leonards-on-Sea, Sussex East.
Gent, Ann, Newport, Wales.
Gent, W., Horsham, Sussex West.
Gentle Antiques, Rupert, Milton Lilbourne, Wilts.
Gentry, M., Grays Antique Market, London W1.
Geometrica, Sherborne, Dorset.
George Street Antiques Centre, Hastings, Sussex East.
George, C., Hingham, Norfolk.
George, Dr J.D., London SW1.
Georgia Antiques, Pulborough, Sussex West.
Georgian Antiques, Edinburgh, Scotland.
Georgian Gems Antique Jewellers, Swanage, Dorset.
Georgian House Antiques, Chipping Norton, Oxon.
Georgian Village Antiques Market, London E17.
Georgian Village, London N1.
Gerard Guy Antiques, Bewdley, Worcs.
Germain, T.C., Burnham-on-Sea, Somerset.
German Antiques Ltd, Michael, London W8.
German, P., Almshouses Arcade,Chichester, Sussex West
Gerrish, Olivia, Grays Antique Market, London W1.
Gerwat-Clark, Brenda, Alfies, London NW8.
Geshua, Anthea, Grays Antique Market, London W1.
Get Stuffed, London N1.
Gewirtz, J., London N1.
Gholam, J. and J. M., Ringway, Cheshire.
Gibb's Bookshop Ltd, Manchester, Lancs.
Gibbard, A. & T., Eastbourne, Sussex East.
Gibbins Antiques, David, Woodbridge, Suffolk.
Gibbon, Richard, Alfies, London NW8.

Gibbons Peter, Jubilee Hall Antiques Centre, Lechlade, Glos.
Gibbons, Stanley, London WC2.
Gibbs Antiques and Decorative Arts, Paul, Conwy, Wales.
Gibbs Ltd, Christopher, London SW1.
Gibson, A., Antiquarius, London SW3.
Gibson, Roderick, Nantwich, Cheshire.
Giddings, J.C., Wiveliscombe, Somerset.
Gifford-Mead, Nicholas, London SW1.
Gilbert & Dale, Ilchester, Somerset.
Gilbert and Son, H.M., Southampton, Hants.
Gilbert Antiques, David, Sandgate, Kent.
Gilbert Antiques, John, Robin Hood's Bay, Yorks. North.
Gilbert, David, Sutton Coldfield, West Mids.
Gilbert, M., Uppingham, Rutland.
Gilbert, Philip, Horsell, Surrey.
Gilbert, R.C. and A.M., Southampton, Hants.
Gilberthorpe, Anthony, York, Yorks. North.
Gilberthorpe, Anthony, York, Yorks. North.
Gilberts of Uppingham, Uppingham, Rutland.
Gilded Lily, The, Grays Antique Market, London W1.
Gilham, J.E., Cawood, Yorks. North.
Gill, David, London SW3.
Gill, Yvonne, London N1.
Gillett, Dorothea, Chester, Cheshire.
Gillett, R. and A., Petworth, Sussex West.
Gilligan, M.T., Leek, Staffs.
Gilligans Antiques, Leek, Staffs.
Gillingham Ltd, G. and F., London NW2.
Gillman, G.W., Newton Abbot, Devon.
Gillmark Gallery, Hertford, Herts.
Gillou, Jean, Alfies, London NW8.
Gilmartin, S., The Mall Antiques Arcade, London N1.
Giltsoff, C., Honiton, Devon.
Giltwood Gallery, Cheltenham, Glos.
Ginger Antiques, G. & D., Ludlow, Shrops.
Ginnel Antiques Centres - P. Stephenson, York, Yorks. North.
Ginnel, The, Harrogate, Yorks. North.
Ginnell Gallery Antique Centre, The, Manchester, Lancs.
Ginty, John, Ampthill, Beds.
Gittings and Beynon, Bridgend, Wales.
Gittins, R., Sutton Bridge, Lincs.
Giuntini, Mr and Mrs M.J., Barham, Kent.
Glade Antiques, Marlow, Bucks.
Gladrags, Edinburgh, Scotland.
Glaisyer, David, Nanette & Caradoc, Moreton-in-Marsh, Glos.
Glaisyer, David, Nanette and Caradoc, Stretton-on-Fosse, Warks.
Glaisyer, Richard and Cherry, Stow-on-the-Wold, Glos.
Glance Back Bookshop, Chepstow, Wales.
Glance Gallery, Chepstow, Wales.

Haley, S., Halifax, Yorks. West.

Halford Bridge Antiques, Shipston-on-Stour, Warks.

Haliden Oriental Rug Shop, Bath, Somerset.

Halifax Antiques Centre, Halifax, Yorks. West.

Hall Antiques, Jacqueline, Tetbury, Glos.

Hall Ltd, Douglas, Brighton, Sussex East.

Hall's Bookshop, Tunbridge Wells, Kent.

Hall, Anthony C., Twickenham, Middx.

Hall, L.M., Great Malvern, Worcs.

Hall, Liza, Nutley, Sussex East.

Hall, R. and J., Ash Priors, Somerset.

Hall, Robert, London W1.

Hall, S., Burford, Oxon.

Hall-Bakker, Liz, Span Antiques, Woodstock, Oxon

Hallberg, Mrs Vivien, Horncastle, Lincs.

Haller, Mrs B. J., Deddington, Oxon.

Hallesy, H., Swansea, Wales.

Hallidays (Fine Antiques) Ltd, Dorchester-on-Thames, Oxon.

Hallmark Antiques, The Mall Antiques Arcade, London N1.

Hallmark Jewellers, Brighton, Sussex East.

Halsall Hall Antiques, Southport Antiques Centre, Southport, Merseyside

Halstead Hall Antiques, Grays Antique Market, London W1.

Hamblin, J. and M. A., Yeovil, Somerset.

Hamblin, John, Yeovil, Somerset.

Hamilton and Co, A.D., Glasgow, Scotland.

Hamilton Antiques, Anne, Burnham Market, Norfolk.

Hamilton Antiques, Woodbridge, Suffolk.

Hamilton Billiards & Games Co., Knebworth, Herts.

Hamilton Ltd, Ross, London SW1.

Hamilton, Angela, Birmingham, West Mids.

Hamilton, H., Knebworth, Herts.

Hamilton, K. and J.E., Grantham, Lincs.

Hamilton, London Silver Vaults, London WC2.

Hamilton, Nikki, Long Melford, Suffolk.

Hamilton, S., Brockenhurst, Hants.

Hamilton, Sheelagh, Fernhurst, Sussex West.

Hamlyn Lodge, Ollerton, Notts.

Hammond Antiques, Jeffery, Leominster, Herefs.

Hammond, D. and R., Buxton, Derbys.

Hammond, G., Chipping Campden, Glos.

Hammond, J. and E., Leominster, Herefs.

Hampden Trading Company, The, Great Missenden, Bucks.

Hampshire Gallery, Bournemouth, Dorset.

Hampshires of Dorking, Dorking, Surrey.

Hampstead Antique and Craft Market, London NW3.

Hampton Court Emporium, East Molesey, Surrey.

Hampton Court Palace Antiques, East Molesey, Surrey.

Hampton Gallery, Tetbury, Glos.

Hampton, G., Christchurch, Dorset.

Hamptons, Christchurch, Dorset.

Hanborough Antiques, Long Hanborough, Oxon.

Hanbury Antiques, Hitchin, Herts.

Hanbury, Mrs M.D., Hitchin, Herts.

Hance, J. and D., Stow-on-the-Wold, Glos.

Hancock Antiques, Peter, Chichester, Sussex West.

Hancocks and Co, London W1.

Hancox, G. and D., Wolseley Bridge, Staffs.

Hand in Hand, Coldstream, Scotland.

Hand, Mrs Ruth, Coldstream, Scotland.

Handbury-Madin, Ruth and Greville, Shrewsbury, Shrops.

Hanham, William, London W1.

Hanlon, W. and J., Menston, Yorks. West.

Hannam, Nick, London SW4.

Hannen, L.G., London W1.

Hanover Antiques & Collectables, Scarborough, Yorks. North.

Hansen Chard Antiques, Pershore, Worcs.

Hanshan Tang Books, London SW15.

Hansord & Son, David J., Lincoln, Lincs.

Hansord, David, John and Anne, Lincoln, Lincs.

Harby, Diane, Grays Antique Market, London W1.

Harcourt Antiques, London W1.

Harcourt, P., London W1.

Hardie Antiques, Perth, Scotland.

Hardie, T., Edinburgh, Scotland.

Hardie, T.G., Perth, Scotland.

Harding's World of Mechanical Music, Keith, Northleach, Glos.

Harding, FBHI, K., Northleach, Glos.

Harding, Mrs J., Duffield, Derbys.

Harding, Mrs Janet, Depden, Suffolk.

Harding, N.J., Tunbridge Wells, Kent.

Harding, T., Fyfield, Essex.

Harding,R., London W1.

Hardwick Antiques, Walsall, West Mids.

Hardwick, Trevor and Linda, Rotherham, Yorks. South.

Hardy, A., London W1.

Hardy and Co, James, London SW3.

Hardy Country, Melbury Osmond, Dorset.

Hardy Pine and Country Furniture, Joyce, Hacheston, Suffolk.

Hardy's Clobber, Bournemouth, Dorset.

Hardy's Collectables, Bournemouth, Dorset.

Hardy, J., Bournemouth, Dorset.

Hardy, J.W., Bournemouth, Dorset.

Harefield Antiques, Harefield, Middx.

Hare-Walker, Terry, Old Cornmarket Antiques Centre, Warwick, Warks.

Hares, Cirencester, Glos.

Hargreaves-Jones, Gay, Wilmslow, Cheshire.

Harkness, C. S., Edinburgh, Scotland.

Harlequin Antiques, Edinburgh, Scotland.

Harlequin Antiques, Grantham, Lincs.

Harlequin Antiques, Nottingham, Notts.

Harlequin Antiques, Porthcawl, Wales.

Harlequin Gallery, Lincoln, Lincs.

Harley Antiques, Christian Malford, Wilts.

Harley, Anthony, London SW6.

Harley, G.J., Christian Malford, Wilts.

Harman Antiques, Robert, Ampthill, Beds.

Harman's Antiques, Dorking, Surrey.

Harman, Paul and Nicholas, Dorking, Surrey.

Harmandian, G., Bath, Somerset.

Harmer, Steve, Eye, Suffolk.

Harms, A., London N6.

Harness Antiques, Jack, Marlow, Bucks.

Harold's Place, London W5.

Harper Antiques, Martin and Dorothy, Bakewell, Derbys.

Harper Fine Paintings, Poynton, Cheshire.

Harper, D. A., Derby, Derbys.

Harper, P.R., Poynton, Cheshire.

Harper-James, Montrose, Scotland.

Harpers Jewellers, The Swan at Tetsworth, Oxon.

Harpers, The Ginnel, Harrogate, Yorks North

Harrap, B., Sheffield, Yorks. South.

Harries, Charles, Malvern Link, Worcs.

Harriet Ann Sleigh Beds, Rolvenden, Kent.

Harriman, Ellen, Rickmansworth, Herts.

Harrington, Adrian, London W8.

Harrington, Mrs M., London SW3.

Harris & Holt, Chester, Cheshire.

Harris (Jewellery) Ltd, Jonathan, London EC1.

Harris Antiques (Stansted), Stansted, Essex.

Harris Antiques, Colin, Eversley, Hants.

Harris Antiques, Colin, Hartley Wintney, Hants.

Harris, F.A.D. and B.D.A., Stansted, Essex.

Harris Lindsay, London SW1.

Harris, A.R., Stourbridge, West Mids.

Harris, Anita, Durham House Antiques Centre, Stow-on-the-Wold, Glos.

Harris, Anita, Jubilee Hall Antiques Centre, Lechlade, Glos.

Harris, C. J., Lewes, Sussex East.

Harris, E.C., D. I. and J., London EC1.

Harris, Ian, Bond Street Antiques Centre, London W1.

Harris, K., Coventry, West Mids.

Harris, M. S., Swinford, Leics.

Harris, Martin, Grays Antique Market, London W1.

Harris, S., Manchester, Lancs.

Harris, Sandra, Chester, Cheshire.

Harris, Steve, Hawarden, Wales.

Harrison Antiques Centre, Anna, Gosforth, Tyne and Wear.

Harrison Fine Antiques, Anna, Gosforth, Tyne and Wear.
Harrison Fine Art, John, Aston Tirrold, Oxon.
Harrison House Antiques, North Petherton, Somerset.
Harrison Steen Ltd, Chorley, Lancs.
Harrison, Beryl and Brian, Durham House Antiques Centre, Stow-on-the-Wold, Glos.
Harrison, J., Newtonmore, Scotland.
Harrison, J.M.C., Aston Tirrold, Oxon.
Harrison, John, Chepstow, Wales.
Harrison, R., London W11.
Harrison, Richard, Grays Antique Market, London W1.
Harrison, Ruth, Sevenoaks, Kent.
Harrods Ltd, London SW1.
Harrop Fold Clocks (F. Robinson), Bolton-by-Bowland, Lancs.
Hart and John Giles, Sheila, Aylsham, Norfolk.
Hart Antiques, Bridgend, Wales.
Hart, Ann and Bernard, London NW3.
Hart, J.A. and N., Bletchingley, Surrey.
Hart, Mrs Cheryl, Bridgend, Wales.
Hart, Mrs Elizabeth, Ceres, Scotland.
Hart, Rosemary, London N1.
Hart, Sylvia, Bournemouth, Dorset.
Hartley Antiques Ltd, J., Ripley, Surrey.
Hartley, Philip, Deal, Kent.
Hartley, S.N., Wingham, Kent.
Hartnett and Ann Davey, Annie, Alfies, London NW8.
Hartnoll, Julian, London SW1.
Harvey & Co (Antiques) Ltd, W.R., Witney, Oxon.
Harvey and Gore, London SW1.
Harvey Antiques and Decoration, Patricia, London NW8.
Harvey, C.S., Ludlow, Shrops.
Harvey, Kenneth, The Furniture Cave, London SW10.
Harvey, Korin, Grays Antique Market, London W1.
Harvey, Mrs Jacqui, Longhaven, Scotland.
Harvey, Mrs. P., Weybridge, Surrey.
Harvey, Victoria, London NW8.
Harvey-Jones, A., Woodbridge, Suffolk.
Harvey-Lee, Elizabeth, North Aston, Oxon.
Harvey-Morgan, R., Stratford-upon-Avon, Warks.
Harwich Antiques Centre, Harwich, Essex.
Haslam and Whiteway, London W8.
Haslam, Catherine, Olney, Bucks.
Haslam, N. and C.A., Chesterfield, Derbys.
Haslam-Hopwood, R.G.G., Wadebridge, Cornwall.
Haslemere Antique Market, Haslemere, Surrey.
Hassell, Geoff, Cheltenham, Glos.
Hastie, Caroline, London SW10.
Hastings Antique Centre, The, St. Leonards-on-Sea, Sussex East.
Hastings-Spital, K., Bath, Somerset.
Hatch Rugs, Gideon, London SW11.

Hatchwell Antiques, Simon, The Furniture Cave, London SW10.
Hatherleigh Antiques, Hatherleigh, Devon.
Hatrell, Satoe, Grays Antique Market, London W1.
Haughey Antiques, Kirkby Stephen, Cumbria.
Haughey, D.M., Kirkby Stephen, Cumbria.
Haughton Antiques, Brian, London W1.
Havard and Havard, Cowbridge, Wales.
Havard, Philip and Christine, Cowbridge, Wales.
Havard, T. and P., Harpole, Northants.
Havelocks, Harrogate, Yorks. North.
Haven Antiques, Wainfleet, Lincs.
Havenplan's Architectural Emporium, Killamarsh, Derbys.
Haw, S., Haslemere, Surrey.
Hawkey, V., Grimsby, Lincs.
Hawkins & Hawkins, Edinburgh, Scotland.
Hawkins The Lanes Armoury, Mark and David, Brighton, Sussex East.
Hawkins, B., London E11.
Hawkins, Emma H., Edinburgh, Scotland.
Hawkins, G. and J., Cambridge, Glos.
Hawkridge, Mrs M., Skipton, Yorks. North.
Hawley (MBHI) Antique Clocks, John, Badgworth, Somerset.
Hawley Antiques, Beverley, Yorks. East.
Haworth Antiques, Harrogate, Yorks. North.
Haworth, Peter, Beetham, Cumbria.
Hawthorn Ltd, Gerard, London W1.
Hay Antique Market, Hay-on-Wye, Wales.
Hay Green Antiques, Fyfield, Essex.
Hay, Henry, Alfies, London NW8.
Hay, J.D., Glasgow, Scotland.
Haybarn and Bridgebarn Antique Centres, Battlesbridge Antique Centre, Essex
Haydon, Brian, Whitwick, Leics.
Haydon, Mrs. Maureen, Chichester, Sussex West.
Hayes Gallery, Paul, Auchterarder, Scotland.
Hayes, Miss M.L., North Shields, Tyne and Wear.
Haygate Gallery, Telford, Shrops.
Hayhurst Fine Glass, Jeanette, London W8.
Haylett, A.P. and M.A., Outwell, Cambs.
Hayman & Hayman, Antiquarius, London SW3.
Haynes - Antiques Finder, Roger, Leek, Staffs.
Haynes Fine Art of Broadway - Picton House Galleries, Broadway, Worcs.
Haynes, John, Littlehampton, Sussex West.
Haynes, John, Littlehampton, Sussex West.
Haynes, Michael, Leicester, Leics.
Hayter's, Ryde, Isle of Wight.
Hayter, R.W. and F.L., Ryde, Isle of Wight.

Hayward, Andy, Cirencester, Glos.
Hayward, D.H. and M.S., Kingsbridge, Devon.
Hayward, Pat, Lamb Arcade, Wallingford, Oxon
Hayward, Rachel, London N1.
Hazel of Brecon, Brecon, Wales.
Hazel, Guy, Sonning-on-Thames, Berks.
Hazell, S.B. and M.J., London SW8.
Hazell, S.B. and M.J., York, Yorks. North.
Hazledine, Anthony, Fairford, Glos.
Hazlitt, Gooden and Fox Ltd, London SW1.
Head, J. and J., Salisbury, Wilts.
Head, P., St. Peter Port, Guernsey, C.I.
Headrow Antiques Centre, Leeds, Yorks. West.
Heads 'n' Tails, Wiveliscombe, Somerset.
Heap, Mrs M.M., Burnham-on-Sea, Somerset.
Heape's Antiques, Burnham-on-Sea, Somerset.
Hearn, K.E., Penzance, Cornwall.
Hearnden, J. and S., Dorchester-on-Thames, Oxon.
Hearne, N.J., Beaconsfield, Bucks.
Hearne, R.E.W., Beaconsfield, Bucks.
Heart of England Antiques, Weedon, Northants.
Hearth & Home, Penrith, Cumbria.
Heath Antiques, Mike, Newport, Isle of Wight.
Heath, K.W. and Y., Moreton-in-Marsh, Glos.
Heath, M. and B., Newport, Isle of Wight.
Heath-Bullock, Roger, Mary and Charlotte, Godalming, Surrey.
Heath-Bullocks, Godalming, Surrey.
Heathcote Antiques, Cross Hills, Yorks. North.
Heather Antiques, The Mall Antiques Arcade, London N1.
Heather, J.C., Woolpit, Suffolk.
Heathfield Antiques & Country Pine, Holt, Norfolk.
Heathfield, J.E., H.B. and S.M., Holt, Norfolk.
Heaton Antiques, Bradford, Yorks. West.
Hebbard, I., Titchfield, Hants.
Hebbard, P.E., Hay-on-Wye, Wales.
Hebbards of Hay, Hay-on-Wye, Wales.
Hebeco, Dorking, Surrey.
Hebert, Janice, Hurst Green, Sussex East.
Hedges, J., Salisbury, Wilts.
Hedingham Antiques & Interiors, Sible Hedingham, Essex.
Hedley's of Hexham, Hexham, Northumbs.
Hedley, Mrs E., Maldon, Essex.
Heffers Booksellers, Cambridge, Cambs.
Heidarieh, M., Alfies, London NW8.
Heirloom & Howard Limited, West Yatton, Wilts.
Heirlooms Antique Jewellers and Silversmiths, Wareham, Dorset.
Heirlooms, Worcester, Worcs.

James and Son Ltd, Anthony, London SW3.
James Antiques, Brian, Telford, Shrops.
James Antiques, Joseph, Penrith, Cumbria.
James Antiques, Peter, Sheffield, Yorks. South.
James Antiques, R. A., Sileby, Leics.
James of St Albans, St. Albans, Herts.
James, Allan, Woodstock, Oxon.
James, D.R., Montrose, Scotland.
James, J.A.R. and J.W., East Dereham, Norfolk.
James, Jonathan, London N1.
James, Maurice and Anita, Leigh-on-Sea, Essex.
James, Michael, London SW1.
James, Mr and Mrs N., Dorking, Surrey.
James, N., Winchester, Hants.
James, P.L. & M., London SW6.
James, R.M. and E., Bishops Cleeve, Glos.
James, Rob and Alison, Tutbury, Staffs.
James, S.N. and W., St. Albans, Herts.
James, Stuart, East Molesey, Surrey.
Jameson and Co, A.E., Sheffield, Yorks. South.
Jameson, Clare, Thirsk, Yorks. North.
Jameson, P., Sheffield, Yorks. South.
Jane, Mrs M., Wallingford, Oxon.
Japanese Gallery, London N1.
Japanese Gallery, London W8.
Jardinique, Beech, Hants.
Jarrett, L.S.A. and C.J., Witney, Oxon.
Jarrett, P., Arundel, Sussex West.
Jarrett-Scott, R.R., Witney, Oxon.
Jartelius, M., The Mall Antiques Arcade, London N1.
Jarvill, Derek and Joanne, Middleham, Yorks. North.
Jasper Antiques, Span Antiques, Woodstock, Oxon
Jay and Gee, Alfies, London NW8.
Jeacott-Smith, B. and D., Leek, Staffs.
Jebb, G., Cookstown, Co. Tyrone, N. Ireland.
Jefferson Ltd, Patrick, London W1.
Jefferson, Patrick, London W1.
Jefferson, R. Y., Abridge, Essex.
Jeffery, A. M. & M. H., Barton, Cambs.
Jeffs - Aesthetics, Peter & Philip, Antiquarius, London SW3.
Jellicoe, Roderick, London W8.
Jellinek Antiques, Tobias, Twickenham, Middx.
Jellinek, Mrs D.L. and T.P., Twickenham, Middx.
Jellings, Bill, Holkham, Norfolk.
Jenkins BA, V. and A., Bradford-on-Avon, Wilts.
Jenkins, Allan, Modbury, Devon.
Jenkins, C.B., Burford, Oxon.
Jenkins, J., London SE26.
Jenner, Sandy, Cheam, Surrey.
Jennings Antiques, Paul, Angarrack, Cornwall.
Jennings, R., Barnstaple, Devon.
Jennings, R., Bideford, Devon.
Jennywell Hall Antiques, Crosby Ravensworth, Cumbria.

Jeremiah's Antiques, St Helier, Jersey, C.I.
Jeremy Ltd, London SW1.
Jeremy's (Oxford Stamp Centre), Oxford, Oxon.
Jeremy, Laura, Pontarddulais, Wales.
Jericho Books, Oxford, Oxon.
Jerram, Mark, Stockbridge, Hants.
Jesse, John, London W8.
Jessop Classic Photographica, London WC1.
Jester Antiques, Tetbury, Glos.
Jethwa, Baba, Grays Antique Market, London W1.
Jevons, Francis, London SE21.
Jewel Antiques, Leek, Staffs.
Jewell Ltd, S. and H., London WC2.
Jezebel, Brighton, Sussex East.
Jia, Lei, London SW6.
Jillings Antiques - Distinctive Antique Clocks, Newent, Glos.
Jillings, Doro and John, Newent, Glos.
Joan's Antiques, Littlehampton, Sussex West.
Joel, Mrs J., Dorking, Surrey.
Joel, Mrs J., London SW6.
John (Rare Rugs) Ltd, C., London W1.
John Anthony Antiques, Bletchingley, Surrey.
John, Michael, Richmond, Surrey.
Johns Ltd, Derek, London SW1.
Johns, T., Lytchett Minster, Dorset.
Johnson and Sons, Rex, Birmingham, West Mids.
Johnson Gibbs, Ilona, Chipping Campden, Glos.
Johnson Medals & Militaria, Steve, Newcastle-upon-Tyne, Tyne and Wear.
Johnson Walker & Tolhurst Ltd, London W1.
Johnson's, Leek, Staffs.
Johnson, D., Birmingham, West Mids.
Johnson, D.A., Kilmarnock, Scotland.
Johnson, Lucy, Burford, Oxon.
Johnson, M., Hainault, Essex.
Johnson, Peter, Penzance, Cornwall.
Johnson, Quentin, Tenterden, Kent.
Johnson, R. and R., Birmingham, West Mids.
Johnson, Roger and Bridget, Henley-on-Thames, Oxon.
Johnston, Nigel, The Swan at Tetsworth, Oxon.
Jones - The Silver Shop, Howard, London W8.
Jones Antique Lighting, London W11.
Jones Antiques, Alan, Okehampton, Devon.
Jones Antiques, Christopher, Flore, Northants.
Jones Antiques, Christopher, London SW6.
Jones at PJ2, Peter, London SW3.
Jones Jeweller, Michael, Northampton, Northants.
Jones, A., Colchester, Essex.
Jones, A.P., Norton, Glos.
Jones, Ashley, London WC1.
Jones, Danny, Barmouth, Wales.
Jones, E., Chester, Cheshire.

Jones, G. Trefor, Alfies, London NW8.
Jones, G., Godalming, Surrey.
Jones, Gareth, Edinburgh, Scotland.
Jones, I. and Mrs A. S., Chester, Cheshire.
Jones, Judy, London W11.
Jones, Keith, Shrewsbury, Shrops.
Jones, Ken, Bath, Somerset.
Jones, L., Ludlow, Shrops.
Jones, M.R.T. and J.A., Cromer, Norfolk.
Jones, Madalyn S., Cawthorne, Yorks South.
Jones, Mr and Mrs P., Chepstow, Wales.
Jones, Nick, Alfies, London NW8.
Jones, P., Watton, Norfolk.
Jones, P.W., Oakham, Rutland.
Jones, Sally and Neil Brent, Sherborne, Dorset.
Jones-Fenleigh, Jennifer, Great Glen, Leics.
Jonkers, Christiaan, Henley-on-Thames, Oxon.
Jordan (Fine Paintings), T.B. and R., Eaglescliffe, Durham.
Jordan, James A., Lichfield, Staffs.
Jordan, Robert A., Barnard Castle, Durham.
Jorgen Antiques, London SW15.
Joseph and Pearce Ltd, London EC1.
Jowitt, C.S., Brasted, Kent.
Joy, F. and E., Grays Antique Market, London W1.
Jubilee Antiques, Tottenhill, Norfolk.
Jubilee Hall Antiques Centre, Lechlade, Glos.
Jubilee Photographica, London N1.
Judge, D., Emsworth, Hants.
Judge, S., The Ginnel, Harrogate, Yorks North
Judge, Susan, Red House Antiques Centre, York, Yorks. North
Jukes, Mr and Mrs G., St. Leonards-on-Sea, Sussex East.
Julian Alexander Antiques, London N20.
Julian Antiques, Hurstpierpoint, Sussex West.
Junk Box, The, London SE10.
Junk Shop, The, London SE10.
Junktion, New Bolingbroke, Lincs.
Juno Antiques, Brackley, Northants.
Juran and Co, Alexander, London N4.
Jury, D., Bristol, Glos.
JUS Watches, Grays Antique Market, London W1.
Just a Second, London SW18.
Just Desks, London NW8.
Just Glass, Alston, Cumbria.

K

K & M Antiques, Grays Antique Market, London W1.
K D Antiques, Chester, Cheshire.
K. & Y. Oriental Art, Grays Antique Market, London W1.
K.C. Antiques, Darwen, Lancs.
K.L.M. & Co. Antiques, Lepton, Yorks. West.
Kaae, Andre and Minoo, Grays Antique Market, London W1.
Kailas, M., London SW6.

DEALERS' INDEX

Kaimes Smithy Antiques, Edinburgh, Scotland.
Kaizen International Ltd, Rochester, Kent.
Kalms, S., London Silver Vaults, London WC2.
Kames Antiques & Jewellery, Brodick and Whiting Bay, Scotland.
Kanetti, A., Antiquarius, London SW3.
Karpelowsky, Raymond, The Mall Antiques Arcade, London N1.
Kashan Carpets Ltd., Brasted, Kent.
Kate, Hemswell Cliff, Lincs.
Katharine House Gallery, Marlborough, Wilts.
Katz, G., Richmond, Surrey.
Kavanagh, Christine, Newark, Notts.
Kay, Barbara, Ashtead, Surrey.
Kaye of Lyndhurst, Lita, Lyndhurst, Hants.
Kaye, N.J., Chester, Cheshire.
Kayes of Chester, Chester, Cheshire.
Kayll, J., London W1.
Kear, P.W., Cranborne, Dorset.
Kearin, J. and J., White Colne, Essex.
Kearney & Sons, T.H., Belfast, N. Ireland.
Keddie, Mrs A.C., East Grinstead, Sussex West.
Keeble Antiques, Sherborne, Dorset.
Keeble, C.P., Sherborne, Dorset.
Keeble, E.J., Fareham, Hants.
Keelman Antiques, Red House Antiques Centre, York, Yorks. North
Keene Gallery, The Barry, Henley-on-Thames, Oxon.
Keene, B.M. and J.S., Henley-on-Thames, Oxon.
Keepsakes, Innerleithen, Scotland.
Keil (Cheltenham) Ltd, H.W., Cheltenham, Glos.
Keil Ltd, H.W., Broadway, Worcs.
Keil Ltd, John, London SW3.
Kellam, I., Moreton-in-Marsh, Glos.
Kellam, Ian, Durham House Antiques Centre, Stow-on-the-Wold, Glos.
Keller, Patrica, Saintfield, Co Down, N. Ireland.
Kelly Antiques, Rodley, Glos.
Kelly, D., Antiquarius, London SW3.
Kelly, G., Rodley, Glos.
Kelsey Antiques, Peter, Chappells & The Antiques Centre, Bakewell, Derbys.
Kelsey, P., Bramley, Surrey.
Kelvedon Antiques, Kelvedon, Essex.
Kembery Antique Clocks (inc. K & D Antique Clocks), Bath, Somerset.
Kembery, E., Bath, Somerset.
Kemp Ltd, Melville, Nottingham, Notts.
Kemp, Chris and Ann, Bath, Somerset.
Kemp, Martin, London SE10.
Kemp, Peter, London W8.
Kemp, R.J., Broadway, Worcs.
Kemp, Valerie and Tony, Wrentham, Suffolk.
Kemp, W., Newport, Essex.
Kemps, Bristol, Glos.
Kendal Studios Antiques, Kendal, Cumbria.
Kendall, G., The Ginnel, Harrogate, Yorks North

Kendall, G., Red House Antiques Centre, York, Yorks. North
Kendall, The English Watercolour Gallery, Beryl, London W9.
Kendons, Ingatestone, Essex.
Kennaugh, P. and C., London SW10.
Kennedy Carpets, London N4.
Kennedy, K., London NW5.
Kennedy, M., London N4.
Kennedy, Robin, Richmond, Surrey.
Kenny, Mrs S.M. and D.E., Dorking, Surrey.
Kensington Church Street Antiques Centre, London W8.
Kensington Tower Antiques Ltd, Liverpool, Merseyside.
Kent & Sussex Gold Refiners, Tunbridge Wells, Kent.
Kent Cottage, Rolvenden, Kent.
Kent House Antiques, Haverfordwest, Wales.
Kent, G. and P., Marlborough, Wilts.
Kentdale Antiques, Tunbridge Wells, Kent.
Kentish, M., Dorridge, West Mids.
Kenulf Fine Arts, Stow-on-the-Wold, Glos.
Kenyon, David S., Burnham Market, Norfolk.
Ker, David, London SW1.
Kern, R.A.B., London SW1.
Kern, Virginia, London SW3.
Kern, Virginia, Stow-on-the-Wold, Glos.
Kerr - Gatehouse Bookshop, Norman, Cartmel, Cumbria.
Kerr Antiques Ltd, Thomas, London SW10.
Kerr, Andrew and Suszanna, Stratford-upon-Avon, Warks.
Keshishian, London SW1.
Kessler Ford, Ashburton, Devon.
Kessler, Elisabeth, Ashburton, Devon.
Keswick Bookshop, Keswick, Cumbria.
Ketley Antiques, Carol, London N1.
Kettle House, The, Chipping Campden, Glos.
Kettle Ltd, Thomas, London WC2.
Kettle, Michael, Brightlingsea, Essex.
Kettle, Mrs Sheila, Eccleshall, Staffs.
Keverne, Roger, London W1.
Key Antiques, Chipping Norton, Oxon.
Key, Sarah, Cambridge, Cambs.
Keymer Son & Co. Ltd, Brasted, Kent.
Keystone Antiques, Coalville, Leics.
Khachadourian, Simon, London SW1.
Khan, Jo, Alfies, London NW8.
Khawaja, A.H., London SW1.
Ki Design, London SW6.
Kiadah, R.P., Grays Antique Market, London W1.
Kidwelly Antiques, Kidwelly, Wales.
Kikuchi Trading Co Ltd, Grays Antique Market, London W1.
Kilby, Mrs M., Northfleet, Kent.
Kilgarriff, A., Biggleswade, Beds.
Kilim Warehouse Ltd, The, London SW12.
Kilmacolm Antiques Ltd, Kilmacolm, Scotland.
Kimber & Son, Malvern Link, Worcs.

Kime Antiques, Robert, Marlborough, Wilts.
King Antiques, Roger, Hungerford, Berks.
King St. Antiques, Southport Antiques Centre, Southport, Merseyside
King Street Antiques, Southport, Merseyside.
King Street Curios, Melksham, Wilts.
King Street Curios, Tavistock, Devon.
King's Cottage Antiques, Leamington Spa, Warks.
King's Court Galleries, Dorking, Surrey.
King's Court Galleries, London SW6.
King's Mill Antique Centre, Burnley, Lancs.
King, Ann, Bath, Somerset.
King, Cindy, Dorking, Surrey.
King, J.H., St. Leonards-on-Sea, Sussex East.
King, John, London SW1.
King, John, Much Wenlock, Shrops.
King, M., Wymondham, Norfolk.
King, Mr and Mrs R.F., Hungerford, Berks.
King, Wymondham, Norfolk.
King-Smith & Simon W. Nutter, T.M., Stow-on-the-Wold, Glos.
Kingham, Mrs G., London SE21.
Kings Fireplaces, Antiques and Interiors, Cardiff, Wales.
Kingsclere Old Bookshop, Kingsclere, Hants.
Kingston Antique Market, Kingston-upon-Thames, Surrey.
Kingston, Richard J., Henley-on-Thames, Oxon.
Kingswood, T., London WC2.
Kinloch, Clare, Hastings Antique Centre, St. Leonards-on-Sea, E. Sussex
Kinnaird, Jane and John, Keswick, Cumbria.
Kirby Antiques, R., Acrise, Kent.
Kirk Ports Gallery, North Berwick, Scotland.
Kirk, R., Honiton, Devon.
Kirkgate Fine Art & Conservation, Thirsk, Yorks. North.
Kirkham, H., Tenterden, Kent.
Kirkland, Chris, Tetbury, Glos.
Kirkland, G., London SW6.
Kirton Antiques, Kirton, Lincs.
Kitchen and Country Antiques, Still Too Few, London W11.
Kitchen Bygones, Alfies, London NW8.
Kitchenalia, London W5.
Kitching, Mr. A.T. and Mrs. V.M., Bognor Regis, Sussex West.
Klaber and Klaber, London NW3.
Klaber, Miss P., London NW3.
Klaber, Mrs B., London NW3.
Kleanthous Antiques Ltd, Kleanthous Antiques, London W11.
Kleanthous Antiques, London W11.
Kleinman, Patricia, The Mall Antiques Arcade, London N1.
Kluth, Paula and S., Alfies, London NW8.
Knicks Knacks Emporium, Sutton-on-Sea, Lincs.
Knight and Sons, B.R., St. Ives, Cambs.

Knight, M., St. Ives, Cambs.
Knight, P., Christchurch, Dorset.
Knight-Mudie, George, Aberdeen, Scotland.
Knights, P.H., Norwich, Norfolk.
Knightsbridge Coins, London SW1.
Knowles, Angela, Castle Gate Antiques Centre, Newark, Notts.
Knowles, Susan and Arnie, Hungerford, Berks.
Knowles, W.A. and M.A., Penkridge, Staffs.
Knutsford Antiques Centre, Knutsford, Cheshire.
Koch, Mrs Sally, Sidmouth, Devon.
Kojis Antique Jewellery Ltd, London SW1.
Koll, A., London SW1.
Kollectables, Glasgow, Scotland.
Korn, E., London N10.
Korn, M.E., London N10.
Kowalski, K. S., Macclesfield, Cheshire.
Koziell, Sasha, London SW1.
Kreckovic, L. and E., London SW6.
Krucker, S., Stroud, Glos.
Kuhn, Nick, Bath, Somerset.
Kunz Armin, London SW1.
Kuznierz, Mrs M., Telford, Shrops.

L

L.P. Antiques (Mids) Ltd, Walsall, West Mids.
La Chaise Antique, Stow-on-the-Wold, Glos.
La Maison, Bourne End, Bucks.
La Trobe, H., Brasted, Kent.
Laburnum Antiques, Poole, Dorset.
Laburnum Cottage Antiques, Eye, Suffolk.
Lace Basket, The, Tenterden, Kent.
Lace Shop, The, Antiquarius, London SW3.
Lacewing Fine Art Gallery, Winchester, Hants.
Lack, Stephen, Grays Antique Market, London W1.
Lacquer Chest, The, London W8.
Lacy Gallery, London W11.
Laffling, Graham, Wickham Market, Suffolk.
Lafleure Antiques & Decoration, Wooburn, Bucks.
Lagden, J., Penzance, Cornwall.
Laikin, Michael, Leatherhead, Surrey.
Laithwaite, Miss S., Macclesfield, Cheshire.
Lake Antiques, Lake, Isle of Wight.
Laker, I.A. and E.K., Somerton, Somerset.
Lakes Crafts & Antiques Gallery, Grasmere, Cumbria.
Laleham Antiques, Laleham, Surrey.
Lamb Antiques & Works of Art, Roger, Stow-on-the-Wold, Glos.
Lamb Arcade, The, Wallingford, Oxon.
Lamb, B., Swanage, Dorset.
Lamb, Malcolm C. and Rebecca, Altrincham, Cheshire.
Lamb, S. and Mrs K., Sherborne, Dorset.
Lambden, J., Warboys, Cambs.

Lambe, Charlotte and John, Belfast, N. Ireland.
Lambert Antiques, Dorrian, Lincoln, Lincs.
Lambert's Barn, Woodbridge, Suffolk.
Lambert, N., Woodbridge, Suffolk.
Lambert, R., Lincoln, Lincs.
Lamberty, The Furniture Cave, London SW10.
Lambourn-Brown, Mick, Great Shelford, Cambs.
Lamont Antiques Ltd, LLeigh, B., London SW19.
Lamont, N., London SE10.
Lampard, Mrs P., Headcorn, Kent.
Lampard, Penny, Headcorn, Kent.
Lampert, B., London Silver Vaults, London WC2.
Lancaster Leisure Park Antiques Centre, Lancaster, Lancs.
Lancaster, Liz, Croydon, Surrey.
Lancaster, Peter A., Beverley, Yorks. East.
Lancaster, T.J., Leek, Staffs.
Lancastrian Antiques & Co, Lancaster, Lancs.
Landen Antiques, Rupert, Reading, Berks.
Landsman, Barry, Alfies, London NW8.
Lane Antiques, Russell, Warwick, Warks.
Lane Antiques, Stockbridge, Hants.
Lane Fine Art Ltd, London SW10.
Lane, E.K., Stockbridge, Hants.
Lane, Mrs N., London W5.
Lane, Peter, Wooburn, Bucks.
Lane, R., Horsebridge, Sussex East.
Lane, R.G.H., Warwick, Warks.
Lang, P., London SW19.
Langer, M.T., Chipping Norton, Oxon.
Langford's Marine Antiques, London SW10.
Langford, J. and R., Llangollen, Wales.
Langford, J., Shrewsbury, Shrops.
Langford, L.L., London SW10.
Langfords, London Silver Vaults, London WC2.
Langley Galleries, Rochester, Kent.
Langton Family, Sheffield, Yorks. South.
Langton Street Gallery, London SW10.
Langtons, M., Hull, Yorks. East.
Langtons Antiques & Collectables, Sheffield, Yorks. South.
Lanham, Miss A., Newmarket, Suffolk.
Lankester Antiques and Books, Saffron Walden, Essex.
Lankester, Barbara, Grays Antique Market, London W1.
Lankester, P., Saffron Walden, Essex.
Lannards Gallery, Billingshurst, Sussex West.
Lansdown Antiques, Bath, Somerset.
Lantern Shop Gallery, The, Sidmouth, Devon.
Larner, P., Cirencester, Glos.
Larpari, Mrs, Antiquarius, London SW3.
Lascelles, R., London SW6.
Lassalle, Judith, London N1.
LASSCo, London EC2.
Lassere, Michael, Alfies, London NW8.

Last Century Antiques, Innerleithen, Scotland.
Latchford Antiques, Cheltenham, Glos.
Latchford, K. and R., Cheltenham, Glos.
Latford, Joan, Alfies, London NW8.
Latham Antiques, R.H., Tarleton, Lancs.
Latreville, C. and M., Antiquarius, London SW3.
Latter Antiques, John, Newcastle Emlyn, Wales.
Laura Antiques, Red House Antiques Centre, York, Yorks. North
Laurel Bank Antiques, Red House Antiques Centre, York, Yorks. North
Laurence Corner, London NW1.
Laurens Antiques, Whitstable, Kent.
Laurens, G. A., Whitstable, Kent.
Laurie (Antiques) Ltd, John, London N1.
Laurie Antiques, Peter, London SE10.
Lavender (Antiques) Ltd, D.S., London W1.
Lavian, Joseph, London N4.
Law, Mr and Mrs R., Chichester, Sussex West.
Law, Rathbone, Chichester, Sussex West.
Lawrence and Sons, F.G., Redhill, Surrey.
Lawrence Gallery, Bob, London SW1.
Lawrence, F., Tunbridge Wells, Kent.
Lawrence, T., Westerham, Kent.
Lawson and Co, E.M., East Hagbourne, Oxon.
Lawson Antique Clocks, Keith, Scratby, Norfolk.
Lawson Antiques Limited, Hurst Green, Sussex East.
Lawson Antiques, F. and T., Richmond, Surrey.
Lawson Gallery, The, Cambridge, Cambs.
Lawson, B. and A., Newcastle-upon-Tyne, Tyne and Wear.
Lawson, Jennifer, Bridgend, Wales.
Lawson, W.J. and K.M., East Hagbourne, Oxon.
Laywood, Anthony W., Knipton, Leics.
Lazarell, Grays Antique Market, London W1.
Lazarus Antiques, David, Hartley Wintney, Hants.
Le Shop, Antiquarius, London SW3.
Le Strange Old Barns Antiques, Arts & Craft Centre, Hunstanton, Norfolk.
Le Vesconte's Collectables, Peter, St Helier, Jersey, C.I.
Leadlay Gallery, The Warwick, London SE10.
Leask Ward, London NW3.
Leatherland Antiques, P.D., Reading, Berks.
Lechlade Arcade, Lechlade, Glos.
Leckey, Joseph, Saintfield, Co. Down, N. Ireland.
Ledger Antiques, Sue, Stockport, Cheshire.
Lee's Antiques, Clitheroe, Lancs.
Lee, A.J. and J.K., King's Lynn, Norfolk.
Lee, C.G., Llandudno, Wales.

Lloyd, Gary, Grays Antique Market, London W1.
Lloyd, J., London W1.
Lloyd, M.R., Sandgate, Kent.
Lloyds of Kew, Kew, Surrey.
Lo, Monty, Grays Antique Market, London W1.
Lock, S.J., South Molton, Devon.
Lodge Antiques, Red House Antiques Centre, York, Yorks. North
Lodge, John C., Salisbury, Wilts.
Loewenthal Antiques, Tillington, Sussex West.
Loftus-Potter, N., Deal, Kent.
Loire Valley Antiques, The Swan at Tetsworth, Oxon.
Lombard Antiques, Honiton, Devon.
Lombard Antiques, Newark, Notts.
London Antique Gallery, London W8.
London Cigarette Card Co. Ltd, The, Somerton, Somerset.
London House Antiques, Westerham, Kent.
London House Oriental Rugs and Carpets, Boston Spa, Yorks. West.
London House Oriental Rugs and Carpets, Harrogate, Yorks. North.
London Militaria Market, London N1.
London Road Antiques, Edinburgh, Scotland.
London Silver Vaults, The, London WC2.
London, Sue, Stow-on-the-Wold, Glos.
Long Melford Antiques Centre, Long Melford, Suffolk.
Long, J.W.H., Aberford, Yorks. West.
Long, Michael D., Nottingham, Notts.
Long, Stephen, London SW10.
Longhi, Janice, Broadway, Worcs.
Longmire Ltd (Three Royal Warrants), London SW1.
Longmore, Michael, Grays Antique Market, London W1.
Longmynd Antiques, Church Stretton, Shrops.
Longthorne, K.J., Brighton, Sussex East.
Lonsdale Antiques, Southend-on-Sea, Essex.
Lonsdale, Elaine, Hemswell Cliff, Lincs.
Looking Glass of Bath, Bath, Somerset.
Loomes, Brian, The Ginnel, Harrogate, Yorks North
Loomes, Brian, Pateley Bridge, Yorks. North.
Loquens Gallery, The, Cheltenham, Glos.
Loquens Gallery, The, Stratford-upon-Avon, Warks.
Loquens, S. and J., Stratford-upon-Avon, Warks.
Loraine Antiques Gordon, Rait Village Antiques Centre, Scotland
Loraine, Liane and Gordon, Rait Village Antiques Centre, Scotland
Lord Antiques, Alan, Folkestone, Kent.
Lord, A.G., J.A. and R.G., Folkestone, Kent.
Lord, J.R. and A.A., Taunton, Somerset.
Lords Antiques, Taunton, Somerset.
Lorenzo, Maurizio, Kensington Church Street Antiques Centre, London W8.

Loska, John, Brighton, Sussex East.
Lothian, D., Tewkesbury, Glos.
Lott, Mr and Mrs G.E., Arundel, Sussex West.
Loudon, W.I., Burnham-on-Sea, Somerset.
Lough, Catherine, Red House Antiques Centre, York, Yorks. North
Lovatt, M., Winchcombe, Glos.
Love Lane Antiques, Nantwich, Cheshire.
Love, David, Harrogate, Yorks. North.
Love, Miss M.A., Worsley, Lancs.
Love, R.M., Worsley, Lancs.
Lovegrove, Candy and Julian, West Malling, Kent.
Lovett, M.J., Northampton, Northants.
Low Antiques, Michael, Forres, Scotland.
Lowcock, Marie-Louise, Alfies, London NW8
Lowe and Sons, Chester, Cheshire.
Lowe of Loughborough, Loughborough, Leics.
Lowe, Andrew, London EC1.
Lowe, D., Mansfield, Notts.
Lowe, Valerie, Grays Antique Market, London W1.
Lower House Fine Antiques, Redditch, Worcs.
Lower, Graham, Flimwell, Sussex East.
Lowrie, Mr and Mrs David, Otford, Kent.
Lucas Gallery, Fay, London W8.
Lucas, N., Amersham, Bucks.
Luck, R.J., Hastings, Sussex East.
Luck, S., Wallingford, Oxon.
Luck, S.L., West Malling, Kent.
Luckmans Antiques, Coventry, West Mids.
Luczyc-Wyhowska, J., London SW12.
Luffman, J., Haslington, Cheshire.
Lugley Street Antiques, Newport, Isle of Wight.
Lukies, Pearse, Aylsham, Norfolk.
Lumb and Sons Ltd, Charles, Harrogate, Yorks. North.
Lumb, F. and A.R., Harrogate, Yorks. North.
Lummis Fine Art, Sandra, London N8.
Lummis, Dr T., London N8.
Lummis, Mrs S., London N8.
Luna, Nottingham, Notts.
Lunn Antiques Ltd, London SW6.
Lunn, R.J. and Mrs. S.Y., Dorchester, Dorset.
Lury, R. and J., Cambridge, Cambs.
Lusted, Maureen, Grays Antique Market, London W1.
Luther Antiques, Michael, London SW6.
Luther, Michael, London SW6.
Lyall Antiques, Alexander, Long Melford, Suffolk.
Lyall, A.J., Long Melford, Suffolk.
Lycurgus Glass, Red House Antiques Centre, York, Yorks. North
Lye Antique Furnishings, Lye, West Mids.
Lyle-Cameron, E., Burford, Oxon.
Lymington Antiques Centre, Lymington, Hants.

Lynas, P., Easingwold, Yorks. North.
Lynch, J., Edinburgh, Scotland.
Lynch, R.C., Feniscowles, Lancs.
Lyndhurst Antiques Centre, Lyndhurst, Hants.
Lyon Oliver Antiques, Oaksey, Wilts.
Lyons, A., Sevenoaks, Kent.
Lyons, H.S., London W8.
Lysaght, Jonathan, Warwick, Warks.
Lysaght, J., Old Cornmarket Antiques Centre, Warwick, Warks.
Lythe Cottage Antiques, Lythe, Yorks. North.

M

M & L Silver Partnership, Bond Street Silver Galleries, London W1.
M B G Antiques, Fine Art & Jewellery, Newark, Notts.
M.C.N. Antiques, London W11.
M.G.R. Exports, Bruton, Somerset.
Maas Gallery, London W1.
Maas, R.N., London W1.
Mabey, Sarah, Kelvedon, Essex.
Macadie, Mrs M., Crosby Ravensworth, Cumbria.
MacConnal-Mason Gallery, London SW1.
MacDonald Fine Art, Gosforth, Tyne and Wear.
MacDonald, Brian, Stow-on-the-Wold, Glos.
MacDonald, G., Inverness, Scotland.
MacDonald, T. and C., Gosforth, Tyne and Wear.
Macdonald, A. and Mrs M., Amersham, Bucks.
MacGillivray, G., Whitchurch, Shrops.
MacGregor, Bill and Nora, Perth, Scotland.
MacHenry Antiques, Newtownabbey, Co. Antrim, N. Ireland.
MacHenry, R. and A., Newtownabbey, Co. Antrim, N. Ireland.
MacInnes Antiques, Kilmarnock, Scotland.
MacInnes, Mrs M., Kilmarnock, Scotland.
Mack Antiques, David, Branksome, Dorset.
Mackay, N.A., Bath, Somerset.
Maclean, H., Kilmacolm, Scotland.
Maclean, Mrs J., Dornoch, Scotland.
MacNaughton-Smith, J., The Swan at Tetsworth, Oxon.
Macrow, S.K., Solihull, West Mids.
Maddermarket Antiques, Norwich, Norfolk.
Made of Honour, Chester, Cheshire.
Madeira, Mrs. C., Flore, Northants.
Madison Gallery, The, Petworth, Sussex West.
Magee, D.A., Canterbury, Kent.
Maggie May's, North Shields, Tyne and Wear.
Maggs Bros Ltd, London W1.
Maggs Shipping Ltd, Liverpool, Merseyside.
Maggs, J.F., B.D. and E.F., London W1.
Maggs, John, Falmouth, Cornwall.
Magic Lantern, The, Dunecht, Scotland.

Martin, F., Crewkerne, Somerset.

Martin, J., Farnborough, Hants.

Martin, John R., Edinburgh, Scotland.

Martin, Malcolm, Antiquarius, London SW3.

Martin, Mrs Truda K., Saintfield, Co. Down, N. Ireland.

Martin, Nigel, Alfies, London NW8.

Martin, Paul, London W11.

Martin, Peter J., Windsor and Eton, Berks.

Martin, R. and S., Risby, Suffolk.

Martin, Tony, Looe, Cornwall.

Martin-Quick Antiques, Wolverhampton, West Mids.

Martin-Taylor Antiques, David, London SW6.

Martinez Antiques, J., Edinburgh, Scotland.

Martinez-Negrilo, Mr., Antiquarius, London SW3.

Martire, Francesca, Alfies, London NW8.

Martlesham Antiques, Martlesham, Suffolk.

Martony Antiques & Collectables, Amersham, Bucks.

Maryam, Alfies, London NW8.

Mascaro, R., Plymouth, Devon.

Mason (Sainsbury & Mason), Jeremy, London SW1.

Mason Gallery, Paul, London SW1.

Mason Jewellers Ltd, John, Rotherham, Yorks. South.

Mason, Ann, Newark, Notts.

Mason, Bill & Sue, Great Shelford, Cambs.

Mason, C.G. and P.G., Bewdley, Worcs.

Mason, Harry, Brighton, Sussex East.

Mason, M. and Mrs R., Peterborough, Cambs.

Massada Antiques, Bond Street Antiques Centre, London W1.

Massey and Son, D.J., Alderley Edge, Cheshire.

Massey and Son, D.J., Macclesfield, Cheshire.

Massey, Alison, Grays Antique Market, London W1.

Massey, J.C., Long Melford, Suffolk.

Massingham Antiques, Roy, Brasted, Kent.

Mathaf Gallery Ltd, London SW1.

Mathers Antiques, Megan, London SW6.

Matheson, T., Portsoy, Scotland.

Mathews, M.R., Tetbury, Glos.

Mathias, Gerald, Antiquarius, London SW3.

Mathias, R., Guildford, Surrey.

Mathias, R., St. Albans, Herts.

Mathias, Richard, Oxford, Oxon.

Mathias, Richard, Windsor and Eton, Berks.

Mathieson and Co, John, Edinburgh, Scotland.

Matlock Antiques and Collectables Centre, Matlock, Derbys.

Matsell, Brian, Derby, Derbys.

Matson, J., Liverpool, Merseyside.

Matthiesen Fine Art Ltd., London SW1.

Maufe, D.H. and J., Burnham Market, Norfolk.

Mautner, Mrs Sue, Antiquarius, London SW3.

Mawby, Mrs P., Northampton, Northants.

Maxtone Graham, Mr and Mrs R.M., Hythe, Kent.

Maxwell, Margaret, Innerleithen, Scotland.

May Antiques & Collectables, Shirley, Chappells & The Antiques Centre, Bakewell, Derbys.

May Avenue, Antiquarius, London SW3.

Maya Antiques, Honiton, Devon.

Mayfair Antiques International Ltd, Grays Antique Market, London W1.

Mayfair Antiques, Dorking, Surrey.

Mayfair Antiques, Otley, Yorks. West.

Mayfair Carpet Gallery Ltd, London W1.

Mayfair Gallery, London W1.

Mayflower Antiques, Harwich, Essex.

Mayflower Antiques, London W11.

Mayle, Mr and Mrs, Marlow, Bucks.

Maynard Antiques, Mark, London SW6.

Maynard, John, Sawbridgeworth, Herts.

Mayne, R., Newhaven, Sussex East.

Mays, Maggie, Buxton, Derbys.

Maze, The, Alfies, London NW8.

McAleer, M., London W2.

McAleer, M.J., London W2.

McAskie, Pete, Grays Antique Market, London W1.

McAuley - The Antique Shop, Marjorie, Greyabbey, Co. Down, N. Ireland.

McBain, I.S., G., R. and M., McBains Antiques, Exeter, Devon

McBains Antique Exports, McBains Antiques, Exeter, Devon

McBains Antiques, Exeter, Devon.

McCall, B., Aberdeen, Scotland.

McCall, Sandra, Chacewater, Cornwall.

McCalls (Aberdeen), Aberdeen, Scotland.

McCalls Limited, Aberdeen, Scotland.

McCann, Mrs. A.D., Holyhead (Anglesey), Wales.

McCarthy, Ian, Clutton, Somerset.

McCarthy, Margaret, London SE1.

McCartney, Cordelia, Wrotham, Kent.

McClaren, J., Gosport, Hants.

McClean, Maria, Antiquarius, London SW3.

McClenaghan, London SW1.

McClure-Buckie, G., Cambridge, Cambs.

McCollum, D.C., Stockland, Devon.

McConnell, Audrey, Durham House Antiques Centre, Stow-on-the-Wold, Glos.

McCourt, Eddie, The Swan at Tetsworth, Oxon.

McCoy, Robert, Alfies, London NW8.

McCreddie, B.S., Ludlow, Shrops.

McCulloch Antiques, John, Felixstowe, Suffolk.

McDonald Antiques, Joy, London SW13.

McDonald, Nigel, Alfies, London NW8.

McDonald, Stella, Antiquarius, London SW3.

McDonald-Hobley, Mrs N., Antiquarius, London SW3.

McErlain, Oliver, Tetbury, Glos.

McEvoy, Mrs M., Comberton, Cambs.

McEwan Gallery, The, Ballater, Scotland.

McEwan, D., P. and R., Ballater, Scotland.

McGill, J., Meigle, Scotland.

McGill, Mrs Jeannette, Alyth, Scotland.

McGlynn, Thomas, Long Melford, Suffolk.

McGrath, Bernard J., Newark, Notts.

McGregor, Veronica, Halstead, Essex.

McHale, Tom, Chichester, Sussex West.

McHugo, M., Lye, West Mids.

McHugo, M., Stourbridge, West Mids.

McKean, Sarah, The Swan at Tetsworth, Oxon.

McKeivor, Mrs J., Chilcompton, Somerset.

McKenna and Co, London SW3.

McKenna, C. and M., London SW3.

McKenzie, J.W., Ewell, Surrey.

McKinley, D., Wiveliscombe, Somerset.

McKinnon, Georgina, Newington, Kent.

McKnight, E.W., Bury St. Edmunds, Suffolk.

McLaughlin, A.J. and Mrs B., Manchester, Lancs.

McLay "Saratoga Trunk", Cathy, Victorian Village, Glasgow, Scotland

McLean, D., Portsoy, Scotland.

McLeod, David and Patricia, Knutsford, Cheshire.

McLeod-Brown, William, Antiquarius, London SW3.

McLoughlin, Alan, Truro, Cornwall.

McMullan & Son, D., Manchester, Lancs.

McNaught, Shirley and David, Bury St Edmunds, Suffolk.

McNaughtan's Bookshop, Edinburgh, Scotland.

McNulty Wholesalers, Coleraine, Co. Londonderry, N. Ireland.

McNulty Wholesalers, Market Drayton, Shrops.

McPherson, I. and H., Coalville, Leics.

McPherson, Robert, London W8.

McQuade Antiques, Kilbarchan, Scotland.

McQuade, W. G. & W. J., Kilbarchan, Scotland.

McRoberts, R.J., Carlisle, Cumbria.

McTague of Harrogate, Harrogate, Yorks. North.

McTague, P., Harrogate, Yorks. North.

McVeigh & Charpentier, London SW10.

McWhirter, James, London SW10.

McWhirter, London SW10.

Mead, T, Launceston, Cornwall.

Meader, Kay, Littlehampton, Sussex West.

Medd, N.P., Clitheroe, Lancs.

Medina Gallery, Barnstaple, Devon.

Medina Gallery, Bideford, Devon.

Mee, R., London W8.

Meeks & Co, F., Birmingham, West Mids.

Megarry's and Forever Summer, Blackmore, Essex.

Mejia, Ginny, London SW10.

Melbourne Antiques & Interiors, London SE22.

Meldrum, D., Chagford, Devon.

Melford Antique Warehouse, Long Melford, Suffolk.

Mellor, C.R.J. and P.J., Lichfield, Staffs.

Mellor, Mrs R., Bath, Somerset.

Melnick House of Ascot, Ascot, Berks.

Melody's Antique Galleries, Chester, Cheshire.

Melody, M., Chester, Cheshire.

Melton Antiques, Woodbridge, Suffolk.

Melton's, London W1.

Meltzer, L., London W11.

Melville Watercolours, Margaret, Staines, Surrey.

Melvin, R., Edinburgh, Scotland.

Memories, Bramley, Surrey.

Memories, Great Dunmow, Essex.

Memories, Rochester, Kent.

Memory Lane Antiques Centre, Ripley, Derbys.

Memory Lane Antiques, Great Bookham, Surrey.

Memory Lane Antiques, Lower Stondon, Beds.

Memory Lane, Sowerby Bridge, Yorks. West.

Mennis, G., Hastings Antique Centre, St. Leonards-on-Sea, E. Sussex

Mercado, Mr and Mrs K., Baythorne End, Essex.

Mercat-Hughes Antiques, Glasgow, Scotland.

Mercer (Chronometers) Ltd, Thomas, London SW1.

Mercer Antiques, Noel, Long Melford, Suffolk.

Merchant House Antiques, Grays Antique Market, London W1.

Merchant House Antiques, Honiton, Devon.

Merchants House Antiques, Ross-on-Wye, Herefs.

Mercury Antiques, London W11.

Mere Antiques, Fowlmere, Cambs.

Mere Antiques, Topsham, Devon.

Meredith, John, Chagford, Devon.

Mereside Books, Macclesfield, Cheshire.

Merkel, M.P., Dartmouth, Devon.

Merlin Antiques, Tetbury, Glos.

Merlins Antiques, Carmarthen, Wales.

Merrifield, Mr and Mrs B., Paisley, Scotland.

Messums (Contemporary), London W1.

Messums, London SW1.

Metcalf, R. W., Eccleston, Lancs.

Metcalfe, C.W. and M., West Auckland, Durham.

Metcalfe, Mrs A., Helsby, Cheshire.

Mews Antique Emporium, Holt, Norfolk.

Meyer, Mr T., London W8.

Meyler, Olivia, Red House Antiques Centre, York, Yorks. North

Meysey-Thompson Antiques, Sarah, Woodbridge, Suffolk.

MGJ Jewellers Ltd., Wallingford, Oxon.

Miall, Margaret, Alfies, London NW8.

Mibus, Adrian, London SW1.

Micawber Antiques, Bridgnorth, Shrops.

Michael Coins, London W8.

Michael, Judith, Corbridge, Northumbs.

Michelson, Mrs E., Bond Street Antiques Centre, London W1.

Michieli, Robert, St Helier, Jersey, C.I.

Middleham Antiques, Middleham, Yorks. North.

Middlemiss, Janet, Sonning-on-Thames, Berks.

Middleton, Arthur, London WC2.

Middleton, Bobbie, Tetbury, Glos.

Middleton, Ms Fiona, Portree, Scotland.

Middleton, Helen, Durham House Antiques Centre, Stow-on-the-Wold, Glos.

Midgley, J.L. and N.M., Settle, Yorks. North.

Midland Goss and Commemoratives, Old Cornmarket Antiques Centre, Warwick, Warks.

Midwinter Antiques, Richard, Newcastle-under-Lyme, Staffs.

Midwinter, Mr and Mrs R., Newcastle-under-Lyme, Staffs.

Mighell, J., London N5.

Mildenhall Antiques, Mildenhall, Suffolk.

Mildwurf and Partners, L., Penrith, Cumbria.

Mileham, Peter, Saffron Walden, Essex.

Miles Antiques, Kinross, Scotland.

Miles Bookshop, Archie, Gosforth, Cumbria.

Miles, David, Canterbury, Kent.

Miles, K. and S., Kinross, Scotland.

Milestone Antiques, Easingwold, Yorks. North.

Milestone Antiques, Lichfield, Staffs.

Milewski, D., Richmond, Surrey.

Milford Haven Antiques, Milford Haven, Wales.

Military Antiques, The Mall Antiques Arcade, London N1.

Military Curios, HQ84, Gloucester, Glos.

Military History Bookshop, London NW1.

Military Parade Bookshop, The, Marlborough, Wilts.

Mill Antiques of Bibury, Bibury, Glos.

Mill Antiques, Sleaford, Lincs.

Mill Farm Antiques, Disley, Cheshire.

Mill Gallery, Ermington, Devon.

Mill House Antiques, Goudhurst, Kent.

Millennium Antiques, Chappells & The Antiques Centre, Bakewell, Derbys.

Miller Antiques, Cullompton, Devon.

Miller Antiques, James, Wooler, Northumbs.

Miller Fine Arts, Duncan R., London NW3.

Miller, Gill and Keith, Innerleithen, Scotland.

Miller, I.E.G., Petworth, Sussex West.

Miller, Iris, Rait Village Antiques Centre, Scotland

Miller, Nick, Cullompton, Devon.

Miller, P., York, Yorks. North.

Miller, Robert, Hemswell Cliff, Lincs.

Miller, Robert, Ludlow, Shrops.

Miller, S., Lewes, Sussex East.

Millers of Chelsea Antiques Ltd, Ringwood, Hants.

Millgate Pine & Antiques, Thirsk, Yorks. North.

Millington, K.L. & J., Lepton, Yorks. West.

Millner, Arthur, London W1.

Millroyal Antiques, The Swan at Tetsworth, Oxon.

Mills Antiques, Cullompton, Devon.

Mills Antiques, Mrs, Ely, Cambs.

Mills Architectural Antiques Ltd, Robert, Bristol, Glos.

Mills, Claire, Rait Village Antiques Centre, Scotland

Mills, Doreen, Poole, Dorset.

Mills, G. and J.E., Honiton, Devon.

Mills, Geoffrey, Penzance, Cornwall.

Millward, J., Norwich, Norfolk.

Milne and Moller, London W11.

Milne Ltd, Nigel, London SW1.

Milne, Andy, Aberdeen, Scotland.

Milnthorpe and Daughters Antique Shop, Mary, Settle, Yorks. North.

Milton Antiques, Blandford Forum, Dorset.

Mimbridge Antiques Centre, Chobham, Surrey.

Mimi Fifi, London W11.

Miners, Steve, Alfies, London NW8.

Minster Antiques, York, Yorks. North.

Minster Books, Wimborne Minster, Dorset.

Minster Gate Bookshop, York, Yorks. North.

Mir Russki, Linlithgow, Scotland.

Mirabaud, S., Lewes, Sussex East.

Miscellany Antiques, Great Malvern, Worcs.

Miscellany Antiques, McBains Antiques, Exeter, Devon.

Misell, Ella, Grays Antique Market, London W1.

Miskimmin, W., Rochester, Kent.

Miss Elany, Long Eaton, Derbys.

Mitchell and Son, John, London W1.

Mitchell Antiques Ltd, Laurence, London N1.

Mitchell Fine Paintings, Anthony, Nottingham, Notts.

Mitchell Ltd, Paul, London W1.

Mitchell's Antiques, Blackburn, Lancs.

Mitchell's Gallery, Sally, Tuxford, Notts.

Mitchell, David and Robert A., Kirkcudbright, Scotland.

Mitchell, G., Burford, Oxon.

Mitchell, L.P.J., London N1.

Mitchell, M., Nottingham, Notts.

Mitchell, Mr and Mrs M. J., Coxley, Somerset.

Mitchell, Nicholas, The Swan at Tetsworth, Oxon.

Mitchell, R.S., Norwich, Norfolk.

North Wilts Exporters, Brinkworth, Wilts.

North, Desmond and Amanda, East Peckham, Kent.

Northcote Road Antiques Market, London SW11.

Northern Antiques Company, Norton, Yorks. North.

Northern Clocks, Worsley, Lancs.

Northfleet Hill Antiques, Northfleet, Kent.

Northumbria Pine, Whitley Bay, Tyne and Wear.

Northwich Antiques Centre, Northwich, Cheshire.

Northwood, Paul and Elizabeth, Ampthill, Beds.

Norton Antiques, Twyford, Norfolk.

Norton, M.S., N.E.L., J.P. and F.E., London W1.

Norton-Gore, Teresa, Alfies, London NW8.

Norton-Grant, K., Alfies, London NW8.

Nortonbury Antiques, London WC1.

Norwich City Council, Norwich, Norfolk.

Nostalgia Architectural Antiques, Stockport, Cheshire.

Nostalgia, Blackpool, Lancs.

Nostalgia, Clevedon, Somerset.

Nostradamus Centre, The, East Molesey, Surrey.

Nostradamus II, East Molesey, Surrey.

Not Just Silver, Weybridge, Surrey.

Notions Antiques Centre, Grantham, Lincs.

Now and Then (Toy Centre), Edinburgh, Scotland.

Nowell, Edward A., Wells, Somerset.

NS Watches, Alfies, London NW8.

NSE Medal Dept., Nottingham, Notts.

Number Nineteen, London N1.

Number One The Mall, The Mall Antiques Arcade, London N1.

Nunn, C.C., Falmouth, Cornwall.

Nutley Antiques, Nutley, Sussex East.

Nutt, Frank, Hereford, Herefs.

Nutting, Mrs B.H., Brackley, Northants.

O

O'Brien and Son Antiques Ltd, R.J., Manchester, Lancs.

O'Connor Brothers, Windsor and Eton, Berks.

O'Connor, Glenda, Grays Antique Market, London W1.

O'Donnell Antiques, Chris and Lin, Wallingford, Oxon.

O'Donnell, Mr and Mrs M., Chester, Cheshire.

O'Flynn, The Ginnel, Harrogate, Yorks North

O'Gara, M., Faringdon, Oxon.

O'Gara, P., Faringdon, Oxon.

O'Grady, Mrs, London W4.

O'Keefe, B., Hadleigh, Suffolk.

O'Keeffe, K.J., St Helier, Jersey, C.I.

O'Kelly, A. and J., London E8.

O'Shea Gallery, The, London W1.

O'Sullivan Antiques, A.J., Darlton, Notts.

O'Toole, Mrs G., Tarvin, Cheshire.

Oak Antiques, Jubilee Hall Antiques Centre, Lechlade, Glos.

Oakes and Son, G., Bolton, Lancs.

Oakleigh Antiques, Eldwick, Yorks. West.

Oakley, N., Alfies, London NW8.

Oaktree Antiques, Lubenham, Leics.

Oakwood Gallery, Leeds, Yorks. West.

Oasis Antiques, Brighton, Sussex East.

Oban Antiques, Oban, Scotland.

Obelisk Antiques, Warminster, Wilts.

Objects of Vertu, Huddersfield, Yorks. West.

Occultique, Northampton, Northants.

Octavia Antiques, The Ginnel, Harrogate, Yorks North

Octavia Antiques, Petworth, Sussex West.

Odd Lot, The, Aberdeen, Scotland.

Oddiquities, London SE23.

Odeon Antiques, Leek, Staffs.

Odgers, J.W., Harwich, Essex.

Odgers, J.W., London W11.

Odiham Gallery, The, Odiham, Hants.

Odin Antiques, Brighton, Sussex East.

Odling, David, Antiquarius, London SW3.

Off the Wall, Hemel Hempstead, Herts.

Offa's Dyke Antique Centre, Knighton, Wales.

Offer Waterman and Co. Fine Art, London SW10.

Ogden Ltd, Richard, London W1.

Ogden of Harrogate Ltd, Harrogate, Yorks. North.

Ogden, G. and D., Alsager, Cheshire.

Okeeffe, Timothy, Prestwick, Scotland.

Okker, Nadine, The Mall Antiques Arcade, London N1.

Old & Gold, Durham, Durham.

Old Bakehouse Antiques and Gallery, Broughton Astley, Leics.

Old Bakery Antiques, The, Wheathampstead, Herts.

Old Bakery Antiques, The, Woolhampton, Berks.

Old Barn Antiques & Furnishings, Sutton Bridge, Lincs.

Old Barn Antiques Warehouse, Sutton Bridge, Lincs.

Old Barn Antiques, Thornwood Common, Essex.

Old Brigade, The, Kingsthorpe, Northants.

Old Button Shop Antiques, Lytchett Minster, Dorset.

Old Chair Company, The Swan at Tetsworth, Oxon.

Old Chapel Antique & Collectables Centre, Tutbury, Staffs.

Old Church Galleries, London SW3.

Old Cinema Antique Department Store, The, London W4.

Old Clock Shop, The, West Malling, Kent.

Old Corner House Antiques, Wittersham, Kent.

Old Cornmarket Antiques Centre, The, Warwick, Warks.

Old Cottage Antiques, London E11.

Old Country Antiques, Chappells & The Antiques Centre, Bakewell, Derbys.

Old Curiosity Shop, King's Lynn, Norfolk.

Old Curiosity Shop, The, Bredbury, Cheshire.

Old Curiosity Shop, The, Sidmouth, Devon.

Old Curiosity Shop, The, St. Sampson, Guernsey, C.I.

Old Custom House, The, Penzance, Cornwall.

Old English Oak, Sandgate, Kent.

Old English Pine, Sandgate, Kent.

Old Father Time Clock Centre, London W11.

Old Flames, Easingwold, Yorks. North.

Old Forge Cottage Antiques, Hartley Wintney, Hants.

Old Forge, The, Stretton-under-Fosse, Warks.

Old French Mirror Company Ltd, The, Henley-on-Thames, Oxon.

Old Furniture Store, The, Brighton, Sussex East.

Old George Inn Antique Galleries, Burford, Oxon.

Old Granary Antique and Craft Centre, The, Battlesbridge Antique Centre, Essex

Old Granary Antiques and Collectors Centre, The, King's Lynn, Norfolk.

Old Hall Antiques, Burton Salmon, Yorks. North.

Old Hall Bookshop, The, Brackley, Northants.

Old Hall Farm, Long Clawson, Leics.

Old House Antique Centre, Adversane, Sussex West.

Old House Gallery, The, Oakham, Rutland.

Old House, The, Seaford, Sussex East.

Old Ironmongers Antiques Centre, The, Lechlade, Glos.

Old Malthouse, The, Hungerford, Berks.

Old Maltings Antique Centre, Louth, Lincs.

Old Manor House Antiques, Brasted, Kent.

Old Maps and Prints, London SW1.

Old Mill Antique Centre, Bridgnorth, Shrops.

Old Mill Market Shop, Tetbury, Glos.

Old Mint House, The, Pevensey, Sussex East.

Old Mother Hubbard's, Biggleswade, Beds.

Old Palace Antiques, Lostwithiel, Cornwall.

Old Post House, The, Axbridge, Somerset.

Old School (Gardens & Interiors), London N19.

Old School Antiques, Penryn, Cornwall.

Old Shoe Box, Leominster, Herefs.

Old Smithy, Feniscowles, Lancs.

Old Sofa Warehouse, The, Wilmslow, Cheshire.

Old Soke Books, Peterborough, Cambs.

Old St. Andrews Gallery, St. Andrews, Scotland.

Park House Tearoom & Antiques, Bladon, Oxon.

Park View Antiques, Wadhurst, Sussex East.

Park Walk Gallery, London SW10.

Parker Gallery, The Ginnel, Harrogate, Yorks North

Parker Gallery, The, London SW1.

Parker, Richard, Baildon, Yorks. West.

Parker, S., Quorn, Leics.

Parkes, Pauline, Durham House Antiques Centre, Stow-on-the-Wold, Glos.

Parkhouse Antiques and Jewellery, Mark, Barnstaple, Devon.

Parkin Fine Art Ltd, Michael, London SW1.

Parkin, E.J., Bristol, Glos.

Parks, Clive, Brighton, Sussex East.

Parks, Richard and Sheila, Sheringham, Norfolk.

Paros, Mark, Grays Antique Market, London W1.

Parriss, J.H., Sheringham, Norfolk.

Parriss, Sheringham, Norfolk.

Parry Ltd, H. and R.L., Sutton Coldfield, West Mids.

Parry, H., Edinburgh, Scotland.

Parry, H., Sutton Coldfield, West Mids.

Parry, Owen, Bath, Somerset.

Parry, R.C., Exeter, Devon.

Parsons, E.J. and C.P., Parkstone, Dorset.

Parsons, Mrs B.D., Tonbridge, Kent.

Partner, John, Durham House Antiques Centre, Stow-on-the-Wold, Glos.

Partners in Pine, Coggeshall, Essex.

Partridge Antiques, Timothy, Eastbourne, Sussex East.

Partridge Fine Arts plc, London W1.

Parvin, T.D. and M., Thirsk, Yorks. North.

Pash & Son, A., Bond Street Silver Galleries, London W1.

Passers Buy (Marie Evans), Llangollen, Wales.

Passiflora, Brewood, Staffs.

Past & Present, Hingham, Norfolk.

Past and Present, Red House Antiques Centre, York, Yorks. North

Past and Present, Totnes, Devon.

Past Caring, Holt, Norfolk.

Past Reflections, The Ginnel, Harrogate, Yorks North

Past Reflections, Red House Antiques Centre, York, Yorks. North

Past Treasures, Wendover, Bucks.

Pastimes Vintage Toys, Glasgow, Scotland.

Pastimes, Bristol, Glos.

Pastorale Antiques, Lewes, Sussex East.

Pateley Bridge Antiques, Pateley Bridge, Yorks. North.

Patterson Fine Arts Ltd, W.H., London W1.

Patterson Liddle, Bath, Somerset.

Patterson, A., Manningtree, Essex.

Patterson, C., Kew, Surrey.

Patterson, John B, Hexham, Northumbs.

Patterson, P., Sible Hedingham, Essex.

Patterson, T., Cavendish, Suffolk.

Patterson, W.H. and Mrs. P.M., London W1.

Pattison's Architectural Antiques incorporating The Architectural Salvage Store, Chorleywood, Herts.

Pattison, Tony, Chorleywood, Herts.

Paul Antiques, Robert, Hastings Antique Centre, St. Leonards-on-Sea, E. Sussex

Pauw Antiques, M., London SW6.

Pawsey and Payne, London W8.

Pawson - Clocks, T. W., Somersham, Cambs.

Payder, G., Alfies, London NW8.

Payne and Son (Goldsmiths) Ltd, Oxford, Oxon.

Payne and Son Ltd, Geo. A., Bournemouth, Dorset.

Payne, B.J., Alcester, Warks.

Payne, Clive, Jubilee Hall Antiques Centre, Lechlade, Glos.

Payne, E.P., G.N. and J.D., Oxford, Oxon.

Payne, H.G. and N.G., Bournemouth, Dorset.

Payne, M., Alfies, London NW8.

Payne, S., Grampound, Cornwall.

Payton, S., Mansfield, Notts.

Pearce, Stevie, Alfies, London NW8.

Pearl Cross Ltd, London WC2.

Pearl Gallery, The, Grays Antique Market, London W1.

Pearman, John, The Mall Antiques Arcade, London N1.

Pearson - Frasco International Ltd, W.M., London SW1.

Pearson Antique Clock Restoration, John, Birstwith, Yorks. North.

Pearson Antiques, John A., Horton, Berks.

Pearson Antiques, Michael, Canterbury, Kent.

Pearson Paintings Prints and Works of Art, Sebastian, Cambridge, Cambs.

Pearson, J., Kirkby Lonsdale, Cumbria.

Pearson, J., Nantwich, Cheshire.

Pearson, J., Nottingham, Notts.

Pearson, Sue, Brighton, Sussex East.

Peasenhall Art and Antiques Gallery, Peasenhall, Suffolk.

Peco, Hampton, Middx.

Pedlars Pack Books, Totnes, Devon.

Pedlars, Chipping Campden, Glos.

Pedler, R.S., London SW15.

Pegasus Antiques, Nottingham, Notts.

Pegler, Philip and Wendy, Chichester, Sussex West.

Pelham Galleries Ltd, London W1.

Pembery, M.J., Bakewell, Derbys.

Pembleton, Mrs A., Nottingham, Notts.

Pembleton, S., Nottingham, Notts.

Pembroke Antiques Centre, Pembroke, Wales.

Pembroke Antiques, Cambridge, Cambs.

Pendle Antiques Centre Ltd, Sabden, Lancs.

Pendulum of Mayfair Ltd, London W1.

Penman Clockcare, Spalding, Lincs.

Penman, J., Kingston-on-Spey, Scotland.

Penn Barn, Penn, Bucks.

Pennard House Antiques, East Pennard, Somerset.

Pennel, Mary, Jubilee Hall Antiques Centre, Lechlade, Glos.

Penney, David, Bishop's Stortford, Herts.

Pennies, Topsham, Devon.

Penny Farthing Antiques Arcade, Swindon, Wilts.

Penny Farthing Antiques, London SE1.

Penny Farthing Antiques, North Cave, Yorks. East.

Penny Farthing, North Berwick, Scotland.

Penny Post Antiques, The, Buxton, Derbys.

Penny's Antiques, Northampton, Northants.

Pennyfarthing Antiques, Salisbury, Wilts.

Penrith Coin and Stamp Centre, Penrith, Cumbria.

Pentecost, David, Paignton, Devon.

Pepper, M.E., Bury St. Edmunds, Suffolk.

Peppers Period Pieces, Bury St. Edmunds, Suffolk.

Peppitt, Judith, Snargate, Kent.

Pepys Antiques, Beckenham, Kent.

Percival Antiques, R. and S. M., Ruthin, Wales.

Percy's, London Silver Vaults, London WC2.

Perera Fine Art, Robert, Lymington, Hants.

Perera, R.J.D., Lymington, Hants.

Perez Antique Carpets Gallery, London SW6.

Perez, London SW3.

Perez, Maria, Antiquarius, London SW3.

Period Fireplaces, Bristol, Glos.

Period Furniture Showrooms, Beaconsfield, Bucks.

Period Pictures, Red House Antiques Centre, York, Yorks. North

Periwinkle Press, Newnham, Kent.

Perkins Antiques, Bryan, Wellingborough, Northants.

Perkins, J., B.H. and S.C., Wellingborough, Northants.

Perry, A, Trecastle, Wales.

Perry, Mrs J.R., Carmarthen, Wales.

Persian Carpet Gallery of Petworth, Petworth, Sussex West.

Persian Carpet Studio, The, Long Melford, Suffolk.

Persiflage, Alfies, London NW8.

Peter Pan's Bazaar, Gosport, Hants.

Peter Pan's of Gosport, Gosport, Hants.

Peters Antiques, Christopher, Brinklow, Warks.

Peters Antiques, Paul M., Harrogate, Yorks. North.

Peters, Chris and Jill, Brinklow, Warks.

Peters, Ian, London SE22.

Peters, Mrs D., Worthing, Sussex West.

Peters, Mrs J., Great Missenden, Bucks.

Peters, Sam, Alfies, London NW8.

Petersen, Lynne, Tetbury, Glos.

Petersfield Bookshop, The, Petersfield, Hants.

DEALERS' INDEX

Rand, Vivien and Eddie, Windsor and Eton, Berks.

Randall, Peter, Marlborough, Wilts.

Randolph, Hadleigh, Suffolk.

Rankin and Ian Conn, Daphne, London SW6.

Rankin Coin Co. Ltd, George, London E2.

Ransom Limited, Mark, The Furniture Cave, London SW10.

Ransom Ltd, Mark, London SW1.

Rapscallion Antiques Ltd, London SW16.

Rare Art, London Silver Vaults, London WC2.

Rare Jewellery Collections Limited, Bond Street Silver Galleries, London W1.

Rasoul, Ghulam, Grays Antique Market, London W1.

Rastro Antiques, Canterbury, Kent.

Ratcliff Ltd, G.T., Kelvedon, Essex.

Ratcliff, J., Todmorden, Yorks. West.

Ratcliffe, A.M., Beccles, Suffolk.

Ratcliffe, J. and R., Waddington, Lincs.

Ratner, R.A., Dorking, Surrey.

Raw, M.J., Keswick, Cumbria.

Rawlinson, John, Cirencester, Glos.

Ray & Scott Ltd, St Sampson, Guernsey, C.I.

Ray, M. T., Nottingham, Notts.

Rayfield, T., Tunbridge Wells, Kent.

Rayment Antiques, Derek and Tina, Barton, Cheshire.

Rayment, D.J. and K.M., Barton, Cheshire.

Rayment, D.M., Petworth, Sussex West.

Raymond, Robert, Antiquarius, London SW3.

Raynalds Mansion, Much Wenlock, Shrops.

Rayner, Barry, Tenterden, Kent.

Rayner, Michael, Cheltenham, Glos.

Rayso, Gill, Henley-in-Arden, Warks.

RBR Grp, Grays Antique Market, London W1.

Rea, C.J., Whitby, Yorks. North.

Read - Period Furniture, Alan, Horncastle, Lincs.

Read Antique Sciences, Mike, St. Ives, Cornwall.

Read, John, Martlesham, Suffolk.

Real Macoy, Keighley, Yorks. West.

Reason, Mrs C., Limpsfield, Surrey.

Recollect Dolls Hospital, Burgess Hill, Sussex West.

Recollections, Bournemouth, Dorset.

Recollections, Brighton, Sussex East.

Recollections, Poyton, Cheshire.

Record Detector, London E4.

Red Goblet Ltd, Petersfield, Hants.

Red House Antiques Centre, The, York, Yorks. North.

Red House Antiques, Yoxford, Suffolk.

Red Lane Antiques, Jubilee Hall Antiques Centre, Lechlade, Glos.

Red Lion Antiques Arcade, The, London W11.

Red Lion Antiques, Petworth, Sussex West.

Red Lodge Antiques, Screveton, Notts.

Red Shop, The, Wolverhampton, West Mids.

Redford Antiques & Interiors, Robert, Altrincham, Cheshire.

Redford, S. and R., Altrincham, Cheshire.

Redleaf Gallery, Tunbridge Wells, Kent.

Redmile, Anthony, The Furniture Cave, London SW10.

Redroom, London SW6.

Reece Gallery, The Gordon, Knaresborough, Yorks. North.

Reed, Anthony, Bath, Somerset.

Reed, Marilyn, Topsham, Devon.

Rees, Mrs G., Weybridge, Surrey.

Reeve, James, Warwick, Warks.

Reeves, P.W. and L., Gomshall, Surrey.

Reeves, Paul, London W8.

Reeves, V., Canterbury, Kent.

Reference Works, Swanage, Dorset.

Reffold, London SW6.

Reflections, Lymm, Cheshire.

Regal Antiques, Westerham, Kent.

Regal Watches, Grays Antique Market, London W1.

Regan, David M., Southport, Merseyside.

Regana, Angela, Alfies, London NW8.

Regency Antique Trading Centre, Stourbridge, West Mids.

Regent Antiques, London N1.

Regent House Gallery, London SW11.

Reid and Lefevre Ltd, Alex, London W1.

Reid, D.C., Edinburgh, Scotland.

Reid-Davies, Alison and Graeme, Berkhamsted, Herts.

Reigate Galleries, Reigate, Surrey.

Reilly, K., Antiquarius, London SW3.

Reindeer Antiques Ltd, London W8.

Reindeer Antiques Ltd, Potterspury, Northants.

Relcy Antiques, London SE10.

Relf Antiques, Ian, Tunbridge Wells, Kent.

Relic Antiques at Camden Passage, London N1.

Relic Antiques Trade Warehouse, London NW1.

Relics - Pine Furniture, Bristol, Glos.

Relics, Ilfracombe, Devon.

Remember When, London W3.

Remington, Reg and Philip, London WC2.

Renaissance Antiques, Chappells & The Antiques Centre, Bakewell, Derbys.

Renaissance Antiques, Cowbridge, Wales.

Renaissance Furniture Store, The, Glasgow, Scotland.

Renaissance, Solihull, West Mids.

Rendezvous Gallery, The, Aberdeen, Scotland.

Renishaw Antiques, Sheffield, Yorks. South.

Renney Antiques, Hexham, Northumbs.

Rennie, Paul and Karen, London WC1.

Rennies, London WC1.

Repetto-Wright, R., Aslockton, Notts.

Resner's, Bond Street Antiques Centre, London W1.

Resner, S. and G.R., Bond Street Antiques Centre, London W1.

Restall Brown and Clennell Ltd, London N1.

Retro Antiques, Lye, West Mids.

Retro, Stourbridge, West Mids.

Revell Antiques, Sheila, Hartley Wintney, Hants.

Revival, Abridge, Essex.

Revival, Colchester, Essex.

Rex Antiques, Chagford, Devon.

Reynold, A., London WC2.

Reynolds Antiques, C., Oakham, Rutland.

Reynolds Antiques, C.H., Pickering, Yorks. North.

Reynolds, Julia, Warwick, Warks.

Reynolds, Mr, Aberdeen, Scotland.

Reynolds, Mrs B.A.S., Easingwold, Yorks. North.

Rezai Persian Carpets, London W11.

Rezai, A., Grays Antique Market, London W1.

Rhodes Antiques, Colin, Yealmpton, Devon.

Rhodes, Isobel, Woodbridge, Suffolk.

Rhodes, Mrs J., London SW6.

Rhudle Mill, Kilmichael Glassary, Scotland.

Rice, Robert J., Great Malvern, Worcs.

Rich & Michael Rich, Steven, London SW1.

Richards and Sons, David, London W1.

Richards, L., London W11.

Richards, M. and E., London W1.

Richardson and Kailas Icons, London SW6.

Richardson Antiques Ltd, Nantwich, Cheshire.

Richardson Antiques, Lindsey, Durham House Antiques Centre, Stow-on-the-Wold, Glos.

Richardson, Ashley and Karen, Lindfield, Sussex West.

Richardson, C., London SW6.

Richardson, S. and E., Blewbury, Oxon.

Richardson, Terry, Nantwich, Cheshire.

Richmond Antiques, Bowdon, Cheshire.

Richmond Antiques, Old Cornmarket Antiques Centre, Warwick, Warks.

Rickett & Co. Antiques, Shepperton, Surrey.

Ricketts, Robert, Dunster, Somerset.

Rideal, Mrs Elizabeth, Waverton, Cheshire.

Ridgeway Antiques, Westcliff-on-Sea, Essex.

Ridgeway, D.A. and J.R., Bridgnorth, Shrops.

Ridings, I. and B., Holmfirth, Yorks. West.

Ridler, P.W., Pershore, Worcs.

Ridout, S.J., Hindhead, Surrey.

Ries, M.A. and Mrs I.T.H., Boston Spa, Yorks. West.

Rigby, B., Kirkby Lonsdale, Cumbria.

Right Angle, Brackley, Northants.

Rignault, Mrs F., Hythe, Kent.

Riley, Angela and Martin, Woodbridge, Suffolk.

Scottish Antique & Arts Centre, Doune, Scotland.
Scottish Gallery, The, Edinburgh, Scotland.
Scratchley, K.S., Sidmouth, Devon.
Scrummager's, Barnet, Herts.
Scull, T. and S.E., Bristol, Glos.
Sea View Antiques, Pontllyfrii, Wales.
Seabrook Antiques, Long Melford, Suffolk.
Seabrook Antiques, Mark, West Haddon, Northants.
Seaby Antiquities, London W1.
Seaford House Antiques, Moreton-in-Marsh, Glos.
Seaford's "Barn Collectors' Market" and Studio Bookshop, Seaford, Sussex East.
Seager Antiques, Arthur, Stow-on-the-Wold, Glos.
Seago, A.E., Cromer, Norfolk.
Seago, D.C., Cromer, Norfolk.
Seal, D., Keighley, Yorks. West.
Sealby, K. and R., Greystoke, Cumbria.
Seale Antiques/Interiors, Jeremy, London WC1.
Seals, B., Leeds, Yorks. West.
Seaman, Ray and Mollie, Axbridge, Somerset.
Sear, Richard, Flore, Northants.
Search, M. J., St Sampson, Guernsey, C.I.
Searle and Co Ltd, London EC3.
Seaview Antiques, Horncastle, Lincs.
Seaward and Around the Clock, Brixham, Devon.
Sebley, Oswald, Norwich, Norfolk.
Second Edition, Edinburgh, Scotland.
Second Hand Rose, Hindhead, Surrey.
Second Notions Antiques, Kirkcaldy, Scotland.
Second Time Around Ltd/Jadefare, Grays Antique Market, London W1.
Second Time Around, Hemswell Cliff, Lincs.
Secondhand and Rare Books, Manchester, Lancs.
Secondhand Bookshop, Oxted, Surrey.
Sedler, M., Bond Street Silver Galleries, London W1.
Sedman Antiques, Bridlington, Yorks. East.
Sedman, R.H.S. and M.A., Bridlington, Yorks. East.
Seidler, Chris, Grays Antique Market, London W1.
Selected Antiques & Collectables, Barnstaple, Devon.
Selective Eye Gallery, The, St. Helier, Jersey, C.I.
Seligmann, M. and D., London NW3.
Sellors, Peter, Warwick, Warks.
Selvester, Mark, Great Malvern, Worcs.
Selwoods, Taunton, Somerset.
Semke, B.W., Warminster, Wilts.
Serendipity Antiques & Crafts, Haslemere, Surrey.
Serendipity, Deal, Kent.
Serendipity, Ledbury, Herefs.
Serle, Mark A., Lechlade, Glos.
Seventh Heaven, Chirk, Wales.

Severn, D., Truro, Cornwall.
Seville, R., Bristol, Glos.
Shabby Tiger Antiques, Stroud, Glos.
Shackleton, Antony, David & Ann, Snainton, Yorks. North.
Shadad Antiques, Grays Antique Market, London W1.
Shaikh and Son (Oriental Rugs) Ltd, London SW19.
Shaikh, M., London SW19.
Shambles, The, Ashburton, Devon.
Shamsa, Mr, Hemswell Cliff, Lincs.
Shanklin Gallery, The, Shanklin, Isle of Wight.
Shapero Rare Books, Bernard J., London W1.
Shapiro & Co, Grays Antique Market, London W1.
Shardlow Antiques Warehouse, Shardlow, Derbys.
Shariff, Y., London WC1.
Sharland, T.H.A. & F.M., The Swan at Tetsworth, Oxon.
Sharp Antiques, Ian, Tynemouth, Tyne and Wear.
Sharp, Alan, The Ginnel, Harrogate, Yorks North
Sharp, Heather, St. Albans, Herts.
Sharp, Prof. Dennis, London WC1.
Sharp, Trisha, Olney, Bucks.
Sharpe, Andrew and Janet, Bolton Abbey, Yorks. North.
Sharpe, Andrew and Janet, Ilkley, Yorks. West.
Sharpe, J. T., London W1.
Sharrington Antiques, Sharrington, Norfolk.
Shaston Antiques, Shaftesbury, Dorset.
Shave, K.J., Cheltenham, Glos.
Shaw and Co, Jack, Ilkley, Yorks. West.
Shaw Antiques, Laurence, Horncastle, Lincs.
Shaw, Paul, Malvern Link, Worcs.
Shea, Sonia, The Mall Antiques Arcade, London N1.
Sheffield Antiques Emporium and the Chapel, Sheffield, Yorks. South.
Sheldon, Tom, Frinton-on-Sea, Essex.
Shelley, A. and J., Lewes, Sussex East.
Shenton, Rita, Twickenham, Middx.
Shepheard, S., Bourne End, Bucks.
Shepherd Antiques, Peter, Hurst, Berks.
Shepherd, G. and F., Wittersham, Kent.
Sheppard, J., Christchurch, Dorset.
Sheppard, K. and J., Balderton, Notts.
Sheppard, Mary P., Falmouth, Cornwall.
Sheppard, P., Baldock, Herts.
Sheppard, S., Lechlade, Glos.
Sheppee, William, Salisbury, Wilts.
Sheraton House Antiques, Torquay, Devon.
Sherborne World of Antiques, Sherborne, Dorset.
Shere Antiques Centre, Shere, Surrey.
Sheridan's Bookshop, Ian, Hampton, Middx.
Sherlock Antiques, George, London SW6.
Sherman and Waterman Associates Ltd, London WC2.

Sherston-Baker, Bt., Sir Robert, Canterbury, Kent.
Sherwood Antiques Ltd, D.W., Rushden, Northants.
Shield Antiques, Robin, Swinstead, Lincs.
Shifrin, Maurice, Wheathampstead, Herts.
Shimizu, Mrs F.K., London W8.
Shindler, A., Chester, Cheshire.
Shiners, Snobs Knobs, Newcastle-upon-Tyne, Tyne and Wear.
Shinn Decorative Textiles, Catherine, Cheltenham, Glos.
Shinn, Catherine and Jenny, Cheltenham, Glos.
Shipwreck, The, Brightlingsea, Essex.
Shiraz Antiques, Grays Antique Market, London W1.
Shirley Ann's Antiques - International Interiors, Brighton, Sussex East.
Shockett, Byron and Orford, Grays Antique Market, London W1.
Shooter, J., Stickney, Lincs.
Shorrick, Harry and Mrs Sheila, Gosforth, Tyne and Wear.
Short Antiques, C, Great Torrington, Devon.
Short, C J, Great Torrington, Devon.
Short, Dr. Roy, Leicester, Leics.
Short, M. and K., Deal, Kent.
Shortle, Mary, Red House Antiques Centre, York, Yorks. North.
Shortmead Antiques, Biggleswade, Beds.
Shotton Antiquarian Books, Prints and Coins, J., Durham, Durham.
Shrewsbury Antique Centre, Shrewsbury, Shrops.
Shrewsbury Antique Market, Shrewsbury, Shrops.
Shure and Co, David S., London Silver Vaults, London WC2.
Shuster, Stuart, London NW8.
Shuttleworth, L.R., Scarborough, Yorks. North.
Shuttleworths, Scarborough, Yorks. North.
Sidcup Antique and Craft Centre, Sidcup, Kent.
Sidmouth Antiques and Collectors Centre, Sidmouth, Devon.
Sieff, Tetbury, Glos.
Sigaroudinia, Parvis, Lisburn, Co. Antrim, N. Ireland.
Sigma Antiques and Fine Art, Ripon, Yorks. North.
Silstar, London Silver Vaults, London WC2.
Silver Belle, London NW8.
Silver Fox Gallery (Portobello), The, London W11.
Silver Mouse Trap, The, London WC2.
Silver Street Antiques and Things, Cirencester, Glos.
Silver Thimble Antiques, Red House Antiques Centre, York, Yorks. North
Silver Thimble, The, Kendal, Cumbria.
Silver, Allen and Anne, London NW8.
Silverman, B., London Silver Vaults, London WC2.

DEALERS' INDEX

Thesaurus (Jersey) Ltd, St. Helier, Jersey, C.I.
thesilverfund.com, London SW1.
Theta Gallery, Liverpool, Merseyside.
Thirkill Antiques, Leyburn, Yorks. North.
This and That (Furniture), London NW1.
Thistle Antiques, Aberdeen, Scotland.
Thistlethwaite, E., Settle, Yorks. North.
Thomas H. Parker Ltd, London SW1.
Thomas, Andrew, Stamford, Lincs.
Thomas, H.R. and T., Bladon, Oxon.
Thomas, Jill, Bishop's Castle, Shrops.
Thomas, M. and V., Penn, Bucks.
Thomas, Rena, Norton, Durham.
Thomas, S., Church Stretton, Shrops.
Thomas, Steve, The Furniture Cave, London SW10.
Thomas, Wing Cdr. R.G., Midsomer Norton, Somerset.
Thompson Antiques, John, Knaresborough, Yorks. North.
Thompson's Gallery, Aldeburgh, Suffolk.
Thompson's, Ipswich, Suffolk.
Thompson, B., London N1.
Thompson, C.A. and A.L., Bourne, Lincs.
Thompson, Colin, Alfies, London NW8.
Thompson, D., Ipswich, Suffolk.
Thompson, J. and S., Aldeburgh, Suffolk.
Thompson, J.J., Easingwold, Yorks. North.
Thompson, John, Tunbridge Wells, Kent.
Thompson, Marlene and Dave, Brinklow, Warks.
Thompson, N.D.A. and E.K., Honiton, Devon.
Thompson, N.F., Buxton, Derbys.
Thomson - Albany Gallery, Bill, London SW1.
Thomson, I.G.F., Chappells & The Antiques Centre, Bakewell, Derbys.
Thomson Antiques, Joan, St. Helier, Jersey, C.I.
Thomson's, St Helier, Jersey, C.I.
Thomson, D., Ripon, Yorks. North.
Thomson, W.B., London SW1.
Thorn, David J., Budleigh Salterton, Devon.
Thornber, Peter, Chester, Cheshire.
Thornbridge Antiques, Bakewell, Derbys.
Thornbury Antiques, Thornbury, Glos.
Thornbury, M., Brinkworth, Wilts.
Thorne, S., Hursley, Hants.
Thornhill Galleries Ltd, London SW6.
Thornhill Galleries Ltd. in association with A. & R. Dockerill Ltd, London SW15.
Thornhill, J., Shrewsbury, Shrops.
Thornhill, Val, Red House Antiques Centre, York, Yorks. North
Thornley Antiques Betty, Durham House Antiques Centre, Stow-on-the-Wold, Glos.
Thornley, G. and E.M., Helmsley, Yorks. North.

Thornton Antiques Supermarket, J.W., Bowness-on-Windermere, Cumbria.
Thornton Antiques, Joseph, Windermere, Cumbria.
Thornton Architectural Antiques Ltd, Andy, Halifax, Yorks. West.
Thornton, D., Oxford, Oxon.
Thornton, J.W., Ulverston, Cumbria.
Thornton, J.W., Windermere, Cumbria.
Thornton, John, London SW10.
Thorntons of Harrogate, Harrogate, Yorks. North.
Thorntons of Oxford Ltd, Oxford, Oxon.
Thorp Bookseller, Thomas, Guildford, Surrey.
Thorp, John, Market Bosworth, Leics.
Thorpe and Foster Ltd, Dorking, Surrey.
Thorpe, P., Haverfordwest, Wales.
Those were the Days, Cambridge, Cambs.
Thrie Estaits, The, Edinburgh, Scotland.
Throckmorton, Lady Isabel, Arthingworth, Northants.
Through the Looking Glass Ltd, London SW6.
Through the Looking Glass Ltd, London W8.
Throup, M., Eldwick, Yorks. West.
Thrower, D. and V., Petworth, Sussex West.
Thuillier, William, London W1.
Thurlow, Kate, London W14.
Thurstans, C.M. and D., Stillington, Yorks. North.
Thwaites and Co, Oxhey, Herts.
Tiernan, Eugene, Alfies, London NW8.
Tiffany Antiques, Shrewsbury, Shrops.
Tiffins Antiques, Emsworth, Hants.
Tildesley, B. and J., Thirsk, Yorks. North.
Tileke - Antique Prints & Engravings, David, Alfies, London NW8.
Tilings Antiques, Brasted, Kent.
Till, Michael J., London N1.
Tilley's Vintage Magazine Shop, Sheffield, Yorks. South.
Tilley, A.G.J. and A.A.J.C., Sheffield, Yorks. South.
Tilley, J.C., Macclesfield, Cheshire.
Tilleys Antiques, Solihull, West Mids.
Tilly's Antiques, Leigh-on-Sea, Essex.
Timbers Antique & Collectables Centre, The, Lavenham, Suffolk.
Time & Tide Antiques, Portaferry, Co. Down, N. Ireland.
Time and Motion, Beverley, Yorks. East.
Time in Hand, Shipston-on-Stour, Warks.
Time to Remember, Sevenoaks, Kent.
Timecraft Clocks, Sherborne, Dorset.
Timepiece Repairs, Lincoln, Lincs.
Timepiece, Teignmouth, Devon.
Times Past Antiques, Auchterarder, Scotland.
Times Past Antiques, Potter Heigham, Norfolk.
Times Past Antiques, Windsor and Eton, Berks.
Times Past, Durham House Antiques Centre, Stow-on-the-Wold, Glos.

Timespec, Grays Antique Market, London W1.
Timms Antiques Ltd, S. and S., Shefford, Beds.
Timms, Nigel, Chris and Russell, Twyford, Berks.
Tina's Antiques, Codford, Wilts.
Tincknell, R., Wedmore, Somerset.
Tintern Antiques, Tintern, Wales.
Tinworth, J.F. and M.A, Lavenham, Suffolk.
Tisdall & Defries Antiques, London N1.
Tisdall, M., London N1.
Titchner and Sons, John, Littleton, Cheshire.
Titian Gallery, The, Chipping Campden, Glos.
Titterton, Peter G., Brackley, Northants.
Titus Omega, London N1.
Tobias and The Angel, London SW13.
Toby's Architectural Antiques, Torquay, Devon.
Todd and Austin Antiques of Winchester, Winchester, Hants.
Todd's, Launceston, Cornwall.
Todd, A., Stockport, Cheshire.
Todd, E., Stockport, Cheshire.
Todd, M.S., Nether Stowey, Somerset.
Todmorden Antiques Centre, Todmorden, Yorks. West.
Toll House Bookshop, The, Holmfirth, Yorks. West.
Tomasso Brothers, Leeds, Yorks. West.
Tomasso, D., G. & R., Leeds, Yorks. West.
Tombland Antiques Centre, Norwich, Norfolk.
Tombland Bookshop, The, Norwich, Norfolk.
Tombland Jewellers & Silversmiths, Norwich, Norfolk.
Tomkinson Stained Glass, London W11.
Tomkinson, S., London W11.
Tomlin, D.S., London SE25.
Tomlinson & Sotiris Papadimitriou, G., Antiquarius, London SW3.
Tomlinson and Son, F., Stockport, Cheshire.
Tomlinson Antiques Ltd. & Period Furniture Ltd, Tockwith, Yorks. North.
Tomtom, London WC2.
Tonkinson, Roger and Anne, St. Ives, Cornwall.
Tonks, Alan and Terri, Warsash, Hants.
Tonks, Mrs B., Wolverhampton, West Mids.
Tooke, M.D., Guildford, Surrey.
Tool Shop, The, Needham Market, Suffolk.
Toole, J., Liverpool, Merseyside.
Tooley Adams & Co, Wallingford, Oxon.
Tooley, CMBHI, M.V., Chesham, Bucks.
Toon, Roger, Church Stretton, Shrops.
Top Floor Antiques, Bidford-on-Avon, Warks.
Top Hat Antique Centre, Sheffield, Yorks. South.

818

DEALERS' INDEX

Underwood Oak, Alresford, Hants.
Underwood Thompson, Nick, London SW11.
Underwoodhall Antiques, Woodhall Spa, Lincs.
Unicorn Antiques & Reproductions, Kingswinford, West Mids.
Unicorn Antiques, Edinburgh, Scotland.
Unsworth Antiques, Robin, Olney, Bucks.
Unsworth, R. and Z. M., Olney, Bucks.
Up Country, Tunbridge Wells, Kent.
Upchurch, Kenneth, Ashbourne, Derbys.
Upham, Matthew, London SW6.
Upperbridge Antiques, Holmfirth, Yorks. West.
Upstairs, Downstairs, The Ginnel, Harrogate, Yorks North.
Upstairs, Downstairs, Honiton, Devon.
Urbach, A., London Silver Vaults, London WC2.
Uriah's Heap, Royal Victoria Arcade, Ryde, I. of Wight
Uriah's Heap, Ryde, Isle of Wight.
Usher and Son Ltd, James, Lincoln, Lincs.
Usher Antiques, Richard, Cuckfield, Sussex West.
Utopia Antiques Ltd, Low Newton, Cumbria.

V

V & A Antiques, Bognor Regis, Sussex West.
V.O.C. Antiques, Woodhall Spa, Lincs.
Vale Antiques, London W9.
Vale Stamps and Antiques, London SE3.
Valentine-Ketchum, V.A. and B.J., Stamford, Lincs.
Valentyne Dawes Gallery, Ludlow, Shrops.
Valledy, S., Wendover, Bucks.
Valley Antiques, Oldham, Lancs.
Valls Ltd, Rafael, London SW1.
Valmar Antiques, Stansted, Essex.
Valued History, Cambridge, Cambs.
Van Haeften Ltd, Johnny, London SW1.
Van Haeften, J. and S., London SW1.
Van Hefflin, Mr, Kirton in Lindsey, Lincs.
Van Wyngaarden, H., Little Malvern, Worcs.
van Beers Oriental Art, Jan, London W1.
van den Berg, Jollke, Jubilee Hall Antiques Centre, Lechlade, Glos.
van der Werf, Hanneke, London W11.
van Heck, Mrs S. M., Totnes, Devon.
Van-Hay Antiques, Geoffrey, Merstham, Surrey.
Vanbrugh House Antiques, Stow-on-the-Wold, Glos.
Vandeleur Antiquarian Books, Epsom, Surrey.
Vane House Antiques, London N1.
Variety Box, Tunbridge Wells, Kent.
Varnham, H.J. and R.P., London SE3.
Vaughan Antiques, Stamford, Lincs.
Vaughan Ltd, London SW10.
Vaughan, Barry and Lindy, Stamford, Lincs.

Vaughan, C.M., Stratford-upon-Avon, Warks.
Vaughan, J. and J., Deddington, Oxon.
Vaughan, J.C., Kingswinford, West Mids.
Vaughan, L., Malton, Yorks. North.
Vaughan, Robert, Stratford-upon-Avon, Warks.
Vee Design - Birch House Antiques, Michael, Melrose, Scotland.
Vee, Michael, Melrose, Scotland.
Veevers, Chester, Cheshire.
Vella, J.D. and H., Olney, Bucks.
Venn, D., Worcester, Worcs.
Venn, Edward, Williton, Somerset.
Ventnor Rare Books, Ventnor, Isle of Wight.
Ventura-Pauly, Michael, Grays Antique Market, London W1.
Venus, M. A., Barnard Castle, Durham.
Verey, Denzil, Barnsley, Glos.
Vescovi, Luigino, Morecambe, Lancs.
Vestry Antiques, Cranbrook, Kent.
Vice, D., Birmingham, West Mids.
Vickers, T. and M., Sheffield, Yorks. South.
Victor, June, Alfies, London NW8.
Victoria and Edward Antiques Centre, Dorking, Surrey.
Victoria Antiques Ltd, Glasgow, Scotland.
Victoria Antiques, Alderney, Alderney, C.I.
Victoria Antiques, London E18.
Victoria Antiques, Wadebridge, Cornwall.
Victoria Antiques/City Strippers, Wallasey, Merseyside.
Victoria Bookshop, Swindon, Wilts.
Victoria Centre, The, Saltaire, Yorks. West.
Victoria Gallery & Bookshop, Camborne, Cornwall.
Victorian Brass Bedstead Company, The, Cocking, Sussex West.
Victorian Chairman, Bournemouth, Dorset.
Victorian Fireplace, Canterbury, Kent.
Victorian Ironmonger, The, Brinklow, Warks.
Victorian Shop, The, St. Annes-on-Sea, Lancs.
Victorian Village Antiques, The, Glasgow, Scotland.
Victoriana Dolls, London W11.
Vieux-Pernon, B., London SW1.
Vigo Carpet Gallery, London W1.
Village Antique Centre, The, Brasted, Kent.
Village Antique Market, The, Weedon, Northants.
Village Antiques, Castle Gate Antiques Centre, Newark, Notts.
Village Antiques, Cheam, Surrey.
Village Antiques, Cobham, Surrey.
Village Antiques, Manchester, Lancs.
Village Antiques, Weybridge, Surrey.
Village Books, East Dereham, Norfolk.
Village Clocks, Coltishall, Norfolk.
Village Clocks, Long Melford, Suffolk.
Vince, N.B., Bawdeswell, Norfolk.

Vincent Antique Arms and Armour, Garth, Allington, Lincs.
Vine, Mr. and Mrs. P.A., Chappells & The Antiques Centre, Bakewell, Derbys.
Vinery, The, Dorking, Surrey.
Vintage Antiques Centre, Warwick, Warks.
Vintage Cameras Ltd, London SE26.
Vintage Pine, Long Melford, Suffolk.
Vintage Toy and Train Shop, The, Sidmouth, Devon.
Vintage Watch Co., The, Tunbridge Wells, Kent.
Vintage Wireless Shop, Nottingham, Notts.
Violin Shop, The, Hexham, Northumbs.
Virginia, London W11.
Visto, London W11.
Viventi, G., Burford, Oxon.
Viventi, Giovanni, London SE1.
Vollaro, Mrs A., Chalfont St. Giles, Bucks.
Von Pflugh Antiques, Johnny, London W11.
von Beregshasy, Count Alexander, The Mall Antiques Arcade, London N1.
von Bülow, Karen E., Dorking, Surrey.
von Dahlen, Baroness V., Long Melford, Suffolk.
Vosburgh, Beryl, London N1.

W

W.13 Antiques, London W13.
W.R.S. Architectural Antiques, Low Newton, Cumbria.
Wace Ancient Art Ltd, Rupert, London W1.
Wachsman, Johnny, Grays Antique Market, London W1.
Waddington Antique Clocks, Trevor, Bradford-on-Avon, Wilts.
Wade Antiques, Ray, Poulton-le-Fylde, Lancs.
Wadey, Ian J., Storrington, Sussex West.
Wadey, Ian. J., Houghton, Sussex West.
Wadge Clocks, Chris, Salisbury, Wilts.
Waghorn, Dee, Windsor and Eton, Berks.
Wagstaff, Cara, Cheltenham, Glos.
Wagstaff, Mrs J., Oxted, Surrey.
Wagstaffs, Oxted, Surrey.
Wagstaffs, Oxted, Surrey.
Wain, J.I., Ripon, Yorks. North.
Wain, John, Hungerford, Berks.
Wain, Mrs M.R., Weedon, Northants.
Wain, Peter, Market Drayton, Shrops.
Wain, William, Antiquarius, London SW3.
Wainford, Frances, Still Too Few, London W11.
Wainwright, David, London NW3.
Wainwright, David, London W11.
Wainwright, P.J., Bridgnorth, Shrops.
Wakefield, Anthony, Dorking, Surrey.
Wakelin and Helen Linfield, Michael, Billingshurst, Sussex West.
Walcot Reclamation, Bath, Somerset.
Waldron Antiques, Patrick, Cirencester, Glos.

Walkden, J., Littlehampton, Sussex West.
Walker Antiques, John, Dorchester, Dorset.
Walker Antiques, John, Sherborne, Dorset.
Walker Galleries Ltd, Harrogate, Yorks. North.
Walker, A.E., Burford, Oxon.
Walker, Alan, Halfway, Berks.
Walker, D., Nottingham, Notts.
Walker, G.R., Penrith, Cumbria.
Walker, I., Odiham, Hants.
Walker, John, Stanley, Scotland.
Walker, K., Bristol, Glos.
Walker, M.W., Coleraine, Co. Londonderry, N. Ireland.
Walker, Mrs S. Kitching, Thornton le Dale, Yorks. North.
Walker-Sherriff, C., Red House Antiques Centre, York, Yorks. North
Walkers, Burford, Oxon.
Walking Stick Shop, The, Arundel, Sussex West.
Wallace Antiques Ltd, London SE3.
Wallace, N., York, Yorks. North.
Wallhead Antiques, Sandra, Chappells & The Antiques Centre, Bakewell, Derbys.
Wallis, D. F., Alfies, London NW8.
Wallis, G.M.A., Wingham, Kent.
Wallis, Gary Lloyd, Cookham Rise, Berks.
Wallop, Hon. N.V.B. and L.N.J., London W8.
Wallrock, Mr and Mrs C., Lymington, Hants.
Walls, C., Tenterden, Kent.
Walpole Gallery, London W1.
Walsh, David, Castle Gate Antiques Centre, Newark, Notts.
Walsh, N., Great Harwood, Lancs.
Walter Antiques Ltd, William, London Silver Vaults, London WC2.
Walter, R.W., London Silver Vaults, London WC2.
Walters, B., Weedon, Northants.
Walters, J.D. and R.M., Rolvenden, Kent.
Walton, Anji, Middleham, Yorks. North.
Walton, P., Warminster, Wilts.
Walton, Peter, Buckingham, Bucks.
Wandle's Workshop Ltd, Mr, London SW18.
Warboys Antiques, Warboys, Cambs.
Warburton, E., Stockport, Cheshire.
Ward and Son, L.L., Brandsby, Yorks. North.
Ward Antiques, London SE7.
Ward Antiques, Paul, Sheffield, Yorks. South.
Ward Antiques, Sidcup, Kent.
Ward Fine Paintings, Peter, Cheltenham, Glos.
Ward Properties, Stewart, Westerham, Kent.
Ward, Charles H., Derby, Derbys.
Ward, E.H., The Ginnel, Harrogate, Yorks North
Ward, Jessica, Alfies, London NW8.

Ward, Jim and Janet, Rushden, Northants.
Ward, M.G., Derby, Derbys.
Ward, Miss Pamela, Huddersfield, Yorks. West.
Ward, R., Brandsby, Yorks. North.
Ward, T. and M., London SE7.
Ward, T. and M., Sidcup, Kent.
Ward-Lee, B., Four Elms, Kent.
Wardale, A., Red House Antiques Centre, York, Yorks. North
Warde, J., Farnborough, Hants.
Wardrobe, Brighton, Sussex East.
Wardrope, J., Carlisle Antique and Craft Centre, Cumbria
Wareside Antiques, Cottered, Herts.
Warings of Hereford, Hereford, Herefs.
Warley Antique Centre, Birmingham, West Mids.
Warminster Antiques Centre, Warminster, Wilts.
Warn, Penelope J., Ramsgate, Kent.
Warne Family, The, Tregony, Cornwall.
Warner (Antiques), W.W., Brasted, Kent.
Warner and Son Ltd, Robert, Worthing, Sussex West.
Warner, Marie, Alfies, London NW8.
Warren Antiques, Jimmy, Littlebourne, Kent.
Warren, B., Seaton, Devon.
Warren, J.R., Leiston, Suffolk.
Warren, M., London N1.
Warren-Thomas, N. and A., Nayland, Suffolk.
Warrender and Co, S., Sutton, Surrey.
Warrender, F.R., Sutton, Surrey.
Warrens Antiques Warehouse, Leiston, Suffolk.
Wartski Ltd, London W1.
Warwick Antique Centre, The, Warwick, Warks.
Warwick Antiques, Carlisle Antique and Craft Centre, Cumbria
Warwick Antiques, Warwick, Warks.
Warwick, D.C., Weymouth, Dorset.
Wass, Nick, Williton, Somerset.
Water Lane Antiques, Bakewell, Derbys.
Waterfield's, Oxford, Oxon.
Waterfront Antiques Market, Falmouth, Cornwall.
Watergate Antiques, Chester, Cheshire.
Waterhouse and Dodd, London W1.
Waterhouse, R., London W1.
Waterloo Antiques, Oldham, Lancs.
Waterloo Trading Co., The, London SE10.
Waterman Fine Art Ltd, London SW1.
Waterman, T. and R., London SW1.
Watermill Antiques, Nayland, Suffolk.
Waters Violins, Lamb Arcade, Wallingford, Oxon
Waters, Geoffrey, Antiquarius, London SW3.
Waterside Antiques Centre, Ely, Cambs.
Waterworth, Mrs. F.S., Alderley Edge, Cheshire.
Watkins Books Ltd, London WC2.
Watkins, I., Knighton, Wales.
Watkins, Islwyn, Knighton, Wales.
Watling Antiques, Crayford, Kent.

Watson Ltd, Gordon, London SW3.
Watson, Jean, Shere, Surrey.
Watson, M.E., Market Weighton, Yorks. East.
Watson, P., Moreton-in-Marsh, Glos.
Watson, Pauline, Ashtead, Surrey.
Watson, Pauline, Dorking, Surrey.
Watts, Captain O.M., London W1.
Watts, Chris, Salisbury, Wilts.
Watts, Sue and Bruce, Huntly, Scotland.
Waverley Antiques, Upper Largo, Scotland.
Way Bookseller, Richard, Henley-on-Thames, Oxon.
Way, R.E. and G.B., Newmarket, Suffolk.
Way, Richard, Henley-on-Thames, Oxon.
Waymouth, Edwin, Honiton, Devon.
Wayne "The Razor Man", Neil, Belper, Derbys.
Wayside Antiques, Duffield, Derbys.
Wayside Antiques, Tattershall, Lincs.
Weatherell's of Harrogate Antiques and Fine Arts, Harrogate, Yorks. North.
Weaver Antiques, Bernard, Cirencester, Glos.
Weaver, Peter, Aldeburgh, Suffolk.
Weaver, Trude, London W11.
Webb Fine Art, Michael, Llangristiolus (Anglesey), Wales.
Webb Fine Arts, Winchester, Hants.
Webb, Anne and Tony, Brancaster Staithe, Norfolk.
Webb, D.H., Winchester, Hants.
Webb, David, Bond Street Silver Galleries, London W1.
Webb, Graham, Brighton, Sussex East.
Webb, M., London N1.
Webb, Michael, London N13.
Webb, R. and J., Leigh-on-Sea, Essex.
Webb, Roy, Wickham Market, Suffolk.
Webster, A.J., Coleshill, Warks.
Webster, Duncan, The Swan at Tetsworth, Oxon.
Webster, E.T., Blythburgh, Suffolk.
Webster, G., Liverpool, Merseyside.
Webster, M., Cross Hills, Yorks. North.
Webster-Speakman, S. J., Southwold, Suffolk.
Weedon Bec Antiques, Weedon, Northants.
Weeks, Brian, Fakenham, Norfolk.
Weidenbaum, R., Manchester, Lancs.
Weijand Fine Oriental Carpets, Karel, Farnham, Surrey.
Weiner, G.G., Brighton, Sussex East.
Weiner, M., Ipswich, Suffolk.
Weir, Mr and Mrs D., Bottisham, Cambs.
Weiss Gallery, The, London W1.
Weiss, A. and G., London Silver Vaults, London WC2.
Weiss, Peter K., London Silver Vaults, London WC2.
Welch Jeweller, M.G., Taunton, Somerset.
Welch, K. and A., Warminster, Wilts.
Welch, Mark and Liz, Taunton, Somerset.

Stop Press

The Walpole Galleries

Commonwealth Buildings, Woolwich Church St. SE18 5NS. (Graham Walpole). Est. 1976. Open by appointment only. SIZE: Large. *STOCK: Paintings, 1770-1940, £500-£50,000; works of art, 1700-1920, £250-£10,000; furniture, 1780-1920, £500-£25,000.* LOC: Immediately off A206 - main road from London through Greenwich and east to Woolwich, 1/4 mile from Woolwich ferry. PARK: Own. TEL: 020 8316 7324; fax - same; mobile - 07831 561042. FAIRS: Olympia (June). VAT: Stan/Spec.

James Hardy Antiques Ltd

12 The Bank. DL12 8PQ. (Alan Hardy). Est. 1994. Open 10-5. CL: Thurs. SIZE: Medium. *STOCK: Furniture, 18th C to Edwardian, £500-£25,000; silver and porcelain, 18th-20th C, £50-£5,000.* PARK: Nearby. TEL: 01833 695135; fax - same; mobile - 07710 162003; e-mail - alan@jameshardyantiques.co.uk; website - www.jameshardyantiques.co.uk. SER: Restorations (silver and furniture); buys at auction (furniture). FAIRS: Harrogate; NEC. VAT: Spec.

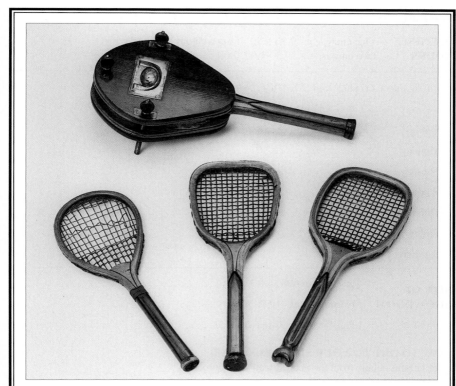

Four miniature lawn tennis rackets and a multiple press made possibly as workshop or salesman's samples or even as apprentice pieces, c.1885.

From an article entitled 'Lawn Tennis Memorabilia' by Gerald Gurney which appeared in the June 2001 issue of **Antique Collecting** magazine. For more details and to subscribe see page 147.

PLEASE USE THIS FORM FOR A NEW OR SUBSTANTIALLY ALTERED ENTRY

Please complete and return this form; there is no charge

NAME OF SHOP . . . .

ADDRESS OF SHOP . . . .

. . . .

. . . .

full address including actual county (not postal code)

Name (or names) and initials of proprietor(s) . . . .

(Mr/Mrs/Miss/or title)

Previous trading address (if applicable) . . . .

State whether 'Trade Only' (Yes or No) . . . .

BADA (Yes or No) . . . . LAPADA (Yes or No) . . . .

Year Established . . . . Resident on premises (Yes or No) . . . .

OPENING: (One entry, e.g. '9.30-5.30' if open all day or part day
HOURS: Two entries, e.g. '9.30-1.00, 2.00-5.30' if closed for lunch)

Please put 'CLOSED' and 'BY APPT.' where applicable

	Morning	Afternoon
Sunday	. . . .
Monday	. . . .
Tuesday	. . . .
Wednesday	. . . .
Thursday	. . . .
Friday	. . . .
Saturday	. . . .

SIZE OF SHOWROOM

Small (up to 600 sq.ft.) . . . .

Medium (600 to 1,500 sq.ft.) . . . .

Large (over 1,500 sq.ft.) . . . .

HOW TO GET TO YOUR SHOP (BUSINESS)
Brief helpful details from the nearest well-known road:

. . . .

. . . .

. . . .

. . . .

OF WHAT DOES OUR STOCK CHIEFLY CONSIST?

(A) Please list in order of importance	(B) Approximate period or date of stock	(C) Indication of price range of stock eg £50-£100 or £5-£25
1. (Principal stock)		
2.		
3.		

IS PARKING *OUTSIDE* YOUR SHOP (BUSINESS) Easy (Yes or No)

TELEPHONE NUMBER   Business ....

Home ....

(only if customers can ring for appointments outside business hours)

V.A.T. scheme operated – Standard/Special/Both ....

SERVICES OFFERED:

Valuations (Yes or No) ....

Restorations (Yes or No) ....

Type of work ....

Buying specific items at auction for a commission (Yes or No) ....

Type of item ....

FAIRS:
At which fairs (if any) do you normally exhibit? ....

....

....

CERTIFICATION:
The information given above is accurate and you may publish it in the Guide.
I understand that this entry is entirely free.

Signed .... Date ....

ENGLAND
& WALES
COUNTIES

NORTHUMBERLAND

TYNE & WEAR

DURHAM

CUMBRIA

NORTH YORKSHIRE

EAST YORKSHIRE

LINCOLN

WEST
YORKSHIRE

SOUTH YORKSHIRE

NOTTINGHAM

DERBY

LANCASHIRE

MERSEYSIDE

CHESHIRE

STAFFORD

CLWYD

GWYNEDD

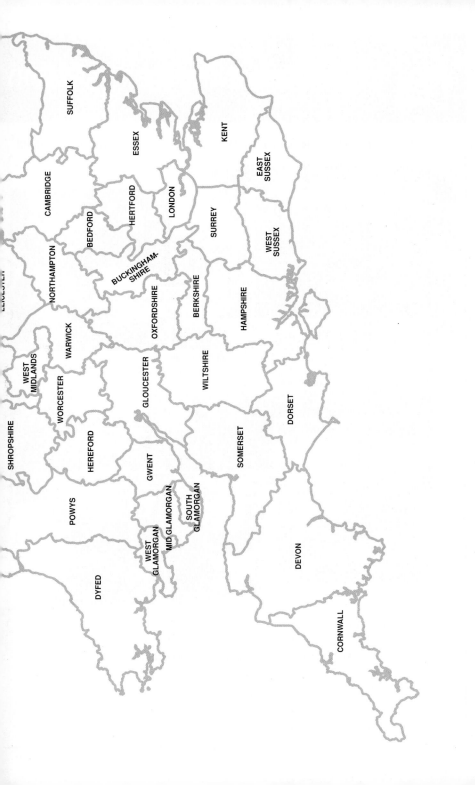